Table of Atomic Masses*

Element	Symbol	Atomic Number	Atomic Mass	Element	Symbol	Atomic Number	Atomic Mass	Element	Symbol	Atomic Number	Atomic Mass
Actinium	Ac	89	(227)†	Gold	Au	79	197.0	Praseodymium	Pr	59	140.9
Aluminum	Al	13	26.98	Hafnium	Hf	72	178.5	Promethium	Pm	61	(145)
Americium	Am	95	(243)	Hassium	Hs	108	(265)	Protactinium	Pa	91	(231)
Antimony	Sb	51	121.8	Helium	He	2	4.003	Radium	Ra	88	226
Argon	Ar	18	39.95	Holmium	Ho	67	164.9	Radon	Rn	86	(222)
Arsenic	As	33	74.92	Hydrogen	H	1	1.008	Rhenium	Re	75	186.2
Astatine	At	85	(210)	Indium	In	49	114.8	Rhodium	Rh	45	102.9
Barium	Ba	56	137.3	Iodine	I	53	126.9	Rubidium	Rb	37	85.47
Berkelium	Bk	97	(247)	Iridium	Ir	77	192.2	Ruthenium	Ru	44	101.1
Beryllium	Be	4	9.012	Iron	Fe	26	55.85	Rutherfordium	Rf	104	(261)
Bismuth	Bi	83	209.0	Krypton	Kr	36	83.80	Samarium	Sm	62	150.4
Bohrium	Bh	107	(264)	Lanthanum	La	57	138.9	Scandium	Sc	21	44.96
Boron	B	5	10.81	Lawrencium	Lr	103	(260)	Seaborgium	Sg	106	(263)
Bromine	Br	35	79.90	Lead	Pb	82	207.2	Selenium	Se	34	78.96
Cadmium	Cd	48	112.4	Lithium	Li	3	6.941	Silicon	Si	14	28.09
Calcium	Ca	20	40.08	Lutetium	Lu	71	175.0	Silver	Ag	47	107.9
Californium	Cf	98	(251)	Magnesium	Mg	12	24.31	Sodium	Na	11	22.99
Carbon	C	6	12.01	Manganese	Mn	25	54.94	Strontium	Sr	38	87.62
Cerium	Ce	58	140.1	Meitnerium	Mt	109	(268)	Sulfur	S	16	32.07
Cesium	Cs	55	132.9	Mendelevium	Md	101	(258)	Tantalum	Ta	73	180.9
Chlorine	Cl	17	35.45	Mercury	Hg	80	200.6	Technetium	Tc	43	(98)
Chromium	Cr	24	52.00	Molybdenum	Mo	42	95.94	Tellurium	Te	52	127.6
Cobalt	Co	27	58.93	Neodymium	Nd	60	144.2	Terbium	Tb	65	158.9
Copper	Cu	29	63.55	Neon	Ne	10	20.18	Thallium	Tl	81	204.4
Curium	Cm	96	(247)	Neptunium	Np	93	(237)	Thorium	Th	90	232.0
Darmstadtium	Ds	110	(281)	Nickel	Ni	28	58.69	Thulium	Tm	69	168.9
Dubnium	Db	105	(262)	Niobium	Nb	41	92.91	Tin	Sn	50	118.7
Dysprosium	Dy	66	162.5	Nitrogen	N	7	14.01	Titanium	Ti	22	47.88
Einsteinium	Es	99	(252)	Nobelium	No	102	(259)	Tungsten	W	74	183.9
Erbium	Er	68	167.3	Osmium	Os	76	190.2	Uranium	U	92	238.0
Europium	Eu	63	152.0	Oxygen	O	8	16.00	Vanadium	V	23	50.94
Fermium	Fm	100	(257)	Palladium	Pd	46	106.4	Xenon	Xe	54	131.3
Fluorine	F	9	19.00	Phosphorus	P	15	30.97	Ytterbium	Yb	70	173.0
Francium	Fr	87	(223)	Platinum	Pt	78	195.1	Yttrium	Y	39	88.91
Gadolinium	Gd	64	157.3	Plutonium	Pu	94	(244)	Zinc	Zn	30	65.38
Gallium	Ga	31	69.72	Polonium	Po	84	(209)	Zirconium	Zr	40	91.22
Germanium	Ge	32	72.59	Potassium	K	19	39.10				

*The values given here are to four significant figures where possible. †A value given in parentheses denotes the mass of the longest-lived isotope.

General Chemistry 142

Includes STUDENT SOLUTIONS MANUAL

Steven S. Zumdahl | Donald J. DeCoste

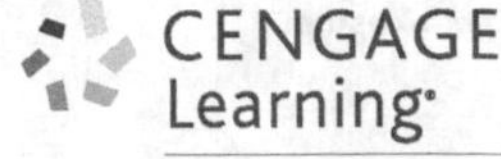

Australia • Brazil • Japan • Korea • Mexico • Singapore • Spain • United Kingdom • United States

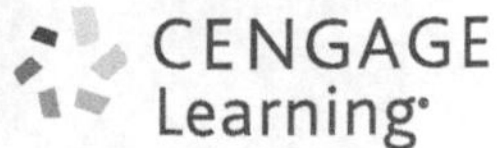

General Chemistry 142: Includes STUDENT SOLUTIONS MANUAL

Chemical Principles, 7th Edition
Steven S. Zumdahl | Donald J. DeCoste

Student Solutions Manual for Chemical Principles, 7th Edition
Steven S. Zumdahl | Donald J. DeCoste

Executive Editors:
Maureen Staudt
Michael Stranz

Senior Project Development Manager:
Linda deStefano

Marketing Specialist:
Courtney Sheldon

Senior Production/Manufacturing Manager:
Donna M. Brown

Production Editorial Manager:
Kim Fry

Sr. Rights Acquisition Account Manager:
Todd Osborne

ISBN-13: 978-1-285-10988-6

ISBN-10: 1-285-10988-0

Cengage Learning
5191 Natorp Boulevard
Mason, Ohio 45040
USA

Cengage Learning is a leading provider of customized learning solutions with office locations around the globe, including Singapore, the United Kingdom, Australia, Mexico, Brazil, and Japan. Locate your local office at:
international.cengage.com/region.
Cengage Learning products are represented in Canada by Nelson Education, Ltd.
For your lifelong learning solutions, visit **www.cengage.com/custom.**
Visit our corporate website at **www.cengage.com.**

Printed in the United States of America

CONTENTS 142

*(*Note – this is a "custom" textbook that has been designed specifically for this course in a joint effort between your instructor and the publisher. Please note that some chapters may have been removed intentionally and some pages may be black & white as dictated by the changes and/or additions.)*

STUDENT SOLUTIONS MANUAL

Chemists and Chemistry

chapter 1

1.1 Thinking Like a Chemist

1.2 A Real-World Chemistry Problem

1.3 The Scientific Method

1.4 Industrial Chemistry

1.5 Polyvinyl Chloride (PVC): Real-World Chemistry

A variety of chemistry glassware.

OWL
Sign in to OWL at www.cengage.com/owl to view tutorials and simulations, develop problem-solving skills, and complete online homework assigned by your professor.

go Chemistry
Download mini lecture videos for key concept review and exam prep from OWL or purchase them from www.cengagebrain.com.

Chemistry. It is a word that evokes various, and often dramatic, responses. It is a word that is impossible to define concisely, because the field is so diverse and its practitioners perform such an incredible variety of jobs. Chemistry mainly deals with situations in which the nature of a substance is changed by altering its composition; entirely new substances are synthesized, or the properties of existing substances are enhanced.

There are many misconceptions about the practitioners of chemistry. Many people picture a chemist as a solitary figure who works in a laboratory and does not talk to anyone else for days at a time. Nothing could be further from the truth. Many chemists do indeed work in laboratories, but rarely by themselves. A typical day for a modern chemist would be spent as a member of a team solving a particular problem important to his or her company. This team might consist of chemists from various specialties, chemical engineers, development specialists, and possibly even lawyers. Figure 1.1 represents the people and organizations with which typical laboratory chemists might expect to interact in the course of their jobs.

On the other hand, many persons trained as chemists do not perform actual laboratory work but may work as patent lawyers, financial analysts, plant managers, salespeople, personnel managers, and so on. Also, it is quite common for a person trained as a chemist to have many different jobs during a career.

In Chapters 2 through 21 of this text we will concentrate on the formal discipline of chemistry—its observations, theories, and applications. The goal of Chapter 1 is to introduce some of the important aspects of chemistry not typically discussed in connection with learning chemistry. The chapter includes an introduction to the world of commercial chemistry and provides a couple of specific examples of the types of problems confronted by the practitioners of

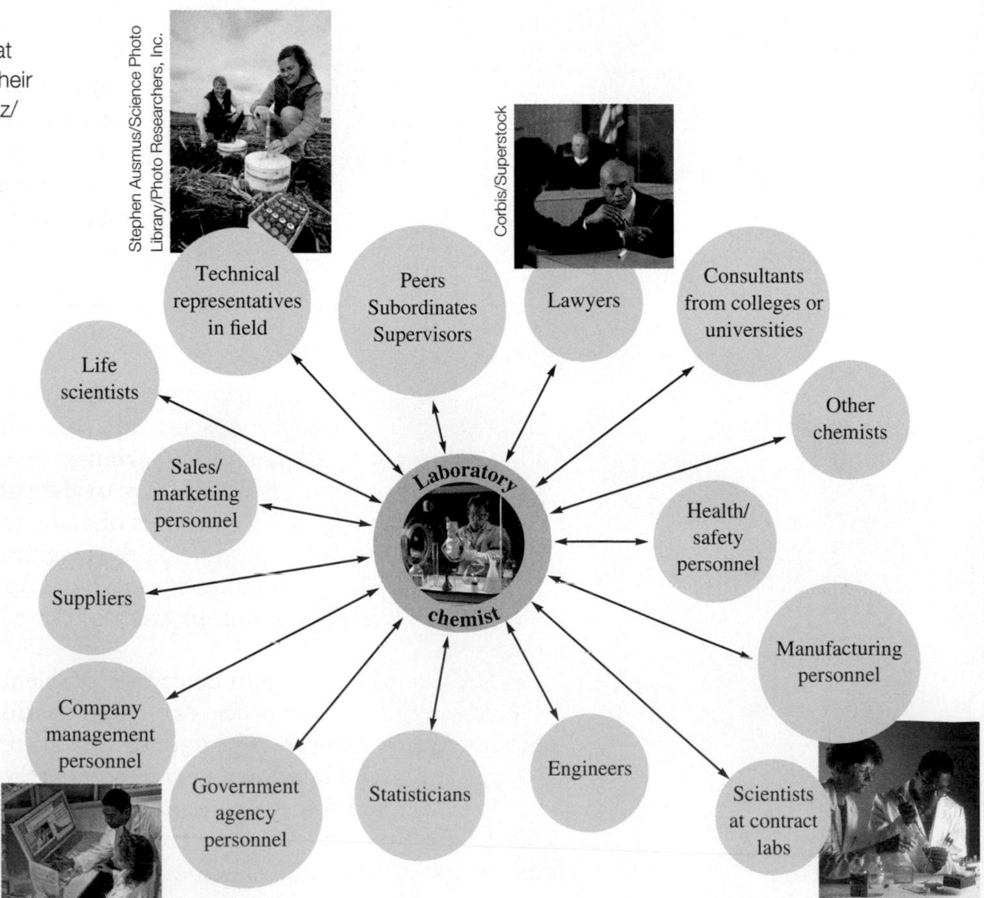

Figure 1.1
Typical chemists interact with a great variety of other people while doing their jobs. (Center photo: Lester Lefkowitz/ Corbis #SC-019-0199)

the "chemical arts." We begin by considering the chemical scientist as a problem solver.

1.1 Thinking Like a Chemist

Much of your life, both personal and professional, will involve problem solving. Most likely, the more creative you are at solving problems, the more effective and successful you will be. Chemists are usually excellent problem solvers because they get a lot of practice. Chemical problems are frequently very complicated—there is usually no neat and tidy solution. Often it is difficult to know where to begin. In response to this dilemma, a chemist makes an educated guess (formulates a hypothesis) and then tests it to see if the proposed solution correctly predicts the observed behavior of the system. This process of trial and error is virtually a way of life for a chemist. Chemists rarely solve a complex problem in a straightforward, elegant manner. More commonly, they poke and prod the problem and make progress only in fits and starts.

It's very important to keep this in mind as you study chemistry. Although "plug and chug" exercises are necessary to familiarize you with the relationships that govern chemical behavior, your ultimate goal should be to advance beyond this stage to true problem solving. Unfortunately, it is impossible to give a formula for becoming a successful problem solver. Creative problem solving is a rather mysterious activity that defies simple analysis. However, it is clear that practice helps. That's why we will make every attempt in this text to challenge you to be creative with the knowledge of chemistry you will be acquiring. Although this process can be frustrating at times, it is definitely worth the struggle—both because it is one of the most valuable skills you can develop and because it helps you test your understanding of chemical concepts. If your understanding of these concepts is not sufficient to allow you to solve problems involving "twists" that you have never encountered before, your knowledge is not very useful to you. The only way to develop your creativity is to expose yourself to new situations in which you need to make new connections. A substantial part of creative problem solving involves developing the confidence necessary to think your way through unfamiliar situations. You must recognize that the entire solution to a complex problem is almost never visible in the beginning. Typically, one tries first to understand pieces of the problem and then puts those pieces together to form the solution.

1.2 A Real-World Chemistry Problem

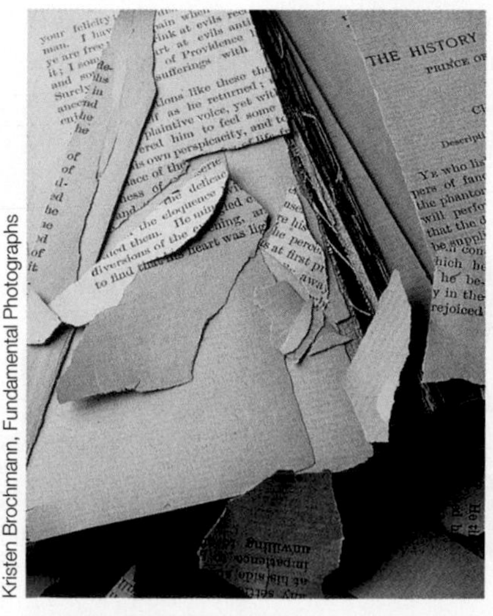

Kristen Brochmann, Fundamental Photographs

Acid-damaged paper.

As discussed, the professional chemist is primarily a problem solver—one who daily confronts tough, but fascinating, situations that must be understood. To illustrate, we will consider an important current problem that requires chemical expertise to solve: the crumbling of the paper in many of the books published in the past century. The pages of many of these books are literally falling apart. To give some perspective on the magnitude of the problem, if the books in the New York Public Library were lined up, they would stretch for almost 100 miles. Currently, about 40 miles of these books are quietly crumbling to dust.

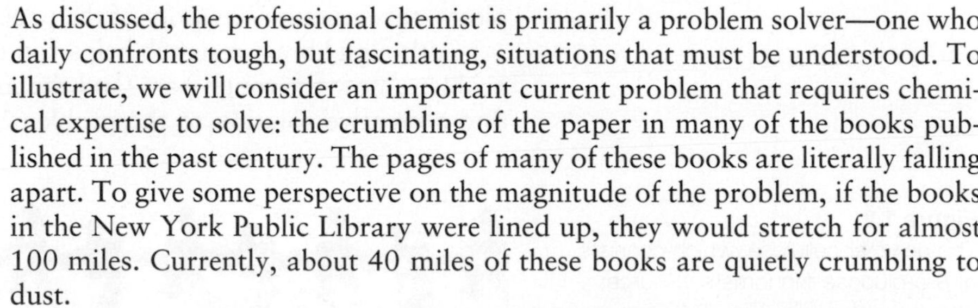

Because of the magnitude of this problem, the company that develops a successful preservation process will reap considerable financial rewards, in addition to performing an important service to society. Assume that you work for a company that is interested in finding a method for saving the crumbling paper in books and that you are put in charge of your company's efforts to develop such a process. What do you know about paper? Probably not much. So the first step is to go to the library to learn all you can about paper. Because paper manufacturing is a mature industry, a great deal of information is avail-

Chemistry Explorers

Alison Williams's Focus: The Structure of Nucleic Acids

Alison Williams started her scientific career as a high school student when she worked part-time at the Ohio State Agricultural Research and Development Center in Wooster, Ohio. She subsequently received her undergraduate degree from Wesleyan University, and then her master's degree and Ph.D. in biophysical chemistry. Dr. Williams has taught at Swarthmore College, Wesleyan University, Princeton University, and is now a senior lecturer at Barnard College.

Dr. Williams's primary interest is to understand the thermodynamic and kinetic behavior of nucleic acid structure. Nucleic acids, in the form of the huge polymers DNA and RNA, are central to the genetic machinery of cells. Dr. Williams and her research group are studying shorter nucleic acids, with the goal of determining how conditions such as the presence of ions in the cellular solutions affect the structures of those nucleic acids. This is significant because ion concentrations in cells vary depending on the type of cell and its growth rate. Dr. Williams's work in this area and related areas should shed light on many important biological processes.

Denise Applewhite/Office of Communications/Princeton University

Alison Williams.

able. Research at the library will show that paper is made of cellulose obtained from wood pulp and that the finished paper is "sized" to give it a smooth surface that prevents ink from "fuzzing." The agent typically used for sizing is alum [$Al_2(SO_4)_3$], which is the cause of the eventual decomposition of the paper. This happens as follows: In the presence of moisture, the Al^{3+} ions from alum become hydrated, forming $Al(H_2O)_6{}^{3+}$. The $Al(H_2O)_6{}^{3+}$ ion acts as an acid because the very strong Al^{3+}—O bond causes changes in the O—H bonds of the attached water molecules, thus allowing H^+ ions to be produced by the following reaction:

$$Al(H_2O)_6{}^{3+} \rightleftharpoons [Al(OH)(H_2O)_5]^{2+} + H^+$$

Therefore, paper sized with alum contains significant numbers of H^+ ions. This is important because the H^+ assists in the breakdown of the polymeric cellulose structure of paper. Cellulose is composed of glucose molecules ($C_6H_{12}O_6$) bonded together to form long chains. A segment of cellulose is shown in Fig. 1.2. When the long chains of glucose units in cellulose are broken into shorter pieces, the structural integrity of the paper fails and it crumbles.

Although library research helps you to understand the fundamentals of the problem, now the tough part (and the most interesting part) begins. Can you find a creative solution to the problem? Can the paper in existing books be

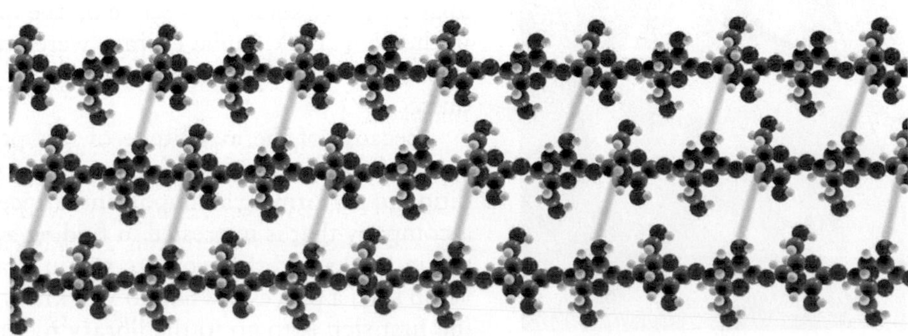

Figure 1.2
The polymer cellulose, which consists of β-D-glucose monomers. (Source: http://en.wikipedia.org/wiki/File:Cellulose_spacefilling_model.jpg)

Chemistry Explorers

Stephanie Burns: Chemist, Executive

Stephanie Burns was always interested in science, even as a little girl. This interest intensified over the years until she obtained a Ph.D. in organic chemistry from Iowa State University, where she specialized in the organic chemistry of silicon. Her career path led her to a job with Dow Corning Company, where she developed useful products containing silicon. Eventually her career path led to several positions involving product development, marketing, and business management. Her outstanding performance in these positions resulted in her appointment as an executive vice president. In early 2003, Dr. Burns, at age 48, was promoted to President and Chief Operating Officer for Dow Corning. In 2004 she became Chief Executive Officer, and in 2006 she was elected Chairman. She has repeatedly been on *Forbes*'s list of the 100 most powerful women.

Dr. Burns says "there was no magic" in reaching the position of Chairman and Chief Executive Officer of Dow Corning. "I'm driven by the science and technology of the company. It's in my blood," she says. Burns says her top priority is to encourage her company's scientists to develop innovative products and expand business built on silicon-based chemistry.

Courtesy Dow Corning. Photo by Jeffrey Glen.

Stephanie Burns.

treated to stop the deterioration in a way that is economical, permanent, and safe?

The essence of the problem seems to be the H^+ present in the paper. How can it be removed or at least rendered harmless?

Your general knowledge of chemistry tells you that some sort of base (a substance that reacts with H^+) is needed. One of the most common and least expensive bases is sodium hydroxide. Why not dip the affected books in a solution of sodium hydroxide and remove the H^+ by the reaction: $H^+ + OH^- \rightarrow H_2O$? This seems to be a reasonable first idea, but as you consider it further and discuss it with your colleagues, several problems become apparent:

1. The NaOH(*aq*) is a strong base and is therefore quite corrosive. It will destroy the paper by breaking down the cellulose just as acid does.
2. The book bindings will be destroyed by dipping the books in water, and the pages will stick together after the books dry.
3. The process will be very labor-intensive, requiring the handling of individual books.

Some of these difficulties can be addressed. For example, a much weaker base than sodium hydroxide could be used. Also, the pages could be removed from the binding, soaked one at a time, dried, and then rebound. In fact, this process is used for some very rare and valuable books, but the labor involved makes it very expensive—much too expensive for the miles of books in the New York Public Library. Obviously, this process is not what your company is seeking.

You need to find a way to treat large numbers of books without disassembling them. How about using a gaseous base? The books could be sealed in a chamber and the gaseous base allowed to permeate them. The first candidate that occurs to you is ammonia, a readily available gaseous base that reacts with H^+ to form NH_4^+:

$$NH_3 + H^+ \longrightarrow NH_4^+$$

This seems like a very promising idea, so you decide to construct a pilot treatment chamber. To construct this chamber, you need some help from coworkers. For example, you might consult a chemical engineer for help in the design of the plumbing and pumps needed to supply ammonia to the chamber. You might also consult a mechanical engineer about the appropriate material to use for the chamber and then discuss the actual construction of the chamber with machinists and other personnel from the company's machine shop. In addition, you probably would consult a safety specialist and possibly a toxicologist about the hazards associated with ammonia.

Before the chamber is built, you also have to think carefully about how to test the effectiveness of the process. How could you evaluate, in a relatively short time, how well the process protects paper from deterioration? At this stage, you would undoubtedly do more library research and consult with other experts, such as a paper chemist your company hires as an outside consultant.

Assume now that the chamber has been constructed and that the initial tests look encouraging. At first the H^+ level is greatly reduced in the treated paper. However, after a few days the H^+ level begins to rise again. Why? The fact that ammonia is a gas at room temperature (and pressure) is an advantage because it allows you to treat many books simultaneously in a dry chamber. However, the volatility of ammonia works against you after the treatment. The process

$$NH_4^+ \longrightarrow NH_3\uparrow + H^+$$

allows the ammonia to escape after a few days. Thus this treatment is too temporary. Even though this effort failed, it was still useful because it provided an opportunity to understand what is required to solve this problem. You need a gaseous substance that *permanently* reacts with the paper and that also consumes H^+.

In discussing this problem over lunch, a colleague suggests the compound diethyl zinc [$(C_2H_5)_2Zn$], which is quite volatile (boiling point = 117°C) and which reacts with water (moisture is present in paper) as follows:

$$(C_2H_5)_2Zn + H_2O \longrightarrow ZnO + 2C_2H_6$$

The C_2H_6 (ethane) is a gas that escapes, but the white solid, ZnO, becomes an integral part of the paper. The important part of ZnO is the oxide ion, O^{2-}, which reacts with H^+ to form water:

$$O^{2-} + 2H^+ \longrightarrow H_2O$$

Thus the ZnO is a nonvolatile base that can be placed in the paper by a gaseous substance. This process seems very promising. However, the major disadvantage of this process (there are always disadvantages) is that diethyl zinc is *very* flammable and great care must be exercised in its use. This leads to another question: Is the treatment effective enough to be worth the risks involved? As it turns out, the Library of Congress used diethyl zinc until 1994, but the process was discontinued because of its risks. Since then, a process known as Bookkeeper has been used. In this process, the book is immersed into a suspension of magnesium oxide (MgO). Small particles (submicron) of MgO are deposited in the pages, and these neutralize the acid and, like ZnO formed from diethyl zinc, become an integral part of the paper. The advantages are the simplicity of the application and the safety of the method.

The type of problem solving illustrated by investigation of the acid decomposition of paper is quite typical of that which a practicing chemist confronts

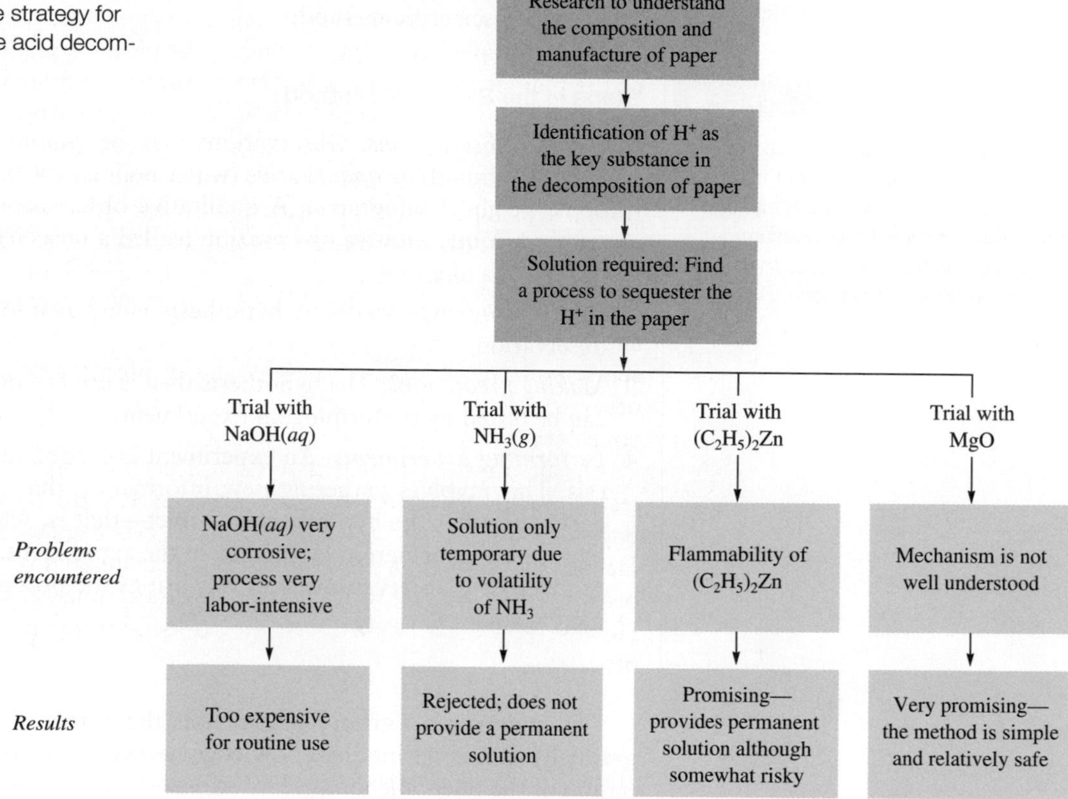

Figure 1.3
Schematic diagram of the strategy for solving the problem of the acid decomposition of paper.

daily. The first step in successful problem solving is to identify the exact nature of the problem. Although this may seem trivial, it is often the most difficult and most important part of the process. Poor problem solving often results from a fuzzy definition of the problem. You cannot efficiently solve a problem if you do not understand the essence of the problem. Once the problem is well defined, then solutions can be advanced, usually by a process of intelligent trial and error. This process typically involves starting with the simplest potential solution and iterating to a final solution as the feedback from earlier attempts is used to refine the approach. Rarely, if ever, is the solution to a complex problem obvious immediately after the problem is defined. The best solution becomes apparent only as the results from various trial solutions are evaluated. A schematic summarizing the approach for dealing with the acid decomposition of paper is shown in Fig. 1.3.

1.3 The Scientific Method

Science is a framework for gaining and organizing knowledge. Science is not simply a set of facts but is also a plan of action—a *procedure* for processing and understanding certain types of information. Scientific thinking is useful in all aspects of life, but in this text we will use it to understand how the chemical world operates. The process that lies at the center of scientific inquiry is called the **scientific method.** There are actually many scientific methods depending on the nature of the specific problem under study and on the particular investigator involved. However, it is useful to consider the following general framework for a generic scientific method:

STEPS

See Appendix A1.6 for conventions regarding the use of significant figures in connection with measurements and the calculations involving measurements. Appendix 2 discusses methods for converting among various units.

Steps in the Scientific Method

1 *Making observations.* Observations may be *qualitative* (the sky is blue; water is a liquid) or *quantitative* (water boils at 100°C; a certain chemistry book weighs 2 kilograms). A qualitative observation does not involve a number. A quantitative observation (called a **measurement**) involves both a number and a unit.

2 *Formulating hypotheses.* A hypothesis is a *possible* explanation for the observation.

3 *Making predictions.* The hypothesis then is used to make a prediction that can be tested by performing an experiment.

4 *Performing experiments.* An experiment is carried out to test the hypothesis. This involves gathering new information that enables a scientist to decide whether the hypothesis is correct—that is, whether it is supported by the new information learned from the experiment. Experiments always produce new observations, and this brings the process back to the beginning again.

To understand a given phenomenon, these steps are repeated many times, gradually accumulating the knowledge necessary to provide a possible explanation of the phenomenon.

As scientists observe nature, they often see that the same observation applies to many different systems. For example, innumerable chemical changes have shown that the total observed mass of the materials involved is the same before and after the change. Such generally observed behavior is formulated into a statement called a **natural law.** For example, the observation that the total mass of materials is not affected by a chemical change in those materials is called the law of conservation of mass. This law tells us *what* happens, but it does not tell us *why.* To try to explain why, we continue to make observations, formulate hypotheses, and test these against observations.

Once a set of hypotheses that agree with the various observations is obtained, the hypotheses are assembled into a theory. A **theory,** which is often called a *model,* is a set of tested hypotheses that gives an overall explanation of some natural phenomenon.

This portrayal of the classical scientific method probably overemphasizes the importance of observations in current scientific practice. Now that we know a great deal about the nature of matter, scientists often start with a hypothesis that they try to refute as they push forward the frontiers of science. See the writings of Karl Popper for more information on this view.

It is very important to distinguish between observations and theories. An observation is something that is witnessed and can be recorded. A theory is an *interpretation*—a possible explanation of *why* nature behaves in a particular way. For example, in Chapter 2 we will read about Dalton's atomic theory, in which John Dalton proposed that a chemical reaction is a reorganization of atoms in reacting substances to produce new substances. As we discussed, we know that mass is conserved (it is a natural law), and we can explain it by claiming that all matter is made of nonchanging atoms (the theory).

Theories inevitably change as more information becomes available. For example, we will also see in Chapter 2 that with further experimentation and observations, the atomic theory came to include subatomic particles—electrons, protons, and neutrons. The "indivisible" atom of Dalton is not indivisible after all. We see the idea of changing theories in all realms of science. For example, the motions of the sun and stars have remained virtually the same over the thousands of years during which humans have been observing them, but our explanations—our theories—for these motions have changed greatly since ancient times.

Critical Units!

Chemical Insights

How important are conversions from one unit to another? If you ask the National Aeronautics and Space Administration (NASA), very important! In 1999 NASA lost a $125 million Mars Climate Orbiter because of a failure to convert from English to metric units.

The problem arose because two teams working on the Mars mission were using different sets of units. NASA's scientists at the Jet Propulsion Laboratory in Pasadena, California, assumed that the thrust data for the rockets on the orbiter they received from Lockheed Martin Astronautics in Denver, which built the spacecraft, were in metric units. In reality, the units were English. As a result the orbiter dipped 100 kilometers lower into the Mars atmosphere than planned and the friction from the atmosphere caused the craft to burn up.

NASA's mistake refueled the controversy over whether Congress should require the United States to switch to the metric system. About 95% of the world now uses the metric system, and the United States is slowly switching from English to metric. For example, the automobile industry has adopted metric fasteners and we buy our soda in 2-liter bottles.

NASA

Artist's conception of the lost Mars Climate Orbiter.

Units can be very important. In fact, they can mean the difference between life and death on some occasions. In 1983, for example, a Canadian jetliner almost ran out of fuel when someone pumped 22,300 pounds of fuel into the aircraft instead of 22,300 kilograms. Remember to watch your units!

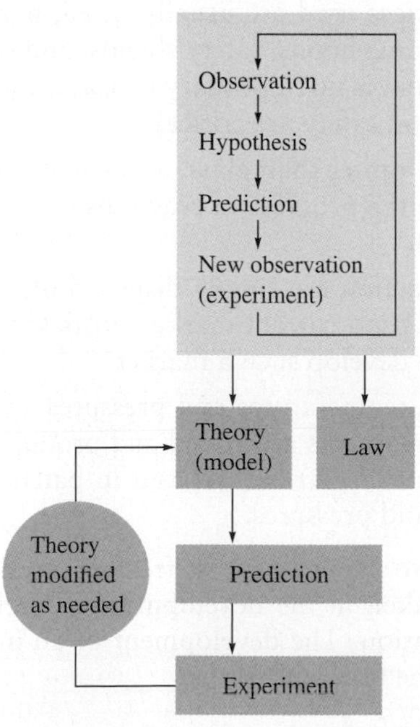

Figure 1.4
The various parts of the scientific method.

The point is that scientists do not stop asking questions just because a given theory seems to account satisfactorily for some aspect of natural behavior. They continue doing experiments to refine or replace the existing theories. This is generally done by using the currently accepted theory to make a prediction and then performing an experiment (making a new observation) to see whether the results bear out this prediction.

Always remember that theories (models) are human inventions. They represent attempts to explain observed natural behavior in terms of human experiences. A theory is actually an educated guess. We must continue to do experiments and to refine our theories (making them consistent with new knowledge) if we hope to approach a more nearly complete understanding of nature.

In this section we have described the scientific method as it might ideally be applied (Fig. 1.4). However, it is important to remember that science does not always progress smoothly and efficiently. For one thing, hypotheses and observations are not totally independent of each other, as we have assumed in the description of the idealized scientific method. The coupling of observations and hypotheses occurs because once we begin to proceed down a given theoretical path, our hypotheses are unavoidably couched in the language of those theoretical underpinnings. In other words, we tend to see what we expect to see and often fail to notice things that we do not expect. Thus the theory we are testing helps us because it focuses our questions. However, at the very same time, this focusing process may limit our ability to see other possible explanations.

It is also important to keep in mind that scientists are human. They have prejudices; they misinterpret data; they become emotionally attached to their theories and thus lose objectivity; and they play politics. Science is affected by profit motives, budgets, fads, wars, and religious beliefs. Galileo, for example, was forced to recant his astronomical observations in the face of strong religious resistance. Lavoisier, the father of modern chemistry, was beheaded because of his political affiliations. And great progress in the chemistry of nitrogen fertilizers resulted from the desire to produce explosives to fight wars. The progress of science is often affected more by the frailties of humans and their institutions than by the limitations of scientific measuring devices. The scientific methods are only as effective as the humans using them. They do not automatically lead to progress.

1.4 Industrial Chemistry

Christian Lagerek/ Shutterstock.com #56046928

Industrial processes require large plants for the production of chemicals.

The impact of chemistry on our lives is due in no small measure to the many industries that process and manufacture chemicals to provide the fuels, fabrics, fertilizers, food preservatives, detergents, and many other products that affect us daily. The chemical industry can be subdivided in terms of three basic types of activities:

1. The isolation of naturally occurring substances for use as raw materials
2. The processing of raw materials by chemical reactions to manufacture commercial products
3. The use of chemicals to provide services

A given industry may participate in one, two, or all of these activities.

Producing chemicals on a large industrial scale is very different from an academic laboratory experiment. Some of the important differences are described below.

- In the academic laboratory, practicality is typically the most important consideration. Because the amounts of substances used are usually small, hazardous materials can be handled by using fume hoods, safety shields, and so on; expense, although always a consideration, is not a primary factor. However, for any industrial process, economy and safety are critical.
- In industry, containers and pipes are metal rather than glass, and corrosion is a constant problem. In addition, because the progress of reactions cannot be monitored visually, gauges must be used.
- In the laboratory, any by-products of a reaction are simply disposed of; in industry, they are usually recycled or sold. If no current market exists for a given by-product, the manufacturer tries to develop such a market.
- Industrial processes often run at very high temperatures and pressures and ideally are *continuous flow,* meaning that reactants are added and products are extracted continuously. In the laboratory, reactions are run in batches and typically at much lower temperatures and pressures.

The many criteria that must be satisfied to make a process feasible on the industrial scale require that great care be taken in the development of each process to ensure safe and economical operation. The development of an industrial chemical process typically involves the following steps:

Step 1: A need for a particular product is identified.

Step 2: The relevant chemistry is studied on a small scale in a laboratory. Various ways of producing the desired material are evaluated in terms of costs and potential hazards.

A Note-able Achievement

Chemical Insights

Post-it Notes, a product of the 3M Corporation, revolutionized casual written communications and personal reminders. Introduced in the United States in 1980, these sticky-but-not-too-sticky notes have now found countless uses in offices, cars, and homes throughout the world.

The invention of sticky notes occurred over a period of about 10 years and involved a great deal of serendipity. The adhesive for Post-it Notes was discovered by Dr. Spencer F. Silver of 3M in 1968. Silver found that when an acrylate polymer material was made in a particular way, it formed cross-linked microspheres. When suspended in a solvent and sprayed on a sheet of paper, this substance formed a "sparse monolayer" of adhesive after the solvent evaporated. Scanning electron microscope images of the adhesive show that it has an irregular surface, a little like the surface of a gravel road. In contrast, the adhesive on cellophane tape looks smooth and uniform, like a superhighway. The bumpy surface of Silver's adhesive caused it to be sticky but not so sticky as to produce permanent adhesion because the number of contact points between the binding surfaces was limited.

When he invented this adhesive, Silver had no specific ideas for its use, so he spread the word of his discovery to his fellow employees at 3M to see if anyone had an application for it. In addition, over the next several years development was carried out to improve the adhesive's properties. It was not until 1974 that the idea for Post-it Notes popped up. One Sunday, Art Fry, a chemical engineer for 3M, was singing in his church choir when he became annoyed that the bookmark in his hymnal kept falling out. He thought to himself that it would be nice if the bookmark were sticky enough to stay in place but not so sticky that it couldn't be moved. Luckily, he remembered Silver's glue—and the Post-it Note was born.

For the next three years, Fry worked to overcome the manufacturing obstacles associated with the product. By 1977 enough Post-it Notes were being produced to supply 3M's corporate headquarters, where the employees quickly became addicted to their many uses. Post-it Notes are now available in 62 colors and 25 shapes.

In the years since their introduction, 3M has heard some remarkable stories connected to the use of these notes. For example, a Post-it Note was applied to the nose of a corporate jet, where it was intended to be read by the plane's Las Vegas ground crew. Someone forgot to remove it, however. The note was still on the nose of the plane when it landed in Minneapolis, having survived a takeoff and landing and speeds of 500 miles per hour at temperatures as low as $-56°F$. Stories on the 3M website also describe how a Post-it Note on the front door of a home survived the 140 mile per hour winds of Hurricane Hugo and how a foreign official accepted Post-it Notes in lieu of cash when a small bribe was needed to cut through bureaucratic hassles.

Post-it Notes have definitely changed the way we communicate and remember things.

Step 3: The data are evaluated by chemists, chemical engineers, business managers, safety engineers, and others to determine which possibility is most feasible.

Step 4: A *pilot-plant test* of the process is carried out. The scale of the pilot plant is between that of the laboratory and that of a manufacturing plant. This test has several purposes: to make sure that the reaction is efficient at a larger scale, to test reactor (reaction container) designs, to determine the costs of the process, to evaluate the hazards, and to gather information on environmental impact.

1.5 Polyvinyl Chloride (PVC): Real-World Chemistry

To get a little better feel for how the world of industrial chemistry operates, we will now consider a particular product, polyvinyl chloride (PVC), to see what types of considerations have been important in making this a successful and important consumer product.

When you put on a nylon jacket, use a polyethylene wash bottle in the lab, wear contact lenses, or accidentally drop your telephone (and it doesn't break), you are benefiting from the properties of polymers. Polymers are very large molecules that are assembled from small units (called monomers). Because of their many useful properties, polymers are manufactured in huge quantities. In fact, it has been estimated that more than 50% of all industrial chemists have jobs that are directly related to polymers.

One particularly important polymer is polyvinyl chloride (PVC), which is made from the molecule commonly called vinyl chloride:

$$\begin{array}{ccc} H & & H \\ & C=C & \\ H & & Cl \end{array}$$

When many of these units are joined together, the polymer PVC results:

$$\begin{array}{cccccccccccc} & H & & H & & H & & H & & H & & H \\ & | & & | & & | & & | & & | & & | \\ \sim\sim & C & - & C & - & C & - & C & - & C & - & C\sim\sim \\ & | & & | & & | & & | & & | & & | \\ & H & & Cl & & H & & Cl & & H & & Cl \end{array}$$

This can be represented as

$$\left(\begin{array}{ccc} H & & H \\ | & & | \\ C & - & C \\ | & & | \\ H & & Cl \end{array} \right)_n$$

where n is usually greater than 1000.

Because the development of PVC into a useful, important material is representative of the type of problem solving encountered in industrial chemistry, we will consider it in some detail.

In pure form PVC is a hard, brittle substance that decomposes easily at the high temperatures necessary to process it. This makes it almost useless. The fact that it has become a high-volume plastic ($\approx$10 billion pounds per year produced in the United States) is a tribute to chemical innovation. Depending on the additives used, PVC can be made rigid or highly flexible, and it can be tailored for use in inexpensive plastic novelty items or for use in precision engineering applications.

A scientist inspecting a product being formed from polyvinyl plastic.

Brownie Harris/Stock Market/Corbis

The development of PVC illustrates the interplay of logic and serendipity, as well as the importance of optimizing properties both for processing and for applications. PVC production has been beset with difficulties from the beginning, but solutions have been found for each problem through a combination of chemical deduction and trial and error. For example, many additives have been found that provide temperature stability so that PVC can be processed as a melt (liquid) and so that PVC products can be used at high temperatures. However, there is still controversy among chemists about exactly how PVC decomposes thermally, and thus the reason these stabilizers work is not well understood. Also, there are approximately 100 different plasticizers (softeners) available for PVC, but the theory of its plasticization is too primitive to predict accurately which compounds might produce even better results.

PVC was discovered by a German chemical company in 1912, but its brittleness and thermal instability proved so problematical that in 1926 the company stopped paying the fees to maintain its patents. That same year Waldo Semon, a chemist at B. F. Goodrich, found that PVC could be made flexible by the addition of phosphate and phthalate esters. Semon also found that white lead [$Pb_3(OH)_2(CO_3)_2$] provided thermal stability to PVC. These advances led to the beginning of significant U.S. industrial production of PVC ($\approx$4 million pounds per year by 1936). In an attempt to further improve PVC, T. L. Gresham (also a chemist at B. F. Goodrich) tried approximately 1000 compounds, searching for a better plasticizer. The compound that he found (its identity is not important here) remains the most common plasticizer added to PVC. The types of additives commonly used in the production of PVC are listed in Table 1.1.

Although the exact mechanism of the thermal, heat-induced decomposition of PVC remains unknown, most chemists agree that the chlorine atoms present in the polymer play an important role. Lead salts are added to PVC both to provide anions less reactive than chloride and to provide lead ions to combine with the released chloride ions. As a beneficial side effect, the lead chloride formed gives PVC enhanced electrical resistance, making lead stabilizers particularly useful in producing PVC for electrical wire insulation.

One major use of PVC is for pipes in plumbing systems. Here, even though the inexpensive lead stabilizers would be preferred from an economic standpoint, the possibility that the toxic lead could be leached from the pipes into the drinking water necessitates the use of more expensive tin and antimony compounds as thermal stabilizers. Because about one-half of the annual U.S. production of PVC is formed into piping, the PVC formulation used for pipes represents a huge market for companies that manufacture additives, and the competition is very intense. A recently developed low-cost thermal stabilizer for PVC is a mixture of antimony and calcium salts. This mixture has replaced stabilizers containing tin compounds that have become increasingly costly in recent years.

Outdoor applications of PVC often require that it contain ultraviolet light absorbers to protect against damage from sunlight. For pigmented applications

Table 1.1

Types of Additives Commonly Used in the Production of PVC

Type of Additive	Effect
Plasticizer	Softens the material
Heat stabilizer	Increases resistance to thermal decomposition
Ultraviolet absorber	Prevents damage by sunlight
Flame retardant	Lowers flammability
Biocide	Prevents bacterial or fungal attack

such as vinyl siding, window frames, and building panels, titanium(IV) oxide (TiO_2) is usually used. For applications in which the PVC must be transparent, other compounds are needed.

The additives used in PVC in the largest amounts are plasticizers, but one detrimental effect of these additives is an increase in flammability. Rigid PVC, which contains little plasticizer, is quite flame resistant because of its high chloride content. However, as more plasticizer is added for flexibility, the flammability increases to the point where fire retardants must be added, the most common being antimony(III) oxide (Sb_2O_3). As the PVC is heated, this oxide forms antimony(III) chloride ($SbCl_3$), which migrates into the flame, where it inhibits the burning process. Because antimony(III) oxide is a white salt, it cannot be used for transparent or darkly colored PVC. In these cases sodium antimonate (Na_3SbO_4), a transparent salt, is used.

Once the additives have been chosen for a particular PVC application, the materials must be blended. This is often done in a dry-blending process, which produces a powder that is then used for fabrication of the final product. The powdered mixture also can be melted and formed into pellets, which are easily shipped to manufacturing plants, where they are remelted and formed into the desired products.

The production of PVC provides a good case study of an industrial process. It illustrates many of the factors that must be taken into account when any product is manufactured: effectiveness of the product, cost, ease of production, safety, and environmental impact. The last issue is becoming ever more important as our society struggles both to reduce the magnitude of the waste stream by recycling and to improve our waste disposal methods.

Key Terms

Section 1.3
scientific method
measurement
natural law
theory

For Review

OWL and go Chemistry

Sign in at **www.cengage.com/owl** to:

- View tutorials and simulations, develop problem-solving skills, and complete online homework assigned by your professor.
- Download Go Chemistry mini lecture modules for quick review and exam prep from OWL (or purchase them at **www.cengagebrain.com**)

Thinking like a chemist

- Problem solving often requires trial and error.
- Practice helps one become a better problem solver.

Scientific method

- Make observations.
- Formulate hypotheses.
- Make predictions.
- Perform experiments.

Difference between a law and a theory

- A law summarizes what happens; it comes from generally observed behavior.
- A theory is an attempt at an explanation of why nature behaves in a particular way; it is subject to modifications over time and sometimes fails.

Three general types of activities in industrial chemistry

- Isolating naturally occurring substances for use as raw materials
- Processing raw materials into commercial products via chemical reactions
- Using chemicals to provide services

Atoms, Molecules, and Ions

2 chapter

Computer graphic of a carbon nanotube.

Oxford Scientific PhotoLibrary #2104025l

In this chapter we present very briefly many of the fundamental concepts and some of the vocabulary of chemistry plus something about how the science developed. Depending on your specific background in chemistry, much of this material may be review. However, whatever your background, read this chapter carefully to be sure this material is fresh in your mind as we pursue the study of reaction chemistry in Chapters 3 and 4.

2.1 The Early History of Chemistry

Sign in to OWL at www.cengage.com/owl to view tutorials and simulations, develop problem-solving skills, and complete online homework assigned by your professor.

go Chemistry

Download mini lecture videos for key concept review and exam prep from OWL or purchase them from www.cengagebrain.com.

Chemistry has been important since ancient times. The processing of natural ores to produce metals for ornaments and weapons and the use of embalming fluids are two applications of chemical phenomena that were used before 1000 B.C.

The Greeks were the first to try to explain why chemical changes occur. By about 400 B.C. they had proposed that all matter was composed of four fundamental substances: fire, earth, water, and air. The Greeks also considered the question of whether matter is continuous, and thus infinitely divisible into smaller pieces, or composed of small indivisible particles. One supporter of the latter position was Democritus, who used the term *atomos* (which later became *atoms*) to describe these ultimate particles. However, because the Greeks had no experiments to test their ideas, no definitive conclusion about the divisibility of matter was reached.

The next 2000 years of chemical history were dominated by a pseudoscience called alchemy. Alchemists were often mystics and fakes who were obsessed with the idea of turning cheap metals into gold. However, this period also saw important discoveries: Elements such as mercury, sulfur, and antimony were discovered, and alchemists learned how to prepare the mineral acids.

Roald Hoffman/Cornell University

The Priestley Medal is the highest honor given by the American Chemical Society. It is named for **Joseph Priestley,** who was born in England on March 13, 1733. He performed many important scientific experiments, one of which led to the discovery that a gas later identified as carbon dioxide could be dissolved in water to produce *seltzer.* Also, as a result of meeting Benjamin Franklin in London in 1766, Priestley became interested in electricity and was the first to observe that graphite was an electrical conductor. However, his greatest discovery occurred in 1774, when he isolated oxygen by heating mercuric oxide.

Because of his nonconformist political views, he was forced to leave England. He died in the United States in 1804.

The foundations of modern chemistry were laid in the sixteenth century with the development of systematic metallurgy (extraction of metals from ores) by a German, Georg Bauer, and the medicinal application of minerals by the Swiss alchemist Paracelsus.

The first "chemist" to perform truly quantitative experiments was Robert Boyle (1627–1691), an Irish scientist, who carefully measured the relationship between the pressure and volume of gases. When Boyle published his book *The Sceptical Chemist* in 1661, the quantitative sciences of physics and chemistry were born. In addition to his results on the quantitative behavior of gases, Boyle's other major contribution to chemistry consisted of his ideas about the chemical elements. Boyle held no preconceived notion about the number of elements. In his view a substance was an element unless it could be broken down into two or more simpler substances. As Boyle's experimental definition of an element became generally accepted, the list of known elements began to grow, and the Greek system of four elements finally died. Although Boyle was an excellent scientist, he was not always right. For example, he clung to the alchemist's views that metals were not true elements and that a way would eventually be found to change one metal to another.

The phenomenon of combustion evoked intense interest in the seventeenth and eighteenth centuries. The German chemist Georg Stahl (1660–1734) suggested that a substance he called phlogiston flowed out of the burning material. Stahl postulated that a substance burning in a closed container eventually stopped burning because the air in the container became saturated with phlogiston. Oxygen gas, discovered by Joseph Priestley (1733–1804), an English clergyman and scientist, was found to support vigorous combustion and was thus supposed to be low in phlogiston. In fact, oxygen was originally called "dephlogisticated air." It is important to note that the observations made by

Joseph Priestley did not contradict those made by Georg Stahl. However, Priestley's theory to explain what he saw was vastly different. As we stated in Chapter 1, *what* happens doesn't change, but our ideas about *why* a phenomenon occurs can change. Such is the nature of science.

2.2 Fundamental Chemical Laws

By the late eighteenth century, combustion had been studied extensively; the gases carbon dioxide, nitrogen, hydrogen, and oxygen had been discovered; and the list of elements continued to grow. However, it was Antoine Lavoisier (1743–1794), a French chemist (Fig. 2.1), who finally explained the true nature of combustion, thus clearing the way for the tremendous progress that was made near the end of the eighteenth century. Lavoisier, like Boyle, regarded measurement as the essential operation of chemistry. His experiments, in which he carefully weighed the reactants and products of various reactions, suggested that *mass is neither created nor destroyed.* Lavoisier's discovery of this **law of conservation of mass** was the basis for the developments in chemistry in the nineteenth century.

Lavoisier's quantitative experiments showed that combustion involved oxygen (which Lavoisier named), not phlogiston. He also discovered that life was supported by a process that also involved oxygen and was similar in many ways to combustion. In 1789 Lavoisier published the first modern chemistry textbook, *Elementary Treatise on Chemistry,* in which he presented a unified picture of the chemical knowledge assembled up to that time. Unfortunately, in the same year the text was published, the French Revolution began. Lavoisier, who had been associated with collecting taxes for the government, was executed on the guillotine as an enemy of the people in 1794.

After 1800, chemistry was dominated by scientists who, following Lavoisier's lead, performed careful weighing experiments to study the course of chemical reactions and to determine the composition of various chemical compounds. One of these chemists, a Frenchman, Joseph Proust (1754–1826), showed that *a given compound always contains exactly the same proportion of elements by mass.* For example, Proust found that the substance copper car-

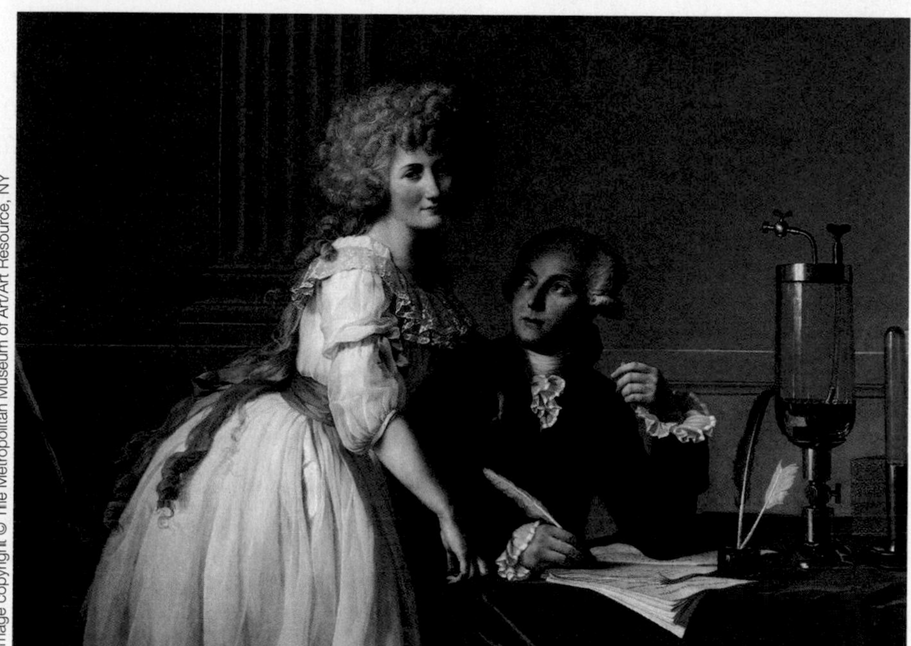

Figure 2.1
Antoine Lavoisier with his wife. Lavoisier was born in Paris on August 26, 1743. From the beginning of his scientific career, Lavoisier recognized the importance of accurate measurements. His careful weighings showed that mass is conserved in chemical reactions and that combustion involves reaction with oxygen. Also, he wrote the first modern chemistry textbook. He is often called the father of modern chemistry.

Because of his connection to a private tax-collecting firm, radical French revolutionaries demanded his execution, which occurred on the guillotine on May 8, 1794.

Manchester Literary & Philosophical Society

Figure 2.2
John Dalton (1766–1844), an Englishman, began teaching at a Quaker school when he was 12. His fascination with science included an intense interest in meteorology (he kept careful daily weather records for 46 years), which led to an interest in the gases of the air and their ultimate components, atoms. Dalton is best known for his atomic theory, in which he postulated that the fundamental differences among atoms are their masses. He was the first to prepare a table of relative atomic weights.

Dalton was a humble man with several apparent handicaps: He was poor; he was not articulate; he was not a skilled experimentalist; and he was color-blind, a terrible problem for a chemist. Despite these disadvantages, he helped revolutionize the science of chemistry.

bonate is always 5.3 parts copper to 4 parts oxygen to 1 part carbon (by mass). The principle of the constant composition of compounds, originally called Proust's law, is now known as the **law of definite proportion.**

Proust's discovery stimulated John Dalton (1766–1844), an English schoolteacher (Fig. 2.2), to think about atoms. Dalton reasoned that if elements were composed of tiny individual particles, a given compound should always contain the same combination of these atoms. This concept explained why the same relative masses of elements were always found in a given compound.

But Dalton discovered another principle that convinced him even more of the existence of atoms. He noted, for example, that carbon and oxygen form two different compounds that contain different relative amounts of carbon and oxygen, as shown by the following data:

	Mass of Oxygen That Combines with 1 g of Carbon
Compound I	1.33 g
Compound II	2.66 g

Dalton noted that compound II contained twice as much oxygen per gram of carbon as compound I, a fact that could be easily explained in terms of atoms. Compound I might be CO, and compound II might be CO_2. This principle, which was found to apply to compounds of other elements as well, became known as the **law of multiple proportions:** *When two elements form a series of compounds, the ratios of the masses of the second element that combine with 1 gram of the first element can always be reduced to small whole numbers.*

These ideas are also illustrated by the compounds of nitrogen and oxygen, as shown by the following data:

	Mass of Nitrogen That Combines with 1 g of Oxygen
Compound I	1.750 g
Compound II	0.8750 g
Compound III	0.4375 g

which yield the following ratios:

$$\frac{\text{I}}{\text{II}} = \frac{1.750}{0.8750} = \frac{2}{1}$$

$$\frac{\text{II}}{\text{III}} = \frac{0.8750}{0.4375} = \frac{2}{1}$$

$$\frac{\text{I}}{\text{III}} = \frac{1.750}{0.4375} = \frac{4}{1}$$

The significance of these data is that compound I contains twice as much nitrogen (N) per gram of oxygen (O) as does compound II and that compound II contains twice as much nitrogen per gram of oxygen as does compound III. In terms of the numbers of atoms combining, these data can be explained by any of the following sets of formulas:

Compound I	N_2O		NO		N_4O_2
Compound II	NO	or	NO_2	or	N_2O_2
Compound III	NO_2		NO_4		N_2O_4

In fact, an infinite number of other possibilities exists. Dalton could not deduce absolute formulas from the available data on relative masses. However, the data on the composition of compounds in terms of the relative masses of the elements supported his hypothesis that each element consisted of a certain type of atom and that compounds were formed from specific combinations of atoms.

2.3 Dalton's Atomic Theory

In 1808 Dalton published *A New System of Chemical Philosophy,* in which he presented his theory of atoms.

These statements are a modern paraphrase of Dalton's ideas.

Dalton's Model

1. Each element is made up of tiny particles called atoms.
2. The atoms of a given element are identical; the atoms of different elements are different in some fundamental way or ways.
3. Chemical compounds are formed when atoms combine with one another. A given compound always has the same relative numbers and types of atoms.
4. Chemical reactions involve reorganization of the atoms—changes in the way they are bound together. The atoms themselves are not changed in a chemical reaction.

It is instructive to consider Dalton's reasoning on the relative masses of the atoms of the various elements. In Dalton's time, water was known to be composed of the elements hydrogen and oxygen, with 8 grams of oxygen present for every 1 gram of hydrogen. If the formula for water were OH, an oxygen atom would have to have eight times the mass of a hydrogen atom. However, if the formula for water were H_2O (two atoms of hydrogen for every oxygen atom), this would mean that each atom of oxygen is 16 times as heavy as *each* atom of hydrogen (since the ratio of the mass of one oxygen to that of *two* hydrogens is 8 to 1). Because the formula for water was not then known, Dalton could not specify the relative masses of oxygen and hydrogen unambiguously. To solve the problem, Dalton made a fundamental assumption: He decided that nature would be as simple as possible. This assumption led him to conclude that the formula for water should be OH. He thus assigned hydrogen a mass of 1 and oxygen a mass of 8.

mass (m): the quantity of matter in a body

weight: $m \times g$

Using similar reasoning for other compounds, Dalton prepared the first table of **atomic masses** (formerly called atomic weights by chemists, since mass is usually determined by comparison to a standard mass—a process called *weighing**). Many of the masses were later proved to be wrong because of Dalton's incorrect assumptions about the formulas of certain compounds, but the construction of a table of masses was an important step forward.

Although not recognized as such for many years, the keys to determining absolute formulas for compounds were provided in the experimental work of the French chemist Joseph Gay-Lussac (1778–1850) and by the hypothesis of an Italian chemist named Amedeo Avogadro (1776–1856). In 1809 Gay-Lussac performed experiments in which he measured (under the same conditions of temperature and pressure) the volumes of gases that reacted with one another. For example, Gay-Lussac found that 2 volumes of hydrogen react with 1 volume of oxygen to form 2 volumes of gaseous water and that 1 vol-

*Technically, weight is the force exerted on an object by gravitational attraction to a body such as the earth (weight = mass × acceleration due to gravity). It is mass (the quantity of matter in a body), not weight, that chemists use in their measurements, although the two terms are sometimes used interchangeably.

Joseph Louis Gay-Lussac (1778–1850), a French physicist and chemist, was remarkably versatile. Although he is now primarily known for his studies on the combining of volumes of gases, Gay-Lussac was instrumental in the studies of many of the other properties of gases. Some of Gay-Lussac's motivation to learn about gases arose from his passion for ballooning. In fact, he made ascents to heights of over 4 miles to collect air samples, setting altitude records that stood for approximately 50 years. Gay-Lussac also was the codiscoverer of boron and the developer of a process for manufacturing sulfuric acid. As chief assayer of the French mint, Gay-Lussac developed many techniques for chemical analysis and invented many types of glassware now used routinely in labs. Gay-Lussac spent his last 20 years as a lawmaker in the French government.

ume of hydrogen reacts with 1 volume of chlorine to form 2 volumes of hydrogen chloride.

In 1811 Avogadro interpreted these results by proposing that, *at the same temperature and pressure, equal volumes of different gases contain the same number of particles.* This assumption (called **Avogadro's hypothesis**) makes sense if the distances between the particles in a gas are very great compared with the sizes of the particles. Under these conditions the volume of a gas is determined by the number of molecules present, not by the size of the individual particles.

If Avogadro's hypothesis is correct, Gay-Lussac's result,

2 volumes of hydrogen react with 1 volume of oxygen
$\longrightarrow$ 2 volumes of water vapor

can be expressed as follows:

2 molecules of hydrogen react with 1 molecule of oxygen
$\longrightarrow$ 2 molecules of water

These observations can be explained best by assuming that gaseous hydrogen, oxygen, and chlorine are all composed of diatomic (two-atom) molecules: H_2, O_2, and Cl_2, respectively. Gay-Lussac's results can then be represented as shown in Fig. 2.3. (Note that this reasoning suggests that the formula for water is H_2O, not OH as Dalton believed.)

Unfortunately, Avogadro's interpretations were not accepted by most chemists. The main stumbling block seems to have been the prevailing belief that only atoms of different elements could attract each other to form molecules. Dalton and the other prominent chemists of the time assumed that identical atoms had no "affinity" for each other and thus would not form diatomic molecules.

Because no general agreement existed concerning the formulas for elements such as hydrogen, oxygen, and chlorine or for the compounds formed from these elements, chaos reigned in the first half of the nineteenth century. Although during this period chemists, such as the Swedish chemist Jöns Jakob Berzelius (1779–1848), made painstaking measurements of the masses of various elements that combined to form compounds, these results were interpreted in many different ways, depending on the assumptions about the formulas of the elements and compounds, and this led to many different tables of atomic masses. The situation was so confused that 19 different formulas for the com-

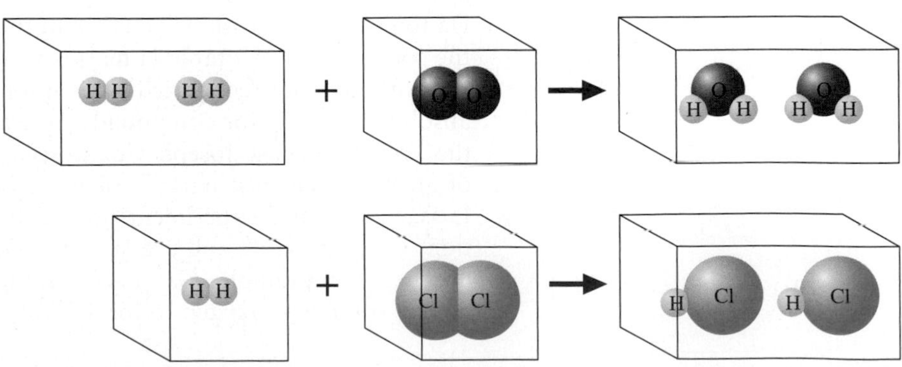

Figure 2.3
A representation of combining gases at the molecular level. The spheres represent atoms in the molecules, and the boxes represent the relative volumes of the gases.

pound acetic acid were given in a textbook written in 1861 by F. August Kekulé (1829–1896). In the next section we will see how this mess was finally cleaned up, primarily because of the leadership of the Italian chemist Stanislao Cannizzaro (1826–1910).

2.4 Cannizzaro's Interpretation

Convinced that chemists had to find a way to agree on a common set of atomic masses, the German chemist F. August Kekulé organized the First International Chemical Congress held in 1860 at Karlsruhe, Germany. At this meeting the young Italian chemist Stanislao Cannizzaro presented his ideas so clearly and forcefully, both in formal and informal talks, that a consensus about atomic masses began to develop in the chemical community. Cannizzaro was guided by two main beliefs:

1. Compounds contained whole numbers of atoms as Dalton postulated.
2. Avogadro's hypothesis was correct—equal volumes of gases under the same conditions contain the same number of molecules.

Applications of Avogadro's hypothesis to Gay-Lussac's results of combining volumes of gas convinced Cannizzaro that hydrogen gas consisted of H_2 molecules. Thus he arbitrarily assigned the relative molecular mass of hydrogen (H_2) to be 2. He then set out to measure the relative molecular masses for other gaseous substances. He did so by comparing the mass of 1 liter of a given gas with the mass of 1 liter of hydrogen gas (both gases at the same conditions of temperature and pressure). For example, the ratio of the masses of 1-liter samples of oxygen and hydrogen gas is 16:

Both gases are at the same temperature and pressure.

$$\frac{\text{Mass of 1.0 L oxygen gas}}{\text{Mass of 1.0 L hydrogen gas}} = \frac{16}{1} = \frac{32}{2}$$

Since by Avogadro's hypothesis both samples of gas contain the same number of molecules, the mass of an oxygen molecule (which he assumed to be O_2) must be 32 relative to a mass of 2 for the H_2 molecule. Since each molecule contains two atoms, the relative atomic masses for oxygen and hydrogen are then 16 and 1, respectively. Using this same method, Cannizzaro found the relative molecular mass of carbon dioxide to be 44 (relative to 2 for H_2). Chemical analysis of carbon dioxide had shown it to contain 27% carbon (by mass). This percentage corresponds to (0.27)(44 g), or 12 g, of carbon in 44 g of carbon dioxide, and 44 g − 12 g = 32 g of oxygen. Recall that the oxygen atom has a relative mass of 16. Thus if the formula of carbon dioxide is assumed to be CO_2, then the relative mass of carbon is 12 because 12 + 2(16) = 44. However, if the formula of carbon dioxide is C_2O_2, then 12 represents the relative mass of two carbon atoms, giving carbon a relative mass of 6. Similarly, the formula C_3O_2 for carbon dioxide gives a relative mass of 4 for carbon. Thus the relative mass of the carbon atom cannot be determined from these data without knowing the formula for carbon dioxide. This is exactly the type of problem that had plagued chemists all along and was the reason for so many different mass tables.

Cannizzaro addressed this problem by obtaining the relative molecular masses of many other compounds containing carbon. For example, consider the data shown in Table 2.1. Notice from these data that the relative mass of carbon present in the compounds is always a multiple of 12. This observation strongly suggests that the relative mass of carbon is 12, which in turn would mean that the formula for carbon dioxide is CO_2.

Chemical Insights Seeing Atoms

There are many pieces of evidence that convince us that matter is made up of atoms. Some of the most compelling evidence comes from scanning probe microscopy. This technique employs a microscopic tip, which responds to a surface to reveal its architecture. The principal methods of scanning probe microscopy are scanning tunneling microscopy (STM) and atomic force microscopy (AFM).

The scanning tunneling microscope was invented at IBM's Zurich Research Laboratory in Switzerland in the early 1980s by Gerd K. Binning and Heinrich Rohrer, who subsequently won the Nobel Prize in Physics for their work. STM uses an ultrasharp metal tip that is brought to within about 1 nm of the surface. A small voltage is applied to the tip, which produces current flow between the surface and the tip. This tunneling* current is strongly dependent on the distance of the tip from the surface. A feedback circuit, which senses the current flow, keeps the tip at a constant distance from the surface. The tip can also be used to move atoms around on the surface, as illustrated by the elliptical arrangement of cobalt atoms shown in Fig. 2.4.

AFM is similar in many ways to STM. In AFM, the attractive and repulsive forces acting on a tiny arm near the surface are measured, and a relief map is produced from the results.

Recently, IBM researcher Leo Gross and his coworkers have found that the image produced by AFM can be greatly improved by inserting a carbon monoxide (CO) molecule at the end of the gold AFM tip. This technique enables the AFM probe to produce a detailed image of an entire molecule such as pentacene ($C_{22}H_{14}$) as depicted in Figure 2.5.

*The term *tunneling* refers to the ability of electrons from the surface to escape even though they do not apparently possess enough energy to overcome the large potential energy holding them there. This quantum mechanical phenomenon is known as tunneling (the electron "tunnels through" the potential barrier).

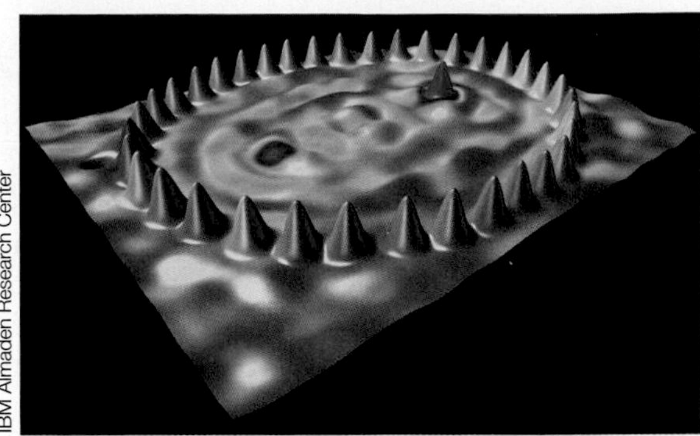

IBM Almaden Research Center

Figure 2.4
Image of a ring of cobalt atoms placed on a copper surface.

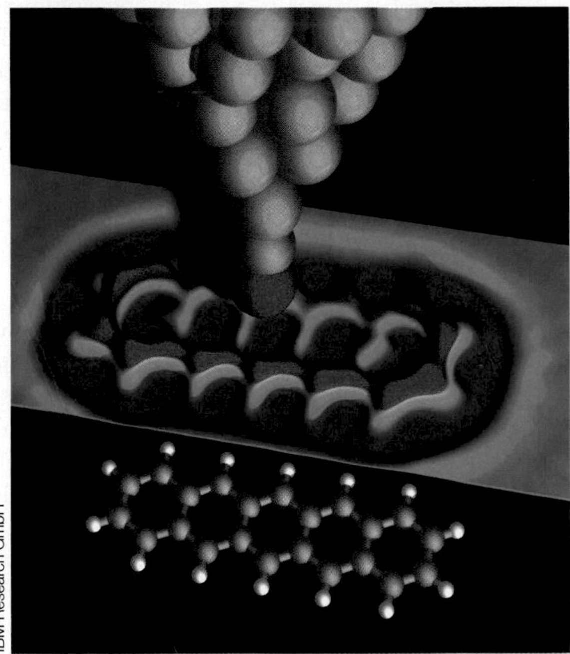

IBM Research GmbH

Figure 2.5
Top, A depiction of the EMF tip in which a CO molecule has been added to the tip (consisting of gold atoms). The image of the pentacene molecule is shown in blue, green, and red.
Bottom, A ball and stick model of the pentacene ($C_{22}H_{14}$) molecule (carbon atoms are black, hydrogen atoms are white)

Table 2.1

Relative Mass Data for Several Gases Containing Carbon

Compound	Relative Molecular Mass	Percent Carbon (by Mass)	Relative Mass of Carbon Present
Methane	16	75	12
Ethane	30	80	24
Propane	44	82	36
Butane	58	83	48
Carbon dioxide	44	27	12

EXAMPLE 2.1

The first four compounds listed in Table 2.1 contain only carbon and hydrogen. Predict the formulas for these compounds.

Solution Since the compounds contain only carbon and hydrogen, the percent hydrogen in each compound (by mass) is 100 − % carbon. We can then find the relative mass of hydrogen present as follows:

$$\text{Relative mass of hydrogen} = \frac{\text{percent hydrogen}}{100} \times \text{relative molecular mass}$$

In tabular form the results are as follows:

Compound	Relative Molecular Mass	Percent Hydrogen	Relative Mass of Hydrogen
Methane	16	25	4
Ethane	30	20	6
Propane	44	18	8
Butane	58	17	10

Combining the preceding results with those from Table 2.1, we find that methane contains relative masses of carbon and hydrogen of 12 and 4, respectively. Using the relative atomic mass values of 12 and 1 for carbon and hydrogen gives a formula of CH_4 for methane. Similarly, the relative masses of carbon and hydrogen in ethane of 24 and 6, respectively, lead to a formula of C_2H_6 for ethane. Similar reasoning gives formulas for propane and butane of C_3H_8 and C_4H_{10}, respectively.

Bettmann/Corbis

Stanislao Cannizzaro (1826–1910). Cannizzaro's work ended the confusion of atomic mass values.

Cannizzaro's work was so convincing because he collected data on so many compounds. Although he couldn't absolutely prove that his atomic mass values were correct (because he had no way to verify absolutely the formulas of the compounds), the consistency of the large quantity of data he had collected eventually convinced virtually everyone that his interpretation made sense and that the relative values of atomic mass that he had determined were correct. The confusion was finally over. Chemistry had the universal (relative) mass standards that it needed.

It is worthwhile to note that Cannizzaro's work led to *approximate* values of the relative atomic masses. His goal was not to determine highly precise values for atomic masses but rather to pin down the approximate values (for example, to show that oxygen's relative mass was 16 rather than 8). The most precise values for atomic masses were determined by quantitative experiments in which the combining masses of elements were carefully measured, such as in the work of Berzelius.

In the next chapter we will have much more to say about atomic masses, including the origin of the very precise values used by today's chemists.

2.3 Early Experiments to Characterize the Atom

On the basis of the work of Dalton, Gay-Lussac, Avogadro, Cannizzaro, and others, chemistry was beginning to make sense. The concept of atoms was clearly a good idea. Inevitably, scientists began to wonder about the nature of the atom. What is an atom made of, and how do the atoms of the various elements differ?

The Electron

The first important experiments that led to an understanding of the composition of the atom were done by the English physicist J. J. Thomson (1856–1940), who studied electrical discharges in partially evacuated tubes called *cathode-ray tubes* (Fig. 2.6) during the period from 1898 to 1903. Thomson found that when high voltage was applied to the tube, a "ray" he called a **cathode ray** (because it emanated from the negative electrode, or cathode) was produced. Because this ray was produced at the negative electrode and was repelled by the negative pole of an applied electric field (Fig. 2.7), Thomson postulated that the ray was a stream of negatively charged particles, now called **electrons.** From experiments in which he measured the deflection of the beam of electrons in a magnetic field, Thomson determined the *charge-to-mass ratio* of an electron:

$$\frac{e}{m} = -1.76 \times 10^8 \text{ C/g}$$

where *e* represents the charge on the electron in coulombs and *m* represents the electron mass in grams.

One of Thomson's primary goals in his cathode-ray tube experiments was to gain an understanding of the structure of the atom. He reasoned that since electrons could be produced from electrodes made of various types of metals, *all* atoms must contain electrons. Since atoms were known to be electrically neutral, Thomson further assumed that atoms also must contain some positive charge. Thomson postulated that an atom consisted of a diffuse cloud of positive charge with the negative electrons embedded randomly in it. This model,

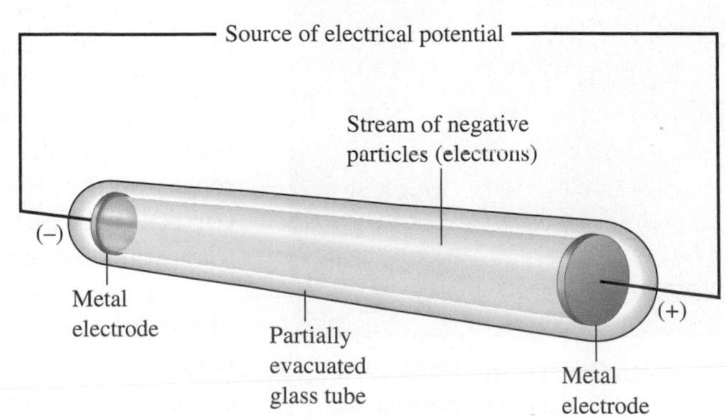

Figure 2.6
A cathode-ray tube. The fast-moving electrons excite the gas in the tube, causing a glow between the electrodes. The green color in the photo is due to the response of the screen (coated with zinc sulfide) to the electron beam.

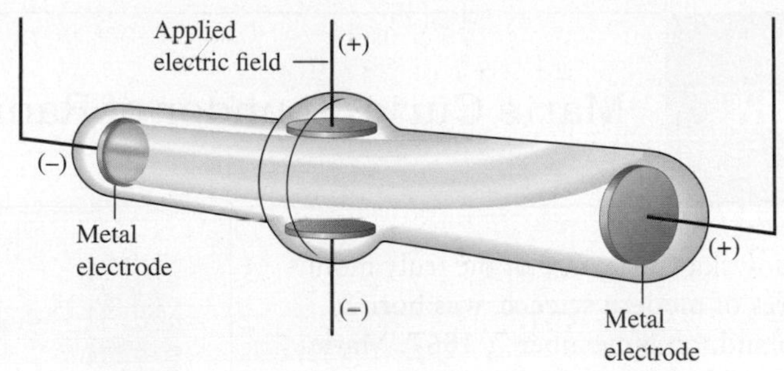

Figure 2.7
Deflection of cathode rays by an applied electric field.

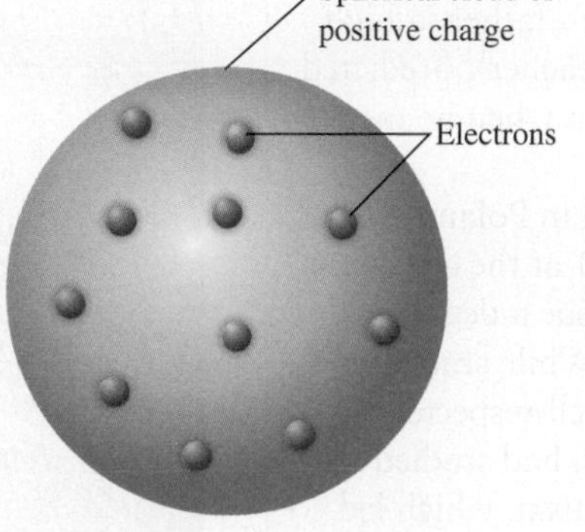

Figure 2.8
Thomson's plum pudding model.

C. Byatt-norman/ Shutterstock.com #19116133

A classic English plum pudding.

shown in Fig. 2.8, is often called the *plum pudding model* because the electrons are like raisins dispersed in a pudding (the positive-charge cloud), as in plum pudding, a favorite English dessert.*

In 1909 Robert Millikan (1868–1953), working at the University of Chicago, performed very clever experiments involving charged oil drops. These experiments allowed him to determine the magnitude of the electron charge (Fig. 2.9). With this value and the charge-to-mass ratio determined by Thomson, Millikan was able to calculate the mass of the electron as 9.11×10^{-31} kilogram.

Bettmann/Corbis #BE042343

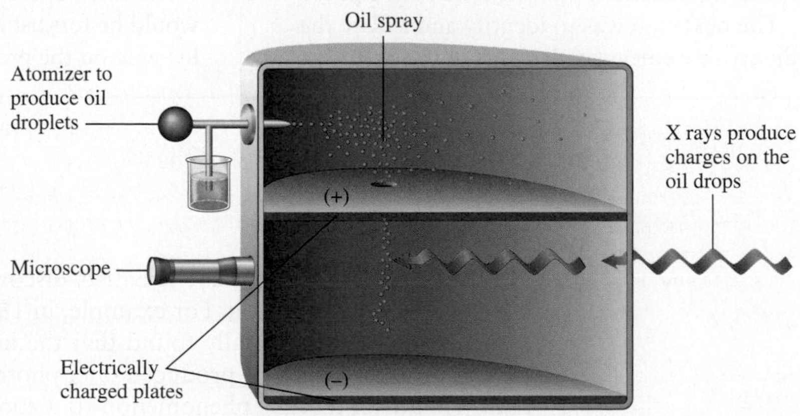

Figure 2.9
A schematic representation of the apparatus Millikan used to determine the charge on the electron. The fall of charged oil droplets due to gravity can be halted by adjusting the voltage across the two plates. The voltage and the mass of an oil drop can then be used to calculate the charge on the oil drop. Millikan's experiments showed that the charge on an oil drop is always a whole-number multiple of the electron charge.

*Although J. J. Thomson is generally given credit for this model, the idea was apparently first suggested by the English mathematician and physicist William Thomson (better known as Lord Kelvin and not related to J. J. Thomson).

Chemical Insights — Marie Curie: Founder of Radioactivity

Marie Sklodowska Curie, one of the truly monumental figures of modern science, was born in Warsaw, Poland, on November 7, 1867. Marie developed an early interest in chemistry, and it is interesting that Dmitri Mendeleev, creator of the periodic table and friend of Marie's father (a high school mathematics and physics teacher), predicted great success for the young woman when he met her in Warsaw.

To escape political persecution in Poland by the Russians, Marie emigrated in 1891 at the age of 24 to Paris, where she decided to pursue a degree in science at the Sorbonne Institute. While studying there, Marie met Pierre Curie, a well-respected physicist who, among other things, had studied the temperature dependence of magnetism, which led to the formulation of Curie's law. Marie and Pierre were married in 1895, after which Marie decided to pursue a doctorate in physics. As the subject of her doctoral thesis, she decided to study the strange radiation emitted by uranium ore, which had been accidentally discovered by Henri Becquerel. Marie was recruited for the task by Becquerel himself. As she began her studies, Madame Curie noticed that pitchblende produced more radiation than uranium, and she became convinced that an as-yet-unknown element in pitchblende was responsible for this "radioactivity"—a term that she coined.

The next step was to identify and isolate the radioactive element or elements in pitchblende.

Bettmann/Corbis

Marie Sklodowska Curie (1867–1934) in her laboratory.

Pierre interrupted his own research—he thought it would be for just a few weeks—to collaborate with his wife on the project. The Curies actually bor-

Radioactivity

In the late nineteenth century, scientists discovered that certain elements produce high-energy radiation. For example, in 1896 the French scientist Antoine Henri Becquerel accidentally found that the image of a piece of mineral containing uranium could be produced on a photographic plate in the absence of light. He attributed this phenomenon to a spontaneous emission of radiation by the uranium, which his student, Marie Curie, called **radioactivity.** Studies in the early twentieth century demonstrated three types of radioactive emission: gamma (γ) rays, beta (β) particles, and alpha (α) particles. A γ ray is high-energy "light"; a β particle is a high-speed electron; and an α particle has a 2+ charge—that is, a charge twice that of the electron and with the opposite sign. The mass of an α particle is 7300 times that of an electron. More modes of radioactivity are now known, and we will discuss them in Chapter 20. Here

rowed money to support themselves and convinced the Austrian government to send them 1 ton of pitchblende from the mines at Joachimsthal. After receiving this 5 cubic foot pile of "sand" from Austria, the Curies worked to chemically digest the ore. In this process they worked with batches as large as 40 pounds at a time in an improvised laboratory with a leaky roof. Working through the bitter winter of 1896 and all through 1897 (in which they had their first daughter, Iréne, who also became a prominent scientist), in July 1898 the Curies finally isolated a previously unknown element they named polonium after Marie's homeland. Although most people would be satisfied by discovering a new element 400 times more radioactive than uranium, the Curies kept working. By this time, the 1 ton of pitchblende had been concentrated to an amount that would fit into an ordinary flask. Marie continued to extract and crystallize increasingly smaller amounts of material. Finally, in November 1898 she obtained crystals of the salt of another new element that the Curies named radium, which turned out to be 900 times more radioactive than uranium.

For their work the Curies were awarded the Nobel Prize in Physics in 1903, sharing the award with Henri Becquerel. In 1904, Pierre was awarded a chair in physics at the Sorbonne. He was killed tragically on the streets of Paris on April 19, 1906, when he was knocked down by a cab and the wheels of a heavy van passing in the opposite direction ran over his head. After mourning for just a few weeks, Marie Curie decided to proceed with the research on radium. In an unprecedented action, she was awarded her late husband's chair and became the first woman to teach at the Sorbonne.

Marie Curie worked tirelessly to develop radioactivity as a new discipline in physics. With the help of five assistants, she studied the effects of radioactivity and developed the atomic theory of its origin. In 1911, Marie was awarded her second Nobel Prize, this time in chemistry, for the chemical processes discovered in the identification of radium and polonium and for the subsequent characterization of those elements. During World War I, she trained doctors in the new methods of radiology and, after learning to drive, personally transported medical equipment to hospitals. After the war, Madame Curie assumed leadership of the newly built Radium Institute in Paris. In 1920, a campaign was mounted in the United States to produce 1 gram of radium for Marie to support her research. She traveled to the United States to receive the precious vial of radium at the White House in 1921.

Marie Curie continued her studies of radioactivity until just before her death of leukemia in 1934. She was truly one of the greatest scientists of the twentieth century.

we will consider only α particles because they were used in some crucial early experiments.

The Nuclear Atom

In 1911 Ernest Rutherford (Fig. 2.10), who performed many of the pioneering experiments to explore radioactivity, carried out an experiment to test Thomson's plum pudding model. The experiment involved directing α particles at a thin sheet of metal foil, as illustrated in Fig. 2.11. Rutherford reasoned that if Thomson's model were accurate, the massive α particles should crash through the thin foil like cannonballs through gauze, as shown in Fig. 2.12(a). He expected the α particles to travel through the foil with, at the most, very minor deflections in their paths. The results of the experiment were very different from those Rutherford anticipated. Although most of the α particles passed

Figure 2.10
Ernest Rutherford (1871–1937) was born on a farm in New Zealand. In 1895 he placed second in a scholarship competition to attend Cambridge University but was awarded the scholarship when the winner decided to stay home and get married. As a scientist in England, Rutherford did much of the early work on characterizing radioactivity. He named the α and β particles and the γ ray and coined the term *half-life* to describe an important attribute of radioactive elements. His experiments on the behavior of α particles striking thin metal foils led him to postulate the nuclear atom. He also invented the name *proton* for the nucleus of the hydrogen atom. He received the Nobel Prize in Chemistry in 1908.

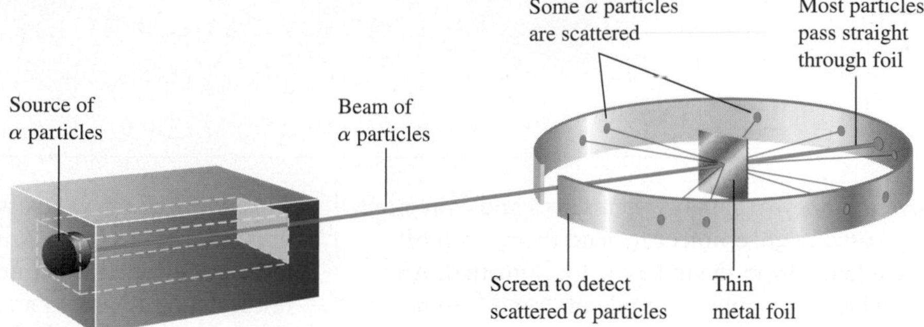

Figure 2.11
Rutherford's experiment on α-particle bombardment of metal foil. (Gold foil was used in the original experiments because it can be hammered into extremely thin sheets.)

straight through, many of the particles were deflected at large angles, as shown in Fig. 2.12(b), and some were reflected, never hitting the detector. This outcome was a great surprise to Rutherford. (He wrote that this result was comparable to shooting a howitzer at a piece of paper and having the shell reflected back.)

Rutherford knew from these results that the plum pudding model for the atom could not be correct. The large deflections of the α particles could be caused only by a center of concentrated positive charge that contains most of the atom's mass, as illustrated in Fig. 2.12(b). Most of the α particles pass directly through the foil because the atom is mostly open space. The deflected α particles are those that had a "close encounter" with the massive positive center of the atom, and the few reflected α particles are those that made a "direct hit" on the much more massive positive center.

In Rutherford's mind these results could be explained only in terms of a **nuclear atom**—an atom with a dense center of positive charge (the **nucleus**) and electrons moving around the nucleus at a distance that is large relative to the nuclear radius.

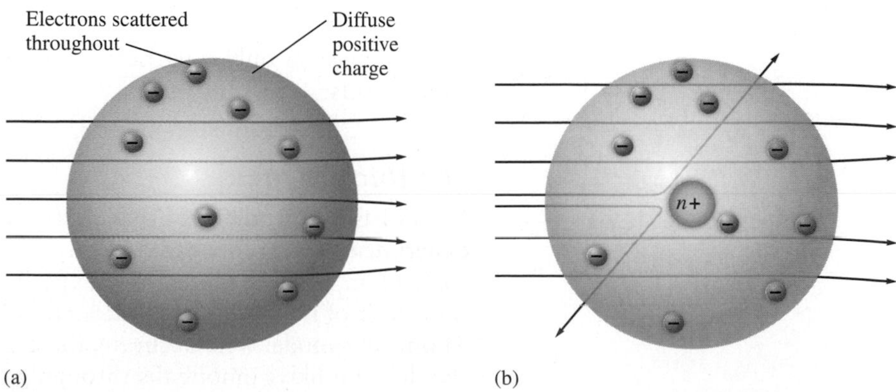

Figure 2.12
(a) The expected results of the metal foil experiment if Thomson's model were correct.
(b) Actual results.

2.6 The Modern View of Atomic Structure: An Introduction

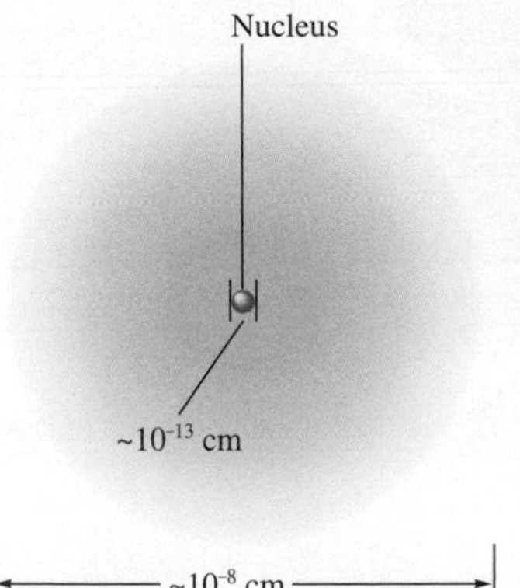

Figure 2.13
A nuclear atom viewed in cross section.

In the years since Thomson and Rutherford, a great deal has been learned about atomic structure. Because much of this material will be covered in detail in later chapters, only an introduction will be given here. The simplest view of the atom is that it consists of a tiny nucleus with a diameter of about 10^{-13} cm and electrons that move about the nucleus at an average distance of about 10^{-8} cm away from it (Fig. 2.13).

As we will see later, the chemistry of an atom mainly results from its electrons. For this reason chemists can be satisfied with a relatively crude nuclear model. The nucleus is assumed to contain **protons,** which have a positive charge equal in magnitude to the electron's negative charge, and **neutrons,** which have virtually the same mass as a proton but no charge. The masses and charges of the electron, proton, and neutron are shown in Table 2.2.

Two striking things about the nucleus are its small size, compared with the overall size of the atom, and its extremely high density. The tiny nucleus accounts for almost all of the atom's mass. Its great density is dramatically demonstrated by the fact that a piece of nuclear material about the size of a pea would have a mass of 250 million tons!

The *chemistry* of an atom arises from its electrons.

As with any theory in science, although it provides answers to questions, it also brings about more questions. An important question to consider at this point is, *"If all atoms are composed of these same components, why do different atoms have different chemical properties?"* The answer to this question lies in the number and the arrangement of the electrons. The electrons constitute most of the atomic volume and thus are the parts that "intermingle" when atoms combine to form molecules. Therefore, the number of electrons possessed by a given atom greatly affects its ability to interact with other atoms. As a result, the atoms of different elements, which have different numbers of protons and electrons, show different chemical behavior.

A sodium atom has 11 protons in its nucleus. Since atoms have no net charge, the number of electrons must equal the number of protons. Therefore, a sodium atom has 11 electrons moving around its nucleus. It is *always* true that a sodium atom has 11 protons and 11 electrons. However, each sodium atom also has neutrons in its nucleus, and different types of sodium atoms exist that have different numbers of neutrons. For example, consider the sodium atoms represented in Fig. 2.14. These two atoms are **isotopes,** or *atoms with*

Table 2.2
The Mass and Charge of the Electron, Proton, and Neutron

Particle	Mass	Charge*
Electron	9.11×10^{-31} kg	1−
Proton	1.67×10^{-27} kg	1+
Neutron	1.67×10^{-27} kg	None

*The magnitude of the charge of the electron and the proton is 1.60×10^{-19} C.

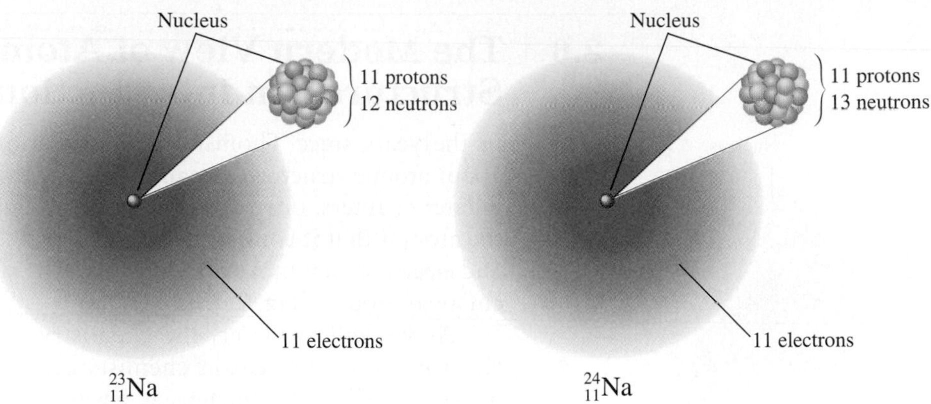

Figure 2.14
Two isotopes of sodium. Both have 11 protons and 11 electrons, but they differ in the number of neutrons in their nuclei. Sodium-23 is the only naturally occurring form of sodium. Sodium-24 does not occur naturally but can be made artificially.

the same number of protons but different numbers of neutrons. Note that the symbol for one particular type of sodium atom is written

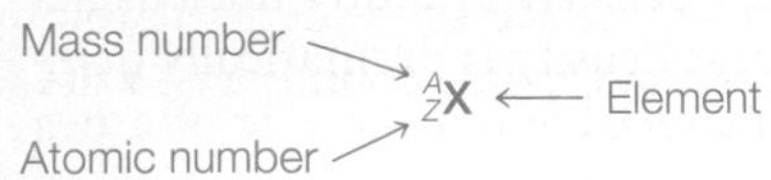

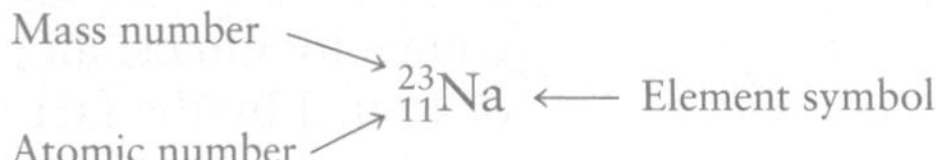

where the **atomic number,** Z (number of protons), is written as a subscript and the **mass number,** A (the total number of protons and neutrons), is written as a superscript. (The particular atom represented here is called "sodium-23." It has 11 electrons, 11 protons, and 12 neutrons.) Because the chemistry of an atom arises from its electrons, isotopes show almost identical chemical properties. In nature most elements contain a mixture of isotopes.

2.7 Molecules and Ions

From a chemist's viewpoint, the most interesting characteristic of an atom is its ability to combine with other atoms to form compounds. It was John Dalton who first recognized that chemical compounds were collections of atoms, but he could not determine the structure of atoms or their means for binding to one another. During the twentieth century, scientists have learned that atoms have electrons and that these electrons participate in the bonding of one atom to another. We will discuss bonding thoroughly in Chapters 13 and 14; here we will consider some definitions that will be useful in the next few chapters.

The forces that hold atoms together in compounds are called **chemical bonds.** One way that atoms can form bonds is by *sharing electrons.* These bonds are called **covalent bonds,** and the resulting collection of atoms is called a **molecule.** Molecules can be represented in several different ways. The simplest method is the **chemical formula,** in which the symbols for the elements are used to indicate the types of atoms present and subscripts are used to indicate the relative numbers of atoms. For example, the formula for carbon dioxide is CO_2, meaning, of course, that each molecule contains 1 atom of carbon and 2 atoms of oxygen.

Familiar examples of molecules that contain covalent bonds are hydrogen (H_2), water (H_2O), oxygen (O_2), ammonia (NH_3), and methane (CH_4). More information about a molecule is given by its **structural formula,** in which the individual bonds are shown (indicated by lines). Structural formulas may or may not indicate the actual shape of the molecule. For example, water might be represented as

$$\mathrm{H{-}O{-}H} \quad \text{or} \quad \begin{array}{c} \mathrm{O} \\ \mathrm{H} \diagup \;\; \diagdown \mathrm{H} \end{array}$$

The structure on the right shows the actual shape of the water molecule, based on experimental evidence. Other examples of structural formulas are

$$\begin{array}{c} \mathrm{H} \\ | \\ \mathrm{H{-}N} \\ | \\ \mathrm{H} \end{array} \quad \text{or} \quad \begin{array}{c} \mathrm{N} \\ \mathrm{H\;\;H\;\;H} \end{array} \qquad\qquad \begin{array}{c} \mathrm{H} \\ | \\ \mathrm{H{-}C{-}H} \\ | \\ \mathrm{H} \end{array} \quad \text{or} \quad \begin{array}{c} \mathrm{H} \\ | \\ \mathrm{C} \\ \mathrm{H\;\;H\;\;H} \end{array}$$

Ammonia   Methane

In the actual structures on the right, the central atom and the solid lines are understood to be in the plane of the page. Atoms connected to the central atom by dashed lines are behind the plane of the page, and atoms connected to the central atom by wedges are in front of the plane of the page.

In a compound composed of molecules, the individual molecules move around as independent units. For example, a methane molecule is represented in Fig. 2.15 using a **space-filling model.** These models show the relative sizes of the atoms, as well as their relative orientation in the molecule. Figure 2.16 shows other examples. **Ball-and-stick models** are also used to represent molecules. The ball-and-stick model of methane is shown in Fig. 2.17.

A second type of chemical bonding results from attractions among ions. An **ion** is an atom or group of atoms that has a net positive or negative charge. The best-known ionic compound is common table salt, or sodium chloride, which forms when neutral chlorine and sodium react.

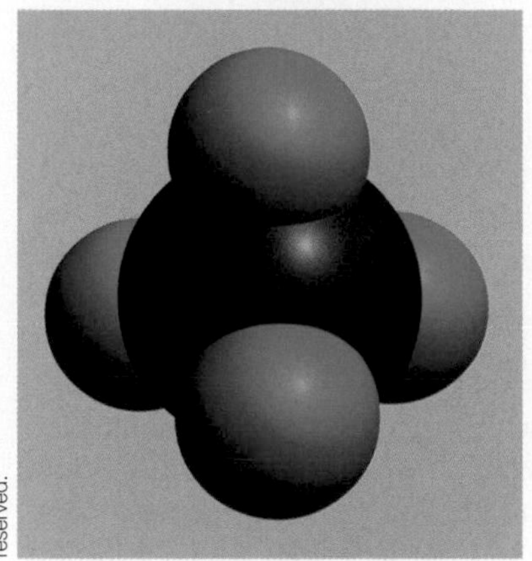

Figure 2.15
Space-filling model of the methane molecule. This type of model shows both the relative sizes of the atoms in the molecule and their spatial relationships.

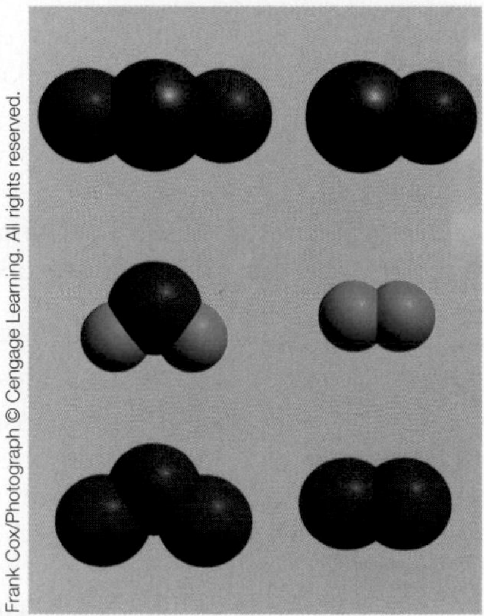

Figure 2.16
Space-filling models of various molecules.

Figure 2.17
Ball-and-stick model of methane.

To see how ions are formed, consider what happens when an electron is transferred from sodium to chlorine (the neutrons in the nuclei will be ignored):

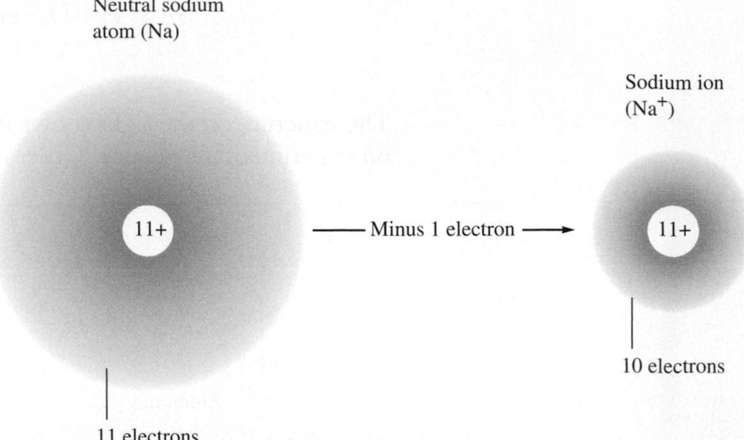

With one electron stripped off, the sodium with its 11 protons and only 10 electrons has become a *positive ion* with a net 1+ charge. A positive ion is called a **cation.** The process can be represented in shorthand form as

$$Na \longrightarrow Na^+ + e^-$$

If an electron is added to chlorine,

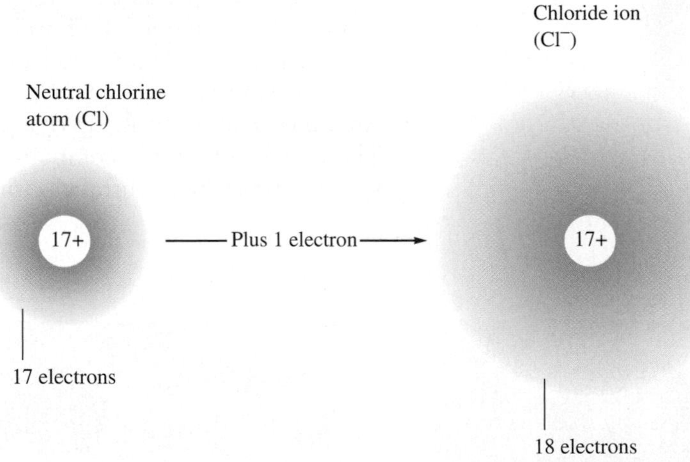

the 18 electrons produce a net 1− charge; the chlorine has become an *ion with a negative charge*—an **anion.** This process is represented as

$$Cl + e^- \longrightarrow Cl^-$$

Because anions and cations have opposite charges, they attract each other. This *force of attraction between oppositely charged ions* is called **ionic bonding.** As shown in Fig. 2.19, sodium metal and chlorine gas (a green gas composed of Cl_2 molecules) react to form solid sodium chloride, which contains many Na^+ and Cl^- ions packed together. The solid forms beautiful, colorless cubic crystals.

A solid consisting of oppositely charged ions is called an *ionic solid,* or (often) a *salt.* Ionic solids can consist of simple ions, as in sodium chloride, or of **polyatomic** (many-atom) **ions,** as in ammonium nitrate (NH_4NO_3), which contains ammonium cations (NH_4^+) and nitrate anions (NO_3^-). The ball-and-stick models of these ions are shown in Fig. 2.18.

Figure 2.18
Ball-and-stick models of the ammonium ion (NH_4^+) and the nitrate ion (NO_3^-).

Figure 2.19
Sodium metal (which is so soft it can be cut with a knife and which consists of individual sodium atoms) reacts with chlorine gas (which contains Cl_2 molecules) to form solid sodium chloride (which contains Na^+ and Cl^- ions packed together).

Na
Na

Cl Cl

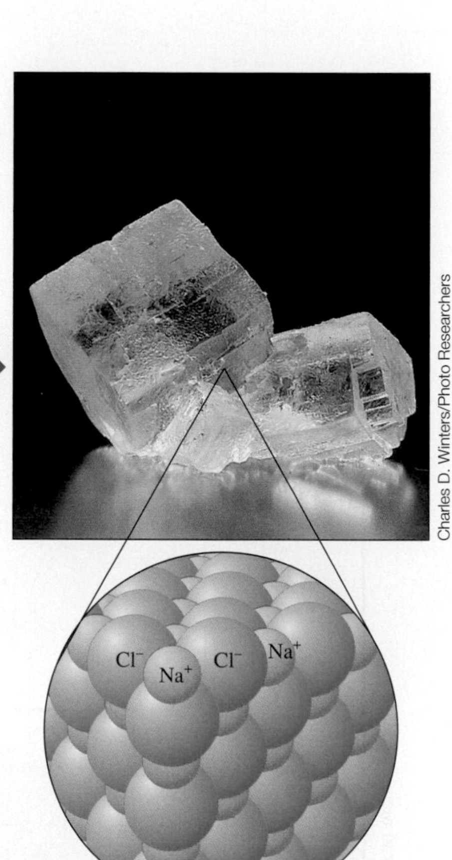

2.8 An Introduction to the Periodic Table

In a room where chemistry is taught or practiced, a chart called the **periodic table** is almost certain to be found hanging on the wall. Recall that this chart shows all the known elements and provides a good deal of information about each. As your knowledge of chemistry increases, the periodic table will become more and more useful to you. In this section we will remind you about its fundamental aspects.

A simple version of the periodic table is shown in Fig. 2.20. The letters given in the boxes are the symbols for the elements, and the number shown above each symbol is the atomic number (number of protons) for that element. Most of the elements are **metals.** Metals have characteristic physical properties such as efficient conduction of heat and electricity, malleability (they can be hammered into thin sheets), ductility (they can be pulled into wires), and (often) a lustrous appearance. Chemically, metal atoms tend to *lose* electrons to form positive ions. For example, copper is a typical metal. It is lustrous (although it tarnishes readily); it is an excellent conductor of electricity (it is widely used in electrical wires); and it is readily formed into various shapes such as pipes for water systems. Copper is also found in many salts, such as the beautiful blue copper sulfate, in which copper is present as Cu^{2+} ions. Copper

Figure 2.20
The periodic table continues to expand as new elements are synthesized in particle accelerators.

Alkali metals (group 1) · Alkaline earth metals (group 2) · Transition metals (groups 3–12) · Halogens (group 17) · Noble gases (group 18)

1 1A	2 2A	3	4	5	6	7	8	9	10	11	12	13 3A	14 4A	15 5A	16 6A	17 7A	18 8A
1 H																	2 He
3 Li	4 Be											5 B	6 C	7 N	8 O	9 F	10 Ne
11 Na	12 Mg											13 Al	14 Si	15 P	16 S	17 Cl	18 Ar
19 K	20 Ca	21 Sc	22 Ti	23 V	24 Cr	25 Mn	26 Fe	27 Co	28 Ni	29 Cu	30 Zn	31 Ga	32 Ge	33 As	34 Se	35 Br	36 Kr
37 Rb	38 Sr	39 Y	40 Zr	41 Nb	42 Mo	43 Tc	44 Ru	45 Rh	46 Pd	47 Ag	48 Cd	49 In	50 Sn	51 Sb	52 Te	53 I	54 Xe
55 Cs	56 Ba	57 La*	72 Hf	73 Ta	74 W	75 Re	76 Os	77 Ir	78 Pt	79 Au	80 Hg	81 Tl	82 Pb	83 Bi	84 Po	85 At	86 Rn
87 Fr	88 Ra	89 Ac†	104 Rf	105 Db	106 Sg	107 Bh	108 Hs	109 Mt	110 Ds	111 Rg	112 Cn	113 Uut	114 Uuq	115 Uup		117 Uus	118 Uuo

*Lanthanides	58 Ce	59 Pr	60 Nd	61 Pm	62 Sm	63 Eu	64 Gd	65 Tb	66 Dy	67 Ho	68 Er	69 Tm	70 Yb	71 Lu
†Actinides	90 Th	91 Pa	92 U	93 Np	94 Pu	95 Am	96 Cm	97 Bk	98 Cf	99 Es	100 Fm	101 Md	102 No	103 Lr

Samples of the alkali metals lithium, sodium, and potassium.

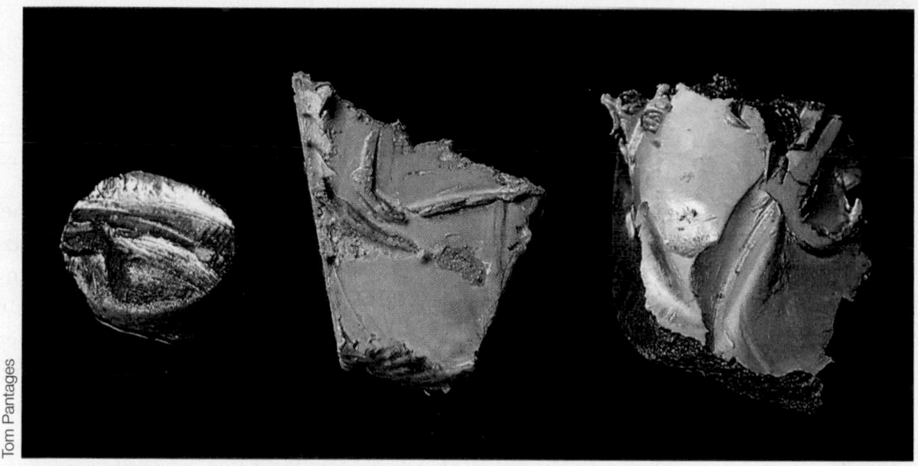

Tom Pantages

is a member of the transition metals—the metals shown in the center of the periodic table.

The relatively few **nonmetals** appear in the upper right-hand corner of the table (to the right of the heavy line in Fig. 2.20), except hydrogen, a nonmetal that is grouped with the metals. The nonmetals typically lack the physical properties that characterize the metals. Chemically, they tend to *gain* electrons to form anions in reactions with metals. Nonmetals often bond to each other by forming covalent bonds. For example, chlorine is a typical nonmetal. Under normal conditions, it exists as Cl_2 molecules; it reacts with metals to form salts containing Cl^- ions (NaCl, for example); and it forms covalent bonds with nonmetals (for example, hydrogen chloride gas, or HCl).

Metals tend to form positive ions; nonmetals tend to form negative ions.

The periodic table is arranged so that elements in the same vertical columns (called **groups** or **families**) have *similar chemical properties.* For example, all of the **alkali metals,** members of Group 1A—lithium (Li), sodium (Na), potassium (K), rubidium (Rb), cesium (Cs), and francium (Fr)—are very active elements that readily form ions with a 1+ charge when they react with nonmetals. The members of Group 2A—beryllium (Be), magnesium (Mg), calcium (Ca), strontium (Sr), barium (Ba), and radium (Ra)—are called the **alkaline earth metals.** They all form ions with a 2+ charge when they react with nonmetals. The **halogens,** the members of Group 7A—fluorine (F), chlorine (Cl), bromine (Br), iodine (I), and astatine (At)—all form diatomic molecules. Fluorine, chlorine, bromine, and iodine all react with metals to form salts containing ions with a 1− charge (F^-, Cl^-, Br^-, and I^-). The members of Group 8A—helium (He), neon (Ne), argon (Ar), krypton (Kr), xenon (Xe), and radon (Rn)—are known as the **noble gases.** They all exist under normal conditions as monatomic (single-atom) gases and have little chemical reactivity.

Tom Pantages

Three members of the halogen family: chlorine, bromine, and iodine.

The horizontal rows of elements in the periodic table are called **periods.** Horizontal row one is called the first period (it contains H and He), row two is called the second period (elements Li through Ne), and so on.

We will learn much more about the periodic table as we continue with our study of chemistry. Meanwhile, when an element is introduced in this text, you should always note its position on the periodic table.

2.9 Naming Simple Compounds

When chemistry was an infant science, there was no system for naming compounds. Names such as sugar of lead, blue vitriol, quicklime, Epsom salts, milk of magnesia, gypsum, and laughing gas were coined by early chemists. Such names are called *common names.* As chemistry grew, it became clear that using

Chemical Insights | Hassium Fits Right In

Hassium, element 108, does not exist in nature but must be made in a particle accelerator. It was first created in 1984 and can be made by shooting magnesium-26 ($^{26}_{12}Mg$) atoms at curium-248 ($^{248}_{96}Cm$) atoms. The collisions between these atoms produce some hassium-265 ($^{265}_{108}Hs$) atoms. The position of hassium in the periodic table (see Fig. 2.20) in the vertical column containing iron, ruthenium, and osmium suggests that hassium should have chemical properties similar to these metals. However, it is not easy to test this prediction—only a few atoms of hassium can be made at a given time and they last for only about 9 seconds. Imagine having to get your next lab experiment done in 9 seconds!

Amazingly, a team of chemists from the Lawrence Berkeley National Laboratory in California, the Paul Scherrer Institute and the University of Bern in Switzerland, and the Institute of Nuclear Chemistry in Germany have done experiments to characterize the chemical behavior of hassium. For example, they have observed that hassium atoms react with oxygen to form a hassium oxide compound of the type expected from its position on the periodic table. The team has also measured other properties of hassium, including the energy released as it undergoes nuclear decay to another atom.

This work would have surely pleased Dmitri Mendeleev, who originally developed the periodic table and showed its power to predict chemical properties.

common names for compounds would lead to unacceptable chaos. More than 4 million chemical compounds are currently known. Memorizing common names for these compounds would be an impossible task.

The solution, of course, is to adopt a *system* for naming compounds in which the name tells something about the composition of the compound. After learning the system, a chemist given a formula should be able to name the compound, or given a name should be able to construct the compound's formula. In this section we will specify the most important rules for naming compounds other than organic compounds (those based on chains of carbon atoms).

The systematic naming of organic compounds will be discussed in Chapter 21.

We will begin with the systems for naming inorganic **binary compounds**—compounds composed of two elements—which we classify into various types for easier recognition. We will consider both ionic and covalent compounds.

Binary Compounds (Type I; Ionic)

Binary ionic compounds contain a positive ion (cation), always written first in the formula, and a negative ion (anion). In the naming of these compounds, the following rules apply:

1. The cation is always named first and the anion second.
2. A monatomic (meaning from one atom) cation takes its name from the name of the element. For example, Na^+ is called sodium in the names of compounds containing this ion.
3. A monatomic anion is named by taking the first part of the element name and adding *-ide*. Thus the Cl^- ion is called chloride.

A monatomic cation has the same name as its parent element.

Some common monatomic cations and anions and their names are given in Table 2.3.

Table 2.3

Common Monatomic Cations and Anions

Cation	Name	Anion	Name
H^+	Hydrogen	H^-	Hydride
Li^+	Lithium	F^-	Fluoride
Na^+	Sodium	Cl^-	Chloride
K^+	Potassium	Br^-	Bromide
Cs^+	Cesium	I^-	Iodide
Be^{2+}	Beryllium	O^{2-}	Oxide
Mg^{2+}	Magnesium	S^{2-}	Sulfide
Ca^{2+}	Calcium	N^{3-}	Nitride
Ba^{2+}	Barium	P^{3-}	Phosphide
Al^{3+}	Aluminum		
Ag^+	Silver		
Zn^{2+}	Zinc		

A Type I binary ionic compound contains a metal that forms only one type of cation. The rules for naming Type I compounds are illustrated by the following examples:

In formulas of ionic compounds, simple ions are represented by the element symbol: Cl means Cl^-, Na means Na^+, and so on.

Compound	*Ions Present*	*Name*
NaCl	Na^+, Cl^-	Sodium chloride
KI	K^+, I^-	Potassium iodide
CaS	Ca^{2+}, S^{2-}	Calcium sulfide
Li_3N	Li^+, N^{3-}	Lithium nitride
CsBr	Cs^+, Br^-	Cesium bromide
MgO	Mg^{2+}, O^{2-}	Magnesium oxide

Type II binary ionic compounds contain a metal that can form more than one type of cation.

Binary Compounds (Type II; Ionic)

In the ionic compounds considered previously (Type I), the metal involved forms only a single type of cation. That is, sodium forms only Na^+, calcium forms only Ca^{2+}, and so on. However, as we will see in more detail later in the text, many metals can form more than one type of positive ion and thus form more than one type of ionic compound with a given anion. For example, the compound $FeCl_2$ contains Fe^{2+} ions, and the compound $FeCl_3$ contains Fe^{3+} ions. In cases such as these, the *charge on the metal ion must be specified.* The systematic names for these two iron compounds are iron(II) chloride and iron(III) chloride, respectively, where the *Roman numeral indicates the charge of the cation.*

A compound containing a metal that forms multiple cations must have a Roman numeral in its name.

Another system for naming these ionic compounds that is seen in the older literature was used for metals that form only two ions. *The ion with the higher charge has a name ending in* -ic, *and the one with the lower charge has a name ending in* -ous. In this system, for example, Fe^{3+} is called the ferric ion, and Fe^{2+} is called the ferrous ion. The names for $FeCl_3$ and $FeCl_2$ are then ferric chloride and ferrous chloride, respectively.

Table 2.4 gives both names for many common Type II cations. The system that uses Roman numerals will be used exclusively in this text.

Note that the use of a Roman numeral in a systematic name is required only in cases in which more than one ionic compound forms between a given pair of elements. This case most commonly occurs for compounds containing transition metals, which often form more than one cation. *Elements that form only one cation do not need to be identified by a Roman numeral.* Common metals that do not require Roman numerals are the Group 1A elements, which form only 1+ ions; the Group 2A elements, which form only 2+ ions; and

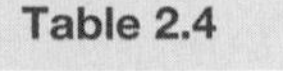

Table 2.4

Common Type II Cations

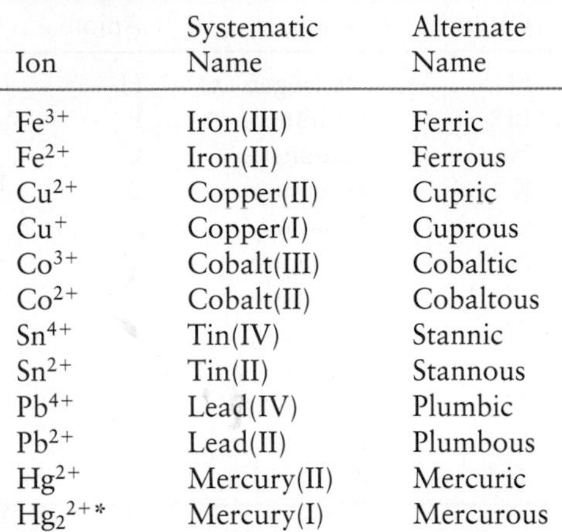

Ion	Systematic Name	Alternate Name
Fe^{3+}	Iron(III)	Ferric
Fe^{2+}	Iron(II)	Ferrous
Cu^{2+}	Copper(II)	Cupric
Cu^{+}	Copper(I)	Cuprous
Co^{3+}	Cobalt(III)	Cobaltic
Co^{2+}	Cobalt(II)	Cobaltous
Sn^{4+}	Tin(IV)	Stannic
Sn^{2+}	Tin(II)	Stannous
Pb^{4+}	Lead(IV)	Plumbic
Pb^{2+}	Lead(II)	Plumbous
Hg^{2+}	Mercury(II)	Mercuric
Hg_2^{2+}*	Mercury(I)	Mercurous

*Note that mercury(I) ions always occur bound together to form Hg_2^{2+}.

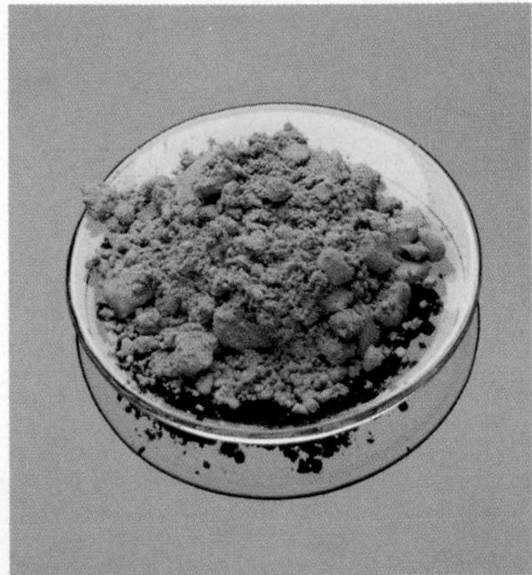

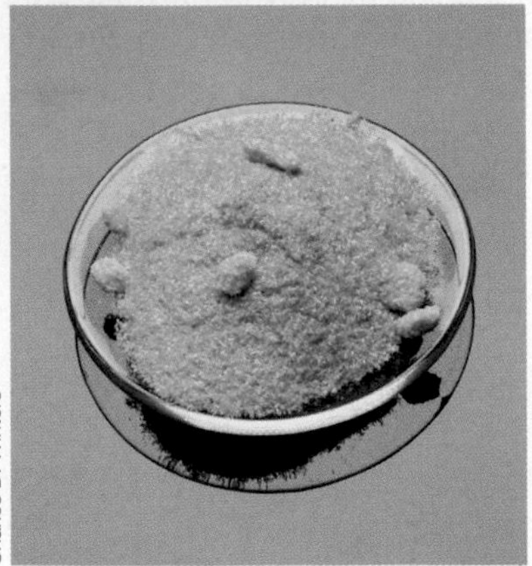

Charles D. Winters

(top) Copper(I) chloride.
(bottom) Copper(II) chloride.

aluminum, which forms only Al^{3+}. Common transition metals that do not require a Roman numeral (because they form only one ion) are zinc (Zn^{2+}) and silver (Ag^{+}).

When a metal ion that forms more than one type of cation is present, the charge on the metal ion must be determined by balancing the positive and negative charges of the compound. To make this determination, you must be able to recognize the common cations and anions and know their charges (see Tables 2.3 and 2.5).

The following flowchart is useful when you are naming binary ionic compounds:

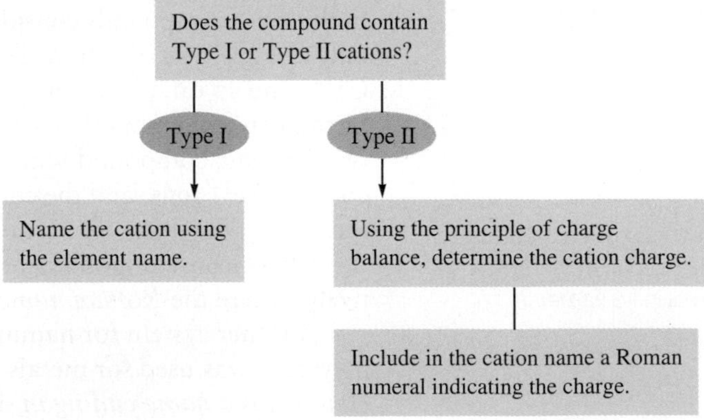

Various chromium compounds dissolved in water. From left to right: $CrCl_2$, $K_2Cr_2O_7$, $Cr(NO_3)_3$, $CrCl_3$, K_2CrO_4.

EXAMPLE 2.2

Give the systematic name of each of the following compounds.

a. $CoBr_2$ **b.** $CaCl_2$ **c.** Al_2O_3 **d.** $CrCl_3$

Solution

Compound	*Name*	*Comment*
a. $CoBr_2$	Cobalt(II) bromide	Cobalt is a transition metal that requires a Roman numeral. The two Br^- ions must be balanced by a Co^{2+} cation.

b. $CaCl_2$	Calcium chloride	Calcium, an alkaline earth metal, forms only the Ca^{2+} ion. A Roman numeral is not necessary.
c. Al_2O_3	Aluminum oxide	Aluminum forms only Al^{3+}. A Roman numeral is not necessary.
d. $CrCl_3$	Chromium(III) chloride	Chromium is a transition metal that must have a Roman numeral. $CrCl_3$ contains Cr^{3+}.

Ionic Compounds with Polyatomic Ions

Ionic compounds that contain polyatomic ions are not binary compounds.

We have not yet considered ionic compounds that contain polyatomic ions. For example, the compound ammonium nitrate (NH_4NO_3) contains the polyatomic ions NH_4^+ and NO_3^-. Polyatomic ions are assigned special names that *must be memorized* to name the compounds containing them. The most important polyatomic ions and their names are listed in Table 2.5.

Note in Table 2.5 that several series of anions contain an atom of a given element and different numbers of oxygen atoms. These anions are called **oxyanions.** When there are two members in such a series, the name of the one with the smaller number of oxygen atoms ends in *-ite,* and the name of the one with the larger number ends in *-ate*—for example, sulfite (SO_3^{2-}) and sulfate (SO_4^{2-}). When more than two oxyanions make up a series, *hypo-* (less than) and *per-* (more than) are used as prefixes to name the members of the series with the fewest and the most oxygen atoms, respectively. The best example involves the oxyanions containing chlorine, as shown in Table 2.5.

In binary covalent compounds, the element names follow the same rules as those for binary ionic compounds.

Binary Compounds (Type III; Covalent—Contain Two Nonmetals)

Binary covalent compounds are formed between *two nonmetals.* Although these compounds do not contain ions, they are named very similarly to binary ionic compounds.

Table 2.5

Common Polyatomic Ions

Ion	Name	Ion	Name
NH_4^+	Ammonium	CO_3^{2-}	Carbonate
NO_2^-	Nitrite	HCO_3^-	Hydrogen carbonate (bicarbonate is a widely used common name)
NO_3^-	Nitrate		
SO_3^{2-}	Sulfite		
SO_4^{2-}	Sulfate	$C_2H_3O_2^-$	Acetate
HSO_4^-	Hydrogen sulfate (bisulfate is a widely used common name)	MnO_4^-	Permanganate
		$Cr_2O_7^{2-}$	Dichromate
		CrO_4^{2-}	Chromate
OH^-	Hydroxide	O_2^{2-}	Peroxide
CN^-	Cyanide		
PO_4^{3-}	Phosphate	ClO^-	Hypochlorite
HPO_4^{2-}	Hydrogen phosphate	ClO_2^-	Chlorite
$H_2PO_4^-$	Dihydrogen phosphate	ClO_3^-	Chlorate
		ClO_4^-	Perchlorate

Table 2.6

Prefixes Used to Indicate Number in Chemical Names

Prefix	Number Indicated
mono-	1
di-	2
tri-	3
tetra-	4
penta-	5
hexa-	6
hepta-	7
octa-	8

In the naming of binary covalent compounds, the following rules apply:

1. The first element in the formula is named first, using the full element name.
2. The second element is named as if it were an anion.
3. Prefixes are used to denote the numbers of atoms present. These prefixes are given in Table 2.6.
4. The prefix *mono-* is never used for naming the first element. For example, CO is called carbon monoxide, *not* monocarbon monoxide.

To see how these rules apply, we will now consider the names of the several covalent compounds formed by nitrogen and oxygen:

Compound	*Systematic Name*	*Common Name*
N_2O	Dinitrogen monoxide	Nitrous oxide
NO	Nitrogen monoxide	Nitric oxide
NO_2	Nitrogen dioxide	
N_2O_3	Dinitrogen trioxide	
N_2O_4	Dinitrogen tetroxide	
N_2O_5	Dinitrogen pentoxide	

Notice from the preceding examples that to avoid awkward pronunciations, we often drop the final *o* or *a* of the prefix when the element begins with a vowel. For example, N_2O_4 is called dinitrogen tetroxide, *not* dinitrogen tetr*a*oxide; and CO is called carbon monoxide, *not* carbon monooxide.

Some compounds are always referred to by their common names. The two best examples are water and ammonia. The systematic names for H_2O and NH_3 are never used.

The rules for naming binary compounds are summarized in Fig. 2.21. Notice that prefixes to indicate the number of atoms are used only in Type III binary compounds (those containing two nonmetals). An overall strategy for naming compounds is summarized in Fig. 2.22.

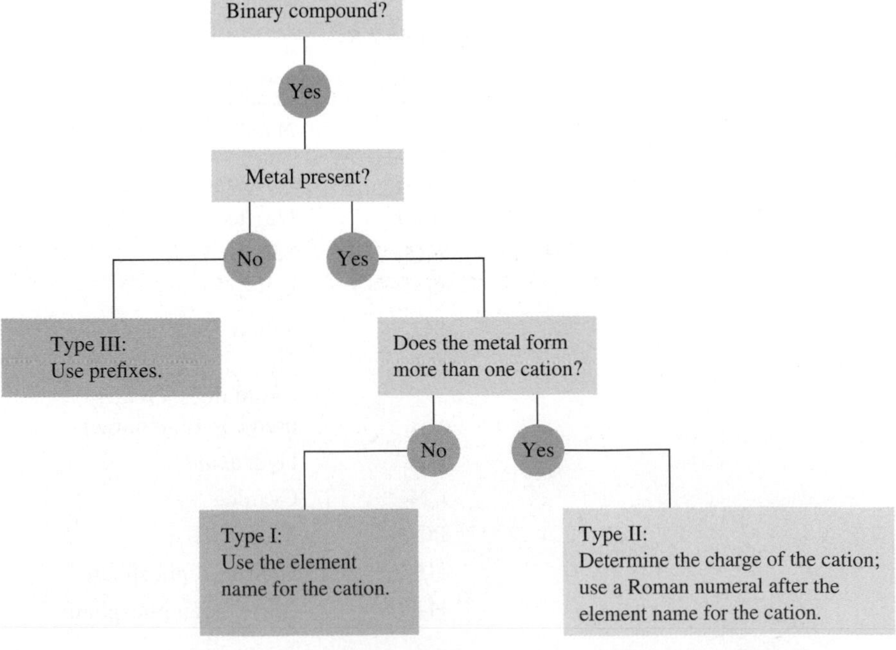

Figure 2.21
A flowchart for naming binary compounds.

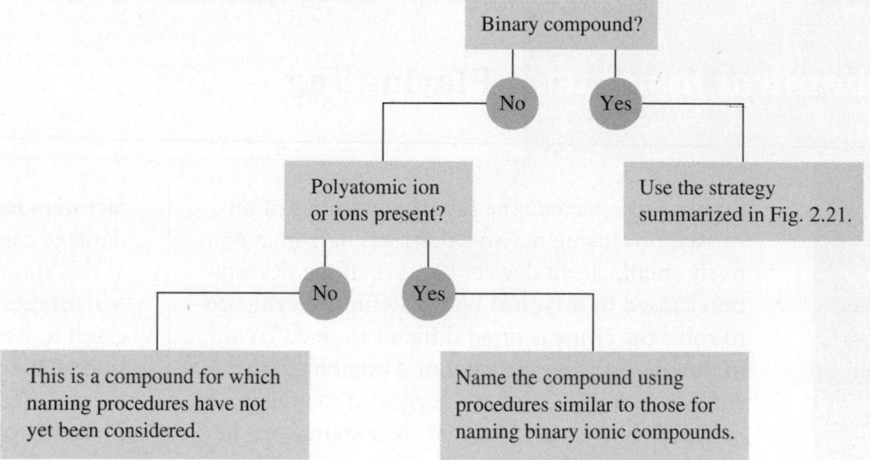

Figure 2.22
Overall strategy for naming chemical compounds.

OWL INTERACTIVE EXAMPLE 2.3

Give the systematic name of each of the following compounds.

a. Na_2SO_4
b. KH_2PO_4
c. $Fe(NO_3)_3$
d. $Mn(OH)_2$
e. Na_2SO_3
f. Na_2CO_3
g. $NaHCO_3$
h. $CsClO_4$
i. $NaOCl$
j. Na_2SeO_4
k. $KBrO_3$

Solution

Compound	*Name*	*Comment*
a. Na_2SO_4	Sodium sulfate	
b. KH_2PO_4	Potassium dihydrogen phosphate	
c. $Fe(NO_3)_3$	Iron(III) nitrate	Transition metal that requires a Roman numeral. Fe^{3+} ion balances three NO_3^- ions.
d. $Mn(OH)_2$	Manganese(II) hydroxide	Transition metal that requires a Roman numeral. Mn^{2+} ion balances two OH^- ions.
e. Na_2SO_3	Sodium sulfite	
f. Na_2CO_3	Sodium carbonate	
g. $NaHCO_3$	Sodium hydrogen carbonate	Often called sodium bicarbonate.
h. $CsClO_4$	Cesium perchlorate	
i. $NaOCl$	Sodium hypochlorite	
j. Na_2SeO_4	Sodium selenate	Atoms in the same group, such as sulfur and selenium, often form similar ions that are named similarly. Thus SeO_4^{2-} is selenate, like SO_4^{2-} (sulfate).
k. $KBrO_3$	Potassium bromate	As above BrO_3^- is bromate, like ClO_3^- (chlorate).

Chemical Insights Playing Tag

Bombs have become the favorite weapons of terrorists, producing massive destruction from a relatively small, cheap device. Because of the devastation caused by a typical bomb, definitive evidence to solve the crime is often difficult to find. To aid in the forensic investigation of a bombing, law enforcement agencies have suggested that explosive materials be "tagged" so that their source can be readily identified. One method for tagging explosives was developed in the 1970s by Richard Livesag, a research chemist at 3M Corporation. Called Microtaggant, the tagging material consists of irregularly shaped particles approximately 0.1 millimeter in diameter. Examined under a microscope, the tiny specks reveal a laminated structure of 10 layers of melamine plastic, a chemically unreactive substance that is very difficult to destroy. The colored layers of the chips act as a kind of bar code, identifying the manufacturer, the date of production, and the name of the distributor of the explosive. Fluorescent and magnetic materials added to the chips aid in their detection at the scene of an explosion.

Although it seems that the tagging of explosives should be noncontroversial, this has not proved to be the case. Manufacturers of explosive materials and gun owners' associations have opposed the use of taggants, arguing that the added substances produce instabilities in the explosives. Also, manufacturers fear that they will be held liable for the damage caused by misuse of their products. Thus, at this stage, only Switzerland routinely uses Microtaggant to label explosives, and the Swiss claim to have solved nearly 600 bombing cases since 1984 using the taggant evidence.

A different tagging method has been pioneered by Isotag of Houston, Texas. Isotag labels explosives by inserting unusual atomic isotopes of the atoms present in the ions or molecules of the explosive substance. The isotopic labeling is done in a way that makes the tagged substances distinctly different from naturally occurring substances. For example, if labeled ammonium nitrate were used in a bomb, residue at the scene could be collected and analyzed with a mass spectrometer to show the unique isotopic patterns present, which could be used to trace the origin of the compound. Although Isotag claims its system to be safe and effective, manufacturers of fertilizers containing ammonium nitrate are reluctant to allow tagging because of fears of liability.

The U.S. Antiterrorism and Effective Death Penalty Act of 1996 authorized a thorough study of taggants. The results of this study and the outcome of the political struggle over taggants will determine whether the United States will follow Switzerland and require taggants for some or all explosive substances.

Formulas from Names

So far we have started with the chemical formula of a compound and decided on its systematic name. The reverse process is also important. For example, given the name calcium hydroxide, we can write the formula as $Ca(OH)_2$, since we know that calcium forms only Ca^{2+} ions and that, since hydroxide is OH^-, two of these anions will be required to give a neutral compound. Similarly, the name iron(II) oxide implies the formula FeO, since the Roman numeral II indicates the presence of Fe^{2+} and the oxide ion is O^{2-}.

OWL INTERACTIVE EXAMPLE 2.4

Given the following systematic names, write the formula for each compound.

a. Ammonium sulfate
b. Vanadium(V) fluoride
c. Dioxygen difluoride
d. Rubidium peroxide
e. Gallium oxide

Microtrace, LLC

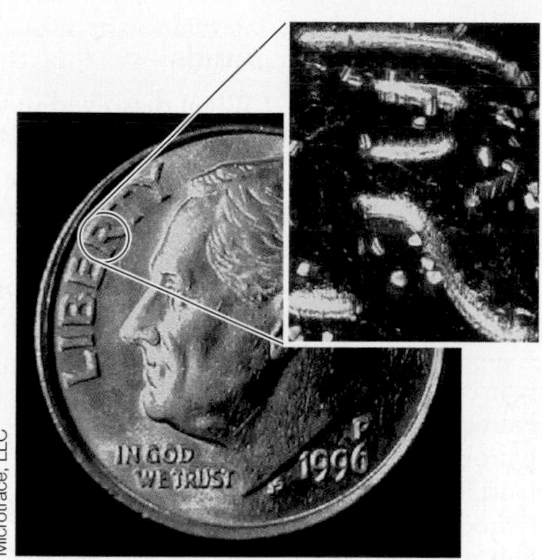

Microtrace, LLC

The multilayered plastic particles of Microtaggants (left) can produce over 37 million unique codes that can be used to identify substances. The tiny size of the taggants is shown (right) compared with the "R" on a dime.

Although taggants for explosives have proved controversial, approximately 500 consumer items already contain Microtaggants to authenticate brand-name products and discourage counterfeiting. For example, taggants are found in shampoo, paint, and carpet adhesives. The latter application enables business owners to check that a requested brand-name glue has been used to secure carpet rather than cheaper off-brand substitutes. Isotag markets taggants for substances such as gasoline and perfume, in which the plastic Microtaggant chips are impractical. For instance, isotopic tagging of perfumes enables a manufacturer to protect its product against dilution by an unethical distributor who might seek to increase profits by selling a diluted perfume.

So chemical taggants represent an increasing market. However, the question of whether explosives will be tagged remains a technical and political question mark.

Solution

Name	*Chemical Formula*	*Comment*
a. Ammonium sulfate	$(NH_4)_2SO_4$	Two ammonium ions (NH_4^+) are required for each sulfate ion (SO_4^{2-}) to achieve charge balance.
b. Vanadium(V) fluoride	VF_5	The compound contains V^{5+} ions and requires five F^- ions for charge balance.
c. Dioxygen difluoride	O_2F_2	The prefix *di-* indicates two of each atom.
d. Rubidium peroxide	Rb_2O_2	Since rubidium is in Group 1A, it forms only 1+ ions. Thus two Rb^+ ions are needed to balance the 2− charge on the peroxide ion (O_2^{2-}).

Name	*Chemical Formula*	*Comment*
e. Gallium oxide	Ga_2O_3	Gallium in Group 3A, like aluminum, forms only 3+ ions. Two Ga^{3+} ions are required to balance the charge on three O^{2-} ions.

Acids

When dissolved in water, certain molecules produce a solution containing free H^+ ions (protons). These substances, acids, will be discussed in detail in Chapters 4, 7, and 8. Here we will simply present the rules for naming acids.

An acid can be viewed as a molecule with one or more H^+ ions attached to an anion. The rules for naming acids depend on whether the anion contains oxygen. If the *anion does not contain oxygen,* the acid is named with the prefix *hydro-* and the suffix *-ic*. For example, when gaseous HCl is dissolved in water, it forms hydrochloric acid. Similarly, HCN and H_2S dissolved in water are called hydrocyanic and hydrosulfuric acid, respectively.

When the *anion contains oxygen,* the acid name is formed from the root name of the anion with a suffix of *-ic* or *-ous*. If the anion name ends in *-ate,* the acid name ends with *-ic* (or sometimes *-ric*). For example, H_2SO_4 contains the sulfate anion (SO_4^{2-}) and is called sulfuric acid; H_3PO_4 contains the phosphate anion (PO_4^{3-}) and is called phosphoric acid; and $HC_2H_3O_2$ contains the acetate ion ($C_2H_3O_2^-$) and is called acetic acid. If the anion has an *-ite* ending, the acid name ends with *-ous*. For example, H_2SO_3, which contains sulfite (SO_3^{2-}), is named sulfurous acid; HNO_2, which contains nitrite (NO_2^-), is named nitrous acid. The application of these rules can be seen in the names of the acids of the oxyanions of chlorine:

Acid	*Anion*	*Name*
$HClO_4$	Perchlor*ate*	Perchlor*ic* acid
$HClO_3$	Chlor*ate*	Chlor*ic* acid
$HClO_2$	Chlor*ite*	Chlor*ous* acid
HClO	Hypochlor*ite*	Hypochlor*ous* acid

The names of the most important acids are given in Tables 2.7 and 2.8. An overall strategy for naming acids is shown in Fig. 2.23.

Table 2.7

Names of Acids That Do Not Contain Oxygen

Acid	Name
HF	Hydrofluoric acid
HCl	Hydrochloric acid
HBr	Hydrobromic acid
HI	Hydroiodic acid
HCN	Hydrocyanic acid
H_2S	Hydrosulfuric acid

Table 2.8

Names of Some Oxygen-Containing Acids

Acid	Name
HNO_3	Nitric acid
HNO_2	Nitrous acid
H_2SO_4	Sulfuric acid
H_2SO_3	Sulfurous acid
H_3PO_4	Phosphoric acid
$HC_2H_3O_2$	Acetic acid

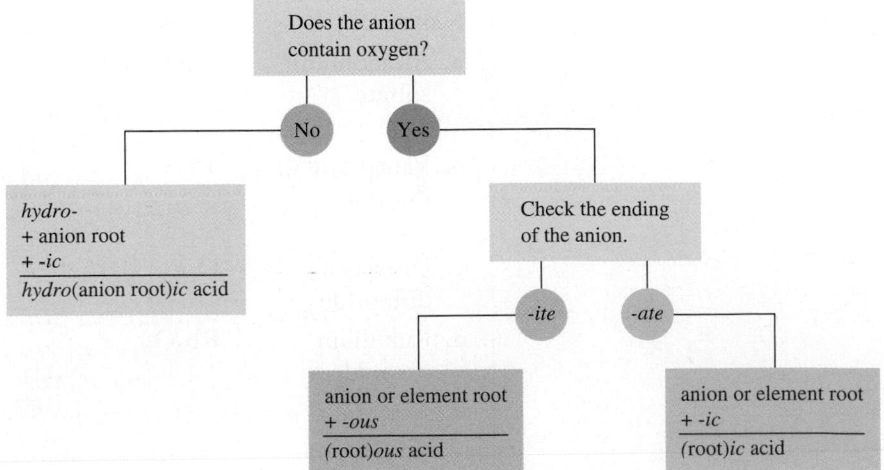

Figure 2.23
A flowchart for naming acids. The acid has one or more H^+ ions attached to an anion.

Key Terms

Section 2.2
law of conservation of mass
law of definite proportion
law of multiple proportions

Section 2.3
atomic masses
Avogadro's hypothesis

Section 2.5
cathode ray
electrons
radioactivity
nuclear atom
nucleus

Section 2.6
protons
neutrons
isotopes
atomic number
mass number

Section 2.7
chemical bonds
covalent bonds
molecule
chemical formula
structural formula
space-filling model
ball-and-stick models
ion
cation
anion
ionic bonding
polyatomic ion

Section 2.8
periodic table
metals
nonmetals
groups (families)
alkali metals
alkaline earth metals
halogens
noble gases
periods

Section 2.9
binary compounds
binary ionic compounds
oxyanions
binary covalent compounds

For Review

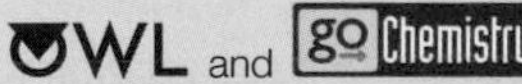

Sign in at **www.cengage.com/owl** to:

- View tutorials and simulations, develop problem-solving skills, and complete online homework assigned by your professor.
- Download Go Chemistry mini lecture modules for quick review and exam prep from OWL (or purchase them at **www.cengagebrain.com**)

Fundamental laws

- Conservation of mass
- Definite proportion
- Multiple proportions

Dalton's atomic theory

- All elements are composed of atoms.
- All atoms of a given element are identical.
- Chemical compounds are formed when atoms combine.

Early atomic experiments

- Thomson model: electrons in a diffuse cloud of positive charge
- Millikan experiment: determined mass of electron
- Rutherford experiment: nuclear atom

Atomic structure

- Small dense nucleus contains protons and neutrons.
  - Protons—positive charge
  - Neutrons—no charge
- Electrons reside outside the nucleus in the relatively large remaining atomic volume.
  - Electrons—negative charge, small mass (1/1840 of proton)
- Isotopes have the same atomic number but different mass numbers.

Formation of molecules

- Atoms combine to form molecules by sharing electrons to form covalent bonds.
- Molecules are described by chemical formulas.
- Chemical formulas show number and type of atoms.
  - Structural formula
  - Ball-and-stick model
  - Space-filling model

Formation of ions

- Cation—formed by a loss of an electron, positive charge
- Anion—formed by gain of an electron, negative charge
- Ionic bonds—formed by interaction of cations and anions

Periodic table

- Elements are organized in order of increasing atomic number.
- Elements with similar properties are in columns, or groups.
- Metals are in the majority and tend to form cations.
- Nonmetals tend to form anions.

Naming of compounds

- Binary compounds
  - Type I—contain a metal that always forms the same cation
  - Type II—contain a metal that can form more than one cation
  - Type III—contain two nonmetals
- Compounds containing a polyatomic ion
- Acids

Discussion Questions

These questions are designed to be considered by groups of students in class. Often these questions work well for introducing a particular topic in class.

1. You may have noticed that when water boils, you can see bubbles that rise to the surface of the water. What is inside these bubbles? Explain.
   a. air
   b. hydrogen and oxygen gas
   c. oxygen gas
   d. water vapor
   e. carbon dioxide gas
2. Which of the following is true about an individual atom?
   a. An individual atom should be considered a solid.
   b. An individual atom should be considered a liquid.
   c. An individual atom should be considered a gas.
   d. The state of the atom depends on which element it is.
   e. An individual atom cannot be considered a solid, liquid, or gas.

   Justify your choice, and for those you did not choose, explain why they are incorrect.
3. How would you go about finding the number of "chalk molecules" it takes to write your name on the board? Explain what you would need to do and provide a sample calculation.
4. These questions concern the work of J. J. Thomson:
   a. From what you know of Thomson's work, which particles do you think he would believe are most important in the formation of compounds (chemical changes) and why?
   b. Of the remaining two subatomic particles, which do you place second in importance for forming compounds and why?
   c. Propose three models that explain Thomson's findings and evaluate them. Include Thomson's findings.
5. Heat is applied to an ice cube in a closed container until only steam is present. Draw a representation of this process, assuming you can see it at an extremely high level of magnification. What happens to the size of the molecules? What happens to the total mass of the sample?
6. You have a chemical in a sealed glass container filled with air. The setup is sitting on a balance, as shown. The chemical is ignited by means of a magnifying glass focusing sunlight on the reactant. After the chemical has completely burned, which of the following is true? Explain your answer.
   a. The balance will read less than 250.0 g.
   b. The balance will read 250.0 g.
   c. The balance will read greater than 250.0 g.
   d. Cannot be determined without knowing the identity of the chemical.

7. The vitamin niacin (nicotinic acid, $C_6H_5NO_2$) can be isolated from a variety of natural sources such as liver, yeast, milk, and whole grain. It also can be synthesized from commercially available materials. From a nutritional point of view, which source of nicotinic acid is best for use in a multivitamin tablet? Why?
8. One of the best indications of a useful theory is that it raises more questions for further experimentation than it originally answered. Is this true of Dalton's atomic theory? Give examples.
9. Dalton assumed that all atoms of the same element are identical in all their properties. Explain why this assumption is not valid.
10. How does Dalton's atomic theory account for each of the following?
    a. the law of conservation of mass
    b. the law of definite proportion
    c. the law of multiple proportions
11. What refinements had to be made in Dalton's atomic theory to account for Gay-Lussac's results on the combining volumes of gases?
12. Which (if any) of the following can be determined by knowing the number of protons in a neutral element? Explain your answer.
    a. the number of neutrons in the neutral element
    b. the number of electrons in the neutral element
    c. the name of the element
13. The average mass of a carbon atom is 12.011. Assuming you were able to pick up only one carbon atom, the chance that you would randomly get one with a mass of 12.011 is
    a. 0%.
    b. 0.011%.
    c. about 12%.
    d. 12.011%.
    e. greater than 50%.
    f. None of these is true.

    Explain.
14. Which of the following explain how an ion is formed? Explain your answer.
    a. adding or subtracting protons to/from an atom
    b. adding or subtracting neutrons to/from an atom
    c. adding or subtracting electrons to/from an atom
15. The formula of water is H_2O. Which of the following is indicated by this formula? Explain your answer.
    a. the mass of hydrogen is twice that of oxygen in each molecule
    b. there are two hydrogen atoms and one oxygen atom per water molecule
    c. the mass of oxygen is twice that of hydrogen in each molecule
    d. there are two oxygen atoms and one hydrogen atom per water molecule
16. Why do we call $Ba(NO_3)_2$ barium nitrate, but we call $Fe(NO_3)_2$ iron(II) nitrate?
17. Why is calcium dichloride not the correct systematic name for $CaCl_2$?

Exercises

OWL Interactive versions of these problems may be assigned in OWL.

A blue exercise number indicates that the answer to that exercise appears at the back of this book and a solution appears in the *Solutions Guide.*

Development of the Atomic Theory

18. Explain the law of conservation of mass, the law of definite proportion, and the law of multiple proportions.

19. A reaction of 1 L of chlorine gas (Cl_2) with 5 L of fluorine gas (F_2) yields 2 L of a gaseous product. All gas volumes are at the same temperature and pressure. What is the formula of the gaseous product?

20. When mixtures of gaseous H_2 and gaseous Cl_2 react, a product forms that has the same properties regardless of the relative amounts of H_2 and Cl_2 used.
    a. How is this result interpreted in terms of the law of definite proportion?
    b. When a volume of H_2 reacts with an equal volume of Cl_2 at the same temperature and pressure, what volume of product having the formula HCl is formed?

21. Observations of the reaction between nitrogen gas and hydrogen gas show us that 1 volume of nitrogen reacts with 3 volumes of hydrogen to make 2 volumes of gaseous product, as shown below:

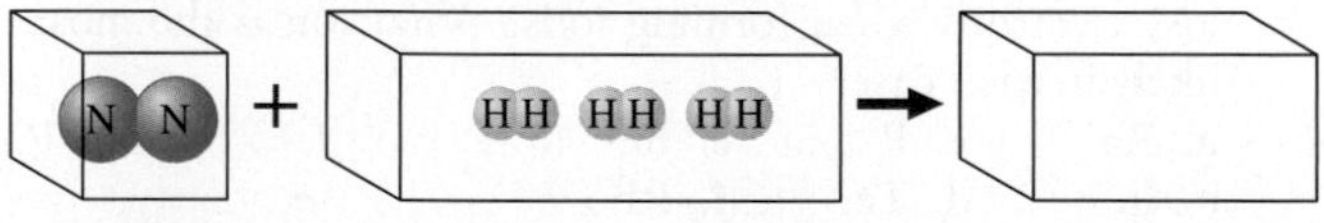

Determine the formula of the product and justify your answer.

22. The three most stable oxides of carbon are carbon monoxide (CO), carbon dioxide (CO_2), and carbon suboxide (C_3O_2). The molecules can be represented as

Explain how these molecules illustrate the law of multiple proportions.

23. Hydrazine, ammonia, and hydrogen azide all contain only nitrogen and hydrogen. The mass of hydrogen that combines with 1.00 g of nitrogen for each compound is 1.44×10^{-1} g, 2.16×10^{-1} g, and 2.40×10^{-2} g, respectively. Show how these data illustrate the law of multiple proportions.

24. Consider 100.0-g samples of two different compounds consisting only of carbon and oxygen. One compound contains 27.2 g of carbon, and the other has 42.9 g of carbon. How can these data support the law of multiple proportions if 42.9 is not a multiple of 27.2? Show that these data support the law of multiple proportions.

25. Early tables of atomic weights (masses) were generated by measuring the mass of a substance that reacts with 1.00 g of oxygen. Given the following data and taking the atomic mass of hydrogen as 1.00, generate a table of relative atomic masses for oxygen, sodium, and magnesium.

Element	Mass That Combines with 1.00 g Oxygen	Assumed Formula
Hydrogen	0.126 g	HO
Sodium	2.875 g	NaO
Magnesium	1.500 g	MgO

How do your values compare with those in the periodic table? How do you account for any differences?

The Nature of the Atom

26. What evidence led to the conclusion that cathode rays had a negative charge? Is there a difference between a cathode ray and a β particle?

27. From the information in this chapter on the mass of the proton, the mass of the electron, and the sizes of the nucleus and the atom, calculate the densities of a hydrogen nucleus and a hydrogen atom.

28. A chemistry instructor makes the following claim: "Consider that if the nucleus were the size of a grape, the electrons would be about 1 *mile* away on average." Is this claim reasonably accurate? Provide mathematical support.

29. A chemist in a galaxy far, far away performed the Millikan oil drop experiment and got the following results for the charge on various drops. What is the charge of the electron in zirkombs?

2.56×10^{-12} zirkombs	7.68×10^{-12} zirkombs
3.84×10^{-12} zirkombs	6.40×10^{-13} zirkombs

30. Do the proton and the neutron have exactly the same mass? How do the masses of the proton and the neutron compare with the mass of the electron? Which particles make the greatest contribution to the mass of an atom? Which particles make the greatest contribution to the chemical properties of an atom?

31. Consider Ernest Rutherford's α-particle bombardment experiment illustrated in Fig. 2.11. How did the results of this experiment lead Rutherford away from the plum pudding model of the atom to propose the nuclear model of the atom?

Elements, Ions, and the Periodic Table

32. Distinguish between the following terms.
   a. molecule versus ion
   b. covalent bonding versus ionic bonding
   c. molecule versus compound
   d. anion versus cation
33. What is the distinction between atomic number and mass number? Between mass number and atomic mass?
34. a. Classify the following elements as metals or nonmetals.

Mg	Si	Rn
Ti	Ge	Eu
Au	B	Am
Bi	At	Br

   b. The distinction between metals and nonmetals is really not a clear one. Some elements, called *metalloids,* are intermediate in their properties. Which of these elements would you reclassify as metalloids? What other elements in the periodic table would you expect to be metalloids?
35. a. List the noble gas elements. Which of the noble gases has only radioactive isotopes? (This situation is indicated on most periodic tables by parentheses around the mass of the element. See inside front cover.)
   b. Which lanthanide element and which transition element have only radioactive isotopes?
36. Consider the elements of the carbon family: C, Si, Ge, Sn, and Pb. What is the trend in metallic character as one goes down a group in the periodic table? What is the trend in metallic character going from left to right across a period in the periodic table?
37. Identify the elements that correspond to the following atomic numbers. Label each as either a noble gas, a halogen, an alkali metal, an alkaline earth metal, a transition metal, a lanthanide metal, or an actinide metal.
   a. 17 e. 2
   b. 4 f. 92
   c. 63 g. 55
   d. 72
38. The number of protons in an atom determines the identity of the atom. What does the number and arrangement of the electrons in an atom determine? What does the number of neutrons in an atom determine?
39. For lighter, stable isotopes, the ratio of the mass number to the atomic number is close to a certain value. What is the value? What happens to the value of the mass number to atomic number ratio as stable isotopes become heavier?
40. Write the atomic symbol ($^{A}_{Z}X$) for each of the isotopes described below.
   a. number of protons = 27, number of neutrons = 31
   b. the isotope of boron with mass number 10
   c. $Z = 12$, $A = 23$
   d. atomic number 53, number of neutrons = 79
   e. $Z = 9$, number of neutrons = 10
   f. number of protons = 29, mass number 65
41. How many protons, neutrons, and electrons are in each of the following atoms or ions?
   a. $^{24}_{12}Mg$ d. $^{59}_{27}Co^{3+}$ g. $^{79}_{34}Se^{2-}$
   b. $^{24}_{12}Mg^{2+}$ e. $^{59}_{27}Co$ h. $^{63}_{28}Ni$
   c. $^{59}_{27}Co^{2+}$ f. $^{79}_{34}Se$ i. $^{59}_{28}Ni^{2+}$
42. Complete the following table.

Symbol	Number of Protons in Nucleus	Number of Neutrons in Nucleus	Number of Electrons	Net Charge
$^{238}_{92}U$	___	___	___	___
___	20	20	___	2+
___	23	28	20	___
$^{89}_{39}Y$	___	___	___	___
___	35	44	36	___
___	15	16	___	3−

43. What is the symbol for an ion with 63 protons, 60 electrons, and 88 neutrons? If an ion contains 50 protons, 68 neutrons, and 48 electrons, what is its symbol?
44. What is the symbol of an ion with 16 protons, 18 neutrons, and 18 electrons? What is the symbol for an ion that has 16 protons, 16 neutrons, and 18 electrons?
45. Would you expect each of the following atoms to gain or lose electrons when forming ions? What ion is the most likely in each case?
   a. Ra c. P e. Br
   b. In d. Te f. Rb
46. For each of the following atomic numbers, use the periodic table to write the formula (including the charge) for the simple *ion* that the element is most likely to form in ionic compounds.
   a. 13 c. 56 e. 87
   b. 34 d. 7 f. 35

Nomenclature

47. The compounds $AlCl_3$, $CrCl_3$, and ICl_3 have similar formulas, yet each follows a different set of rules to name it. Name these compounds, and then compare and contrast the nomenclature rules used in each case.
48. Each of the following compounds has three possible names listed for it. For each compound, what is the correct name and why aren't the other names used?
   a. N_2O: nitrogen oxide, nitrogen(I) oxide, dinitrogen monoxide
   b. Cu_2O: copper oxide, copper(I) oxide, dicopper monoxide
   c. Li_2O: lithium oxide, lithium(I) oxide, dilithium monoxide

49. Name each of the following compounds.

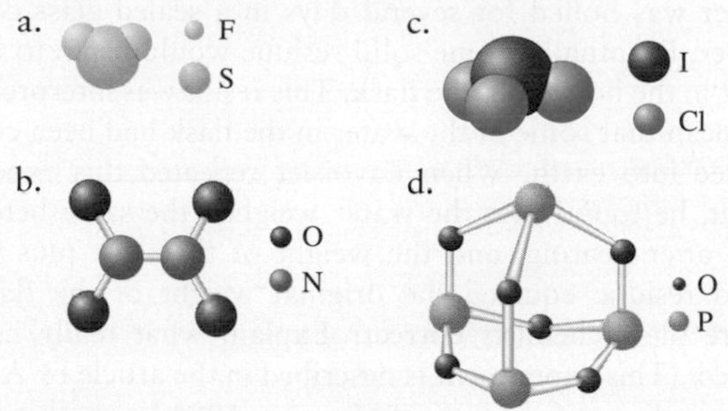

50. Name the following compounds.
a. $NaClO_4$
b. $Mg_3(PO_4)_2$
c. $Al_2(SO_4)_3$
d. SF_2
e. SF_6
f. Na_2HPO_4
g. NaH_2PO_4
h. Li_3N
i. NaOH
j. $Mg(OH)_2$
k. $Al(OH)_3$
l. Ag_2CrO_4

51. Name each of the following compounds.
a. CuI
b. CuI_2
c. CoI_2
d. Na_2CO_3
e. $NaHCO_3$
f. S_4N_4
g. $SeBr_4$
h. NaOCl
i. $BaCrO_4$
j. NH_4NO_3

52. Name the following compounds. Assume the potential acids are dissolved in water.
a. $HC_2H_3O_2$
b. NH_4NO_2
c. Co_2S_3
d. ICl
e. $Pb_3(PO_4)_2$
f. $KClO_3$
g. H_2SO_4
h. Sr_3N_2
i. $Al_2(SO_3)_3$
j. SnO_2
k. Na_2CrO_4
l. HClO

53. Write formulas for the following compounds.
a. Sulfur dioxide
b. Sulfur trioxide
c. Sodium sulfite
d. Potassium hydrogen sulfite
e. Lithium nitride
f. Chromium(III) carbonate
g. Chromium(II) acetate
h. Tin(IV) fluoride
i. Ammonium hydrogen sulfate
j. Ammonium hydrogen phosphate
k. Potassium perchlorate
l. Sodium hydride
m. Hypobromous acid
n. Hydrobromic acid

54. Write formulas for the following compounds.
a. Sodium oxide
b. Sodium peroxide
c. Potassium cyanide
d. Copper(II) nitrate
e. Silicon tetrachloride
f. Lead(II) oxide
g. Lead(IV) oxide (common name lead dioxide)
h. Copper(I) chloride
i. Gallium arsenide
j. Cadmium selenide
k. Zinc sulfide
l. Mercury(I) chloride
m. Nitrous acid
n. Diphosphorus pentoxide

55. The common names and formulas for several substances are given below. What are the systematic names for these substances?

a. Sugar of lead	$Pb(C_2H_3O_2)_2$
b. Blue vitriol	$CuSO_4$
c. Quicklime	CaO
d. Epsom salts	$MgSO_4$
e. Milk of magnesia	$Mg(OH)_2$
f. Gypsum	$CaSO_4$
g. Laughing gas	N_2O

56. Each of the following compounds is incorrectly named. What is wrong with each name, and what is the correct name for each compound?
a. $FeCl_3$, iron chloride
b. NO_2, nitrogen(IV) oxide
c. CaO, calcium(II) monoxide
d. Al_2S_3, dialuminum trisulfide
e. $Mg(C_2H_3O_2)_2$, manganese diacetate
f. $FePO_4$, iron(II) phosphide
g. P_2S_5, phosphorus sulfide
h. Na_2O_2, sodium oxide
i. HNO_3, nitrate acid
j. H_2S, sulfuric acid

57. Name the following acids.

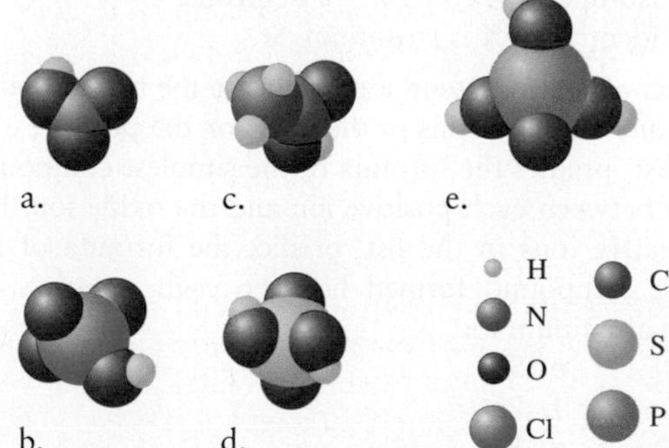

Additional Exercises

58. What discoveries were made by J. J. Thomson, Henri Becquerel, and Lord Rutherford? How did Dalton's model of the atom have to be modified to account for these discoveries?

59. Consider the chemical reaction depicted to the right. Label as much as you can using the terms *atom, molecule, element, compound, ionic, gas,* and *solid.*

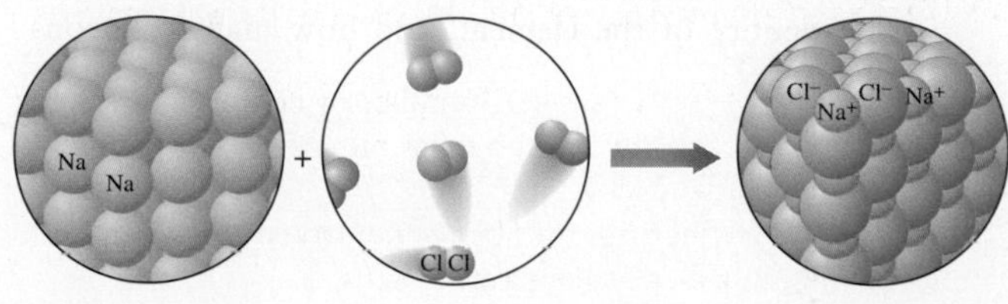

60. Section 2.3 describes the postulates of Dalton's atomic theory. With some modifications, these postulates hold up very well regarding how we view elements, compounds, and chemical reactions today. Answer the following questions concerning Dalton's atomic theory and the modifications made today.
    a. The atom can be broken down into smaller parts. What are the smaller parts?
    b. How are atoms of hydrogen identical to each other, and how can they be different from each other?
    c. How are atoms of hydrogen different from atoms of helium? How can H atoms be similar to He atoms?
    d. How is water different from hydrogen peroxide (H_2O_2) even though both compounds are composed of only hydrogen and oxygen?
    e. What happens in a chemical reaction, and why is mass conserved in a chemical reaction?

61. A sample of chloroform is found to contain 12.0 g of carbon, 106.4 g of chlorine, and 1.01 g of hydrogen. If a second sample of chloroform is found to contain 30.0 g of carbon, what is the total mass of chloroform in the second sample?

62. In a reaction, 34.0 g of chromium(III) oxide reacts with 12.1 g of aluminum to produce chromium and aluminum oxide. If 23.3 g of chromium is produced, what mass of aluminum oxide is produced?

63. The isotope of an unknown element, X, has a mass number of 79. The most stable ion of the isotope has 36 electrons and forms a binary compound with sodium having a formula of Na_2X. Which of the following statements is(are) *true?* Correct the false statements.
    a. The binary compound formed between X and fluorine will be a covalent compound.
    b. The isotope of X contains 38 protons.
    c. The isotope of X contains 41 neutrons.
    d. The identity of X is strontium, Sr.

64. For each of the following ions, indicate the total number of protons and electrons in the ion. For the positive ions in the list, predict the formula of the simplest compound formed between each positive ion and the oxide ion. For the negative ions in the list, predict the formula of the simplest compound formed between each negative ion and the aluminum ion.
    a. Fe^{2+}
    b. Fe^{3+}
    c. Ba^{2+}
    d. Cs^{+}
    e. S^{2-}
    f. P^{3-}
    g. Br^{-}
    h. N^{3-}

65. An element's most stable ion forms an ionic compound with bromine, having the formula XBr_2. If the ion of element X has a mass number of 230 and 86 electrons, what is the identity of the element, and how many neutrons does it have?

66. The early alchemists used to do an experiment in which water was boiled for several days in a sealed glass container. Eventually, some solid residue would begin to appear in the bottom of the flask. This result was interpreted to mean that some of the water in the flask had been converted into earth. When Lavoisier repeated this experiment, he found that the water weighed the same before and after heating, and the weight of the flask plus the solid residue equaled the original weight of the flask. Were the alchemists correct? Explain what really happened. (This experiment is described in the article by A. F. Scott in *Scientific American,* January 1984.)

67. Elements in the same family often form oxyanions of the same general formula. The anions are named in a similar fashion. What are the names of the oxyanions of selenium and tellurium: SeO_4^{2-}, SeO_3^{2-}, TeO_4^{2-}, TeO_3^{2-}?

68. How would you name $HBrO_4$, KIO_3, $NaBrO_2$, and HIO? Refer to Table 2.5 and the acid nomenclature discussion in the text.

69. Indium oxide contains 4.784 g of indium for every 1.000 g of oxygen. In 1869, when Mendeleev first presented his version of the periodic table, he proposed the formula In_2O_3 for indium oxide. Before that time, it was thought that the formula was InO. What values for the atomic mass of indium are obtained using these two formulas? Assume that oxygen has an atomic mass of 16.00.

70. The designations 1A through 8A used for certain families of the periodic table are helpful for predicting the charges on ions in binary ionic compounds. In these compounds, the metals generally take on a positive charge equal to the family number, and the nonmetals take on a negative charge equal to the family number minus 8. Thus the compound formed from sodium and chlorine contains Na^+ and Cl^- ions and has the formula NaCl. Predict the formula and the name of the binary compound formed from the following pairs of elements.
    a. Ca and N
    b. K and O
    c. Rb and F
    d. Mg and S
    e. Ba and I
    f. Al and Se
    g. Cs and P
    h. In and Br

71. A binary ionic compound is known to contain a cation with 51 protons and 48 electrons. The anion contains one-third the number of protons as the cation. The number of electrons in the anion is equal to the number of protons plus 1. What is the formula of this compound? What is the name of this compound?

72. Identify each of the following elements.
    a. a member of the same family as oxygen whose most stable ion contains 54 electrons
    b. a member of the alkali metal family whose most stable ion contains 36 electrons
    c. a noble gas with 18 protons in the nucleus
    d. a halogen with 85 protons and 85 electrons

73. A certain element has only two naturally occurring isotopes: one with 18 neutrons and the other with 20 neutrons. The element forms 1− charged ions when in ionic compounds. Predict the identity of the element. What number of electrons does the 1− charged ion have?

Challenge Problems

74. Reaction of 2.0 L of hydrogen gas with 1.0 L of oxygen gas yields 2.0 L of water vapor. All gases are at the same temperature and pressure. Show how these data support the idea that oxygen gas is a diatomic molecule. Must we consider hydrogen to be a diatomic molecule to explain these results?

75. Each of the statements below is true, but Dalton might have had trouble explaining some of them with his atomic theory. Give explanations for the following statements.
   a. The space-filling models for ethyl alcohol and dimethyl ether are shown below.

   These two compounds have the same composition by mass (52% carbon, 13% hydrogen, and 35% oxygen), yet the two have different melting points, boiling points, and solubilities in water.
   b. Burning wood leaves an ash that is only a small fraction of the mass of the original wood.
   c. Atoms can be broken down into smaller particles.
   d. One sample of lithium hydride is 87.4% lithium by mass, whereas another sample of lithium hydride is 74.9% lithium by mass. However, the two samples have the same properties.

76. You take three compounds, each consisting of two elements (X, Y, and/or Z) and decompose them to their respective elements. To determine the relative masses of X, Y, and Z, you collect and weigh the elements, obtaining the following data:

Elements in Compound	Masses of Elements
1. X and Y	X = 0.4 g, Y = 4.2 g
2. Y and Z	Y = 1.4 g, Z = 1.0 g
3. X and Y	X = 2.0 g, Y = 7.0 g

   a. What are the assumptions needed to solve this problem?
   b. What are the relative masses of X, Y, and Z?
   c. What are the chemical formulas of the three compounds?
   d. If you decompose 21 g of compound XY, how much of each element is present?

77. Two elements, R and Q, combine to form two binary compounds. In the first compound, 14.0 g of R combines with 3.00 g of Q. In the second compound, 7.00 g of R combines with 4.50 g of Q. Show that these data are in accord with the law of multiple proportions. If the formula of the second compound is RQ, what is the formula of the first compound?

78. A single molecule has a mass of 7.31×10^{-23} g. Provide an example of a real molecule that can have this mass.

79. A combustion reaction involves the reaction of a substance with oxygen gas. The complete combustion of any hydrocarbon (binary compound of carbon and hydrogen) produces carbon dioxide and water as the only products. Octane is a hydrocarbon found in gasoline. Complete combustion of octane produces 8 L of carbon dioxide for every 9 L of water vapor (both measured at the same temperature and pressure). What is the ratio of carbon atoms to hydrogen atoms in a molecule of octane?

80. You have two distinct gaseous compounds made from element X and element Y. The mass percents are as follows:

Compound I: 30.43% X, 69.57% Y

Compound II: 63.64% X, 36.36% Y

In their natural standard states, element X and element Y exist as gases. (Monatomic? Diatomic? Triatomic? That is for you to determine.) When you react "gas X" with "gas Y" to make the products, you get the following data (all at standard pressure and temperature):

1 volume "gas X" + 2 volumes "gas Y" $\longrightarrow$ 2 volumes compound I

2 volumes "gas X" + 1 volume "gas Y" $\longrightarrow$ 2 volumes compound II

Assume the simplest possible formulas for reactants and products in these chemical equations. Then determine the relative atomic masses of element X and element Y.

Marathon Problem

81. You have gone back in time and are working with Dalton on a table of relative masses. Following are his data:

    0.602 g gas A reacts with 0.295 g gas B

    0.172 g gas B reacts with 0.401 g gas C

    0.320 g gas A reacts with 0.374 g gas C

    a. Assuming simplest formulas (AB, BC, and AC), construct a table of relative masses for Dalton.
    b. Knowing some history of chemistry, you tell Dalton that if he determines the volumes of the gases reacted at constant temperature and pressure, he need not assume simplest formulas. You collect the following data:

    6 volumes gas A + 1 volume gas B $\longrightarrow$ 4 volumes product

    1 volume gas B + 4 volumes gas C $\longrightarrow$ 4 volumes product

    3 volumes gas A + 2 volumes gas C $\longrightarrow$ 6 volumes product

    Write the simplest balanced equations, and find the actual relative masses of the elements. Explain your reasoning.

Stoichiometry

3

chapter

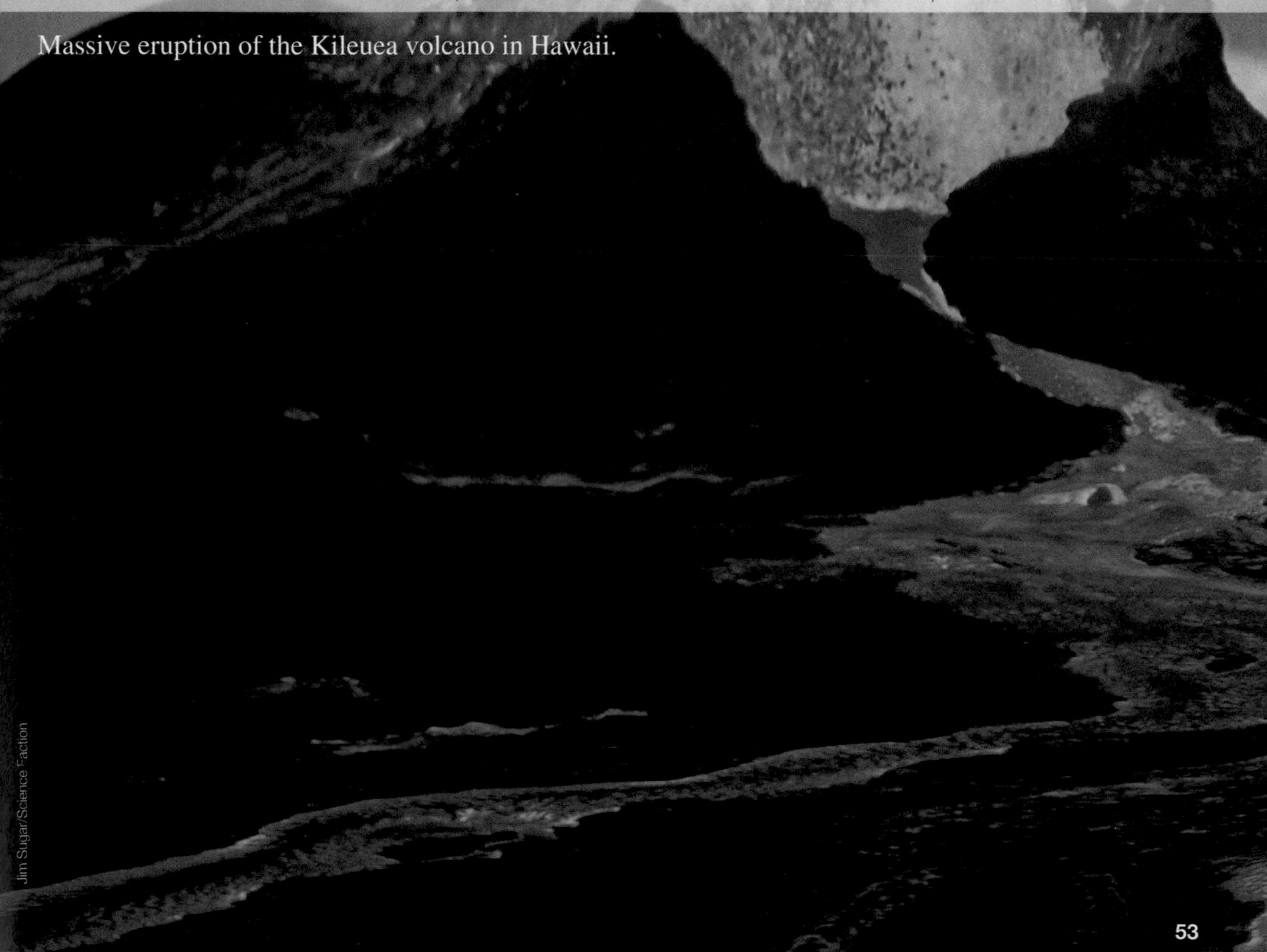

Massive eruption of the Kileuea volcano in Hawaii.

Jim Sugar/Science Faction

OWL

Sign in to OWL at www.cengage.com/owl to view tutorials and simulations, develop problem-solving skills, and complete online homework assigned by your professor.

go Chemistry

Download mini lecture videos for key concept review and exam prep from OWL or purchase them from www.cengagebrain.com.

Chemical reactions have a profound effect on our lives. There are many examples: Food is converted to energy in the human body; nitrogen and hydrogen are combined to form ammonia, which is used as a fertilizer; fuels and plastics are produced from petroleum; the starch in plants is synthesized from carbon dioxide and water using energy from sunlight; human insulin is produced in laboratories by bacteria; cancer is induced in humans by substances from our environment; and so on, in a seemingly endless list. The central activity of chemistry is to understand chemical changes such as these, and the study of reactions occupies a central place in this text. We will examine why reactions occur, how fast they occur, and the specific pathways they follow.

In this chapter we will consider the quantities of materials consumed and produced in chemical reactions. This area of study is called **chemical stoichiometry.** To understand chemical stoichiometry, you must first understand the concept of relative atomic masses.

3.1 Atomic Masses

As we saw in Chapter 2, the first quantitative information about atomic masses came from the work of Dalton, Gay-Lussac, Lavoisier, Avogadro, Cannizzaro, and Berzelius. By observing the proportions in which elements combine to form various compounds, nineteenth-century chemists calculated relative atomic masses. The modern system of atomic masses, instituted in 1961, is based on ^{12}C (carbon-12) as the standard. In this system *^{12}C is assigned a mass of exactly 12 atomic mass units* (amu), and the masses of all other atoms are given relative to this standard.

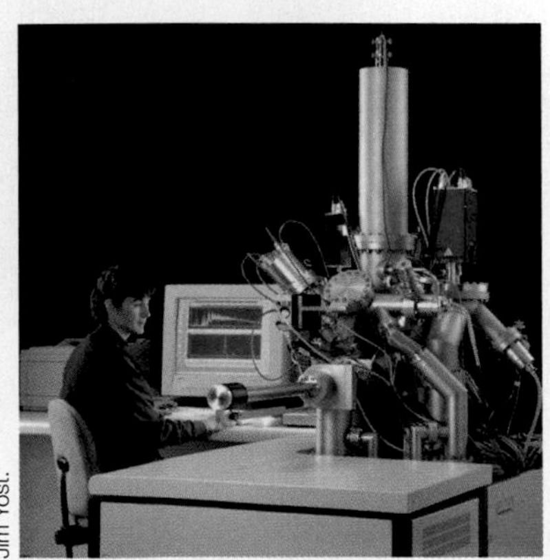

Chemist using a mass spectrometer to analyze for copper in blood plasma.

The most accurate method currently available for comparing the masses of atoms involves the use of the **mass spectrometer.** In this instrument, diagrammed in Fig. 3.1, atoms or molecules are passed into a beam of high-speed electrons. The high-speed electrons knock electrons off the atoms or molecules being analyzed and change them to positive ions. An applied electric field then accelerates these ions through a magnetic field, which deflects the paths of the ions. The amount of path deflection for each ion depends on its mass—the most massive ions are deflected the smallest amount—and this deflection causes the ions to separate, as shown in Fig. 3.1. A comparison of the positions where the ions hit the detector plate gives very accurate values of their relative masses. For example, when ^{12}C and ^{13}C are analyzed in a mass spectrometer, the ratio of their masses is found to be

$$\frac{\text{Mass } ^{13}\text{C}}{\text{Mass } ^{12}\text{C}} = 1.0836129$$

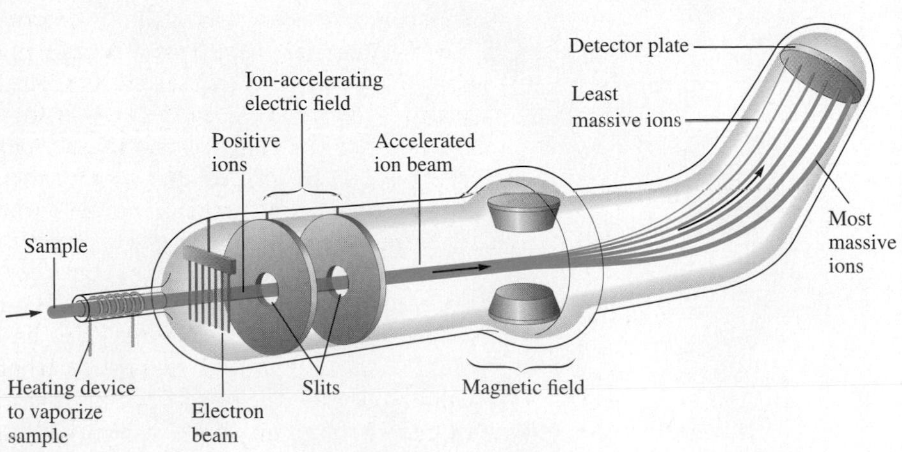

Figure 3.1
Schematic diagram of a mass spectrometer.

Elemental Analysis Catches Elephant Poachers

Chemical Insights

In an effort to combat the poaching of elephants by controlling illegal exports of ivory, scientists are now using the isotopic composition of ivory trinkets and elephant tusks to identify the region of Africa where the elephant lived. Using a mass spectrometer, scientists analyze the ivory for the relative amounts of ^{12}C, ^{13}C, ^{14}N, ^{15}N, ^{86}Sr, and ^{87}Sr to determine the diet of the elephant and thus its place of origin. For example, because grasses use a different photosynthetic pathway to produce glucose than do trees, grasses have a slightly different $^{13}C/^{12}C$ ratio than trees. They have different ratios because each time a carbon is added in going from simpler to more complex compounds, the more massive ^{13}C is disfavored relative to ^{12}C since it reacts more slowly. Because trees use more steps to build up glucose, they end up with a smaller $^{13}C/^{12}C$ ratio in their leaves relative to grasses, and this difference is then reflected in the tissues of elephants. Thus scientists can tell whether a particular tusk came from a savanna-dwelling (grass-eating) elephant or from a tree-browsing elephant.

Similarly, because the ratios of $^{15}N/^{14}N$ and $^{87}Sr/^{86}Sr$ in elephant tusks also vary depending on the region of Africa the elephant inhabited, they can be used to trace the elephant's origin. In fact, using these techniques, scientists have reported being able to discriminate between elephants living only about 100 miles apart.

Kennan Ward/Stock Market/Corbis

A herd of savanna-dwelling elephants.

There is now international concern about the dwindling elephant populations in parts of Africa, where their numbers have decreased dramatically over the past several decades. This concern has led to bans on the export of ivory from many countries in Africa. However, a few nations still allow ivory to be exported. Thus, to enforce the trade restrictions, the origin of a given piece of ivory must be established. It is hoped that the "isotope signature" of the ivory can be used for this purpose.

Since the atomic mass unit is defined such that the mass of ^{12}C is *exactly* 12 atomic mass units, then on this same scale,

$$\text{Mass of } ^{13}\text{C} = (1.0836129)(12 \text{ amu}) = 13.003355 \text{ amu}$$

↑ Exact number, by definition

Most elements occur in nature as mixtures of isotopes; thus atomic masses are generally reported as average values. It turns out the average mass for a given atom varies at different geographical locations, and the new values are given as intervals to reflect this. Carbon, for example, now has an official mass of [12.0096; 12.0116]. This is not due to uncertainty but takes into account variations in atomic masses based on location. This new system has recently been adopted for 10 elements (hydrogen, lithium, boron, carbon, nitrogen, oxygen, silicon, sulfur, chlorine, and thallium). In the text we will continue with the standard method of average atomic masses for these elements.

The masses of other atoms can be determined in a similar manner.

The mass for each element is given in the table inside the front cover of this book. This value, even though it is actually a mass, is sometimes called (for historical reasons) the atomic weight for each element.

Look at the value of the atomic mass of carbon given in the table. You might expect to see 12 since we said the system of atomic masses is based on ^{12}C. However, the number given for carbon is 12.01 because the carbon found on earth (natural carbon) is a mixture of the isotopes ^{12}C, ^{13}C, and ^{14}C. All three isotopes have six protons, but they have six, seven, and eight neutrons, respectively. Because natural carbon is a mixture of isotopes, the atomic mass we use for carbon is an *average value* based on its isotopic composition.

The average atomic mass for carbon is computed as follows. Chemists know that natural carbon is composed of 98.89% ^{12}C atoms and 1.11% ^{13}C atoms. The amount of ^{14}C is negligibly small at this level of precision. Using

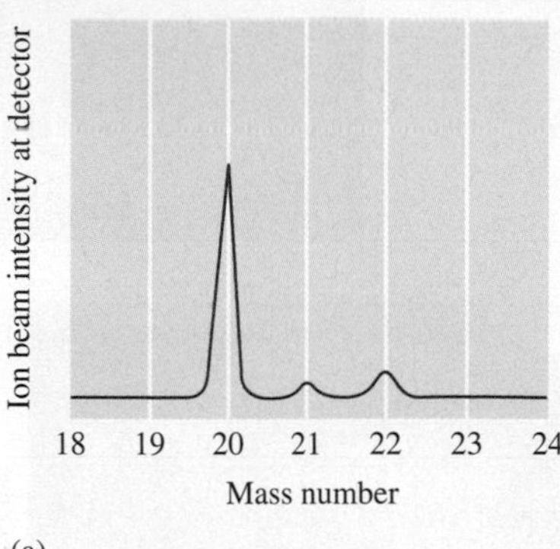

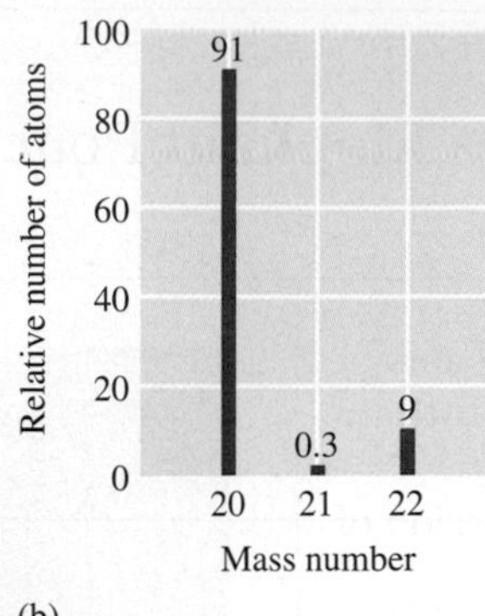

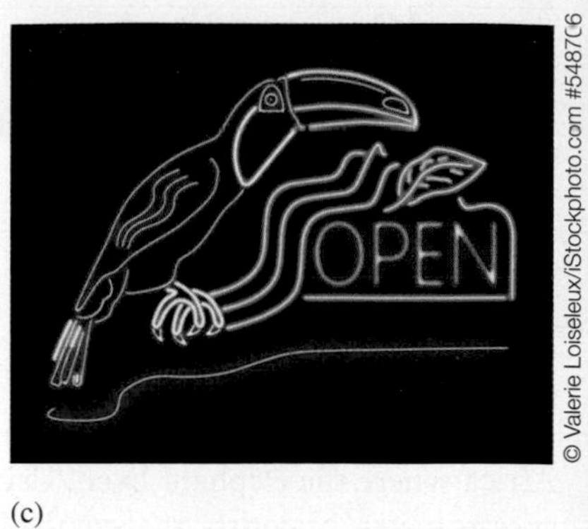

Figure 3.2
The relative intensities of the signals recorded when natural neon is injected into a mass spectrometer, represented in terms of (a) "peaks" and (b) a bar graph. The relative areas of the peaks are 0.9092 (^{20}Ne), 0.00257 (^{21}Ne), and 0.0882 (^{22}Ne); natural neon is therefore 90.92% ^{20}Ne, 0.257% ^{21}Ne, and 8.82% ^{22}Ne. (c) A neon sign.

the masses of ^{12}C (exactly 12 amu) and ^{13}C (13.003355 amu), the average atomic mass for natural carbon can be calculated.

$$98.89\% \text{ of } 12 \text{ amu} + 1.11\% \text{ of } 13.0034 \text{ amu}$$
$$= (0.9889)(12 \text{ amu}) + (0.0111)(13.0034 \text{ amu}) = 12.01 \text{ amu}$$

See Appendix A1.5 for a discussion of significant figures.

This average mass is often called the atomic weight of carbon.

Even though natural carbon does not contain a single atom with mass 12.01, for stoichiometric purposes we consider carbon to be composed of only one type of atom with a mass of 12.01. We do this so that we can count atoms of natural carbon by weighing a sample of carbon. Let's consider a nonchemical example. It is much easier to weigh out 3000 grams of jelly beans (with an average mass of 3 grams per jelly bean) than to count out 1000 of them. Note that none of the jelly beans has to have a mass of 3 grams for this method to work; only the *average* mass must be 3 grams. We extend this same principle to counting atoms. For natural carbon with an average mass of 12.01 atomic mass units, to obtain 1000 atoms would require weighing out 12,010 atomic mass units of natural carbon (a mixture of ^{12}C and ^{13}C).

As in the case of carbon, the mass for each element given in the table inside the front cover of this book is an average value based on the isotopic composition of the naturally occurring element. For instance, the mass listed for hydrogen (1.008) is the average mass for natural hydrogen, which is a mixture of ^{1}H and ^{2}H (deuterium). *No* atom of hydrogen actually has the mass 1.008.

In addition to being used for determining accurate mass values for individual atoms, the mass spectrometer is used to determine the isotopic composition of a natural element. For example, when a sample of natural neon is injected into a mass spectrometer, the results shown in Fig. 3.2 are obtained. The areas of the "peaks" or the heights of the bars indicate the relative numbers of $^{22}_{10}$Ne, $^{22}_{10}$Ne, and $^{22}_{10}$Ne atoms.

Figure 3.3
Mass spectrum of natural copper.

EXAMPLE 3.1

Copper is a very important metal used for water pipes, electrical wiring, roof coverings, and other materials. When a sample of natural copper is vaporized and injected into a mass spectrometer, the results shown in Fig. 3.3 are obtained. Use these data to compute the average mass of natural copper. (The mass values for ^{63}Cu and ^{65}Cu are 62.93 amu and 64.93 amu, respectively.)

Solution As shown by the graph, of every 100 atoms of natural copper, on average 69.09 are ^{63}Cu and 30.91 are ^{65}Cu. Thus the average mass of 100 atoms of natural copper is

$$(69.09 \text{ atoms})\left(62.93 \frac{\text{amu}}{\text{atom}}\right) + (30.9 \text{ atoms})\left(64.93 \frac{\text{amu}}{\text{atom}}\right) = 6355 \text{ amu}$$

The average mass per atom is

$$\frac{6355 \text{ amu}}{100 \text{ atoms}} = 63.55 \text{ amu/atom}$$

This mass value is used in calculations involving the reactions of copper and is the value given in the table inside the front cover of this book.

3.2 The Mole

Because samples of matter typically contain so many atoms, a unit of measure called the mole has been established for use in counting atoms. For our purposes it is most convenient to define the **mole** (abbreviated mol) as *the number equal to the number of carbon atoms in exactly 12 grams of pure* ^{12}C. Modern techniques that allow us to count atoms very precisely have been used to determine this number as 6.022137×10^{23} (6.022×10^{23} will be sufficient for our purposes). This number is called **Avogadro's number** to honor his contributions to chemistry. *One mole of something consists of* 6.022×10^{23} *units of that substance.* Just as a dozen eggs is 12 eggs, a mole of eggs is 6.022×10^{23} eggs.

The SI definition of the mole is the amount of a substance that contains as many entities as there are in exactly 0.012 kg (12 g) of carbon-12.

The magnitude of the number 6.022×10^{23} is very difficult to imagine. To give you some idea, 1 mole of seconds represents a span of time 4 million times as long as the earth has already existed, and 1 mole of marbles is enough to cover the entire earth to a depth of 50 miles! However, since atoms are so tiny, a mole of atoms or molecules is a perfectly manageable quantity to use in a reaction (see Fig. 3.4).

Figure 3.4
Proceeding clockwise from the top, samples containing 1 mole each of copper, aluminum, iron, sulfur, iodine, and (in the center) mercury.

How do we use the mole in chemical calculations? Recall that Avogadro's number is defined as the number of atoms in exactly 12 grams of ^{12}C. Thus 12 grams of ^{12}C contains 6.022×10^{23} atoms. Also, a 12.01-gram sample of natural carbon contains 6.022×10^{23} atoms (a mixture of ^{12}C, ^{13}C, and ^{14}C atoms, with an average mass of 12.01). Since the ratio of the masses of the samples (12 g/12.01 g) is the same as the ratio of the masses of the individual components (12 amu/12.01 amu), the two samples contain the *same number* of components.

To be sure this point is clear, think of oranges with an average mass of 0.5 pound each and grapefruit with an average mass of 1.0 pound each. Any two sacks for which the sack of grapefruit weighs twice as much as the sack of oranges will contain the same number of pieces of fruit. The same idea extends to atoms. Compare natural carbon (average mass of 12.01) and natural helium (average mass of 4.003). A sample of 12.01 grams of natural carbon contains the same number of atoms as 4.003 grams of natural helium. Both samples contain 1 mole of atoms (6.022×10^{23}). Table 3.1 gives more examples that illustrate this basic idea.

The mass of 1 mole of an element is equal to its atomic mass in grams.

Thus the mole is defined such that a sample of a natural element with a mass equal to the element's atomic mass expressed in grams contains 1 mole of atoms. This definition also fixes the relationship between the atomic mass unit

Table 3.1

Comparison of 1-Mole Samples of Various Elements

Element	Number of Atoms	Mass of Sample (g)
Aluminum	6.022×10^{23}	26.98
Gold	6.022×10^{23}	196.97
Iron	6.022×10^{23}	55.85
Sulfur	6.022×10^{23}	32.07
Boron	6.022×10^{23}	10.81
Xenon	6.022×10^{23}	131.30

and the gram. Since 6.022×10^{23} atoms of carbon (each with a mass of 12 amu) have a mass of 12 grams, then

$$(6.022 \times 10^{23} \text{ atoms})\left(\frac{12 \text{ amu}}{\text{atom}}\right) = 12 \text{ g}$$

and

$$6.022 \times 10^{23} \text{ amu} = \underset{\substack{\uparrow \\ \text{Exact number}}}{1} \text{ g}$$

OWL INTERACTIVE EXAMPLE 3.2

Americium is an element that does not occur naturally. It can be made in very small amounts in a device called a particle accelerator. Compute the mass in grams of a sample of americium containing six atoms.

Solution From the table inside the front cover of this book, note that one americium atom has a mass of 243 amu. Thus the mass of six atoms is

$$6 \text{ atoms} \times 243 \frac{\text{amu}}{\text{atom}} = 1.46 \times 10^3 \text{ amu}$$

From the relationship 6.022×10^{23} amu = 1 g, the mass of six americium atoms in grams is

$$1.46 \times 10^3 \text{ amu} \times \frac{1 \text{ g}}{6.022 \times 10^{23} \text{ amu}} = 2.42 \times 10^{-21} \text{ g}$$

This relationship can be used to derive the factor needed to convert between atomic mass units and grams.

Refer to Appendix 2 for a discussion of units and the conversion from one unit to another.

To perform chemical calculations, you must understand what the mole means and how to determine the number of moles in a given mass of a substance. These procedures are illustrated in Example 3.3.

OWL INTERACTIVE EXAMPLE 3.3

A silicon chip used in an integrated circuit of a microcomputer has a mass of 5.68 mg. How many silicon (Si) atoms are present in this chip?

Solution The strategy for doing this problem is to convert from milligrams of silicon to grams of silicon, then to moles of silicon, and finally to atoms of silicon:

$$5.68 \text{ mg Si} \times \frac{1 \text{ g Si}}{1000 \text{ mg Si}} = 5.68 \times 10^{-3} \text{ g Si}$$

$$5.68 \times 10^{-3} \text{ g Si} \times \frac{1 \text{ mol Si}}{28.09 \text{ g Si}} = 2.02 \times 10^{-4} \text{ mol Si}$$

$$2.02 \times 10^{-4} \text{ mol Si} \times \frac{6.022 \times 10^{23} \text{ atoms}}{1 \text{ mol Si}} = 1.22 \times 10^{20} \text{ atoms}$$

It always makes sense to think about orders of magnitude as you do a calculation. In Example 3.3, the 5.68-milligram sample of silicon is clearly much less than 1 mole of silicon (which has a mass of 28.09 grams), so the final answer of 1.22×10^{20} atoms (compared with 6.022×10^{23} atoms) is at least in the right direction. Paying careful attention to units and making sure the answer is sensible can help you detect an inverted conversion factor or a number that was incorrectly entered in your calculator.

Always check to see if your answer is sensible.

3.3 Molar Mass

A chemical compound is, ultimately, a collection of atoms. For example, methane (the major component of natural gas) consists of molecules that each contain one carbon atom and four hydrogen atoms (CH_4). How can we calculate the mass of 1 mole of methane; that is, what is the mass of 6.022×10^{23} CH_4 molecules? Since each CH_4 molecule contains one carbon atom and four hydrogen atoms, 1 mole of CH_4 molecules consists of 1 mole of carbon atoms and 4 moles of hydrogen atoms. The mass of 1 mole of methane can be found by summing the masses of carbon and hydrogen present:

The average atomic mass for carbon to five significant digits is 12.011.

Mass of 1 mol of C	=	12.011 g
Mass of 4 mol of H	=	4×1.008 g
Mass of 1 mol of CH_4	=	16.043 g

OWL INTERACTIVE EXAMPLE 3.4

Isopentyl acetate ($C_7H_{14}O_2$), the compound responsible for the scent of bananas, can be produced commercially. Interestingly, bees release about 1 μg (1×10^{-6} g) of this compound when they sting to attract other bees to join the attack. How many molecules of isopentyl acetate are released in a typical bee sting? How many atoms of carbon are present?

Solution Since we are given a mass of isopentyl acetate and want the number of molecules, we must first compute the molar mass.

The average atomic mass for hydrogen to five significant digits is 1.0079 and that for oxygen is 15.999.

$$7 \text{ mol C} \times 12.011 \frac{\text{g}}{\text{mol}} = 84.077 \text{ g C}$$

$$14 \text{ mol H} \times 1.0079 \frac{\text{g}}{\text{mol}} = 14.111 \text{ g H}$$

$$2 \text{ mol O} \times 15.999 \frac{\text{g}}{\text{mol}} = 31.998 \text{ g O}$$

$$\text{Mass of 1 mol of } C_7H_{14}O_2 = 130.186 \text{ g}$$

Thus 1 mole of isopentyl acetate (6.022×10^{23} molecules) has a mass of 130.186 g.

To find the number of molecules released in a sting, we must first determine the number of moles of isopentyl acetate in 1×10^{6} g:

$$1 \times 10^{-6} \text{ g } C_7H_{14}O_2 \times \frac{1 \text{ mol } C_7H_{14}O_2}{130.186 \text{ g } C_7H_{14}O_2} = 8 \times 10^{-9} \text{ mol } C_7H_{14}O_2$$

Since 1 mol is 6.022×10^{23} units, we can determine the number of molecules:

$$8 \times 10^{-9} \text{ mol } C_7H_{14}O_2 \times \frac{6.022 \times 10^{23} \text{ molecules}}{1 \text{ mol } C_7H_{14}O_2} = 5 \times 10^{15} \text{ molecules}$$

Chemical Insights

Measuring the Masses of Large Molecules or Making Elephants Fly

When a chemist produces a new molecule, one crucial property for making a positive identification is the molecule's mass. There are many ways to determine the molar mass of a compound, but one of the fastest and most accurate methods involves mass spectrometry. This method requires that the substance be put into the gas phase and ionized. The deflection that the resulting ion exhibits as it is accelerated through a magnetic field can be used to obtain a very precise value of its mass. One drawback of this method is that it is difficult to use with large molecules because they are difficult to vaporize. That is, substances that contain large molecules typically have very high boiling points, and these molecules are often damaged when they are vaporized at such high temperatures. A case in point involves proteins, an extremely important class of large biologic molecules that are quite fragile at high temperatures. Typical methods used to obtain the masses of protein molecules are slow and tedious.

Mass spectrometry has not previously been used to obtain protein masses because proteins decompose at the temperatures necessary to vaporize them. However, a relatively new technique called matrix-assisted laser desorption has been developed that allows mass spectrometric determination of protein molar masses. In this technique, the large "target" molecule is embedded in a matrix of smaller molecules. The matrix is then placed in a mass spectrometer and blasted with a laser beam, which causes its disintegration. Disintegration of the matrix frees the large target molecule, which is then swept into the mass spectrometer. One researcher involved in this project likened this method to an elephant on top of a tall building: "The elephant must fly if the building suddenly turns into fine grains of sand."

This technique allows scientists to determine the masses of huge molecules. So far, researchers have measured proteins with masses up to 350,000 daltons (1 dalton is equal to 1 atomic mass unit). This method probably will be extended to even larger molecules such as DNA and could be a revolutionary development in the characterization of biomolecules.

To determine the number of carbon atoms present, we must multiply the number of molecules by 7 (each molecule of isopentyl acetate contains seven carbon atoms):

To show the correct number of significant figures in each calculation, we round off after each step. In your calculations, always carry extra significant figures through to the end; then round off.

$$5 \times 10^{15} \text{ molecules} \times \frac{7 \text{ carbon atoms}}{\text{molecule}} = 4 \times 10^{16} \text{ carbon atoms}$$

Note: In keeping with our practice of always showing the correct number of significant figures, we have rounded off after each step. However, if extra digits are carried throughout this problem, the final answer rounds to 3×10^{16}.

Since the number 16.043 represents the mass of 1 mole of methane molecules, it makes sense to call it the *molar mass* for methane. However, traditionally, the term *molecular weight* has been used to describe the mass of 1 mole of a substance. Thus the terms **molar mass** and **molecular weight** mean exactly the same thing: *the mass in grams of 1 mole of a compound.* The molar mass of a known substance is obtained by summing the masses of the component atoms, as we did for methane.

A substance's molar mass (molecular weight) is the mass in grams of 1 mole of the substance.

Some substances exist as a collection of ions rather than as separate molecules. An example is ordinary table salt, sodium chloride (NaCl), which is composed of an array of Na^+ and Cl^- ions. There are no NaCl molecules present. However, in this text, for convenience, we will apply the term *molar mass* to both ionic and molecular substances. Thus we will refer to 58.44

(22.99 + 35.45) as the molar mass for NaCl. In some texts the term *formula weight* is used for ionic compounds instead of the terms *molar mass* and *molecular weight*.

3.4 Conceptual Problem Solving

One of the great rewards of studying chemistry is to become a good problem solver. Being able to solve complex problems is a talent that will serve you well in all walks of life. It is our purpose in this text to help you learn to solve problems in a flexible, creative way based on understanding the fundamental ideas of chemistry. We call this approach **conceptual problem solving.**

The ultimate goal is to be able to solve new problems (that is, problems you have not seen before) on your own. In this text we will provide problems and offer solutions by explaining how to think about the problems. Although the answers to these problems are important, it is perhaps even more important to understand the process—the thinking necessary to get the answer. While studying the solution, it is crucial that you interactively think through the problem with us. Do not skip the discussion and jump to the answer. Make sure that you understand each step in the process.

A main goal in conceptual problem solving is to get the "big picture"—a real understanding of the situation. This approach to problem solving looks within the problem for a solution. In essence, we ask a series of questions as we proceed and use our knowledge of fundamental principles to answer these questions; we then let the problem (and our questions) guide us as we solve it.

The following organizing principles will be useful to us as we proceed to solve a problem:

- First, we need to read the problem and decide on the final goal. Then we sort through the facts given, focusing on the key words and, when appropriate, drawing a diagram of the problem. In this part of the analysis we need to state the problem as simply as possible. The questions we ask at first are general and similar regardless of the problem. They are basically of the type "What are we trying to solve?" and "What does this mean?"
- We need to work backward from the final goal to decide where to start. Our questions become more specific depending on the given problem, such as, "What are the reactants and products?" "What is the balanced equation?" "What do we mean by molar mass?" and so on. Our understanding of the fundamental principles of chemistry will enable us to answer each of these questions and will eventually lead us to the final solution.
- After getting an answer we should check to see whether it is reasonable. The extent to which we can do this varies with the type of problem. If we are computing mass percents of elements in a compound, do they add up to 100%? Do we get a negative answer for a mass? Sometimes it is more difficult to judge if an answer is reasonable. However, once we get the solution of the problem, we should ask, "Does it make sense?"

In summary, instead of looking outside the problem using a memorized scheme, we will look inside the problem and let the problem help us as we proceed to a solution. Learning this approach requires some patience, but the reward for learning to solve problems this way is that you become an effective solver of any new problem that confronts you in daily life or in your work in any field. You will no longer panic when you see a problem that is different in some ways from those you have solved in the past. Although you might be frustrated at times as you learn this method, we guarantee that it will pay dividends later and should make your experience with chemistry a positive one that will prepare you for any career you choose.

We will model this approach with the examples in this text, beginning with Example 3.5. We will continue this approach throughout the examples in Chapters 3 and 4. We will not, however, discuss all example problems throughout the text to this extent because we expect you to take an increasingly active role in this process. As the problems become more complicated, the method of conceptual problem solving becomes more important, and it is crucial that you work through these on your own before reading the solution.

3.5 Percent Composition of Compounds

So far we have discussed the composition of a compound in terms of the numbers of its constituent atoms. It is often useful to know a compound's composition in terms of the masses of its elements. We can obtain this information from the formula of the compound by comparing the mass of each element present in 1 mole of the compound with the total mass of 1 mole of the compound.

For example, consider ethanol, which has the formula C_2H_5OH. The mass of each element present and the molar mass are obtained through the following procedure:

$$\text{Mass of C} = 2 \text{ mol} \times 12.011 \frac{\text{g}}{\text{mol}} = 24.022 \text{ g}$$

$$\text{Mass of H} = 6 \text{ mol} \times 1.008 \frac{\text{g}}{\text{mol}} = 6.048 \text{ g}$$

$$\text{Mass of O} = 1 \text{ mol} \times 15.999 \frac{\text{g}}{\text{mol}} = \underline{15.999 \text{ g}}$$

$$\text{Mass of 1 mol of } C_2H_5OH = 46.069 \text{ g}$$

The **mass percent** (often called the weight percent) of carbon in ethanol can be computed by comparing the mass of carbon in 1 mole of ethanol with the total mass of 1 mole of ethanol and multiplying the result by 100%:

$$\text{Mass percent of C} = \frac{\text{mass of C in 1 mol } C_2H_5OH}{\text{mass of 1 mol } C_2H_5OH} \times 100\%$$

$$= \frac{24.022 \text{ g}}{46.069 \text{ g}} \times 100\%$$

$$= 52.144\%$$

The mass percents of hydrogen and oxygen in ethanol are obtained in a similar manner:

$$\text{Mass percent of H} = \frac{\text{mass of H in 1 mol } C_2H_5OH}{\text{mass of 1 mol } C_2H_5OH} \times 100\%$$

$$= \frac{6.048 \text{ g}}{46.069 \text{ g}} \times 100\%$$

$$= 13.13\%$$

$$\text{Mass percent of O} = \frac{\text{mass of O in 1 mol } C_2H_5OH}{\text{mass of 1 mol } C_2H_5OH} \times 100\%$$

$$= \frac{15.999 \text{ g}}{46.069 \text{ g}} \times 100\%$$

$$= 34.728\%$$

Notice that the percentages add to 100% if rounded to two decimal places; this is the check of the calculations.

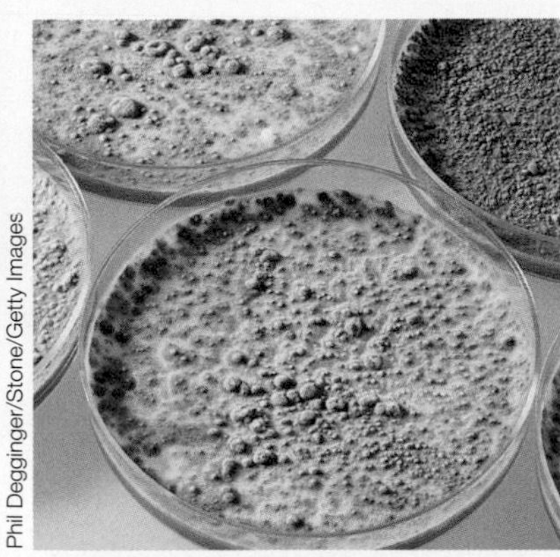

Penicillin is isolated from a mold.

Dorothy Hodgkin (1910–1994) was born in Cairo, Egypt. She became interested in chemistry and in crystals at about the age of 10, and on her 16th birthday she received a book by the Nobel Prize–winning physicist William Bragg. The subject of the book was how to use X rays to analyze crystals, and from that point on, her career path was set.

Dr. Hodgkin used X-ray analysis for three important discoveries. In 1945 she determined the structure of penicillin, which helped manufacturers create penicillin. In 1954 she determined the structure of vitamin B_{12}, which led to her winning the Nobel Prize in Chemistry in 1964. Although both of these are important and useful discoveries, Dr. Hodgkin considered her greatest scientific achievement to be the discovery of insulin (1969), now used in the treatment of diabetes.

OWL INTERACTIVE EXAMPLE 3.5

Penicillin, the first of a now large number of antibiotics (antibacterial agents), was discovered accidentally by the Scottish bacteriologist Alexander Fleming in 1928, but he was never able to isolate it as a pure compound. This and similar antibiotics have saved millions of lives that might have been lost to infections. Penicillin F has the formula $C_{14}H_{20}N_2SO_4$. Compute the mass percent of each element.

Solution As we discussed in Section 3.4, your solution to a problem should begin with questions, the first of which is:

- What is the problem asking us to solve?

In this case you are asked to determine the mass percent of each element in penicillin F. This leads directly to the next question:

- What does this mean?

The mass percent for a given element in a compound is the mass of the element in the compound as a percentage of the mass of the compound. We know the formula for penicillin F is $C_{14}H_{20}N_2SO_4$. The mass percent of carbon, for example, is

$$\text{Mass percent of carbon} = \frac{\text{Mass of carbon in 1 mole of } C_{14}H_{20}N_2SO_4}{\text{Mass of 1 mole of } C_{14}H_{20}N_2SO_4} \times 100\%$$

Notice how we are letting the problem guide us. The original problem was to find the mass percent of each element in a compound. By using the definition of mass percent, we see that we will solve for each element individually. We also have changed the problem to two new and more specific questions:

1. What is the mass of carbon in 1 mole of penicillin F? (the numerator above)
2. What is the mass of 1 mole of penicillin F? (the denominator above)

From the discussion in Section 3.3, we see that the second question is asking for the molar mass of penicillin F. This shows us that although allowing the problem to guide us is important, we also need knowledge of fundamental principles. The molar mass of penicillin F is computed as follows:

$$\text{C:} \quad 14 \text{ mol} \times 12.011 \frac{\text{g}}{\text{mol}} = 168.15 \text{ g}$$

$$\text{H:} \quad 20 \text{ mol} \times 1.008 \frac{\text{g}}{\text{mol}} = 20.16 \text{ g}$$

$$\text{N:} \quad 2 \text{ mol} \times 14.007 \frac{\text{g}}{\text{mol}} = 28.014 \text{ g}$$

$$\text{S:} \quad 1 \text{ mol} \times 32.07 \frac{\text{g}}{\text{mol}} = 32.07 \text{ g}$$

$$\text{O:} \quad 4 \text{ mol} \times 15.999 \frac{\text{g}}{\text{mol}} = \underline{63.996 \text{ g}}$$

$$\text{Mass of 1 mol of } C_{14}H_{20}N_2SO_4 = 312.39 \text{ g}$$

Notice that in solving for the molar mass of penicillin F, we also solved for the mass of each element in 1 mole of the compound. With these masses we can determine the mass percent of each element:

$$\text{Mass percent of C} = \frac{168.15 \text{ g C}}{312.39 \text{ g } C_{14}H_{20}N_2SO_4} \times 100\% = 53.827\%$$

$$\text{Mass percent of H} = \frac{20.16 \text{ g H}}{312.39 \text{ g } C_{14}H_{20}N_2SO_4} \times 100\% = 6.453\%$$

$$\text{Mass percent of N} = \frac{28.014 \text{ g N}}{312.39 \text{ g } C_{14}H_{20}N_2SO_4} \times 100\% = 8.968\%$$

$$\text{Mass percent of S} = \frac{32.07 \text{ g S}}{312.39 \text{ g } C_{14}H_{20}N_2SO_4} \times 100\% = 10.27\%$$

$$\text{Mass percent of O} = \frac{63.996 \text{ g O}}{312.39 \text{ g } C_{14}H_{20}N_2SO_4} \times 100\% = 20.486\%$$

Finally, we can check that the answer is reasonable because the percentages add up to 100%.

Let's summarize the approach:

1. We started with the general question, "What are we trying to solve?"
2. Once we decided on the answer to question 1, we explained what this meant, in this case with a formula.
3. We let the answers guide us to new questions, which were more specific to the problem (such as, "What is the mass of 1 mole of $C_{14}H_{20}N_2SO_4$?").
4. We answered these specific questions using knowledge of fundamental principles.
5. We came to the solution.

This approach will guide you in solving problems throughout the textbook. No matter how complicated the problems become, you should always know specifically what you are trying to solve and then ask (and answer) questions to get to the solution. Your knowledge is important as well, and in chemistry this knowledge builds. Solving this particular problem, for example, would not have been possible without knowing what a chemical formula means and without an understanding of molar mass.

3.6 Determining the Formula of a Compound

When a new compound is prepared, one of the first items of interest is its formula. The formula is often determined by taking a weighed sample of the compound and either decomposing it into its component elements or reacting it with oxygen to produce substances such as CO_2, H_2O, and N_2, which are then collected and weighed. A device for doing this type of analysis is shown in Fig. 3.5. The results of such analyses provide the mass of each type of element in the compound, which can be used to determine the mass percent of each element present.

We will see how information of this type can be used to compute the formula of a compound. Suppose a substance has been prepared that is composed of carbon, hydrogen, and nitrogen. When 0.1156 gram of this compound is reacted with oxygen, 0.1638 gram of carbon dioxide (CO_2) and 0.1676 gram of water (H_2O) are collected. Assuming that all of the carbon in the compound

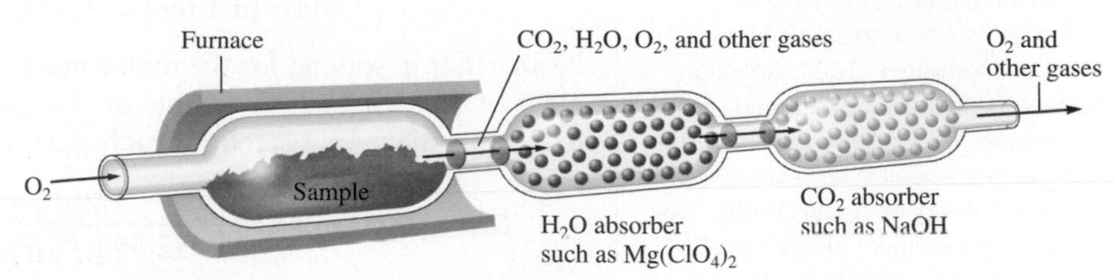

Figure 3.5
A schematic diagram of the combustion device used to analyze substances for carbon and hydrogen. The sample is burned in the presence of excess oxygen, which converts all of its carbon to carbon dioxide and all of its hydrogen to water. These compounds are collected by absorption using appropriate materials, and their amounts are determined by measuring the increase in weights of the absorbents.

is converted to CO_2, we can determine the mass of carbon originally present in the 0.1156-gram sample. To do so, we must use the fraction (by mass) of carbon in CO_2. The molar mass of CO_2 is 12.011 g/mol plus 2(15.999) g/mol, or 44.009 g/mol. The fraction of carbon present by mass (12.011 grams C/44.009 grams CO_2) can now be used to determine the mass of carbon in 0.1638 gram of CO_2:

$$0.1638 \text{ g } CO_2 \times \frac{12.011 \text{ g C}}{44.009 \text{ g } CO_2} = 0.04470 \text{ g C}$$

Remember that this carbon originally came from the 0.1156-gram sample of the unknown compound. Thus the mass percent of carbon in this compound is

$$\frac{0.04470 \text{ g C}}{0.1156 \text{ g compound}} \times 100\% = 38.67\% \text{ C}$$

The same procedure can be used to find the mass percent of hydrogen in the unknown compound. We assume that all of the hydrogen present in the original 0.1156 gram of compound was converted to H_2O. The molar mass of H_2O is 18.015 grams, and the fraction of hydrogen by mass in H_2O is 2.016 grams H/18.015 grams H_2O. Therefore, the mass of hydrogen in 0.1676 gram of H_2O is

$$0.1676 \text{ g } H_2O \times \frac{2.016 \text{ g H}}{18.015 \text{ g } H_2O} = 0.01876 \text{ g H}$$

And the mass percent of hydrogen in the compound is

$$\frac{0.01876 \text{ g H}}{0.1156 \text{ g compound}} \times 100\% = 16.23\% \text{ H}$$

The unknown compound contains only carbon, hydrogen, and nitrogen. So far, we have determined that it is 38.67% carbon and 16.23% hydrogen. The remainder must be nitrogen:

$$100.00\% - (\underset{\%\text{ C}}{\underset{\uparrow}{38.67\%}} + \underset{\%\text{ H}}{\underset{\uparrow}{16.23\%}}) = 45.10\% \text{ N}$$

We have determined that the compound contains 38.67% carbon, 16.23% hydrogen, and 45.10% nitrogen. Next, we use these data to obtain the formula.

Since the formula of a compound indicates the *numbers* of atoms in the compound, we must convert the masses of the elements to numbers of atoms. The easiest way to do this is to work with 100.00 grams of the compound. In the present case 38.67% carbon by mass means 38.67 grams of carbon per 100.00 grams of compound; 16.23% hydrogen means 16.23 grams of hydrogen per 100.00 grams of compound; and so on. To determine the formula, we must calculate the number of carbon atoms in 38.67 grams of carbon, the number of hydrogen atoms in 16.23 grams of hydrogen, and the number of nitrogen atoms in 45.10 grams of nitrogen. We can do this as follows:

$$38.67 \text{ g C} \times \frac{1 \text{ mol C}}{12.011 \text{ g C}} = 3.220 \text{ mol C}$$

$$16.23 \text{ g H} \times \frac{1 \text{ mol H}}{1.008 \text{ g H}} = 16.10 \text{ mol H}$$

$$45.10 \text{ g N} \times \frac{1 \text{ mol N}}{14.007 \text{ g N}} = 3.220 \text{ mol N}$$

Thus 100.00 grams of this compound contains 3.220 moles of carbon atoms, 16.10 moles of hydrogen atoms, and 3.220 moles of nitrogen atoms.

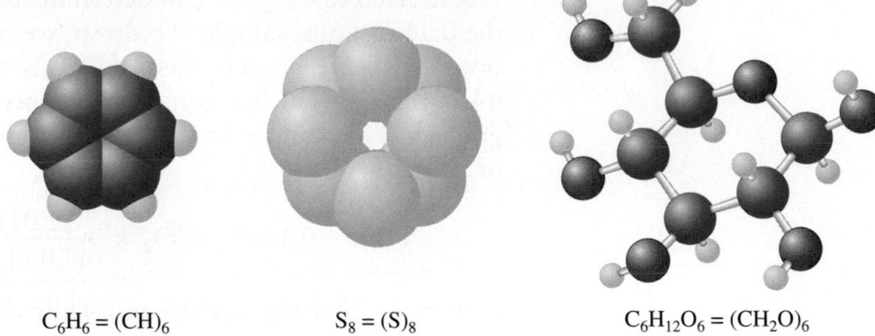

Figure 3.6
Examples of substances whose empirical and molecular formulas differ. Notice that molecular formula = (empirical formula)$_x$, where x is an integer.

We can find the smallest *whole-number ratio* of atoms in this compound by dividing each of the mole values above by the smallest of the three:

$$\text{C:} \quad \frac{3.220}{3.220} = 1$$

$$\text{H:} \quad \frac{16.10}{3.220} = 5$$

$$\text{N:} \quad \frac{3.220}{3.220} = 1$$

Thus the formula of this compound can be written CH_5N. This formula is called the **empirical formula.** It represents the *simplest whole-number ratio of the various types of atoms in a compound.*

If this compound is molecular, then the formula might well be CH_5N. It might also be $C_2H_{10}N_2$, or $C_3H_{15}N_3$, and so on—that is, some multiple of the simplest whole-number ratio. Each of these alternatives also has the correct relative numbers of atoms. Any molecule that can be represented as $(CH_5N)_x$, where x is an integer, has the empirical formula CH_5N. To be able to specify the exact formula of the molecule involved, the **molecular formula,** we must know the molar mass.

Molecular formula = (empirical formula)$_x$, where x is an integer.

Suppose we know that this compound with empirical formula CH_5N has a molar mass of 31.06. How do we determine which of the possible choices represents the molecular formula? Since the molecular formula is always a whole-number multiple of the empirical formula, we must first find the empirical formula mass for CH_5N:

$$\begin{aligned} &1\text{ C:} && 1 \times 12.011\text{ g} = 12.011\text{ g} \\ &5\text{ H:} && 5 \times \ \ 1.008\text{ g} = \ \ 5.040\text{ g} \\ &1\text{ N:} && 1 \times 14.007\text{ g} = \underline{14.007\text{ g}} \\ & && \text{Formula mass of } CH_5N = 31.058\text{ g} \end{aligned}$$

This value is the same as the known molar mass of the compound. Thus, in this case, the empirical formula and the molecular formula are the same; this substance consists of molecules with the formula CH_5N. It is quite common for the empirical and molecular formulas to be different; some examples in which this is the case are shown in Fig. 3.6.

OWL INTERACTIVE EXAMPLE 3.6

A white powder is analyzed and found to contain 43.64% phosphorus and 56.36% oxygen by mass. The compound has a molar mass of 283.88 g. What are the compound's empirical and molecular formulas?

Solution

▪ What are we trying to solve?

In this problem we are asked to solve for the empirical and molecular formulas for a compound.

▪ What does this mean?

The empirical formula is the simplest whole-number ratio of the atoms in the compound, and the molecular formula is the actual formula for the compound. In both cases the formula will look like P_xO_y, and we are trying to solve for x and y.

We know x and y represent numbers of atoms (or relative moles of atoms), but we are given mass percents of the elements in the compound. So now we have a new question:

▪ How can we convert a mass percent of an element to the moles of atoms?

We know we can convert mass to moles of atoms using atomic masses. So, we must convert a mass percent to a mass, and a mass to a number.

One way—although not the only way—is to realize that mass percents have the same value as masses if we assume 100.00 g of the sample. Thus, in 100.00 g of this compound, there are 43.64 g of phosphorus and 56.36 g of oxygen. If we convert these masses to moles, the ratio of the numbers of moles of each element represents the ratio of x to y in the formula. In terms of moles, in 100.00 g of compound we have

$$43.64 \text{ g P} \times \frac{1 \text{ mol P}}{30.97 \text{ g P}} = 1.409 \text{ mol P}$$

$$56.36 \text{ g O} \times \frac{1 \text{ mol O}}{15.999 \text{ g O}} = 3.523 \text{ mol O}$$

These numbers give us a ratio of moles of atoms of P/O, but the empirical formula is the *simplest whole-number ratio* of these atoms. Dividing both mole values by the smaller one gives

$$\frac{1.409}{1.409} = 1 \text{ P} \quad \text{and} \quad \frac{3.523}{1.409} = 2.5 \text{ O}$$

This yields the formula $PO_{2.5}$. Since compounds must contain whole numbers of atoms, the empirical formula should contain only whole numbers. To obtain the simplest set of whole numbers, we multiply both numbers by 2 to give the empirical formula P_2O_5.

To obtain the molecular formula, we must compare the empirical formula mass with the molar mass. The empirical formula mass for P_2O_5 is 141.94.

$$\frac{\text{Molar mass}}{\text{Empirical formula mass}} = \frac{283.88}{141.94} = 2$$

The molecular formula is $(P_2O_5)_2$, or P_4O_{10}.

▪ Does the answer make sense?

The molar mass of the compound is a whole-number multiple of the empirical molar mass, which should make us more confident about the answer. The structural formula of this interesting compound is given in Fig. 3.7.

Figure 3.7
The structural formula of P_4O_{10}. Note that some of the oxygen atoms act as "bridges" between the phosphorus atoms. This compound has a great affinity for water and is often used as a desiccant, or drying agent.

In Example 3.6 we found the molecular formula by comparing the empirical formula mass with the molar mass. There is an alternative way to obtain the molecular formula. The molar mass and the percentages (by mass) of each element present can be used to compute the moles of each element present in one mole of compound. These numbers of moles then represent directly the subscripts in the molecular formula. This procedure is illustrated in Example 3.7.

OWL INTERACTIVE EXAMPLE 3.7

Caffeine, a stimulant found in coffee, tea, chocolate, and some medications, contains 49.48% carbon, 5.15% hydrogen, 28.87% nitrogen, and 16.49% oxygen by mass and has a molar mass of 194.2. Determine the molecular formula of caffeine.

Solution

■ What are we trying to solve?

In this problem we are asked to solve for the molecular formula for caffeine.

■ What does this mean?

The molecular formula will look like $C_aH_bN_cO_d$, where *a*, *b*, *c*, and *d* are whole numbers. We need to solve for *a*, *b*, *c*, and *d*.

This problem is similar to Example 3.6, but in this case, we are going to determine the molecular formula without the empirical formula.

■ How can we use percent by mass data of an element and the molar mass?

By multiplying the molar mass of the compound by the individual percents by mass of each element, we can determine the mass of each element in 1 mole (194.2 g) of caffeine:

$$\frac{49.48 \text{ g C}}{100.0 \text{ g caffeine}} \times \frac{194.2 \text{ g}}{\text{mol}} = \frac{96.09 \text{ g C}}{\text{mol caffeine}}$$

$$\frac{5.15 \text{ g H}}{100.0 \text{ g caffeine}} \times \frac{194.2 \text{ g}}{\text{mol}} = \frac{10.0 \text{ g H}}{\text{mol caffeine}}$$

$$\frac{28.87 \text{ g N}}{100.0 \text{ g caffeine}} \times \frac{194.2 \text{ g}}{\text{mol}} = \frac{56.07 \text{ g N}}{\text{mol caffeine}}$$

$$\frac{16.49 \text{ g O}}{100.0 \text{ g caffeine}} \times \frac{194.2 \text{ g}}{\text{mol}} = \frac{32.02 \text{ g O}}{\text{mol caffeine}}$$

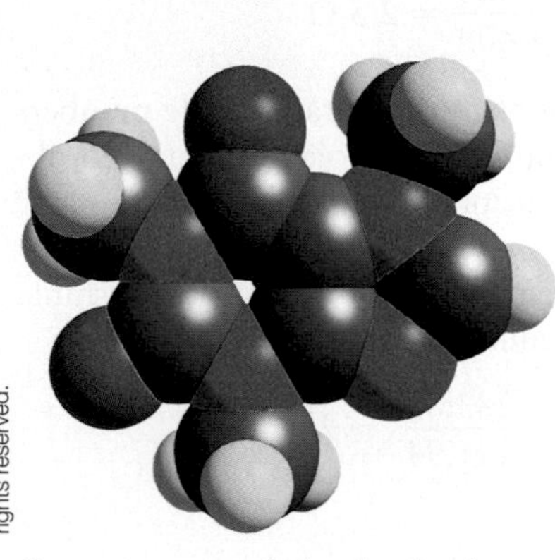

Computer-generated molecule of caffeine.

We have masses and we need moles, which we can compute using atomic masses.

$$\text{C:} \quad \frac{96.09 \text{ g C}}{\text{mol caffeine}} \times \frac{1 \text{ mol C}}{12.011 \text{ g C}} = \frac{8.000 \text{ mol C}}{\text{mol caffeine}}$$

$$\text{H:} \quad \frac{10.0 \text{ g H}}{\text{mol caffeine}} \times \frac{1 \text{ mol H}}{1.008 \text{ g H}} = \frac{9.92 \text{ mol H}}{\text{mol caffeine}}$$

$$\text{N:} \quad \frac{56.07 \text{ g N}}{\text{mol caffeine}} \times \frac{1 \text{ mol N}}{14.01 \text{ g N}} = \frac{4.002 \text{ mol N}}{\text{mol caffeine}}$$

$$\text{O:} \quad \frac{32.02 \text{ g O}}{\text{mol caffeine}} \times \frac{1 \text{ mol O}}{16.00 \text{ g O}} = \frac{2.001 \text{ mol O}}{\text{mol caffeine}}$$

Rounding the numbers to integers gives the molecular formula for caffeine: $C_8H_{10}N_4O_2$.

■ Does the answer make sense?

The answers to the number of moles should be whole numbers, because, unlike the first part of the solution to Example 3.6, we are solving for the actual number of moles of each element in 1 mole of the compound. There is not much rounding needed to get whole numbers for the subscripts. This is a good sign.

The methods for obtaining empirical and molecular formulas are summarized below.

STEPS

Determination of the Empirical Formula

Numbers very close to whole numbers, such as 9.92 and 1.08, should be rounded to whole numbers. Numbers such as 2.25, 4.33, and 2.72 should not be rounded to whole numbers.

1 Since mass percent gives the number of grams of a particular element per 100 grams of compound, base the calculation on 100 grams of compound. Each percent will then represent the mass in grams of that element present in the compound.

2 Determine the number of moles of each element present in 100 grams of compound using the atomic weights (masses) of the elements present.

3 Divide each value of the number of moles by the smallest of the values. If each resulting number is a whole number (after appropriate rounding), these numbers represent the subscripts of the elements in the empirical formula.

4 If the numbers obtained in the previous step are not whole numbers, multiply each number by an integer so that the results are all whole numbers.

STEPS

Determination of the Molecular Formula

Method 1

1 Obtain the empirical formula.

2 Compute the empirical formula mass.

3 Calculate the ratio:

$$\frac{\text{Molar mass}}{\text{Empirical formula mass}}$$

4 The integer from the previous step represents the number of empirical formula units in one molecule. When the empirical formula subscripts are multiplied by this integer, we obtain the molecular formula.

Method 2

1 Using the mass percents and the molar mass, determine the mass of each element present in 1 mole of compound.

2 Determine the number of moles of each element present in 1 mole of compound.

3 The integers from the previous step represent the subscripts in the molecular formula.

3.7 Chemical Equations

Chemical Reactions

A chemical change involves reorganization of the atoms in one or more substances. For example, when the methane (CH_4) in natural gas combines with oxygen (O_2) in the air and burns, carbon dioxide (CO_2) and water (H_2O) are formed. This process is represented by a **chemical equation** with the **reactants** (here methane and oxygen) on the left side of an arrow and the **products** (carbon dioxide and water) on the right side:

$$\underset{\text{Reactants}}{CH_4 + O_2} \longrightarrow \underset{\text{Products}}{CO_2 + H_2O}$$

A flare in a natural gas field is an example of a chemical reaction.

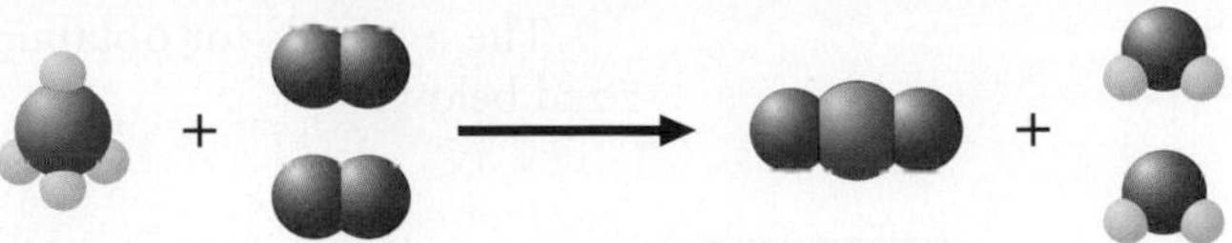

Figure 3.8
The reaction between methane and oxygen to give water and carbon dioxide. Note that no atoms have been gained or lost in the reaction. The reaction simply reorganizes the atoms.

Notice that the atoms have been reorganized. *Bonds have been broken and new ones formed.* Remember that *in a chemical reaction, atoms are neither created nor destroyed. All atoms present in the reactants must be accounted for among the products.* In other words, there must be the same number of each type of atom on the product side as there is on the reactant side of the arrow. Making sure that this rule is followed is called **balancing a chemical equation** for a reaction. The equation just shown for the reaction between CH_4 and O_2 is not balanced. As we will see in the next section, the equation can be balanced to produce

$$CH_4 + 2O_2 \longrightarrow CO_2 + 2H_2O$$

This reaction is shown graphically in Fig. 3.8. We can check whether the equation is balanced by comparing the number of each type of atom on both sides:

$$\underbrace{CH_4}_{1\,C,\ 4\,H} + \underbrace{2O_2}_{4\,O} \longrightarrow \underbrace{CO_2}_{1\,C,\ 2\,O} + \underbrace{2H_2O}_{4\,H,\ 2\,O}$$

The Meaning of a Chemical Equation

The chemical equation for a reaction provides two important types of information: the nature of the reactants and products and the relative numbers of each. The reactants and products in a specific reaction must be identified by experiment. Besides specifying the compounds involved in the reaction, the equation often includes the *physical states* of the reactants and products:

State	Symbol
Solid	(*s*)
Liquid	(*l*)
Gas	(*g*)
Dissolved in water (in aqueous solution)	(*aq*)

For example, when hydrochloric acid in aqueous solution is added to solid sodium hydrogen carbonate, the products carbon dioxide gas, liquid water, and sodium chloride (which dissolves in the water) are formed:

$$HCl(aq) + NaHCO_3(s) \longrightarrow CO_2(g) + H_2O(l) + NaCl(aq)$$

The relative numbers of reactants and products in a reaction are indicated by the *coefficients* in the balanced equation. (The coefficients can be determined since we know that the same number of each type of atom must occur on both sides of the equation.) For example, the balanced equation

$$CH_4(g) + 2O_2(g) \longrightarrow CO_2(g) + 2H_2O(g)$$

can be interpreted in several equivalent ways, as shown in Table 3.2. Note that the total mass is 80 grams for both reactants and products. We should expect this result, since chemical reactions involve only a rearrangement of atoms. Atoms, and therefore mass, are conserved in a chemical reaction.

Table 3.2

Information Conveyed by the Balanced Equation for the Combustion of Methane

Reactants		Products
$CH_4(g) + 2O_2(g)$	$\longrightarrow$	$CO_2(g) + 2H_2O(g)$
1 molecule CH_4 + 2 molecules O_2	$\longrightarrow$	1 molecule CO_2 + 2 molecules H_2O
1 mole of CH_4 molecules + 2 moles of O_2 molecules	$\longrightarrow$	1 mole of CO_2 molecules + 2 moles of H_2O molecules
6.022×10^{23} CH_4 molecules + $2(6.022 \times 10^{23})$ O_2 molecules	$\longrightarrow$	6.022×10^{23} CO_2 molecules + $2(6.022 \times 10^{23})$ H_2O molecules
16 g CH_4 + 2(32 g) O_2	$\longrightarrow$	44 g CO_2 + 2(18 g) H_2O
80 g reactants	$\longrightarrow$	80 g products

From this discussion you can see that a balanced chemical equation gives you a great deal of information.

3.8 Balancing Chemical Equations

An unbalanced chemical equation is of limited use. Whenever you see an equation, you should ask yourself whether it is balanced. The principle that lies at the heart of the balancing process is that atoms are conserved in a chemical reaction. The same number of each type of atom must be found among the reactants and products. Also, remember that the identities of the reactants and products of a reaction are determined by experimental observation. For example, when liquid ethanol is burned in the presence of sufficient oxygen gas, the products will always be carbon dioxide and water. When the equation for this reaction is balanced, the *identities* of the reactants and products must not be changed. *The formulas of the compounds must never be changed when balancing a chemical equation.* That is, the subscripts in a formula cannot be changed, nor can atoms be added or subtracted from a formula.

In balancing equations, start with the most complicated molecule.

Most chemical equations can be balanced by inspection—that is, by trial and error. It is always best to start with the most complicated molecules (those containing the greatest number of atoms). For example, consider the reaction of ethanol with oxygen, given by the unbalanced equation

$$C_2H_5OH(l) + O_2(g) \longrightarrow CO_2(g) + H_2O(g)$$

The most complicated molecule here is C_2H_5OH. We will begin by balancing the products that contain the atoms in C_2H_5OH. Since C_2H_5OH contains two carbon atoms, we place a 2 before the CO_2 to balance the carbon atoms:

$$\underset{\text{2 C atoms}}{C_2H_5OH(l)} + O_2(g) \longrightarrow \underset{\text{2 C atoms}}{2CO_2(g)} + H_2O(g)$$

Since C_2H_5OH contains six hydrogen atoms, the hydrogen atoms can be balanced by placing a 3 before the H_2O:

$$\underset{(5+1)\text{ H}}{C_2H_5OH(l)} + O_2(g) \longrightarrow 2CO_2(g) + \underset{(3\times 2)\text{ H}}{3H_2O(g)}$$

Last, we balance the oxygen atoms. Note that the right side of the preceding equation contains seven oxygen atoms, whereas the left side has only three.

We can correct this by putting a 3 before the O_2 to produce the balanced equation:

$$\underset{1\,O}{C_2H_5OH(l)} + \underset{6\,O}{3O_2(g)} \longrightarrow \underset{(2\times 2)\,O}{2CO_2(g)} + \underset{3\,O}{3H_2O(g)}$$

Now we check:

$$C_2H_5OH(l) + 3O_2(g) \longrightarrow 2CO_2(g) + 3H_2O(g)$$

Reactants	Products
2 C atoms	2 C atoms
6 H atoms	6 H atoms
7 O atoms	7 O atoms

The balanced equation can be represented by space-filling models as follows:

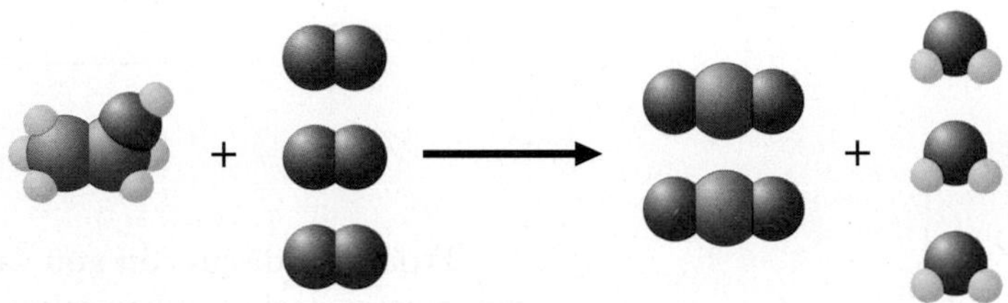

STEPS

Writing and Balancing the Equation for a Chemical Reaction

1 Determine what reaction is occurring. What are the reactants, the products, and the states involved?

2 Write the *unbalanced* equation that summarizes the preceding information.

3 Balance the equation by inspection, starting with the most complicated molecule(s). Determine what coefficients are necessary to ensure that the same number of each type of atom appears on both reactant and product sides. Do not change the identities (formulas) of any of the reactants or products.

OWL INTERACTIVE EXAMPLE 3.8

Chromate and dichromate compounds are suspected carcinogens (cancer-inducing agents) and should be handled carefully.

Chromium compounds exhibit a variety of bright colors. When solid ammonium dichromate, $(NH_4)_2Cr_2O_7$, a vivid orange compound, is ignited, a spectacular reaction occurs, as shown in the two photographs on the next page. Although the reaction is somewhat more complex, let's assume here that the products are solid chromium(III) oxide, nitrogen gas (consisting of N_2 molecules), and water vapor. Balance the equation for this reaction.

Solution From the description given, the reactant is solid ammonium dichromate, $(NH_4)_2Cr_2O_7(s)$, and the products are nitrogen gas, $N_2(g)$; water vapor, $H_2O(g)$; and solid chromium(III) oxide, $Cr_2O_3(s)$. The formula for chromium (III) oxide can be determined by recognizing that the Roman numeral III means that Cr^{3+} ions are present. For a neutral compound the formula must then be Cr_2O_3, since each oxide ion is O^{2-}.

The unbalanced equation is

$$(NH_4)_2Cr_2O_7(s) \longrightarrow Cr_2O_3(s) + N_2(g) + H_2O(g)$$

Note that nitrogen and chromium are balanced (two nitrogen atoms and two chromium atoms on each side), but hydrogen and oxygen are not. A coefficient of 4 for H_2O balances the hydrogen atoms:

$$\underset{(4 \times 2)\ H}{(NH_4)_2Cr_2O_7(s)} \longrightarrow Cr_2O_3(s) + N_2(g) + \underset{(4 \times 2)\ H}{4H_2O(g)}$$

Note that in balancing the hydrogen, we have also balanced the oxygen since there are seven oxygen atoms in the reactants and in the products.

Check: $$\underset{\text{Reactant atoms}}{2\ N, 8\ H, 2\ Cr, 7\ O} \longrightarrow \underset{\text{Product atoms}}{2\ N, 8\ H, 2\ Cr, 7\ O}$$

The equation is balanced.

3.9 Stoichiometric Calculations: Amounts of Reactants and Products

Recall that the coefficients in chemical equations represent *numbers* of molecules, not masses of molecules. However, in the laboratory or chemical plant, when a reaction is to be run, the amounts of substances needed cannot be determined by counting molecules directly. Counting is always done by weighing. In this section we will see how chemical equations can be used to deal with *masses* of reacting chemicals.

To develop the principles involved in dealing with the stoichiometry of reactions, we will consider the combustion of propane (C_3H_8), a hydrocarbon used for gas barbecue grills and often used as a fuel in rural areas where natural gas pipelines are not available. Propane reacts with oxygen to produce carbon dioxide and water. We will consider the question, "What mass of oxygen will react with 96.1 grams of propane?" The first thing that must always be done when performing calculations involving chemical reactions is to *write the balanced chemical equation* for the reaction. In this case the balanced equation is

Before doing any calculations involving a chemical reaction, be sure the equation for the reaction is balanced.

$$C_3H_8(g) + 5O_2(g) \longrightarrow 3CO_2(g) + 4H_2O(g)$$

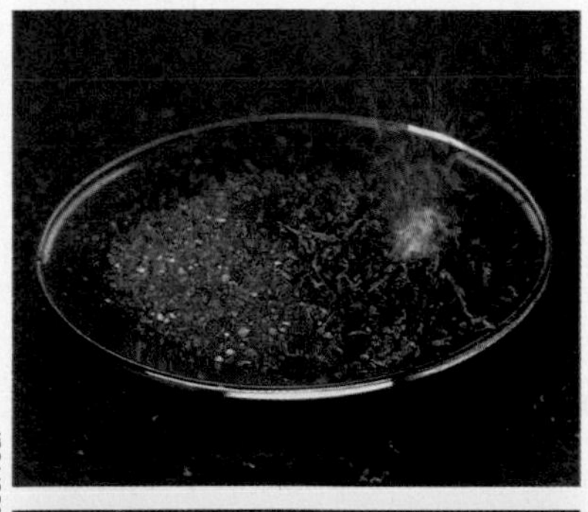

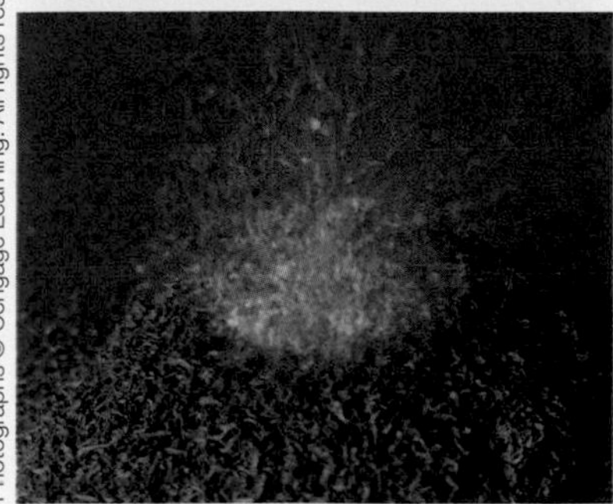

Decomposition of ammonium dichromate.

Recall that this equation means that 1 mole of C_3H_8 will react with 5 moles of O_2 to produce 3 moles of CO_2 and 4 moles of H_2O. To use this equation to find the masses of reactants and products, we must be able to convert between masses and moles of substances. Thus we must first ask, "How many moles of propane are present in 96.1 grams of propane?" The molar mass of propane to three significant figures is 44.1 g/mol. The moles of propane can be calculated as follows:

$$96.1\ g\ C_3H_8 \times \frac{1\ mol\ C_3H_8}{44.1\ g\ C_3H_8} = 2.18\ mol\ C_3H_8$$

Next, we must take into account that each mole of propane reacts with 5 moles of oxygen. The best way to do this is to use the balanced equation to construct a **mole ratio.** In this case we want to convert from moles of propane to moles of oxygen. From the balanced equation we see that 5 moles of O_2 is required for each mole of C_3H_8, so the appropriate ratio is

$$\frac{5\ mol\ O_2}{1\ mol\ C_3H_8}$$

which can be used to calculate the number of moles of O_2 required:

$$2.18\ mol\ C_3H_8 \times \frac{5\ mol\ O_2}{1\ mol\ C_3H_8} = 10.9\ mol\ O_2$$

Chemical Insights High Mountains—Low Octane

The next time you visit a gas station, take a moment to note the octane rating that accompanies the grade of gasoline that you are purchasing. The gasoline is priced according to its octane rating—a measure of the fuel's antiknock properties. In a conventional internal combustion engine, gasoline vapors and air are drawn into the combustion cylinder on the downward stroke of the piston. This air–fuel mixture is compressed on the upward piston stroke (compression stroke), and a spark from the sparkplug ignites the mix. The rhythmic combustion of the air–fuel mix occurring sequentially in several cylinders furnishes the power to propel the vehicle down the road. Excessive heat and pressure (or poor-quality fuel) within the cylinder may cause the premature combustion of the mixture—commonly known as engine "knock" or "ping." Over time, this engine knock can damage the engine, resulting in inefficient performance and costly repairs.

A consumer typically is faced with three choices of gasoline, with octane ratings of 87 (regular), 89 (midgrade), and 93 (premium). But if you happen to travel or live in the higher elevations of the Rocky Mountain states, you might be surprised to find different octane ratings at the gasoline pumps. The reason for this provides a lesson in stoichiometry. At higher elevations the air is less dense—the volume of oxygen per unit volume of air is smaller. Most engines are designed to achieve a 14:1 oxygen-to-fuel ratio in the cylinder prior to combustion. If less oxygen is available, then less fuel is required to achieve this optimal ratio. In turn, the lower volumes of oxygen and fuel result in a lower pressure in the cylinder. Because high pressure tends to promote knocking, the lower pressure within engine cylinders at higher elevations promotes a more controlled combustion of the air–fuel mixture, and therefore, octane requirements are lower. Although consumers in the Rocky Mountain states can purchase three grades of gasoline, the octane ratings of these fuel blends are different from those in the rest of the United States. In Denver, Colorado, regular gasoline is 85 octane, midgrade is 87 octane, and premium is 91 octane—2 points lower than gasoline sold in most of the rest of the country.

Since the original question asked for the mass of oxygen needed to react with 96.1 grams of propane, the 10.9 moles of O_2 must be converted to *grams*, using the molar mass of O_2:

$$10.9 \text{ mol } O_2 \times \frac{32.0 \text{ g } O_2}{1 \text{ mol } O_2} = 349 \text{ g } O_2$$

Therefore, 349 grams of oxygen is required to burn 96.1 grams of propane.

This example can be extended by asking, "What mass of carbon dioxide is produced when 96.1 grams of propane is combusted with oxygen?" In this case we must convert between moles of propane and moles of carbon dioxide. This conversion can be done by inspecting the balanced equation, which shows that 3 moles of CO_2 is produced for each mole of C_3H_8 reacted:

$$2.18 \text{ mol } C_3H_8 \times \frac{3 \text{ mol } CO_2}{1 \text{ mol } C_3H_8} = 6.54 \text{ mol } CO_2$$

Then we use the molar mass of CO_2 (44.0 g/mol) to calculate the mass of CO_2 produced:

$$6.54 \text{ mol } CO_2 \times \frac{44.0 \text{ g } CO_2}{1 \text{ mol } CO_2} = 288 \text{ g } CO_2$$

The process for finding the mass of carbon dioxide produced from 96.1 grams of propane is summarized here:

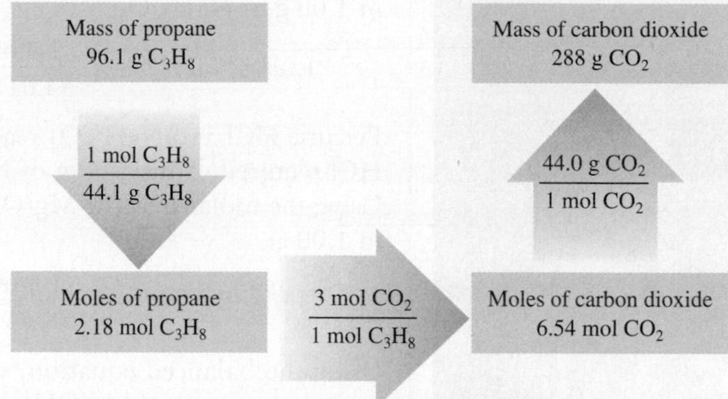

STEPS

Calculation of Masses of Reactants and Products in Chemical Reactions

1. Balance the equation for the reaction.
2. Convert the known masses of the substances to moles.
3. Use the balanced equation to set up the appropriate mole ratios.
4. Use the appropriate mole ratios to calculate the number of moles of the desired reactant or product.
5. Convert from moles back to grams if required by the problem.

OWL INTERACTIVE EXAMPLE 3.9

Baking soda ($NaHCO_3$) is often used as an antacid. It neutralizes excess hydrochloric acid secreted by the stomach:

$$NaHCO_3(s) + HCl(aq) \longrightarrow NaCl(aq) + H_2O(l) + CO_2(aq)$$

Milk of magnesia, which is an aqueous suspension of magnesium hydroxide, is also used as an antacid:

$$Mg(OH)_2(s) + 2HCl(aq) \longrightarrow 2H_2O(l) + MgCl_2(aq)$$

Which is the more effective antacid per gram, $NaHCO_3$ or $Mg(OH)_2$?

Solution

▪ What are we trying to solve?

In this problem we are asked to determine which antacid is more effective.

▪ What does this mean?

The more effective antacid will react with (neutralize) more acid. So to answer this question, we must answer the following:

1. How much HCl is neutralized per gram of $NaHCO_3$?
2. How much HCl is neutralized per gram of $Mg(OH)_2$?

We will then compare the answers and choose the more effective antacid.

▪ How can we determine the amount of base (antacid) that reacts with an amount of acid?

We have balanced chemical equations, which give us the mole ratios of $NaHCO_3$/HCl and $Mg(OH)_2$/HCl. Thus we must convert 1.00 g of each

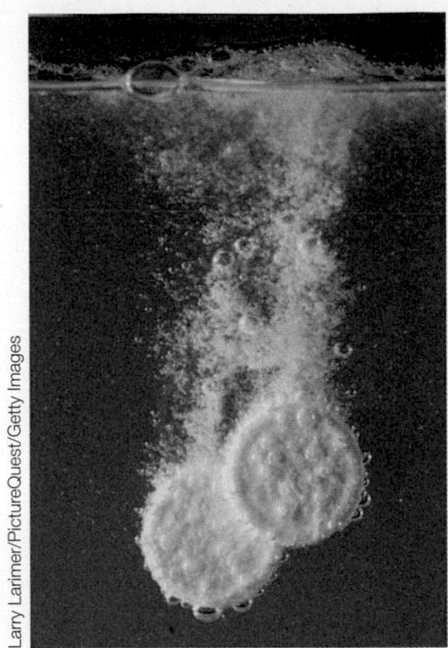

Two antacid tablets containing HCO_3^- dissolve to produce CO_2 gas.

antacid to moles of antacid and then to moles of HCl. The antacid that reacts with the greater number of moles of HCl is the more effective one.

Using the molar mass of $NaHCO_3$, we determine the moles of $NaHCO_3$ in 1.00 g of $NaHCO_3$:

$$1.00 \text{ g NaHCO}_3 \times \frac{1 \text{ mol NaHCO}_3}{84.01 \text{ g NaHCO}_3} = 1.19 \times 10^{-2} \text{ mol NaHCO}_3$$

Because HCl and $NaHCO_3$ react 1:1, this answer also represents the moles of HCl required. Thus 1.00 g of $NaHCO_3$ will neutralize 1.19×10^{-2} mol HCl. Using the molar mass of $Mg(OH)_2$, we next determine the moles of $Mg(OH)_2$ in 1.00 g:

$$1.00 \text{ g Mg(OH)}_2 \times \frac{1 \text{ mol Mg(OH)}_2}{58.32 \text{ g Mg(OH)}_2} = 1.71 \times 10^{-2} \text{ mol Mg(OH)}_2$$

Using the balanced equation, we determine the moles of HCl that will react with this amount of $Mg(OH)_2$:

$$1.71 \times 10^{-2} \text{ mol Mg(OH)}_2 \times \frac{2 \text{ mol HCl}}{1 \text{ mol Mg(OH)}_2} = 3.42 \times 10^{-2} \text{ mol HCl}$$

Thus 1.00 g of $Mg(OH)_2$ will neutralize 3.42×10^{-2} mol HCl. It is a better antacid per gram than $NaHCO_3$.

3.10 Calculations Involving a Limiting Reactant

When chemicals are mixed together to undergo a reaction, they are often mixed in **stoichiometric quantities**—that is, in exactly the correct amounts so that all reactants "run out" (are used up) at the same time. To clarify this concept, let's consider the production of hydrogen for use in the manufacture of ammonia by the Haber process. Ammonia, a very important fertilizer itself and a starting material for other fertilizers, is made by combining nitrogen from the air with hydrogen according to the equation

$$N_2(g) + 3H_2(g) \longrightarrow 2NH_3(g)$$

The hydrogen for this process is produced from the reaction of methane with water:

$$CH_4(g) + H_2O(g) \longrightarrow 3H_2(g) + CO(g)$$

Now consider the following question: What mass of water is required to react with *exactly* 2.50×10^3 kilograms of methane? That is, how much water will just use up all of the 2.50×10^3 kilograms of methane, leaving no methane or water remaining? Using the principles developed in the preceding section, we can calculate that if 2.50×10^3 kilograms of methane is mixed with 2.81×10^3 kilograms of water, both reactants will run out at the same time. The reactants have been mixed in stoichiometric quantities.

If, however, 2.50×10^3 kilograms of methane is mixed with 3.00×10^3 kilograms of water, the methane will be consumed before the water runs out. The water will be in *excess*. In this case the quantity of products formed will be determined by the quantity of methane present. Once the methane is consumed, no more products can be formed, even though some water still remains. In this situation, because the amount of methane *limits* the amount of products that can be formed, it is called the **limiting reactant**, or **limiting reagent.** In any stoichiometry problem it is essential to determine which reactant is the limiting one to calculate correctly the amounts of products that will be formed.

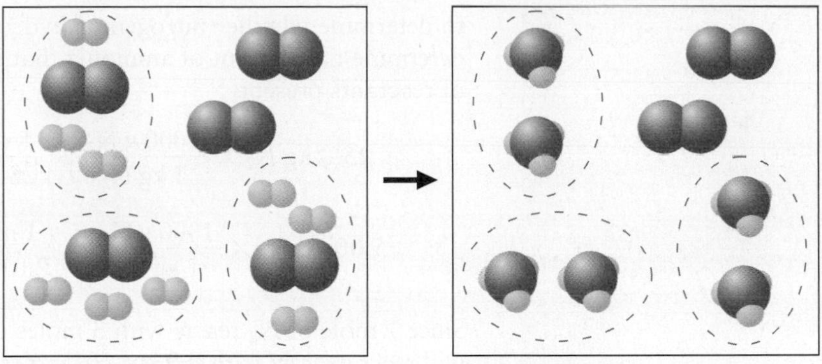

Figure 3.9
Hydrogen and nitrogen react to form ammonia according to the equation $N_2 + 3H_2 \longrightarrow 2NH_3$.

To further explore the idea of a limiting reactant, consider the ammonia synthesis reaction:

$$N_2(g) + 3H_2(g) \longrightarrow 2NH_3(g)$$

Assume that 5 N_2 molecules and 9 H_2 molecules are placed in a flask. Is this a stoichiometric mixture of reactants, or will one of them be consumed before the other runs out? From the balanced equation we know that each N_2 molecule requires 3 H_2 molecules for the reaction to occur:

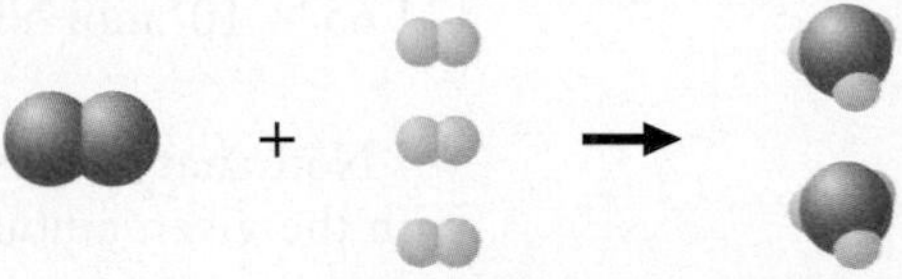

Thus the required H_2/N_2 ratio is $3H_2/1N_2$. In our experiment, we have 9 H_2 and 5 N_2, or a ratio of $9H_2/5N_2 = 1.8H_2/1N_2$.

Since the actual ratio (1.8:1) of H_2/N_2 is less than the ratio required by the balanced equation (3:1), there is not enough hydrogen to react with all the nitrogen. That is, the hydrogen will run out first, leaving some unreacted N_2 molecules. We can visualize this as shown in Fig. 3.9, which shows that 3 of the N_2 molecules react with the 9 H_2 molecules to produce 6 NH_3 molecules:

$$3N_2 + 9H_2 \longrightarrow 6NH_3$$

This leaves 2 N_2 molecules unreacted—the nitrogen is in excess.

What we have shown here is that in this experiment the hydrogen is the limiting reactant. The amount of H_2 initially present determines the amount of NH_3 that can form. The reaction was not able to use up all the N_2 molecules because the H_2 molecules were all consumed by the first 3 N_2 molecules to react.

In the laboratory or chemical plant we work with much larger quantities than the few molecules of the preceding example. Therefore we must use moles to deal with limiting reactants. The ideas are exactly the same, except that we are using moles of molecules instead of individual molecules. For example, suppose 25.0 kilograms of nitrogen and 5.00 kilograms of hydrogen are mixed and reacted to form ammonia. How do we calculate the mass of ammonia produced when this reaction is run to completion (until one of the reactants is completely consumed)?

As in the preceding example, we must use the balanced equation

$$N_2(g) + 3H_2(g) \longrightarrow 2NH_3(g)$$

to determine whether nitrogen or hydrogen is a limiting reactant and then to determine the amount of ammonia that is formed. We first calculate the moles of reactants present:

$$25.0 \text{ kg } N_2 \times \frac{1000 \text{ g } N_2}{1 \text{ kg } N_2} \times \frac{1 \text{ mol } N_2}{28.0 \text{ g } N_2} = 8.93 \times 10^2 \text{ mol } N_2$$

$$5.00 \text{ kg } H_2 \times \frac{1000 \text{ g } H_2}{1 \text{ kg } H_2} \times \frac{1 \text{ mol } H_2}{2.016 \text{ g } H_2} = 2.48 \times 10^3 \text{ mol } H_2$$

Since 1 mole of N_2 reacts with 3 moles of H_2, the number of moles of H_2 that will react exactly with 8.93×10^2 moles of N_2 is

$$8.93 \times 10^2 \text{ mol } N_2 \times \frac{3 \text{ mol } H_2}{1 \text{ mol } N_2} = 2.68 \times 10^3 \text{ mol } H_2$$

Thus 8.93×10^2 moles of N_2 requires 2.68×10^3 moles of H_2 to react completely. However, in this case only 2.48×10^3 moles of H_2 is present. Thus the hydrogen will be consumed before the nitrogen. Therefore, hydrogen is the *limiting reactant* in this particular situation, and we must use the amount of hydrogen to compute the quantity of ammonia formed:

Always check to see which reactant is limiting.

$$2.48 \times 10^3 \text{ mol } H_2 \times \frac{2 \text{ mol } NH_3}{3 \text{ mol } H_2} = 1.65 \times 10^3 \text{ mol } NH_3$$

$$1.65 \times 10^3 \text{ mol } NH_3 \times \frac{17.0 \text{ g } NH_3}{1 \text{ mol } NH_3} = 2.80 \times 10^4 \text{ g } NH_3 = 28.0 \text{ kg } NH_3$$

Note that to determine the limiting reactant, we could have started instead with the given amount of hydrogen and calculated the moles of nitrogen required:

$$2.48 \times 10^3 \text{ mol } H_2 \times \frac{1 \text{ mol } N_2}{3 \text{ mol } H_2} = 8.27 \times 10^2 \text{ mol } N_2$$

Thus 2.48×10^3 moles of H_2 requires 8.27×10^2 moles of N_2. Since 8.93×10^2 moles of N_2 is actually present, the nitrogen is in excess. The hydrogen will run out first, and thus again we find that hydrogen limits the amount of ammonia formed.

A related but simpler way to determine which reactant is limiting is to compare the mole ratio of the substances required by the balanced equation with the mole ratio of reactants actually present. For example, in this case the mole ratio of H_2 to N_2 required by the balanced equation is

$$\frac{3 \text{ mol } H_2}{1 \text{ mol } N_2}$$

That is,

$$\frac{\text{mol } H_2}{\text{mol } N_2} \text{ (required)} = \frac{3}{1} = 3$$

In this experiment we have 2.48×10^3 moles of H_2 and 8.93×10^2 moles of N_2. Thus the ratio

$$\frac{\text{mol } H_2}{\text{mol } N_2} \text{ (actual)} = \frac{2.48 \times 10^3}{8.93 \times 10^2} = 2.78$$

Since 2.78 is less than 3, the actual mole ratio of H_2 to N_2 is too small, and H_2 must be limiting. If the actual H_2/N_2 mole ratio had been greater than 3, then the H_2 would have been in excess and the N_2 would have been limiting.

OWL INTERACTIVE EXAMPLE 3.10

Nitrogen gas can be prepared by passing gaseous ammonia over solid copper(II) oxide at high temperatures. The other products of the reaction are solid copper and water vapor. If 18.1 g of NH_3 is reacted with 90.4 g of CuO, which is the limiting reactant? How many grams of N_2 will be formed?

Solution

■ What are we trying to solve?

In this example we are asked to solve two problems: to determine the limiting reactant and to determine the mass of N_2 that will be formed from a given amount of reactants.

We first need to answer the following two questions: What is meant by the term limiting reactant? and What do we need to do to solve for an amount of N_2?

■ What is meant by the term limiting reactant?

It is the reactant that is completely used up in the reaction. Since a chemical equation gives us the mole ratio of the reactants, we can determine how many moles of a given reactant we need to have compared with what we actually have. To do this we need to have a balanced equation, which we can get from the description of the problem.

$$2NH_3(g) + 3CuO(s) \longrightarrow N_2(g) + 3Cu(s) + 3H_2O(g)$$

To use this equation we have to compare the amounts of reactants in moles to the balanced equation, so we must compute the moles of NH_3 and CuO:

$$18.1 \text{ g } NH_3 \times \frac{1 \text{ mol } NH_3}{17.0 \text{ g } NH_3} = 1.06 \text{ mol } NH_3$$

$$90.4 \text{ g CuO} \times \frac{1 \text{ mol CuO}}{79.5 \text{ g CuO}} = 1.14 \text{ mol CuO}$$

We can now use either one of these to determine the number of moles of the other reactant that would be required to react completely. For example, if all of the NH_3 reacts, what number of moles of CuO is required?

$$1.06 \text{ mol } NH_3 \times \frac{3 \text{ mol CuO}}{2 \text{ mol } NH_3} = 1.59 \text{ mol CuO}$$

Thus 1.59 moles of CuO is required to react with 1.06 moles of NH_3. Since only 1.14 moles of CuO is actually present, the amount of CuO is limiting.

We can verify this conclusion by comparing the mole ratio of CuO to NH_3 required by the balanced equation,

$$\frac{\text{mol CuO}}{\text{mol } NH_3} \text{(required)} = \frac{3}{2} = 1.5$$

with the mole ratio actually present,

$$\frac{\text{mol CuO}}{\text{mol } NH_3} \text{(actual)} = \frac{1.14}{1.06} = 1.08$$

Since the actual ratio is too small (smaller than 1.5), CuO is the limiting reactant.

■ What do we need to do to solve for an amount of N_2?

To determine this we need to use the limiting reactant to calculate the moles, then mass, of N_2.

Because CuO is the limiting reactant, we must use the amount of CuO to calculate the amount of N_2 formed:

$$1.14 \text{ mol CuO} \times \frac{1 \text{ mol } N_2}{3 \text{ mol CuO}} = 0.380 \text{ mol } N_2$$

Using the molar mass of N_2, we can calculate the mass of N_2 produced:

$$0.380 \text{ mol } N_2 \times \frac{28.0 \text{ g } N_2}{1 \text{ mol } N_2} = 10.6 \text{ g } N_2$$

Note: As with most problems, there is more than one way to solve this. We could have answered, "What is meant by the term limiting reactant?" with: the reactant that limits the amount of product. So, another way to solve this is to solve for the number of moles of N_2 produced assuming all of the NH_3 reacts and solve again for moles of N_2 produced assuming all of the CuO reacts. The reactant that results in the smaller amount of product limits the reaction. Once we know the limiting reactant, we can solve for the mass of N_2 produced. We leave this up to you to try.

The amount of a given product formed when the limiting reactant is completely consumed is called the **theoretical yield** of that product. In Example 3.10, 10.6 grams of nitrogen is the theoretical yield. This is the *maximum amount* of nitrogen that can be produced from the quantities of reactants used. Actually, the amount of product predicted by the theoretical yield is seldom obtained because of side reactions (other reactions that involve one or more of the reactants or products) and other complications. The *actual yield* of product is often given as a percentage of the theoretical yield. This value is called the **percent yield:**

Percent yield is important as an indicator of the efficiency of a particular laboratory or industrial reaction.

$$\frac{\text{Actual yield}}{\text{Theoretical yield}} \times 100\% = \text{percent yield}$$

For example, if the reaction considered in Example 3.10 actually produced 6.63 grams of nitrogen instead of the predicted 10.6 grams, the percent yield of nitrogen would be

$$\frac{6.63 \text{ g } N_2}{10.6 \text{ g } N_2} \times 100\% = 62.5\%$$

STEPS

Solving a Stoichiometry Problem Involving Masses of Reactants and Products

1. Write and balance the equation for the reaction.
2. Convert the known masses of substances to moles.
3. By comparing the mole ratio of reactants required by the balanced equation with the mole ratio of reactants actually present, determine which reactant is limiting.
4. Using the amount of the limiting reactant and the appropriate mole ratios, compute the number of moles of the desired product.
5. Convert from moles to grams using the molar mass.

OWL INTERACTIVE EXAMPLE 3.11

Potassium chromate, a bright yellow solid, is produced by the reaction of solid chromite ore ($FeCr_2O_4$) with solid potassium carbonate and gaseous oxygen at high temperatures. The other products of the reaction are solid iron(III) oxide and gaseous carbon dioxide. In a particular experiment, 169 kg of chromite ore, 298 kg of potassium carbonate, and 75.0 kg of oxygen were sealed in a reaction vessel and reacted at a high temperature. The amount of potassium chromate obtained was 194 kg. Calculate the percent yield of potassium chromate.

Solution

■ What are we trying to solve?

This problem asks us to determine percent yield.

■ What does this mean?

$$\text{Percent yield} = \frac{\text{actual yield}}{\text{theoretical yield}} \times 100\%$$

We are given the actual yield of potassium chromate as 194 kg; thus we have

$$\text{Percent yield} = \frac{194\text{ kg}}{\text{theoretical yield}} \times 100\%$$

So we have now changed the problem to, What is the theoretical yield? Once we have this, we can solve for percent yield. This leads us to:

■ What do we mean by theoretical yield?

The theoretical yield is the amount of product we can expect if the reaction is allowed to run to completion. It is the amount of product that we have been calculating using the ideas in Sections 3.8 and 3.9.

We are given the masses (and names) of the three reactants and are told the names of the products. First, we will need a balanced chemical equation.

The unbalanced equation, which can be written from the preceding description of the reaction, is

$$FeCr_2O_4(s) + K_2CO_3(s) + O_2(g) \longrightarrow K_2CrO_4(s) + Fe_2O_3(s) + CO_2(g)$$

The balanced equation is

$$4FeCr_2O_4(s) + 8K_2CO_3(s) + 7O_2(g) \longrightarrow 8K_2CrO_4(s) + 2Fe_2O_3(s) + 8CO_2(g)$$

To determine the theoretical yield, we have to decide on which reactant is limiting and then use this reactant to compute the mass of the product formed. To determine the limiting reactant, we will compare the mole ratios of the reactants required by the balanced equation with the actual mole ratios. The numbers of moles of the various reactants are obtained as follows:

$$169\text{ kg } FeCr_2O_4 \times \frac{1000\text{ g } FeCr_2O_4}{1\text{ kg } FeCr_2O_4} \times \frac{1\text{ mol } FeCr_2O_4}{223.84\text{ g } FeCr_2O_4} = 7.55 \times 10^2\text{ mol } FeCr_2O_4$$

$$298\text{ kg } K_2CO_3 \times \frac{1000\text{ g } K_2CO_3}{1\text{ kg } K_2CO_3} \times \frac{1\text{ mol } K_2CO_3}{138.21\text{ g } K_2CO_3} = 2.16 \times 10^3\text{ mol } K_2CO_3$$

$$75.0\text{ kg } O_2 \times \frac{1000\text{ g } O_2}{1\text{ kg } O_2} \times \frac{1\text{ mol } O_2}{32.00\text{ g } O_2} = 2.34 \times 10^3\text{ mol } O_2$$

Now we must determine which of the three reactants is limiting. For the reactants K_2CO_3 and $FeCr_2O_4$ the required mole ratio is

$$\frac{\text{mol } K_2CO_3}{\text{mol } FeCr_2O_4}\text{ (required)} = \frac{8}{4} = 2$$

The actual mole ratio is

$$\frac{\text{mol } K_2CO_3}{\text{mol } FeCr_2O_4} \text{ (actual)} = \frac{2.16 \times 10^3}{7.55 \times 10^2} = 2.86$$

Since the actual mole ratio is greater than that required, the K_2CO_3 is in excess compared with $FeCr_2O_4$. Thus either $FeCr_2O_4$ or O_2 must be limiting. To determine which of these will limit the amounts of products, we compare the required mole ratio,

$$\frac{\text{mol } O_2}{\text{mol } FeCr_2O_4} \text{ (required)} = \frac{7}{4} = 1.75$$

with the actual mole ratio,

$$\frac{\text{mol } O_2}{\text{mol } FeCr_2O_4} \text{ (actual)} = \frac{2.34 \times 10^3}{7.55 \times 10^2} = 3.10$$

Thus more K_2CO_3 and O_2 are present than required. These reactants are in excess, so $FeCr_2O_4$ is the limiting reactant.

We must use the amount of $FeCr_2O_4$ to calculate the maximum amount of K_2CrO_4 that can be formed:

$$7.55 \times 10^2 \text{ mol } FeCr_2O_4 \times \frac{8 \text{ mol } K_2CrO_4}{4 \text{ mol } FeCr_2O_4} = 1.51 \times 10^3 \text{ mol } K_2CrO_4$$

Using the molar mass of K_2CrO_4, we can determine the mass:

$$1.51 \times 10^3 \text{ mol } K_2CrO_4 \times \frac{194.19 \text{ g } K_2CrO_4}{1 \text{ mol } K_2CrO_4} = 2.93 \times 10^5 \text{ g } K_2CrO_4$$

This value represents the theoretical yield of K_2CrO_4. The actual yield was 194 kg, or 1.94×10^5 g. Thus the percent yield is

$$\frac{1.94 \times 10^5 \text{ g } K_2CrO_4}{2.93 \times 10^5 \text{ g } K_2CrO_4} \times 100\% = 66.2\%$$

Key Terms

chemical stoichiometry

Section 3.1
mass spectrometer

Section 3.2
mole
Avogadro's number

Section 3.3
molar mass

Section 3.4
conceptual problem solving

Section 3.5
molecular weight
mass percent

Section 3.6
empirical formula
molecular formula

Section 3.7
chemical equation
reactants
products
balancing a chemical equation

For Review

OWL and go Chemistry

Sign in at **www.cengage.com/owl** to:

- View tutorials and simulations, develop problem-solving skills, and complete online homework assigned by your professor.
- Download Go Chemistry mini lecture modules for quick review and exam prep from OWL (or purchase them at **www.cengagebrain.com**)

Stoichiometry

- Deals with the amounts of substances consumed and/or produced in a chemical reaction.
- We count atoms by measuring the mass of the sample.
- To relate mass and the number of atoms, the average atomic mass is required.

Mole

- The number of carbon atoms in exactly 12 g of pure ^{12}C
- 6.022×10^{23} units of a substance
- The mass of 1 mole of an element = the atomic mass in grams

Molar mass

- Mass (g) of 1 mole of a compound or element
- Obtained for a compound by finding the sum of the average masses of its constituents

Section 3.9
mole ratio
Section 3.10
stoichiometric quantities
Haber process
limiting reactant (reagent)
theoretical yield
percent yield
	Percent composition
	■ The mass percent on each element in a compound
	■ Mass percent $= \frac{\text{mass of element in 1 mole of substance}}{\text{mass of 1 mole of substance}} \times 100\%$
	Empirical formula
	■ The simplest whole-number ratio of the various types of atoms in a compound
	■ Can be obtained from the mass percent of elements in a compound
	Molecular formula
	■ For molecular substance:
	  ■ The formula of the constituent molecules
	  ■ Always an integer multiple of an empirical formula
	■ For ionic substances:
	  ■ The same as the empirical formula
	Chemical reactions
	■ Reactants are turned into products.
	■ Atoms are neither created nor destroyed.
	■ All of the atoms present in the reactants must also be present in the products.
	Characteristics of a chemical equation
	■ Represents a chemical reaction
	■ Reactants on the left side of the arrow; products on the right side
	■ When balanced, gives the relative numbers of reactant and product molecules or ions
	Stoichiometry calculations
	■ Amounts of reactants consumed and products formed can be determined from the balanced chemical equation.
	■ The limiting reactant is the one consumed first, thus limiting the amount of product that can form.
	Yield
	■ The theoretical yield is the maximum amount that can be produced from a given amount of the limiting reactant.
	■ The actual yield, the amount of product actually obtained, is always less than the theoretical yield.
	■ Percent yield $= \frac{\text{actual yield (g)}}{\text{theoretical yield (g)}} \times 100\%$

Discussion Questions

These questions are designed to be considered by groups of students in class. Often these questions work well for introducing a particular topic in class.

1. The following are actual student responses to the question: Why is it necessary to balance chemical equations?
   a. The chemicals will not react until you have added the correct mole ratios.
   b. The correct products will not be formed unless the right amount of reactants have been added.
   c. A certain number of products cannot be formed without a certain number of reactants.
   d. The balanced equation tells you how much reactant you need and allows you to predict how much product you will make.
   e. A mole-to-mole ratio must be established for the reaction to occur as written.

   What is the best choice? For those you did not choose, explain why they are incorrect. State the fundamental reason why an equation for a reaction must be balanced.

2. Consider the equation $A + 2B \rightarrow AB_2$. Imagine that 10 moles of A is reacted with 26 moles of B. Use a scale from 0 to 10 to express your level of agreement with each of the following statements. Justify and discuss your responses.
   a. There will be some As left over.
   b. There will be some Bs left over.
   c. Because of leftover As, some A_2 molecules will be formed.
   d. Because of leftover Bs, some B_2 molecules will be formed.

e. Even if A is not limiting, A_2 molecules will be formed.
f. Even if B is not limiting, B_2 molecules will be formed.
g. Along with the molecule AB_2, molecules with the formula A_xB_y (other than AB_2) will be formed.

3. What information do we get from a formula? From an equation?
4. A sample of liquid heptane (C_7H_{16}) weighing 11.50 g is reacted with 1.300 moles of oxygen gas. The heptane is burned completely (heptane reacts with oxygen to form both carbon monoxide and water and carbon dioxide and water). After the reaction is complete, the amount of gas present is 1.050 moles (assume that all of the water formed is liquid).
   a. How many moles of CO are produced?
   b. How many moles of CO_2 are produced?
   c. How many moles of O_2 are left over?
5. Nitrogen (N_2) and hydrogen (H_2) react to form ammonia (NH_3). Consider the mixture of N_2( ) and H_2( ) in a closed container as illustrated:

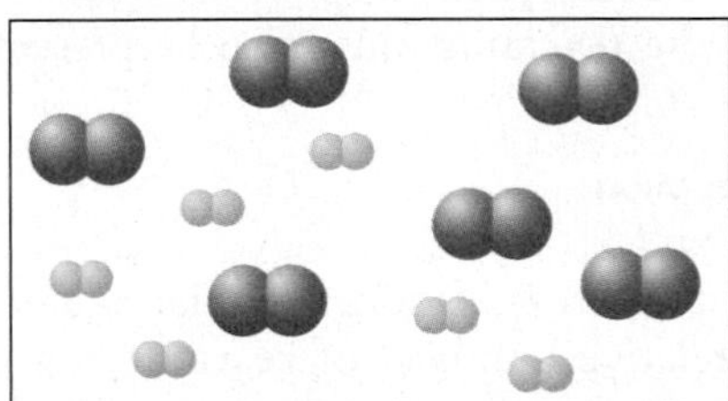

   Assuming that the reaction goes to completion, draw a representation of the product mixture. Explain how you arrived at this representation.
6. For the preceding question, which of the following equations best represents the reaction?
   a. $6N_2 + 6H_2 \rightarrow 4NH_3 + 4N_2$
   b. $N_2 + H_2 \rightarrow NH_3$
   c. $N + 3H \rightarrow NH_3$
   d. $N_2 + 3H_2 \rightarrow 2NH_3$
   e. $2N_2 + 6H_2 \rightarrow 4NH_3$

   Justify your choice. For those you did not choose, explain why they are incorrect.
7. You know that chemical A reacts with chemical B. You react 10.0 g A with 10.0 g B. What information do you need to have to determine the amount of product that will be produced? Explain.
8. A kerosene lamp has a mass of 1.5 kg. You put 0.5 kg of kerosene in the lamp. You burn all the kerosene until the lamp has a mass of 1.5 kg. What is the mass of the gases that are given off? Explain.
9. Consider an iron bar on a balance as shown.

   As the iron bar rusts, which of the following is true? Explain your answer.
   a. The balance will read less than 75.0 g.
   b. The balance will read 75.0 g.
   c. The balance will read greater than 75.0 g.
   d. The balance will read greater than 75.0 g, but if the bar is removed, the rust scraped off, and the bar replaced, the balance will read 75.0 g.
10. You may have noticed that water sometimes drips from an exhaust pipe of a car as it is running. Is this evidence that there is at least a small amount of water originally present in the gasoline? Explain.

Questions 11 and 12 deal with the following situation: You react chemical A with chemical B to make one product. It takes 100 g of A to react completely with 20 g B.

11. What is the mass of the product?
    a. less than 20 g
    b. between 20 and 100 g
    c. between 100 and 120 g
    d. exactly 120 g
    e. more than 120 g
12. What is true about the chemical properties of the product?
    a. The properties are more like those of chemical A.
    b. The properties are more like those of chemical B.
    c. The properties are an average of those of chemical A and chemical B.
    d. The properties are not necessarily like those of either chemical A or chemical B.

    Justify your choice. For those you did not choose, explain why they are incorrect.
13. What is the difference between the empirical and molecular formulas of a compound? Can they ever be the same? Explain.
14. Atoms of three different elements are represented by O, □, and Δ. Which compound is left over when three molecules of OΔ and three molecules of □□Δ react to form O□Δ and OΔΔ?
15. One way of determining the empirical formula is to burn a compound in air and weigh the amounts of carbon dioxide and water given off. For what types of compounds does this work? Explain the assumptions that are made. Why is the formula an empirical formula and not necessarily a molecular formula?
16. In chemistry, what is meant by the term *mole*? What is the importance of the mole concept?
17. Which (if any) of the following is true regarding the limiting reactant in a chemical reaction?
    a. The limiting reactant has the lowest coefficient in a balanced equation.
    b. The limiting reactant is the reactant for which you have the fewest number of moles.
    c. The limiting reactant has the lowest ratio of moles available/coefficient in the balanced equation.
    d. The limiting reactant has the lowest ratio of coefficient in the balanced equation/moles available.

    Justify your choice. For those you did not choose, explain why they are incorrect.
18. Consider the equation $3A + B \rightarrow C + D$. You react 4 moles of A with 2 moles of B. Which of the following is true?
    a. The limiting reactant is the one with the higher molar mass.
    b. A is the limiting reactant because you need 6 moles of A and have 4 moles.

c. B is the limiting reactant because you have fewer moles of B than A.
d. B is the limiting reactant because three A molecules react with each B molecule.
e. Neither reactant is limiting.

Justify your choice. For those you did not choose, explain why they are incorrect.

19. Chlorine exists mainly as two isotopes, ^{37}Cl and ^{35}Cl. Which is more abundant? How do you know?

20. According to the law of conservation of mass, mass cannot be gained or destroyed in a chemical reaction. Why can't you simply add the masses of two reactants to determine the total mass of product?

21. The atomic mass of boron (B) is given in the periodic table as 10.81, yet no single atom of boron has a mass of 10.81 amu. Explain.

22. Why is the actual yield of a reaction often less than the theoretical yield?

Exercises

OWL Interactive versions of these problems may be assigned in OWL.

A blue exercise number indicates that the answer to that exercise appears at the back of this book and a solution appears in the *Solutions Guide*.

Atomic Masses and the Mass Spectrometer

23. An element X has five major isotopes, which are listed below along with their abundances. Calculate the average atomic mass, and identify the element.

Isotope	Percent Natural Abundance	Mass (amu)
^{46}X	8.00	45.95269
^{47}X	7.30	46.951764
^{48}X	73.80	47.947947
^{49}X	5.50	48.947841
^{50}X	5.40	49.944792

24. The stable isotopes of iron are ^{54}Fe, ^{56}Fe, ^{57}Fe, and ^{58}Fe. The mass spectrum of iron looks like the following:

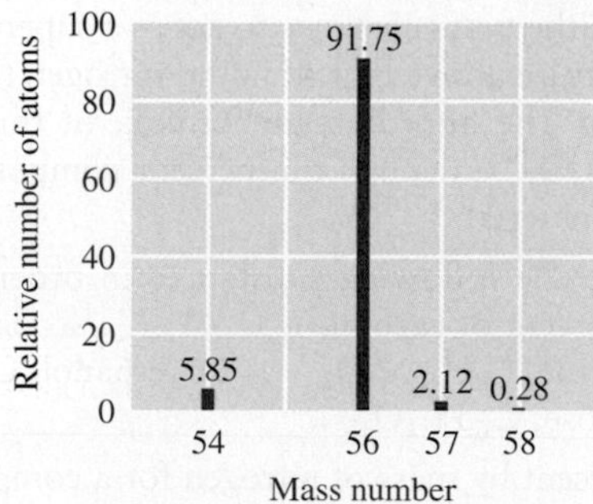

Use the data on the mass spectrum to estimate the average atomic mass of iron and compare it with the value given in the table inside the front cover of this book.

25. The element silver (Ag) has two naturally occurring isotopes: ^{109}Ag and ^{107}Ag with a mass of 106.905 amu. Silver consists of 51.82% ^{107}Ag and has an average atomic mass of 107.868 amu. Calculate the mass of ^{109}Ag.

26. The element europium exists in nature as two isotopes: ^{151}Eu has a mass of 150.9196 amu, and ^{153}Eu has a mass of 152.9209 amu. The average atomic mass of europium is 151.96 amu. Calculate the relative abundance of the two europium isotopes.

27. The element rhenium (Re) has two naturally occurring isotopes, ^{185}Re and ^{187}Re, with an average atomic mass of 186.207 amu. Rhenium is 62.60% ^{187}Re, and the atomic mass of ^{187}Re is 186.956 amu. Calculate the mass of ^{185}Re.

28. An element consists of 1.40% of an isotope with mass 203.973 amu, 24.10% of an isotope with mass 205.9745 amu, 22.10% of an isotope with mass 206.9759 amu, and 52.40% of an isotope with mass 207.9766 amu. Calculate the average atomic mass and identify the element.

29. The mass spectrum of bromine (Br_2) consists of three peaks with the following relative sizes:

Mass (amu)	Relative Size
157.84	0.2534
159.84	0.5000
161.84	0.2466

How do you interpret these data?

30. Naturally occurring tellurium (Te) has the following isotopic abundances:

Isotope	Abundance	Mass (amu)
^{120}Te	0.09%	119.90
^{122}Te	2.46%	121.90
^{123}Te	0.87%	122.90
^{124}Te	4.61%	123.90
^{125}Te	6.99%	124.90
^{126}Te	18.71%	125.90
^{128}Te	31.79%	127.90
^{130}Te	34.48%	129.91

Draw the mass spectrum of H_2Te, assuming that the only hydrogen isotope present is ^{1}H (mass 1.008).

31. Gallium arsenide (GaAs) has gained widespread use in semiconductor devices that interconvert light and electrical signals in fiber-optic communications systems. Gallium

consists of 60.% ^{69}Ga and 40.% ^{71}Ga. Arsenic has only one naturally occurring isotope, ^{75}As. Gallium arsenide is a polymeric material, but its mass spectrum shows fragments with formulas GaAs and Ga_2As_2. What would the distribution of peaks look like for these two fragments?

Moles and Molar Masses

32. Ascorbic acid, or vitamin C ($C_6H_8O_6$), is an essential vitamin. It cannot be stored by the body and must be present in the diet. What is the molar mass of ascorbic acid? Vitamin C tablets are taken as a dietary supplement. If a typical tablet contains 500.0 mg vitamin C, what amount (moles) and what number of molecules of vitamin C does it contain?

33. The molecular formula of acetylsalicylic acid (aspirin), one of the most commonly used pain relievers, is $C_9H_8O_4$.
    a. Calculate the molar mass of aspirin.
    b. A typical aspirin tablet contains 500. mg $C_9H_8O_4$. What amount (moles) of $C_9H_8O_4$ molecules and what number of molecules of acetylsalicylic acid are in a 500.-mg tablet?

34. Complete the following table.

Mass of Sample	Moles of Sample	Molecules in Sample	Total Atoms in Sample
4.24 g C_6H_6	______	______	______
______	0.224 mol H_2O	______	______
______	______	2.71×10^{22} molecules CO_2	______
______	______	______	3.35×10^{22} total atoms in CH_3OH sample

35. What amount (moles) is represented by each of these samples?
    a. 20.0 mg caffeine, $C_8H_{10}N_4O_2$
    b. 2.72×10^{21} molecules of ethanol, C_2H_5OH
    c. 1.50 g of dry ice, CO_2

36. How many atoms of nitrogen are present in 5.00 g of each of the following?
    a. glycine, $C_2H_5O_2N$
    b. magnesium nitride
    c. calcium nitrate
    d. dinitrogen tetroxide

37. Consider the following gas samples: 4.0 g of hydrogen gas, 4.0 g of helium gas, 1.0 mole of fluorine gas, 44.0 g of carbon dioxide gas, and 146 g of sulfur hexafluoride gas. Arrange the gas samples in order of increasing number of total atoms present.

38. Aspartame is an artificial sweetener that is 160 times sweeter than sucrose (table sugar) when dissolved in water. It is marketed as NutraSweet. The molecular formula of aspartame is $C_{14}H_{18}N_2O_5$.
    a. Calculate the molar mass of aspartame.
    b. How many moles of molecules are in 10.0 g of aspartame?
    c. What is the mass in grams of 1.56 moles of aspartame?
    d. How many molecules are in 5.0 mg of aspartame?
    e. How many atoms of nitrogen are in 1.2 g of aspartame?
    f. What is the mass in grams of 1.0×10^9 molecules of aspartame?
    g. What is the mass in grams of one molecule of aspartame?

39. Chloral hydrate ($C_2H_3Cl_3O_2$) is a drug formerly used as a sedative and hypnotic. It is the compound used to make "Mickey Finns" in detective stories.
    a. Calculate the molar mass of chloral hydrate.
    b. How many moles of $C_2H_3Cl_3O_2$ molecules are in 500.0 g of chloral hydrate?
    c. What is the mass in grams of 2.0×10^{-2} mol chloral hydrate?
    d. How many chlorine atoms are in 5.0 g chloral hydrate?
    e. What mass of chloral hydrate would contain 1.0 g Cl?
    f. What is the mass of exactly 500 molecules of chloral hydrate?

40. In the spring of 1984, concern arose over the presence of ethylene dibromide, or EDB, in grains and cereals. EDB has the molecular formula $C_2H_4Br_2$ and until 1984 was commonly used as a plant fumigant. The federal limit for EDB in finished cereal products is 30.0 parts per billion (ppb), where 1.0 ppb = 1.0×10^{-9} g of EDB for every 1.0 g of sample. How many molecules of EDB are in 1.0 lb of flour if 30.0 ppb of EDB is present?

Percent Composition

41. Anabolic steroids are performance enhancement drugs whose use has been banned from most major sporting activities. One anabolic steroid is fluoxymesterone ($C_{20}H_{29}FO_3$). Calculate the percent composition by mass of fluoxymesterone.

42. Calculate the percent composition by mass of the following compounds that are important starting materials for synthetic polymers:
    a. $C_3H_4O_2$ (acrylic acid, from which acrylic plastics are made)
    b. $C_4H_6O_2$ (methyl acrylate, from which Plexiglas is made)
    c. C_3H_3N (acrylonitrile, from which Orlon is made)

43. In 1987 the first substance to act as a superconductor at a temperature above that of liquid nitrogen (77 K) was discovered. The approximate formula of this substance is $YBa_2Cu_3O_7$. Calculate the percent composition by mass of this material.

44. Arrange the following substances in order of increasing mass percent of carbon.
    a. caffeine, $C_8H_{10}N_4O_2$
    b. sucrose, $C_{12}H_{22}O_{11}$
    c. ethanol, C_2H_5OH

45. The percent by mass of nitrogen for a compound is found to be 46.7%. Which of the following could be this species?

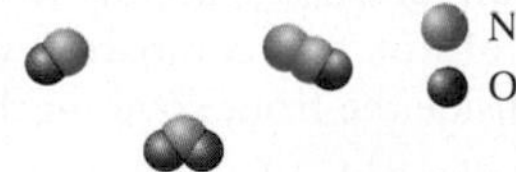

46. Vitamin B_{12}, cyanocobalamin, is essential for human nutrition. It is concentrated in animal tissue but not in higher plants. Although nutritional requirements for the vitamin are quite low, people who abstain completely from animal

products may develop a deficiency anemia. Cyanocobalamin is the form used in vitamin supplements. It contains 4.34% cobalt by mass. Calculate the molar mass of cyanocobalamin, assuming that there is one atom of cobalt in every molecule of cyanocobalamin.

47. Fungal laccase, a blue protein found in wood-rotting fungi, is 0.390% Cu by mass. If a fungal laccase molecule contains four copper atoms, what is the molar mass of fungal laccase?

48. Portland cement acts as the binding agent in concrete. A typical Portland cement has the following composition:

Formula	Name	Mass Percent
Ca_3SiO_5	Tricalcium silicate	50.
Ca_2SiO_4	Dicalcium silicate	25
$Ca_3Al_2O_6$	Tricalcium aluminate	12
Ca_2AlFeO_5	Calcium aluminoferrite	8.0
$CaSO_4 \cdot 2H_2O$	Calcium sulfate dihydrate	3.5
Other substances, mostly MgO		1.5

Assuming that the impurities contain no Ca, Al, or Fe, calculate the mass percent of these elements in this Portland cement.

Empirical and Molecular Formulas

49. Express the composition of each of the following compounds as the mass percent of its elements.
a. formaldehyde, CH_2O
b. glucose, $C_6H_{12}O_6$
c. acetic acid, $HC_2H_3O_2$

Considering your answers, which type of formula—empirical or molecular—can be obtained from elemental analysis that gives mass percent composition? Explain.

50. Give the empirical formula of each of these compounds.

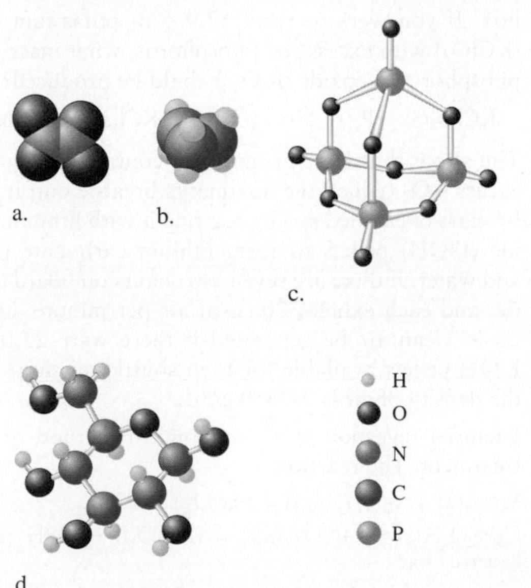

51. Determine the molecular formulas to which the following empirical formulas and molar masses pertain.
a. SNH (188.35 g/mol)
b. $NPCl_2$ (347.64 g/mol)
c. CoC_4O_4 (341.94 g/mol)
d. SN (184.32 g/mol)

52. A sample of urea contains 1.121 g N, 0.161 g H, 0.480 g C, and 0.640 g O. What is the empirical formula of urea?

53. There are two binary compounds of mercury and oxygen. Heating either of them results in the decomposition of the compound, with oxygen gas escaping into the atmosphere while leaving a residue of pure mercury. Heating 0.6498 g of one of the compounds leaves a residue of 0.6018 g. Heating 0.4172 g of the other compound results in a mass loss of 0.016 g. Determine the empirical formula of each compound.

54. The compound adrenaline contains 56.79% C, 6.56% H, 28.37% O, and 8.28% N by mass. What is the empirical formula of adrenaline?

55. A compound contains only carbon, hydrogen, nitrogen, and oxygen. Combustion of 0.157 g of the compound produced 0.213 g of CO_2 and 0.0310 g of H_2O. In another experiment, 0.103 g of the compound produced 0.0230 g of NH_3. What is the empirical formula of the compound? *Hint:* Combustion involves reacting with excess O_2. Assume that all the carbon ends up in CO_2 and all the hydrogen ends up in H_2O. Also assume that all the nitrogen ends up in the NH_3 in the second experiment.

56. Maleic acid is an organic compound composed of 41.39% C, 3.47% H, and the rest oxygen. If 0.129 mole of maleic acid has a mass of 15.0 g, what are the empirical and molecular formulas of maleic acid?

57. Determine the molecular formula of a compound that contains 26.7% P, 12.1% N, and 61.2% Cl, and has a molar mass of 580 g/mol.

58. Terephthalic acid is an important chemical used in the manufacture of polyesters and plasticizers. It contains only C, H, and O. Combustion of 19.81 mg terephthalic acid produces 41.98 mg CO_2 and 6.45 mg H_2O. If 0.250 mole of terephthalic acid has a mass of 41.5 g, determine the molecular formula of terephthalic acid.

59. A compound contains only carbon, hydrogen, and oxygen. Combustion of 10.68 mg of the compound yields 16.01 mg CO_2 and 4.37 mg H_2O. The molar mass of the compound is 176.1 g/mol. What are the empirical and molecular formulas of the compound?

60. ABS plastic is a tough, hard plastic used in applications requiring shock resistance. (See Chapter 21.) The polymer consists of three monomer units: acrylonitrile (C_3H_3N), butadiene (C_4H_6), and styrene (C_8H_8).
a. A sample of ABS plastic contains 8.80% N by mass. It took 0.605 g of Br_2 to react completely with a 1.20-g sample of ABS plastic. Bromine reacts 1:1 (by moles) with the butadiene molecules in the polymer and

nothing else. What is the percent by mass of acrylonitrile and butadiene in this polymer?

b. What are the relative numbers of each of the monomer units in this polymer?

Balancing Chemical Equations

61. The reaction of an element X with element Y is represented in the following diagram. Which of the equations best describes this reaction?

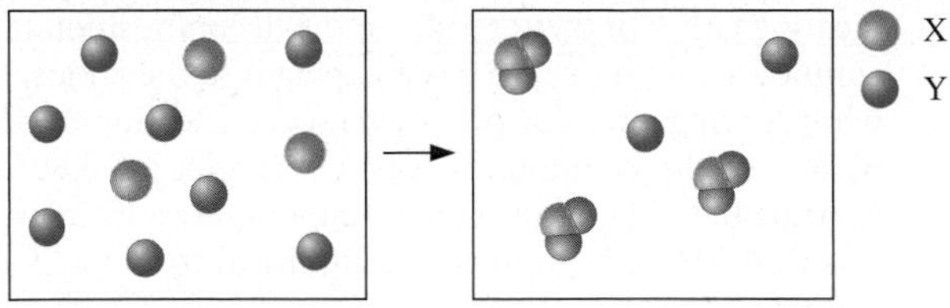

a. $3X + 8Y \rightarrow X_3Y_8$
b. $3X + 6Y \rightarrow X_3Y_6$
c. $X + 2Y \rightarrow XY_2$
d. $3X + 8Y \rightarrow 3XY_2 + 2Y$

62. Silicon is produced for the chemical and electronics industries by the following reactions. Give the balanced equation for each reaction.

a. $SiO_2(s) + C(s) \xrightarrow[\text{arc furnace}]{\text{Electric}} Si_2(s) + CO(g)$

b. Silicon tetrachloride is reacted with very pure magnesium, producing silicon and magnesium chloride.

c. $Na_2SiF_6(s) + Na(s) \longrightarrow Si(s) + NaF(s)$

63. Give the balanced equation for each of the following chemical reactions.

a. Glucose ($C_6H_{12}O_6$) reacts with oxygen gas to produce gaseous carbon dioxide and water vapor.

b. Solid iron(III) sulfide reacts with gaseous hydrogen chloride to form solid iron(III) chloride and hydrogen sulfide gas.

c. Carbon disulfide liquid reacts with ammonia gas to produce hydrogen sulfide gas and solid ammonium thiocyanate (NH_4SCN).

64. Give the balanced equation for each of the following.

a. The combustion of ethanol (C_2H_5OH) forms carbon dioxide and water vapor. A combustion reaction refers to a reaction of a substance with oxygen gas.

b. Aqueous solutions of lead(II) nitrate and sodium phosphate are mixed, resulting in the precipitate formation of lead(II) phosphate with aqueous sodium nitrate as the other product.

65. Balance the following equations.

a. $Cr(s) + S_8(s) \longrightarrow Cr_2S_3(s)$
b. $NaHCO_3(s) \xrightarrow{\text{Heat}} Na_2CO_3(s) + CO_2(g) + H_2O(g)$
c. $KClO_3(s) \xrightarrow{\text{Heat}} KCl(s) + O_2(g)$
d. $Eu(s) + HF(g) \longrightarrow EuF_3(s) + H_2(g)$
e. $C_6H_6(l) + O_2(g) \longrightarrow CO_2(g) + H_2O(g)$

66. Balance each of the following chemical equations.

a. $KO_2(s) + H_2O(l) \rightarrow KOH(aq) + O_2(g) + H_2O_2(aq)$
b. $Fe_2O_3(s) + HNO_3(aq) \rightarrow Fe(NO_3)_3(aq) + H_2O(l)$
c. $NH_3(g) + O_2(g) \rightarrow NO(g) + H_2O(g)$
d. $PCl_5(l) + H_2O(l) \rightarrow H_3PO_4(aq) + HCl(g)$
e. $CaO(s) + C(s) \rightarrow CaC_2(s) + CO_2(g)$
f. $MoS_2(s) + O_2(g) \rightarrow MoO_3(s) + SO_2(g)$
g. $FeCO_3(s) + H_2CO_3(aq) \rightarrow Fe(HCO_3)_2(aq)$

Reaction Stoichiometry

67. The reusable booster rockets of the U.S. space shuttle use a mixture of aluminum and ammonium perchlorate for fuel. A possible equation for this reaction is

$$3Al(s) + 3NH_4ClO_4(s) \longrightarrow Al_2O_3(s) + AlCl_3(s) + 3NO(g) + 6H_2O(g)$$

What mass of NH_4ClO_4 should be used in the fuel mixture for every kilogram of Al?

68. Nitric acid is produced commercially by the Ostwald process. The three steps of the Ostwald process are shown in the following equations:

$$4NH_3(g) + 5O_2(g) \longrightarrow 4NO(g) + 6H_2O(g)$$
$$2NO(g) + O_2(g) \longrightarrow 2NO_2(g)$$
$$3NO_2(g) + H_2O(l) \longrightarrow 2HNO_3(aq) + NO(g)$$

What mass of NH_3 must be used to produce 1.0×10^6 kg of HNO_3 by the Ostwald process, assuming 100% yield in each reaction and assuming the NO produced in the third stage is not recycled?

69. Over the years, the thermite reaction has been used for welding railroad rails, in incendiary bombs, and to ignite solid-fuel rocket motors. The reaction is

$$Fe_2O_3(s) + 2Al(s) \longrightarrow 2Fe(l) + Al_2O_3(s)$$

What masses of iron(III) oxide and aluminum must be used to produce 15.0 g of iron? What is the maximum mass of aluminum oxide that could be produced?

70. The reaction between potassium chlorate and red phosphorus takes place when you strike a match on a matchbox. If you were to react 52.9 g of potassium chlorate ($KClO_3$) with excess red phosphorus, what mass of tetraphosphorus decoxide (P_4O_{10}) could be produced?

$$KClO_3(s) + P_4(s) \longrightarrow P_4O_{10}(s) + KCl(s) \quad \text{(unbalanced)}$$

71. The space shuttle environmental control system handles excess CO_2 (which the astronauts breathe out; it is 4.0% by mass of exhaled air) by reacting it with lithium hydroxide (LiOH) pellets to form lithium carbonate (Li_2CO_3) and water. If there are seven astronauts on board the shuttle, and each exhales 20. L of air per minute, how long could clean air be generated if there were 25,000 g of LiOH pellets available for each shuttle mission? Assume the density of air is 0.0010 g/mL.

72. Bacterial digestion is an economical method of sewage treatment. The reaction

$$5CO_2(g) + 55NH_4^+(aq) + 76O_2(g) \xrightarrow{\text{Bacteria}} \underset{\text{Bacterial tissue}}{C_5H_7O_2N(s)} + 54NO_2^-(aq) + 52H_2O(l) + 109H^+(aq)$$

is an intermediate step in the conversion of the nitrogen in organic compounds into nitrate ions. How much bacterial tissue is produced in a treatment plant for every 1.0×10^4 kg of wastewater containing 3.0% NH_4^+ ions by mass? Assume that 95% of the ammonium ions are consumed by the bacteria.

73. Phosphorus can be prepared from calcium phosphate by the following reaction:

$$2Ca_3(PO_4)_2(s) + 6SiO_2(s) + 10C(s) \longrightarrow 6CaSiO_3(s) + P_4(s) + 10CO(g)$$

Phosphorite is a mineral that contains $Ca_3(PO_4)_2$ plus other non-phosphorus-containing compounds. What is the maximum amount of P_4 that can be produced from 1.0 kg of phosphorite if the phosphorite sample is 75% $Ca_3(PO_4)_2$ by mass? Assume an excess of the other reactants.

74. In the production of printed circuit boards for the electronics industry, a 0.60-mm layer of copper is laminated onto an insulating plastic board. Next, a circuit pattern made of a chemically resistant polymer is printed on the board. The unwanted copper is removed by chemical etching and the protective polymer is finally removed by solvents. One etching reaction is

$$Cu(NH_3)_4Cl_2(aq) + 4NH_3(aq) + Cu(s) \longrightarrow 2Cu(NH_3)_4Cl(aq)$$

A plant needs to manufacture 10,000 printed circuit boards, each 8.0×16.0 cm in area. An average of 80.% of the copper is removed from each board (density of copper = 8.96 g/cm³). What masses of $Cu(NH_3)_4Cl_2$ and NH_3 are needed to do this? Assume 100% yield.

Limiting Reactants and Percent Yield

75. Consider the reaction between NO(g) and O_2(g) represented below.

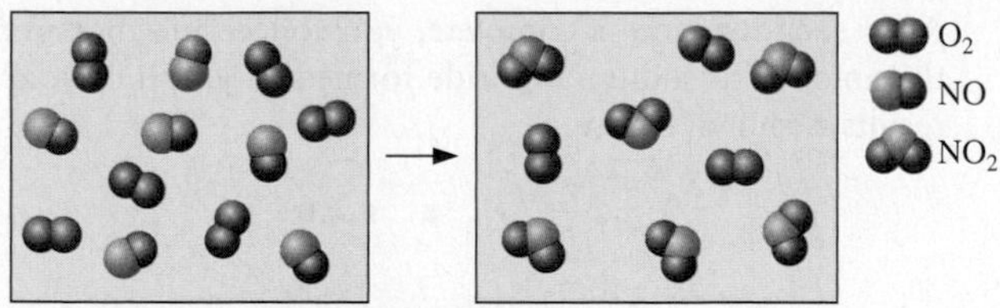

What is the balanced equation for this reaction and what is the limiting reactant?

76. Consider the following reaction:

$$4NH_3(g) + 5O_2(g) \longrightarrow 4NO(g) + 6H_2O(g)$$

If a container were to have 10 molecules of O_2 and 10 molecules of NH_3 initially, how many total molecules (reactants plus products) would be present in the container after this reaction goes to completion?

77. Hydrogen peroxide is used as a cleaning agent in the treatment of cuts and abrasions for several reasons. It is an oxidizing agent that can directly kill many microorganisms; it decomposes upon contact with blood, releasing elemental oxygen gas (which inhibits the growth of anaerobic microorganisms); and it foams upon contact with blood, which provides a cleansing action. In the laboratory, small quantities of hydrogen peroxide can be prepared by the action of an acid on an alkaline earth metal peroxide, such as barium peroxide:

$$BaO_2(s) + 2HCl(aq) \longrightarrow H_2O_2(aq) + BaCl_2(aq)$$

What amount of hydrogen peroxide should result when 1.50 g of barium peroxide is treated with 25.0 mL of hydrochloric acid solution containing 0.0272 g of HCl per mL? What mass of which reagent is left unreacted?

78. Silver sulfadiazine burn-treating cream creates a barrier against bacterial invasion and releases antimicrobial agents directly into the wound. If 25.0 g of Ag_2O is reacted with 50.0 g of $C_{10}H_{10}N_4SO_2$, what mass of silver sulfadiazine ($AgC_{10}H_9N_4SO_2$) can be produced, assuming 100% yield?

$$Ag_2O(s) + 2C_{10}H_{10}N_4SO_2(s) \longrightarrow 2AgC_{10}H_9N_4SO_2(s) + H_2O(l)$$

79. Bornite (Cu_3FeS_3) is a copper ore used in the production of copper. When heated, the following reaction occurs:

$$2Cu_3FeS_3(s) + 7O_2(g) \longrightarrow 6Cu(s) + 2FeO(s) + 6SO_2(g)$$

If 2.50 metric tons of bornite is reacted with excess O_2 and the process has an 86.3% yield of copper, how much copper is produced?

80. DDT, an insecticide harmful to fish, birds, and humans, is produced by the following reaction:

$$\underset{\text{Chlorobenzene}}{2C_6H_5Cl} + \underset{\text{Chloral}}{C_2HOCl_3} \longrightarrow \underset{\text{DDT}}{C_{14}H_9Cl_5} + H_2O$$

In a government lab, 1142 g of chlorobenzene is reacted with 485 g of chloral.

a. What mass of DDT is formed, assuming 100% yield?
b. Which reactant is limiting? Which is in excess?
c. What mass of the excess reactant is left over?
d. If the actual yield of DDT is 200.0 g, what is the percent yield?

81. Hydrogen cyanide is produced industrially from the reaction of gaseous ammonia, oxygen, and methane:

$$2NH_3(g) + 3O_2(g) + 2CH_4(g) \longrightarrow 2HCN(g) + 6H_2O(g)$$

If 5.00×10^3 kg each of NH_3, O_2, and CH_4 are reacted, what mass of HCN and of H_2O will be produced, assuming 100% yield?

82. The production capacity for acrylonitrile (C_3H_3N) in the United States exceeds 2 million pounds per year. Acrylonitrile, the building block for polyacrylonitrile fibers and a variety of plastics, is produced from gaseous propylene, ammonia, and oxygen:

$$2C_3H_6(g) + 2NH_3(g) + 3O_2(g) \longrightarrow 2C_3H_3N(g) + 6H_2O(g)$$

a. What mass of acrylonitrile can be produced from a mixture of 1.00 kg of propylene (C_3H_6), 1.50 kg of ammonia, and 2.00 kg of oxygen, assuming 100% yield?
b. What mass of water is produced, and what masses of which starting materials are left in excess?

83. Consider the following unbalanced reaction:

$$P_4(s) + F_2(g) \longrightarrow PF_3(g)$$

How many grams of F_2 are needed to produce 120. g of PF_3 if the reaction has a 78.1% yield?

84. The aspirin substitute acetaminophen ($C_8H_9O_2N$) is produced by the following three-step synthesis:

I. $C_6H_5O_3N(s) + 3H_2(g) + HCl(aq) \longrightarrow C_6H_8ONCl(s) + 2H_2O(l)$

II. $C_6H_8ONCl(s) + NaOH(aq) \longrightarrow C_6H_7ON(s) + H_2O(l) + NaCl(aq)$

III. $C_6H_7ON(s) + C_4H_6O_3(l) \longrightarrow C_8H_9O_2N(s) + HC_2H_3O_2(l)$

The first two reactions have percent yields of 87% and 98% by mass, respectively. The overall reaction yields 3 moles of acetaminophen product for every 4 moles of $C_6H_5O_3N$ reacted.

a. What is the percent yield by mass for the overall process?
b. What is the percent yield by mass of step III?

Additional Exercises

85. A sample of a hydrocarbon (a compound consisting of only carbon and hydrogen) contains 2.59×10^{23} atoms of hydrogen and is 17.3% hydrogen by mass. If the molar mass of the hydrocarbon is between 55 and 65 g/mol, how many moles of compound are present, and what is the mass of the sample?

86. A binary compound created by the reaction of an unknown element E and hydrogen contains 91.27% E and 8.73% H by mass. If the formula of the compound is E_3H_8, calculate the atomic mass of E.

87. An ionic compound MX_3 is prepared according to the following unbalanced chemical equation:

$$M + X_2 \longrightarrow MX_3$$

A 0.105-g sample of X_2 contains 8.92×10^{20} molecules. The compound MX_3 consists of 54.47% X by mass. What are the identities of M and X, and what is the correct name for MX_3? Starting with 1.00 g each of M and X_2, what mass of MX_3 can be prepared?

88. The empirical formula of styrene is CH; the molar mass of styrene is 104.14 g/mol. How many H atoms are present in a 2.00-g sample of styrene?

89. A 0.755-g sample of hydrated copper(II) sulfate ($CuSO_4 \cdot xH_2O$) was heated carefully until it had changed completely to anhydrous copper(II) sulfate ($CuSO_4$) with a mass of 0.483 g. Determine the value of x. [This number is called the "number of waters of hydration" of copper(II) sulfate. It specifies the number of water molecules per formula unit of $CuSO_4$ in the hydrated crystal.]

90. Many cereals are made with high moisture content so that the cereal can be formed into various shapes before it is dried. A cereal product containing 58% H_2O by mass is produced at the rate of 1000. kg/h. How much water must be evaporated per hour if the final product contains only 20.% water?

91. When aluminum metal is heated with an element from Group 6A of the periodic table, an ionic compound forms. When the experiment is performed with an unknown Group 6A element, the product is 18.56% Al by mass. What is the formula of the compound?

92. A salt contains only barium and one of the halide ions. A 0.158-g sample of the salt was dissolved in water, and an excess of sulfuric acid was added to form barium sulfate ($BaSO_4$), which was filtered, dried, and weighed. Its mass was found to be 0.124 g. What is the formula of the barium halide?

93. A sample of LSD (D-lysergic acid diethylamide, $C_{24}H_{30}N_3O$) is added to some table salt (sodium chloride) to form a mixture. Given that a 1.00-g sample of the mixture undergoes combustion to produce 1.20 g of CO_2, what is the mass percentage of LSD in the mixture?

94. Consider the following unbalanced equation:

$$Ca_3(PO_4)_2(s) + H_2SO_4(aq) \longrightarrow CaSO_4(s) + H_3PO_4(aq)$$

What masses of calcium sulfate and phosphoric acid can be produced from the reaction of 1.0 kg of calcium phosphate with 1.0 kg of concentrated sulfuric acid (98% H_2SO_4 by mass)?

95. A 0.4230-g sample of impure sodium nitrate was heated, converting all the sodium nitrate to 0.2864 g of sodium nitrite and oxygen gas. Determine the percent of sodium nitrate in the original sample.

96. You have seven closed containers, each with equal masses of chlorine gas (Cl_2). You add 10.0 g of sodium to the first sample, 20.0 g of sodium to the second sample, and so on (adding 70.0 g of sodium to the seventh sample). Sodium and chlorine react to form sodium chloride according to the equation

$$2Na(s) + Cl_2(g) \longrightarrow 2NaCl(s)$$

After each reaction is complete, you collect and measure the amount of sodium chloride formed. A graph of your results is shown below.

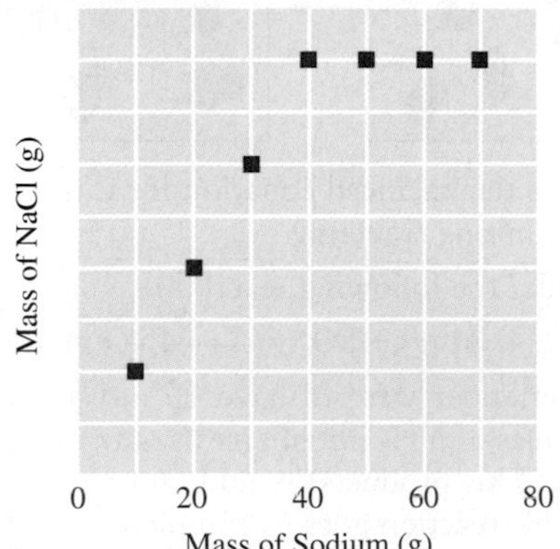

Anwer the following questions:

a. Explain the shape of the graph.
b. Calculate the mass of NaCl formed when 20.0 g of sodium is used.
c. Calculate the mass of Cl_2 in each container.
d. Calculate the mass of NaCl formed when 50.0 g of sodium is used.
e. Identify the leftover reactant and determine its mass for parts b and d.

97. An iron ore sample contains Fe_2O_3 plus other impurities. A 752-g sample of impure iron ore is heated with excess carbon, producing 453 g of pure iron by the following reaction:

$$Fe_2O_3(s) + 3C(s) \longrightarrow 2Fe(s) + 3CO(g)$$

What is the mass percent of Fe_2O_3 in the impure iron ore sample? Assume that Fe_2O_3 is the only source of iron and that the reaction is 100% efficient.

98. In using a mass spectrometer, a chemist sees a peak at a mass of 30.0106. Of the choices $^{12}C_2{}^1H_6$, $^{12}C^1H_2{}^{16}O$, and $^{14}N^{16}O$, which is responsible for this peak? Pertinent masses are ^1H, 1.007825; ^{16}O, 15.994915; and ^{14}N, 14.003074.

99. Natural rubidium has the average mass 85.4678 amu and is composed of isotopes ^{85}Rb (mass = 84.9117 amu) and ^{87}Rb. The ratio of atoms $^{85}Rb/^{87}Rb$ in natural rubidium is 2.591. Calculate the mass of ^{87}Rb.

100. Tetrodotoxin is a toxic chemical found in fugu pufferfish, a popular but rare delicacy in Japan. This compound has an LD_{50} (the amount of substance that is lethal to 50.% of a population sample) of 10. μg per kg of body mass. Tetrodotoxin is 41.38% carbon by mass, 13.16% nitrogen by mass, and 5.37% hydrogen by mass, with the remaining amount consisting of oxygen. What is the empirical formula of tetrodotoxin? If three molecules of tetrodotoxin have a mass of 1.59×10^{-21} g, what is the molecular formula of tetrodotoxin? What number of molecules of tetrodotoxin would be the LD_{50} dosage for a person weighing 165 lb?

101. Consider the following data for three binary compounds of hydrogen and nitrogen:

	% H (by Mass)	% N (by Mass)
I	17.75	82.25
II	12.58	87.42
III	2.34	97.66

When 1.00 L of each gaseous compound is decomposed to its elements, the following volumes of $H_2(g)$ and $N_2(g)$ are obtained:

	H_2 (L)	N_2 (L)
I	1.50	0.50
II	2.00	1.00
III	0.50	1.50

Use these data to determine the molecular formulas of compounds I, II, and III and to determine the relative values for the atomic masses of hydrogen and nitrogen.

102. A 0.200-g sample of protactinium(IV) oxide is converted to another oxide of protactinium by heating in the presence of oxygen to give 0.2081 g of the new oxide, Pa_xO_y. Determine the values of x and y.

103. A 1.000-g sample of XI_2 is dissolved in water, and excess silver nitrate is added to precipitate all of the iodide as AgI. The mass of the dry AgI is found to be 1.375 g. Calculate the atomic weight (mass) of X.

104. A substance X_2Z has the composition (by mass) of 40.0% X and 60.0% Z. What is the composition (by mass) of the compound XZ_2?

105. Vitamin A has a molar mass of 286.4 g and has a general molecular formula of C_xH_yE, where E is an unknown element. If vitamin A is 83.86% C and 10.56% H by mass, what is the molecular formula of vitamin A?

106. Boron consists of two isotopes, ^{10}B and ^{11}B. Chlorine also has two isotopes, ^{35}Cl and ^{37}Cl. Consider the mass spectrum of BCl_3. How many peaks would be present, and what approximate mass would each peak correspond to in the BCl_3 mass spectrum?

Challenge Problems

107. In a mass spectrometer, positive ions are produced when a gaseous mixture is ionized by electron bombardment produced by an electric discharge. When the electric-discharge voltage is low, singly positive ions are produced and the following peaks are observed in the mass spectrum:

Mass (amu)	Relative Intensity
32	0.3743
34	0.0015
40	1.0000

When the electric discharge is increased, still only singly charged ions are produced, but now the peaks observed in the mass spectrum are

Mass (amu)	Relative Intensity
16	0.7500
18	0.0015
40	1.0000

What does the gas mixture consist of, and what is the percent composition by isotope of the mixture?

108. When the supply of oxygen is limited, iron metal reacts with oxygen to produce a mixture of FeO and Fe_2O_3. In a certain experiment, 20.00 g of iron metal was reacted with 11.20 g of oxygen gas. After the experiment, the iron was totally consumed and 3.24 g of oxygen gas remained. Calculate the amounts of FeO and Fe_2O_3 formed in this experiment.

109. Element X forms both a dichloride (XCl_2) and a tetrachloride (XCl_4). Treatment of 10.00 g of XCl_2 with excess chlorine forms 12.55 g of XCl_4. Calculate the atomic weight (mass) of X and identify X.

110. Zinc and magnesium metal each react with hydrochloric acid to make chloride salts of the respective metals and hydrogen gas. A 10.00-g mixture of zinc and magnesium produces 0.5171 g of hydrogen gas upon being mixed with an excess of hydrochloric acid. Determine the percent magnesium by mass in the original mixture.

111. An unknown binary compound containing hydrogen (XH_n) has a density as a gas that is 2.393 times that of oxygen gas under the same conditions. When 2.23×10^{-2} mole of this compound reacts with excess oxygen gas, 0.803 g of water is produced. Identify the element X in this compound.

112. A 2.25-g sample of scandium metal is reacted with excess hydrochloric acid to produce 0.1502 g hydrogen gas. What is the formula of the scandium chloride produced in the reaction?

113. When $M_2S_3(s)$ is heated in air, it is converted to $MO_2(s)$. A 4.000-g sample of $M_2S_3(s)$ shows a decrease in mass of 0.277 g when it is heated in air. What is the average atomic mass of M?

114. Consider a gaseous binary compound with a molar mass of 62.09 g/mol. When 1.39 g of this compound is completely burned in excess oxygen, 1.21 g of water is formed. Determine the formula of the compound.

115. Pure carbon was burned in an excess of oxygen. The gaseous products were

CO_2	72.0 mol%
CO	16.0 mol%
O_2	12.0 mol%

How many moles of O_2 were present in the initial reaction mixture for every mole of carbon?

116. You take 1.00 g of an aspirin tablet (a compound consisting solely of carbon, hydrogen, and oxygen), burn it in air, and collect 2.20 g CO_2 and 0.400 g H_2O. You know that the molar mass of aspirin is between 170 and 190 g/mol. Reacting 1 mole of salicylic acid with 1 mole of acetic anhydride ($C_4H_6O_3$) gives you 1 mole of aspirin and 1 mole of acetic acid ($C_2H_4O_2$). Use this information to determine the molecular formula of salicylic acid.

117. Lanthanum was reacted with hydrogen in a given experiment to produce the nonstoichiometric compound $LaH_{2.90}$. Assuming that the compound contains H^-, La^{2+}, and La^{3+}, calculate the fraction of $La^{2+}$and La^{3+} present.

118. A 9.780-g gaseous mixture contains ethane (C_2H_6) and propane (C_3H_8). Complete combustion to form carbon dioxide and water requires 1.120 moles of oxygen gas. Calculate the mass percent of ethane in the original mixture.

119. Consider a mixture of potassium chloride and potassium nitrate that is 43.2% potassium by mass. What is the percent KCl by mass of the original mixture?

120. A 2.077-g sample of an element, which has an atomic mass between 40 and 55, reacts with oxygen to form 3.708 g of an oxide. Determine the formula of the oxide and identify the element.

121. Ammonia reacts with O_2 to form either $NO(g)$ or $NO_2(g)$ according to these unbalanced equations:

$$NH_3(g) + O_2(g) \longrightarrow NO(g) + H_2O(g)$$

$$NH_3(g) + O_2(g) \longrightarrow NO_2(g) + H_2O(g)$$

In a certain experiment, 2.00 moles of $NH_3(g)$ and 10.00 moles of $O_2(g)$ are contained in a closed flask. After the reaction is complete, 6.75 moles of $O_2(g)$ remains. Calculate the number of moles of $NO(g)$ in the product mixture. (*Hint:* You cannot do this problem by adding the balanced equations, because you cannot assume that the two reactions will occur with equal probability.)

122. A gas contains a mixture of $NH_3(g)$ and $N_2H_4(g)$, both of which react with $O_2(g)$ to form $NO_2(g)$ and $H_2O(g)$. The gaseous mixture (with an initial mass of 61.00 g) is reacted with 10.00 moles O_2, and after the reaction is complete, 4.062 moles of O_2 remains. Calculate the mass percent of $N_2H_4(g)$ in the original gaseous mixture.

Marathon Problems*

123. From the information that follows, determine the mass of substance C that will be formed if 45.0 g of substance A reacts with 23.0 g of substance B. (Assume that the reaction between A and B goes to completion.)
   a. Substance A is a gray solid that consists of an alkaline earth metal and carbon (37.5% by mass). It reacts with substance B to produce substances C and D. Forty million trillion formula units of A have a mass of 4.26 mg.
   b. 47.9 g of substance B contains 5.36 g of hydrogen and 42.5 g of oxygen.
   c. When 10.0 g of substance C is burned in excess oxygen, 33.8 g of carbon dioxide and 6.92 g of water are produced. A mass spectrum of substance C shows a parent molecular ion with a mass-to-charge ratio of 26.
   d. Substance D is the hydroxide of the metal in substance A.

124. Consider the following balanced chemical equation:

$$A + 5B \longrightarrow 3C + 4D$$

*From James H. Burness, "The Use of "Marathon" Problems as Effective Vehicles for the Presentation of General Chemistry Lectures," Journal of Chemical Education, 68(11). Copyright © 1991 American Chemical Society. Reprinted by permission.

a. Equal masses of A and B are reacted. Complete each of the following with either "A is the limiting reactant because ____"; "B is the limiting reactant because ____"; or "We cannot determine the limiting reactant because ____."
   i. If the molar mass of A is greater than the molar mass of B, then
   ii. If the molar mass of B is greater than the molar mass of A, then

b. The products of the reaction are carbon dioxide (C) and water (D). Compound A has a similar molar mass to carbon dioxide. Compound B is a diatomic molecule. Identify compound B and support your answer.

c. Compound A is a hydrocarbon that is 81.71% carbon by mass. Determine its empirical and molecular formulas.

4 Types of Chemical Reactions and Solution Stoichiometry

chapter

When zinc reacts with iodine, the heat produces a cloud of excess iodine.

Sign in to OWL at www.cengage.com/owl to view tutorials and simulations, develop problem-solving skills, and complete online homework assigned by your professor.

Download mini lecture videos for key concept review and exam prep from OWL or purchase them from www.cengagebrain.com.

Much of the chemistry that affects each of us occurs among substances dissolved in water. For example, virtually all of the chemistry that makes life possible occurs in an aqueous environment. Also, various tests for illnesses involve aqueous reactions. Modern medical practice depends heavily on analyses of blood and other body fluids. In addition to the common tests for sugar, cholesterol, and iron, analyses for specific chemical markers allow detection of many diseases before more obvious symptoms occur.

Aqueous chemistry is also important in our environment. In recent years contamination of the groundwater by substances such as chloroform and nitrates has been widely publicized. Water is essential for life, and the maintenance of an ample supply of clean water is crucial to all civilization.

To understand the chemistry that occurs in such diverse places as the human body, the groundwater, the oceans, the local water treatment plant, your hair as you shampoo it, and so on, we must understand how substances dissolved in water react with one another.

However, before we can understand solution reactions, we need to discuss the nature of solutions in which water is the dissolving medium, or *solvent*. These solutions are called **aqueous solutions.** In this chapter we will study the nature of materials after they are dissolved in water and various types of reactions that occur among these substances. You will see that the procedures developed in Chapter 3 to deal with chemical reactions work very well for reactions that take place in aqueous solutions. To understand the types of reactions that occur in aqueous solutions, we must first explore the types of species present. This requires an understanding of the nature of water.

4.1 Water, the Common Solvent

Water is one of the most important substances on earth. It is, of course, crucial for sustaining the reactions that keep us alive, but it also affects our lives in many indirect ways. Water helps moderate the earth's temperature; it cools automobile engines, nuclear power plants, and many industrial processes; it provides a means of transportation on the earth's surface and a medium for the growth of a myriad of creatures we use as food; and much more.

One of the most valuable functions of water involves its ability to dissolve many different substances. For example, salt "disappears" when you sprinkle it into the water used to cook vegetables, as does sugar when you add it to your iced tea. In each case the disappearing substance is obviously still present—you can taste it. What happens when a solid dissolves? To understand this process, we need to consider the nature of water. Liquid water consists of a collection of H_2O molecules. An individual H_2O molecule is "bent" or V-shaped, with an H—O—H angle of about 105°:

H 105° H
O

The O—H bonds in the water molecule are covalent bonds formed by electron sharing between the oxygen and hydrogen atoms. However, the electrons of the bond are not shared equally between these atoms. For reasons we will discuss in later chapters, oxygen has a greater attraction for electrons than does hydrogen. If the electrons were shared equally between the two atoms, both would be electrically neutral because, on average, the number of electrons around each would equal the number of protons in that nucleus. However, because the oxygen atom has a greater attraction for electrons, the shared electrons tend to spend more time close to the oxygen than to either of the hydro-

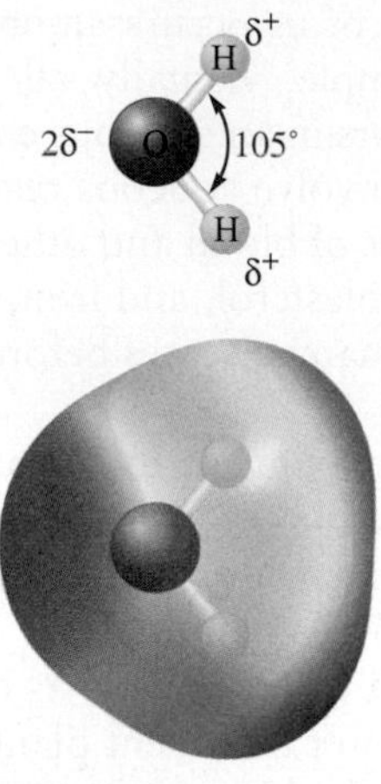

Figure 4.1
(top) The water molecule is polar. (bottom) The electrons in the water molecule are not shared equally between hydrogen and oxygen. This can be represented with a colored map of electrostatic potential. Red areas indicate high electron density, and blue areas represent low electron density. The colors in between indicate varying degrees of electron density.

gens. Thus the oxygen atom gains a slight excess of negative charge, and the hydrogen atoms become slightly positive. This is shown in Fig. 4.1, where δ (delta) indicates a *partial* charge *(less than one unit of charge)*. Because of this unequal charge distribution, water is said to be a **polar molecule.** It is this polarity that gives water its great ability to dissolve compounds.

A schematic of an ionic solid dissolving in water is shown in Fig. 4.2. Note that the "positive ends" of the water molecules are attracted to the negatively charged anions and that the "negative ends" are attracted to the positively charged cations. This process is called **hydration.** The hydration of its ions tends to cause a salt to "fall apart" in the water, or to dissolve. The strong forces present among the positive and negative ions of the solid are replaced by strong water–ion interactions.

It is very important to recognize that when ionic substances (salts) dissolve in water, they break up into the *individual* cations and anions. For instance, when ammonium nitrate (NH_4NO_3) dissolves in water, the resulting solution contains NH_4^+ and NO_3^- ions floating around independently. This process can be represented as

$$NH_4NO_3(s) \xrightarrow{H_2O(l)} NH_4^+(aq) + NO_3^-(aq)$$

where (aq) indicates that the ions are hydrated by unspecified numbers of water molecules.

The solubility of ionic substances in water varies greatly. For example, sodium chloride is quite soluble in water, whereas silver chloride (contains Ag^+ and Cl^- ions) is only very slightly soluble. The differences in the solubilities of ionic compounds in water typically depend on the relative affinities of the ions for each other (these forces hold the solid together) and the affinities of the ions for water molecules [which cause the solid to disperse (dissolve) in water]. Solubility is a complex issue that we will explore in much more detail in Chapter 17. However, the most important thing to remember at this point is that when an ionic solid does dissolve in water, the ions are dispersed and are assumed to move around independently.

Figure 4.2
Polar water molecules interact with the positive and negative ions of a salt, assisting with the dissolving process.

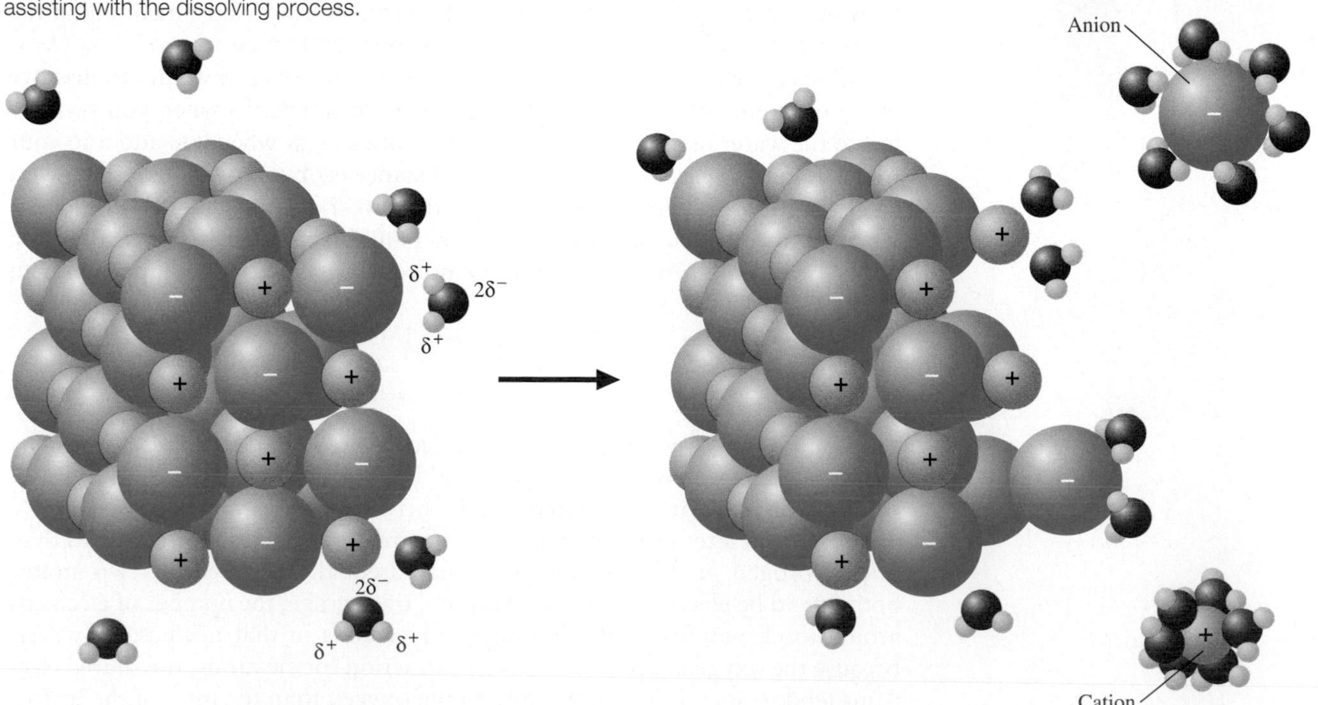

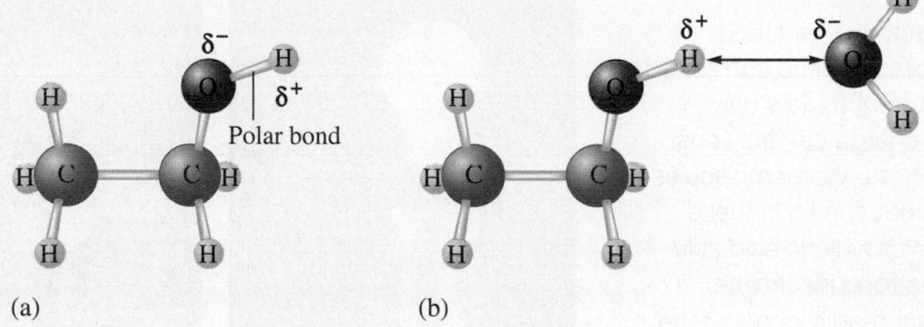

Figure 4.3
(a) The ethanol molecule contains a polar O—H bond similar to those in the water molecule. (b) The polar water molecule interacts strongly with the polar O—H bond in ethanol. This is a case of "like dissolving like."

Water also dissolves many nonionic substances. Ethanol (C_2H_5OH), for example, is very soluble in water. Wine, beer, and mixed drinks are aqueous solutions of alcohol and other substances. Why is ethanol so soluble in water? The answer lies in the structure of the alcohol molecule, which is shown in Fig. 4.3(a). The molecule contains a polar O—H bond like those in water, which makes it very compatible with water. The interaction of water with ethanol is represented in Fig. 4.3(b).

Many substances do not dissolve in water. Pure water will not, for example, dissolve animal fat because fat molecules are nonpolar and do not interact effectively with polar water molecules. In general, polar and ionic substances are expected to be more soluble in water than nonpolar substances. "Like dissolves like" is a useful rule for predicting solubility. We will explore the basis for this generalization when we discuss the details of solution formation in Chapter 17.

4.2 The Nature of Aqueous Solutions: Strong and Weak Electrolytes

Recall that a solution is a homogeneous mixture. It is the same throughout (the first sip of a cup of coffee is the same as the last), but its composition can be varied by changing the amount of dissolved substances (one can make weak or strong coffee). In this section we will consider what happens when a substance, the **solute,** is dissolved in liquid water, the **solvent.**

One useful property for characterizing a solution is its **electrical conductivity,** its ability to conduct an electric current. This characteristic can be checked conveniently by using an apparatus like the one shown in Fig. 4.4. If the solution in the container conducts electricity, the bulb lights. Some solutions conduct current very efficiently, and the bulb shines very brightly; these solutions contain **strong electrolytes.** Other solutions conduct only a small current, and the bulb glows dimly; these solutions contain **weak electrolytes.** Some solutions permit no current to flow, and the bulb remains unlit; these solutions contain **nonelectrolytes.**

The basis for the conductivity properties of solutions was first correctly identified by Svante Arrhenius, then a Swedish graduate student in physics, who carried out research on the nature of solutions at the University of Uppsala in the early 1880s. Arrhenius came to believe that the conductivity of solutions arose from the presence of ions, an idea that was at first scorned by the majority of the scientific establishment. However, in the late 1890s when atoms were found to contain charged particles, the ionic theory suddenly made sense and became widely accepted.

As Arrhenius postulated, the extent to which a solution can conduct an electric current depends directly on the number of ions present. Some materials, such as sodium chloride, readily produce ions in aqueous solution and are thus strong electrolytes. Other substances, such as acetic acid, produce relatively few ions when dissolved in water and are weak electrolytes. A third class

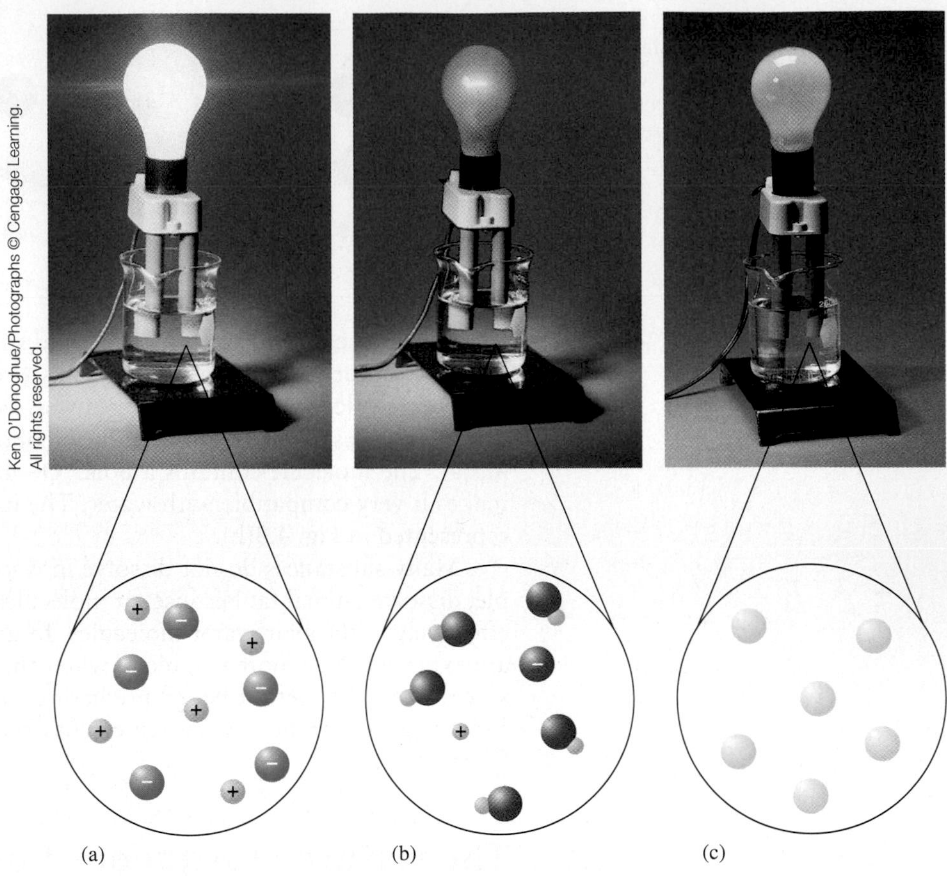

Figure 4.4
Electrical conductivity of aqueous solutions. The circuit will be completed and will allow current to flow only when there are charge carriers (ions) in the solution. *Note:* Water molecules are present but not shown in these pictures. (a) A hydrochloric acid solution, which is a strong electrolyte, contains ions that readily conduct the current and give a brightly lit bulb. (b) An acetic acid solution, which is a weak electrolyte, contains only a few ions and does not conduct as much current as a strong electrolyte. The bulb is only dimly lit. (c) A sucrose solution, which is a nonelectrolyte, contains no ions and does not conduct a current. The bulb remains unlit.

of materials, such as sugar, form virtually no ions when dissolved in water and are nonelectrolytes.

Strong Electrolytes

We will consider several classes of strong electrolytes: (1) soluble salts, (2) strong acids, and (3) strong bases.

As shown in Fig. 4.2, a salt consists of an array of cations and anions that separate and become hydrated when the salt dissolves. **Solubility** is usually measured in terms of the mass (grams) of solute that dissolves per given volume of solvent *or* in terms of the number of moles of solute that dissolve in a given volume of solution. Some salts, such as NaCl, KCl, and NH_4Cl, are very soluble in water. For example, approximately 357 grams of NaCl will dissolve in a liter of water at 25°C. On the other hand, many salts are only very slightly soluble in water; for example, silver chloride (AgCl) dissolves in water only to a slight extent (approximately 2×10^{-3} g/L at 25°C). We will consider only soluble salts at this point.

One of Arrhenius's most important discoveries concerned the nature of **acids.** Acidic behavior was first associated with the sour taste of citrus fruits. In fact, the word *acid* comes directly from the Latin word *acidus,* meaning "sour." The *mineral acids* sulfuric acid (H_2SO_4) and nitric acid (HNO_3), so named because they were originally obtained by the treatment of minerals, were discovered around 1300.

Acids were known to exist for hundreds of years before the time of Arrhenius, but no one had recognized their essential nature. In his studies of solutions, Arrhenius found that when the substances HCl, HNO_3, and H_2SO_4 were dissolved in water, they behaved as strong electrolytes. He postulated that this was the result of ionization reactions in water, for example:

$$HCl \xrightarrow{H_2O} H^+(aq) + Cl^-(aq)$$

$$HNO_3 \xrightarrow{H_2O} H^+(aq) + NO_3^-(aq)$$

$$H_2SO_4 \xrightarrow{H_2O} H^+(aq) + HSO_4^-(aq)$$

The Arrhenius definition of an acid: a substance that produces H^+ ions in solution.

Thus Arrhenius proposed that an *acid is a substance that produces H^+ ions (protons) when it is dissolved in water.*

Perchloric acid, $HClO_4(aq)$, is another strong acid.

Studies of conductivity show that when HCl, HNO_3, and H_2SO_4 are placed in water, *virtually every molecule* dissociates to give ions. These substances are strong electrolytes and are thus called **strong acids.** All three are very important chemicals, and much more will be said about them as we proceed. However, at this point the following facts are important:

Hydrochloric acid, nitric acid, and sulfuric acid are aqueous solutions and should be written in chemical equations as HCl(*aq*), HNO_3(*aq*), and H_2SO_4(*aq*), respectively, although they often appear without the (*aq*) symbol.

A strong acid is one that completely dissociates into its ions. Thus, if 100 molecules of HCl are dissolved in water, 100 H^+ ions and 100 Cl^- ions are produced. Virtually no HCl molecules exist in aqueous solution (see Fig. 4.5).

Sulfuric acid is a special case. The formula H_2SO_4 indicates that this acid can produce two H^+ ions per molecule when dissolved in water. However, only the first H^+ ion is completely dissociated. The second H^+ ion can be pulled off under certain conditions, which we will discuss later. Thus a solution of H_2SO_4 dissolved in water contains mostly H^+ ions and HSO_4^- ions.

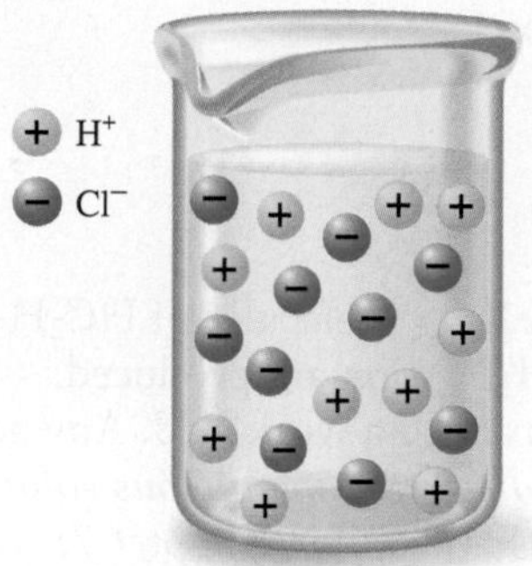

Figure 4.5
HCl(*aq*) is completely ionized.

Strong electrolytes dissociate completely in aqueous solution.

Another important class of strong electrolytes is the **strong bases,** soluble compounds containing the *hydroxide ion* (OH^-) that completely dissociate when dissolved in water. Solutions containing bases have a bitter taste and a slippery feel. The most common basic solutions are those produced when solid sodium hydroxide (NaOH) or potassium hydroxide (KOH) is dissolved in water to produce ions, as follows (Fig. 4.6):

$$NaOH(s) \xrightarrow{H_2O} Na^+(aq) + OH^-(aq)$$

$$KOH(s) \xrightarrow{H_2O} K^+(aq) + OH^-(aq)$$

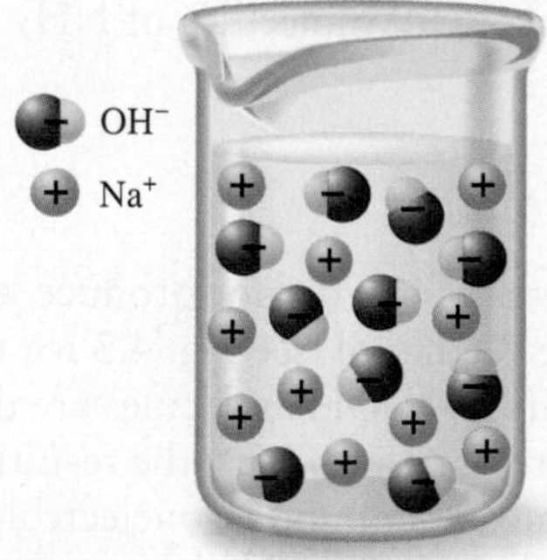

Figure 4.6
An aqueous solution of sodium hydroxide.

Weak Electrolytes

Weak electrolytes are substances that produce relatively few ions when dissolved in water, as shown in Fig. 4.4(b). The most common weak electrolytes are weak acids and weak bases.

The main acidic component of vinegar is acetic acid ($HC_2H_3O_2$). The formula is written to indicate that acetic acid has two chemically distinct types of hydrogen atoms. Formulas for acids are often written with the acidic hydrogen atom or atoms (any that will produce H^+ ions in solution) listed first. If any nonacidic hydrogens are present, they are written later in the formula. Thus the formula $HC_2H_3O_2$ indicates one acidic and three nonacidic hydrogen atoms. The dissociation reaction for acetic acid in water can be written as follows:

$$HC_2H_3O_2(aq) \xrightarrow{H_2O} H^+(aq) + C_2H_3O_2^-(aq)$$

Acetic acid is very different from the strong acids in that only about 1% of its molecules dissociate in aqueous solution (Fig. 4.7). Thus, when 100 molecules

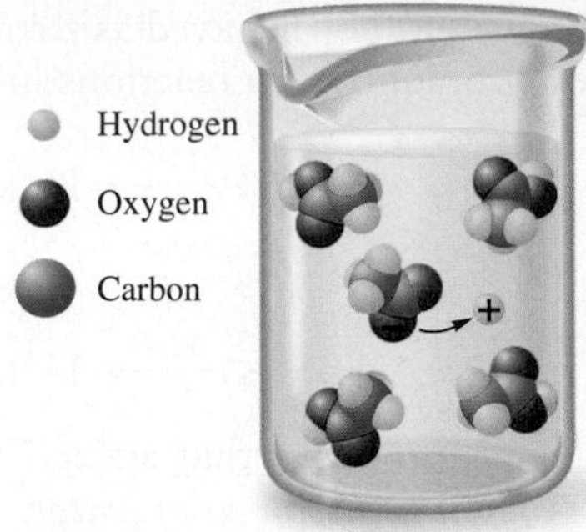

Figure 4.7
Acetic acid ($HC_2H_3O_2$) exists in water mostly as undissociated molecules. Only a small percentage of the molecules are ionized.

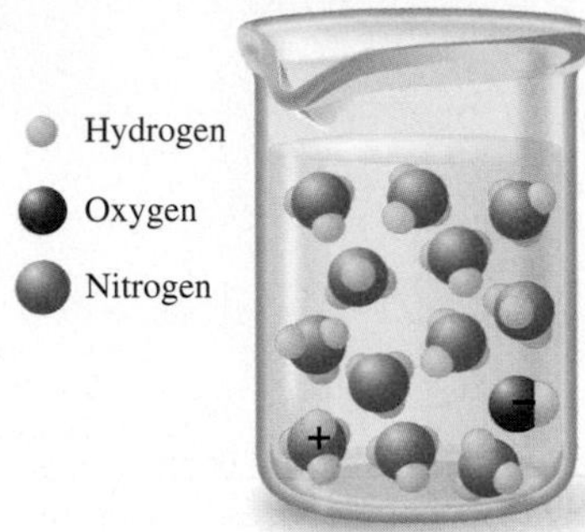

Figure 4.8
The reaction of NH_3 in water. The NH_4^+ and OH^- ions are formed by reaction of an NH_3 molecule with an H_2O molecule.

of $HC_2H_3O_2$ are dissolved in water, approximately 99 molecules of $HC_2H_3O_2$ remain intact, and only one H^+ ion and one $C_2H_3O_2^-$ ion are produced.

Weak electrolytes dissociate only to a small extent in aqueous solution.

Because acetic acid is a weak electrolyte, it is called a **weak acid.** Any acid, such as acetic acid, that *dissociates only to a slight extent in aqueous solution is called a weak acid.* We will explore weak acids in detail in Chapter 7.

The most common **weak base** is ammonia (NH_3). When ammonia is dissolved in water, it reacts as follows:

$$NH_3(aq) + H_2O(l) \longrightarrow NH_4^+(aq) + OH^-(aq)$$

The solution is *basic* since OH^- ions are produced. Ammonia is called a **weak base** because *the resulting solution is a weak electrolyte*—very few ions are present (Fig. 4.8). In fact, for every 100 molecules of NH_3 that are dissolved, only one NH_4^+ ion and one OH^- ion are produced; 99 molecules of NH_3 remain unreacted.

Nonelectrolytes

Nonelectrolytes are substances that dissolve in water but do not produce any ions [Fig. 4.4(c)]. An example of a nonelectrolyte is ethanol (see Fig. 4.3 for the structural formula). When ethanol dissolves, entire C_2H_5OH molecules are dispersed in the water. Since the molecules do not break up into ions, the resulting solution does not conduct an electric current. Another common nonelectrolyte is table sugar (sucrose, $C_{12}H_{22}O_{11}$), which is very soluble in water but produces no ions when it dissolves.

4.3 The Composition of Solutions

Chemical reactions often take place when two solutions are mixed. To perform stoichiometric calculations in such cases, we must know two things: (1) the *nature of the reaction,* which depends on the exact forms the chemicals take when dissolved, and (2) the *amounts of chemicals* present in the solutions, that is, the composition of each solution.

The composition of a solution can be described in many different ways, as we will see in Chapter 17. At this point we will consider only the most commonly used expression of concentration, **molarity** (M), which is defined as *moles of solute per volume of solution (expressed in liters):*

$$M = \text{molarity} = \frac{\text{moles of solute}}{\text{liters of solution}}$$

A solution that is 1.0 molar (written as 1.0 M) contains 1.0 mole of solute per liter of solution.

OWL INTERACTIVE EXAMPLE 4.1

Calculate the molarity of a solution prepared by bubbling 1.56 g of gaseous HCl into enough water to make 26.8 mL of solution.

Solution

- What are we trying to solve?

We are asked to solve for the concentration of a solution in units of molarity.

- What does this mean?

$$\text{Molarity} = \frac{\text{moles of solute}}{\text{liters of solution}}$$

We are given the volume of the solution in milliliters, and we can convert this to liters:

$$26.8 \text{ mL} \times \frac{1 \text{ L}}{1000 \text{ mL}} = 2.68 \times 10^{-2} \text{ L}$$

Thus we have

$$\text{Molarity} = \frac{\text{moles of solute}}{2.68 \times 10^{-2} \text{ L}}$$

To calculate the molarity, we need to determine the moles of solute, so we change the original question to *"How many moles of HCl are in 1.56 g?"* Recall from Chapter 3 that to do this we use the molar mass as follows:

$$1.56 \text{ g HCl} \times \frac{1 \text{ mol HCl}}{36.5 \text{ g HCl}} = 4.27 \times 10^{-2} \text{ mol HCl}$$

We can now determine the concentration as follows:

$$\text{Molarity} = \frac{4.27 \times 10^{-2} \text{ mol HCl}}{2.68 \times 10^{-2} \text{ L solution}} = 1.59 \; M \text{ HCl}$$

Note that the description of a solution's composition may not accurately reflect the true chemical nature of the solution. Solution concentration is always given in terms of the form of the solute *before* it dissolves. For example, consider 1.0 liter of a solution labeled as 1.0 M NaCl. This solution was prepared by dissolving 1.0 mole of solid NaCl in enough water to make 1.0 liter of solution. The label 1.0 M does not mean that the solution contains 1.0 mole of NaCl units. Actually, the solution contains 1.0 mole of Na^+ ions and 1.0 mole of Cl^- ions.

Often we need to determine the number of moles of solute present in a given volume of a solution of known molarity. The procedure for doing so is easily derived from the definition of molarity:

$$M = \frac{\text{moles of solute}}{\text{liters of solution}}$$

$$\text{Liters of solution} \times \text{molarity} = \text{liters of solution} \times \frac{\text{moles of solute}}{\text{liters of solution}}$$

$$= \text{moles of solute}$$

OWL INTERACTIVE EXAMPLE 4.2

Calculate the number of moles of Cl^- ions in 1.75 L of 1.0×10^{-3} M $AlCl_3$.

Solution

■ What are we trying to solve?

We are looking for the number of moles of Cl^- ions, and we are given the volume of the solution and the concentration in molarity, along with the formula for the ionic compound.

We know that molarity is a ratio of moles of solute to liters of solution, or

$$M = \frac{\text{moles of solute}}{\text{liters of solution}}$$

Thus

$$\text{Moles} = M \times \text{volume}$$

This would give us the moles of $AlCl_3$ that would dissolve, but we are looking for the moles of Cl^- ions in solution.

When solid $AlCl_3$ dissolves, it produces ions as follows:

$$AlCl_3(s) \xrightarrow{H_2O} Al^{3+}(aq) + 3Cl^-(aq)$$

Thus a 1.0×10^{-3} M $AlCl_3$ solution contains 1.0×10^{-3} M Al^{3+} ions and 3.0×10^{-3} M Cl^- ions.

To calculate the moles of Cl^- ions in 1.75 L of the 1.0×10^{-3} M $AlCl_3$ solution, we must multiply the volume by the molarity:

$$1.75 \text{ L solution} \times 3.0 \times 10^{-3} \text{ } M \text{ Cl}^-$$

$$= 1.75 \text{ L solution} \times \frac{3.0 \times 10^{-3} \text{ mol Cl}^-}{\text{L solution}}$$

$$= 5.3 \times 10^{-3} \text{ mol Cl}^-$$

OWL INTERACTIVE EXAMPLE 4.3

Typical blood serum is about 0.14 M NaCl. What volume of blood contains 1.0 mg of NaCl?

Solution

■ What are we trying to solve?

We want to determine the volume of blood containing 1.0 mg of NaCl, and we know the concentration of NaCl in molarity. Thus we are looking for a conversion between volume and mass.

We know that molarity is a ratio of moles of solute to liters of solution, so we have a conversion between volume and moles:

$$M = \frac{\text{moles of solute}}{\text{liters of solution}}$$

Thus

$$\text{Volume} = \frac{\text{moles of solute}}{M}$$

We also have a conversion between mass and moles (molar mass). Thus we can convert mass to moles (using molar mass) and moles to volume (using molarity):

We must first determine the number of moles represented by 1.0 mg of NaCl:

$$1.0 \text{ mg NaCl} \times \frac{1 \text{ g NaCl}}{1000 \text{ mg NaCl}} \times \frac{1 \text{ mol NaCl}}{58.45 \text{ g NaCl}} = 1.7 \times 10^{-5} \text{ mol NaCl}$$

Next, we must determine what volume of 0.14 M NaCl solution contains 1.7×10^{-5} mole of NaCl. There is some volume *(V)* that when multiplied by the molarity of this solution yields 1.7×10^{-5} mole of NaCl. That is,

$$V \times \frac{0.14 \text{ mol NaCl}}{\text{L solution}} = 1.7 \times 10^{-5} \text{ mol NaCl}$$

Solving for the volume gives

$$V = \frac{1.7 \times 10^{-5} \text{ mol NaCl}}{\frac{0.14 \text{ mol NaCl}}{\text{L solution}}} = 1.2 \times 10^{-4} \text{ L solution}$$

Thus 0.12 mL of blood contains 1.7×10^{-5} mole of NaCl, or 1.0 mg of NaCl.

A **standard solution** is a solution *whose concentration is accurately known.* Standard solutions, often used in chemical analysis, can be prepared as shown in Fig. 4.9 and in Example 4.4.

OWL INTERACTIVE EXAMPLE 4.4

To analyze the alcohol content of a certain wine, a chemist needs 1.00 L of an aqueous 0.200 M $K_2Cr_2O_7$ (potassium dichromate) solution. How much solid $K_2Cr_2O_7$ must be weighed out to make this solution?

Solution

■ What are we trying to solve?

We are asked to determine the mass of K_2CrO_7 solute required to make 1.00 L of a 0.200 M solution. Knowing that molarity is a ratio of moles of solute to

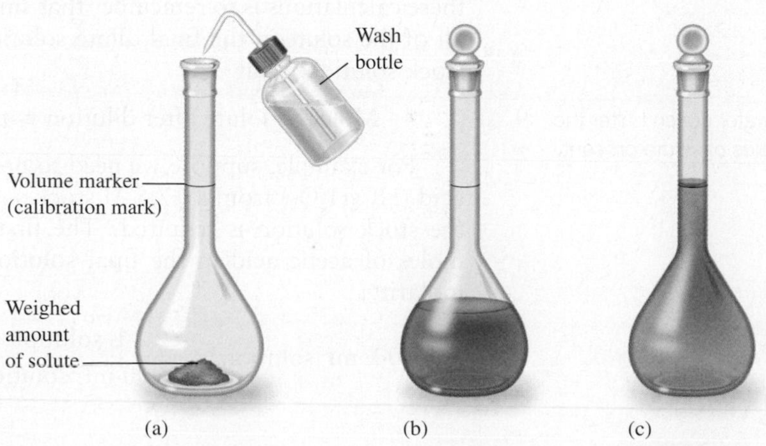

Figure 4.9
Steps involved in the preparation of a standard aqueous solution. (a) Put a weighed amount of a substance (the solute) into the volumetric flask, and add a small quantity of water. (b) Dissolve the solid in the water by gently swirling the flask *(with the stopper in place).* (c) Add more water (with gentle swirling) until the level of the solution just reaches the mark etched on the neck of the flask. Then mix the solution thoroughly by inverting the flask several times.

liters of solution, we can use molarity and volume to determine the moles of solute.

$$M = \frac{\text{moles of solute}}{\text{liters of solution}}$$

Thus

$$\text{Moles} = M \times \text{volume}$$

However, we are asked for mass, so we will need to convert the moles to a mass, and we can do this using the molar mass of the solute.

First, determine the moles of $K_2Cr_2O_7$ required:

$$1.00 \text{ L solution} \times \frac{0.200 \text{ mol } K_2Cr_2O_7}{\text{L solution}} = 0.200 \text{ mol } K_2Cr_2O_7$$

This amount can be converted to grams by using the molar mass of $K_2Cr_2O_7$:

$$0.200 \text{ mol } K_2Cr_2O_7 \times \frac{294.2 \text{ g } K_2Cr_2O_7}{\text{mol } K_2Cr_2O_7} = 58.8 \text{ g } K_2Cr_2O_7$$

Thus, to make 1.00 L of 0.200 M $K_2Cr_2O_7$, the chemist must weigh out 58.8 g of $K_2Cr_2O_7$, put it in a 1.00-L volumetric flask, and add water up to the mark on the flask.

Note: In looking back at the solutions to Examples 4.1 through 4.4, you should notice that the problems are solved similarly. For example, in all cases we need to know what molarity means and how to manipulate the formula for concentration. The problems vary in the details. In Examples 4.1, 4.3, and 4.4, we need to use molar mass = mass/mol. In Example 4.2, we need to understand how an ionic solid dissolves. As discussed in Section 3.4, we need to ask questions that allow the problem to guide us, but we also need a bank of knowledge to draw from.

Dilution

To save time and space in the laboratory, routinely used solutions are often purchased or prepared in concentrated form (these are called *stock solutions*). In a process called **dilution,** water is then added to achieve the molarity desired for a particular solution. For example, the common acids are purchased as concentrated solutions and diluted as needed. A typical dilution calculation involves determining how much water must be added to an amount of stock solution to achieve a solution of the desired concentration. The key to doing these calculations is to remember that since only water is added in the dilution, all of the solute in the final dilute solution must come from the concentrated stock solution. That is,

Dilution with water doesn't alter the number of moles of solute present.

$$\text{Moles of solute after dilution} = \text{moles of solute before dilution}$$

For example, suppose we need to prepare 500. milliliters of 1.00 M acetic acid ($HC_2H_3O_2$) from a 17.5 M stock solution of acetic acid. What volume of the stock solution is required? The first step is to determine the number of moles of acetic acid in the final solution by multiplying the volume by the molarity:

$$500. \text{ mL solution} \times \frac{1 \text{ L solution}}{1000 \text{ mL solution}} \times \frac{1.00 \text{ mol } HC_2H_3O_2}{\text{L solution}}$$
$$= 0.500 \text{ mol } HC_2H_3O_2$$

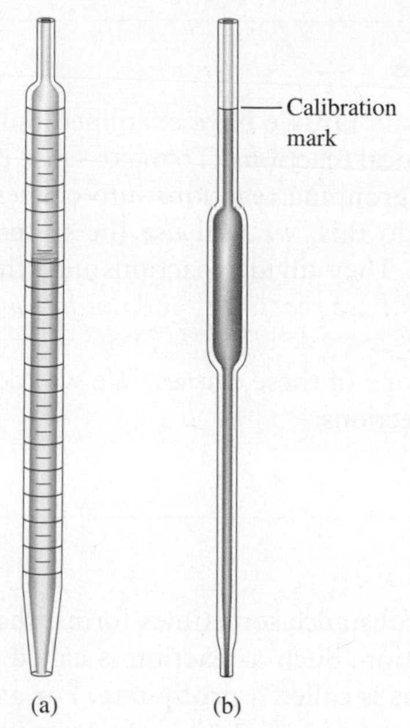

Figure 4.10
(a) A measuring pipet is graduated and can be used to measure various volumes of liquid accurately. (b) A volumetric pipet is designed to measure *one* volume accurately. When filled to the calibration mark, it delivers the volume indicated on the pipet.

Thus we need to use a volume of 17.5 *M* acetic acid that contains 0.500 mole of $HC_2H_3O_2$. That is,

$$V \times \frac{17.5 \text{ mol } HC_2H_3O_2}{\text{L solution}} = 0.500 \text{ mol } HC_2H_3O_2$$

Solving for *V* gives

$$V = \frac{0.500 \text{ mol } HC_2H_3O_2}{\dfrac{17.5 \text{ mol } HC_2H_3O_2}{\text{L solution}}} = 0.0286 \text{ L, or } 28.6 \text{ mL solution}$$

Thus, to make 500. milliliters of a 1.00 *M* acetic acid solution, we can take 28.6 milliliters of 17.5 *M* acetic acid and dilute it to a total volume of 500. milliliters.

A dilution procedure typically involves two types of glassware: a pipet and a volumetric flask. A pipet is a device for accurately measuring and transferring a given volume of solution. There are two common types of pipets: *measuring pipets* and *volumetric pipets,* as shown in Fig. 4.10. Measuring pipets are used to measure out volumes for which a volumetric pipet is not available. For example, we would use a measuring pipet as shown in Fig. 4.11 to deliver 28.6 milliliters of 17.5 *M* acetic acid into a 500-milliliter volumetric flask and then add water to the mark to perform the dilution described above.

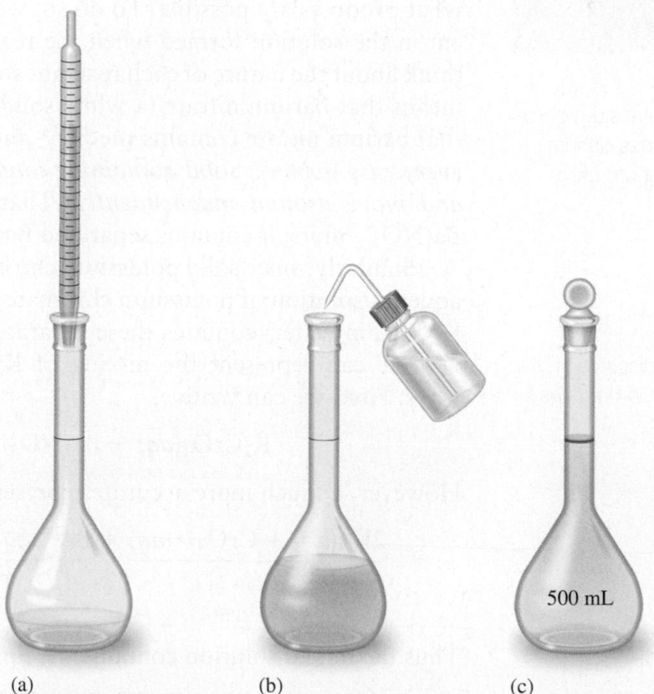

Figure 4.11
(a) A measuring pipet is used to transfer 28.7 mL of 17.4 *M* acetic acid solution to a volumetric flask. (b) Water is added to the flask to the calibration mark. (c) The resulting solution is 1.00 *M* acetic acid.

4.4 Types of Chemical Reactions

Types of Solution Reactions

Precipitation reactions
Acid–base reactions
Oxidation–reduction reactions

Although we have considered many reactions so far, we have examined only a tiny fraction of the millions of possible chemical reactions. To make sense of all these reactions, we need some system for grouping reactions into classes. Although there are many different ways to do this, we will use the system most commonly used by practicing chemists. They divide reactions into the following groups: *precipitation reactions, acid–base reactions,* and *oxidation–reduction reactions.*

Virtually all reactions can be placed into one of these classes. We will define and illustrate each type in the following sections.

4.5 Precipitation Reactions

Figure 4.12
When yellow aqueous potassium chromate is added to a colorless barium nitrate solution, yellow barium chromate precipitates.

When two solutions are mixed, an insoluble substance sometimes forms; that is, a solid forms and separates from the solution. Such a reaction is called a **precipitation reaction,** and the solid that forms is called a **precipitate.** For example, a precipitation reaction occurs when an aqueous solution of potassium chromate [$K_2CrO_4(aq)$], which is yellow, is mixed with a colorless aqueous solution containing barium nitrate [$Ba(NO_3)_2(aq)$]. As shown in Fig. 4.12, when these solutions are mixed, a yellow solid forms. What is the equation that describes this chemical change? To write the equation, we must know the identities of the reactants and products. The reactants have already been described: $K_2CrO_4(aq)$ and $Ba(NO_3)_2(aq)$. Is there some way we can predict the identities of the products? In particular, what is the yellow solid?

The best way to predict the identity of this solid is to think carefully about what products are possible. To do so, we need to know what species are present in the solution formed when the reactant solutions are mixed. First, let's think about the nature of each reactant solution. The designation $Ba(NO_3)_2(aq)$ means that barium nitrate (a white solid) has been dissolved in water. Notice that barium nitrate contains the Ba^{2+} and NO_3^- ions. *Remember: In virtually every case, when a solid containing ions dissolves in water, the ions separate and move around independently.* That is, $Ba(NO_3)_2(aq)$ does not contain $Ba(NO_3)_2$ units; it contains separated Ba^{2+} and NO_3^- ions (Fig. 4.13).

Similarly, since solid potassium chromate contains K^+ and CrO_4^{2-} ions, an aqueous solution of potassium chromate (which is prepared by dissolving solid K_2CrO_4 in water) contains these separated ions (Fig. 4.13).

When ionic compounds dissolve in water, the *resulting solution contains the separated ions.*

We can represent the mixing of $K_2CrO_4(aq)$ and $Ba(NO_3)_2(aq)$ in two ways. First, we can write

$$K_2CrO_4(aq) + Ba(NO_3)_2(aq) \longrightarrow \text{products}$$

However, a much more accurate representation is

$$\underbrace{2K^+(aq) + CrO_4^{2-}(aq)}_{\substack{\text{The ions in}\\ K_2CrO_4(aq)}} + \underbrace{Ba^{2+}(aq) + 2NO_3^-(aq)}_{\substack{\text{The ions in}\\ Ba(NO_3)_2(aq)}} \longrightarrow \text{products}$$

Thus the mixed solution contains the ions

$$K^+,\ CrO_4^{2-},\ Ba^{2+},\ \text{and}\ NO_3^-$$

How can some or all of these ions combine to form the yellow solid observed when the original solutions are mixed? This is not an easy question to answer. In fact, predicting the products of a chemical reaction is one of the hardest things a beginning chemistry student is asked to do. Even an experi-

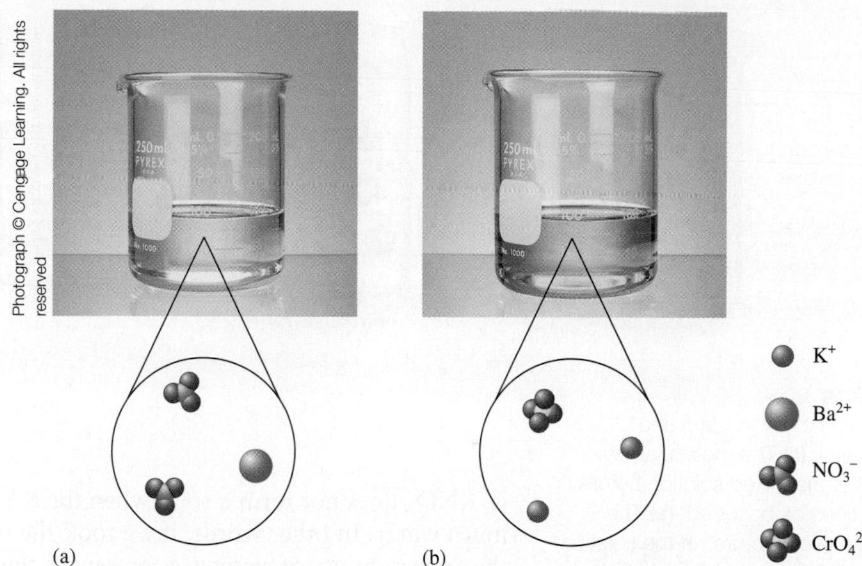

Figure 4.13
Reactant solutions: (a) $Ba(NO_3)_2(aq)$ and (b) $K_2CrO_4(aq)$.

enced chemist, when confronted with a new reaction, is often not sure what will happen. The chemist tries to think of the various possibilities, considers the likelihood of each possibility, and then makes a prediction (an educated guess). Only after identifying each product *experimentally* is the chemist sure what reaction has taken place. However, an educated guess is useful because it provides a place to start. It tells us what kinds of products we are most likely to find.

We already know some things that will help us predict the products:

1. When ions form a solid compound, the compound must have a zero net charge. Thus the products of this reaction must contain *both anions and cations*. For example, K^+ and Ba^{2+} could not combine to form the solid, nor could CrO_4^{2-} and NO_3^-.
2. Most ionic materials contain only two types of ions: one type of cation and one type of anion (for example, NaCl, KOH, Na_2SO_4, K_2CrO_4, $Co(NO_3)_2$, NH_4Cl, and Na_2CO_3).

The possible combinations of a given cation and a given anion from the list of ions K^+, CrO_4^{2-}, Ba^{2+}, and NO_3^- are

$$K_2CrO_4,\ KNO_3,\ BaCrO_4,\ \text{and}\ Ba(NO_3)_2$$

Which of these possibilities is most likely to represent the yellow solid? We know it's not K_2CrO_4 or $Ba(NO_3)_2$. They are the reactants. They were present (dissolved) in the separate solutions that were mixed. The only real possibilities for the solid that formed are

$$KNO_3 \quad \text{and} \quad BaCrO_4$$

To decide which of these possibilities most likely represents the yellow solid, we need more facts. An experienced chemist knows that the K^+ ion and the NO_3^- ion are both colorless. Thus, if the solid is KNO_3, it should be white, not yellow. On the other hand, the CrO_4^{2-} ion is yellow [note in Fig. 4.12 that $K_2CrO_4(aq)$ is yellow]. Thus the yellow solid is almost certainly $BaCrO_4$. Further tests show that this is the case.

So far we have determined that one product of the reaction between $K_2CrO_4(aq)$ and $Ba(NO_3)_2(aq)$ is $BaCrO_4(s)$, but what happened to the K^+ and NO_3^- ions? The answer is that these ions are left dissolved in the solution. That

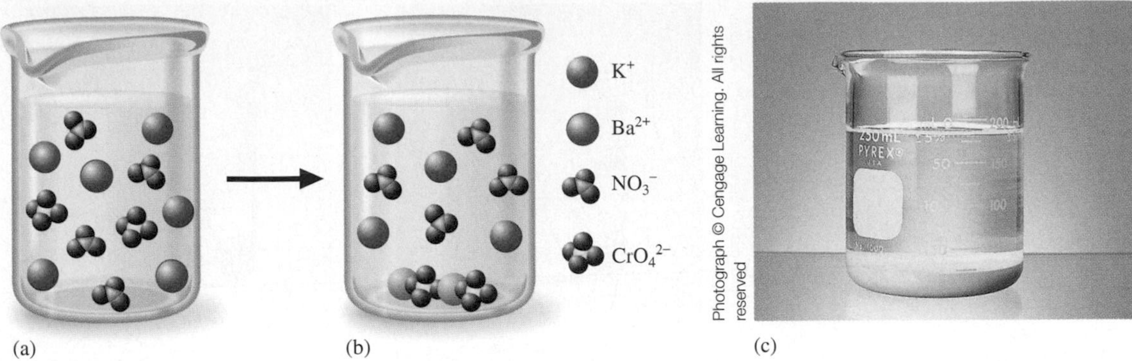

Figure 4.14
The reaction of $K_2CrO_4(aq)$ and $Ba(NO_3)_2(aq)$. (a) The molecular-level "picture" of the mixed solution before any reaction has occurred. (b) The molecular-level "picture" of the solution after the reaction has occurred to form $BaCrO_4(s)$. (c) A photo of the solution after the reaction has occurred, showing the solid $BaCrO_4$ on the bottom.

is, KNO_3 does not form a solid when the K^+ and NO_3^- ions are present in this much water. In other words, if we took the white solid, $KNO_3(s)$, and put it in the same quantity of water as is present in the mixed solution, it would dissolve. Thus, when we mix $K_2CrO_4(aq)$ and $Ba(NO_3)_2(aq)$, $BaCrO_4(s)$ forms, but KNO_3 is left behind in solution [we write it as $KNO_3(aq)$]. This reaction is illustrated in Fig. 4.14. Therefore, the equation for this precipitation reaction is

$$K_2CrO_4(aq) + Ba(NO_3)_2(aq) \longrightarrow BaCrO_4(s) + 2KNO_3(aq)$$

If we removed the solid $BaCrO_4$ by filtration and then evaporated the water, the white solid, KNO_3, would be obtained.

Now let's consider another example. When an aqueous solution of silver nitrate is added to an aqueous solution of potassium chloride, a white precipitate forms. We can represent what we know so far as

$$AgNO_3(aq) + KCl(aq) \longrightarrow \text{unknown white solid}$$

Doing chemistry requires both understanding ideas and remembering facts.

Remembering that when ionic substances dissolve in water, the ions separate, we can write

$$\underbrace{Ag^+, NO_3^-}_{\text{In silver nitrate solution}} + \underbrace{K^+, Cl^-}_{\text{In potassium chloride solution}} \longrightarrow \underbrace{Ag^+, NO_3^-, K^+, Cl^-}_{\text{Combined solution, before reaction}} \longrightarrow \text{white solid}$$

Since we know that the white solid must contain both positive and negative ions, the possible compounds that can be assembled from this collection of ions are

$$AgNO_3,\ KCl,\ AgCl,\ \text{and}\ KNO_3$$

Since $AgNO_3$ and KCl are the substances dissolved in the reactant solutions, we know that they do not represent the white solid product. The only real possibilities are

$$AgCl \quad \text{and} \quad KNO_3$$

From the example considered above, we know that KNO_3 is quite soluble in water. Thus solid KNO_3 will not form when the reactant solutions are mixed. The product must be $AgCl(s)$ (which can be proved by experiment). The equation for the reaction now can be written

$$AgNO_3(aq) + KCl(aq) \longrightarrow AgCl(s) + KNO_3(aq)$$

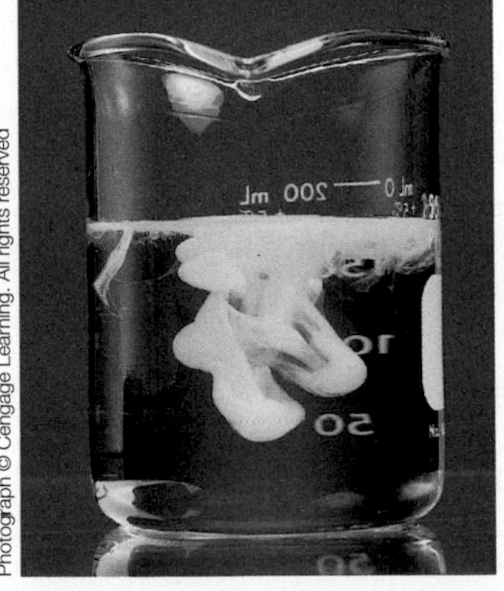

Figure 4.15
Precipitation of silver chloride by mixing solutions of silver nitrate and potassium chloride. The K^+ and NO_3^- ions remain in solution.

Figure 4.15 shows the result of mixing aqueous solutions of $AgNO_3$ and KCl. Figure 4.16 provides a visualization of the reaction.

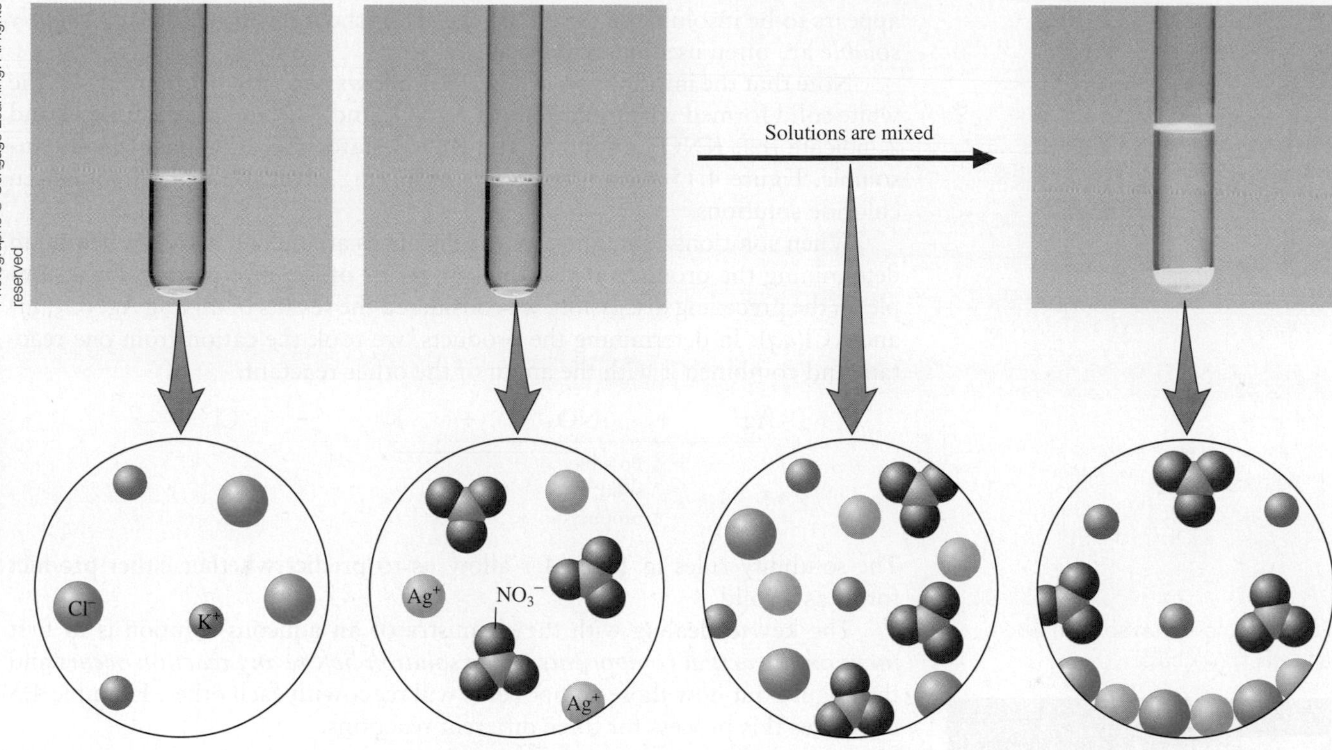

Figure 4.16
Photos and accompanying molecular-level representations illustrating the reaction of KCl(*aq*) with $AgNO_3$(*aq*) to form AgCl(*s*). Note that it is not possible to have a photo of the mixed solution before the reaction occurs because it is an imaginary step that we use to help visualize the reaction. Actually, the reaction occurs immediately when the two solutions are mixed.

Notice that to do these two examples, we had to know both concepts (solids always have a zero net charge) and facts (KNO_3 is very soluble in water, the CrO_4^{2-} is yellow, and so on).

Predicting the identity of the solid product in a precipitation reaction requires knowledge of the solubilities of common ionic substances. As an aid in predicting the products of precipitation reactions, some simple solubility rules are given in Table 4.1. You should memorize these rules.

The phrase "slightly soluble" used in the solubility rules in Table 4.1 means that the tiny amount of solid that dissolves is not noticeable. The solid

Table 4.1

Simple Rules for Solubility of Salts in Water

1. Most nitrate (NO_3^-) salts are soluble.
2. Most salts of Na^+, K^+, and NH_4^+ are soluble.
3. Most chloride salts are soluble. Notable exceptions are AgCl, $PbCl_2$, and Hg_2Cl_2.
4. Most sulfate salts are soluble. Notable exceptions are $BaSO_4$, $PbSO_4$, and $CaSO_4$.
5. Most hydroxide salts are only slightly soluble. The important soluble hydroxides are NaOH, KOH, and $Ca(OH)_2$ (marginally soluble).
6. Most sulfide (S^{2-}), carbonate (CO_3^{2-}), and phosphate (PO_4^{3-}) salts are only slightly soluble.

appears to be insoluble to the naked eye. Thus the terms *insoluble* and *slightly soluble* are often used interchangeably.

Note that the information in Table 4.1 allows us to predict that AgCl is the white solid formed when solutions of $AgNO_3$ and KCl are mixed; Rules 1 and 2 indicate that KNO_3 is soluble, and Rule 3 states that AgCl is (virtually) insoluble. Figure 4.15 shows the results of mixing silver nitrate and potassium chloride solutions.

When solutions containing ionic substances are mixed, it will be helpful in determining the products if you think in terms of *ion interchange*. For example, in the preceding discussion, we considered the results of mixing $AgNO_3(aq)$ and $KCl(aq)$. In determining the products, we took the cation from one reactant and combined it with the anion of the other reactant:

$$Ag^+ + NO_3^- + K^+ + Cl^- \longrightarrow$$

Possible solid products

The solubility rules in Table 4.1 allow us to predict whether either product forms as a solid.

Focus on the ions in solution before any reaction occurs.

The key to dealing with the chemistry of an aqueous solution is to first *focus on the actual components of the solution before any reaction occurs* and then figure out how those components will react with each other. Example 4.5 illustrates this process for three different reactions.

The precipitation of lead(II) sulfate by mixing solutions of lead(II) nitrate and sodium sulfate.

Solid $Fe(OH)_3$ forms when aqueous KOH and $Fe(NO_3)_3$ are mixed.

OWL INTERACTIVE EXAMPLE 4.5

Using the solubility rules in Table 4.1, predict what will happen when the following pairs of solutions are mixed.

a. $KNO_3(aq)$ and $BaCl_2(aq)$
b. $Na_2SO_4(aq)$ and $Pb(NO_3)_2(aq)$
c. $KOH(aq)$ and $Fe(NO_3)_3(aq)$

Solution

a. $KNO_3(aq)$ stands for an aqueous solution obtained by dissolving solid KNO_3 in water to form a solution containing the hydrated ions $K^+(aq)$ and $NO_3^-(aq)$. Likewise, $BaCl_2(aq)$ is a solution formed by dissolving solid $BaCl_2$ in water to produce $Ba^{2+}(aq)$ and $Cl^-(aq)$. When these two solutions are mixed, the resulting solution contains the ions K^+, NO_3^-, Ba^{2+}, and Cl^-. All will be hydrated, but (aq) is omitted for simplicity. To look for possible solid products, combine the cation from one reactant with the anion from the other:

$$K^+ + NO_3^- + Ba^{2+} + Cl^- \longrightarrow$$

Possible solid products

Note from Table 4.1 that the rules predict that both KCl and $Ba(NO_3)_2$ are soluble in water. Thus no precipitate will form when $KNO_3(aq)$ and $BaCl_2(aq)$ are mixed. All the ions will remain dissolved in the solution. No reaction occurs.

b. Using the same procedures as in part a, we find that the ions present in the combined solution before any reaction occurs are Na^+, SO_4^{2-}, Pb^{2+}, and NO_3^-. The possible salts that could form precipitates are

$$Na^+ + SO_4^{2-} + Pb^{2+} + NO_3^- \longrightarrow$$

The compound $NaNO_3$ is soluble, but $PbSO_4$ is insoluble (see Rule 4 in Table 4.1). When these solutions are mixed, $PbSO_4$ will precipitate from the solution. The balanced equation is

$$Na_2SO_4(aq) + Pb(NO_3)_2(aq) \longrightarrow PbSO_4(s) + 2NaNO_3(aq)$$

c. The combined solution (before any reaction occurs) contains the ions K^+, OH^-, Fe^{3+}, and NO_3^-. The salts that might precipitate are KNO_3 and $Fe(OH)_3$. The solubility rules in Table 4.1 indicate that both K^+ and NO_3^- salts are soluble. However, $Fe(OH)_3$ is only slightly soluble (Rule 5) and hence will precipitate. The balanced equation is

$$3KOH(aq) + Fe(NO_3)_3(aq) \longrightarrow Fe(OH)_3(s) + 3KNO_3(aq)$$

4.6 Describing Reactions in Solution

In this section we will consider the types of equations used to represent reactions in solution. For example, when we mix aqueous potassium chromate with aqueous barium nitrate, a reaction occurs to form a precipitate ($BaCrO_4$) and dissolved potassium nitrate. So far we have written the **molecular equation** for this reaction:

$$K_2CrO_4(aq) + Ba(NO_3)_2(aq) \longrightarrow BaCrO_4(s) + 2KNO_3(aq)$$

Although this equation shows the reactants and products of the reaction, it does not give a very clear picture of what actually occurs in solution. As we have seen, aqueous solutions of potassium chromate, barium nitrate, and potassium nitrate contain the individual ions, not molecules, as is implied by the molecular equation. Thus the **complete ionic equation**

$$2K^+(aq) + CrO_4^{2-}(aq) + Ba^{2+}(aq) + 2NO_3^-(aq) \longrightarrow BaCrO_4(s) + 2K^+(aq) + 2NO_3^-(aq)$$

A strong electrolyte is a substance that completely breaks apart into ions when dissolved in water.

better represents the actual forms of the reactants and products in solution. *In a complete ionic equation, all substances that are strong electrolytes are represented as ions.*

The complete ionic equation reveals that only some of the ions participate in the reaction. The K^+ and NO_3^- ions are present in solution both before and after the reaction. Ions such as these that do not participate directly in a reaction in solution are called **spectator ions.** The ions that participate in this reaction are the Ba^{2+} and CrO_4^{2-} ions, which combine to form solid $BaCrO_4$:

$$Ba^{2+}(aq) + CrO_4^{2-}(aq) \longrightarrow BaCrO_4(s)$$

Net ionic equations include only those components that undergo changes in the reaction.

This equation, called the **net ionic equation,** includes only those solution components directly involved in the reaction. Chemists usually write the net ionic equation for a reaction in solution because it gives the actual forms of the reactants and products and includes only the species that undergo a change.

EXAMPLE 4.6

For each of the following reactions, write the molecular equation, the complete ionic equation, and the net ionic equation.

a. Aqueous potassium chloride is added to aqueous silver nitrate to form a silver chloride precipitate plus aqueous potassium nitrate.

b. Aqueous potassium hydroxide is mixed with aqueous iron(III) nitrate to form a precipitate of iron(III) hydroxide and aqueous potassium nitrate.

Solution

a. *Molecular:*

$$KCl(aq) + AgNO_3(aq) \longrightarrow AgCl(s) + KNO_3(aq)$$

Complete ionic (remember that any ionic compound dissolved in water will be present as the separated ions):

$$\underset{\substack{\uparrow \\ \text{Spectator ion}}}{K^+(aq)} + Cl^-(aq) + Ag^+(aq) + \underset{\substack{\uparrow \\ \text{Spectator ion}}}{NO_3^-(aq)} \longrightarrow \underset{\substack{\uparrow \\ \text{Solid, not written as separate ions}}}{AgCl(s)} + \underset{\substack{\uparrow \\ \text{Spectator ion}}}{K^+(aq)} + \underset{\substack{\uparrow \\ \text{Spectator ion}}}{NO_3^-(aq)}$$

Net ionic: Canceling the spectator ions,

$$\cancel{K^+}(aq) + Cl^-(aq) + Ag^+(aq) + \cancel{NO_3^-}(aq) \longrightarrow AgCl(s) + \cancel{K^+}(aq) + \cancel{NO_3^-}(aq)$$

gives the following net ionic equation:

$$Cl^-(aq) + Ag^+(aq) \longrightarrow AgCl(s)$$

b. *Molecular:*

$$3KOH(aq) + Fe(NO_3)_3(aq) \longrightarrow Fe(OH)_3(s) + 3KNO_3(aq)$$

Complete ionic:

$$3K^+(aq) + 3OH^-(aq) + Fe^{3+}(aq) + 3NO_3^-(aq) \longrightarrow Fe(OH)_3(s) + 3K^+(aq) + 3NO_3^-(aq)$$

Net ionic:

$$3OH^-(aq) + Fe^{3+}(aq) \longrightarrow Fe(OH)_3(s)$$

Three Types of Equations Used to Describe Reactions in Solution

1. The *molecular equation* gives the overall reaction stoichiometry but not necessarily the actual forms of the reactants and products in solution.
2. The *complete ionic equation* represents as ions all reactants and products that are strong electrolytes.
3. The *net ionic equation* includes only those solution components undergoing a change. Spectator ions are not included.

4.7 Selective Precipitation

We can use the fact that salts have different solubilities to separate mixtures of ions. For example, suppose we have an aqueous solution containing the cations Ag^+, Ba^{2+}, and Fe^{3+}, and the anion NO_3^-. We want to separate the cations by precipitating them one at a time, a process called **selective precipitation.**

How can the separation of these cations be accomplished? We can perform some preliminary tests and observe the reactivity of each cation toward the anions Cl^-, SO_4^{2-}, and OH^-. For example, to test the reactivity of Ag^+ toward Cl^-, we can mix the $AgNO_3$ solution with aqueous KCl or NaCl. As we have

Chemical Analysis of Cockroaches

Chemical Insights

Cockroaches can be a big problem. Not only are these hardy pests unpleasant to live with, but they also consume significant quantities of the world's precious food and grain supplies. Because the many different species of cockroaches require different control measures, determining which species is causing a particular problem is important. Careful examination of a cockroach can reveal its species, but this process is very time-consuming. However, a new method of cockroach identification, based on gas chromatography, has been developed at the U.S. Department of Agriculture by D. A. Carlson and R. J. Brenner. In gas chromatography, the compounds to be separated are dispersed in a carrier gas that passes through a porous solid. Because different substances have differing tendencies to adhere to the solid, the components of the mixture travel at different rates through the system, causing them to spread out so that they can be separated and identified.

In the cockroach identification study, Carlson and Brenner found that the composition of the outer, waxy layer of a roach is distinct to the particular species. Thus, by dissolving this waxy coating and injecting it into the gas stream of a gas chromatograph, scientists can identify the cockroach unambiguously in less than half an hour. This technique is particularly useful for identifying hybrid Asian–German cockroaches, which have become a major problem for the food industry.

Although biologists might argue that the gas chromatographic method takes the fun and the challenge out of identifying cockroaches, this technique should lead to significant advances in the control of these insects.

seen, this produces a precipitate. When we carry out tests of this type using all the possible combinations, we obtain the results in Table 4.2.

After studying these results, we might proceed to separate the cations as follows:

Step 1

Add an aqueous solution of NaCl to the solution containing the Ag^+, Ba^{2+}, and Fe^{3+} ions. Solid AgCl will form and can be removed, leaving Ba^{2+} and Fe^{3+} ions in solution.

Table 4.2

Testing the Reactivity of the Cations Ag^+, Ba^{2+}, and Fe^{3+} with the Anions Cl^-, SO_4^{2-}, and OH^-

	Test Solution (anion)		
Cation	$NaCl(aq)$ (Cl^-)	$Na_2SO_4(aq)$ (SO_4^{2-})	$NaOH(aq)$ (OH^-)
Ag^+	White precipitate (AgCl)	No reaction	White precipitate that turns brown $\left(\underset{\text{White}}{AgOH} \longrightarrow \underset{\text{Brown}}{Ag_2O}\right)$
Ba^{2+}	No reaction	White precipitate ($BaSO_4$)	No reaction
Fe^{3+}	Yellow color but no solid	No reaction	Reddish brown precipitate [$Fe(OH)_3$]

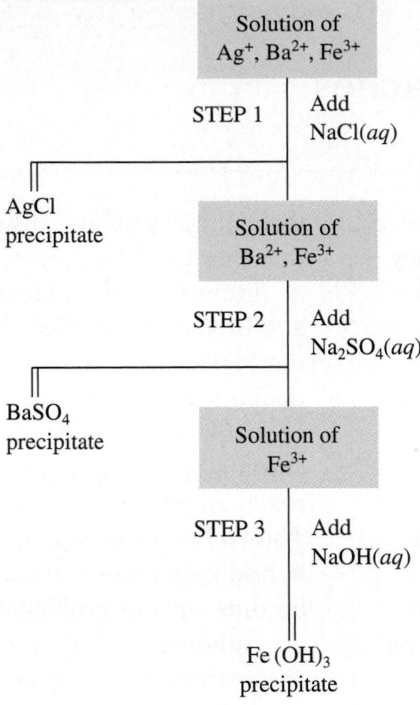

Figure 4.17
Selective precipitation of Ag^+, Ba^{2+}, and Fe^{3+} ions. In this schematic representation, a double line means that a solid forms, and a single line designates a solution.

Step 2

Add an aqueous solution of Na_2SO_4 to the solution containing the Ba^{2+} and Fe^{3+} ions. Solid $BaSO_4$ will form and can be removed, leaving only Fe^{3+} ions in solution.

Step 3

Add an aqueous solution of NaOH to the solution containing the Fe^{3+} ions. Solid $Fe(OH)_3$ will form and can be removed.
Steps 1 through 3 are represented schematically in Fig. 4.17.

Note that adding the anions in this order precipitates the cations one at a time and thus separates them. The process whereby mixtures of ions are separated and identified is called **qualitative analysis.** In this example the qualitative analysis was carried out by selective precipitation, but it can also be accomplished by using other separation techniques that will not be discussed here.

4.8 Stoichiometry of Precipitation Reactions

In Chapter 3 we covered the principles of chemical stoichiometry: the procedures for calculating quantities of reactants and products involved in a chemical reaction. Recall that in performing these calculations, we first convert all quantities to moles and then use the coefficients of the balanced equation to assemble the appropriate molar ratios. In cases in which reactants are mixed, we must determine which reactant is limiting, since the reactant that is consumed first will limit the amounts of products formed. *These same principles apply to reactions that take place in solutions.* However, two points about solution reactions need special emphasis. The first is that it is sometimes difficult to tell immediately which reaction will occur when two solutions are mixed. Usually we must think about the various possibilities and then decide what will happen. The first step in this process *always* should be to write down the species that are actually present in the solution, as we did in Section 4.5.

The second special point about solution reactions is that to obtain the moles of reactants, we must use the volume of a particular solution and its molarity. This procedure was covered in Section 4.3.

We will introduce stoichiometric calculations for reactions in solution in Example 4.7.

OWL INTERACTIVE EXAMPLE 4.7

Calculate the mass of solid NaCl that must be added to 1.50 L of a 0.100 *M* $AgNO_3$ solution to precipitate all the Ag^+ ions in the form of AgCl.

Solution

■ What are we trying to solve?

We want to determine the mass of NaCl to add to a given amount of $AgNO_3(aq)$ to precipitate all of the Ag^+ ions and form AgCl.

■ What does this mean?

We need to recognize that a reaction occurs to form AgCl; thus we will need a balanced equation. First, we must consider what happens chemically.

When added to the $AgNO_3$ solution (which contains Ag^+ and NO_3^- ions), the solid NaCl dissolves to yield Na^+ and Cl^- ions. Thus the mixed solution contains the ions

$$Ag^+, NO_3^-, Na^+, \text{and } Cl^-$$

When a solution of NaCl(*aq*) is added to a solution of $AgNO_3$, the white solid AgCl forms.

$NaNO_3$ is soluble and AgCl is insoluble (Table 4.1), so solid AgCl forms according to the following net ionic reaction:

$$Ag^+(aq) + Cl^-(aq) \longrightarrow AgCl(s)$$

In this case enough Cl^- ions must be added to react with all the Ag^+ ions present. Thus we must calculate the moles of Ag^+ ions present in 1.50 L of a 0.100 *M* $AgNO_3$ solution (remember that a 0.100 *M* $AgNO_3$ solution contains 0.100 *M* Ag^+ ions and 0.100 *M* NO_3^- ions):

$$1.50\text{ L} \times \frac{0.100\text{ mol } Ag^+}{\text{L}} = 0.150\text{ mol } Ag^+$$

Since Ag^+ and Cl^- react in a 1:1 ratio, 0.150 mole of Cl^- ions and thus 0.150 mole of NaCl are required. We calculate the mass of NaCl required as follows:

$$0.150\text{ mol NaCl} \times \frac{58.4\text{ g NaCl}}{\text{mol NaCl}} = 8.76\text{ g NaCl}$$

Notice from Example 4.7 that the procedures for doing stoichiometric calculations for solution reactions are very similar to those for other types of reactions. It is useful to think in terms of the following steps for reactions in solution.

Species present

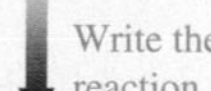

Write the reaction

Balanced net ionic equation

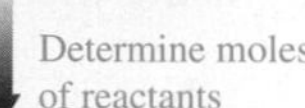

Determine moles of reactants

Identify limiting reactant

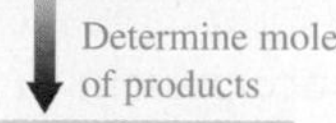

Determine moles of products

Check units of products

STEPS Solving a Stoichiometry Problem Involving Reactions in Solution

1 Identify the species present in the combined solution and determine which reaction occurs.
2 Write the balanced equation for the reaction.
3 Calculate the moles of reactants.
4 Determine which reactant is limiting.
5 Calculate the moles of product or products, as required.
6 Convert to grams or other units, as required.

OWL INTERACTIVE EXAMPLE 4.8

When aqueous solutions of Na_2SO_4 and $Pb(NO_3)_2$ are mixed, $PbSO_4$ precipitates. Calculate the mass of $PbSO_4$ formed when 1.25 L of 0.0500 *M* $Pb(NO_3)_2$ and 2.00 L of 0.0250 *M* Na_2SO_4 are mixed.

Solution

- What are we trying to solve?

We are asked to determine the mass of the precipitant given the amounts of the reactants.

This problem is complex in the sense that it incorporates much of what we have learned in Chapters 3 and 4. The list of what we need to know/do is extensive:

- We need to know what the solutions "look like" at a molecular level.
- We need to be able to write a net ionic equation.
- We must use volume and molarity to determine the number of moles of each reactant.
- Since we are given amounts of both reactants, we will have to determine which reactant is limiting.
- We need to convert moles to mass using molar mass.

However, by now each step of this solution should be familiar to you. Thus, although there are many parts to the solution to this problem, taking it one step at a time makes it less daunting.

When the aqueous solutions of Na_2SO_4 (containing Na^+ and SO_4^{2-} ions) and $Pb(NO_3)_2$ (containing Pb^{2+} and NO_3^- ions) are mixed, the mixed solution contains the ions Na^+, SO_4^{2-}, Pb^{2+}, and NO_3^-. Since $NaNO_3$ is soluble and $PbSO_4$ is insoluble (Table 4.1), solid $PbSO_4$ will form.

The net ionic equation is

$$Pb^{2+}(aq) + SO_4^{2-}(aq) \longrightarrow PbSO_4(s)$$

Since 0.0500 *M* $Pb(NO_3)_2$ contains 0.0500 *M* Pb^{2+} ions, we can calculate the moles of Pb^{2+} ions in 1.25 L of this solution as follows:

$$1.25 \text{ L} \times \frac{0.0500 \text{ mol } Pb^{2+}}{\text{L}} = 0.0625 \text{ mol } Pb^{2+}$$

The 0.0250 *M* Na_2SO_4 solution contains 0.0250 *M* SO_4^{2-} ions, and the number of moles of SO_4^{2-} ions in 2.00 L of this solution is

$$2.00 \text{ L} \times \frac{0.0250 \text{ mol } SO_4^{2-}}{\text{L}} = 0.0500 \text{ mol } SO_4^{2-}$$

Because Pb^{2+} and SO_4^{2-} react in a 1:1 ratio, the amount of SO_4^{2-} will be limiting.

Since the Pb^{2+} ions are present in excess, only 0.0500 mole of solid $PbSO_4$ will be formed. The mass of $PbSO_4$ formed can be calculated by using the molar mass of $PbSO_4$ (303.3):

$$0.0500 \text{ mol } PbSO_4 \times \frac{303.3 \text{ g } PbSO_4}{1 \text{ mol } PbSO_4} = 15.2 \text{ g } PbSO_4$$

One method for determining the amount of a given substance present in a solution is to form a precipitate that includes the substance. The precipitate is then filtered, dried, and weighed. This process, called gravimetric analysis, is illustrated in Example 4.9.

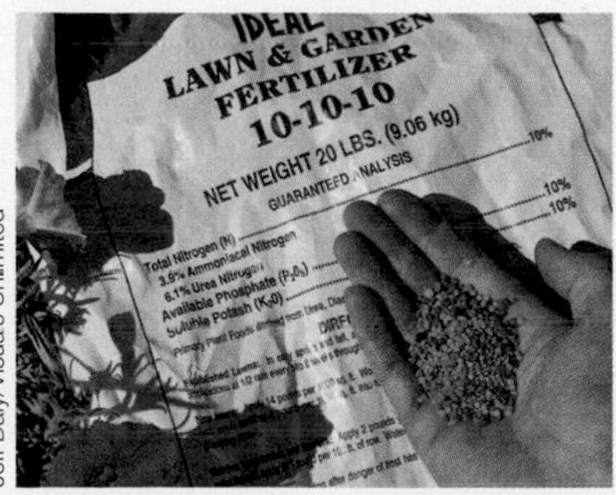

Jeff Daly/Visuals Unlimited

Phosphate rock is used in the manufacture of fertilizer.

EXAMPLE 4.9

Phosphorite, also called *phosphate rock,* is a mineral containing PO_4^{3-} and OH^- anions and Ca^{2+} cations. It is treated with sulfuric acid in the manufacture of phosphate fertilizers (see Chapter 3). A chemist finds the calcium content in an impure sample of phosphate rock by weighing out a 0.4367-g sample, dissolving it in water, and precipitating the Ca^{2+} ions as the insoluble hydrated salt* $CaC_2O_4 \cdot H_2O$ ($C_2O_4^{2-}$ is called the oxalate ion). After being filtered and dried (at a temperature of about 100°C so that the extraneous water is driven off but not the water of hydration), the $CaC_2O_4 \cdot H_2O$ precipitate weighed 0.2920 g. Calculate the mass percent of calcium in the sample of phosphate rock.

Solution

- What are we trying to solve?

We are asked to determine the mass percent of calcium in a sample of phosphate rock.

- What does this mean?

$$\text{Mass percent of calcium in the rock} = \frac{\text{mass of calcium}}{\text{mass of rock sample}} \times 100\%$$

We know that the sample of rock has a mass of 0.4367 g, so to determine the mass percent of calcium we change the question to *"What is the mass of calcium?"*

The gravimetric procedure can be summarized as follows:

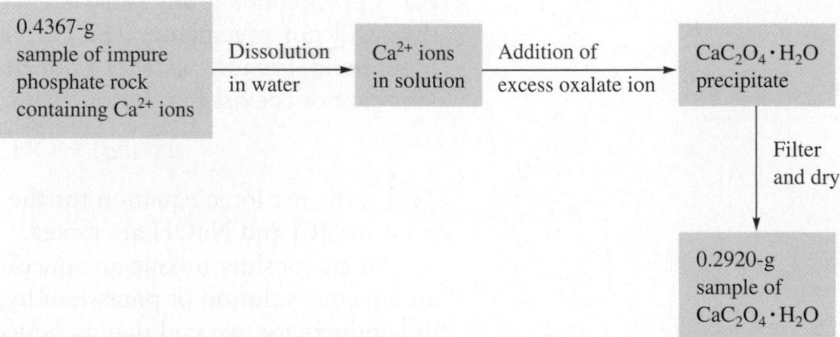

In this analysis, excess $C_2O_4^{2-}$ ions are added to ensure that all Ca^{2+} ions are precipitated. Thus the number of moles of Ca^{2+} ions in the original sample determines the number of moles of $CaC_2O_4 \cdot H_2O$ formed. Using the molar mass of $CaC_2O_4 \cdot H_2O$, we can calculate the moles of $CaC_2O_4 \cdot H_2O$:

$$0.2920 \text{ g } CaC_2O_4 \cdot H_2O \times \frac{1 \text{ mol } CaC_2O_4 \cdot H_2O}{146.12 \text{ g } CaC_2O_4 \cdot H_2O} = 1.998 \times 10^{-3} \text{ mol } CaC_2O_4 \cdot H_2O$$

Thus the original sample of impure phosphate rock contained 1.998×10^{-3} mole of Ca^{2+} ions, which we convert to grams:

$$1.998 \times 10^{-3} \text{ mol } Ca^{2+} \times \frac{40.08 \text{ g } Ca^{2+}}{1 \text{ mol } Ca^{2+}} = 8.009 \times 10^{-2} \text{ g } Ca^{2+}$$

*Hydrated salts contain one or more H_2O molecules per formula unit in addition to the cations and anions. A dot is used in the formula of these salts.

The mass percent of calcium in the original sample is then

$$\frac{8.009 \times 10^{-2}\text{ g}}{0.4367\text{ g}} \times 100\% = 18.34\%$$

4.9 Acid–Base Reactions

Earlier in this chapter we considered Arrhenius's concept of acids and bases: An acid is a substance that produces H^+ ions when dissolved in water, and a base is a substance that produces OH^- ions. Although these ideas are fundamentally correct, it is convenient to have a more general definition of a base, which covers substances that do not produce OH^- ions. Such a definition was provided by Brønsted and Lowry, who defined acids and bases as follows:

The Brønsted–Lowry concept of acids and bases will be discussed in detail in Chapter 7.

An acid is a proton donor.
A base is a proton acceptor.

How do we recognize acid–base reactions? One of the most difficult tasks for someone inexperienced in chemistry is to predict which reaction might occur when two solutions are mixed. With precipitation reactions, we found that the best way to deal with this problem is to focus on the species actually present in the mixed solution. This also applies to acid–base reactions. For example, when an aqueous solution of hydrogen chloride (HCl) is mixed with an aqueous solution of sodium hydroxide (NaOH), the combined solution contains the ions H^+, Cl^-, Na^+, and OH^-, since HCl is a strong acid and NaOH is a strong base. How can we predict what reaction occurs, if any? First, will NaCl precipitate? From Table 4.1 we know that NaCl is soluble in water and thus will not precipitate. The Na^+ and Cl^- ions are spectator ions. On the other hand, because water is a nonelectrolyte, large quantities of H^+ and OH^- ions cannot coexist in solution. They will react to form H_2O molecules:

$$H^+(aq) + OH^-(aq) \longrightarrow H_2O(l)$$

This is the net ionic equation for the reaction that occurs when aqueous solutions of HCl and NaOH are mixed.

Next, consider mixing an aqueous solution of acetic acid ($HC_2H_3O_2$) with an aqueous solution of potassium hydroxide (KOH). In our earlier discussion of conductivity, we said that an aqueous solution of acetic acid is a weak electrolyte. Thus acetic acid does not dissociate into ions to any great extent. In fact, in aqueous solution 99% of the $HC_2H_3O_2$ molecules remain undissociated. However, when solid KOH is dissolved in water, it dissociates completely to produce K^+ and OH^- ions. So, in the solution formed by mixing aqueous solutions of $HC_2H_3O_2$ and KOH, *before any reaction occurs* the principal species are H_2O, $HC_2H_3O_2$, K^+, and OH^-. Which reaction will occur? A possible precipitation reaction involves K^+ and OH^-, but we know that KOH is soluble. Another possibility is a reaction involving the hydroxide ion and a proton donor. Is there a source of protons in the solution? The answer is yes—the $HC_2H_3O_2$ molecules. The OH^- ion has such a strong affinity for protons that it can strip them from the $HC_2H_3O_2$ molecules. Thus the net ionic equation for the reaction is

$$OH^-(aq) + HC_2H_3O_2(aq) \longrightarrow H_2O(l) + C_2H_3O_2^-(aq)$$

This reaction illustrates a very important general principle: *The hydroxide ion is such a strong base that for purposes of stoichiometry it is assumed to react completely with any weak acid dissolved in water.* Of course, OH^- ions also react completely with the H^+ ions in the solutions of strong acids.

We will now deal with the stoichiometry of acid–base reactions in aqueous solutions. The procedure is fundamentally the same as that used previously.

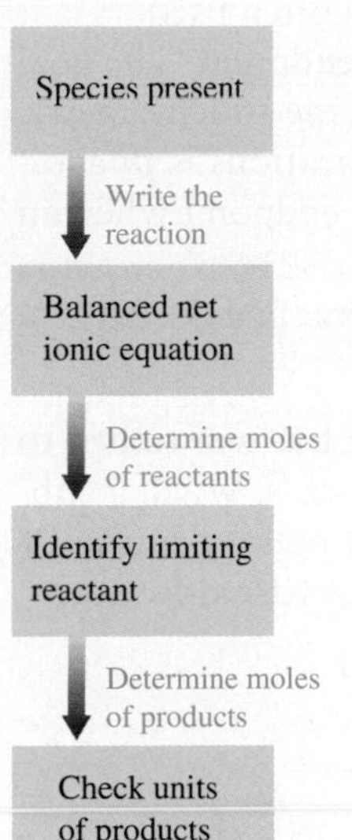

STEPS **Calculations for Acid–Base Reactions**

1 List the species present in the combined solution *before reaction,* and decide which reaction will occur.
2 Write the balanced net ionic equation for this reaction.
3 Change the given quantities of reactants to moles. For reactions in solution, use the volumes of the original solutions and their molarities.
4 Determine the limiting reactant where appropriate.
5 Calculate the moles of the required reactant or product.
6 Convert to grams or a volume of solution, as required by the problem.

An acid–base reaction is often called a **neutralization reaction.** When just enough base is added to react exactly with all of the acid in a solution, we say the acid has been *neutralized.*

Acid–Base Titrations

Acid–base **titrations** are an example of **volumetric analysis,** a technique in which one solution is used to analyze another. The solution used to carry out the analysis is called the **titrant** and is delivered from a device called a buret, which measures the volume accurately. The point in the titration at which enough titrant has been added to react exactly with the substance being determined is called the **equivalence point,** or the **stoichiometric point.** This point is often marked by the change in color of a chemical called an **indicator.** The titration procedure is illustrated in Fig. 4.18.

The following requirements must be met for a titration to be successful:

The concentration of the titrant must be known. Such a titrant is called a *standard solution.*

(a)

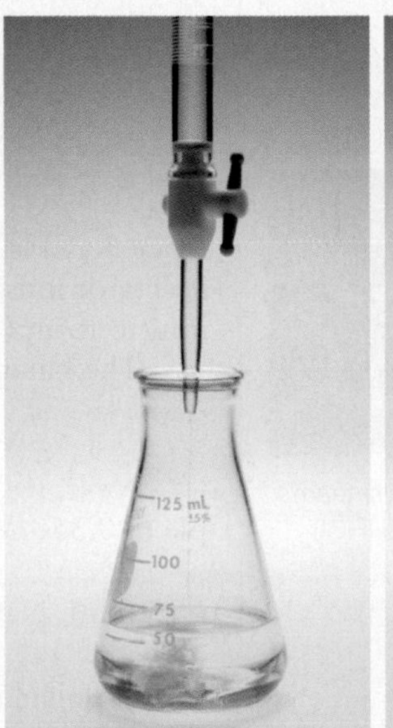

(b)

(c)

Figure 4.18
The titration of an acid with a base. (a) The titrant (the base) is in the buret, and the beaker contains the acid solution along with a small amount of indicator. (b) As base is added drop by drop to the acidic solution in the beaker during the titration, the indicator changes color, but the color disappears on mixing. (c) The stoichiometric (equivalence) point is marked by a permanent indicator color change. The volume of the base added is the difference between the final and initial buret readings.

The exact reaction between titrant and substance being analyzed must be known.

The stoichiometric (equivalence) point must be known. An indicator that changes color at, or very near, the stoichiometric point is often used.

The point at which the indicator changes color is called the **endpoint.** The goal is to choose an indicator whose endpoint coincides with the stoichiometric point. An indicator very commonly used by acid–base titrations is *phenolphthalein,* which is colorless in acid and turns pink at the endpoint when an acid is titrated with a base.

Ideally, the endpoint and stoichiometric point should coincide.

The volume of titrant required to reach the stoichiometric point must be known as accurately as possible.

We will deal with acid–base titrations only briefly here but will return to the topic of titrations and indicators in more detail in Chapter 8. When a substance being analyzed contains an acid, the amount of acid present is usually determined by titration with a standard solution containing hydroxide ions.

OWL INTERACTIVE EXAMPLE 4.10

What volume of a 0.100 *M* HCl solution is needed to neutralize 25.0 mL of a 0.350 *M* NaOH solution?

Solution

■ What are we trying to solve?

We are asked to determine the volume of a solution of HCl required to neutralize a given volume of a solution of NaOH.

■ What does this mean?

The HCl and NaOH react with each other, so we need to use a balanced equation to determine the mole ratio between the two reactants. Since we have volumes and molarities of both, we can determine the moles of each reactant. To do this, we must think about the components in the reactant solutions.

The species present in the mixed solutions before any reaction occurs are

$$\underbrace{H^+, Cl^-,}_{\text{From HCl}(aq)} \quad \underbrace{Na^+, OH^-,}_{\text{From NaOH}(aq)} \quad \text{and} \quad H_2O$$

Which reaction will occur? The two possibilities are

$$Na^+(aq) + Cl^-(aq) \longrightarrow NaCl(s)$$

$$H^+(aq) + OH^-(aq) \longrightarrow H_2O(l)$$

AP Photo/The Herald Bulletin, John F. Cleary

A Hazmat (hazardous materials) team neutralizes a hydrochloric acid (HCl) spill.

Since NaCl is soluble, the first reaction does not take place (Na^+ and Cl^- are spectator ions). However, as we have seen before, the reaction of H^+ and OH^- ions to form H_2O does occur.

The balanced net ionic equation for the reaction is

$$H^+(aq) + OH^-(aq) \longrightarrow H_2O(l)$$

Next, we calculate the number of moles of OH^- ions in the 25.0-mL sample of 0.350 *M* NaOH:

$$25.0 \text{ mL NaOH} \times \frac{1 \text{ L}}{1000 \text{ mL}} \times \frac{0.350 \text{ mol OH}^-}{\text{L NaOH}} = 8.75 \times 10^{-3} \text{ mol OH}^-$$

This problem requires the addition of just enough H^+ ions to react exactly with the OH^- ions present. Thus we need not be concerned with determining a limiting reactant.

Since H^+ and OH^- ions react in a 1:1 ratio, 8.75×10^{-3} mole of H^+ ions is required to neutralize the OH^- ions present.

The volume (V) of 0.100 M HCl required to furnish this amount of H^+ ions can be calculated as follows:

$$V \times \frac{0.100 \text{ mol H}^+}{\text{L}} = 8.75 \times 10^{-3} \text{ mol H}^+$$

Solving for V gives

$$V = 8.75 \times 10^{-2} \text{ L}$$

Thus 8.75×10^{-2} L (87.5 mL) of 0.100 M HCl is required to neutralize 25.0 mL of 0.350 M NaOH.

■ Is the answer reasonable?

The mole ratio between the reactants is 1:1. The NaOH is more concentrated than the HCl, so it makes sense that the volume of HCl is larger than the volume of NaOH.

OWL INTERACTIVE EXAMPLE 4.11

In a certain experiment, 28.0 mL of 0.250 M HNO_3 and 53.0 mL of 0.320 M KOH are mixed. Calculate the amount of water formed in the resulting reaction. What is the concentration of H^+ or OH^- ions in excess after the reaction goes to completion?

Solution

■ What are we trying to solve?

We are asked to determine the amount of water formed and the amount of excess reactant when an acid and base react.

■ What does this mean?

The acid and base react with each other, so we need to use a balanced equation to determine the mole ratio between the two reactants. Since we have volumes and molarities of both, we can determine the moles of each reactant. To do this, we must think about the components in the reactant solutions.

The species available for reaction are

$$\underbrace{H^+, NO_3^-,}_{\text{From HNO}_3\text{ solution}} \qquad \underbrace{K^+, OH^-,}_{\text{From KOH solution}} \qquad \text{and} \qquad H_2O$$

Since KNO_3 is soluble, K^+ and NO_3^- are spectator ions, so the net ionic equation is

$$H^+(aq) + OH^-(aq) \longrightarrow H_2O(l)$$

We next compute the amounts of H^+ and OH^- ions present.

$$28.0 \text{ mL HNO}_3 \times \frac{1 \text{ L}}{1000 \text{ mL}} \times \frac{0.250 \text{ mol H}^+}{\text{L}} = 7.00 \times 10^{-3} \text{ mol H}^+$$

$$53.0 \text{ mL KOH} \times \frac{1 \text{ L}}{1000 \text{ mL}} \times \frac{0.320 \text{ mol OH}^-}{\text{L}} = 1.70 \times 10^{-2} \text{ mol OH}^-$$

Since H^+ and OH^- react in a 1:1 ratio, the limiting reactant is H^+. Thus 7.00×10^{-3} mole of H^+ ions will react with 7.00×10^{-3} mole of OH^- ions to form 7.00×10^{-3} mole of H_2O.

The amount of OH^- ions in excess is obtained from the following difference:

$$\text{Original amount} - \text{amount consumed} = \text{amount in excess}$$

$$1.70 \times 10^{-2} \text{ mol } OH^- - 7.00 \times 10^{-3} \text{ mol } OH^- = 1.00 \times 10^{-2} \text{ mol } OH^-$$

The volume of the combined solution is the sum of the individual volumes:

$$\text{Original volume of } HNO_3 + \text{original volume of KOH} = \text{total volume}$$

$$28.0 \text{ mL} + 53.0 \text{ mL} = 81.0 \text{ mL} = 8.10 \times 10^{-2} \text{ L}$$

Thus the molarity of OH^- ions in excess is

$$M = \frac{\text{mol } OH^-}{\text{L solution}} = \frac{1.00 \times 10^{-2} \text{ mol } OH^-}{8.10 \times 10^{-2} \text{ L}} = 0.123\ M\ OH^-$$

■ Is the answer reasonable?

The mole ratio between the reactants is 1:1. The KOH is more concentrated than the HNO_3, and a greater volume of KOH is used. It makes sense that the OH^- is in excess.

EXAMPLE 4.12

An environmental chemist analyzed the effluent (the released waste material) from an industrial process known to produce the compounds carbon tetrachloride (CCl_4) and benzoic acid ($HC_7H_5O_2$), a weak acid that has one acidic hydrogen atom per molecule. A sample of this effluent weighing 0.3518 g was placed in water and shaken vigorously to dissolve the benzoic acid. The resulting aqueous solution required 10.59 mL of 0.1546 M NaOH for neutralization. Calculate the mass percent of $HC_7H_5O_2$ in the original sample.

Solution

■ What are we trying to solve?

We are asked to determine the mass percent of an acid in a mixture (effluent).

■ What does this mean?

$$\text{Mass percent of benzoic acid} = \frac{\text{mass of benzoic acid}}{\text{mass of mixture}} \times 100\%$$

We know the mass of the mixture is 0.3518 g, so we change the question to *"What is the mass of benzoic acid in the mixture?"*

In this case the sample was a mixture containing CCl_4 and $HC_7H_5O_2$, and it was titrated with OH^- ions. Clearly, CCl_4 is not an acid (it contains no hydrogen atoms), so we can assume it does not react with OH^- ions. However, $HC_7H_5O_2$ is an acid. It donates one H^+ ion per molecule to react with an OH^- ion as follows:

$$HC_7H_5O_2(aq) + OH^-(aq) \longrightarrow H_2O(l) + C_7H_5O_2^-(aq)$$

Although $HC_7H_5O_2$ is a weak acid, the OH^- ion is such a strong base that we can assume that each OH^- ion added will react with a $HC_7H_5O_2$ molecule until all the benzoic acid is consumed.

We must first determine the number of moles of OH^- ions required to react with all of the $HC_7H_5O_2$:

$$10.59 \text{ mL NaOH} \times \frac{1 \text{ L}}{1000 \text{ mL}} \times \frac{0.1546 \text{ mol OH}^-}{\text{L NaOH}}$$

$$= 1.637 \times 10^{-3} \text{ mol OH}^-$$

This number is also the number of moles of $HC_7H_5O_2$ present. The number of grams of the acid is calculated by using its molar mass:

$$1.637 \times 10^{-3} \text{ mol HC}_7\text{H}_5\text{O}_2 \times \frac{122.125 \text{ g HC}_7\text{H}_5\text{O}_2}{1 \text{ mol HC}_7\text{H}_5\text{O}_2} = 0.1999 \text{ g HC}_7\text{H}_5\text{O}_2$$

The mass percent of $HC_7H_5O_2$ in the original sample is

$$\frac{0.1999 \text{ g}}{0.3518 \text{ g}} \times 100\% = 56.82\%$$

The first step in the analysis of a complex solution is to write down the components present and to focus on the chemistry of each one.

Chemical systems often seem difficult to deal with simply because there are many components. Solving a problem involving a solution in which several components are present is simplified if you *think* about the *chemistry* involved. *The key to success is to write down all the components in the solution and to focus on the chemistry of each one.* We have been emphasizing this approach in dealing with the reactions between ions in solution. Make it a habit to write down the components of solutions before trying to decide which reaction(s) might take place.

4.10 Oxidation–Reduction Reactions

As we have seen, many important substances are ionic. Sodium chloride, for example, can be formed by the reaction of elemental sodium and chlorine:

$$2\text{Na}(s) + \text{Cl}_2(g) \longrightarrow 2\text{NaCl}(s)$$

In this reaction, solid sodium, which contains neutral sodium atoms, reacts with chlorine gas, which contains diatomic Cl_2 molecules, to form the ionic solid NaCl, which contains Na^+ and Cl^- ions. This process is represented in Fig. 4.19. *Reactions like this one, in which one or more electrons are transferred, are called* ***oxidation–reduction reactions*** *or* ***redox reactions.***

Many important chemical reactions involve oxidation and reduction. In fact, most reactions used for energy production are redox reactions. In humans the oxidation of sugars, fats, and proteins provides the energy necessary for life. Combustion reactions, which provide most of the energy to power our civilization, also involve oxidation and reduction. An example is the reaction of methane with oxygen:

$$\text{CH}_4(g) + 2\text{O}_2(g) \longrightarrow \text{CO}_2(g) + 2\text{H}_2\text{O}(g) + \text{energy}$$

Even though none of the reactants or products in this reaction is ionic, the reaction is still assumed to involve a transfer of electrons from carbon to oxygen. To explain this, we must introduce the concept of oxidation states.

Oxidation States

The concept of **oxidation states** (also called **oxidation numbers**) provides a way to keep track of electrons in oxidation–reduction reactions. Oxidation states are defined by a set of rules, most of which describe how to divide up the

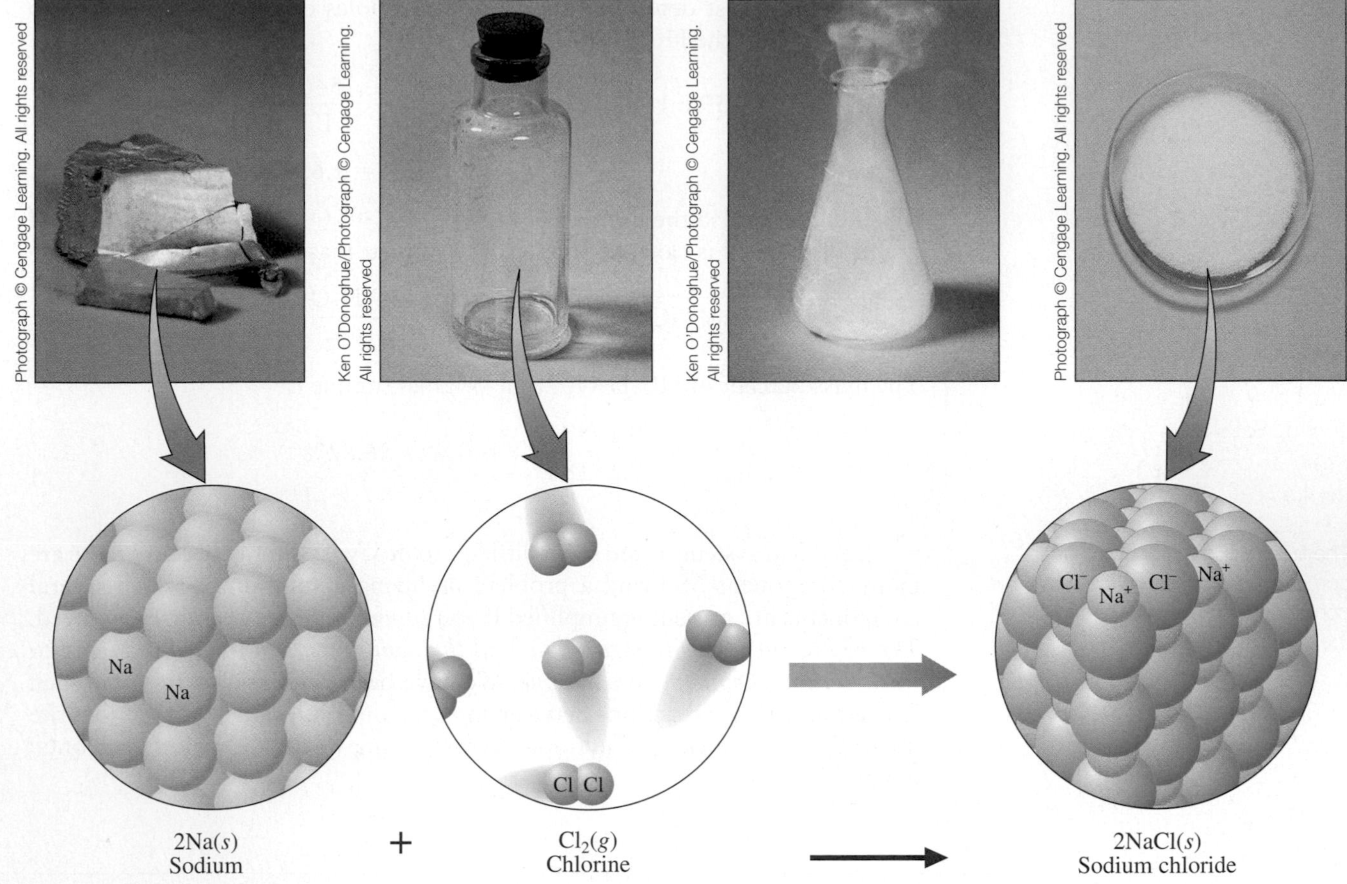

Figure 4.19
The reaction of solid sodium and gaseous chlorine to form solid sodium chloride.

Oxidation of copper metal by nitric acid. The copper atoms lose two electrons to form Cu^{2+} ions, which give a deep green color that becomes turquoise when diluted with water. The brown gas NO_2 is also evolved.

shared electrons in compounds containing covalent bonds. However, before we discuss these rules, we need to discuss the distribution of electrons in a bond.

Recall from the discussion of the water molecule in Section 4.1 that oxygen has a greater attraction for electrons than does hydrogen, causing the O—H bonds in the water molecule to be polar. This phenomenon occurs in other bonds as well, and we will discuss the topic of polarity in detail in Chapter 13. For now we will be satisfied with some general guidelines to help us keep track of electrons in oxidation–reduction reactions. The nonmetals with the highest attraction for shared electrons are in the upper right-hand corner of the periodic table. They are fluorine, oxygen, nitrogen, and chlorine. The relative ability of these atoms to attract shared electrons is

$$F > O > N \approx Cl$$

↗ Greatest attraction for electrons ↖ Least attraction for electrons

That is, fluorine attracts shared electrons to the greatest extent, followed by oxygen, then nitrogen and chlorine.

The rules for assigning oxidation states are given in Table 4.3. Application of these rules allows the assignment of oxidation states in most compounds. The principles are illustrated in Example 4.13.

State-of-the-Art Analysis

Chemical Insights

The real world of chemical analysis is often quite different from what students do in the typical university laboratory. In the real world, chemical analysis must be done quickly, accurately, economically, and often outside the laboratory setting. Analytical accuracy is crucial. A career can hinge on accuracy when a drug test is involved, and sometimes accuracy is truly a life-or-death matter, as in the screening of air travelers' luggage for explosives.

Chemical analysis can turn up in unexpected places. Modern engines in automobiles have been made much more fuel-efficient and less polluting by the inclusion of a sensor to analyze the oxygen (O_2) concentration in the exhaust gases. The signal from this sensor is sent to the computer that controls engine function so that instantaneous adjustments can be made in spark timing and air–fuel mixtures.

The automated screening of luggage for explosives is a very difficult and important analysis problem. One method being developed for luggage screening is called thermal neutron analysis (TNA), in which the substance to be analyzed is bombarded with neutrons. When nuclei in the sample absorb neutrons, they release gamma rays that are characteristic of a specific nucleus. For example, after the nucleus of a nitrogen atom absorbs a neutron, it emits a gamma ray that is unique to nitrogen, whereas an oxygen atom would produce a different gamma ray unique to oxygen, and so on. Thus, when a sample is bombarded by neutrons and the resulting gamma rays are analyzed by a detector connected to a computer, the atoms present in the sample can be specified. In an airport the luggage would pass through the TNA instrument on a conveyor belt and be bombarded by neutrons from californium-252. The detector is set up to look for unusually large quantities of nitrogen because most chemical explosives are based on nitrogen compounds. Although this system is still under development, the Federal Aviation Administration is optimistic that it will work.

Analytical chemists have always admired the supersensitive natural detection devices built into organisms as part of elaborate control systems

Tammy Peluso/Island Effects

A Hawaiian red swimming crab.

used to regulate the levels of various crucial chemicals, such as enzymes, hormones, and neurotransmitters. Because these "biosensors" are so sensitive, chemists are now attaching them to their instruments. For example, the sensory hairs from Hawaiian red swimming crabs can be connected to electrical analyzers and used to detect hormones at concentrations lower than 10^{-12} *M*. Also, slices from the tissues of pineapple cores can be used to detect hydrogen peroxide at levels of $\approx 10^{-6}$ *M*.

Another state-of-the-art detection system contains a surface acoustic wave (SAW) device, which is based on a piezoelectric crystal whose resonant frequency is sensitive to tiny changes in its mass—it can sense a change of 10^{-10} g/cm. In one use of this device as a detector, it was coated with a thin film of zeolite, a silicate mineral. Zeolite has intricate passages of a very uniform size. Thus, it can act as a "molecular sieve," allowing only molecules of a certain size to pass through onto the detector, where their accumulation changes the mass and therefore alters the detector frequency. This sensor has been used to detect amounts of methyl alcohol (CH_3OH) as low as 10^{-9} g.

The face of chemical analysis is changing rapidly. In fact, although wet chemical analyses (titrations, for example) are still quite important in the chemical industry, increasingly these routine analyses are done by robots, which not only perform the analyses automatically but also send the results to a computer for interpretation.

Table 4.3

Rules for Assigning Oxidation States

1. The oxidation state of an atom in an element is 0. For example, the oxidation state of each atom in the substances Na(*s*), $O_2(g)$, $O_3(g)$, and Hg(*l*) is 0.
2. The oxidation state of a monatomic ion is the same as its charge. For example, the oxidation state of the Na^+ ion is +1.
3. In its covalent compounds with nonmetals, hydrogen is assigned an oxidation state of +1. For example, in the compounds HCl, NH_3, H_2O, and CH_4, hydrogen is assigned an oxidation state of +1.
4. Oxygen is assigned an oxidation state of −2 in its covalent compounds, such as CO, CO_2, SO_2, and SO_3. The exception to this rule occurs in peroxides (compounds containing the O_2^{2-} group), where each oxygen is assigned an oxidation state of −1. The best-known example of a peroxide is hydrogen peroxide (H_2O_2).
5. In binary compounds, the element with the greater attraction for the electrons in the bond is assigned a negative oxidation state equal to its charge in its ionic compounds. For example, fluorine is always assigned an oxidation state of −1. That is, for purposes of counting electrons, fluorine is assumed to be F^-. Nitrogen is usually assigned −3. For example, in NH_3, nitrogen is assigned an oxidation state of −3; in H_2S, sulfur is assigned an oxidation state of −2; in HI, iodine is assigned an oxidation state of −1; and so on.
6. The sum of the oxidation states must be zero for an electrically neutral compound and must be equal to the overall charge for an ionic species. For example, the sum of the oxidation states for the hydrogen and oxygen atoms in water is 0; the sum of the oxidation states for the carbon and oxygen atoms in CO_3^{2-} is −2; and the sum of oxidation states for the nitrogen and hydrogen atoms in NH_4^+ is +1.

OWL INTERACTIVE EXAMPLE 4.13

Assign oxidation states to all of the following atoms.

a. CO_2 b. SF_6 c. NO_3^-

Solution

a. The rule that takes precedence here is that oxygen is assigned an oxidation state of −2. The oxidation state for carbon can be determined by recognizing that since CO_2 has no charge, the sum of the oxidation states for oxygen and carbon must be 0. Since each oxygen is −2 and there are two oxygen atoms, the carbon atom must be assigned an oxidation state of +4:

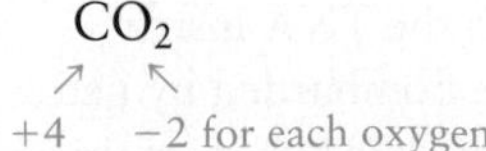

b. Since fluorine has the greater attraction for the shared electrons, we assign its oxidation state first. Because its charge in ionic compounds is 1−, we assign −1 as the oxidation state of each fluorine atom. The sulfur must then be assigned an oxidation state of +6 to balance the total of −6 from the fluorine atoms:

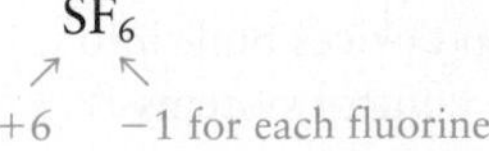

c. Since oxygen has a greater attraction than does nitrogen for the shared electrons, we assign its oxidation state of −2 first. Because the sum of the

Actual charges are given as *n*− or *n*+. Oxidation states *(not actual charges)* are given as −*n* or +*n*. For example, for NO_3^-, the overall charge is 1−; the oxidation state for N is +5 and for O is −2.

oxidation states of the three oxygens is −6 and the net charge on the NO_3^- ion is 1−, the nitrogen must have an oxidation state of +5:

$$\underset{+5\quad -2 \text{ for each oxygen}}{NO_3^-}$$

Next, let's consider the oxidation states of the atoms in Fe_3O_4, which is the main component in magnetite, an iron ore that accounts for the reddish color of many types of rocks and soils. We assign each oxygen atom its usual oxidation state of −2. The three iron atoms must yield a total of +8 to balance the total of −8 from the four oxygens. Thus each iron atom has an oxidation state of $+\frac{8}{3}$. A noninteger value for an oxidation state may seem strange since charge is expressed in whole numbers. However, although they are rare, noninteger oxidation states do occur because of the rather arbitrary way that the electrons are divided up by the rules in Table 4.3. In the compound Fe_3O_4, for example, the rules assume that all of the iron atoms are equal when in fact this compound can best be viewed as containing four O^{2-} ions, two Fe^{3+} ions, and one Fe^{2+} per formula unit. (Note that the "average" charge on iron works out to be $\frac{8}{3}+$, which is equal to the oxidation state we determined above.) Noninteger oxidation states should not intimidate you. They serve the same purpose as integer oxidation states—for keeping track of electrons.

The Characteristics of Oxidation–Reduction Reactions

Oxidation–reduction reactions are characterized by a transfer of electrons. In some cases the transfer occurs in a literal sense to form ions, such as in this reaction:

$$2Na(s) + Cl_2(g) \longrightarrow 2NaCl(s)$$

However, sometimes the transfer occurs in a more formal sense, such as in the combustion of methane (the oxidation state for each atom is given):

$$CH_4(g) + 2O_2(g) \longrightarrow CO_2(g) + 2H_2O(g)$$

Oxidation state: C −4, H +1 (each H); O in O_2: 0; C in CO_2: +4, O −2 (each O); H in H_2O: +1 (each H), O −2

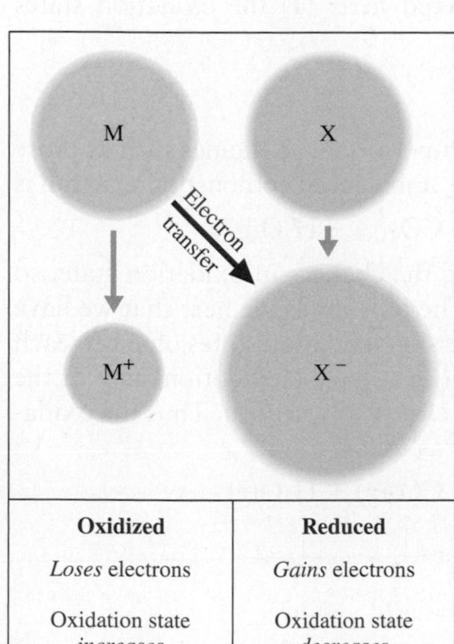

Oxidized	Reduced
Loses electrons	*Gains* electrons
Oxidation state *increases*	Oxidation state *decreases*
Reducing agent	*Oxidizing* agent

Figure 4.20
A summary of an oxidation–reduction process, in which M is oxidized and X is reduced.

Note that the oxidation state of oxygen in O_2 is 0 because it is in elemental form. In this reaction there are no ionic compounds, but we can still describe the process in terms of a transfer of electrons. Note that carbon undergoes a change in oxidation state from −4 in CH_4 to +4 in CO_2. Such a change can be accounted for by a loss of eight electrons (the symbol e^- stands for an electron):

$$\underset{-4}{CH_4} \longrightarrow \underset{+4}{CO_2} + 8e^-$$

On the other hand, each oxygen changes from an oxidation state of 0 in O_2 to −2 in H_2O and CO_2, signifying a gain of two electrons per atom. Since four oxygen atoms are involved, this is a gain of eight electrons:

$$\underset{0}{2O_2} + 8e^- \longrightarrow \underbrace{CO_2 + 2H_2O}_{4(-2)\,=\,-8}$$

No change occurs in the oxidation state of hydrogen, so it is not formally involved in the electron transfer process.

With this background, we can now define some important terms. **Oxidation** is an *increase* in oxidation state (a loss of electrons). **Reduction** is a *decrease* in oxidation state (a gain of electrons). Thus in the reaction

$$\begin{array}{ccccc} 2\text{Na}(s) & + & \text{Cl}_2(g) & \longrightarrow & 2\text{NaCl}(s) \\ \uparrow & & \uparrow & & \uparrow \quad \nwarrow \\ 0 & & 0 & & +1 \quad -1 \end{array}$$

sodium is oxidized and chlorine is reduced. In addition, Cl_2 is called the **oxidizing agent (electron acceptor)**, and Na is called the **reducing agent (electron donor)**. These concepts are summarized in Fig. 4.20.

Concerning the reaction

$$\begin{array}{ccccccc} \text{CH}_4(g) & + & 2\text{O}_2(g) & \longrightarrow & \text{CO}_2(g) & + & 2\text{H}_2\text{O}(g) \\ \uparrow \quad \nwarrow & & \uparrow & & \uparrow \quad \nwarrow & & \uparrow \quad \nwarrow \\ -4 \quad +1 & & 0 & & +4 \quad -2 & & +1 \quad -2 \end{array}$$

Oxidation is an increase in oxidation state. Reduction is a decrease in oxidation state.

A helpful mnemonic device is OIL RIG (*O*xidation *I*nvolves *L*oss; *R*eduction *I*nvolves *G*ain).

An oxidizing agent is reduced and a reducing agent is oxidized in a redox reaction.

we can say the following:

Carbon is oxidized because there is an increase in its oxidation state (carbon has formally lost electrons).

Oxygen is reduced as shown by the decrease in its oxidation state (oxygen has formally gained electrons).

CH_4 is the reducing agent.

O_2 is the oxidizing agent.

Note that when the oxidizing or reducing agent is named, the *whole compound* is specified, not just the element that undergoes the change in oxidation state.

4.11 Balancing Oxidation–Reduction Equations

Oxidation–reduction reactions are often complicated, which means that it can be difficult to balance their equations by simple inspection. Two methods for balancing redox reactions will be considered here: (1) the oxidation states method and (2) the half-reaction method.

The Oxidation States Method

Methanol (CH_3OH) is used as a fuel in high-performance engines such as those in the race cars in the Indianapolis 500. The unbalanced combustion reaction is

$$\text{CH}_3\text{OH}(l) + \text{O}_2(g) \longrightarrow \text{CO}_2(g) + \text{H}_2\text{O}(g)$$

We want to balance this equation by using the changes in oxidation state, so we must first specify all oxidation states. The only molecule here that we have not previously considered is CH_3OH. We assign oxidation states of $+1$ to each hydrogen and -2 to the oxygen, which means that the oxidation state of the carbon must be -2, since the compound is electrically neutral. Thus the oxidation states for the reaction participants are as follows:

$$\begin{array}{ccccccc} \text{CH}_3\text{OH}(l) & + & \text{O}_2(g) & \longrightarrow & \text{CO}_2(g) & + & \text{H}_2\text{O}(g) \\ -2 \quad +1 \text{ (each H)} \quad -2 \quad +1 & & 0 & & +4 \quad -2 \text{ (each O)} & & +1 \text{ (each H)} \quad -2 \end{array}$$

Note that the oxidation state of carbon changes from -2 to $+4$, an increase of 6. On the other hand, the oxidation state of oxygen changes from 0 to -2, a decrease of 2. This means that three oxygen atoms are needed to balance the increase in the oxidation state of the single carbon atom. We can write this relationship as follows:

$$\begin{array}{ccccc} \text{CH}_3\text{OH}(l) & + & \tfrac{3}{2}\text{O}_2(g) & \longrightarrow & \text{products} \\ \uparrow & & \uparrow & & \\ \text{1 carbon atom} & & \text{3 oxygen atoms} & & \end{array}$$

The rest of the equation can be balanced by inspection:

$$CH_3OH(l) + \tfrac{3}{2}O_2(g) \longrightarrow CO_2(g) + 2H_2O(g)$$

We then write it in conventional format (multiply through by 2):

$$2CH_3OH(l) + 3O_2(g) \longrightarrow 2CO_2(g) + 4H_2O(g)$$

In using the oxidation states method to balance an oxidation–reduction equation, we find the coefficients for the reactants that will make the total increase in oxidation state balance the total decrease. The remainder of the equation is then balanced by inspection.

EXAMPLE 4.14

Because metals are so reactive, very few are found in pure form in nature. Metallurgy involves reducing the metal ions in ores to the elemental form. The production of manganese from the ore pyrolusite, which contains MnO_2, uses aluminum as the reducing agent. Using oxidation states, balance the equation for this process.

$$MnO_2(s) + Al(s) \longrightarrow Mn(s) + Al_2O_3(s)$$

Solution First, we assign oxidation states:

$$\underset{+4\ \ -2\ (\text{each O})}{MnO_2(s)} + \underset{0}{Al(s)} \longrightarrow \underset{0}{Mn(s)} + \underset{+3\ (\text{each Al})\ \ -2\ (\text{each O})}{Al_2O_3(s)}$$

Each Mn atom undergoes a decrease in oxidation state of 4 (from +4 to 0), whereas each Al atom undergoes an increase of 3 (from 0 to +3).

Thus we need three Mn atoms for every four Al atoms to balance the increase and decrease in oxidation states:

$$\text{Increase} = 4(3) = \text{decrease} = 3(4)$$

$$3MnO_2(s) + 4Al(s) \longrightarrow \text{products}$$

We balance the rest of the equation by inspection:

$$3MnO_2(s) + 4Al(s) \longrightarrow 3Mn(s) + 2Al_2O_3(s)$$

The procedures for balancing an oxidation–reduction equation by the oxidation states method are summarized below.

STEPS

Balancing an Oxidation–Reduction Equation by the Oxidation States Method

1. Assign the oxidation states of all atoms.
2. Decide which element is oxidized, and determine the increase in oxidation state.
3. Decide which element is reduced, and determine the decrease in oxidation state.
4. Choose coefficients for the species containing the atom oxidized and the atom reduced such that the total increase in oxidation state equals the total decrease in oxidation state.
5. Balance the remainder of the equation by inspection.

The Half-Reaction Method

For oxidation–reduction reactions that occur in aqueous solution, it is often useful to separate the reaction into two **half-reactions:** one involving oxidation and the other involving reduction. For example, consider the unbalanced equation for the oxidation–reduction reaction between cerium(IV) ion and tin(II) ion:

$$Ce^{4+}(aq) + Sn^{2+}(aq) \longrightarrow Ce^{3+}(aq) + Sn^{4+}(aq)$$

This reaction can be separated into a half-reaction involving the substance being *reduced,*

$$Ce^{4+}(aq) \longrightarrow Ce^{3+}(aq)$$

and one involving the substance being *oxidized,*

$$Sn^{2+}(aq) \longrightarrow Sn^{4+}(aq)$$

The general procedure is to balance the equations for the half-reactions separately and then to add them to obtain the overall balanced equation. The half-reaction method for balancing oxidation–reduction equations differs slightly depending on whether the reaction takes place in acidic or basic solution.

STEPS

Balancing Oxidation–Reduction Equations Occurring in Acidic Solution by the Half-Reaction Method

1 Write the equations for the oxidation and reduction half-reactions.

2 For each half-reaction:
- Balance all the elements except hydrogen and oxygen.
- Balance oxygen using H_2O.
- Balance hydrogen using H^+.
- Balance the charge using electrons.

3 If necessary, multiply one or both balanced half-reactions by integers to equalize the number of electrons transferred in the two half-reactions.

4 Add the half-reactions, and cancel identical species.

5 Check to be sure that the elements and charges balance.

These steps are summarized by the following flowchart:

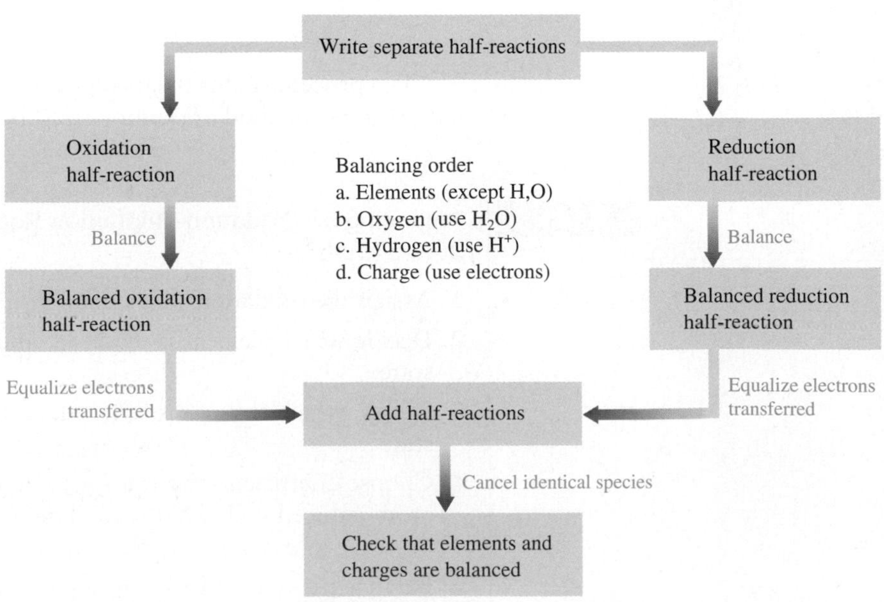
Write separate half-reactions
Oxidation half-reaction
Balance
Balanced oxidation half-reaction
Equalize electrons transferred
Balancing order
a. Elements (except H,O)
b. Oxygen (use H_2O)
c. Hydrogen (use H^+)
d. Charge (use electrons)
Reduction half-reaction
Balance
Balanced reduction half-reaction
Equalize electrons transferred
Add half-reactions
Cancel identical species
Check that elements and charges are balanced

We will illustrate this method by balancing the equation for the reaction between permanganate and iron(II) ions in acidic solution:

$$MnO_4^-(aq) + Fe^{2+}(aq) \xrightarrow{\text{Acidic}} Fe^{3+}(aq) + Mn^{2+}(aq)$$

This reaction is used to analyze iron ore for its iron content.

1. **Identify and write equations for the half-reactions.**
   The oxidation states for the half-reaction involving the permanganate ion show that manganese is reduced:

$$\underset{+7\ \ -2\text{ (each O)}}{MnO_4^-} \longrightarrow \underset{+2}{Mn^{2+}}$$

   This is the *reduction half-reaction.* The other half-reaction involves the oxidation of iron(II) to iron(III) ion and is the *oxidation half-reaction:*

$$\underset{+2}{Fe^{2+}} \longrightarrow \underset{+3}{Fe^{3+}}$$

2. **Balance each half-reaction.**
   For the reduction reaction, we have

$$MnO_4^-(aq) \longrightarrow Mn^{2+}(aq)$$

   a. The manganese is balanced.
   b. We balance oxygen by adding $4H_2O$ to the right side of the equation:

$$MnO_4^-(aq) \longrightarrow Mn^{2+}(aq) + 4H_2O(l)$$

   c. Next, we balance hydrogen by adding $8H^+$ to the left side:

$$8H^+(aq) + MnO_4^-(aq) \longrightarrow Mn^{2+}(aq) + 4H_2O(l)$$

   d. All the elements have been balanced, but we need to balance the charge by using electrons. At this point we have the following charges for reactants and products in the reduction half-reaction:

$$\underbrace{8H^+(aq) + MnO_4^-(aq)}_{\substack{8+\ \ +\ \ 1- \\ 7+}} \longrightarrow \underbrace{Mn^{2+}(aq) + 4H_2O(l)}_{\substack{2+\ \ +\ \ 0 \\ 2+}}$$

   We can equalize the charges by adding five electrons to the left side:

$$\underbrace{5e^- + 8H^+(aq) + MnO_4^-(aq)}_{2+} \longrightarrow \underbrace{Mn^{2+}(aq) + 4H_2O(l)}_{2+}$$

   Both the *elements* and the *charges* are now balanced, so this represents the balanced reduction half-reaction. The fact that five electrons appear on the reactant side of the equation makes sense, since five electrons are required to reduce MnO_4^- (in which Mn has an oxidation state of +7) to Mn^{2+} (in which Mn has an oxidation state of +2).

   For the oxidation reaction,

$$Fe^{2+}(aq) \longrightarrow Fe^{3+}(aq)$$

   the elements are balanced, and we must simply balance the charge:

$$\underbrace{Fe^{2+}(aq)}_{2+} \longrightarrow \underbrace{Fe^{3+}(aq)}_{3+}$$

One electron is needed on the right side to give a net 2+ charge on both sides:

$$\underbrace{Fe^{2+}(aq)}_{2+} \longrightarrow \underbrace{Fe^{3+}(aq) + e^-}_{2+}$$

The number of electrons gained in the reduction half-reaction must equal the number of electrons lost in the oxidation half-reaction.

3. **Equalize the electron transfer in the two half-reactions.**
   Since the reduction half-reaction involves a transfer of five electrons and the oxidation half-reaction involves a transfer of only one electron, the oxidation half-reaction must be multiplied by 5:

$$5Fe^{2+}(aq) \longrightarrow 5Fe^{3+}(aq) + 5e^-$$

4. **Add the half-reactions.**
   The half-reactions are added to give

$$5e^- + 5Fe^{2+}(aq) + MnO_4^-(aq) + 8H^+(aq) \longrightarrow 5Fe^{3+}(aq) + Mn^{2+}(aq) + 4H_2O(l) + 5e^-$$

   Note that the electrons cancel (as they must) to give the final balanced equation:

$$5Fe^{2+}(aq) + MnO_4^-(aq) + 8H^+(aq) \longrightarrow 5Fe^{3+}(aq) + Mn^{2+}(aq) + 4H_2O(l)$$

5. **Check that the elements and charges balance.**

   Elements balance: 5 Fe, 1 Mn, 4 O, 8 H $\longrightarrow$ 5 Fe, 1 Mn, 4 O, 8 H

   Charges balance: $5(2+) + (1-) + 8(1+) = 17+ \longrightarrow 5(3+) + (2+) + 0 = 17+$

   The equation is balanced.

Oxidation–reduction reactions can occur in basic as well as in acidic solutions. The half-reaction method for balancing equations is slightly different in such cases.

STEPS

Balancing Oxidation–Reduction Equations Occurring in Basic Solution by the Half-Reaction Method

1 Use the half-reaction method as specified for acidic solutions to obtain the final balanced equation *as if H^+ ions were present.*

2 To both sides of the equation obtained by the procedure in Step 1, add the number of OH^- ions that is equal to the number of H^+ ions. (We want to eliminate H^+ by forming H_2O.)

3 Form H_2O on the side containing both H^+ and OH^- ions, and eliminate the number of H_2O molecules that appear on both sides of the equation.

4 Check that the elements and charges balance.

This method is summarized by the following flowchart:

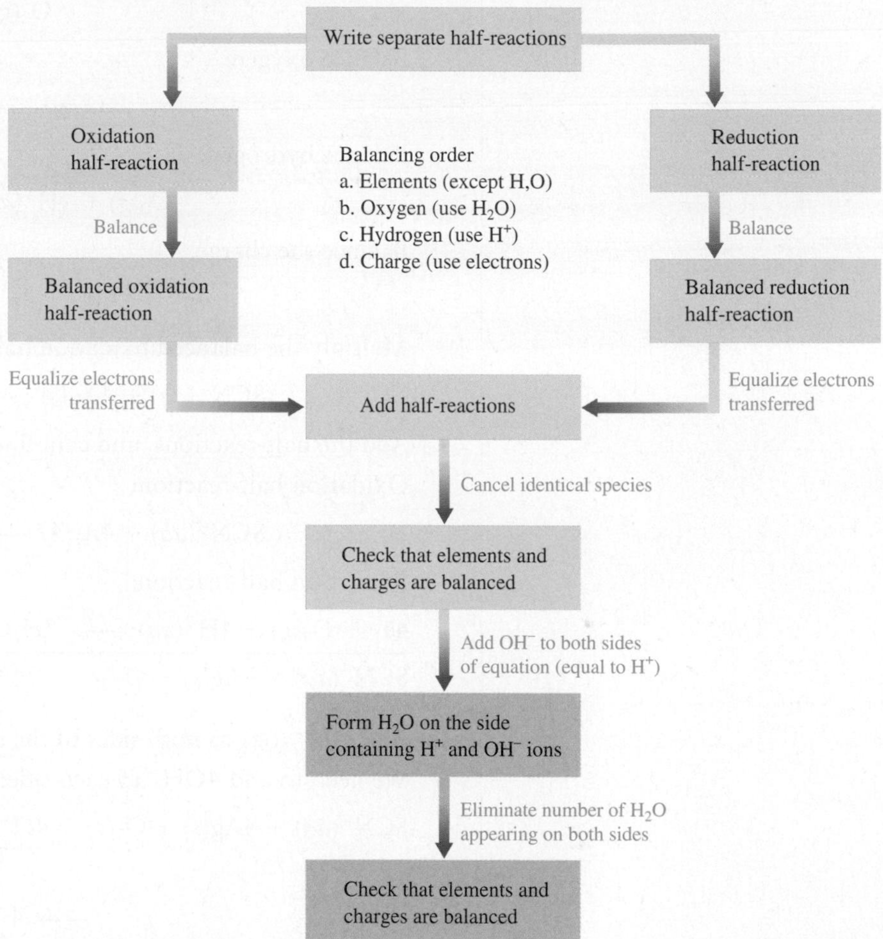
Write separate half-reactions
Oxidation half-reaction
Reduction half-reaction
Balancing order
a. Elements (except H,O)
b. Oxygen (use H_2O)
c. Hydrogen (use H^+)
d. Charge (use electrons)
Balance
Balance
Balanced oxidation half-reaction
Balanced reduction half-reaction
Equalize electrons transferred
Equalize electrons transferred
Add half-reactions
Cancel identical species
Check that elements and charges are balanced
Add OH^- to both sides of equation (equal to H^+)
Form H_2O on the side containing H^+ and OH^- ions
Eliminate number of H_2O appearing on both sides
Check that elements and charges are balanced

OWL INTERACTIVE EXAMPLE 4.15

Silver is sometimes found in nature as large nuggets; more often it is found mixed with other metals and their ores. Cyanide ion is often used to extract the silver by the following reaction that occurs in basic solution:

$$Ag(s) + CN^-(aq) + O_2(g) \xrightarrow{\text{Basic}} Ag(CN)_2^-(aq)$$

Balance this equation by using the half-reaction method.

Solution

1. **Balance the equation as if H^+ ions were present.**

Balance the oxidation half-reaction:

$$CN^-(aq) + Ag(s) \longrightarrow Ag(CN)_2^-(aq)$$

Balance carbon and nitrogen:

$$2CN^-(aq) + Ag(s) \longrightarrow Ag(CN)_2^-(aq)$$

Balance the charge:

$$2CN^-(aq) + Ag(s) \longrightarrow Ag(CN)_2^-(aq) + e^-$$

Balance the reduction half-reaction:

$$O_2(g) \longrightarrow$$

Balance oxygen:

$$O_2(g) \longrightarrow 2H_2O(l)$$

Balance hydrogen:

$$O_2(g) + 4H^+(aq) \longrightarrow 2H_2O(l)$$

Balance the charge:

$$4e^- + O_2(g) + 4H^+(aq) \longrightarrow 2H_2O(l)$$

Multiply the balanced oxidation half-reaction by 4:

$$8CN^-(aq) + 4Ag(s) \longrightarrow 4Ag(CN)_2^-(aq) + 4e^-$$

Add the half-reactions, and cancel identical species:

Oxidation half-reaction:

$$8CN^-(aq) + 4Ag(s) \longrightarrow 4Ag(CN)_2^-(aq) + 4e^-$$

Reduction half-reaction:

$$4e^- + O_2(g) + 4H^+(aq) \longrightarrow 2H_2O(l)$$

$$8CN^-(aq) + 4Ag(s) + O_2(g) + 4H^+(aq) \longrightarrow 4Ag(CN)_2^-(aq) + 2H_2O(l)$$

2. **Add OH^- ions to both sides of the balanced equation.**

   We need to add $4OH^-$ to each side:

$$8CN^-(aq) + 4Ag(s) + O_2(g) + \underbrace{4H^+(aq) + 4OH^-(aq)}_{4H_2O(l)} \longrightarrow 4Ag(CN)_2^-(aq) + 2H_2O(l) + 4OH^-(aq)$$

3. **Eliminate as many H_2O molecules as possible.**

$$8CN^-(aq) + 4Ag(s) + O_2(g) + 2H_2O(l) \longrightarrow 4Ag(CN)_2^-(aq) + 4OH^-(aq)$$

4. **Check that elements and charges balance.**

OWL INTERACTIVE EXAMPLE 4.16

Cerium(IV) ion is a strong oxidizing agent that accepts one electron to produce cerium(III) ion:

$$Ce^{4+}(aq) + e^- \longrightarrow Ce^{3+}(aq)$$

A solution containing an unknown concentration of Sn^{2+} ions was titrated with a solution containing Ce^{4+} ions, which oxidize the Sn^{2+} ions to Sn^{4+} ions. In one titration, 1.00 L of the unknown solution required 46.45 mL of a 0.1050 *M* Ce^{4+} solution to reach the stoichiometric point. Calculate the concentration of Sn^{2+} ions in the unknown solution.

Solution

- What are we trying to solve?

We are asked to determine the concentration of 1.00 L of a solution of Sn^{2+} required to react with a given volume and molarity of a Ce^{4+} solution.

■ What does this mean?

The Sn^{2+} and Ce^{4+} react with each other, so we need to use a balanced equation to determine the mole ratio between the two reactants. From the volume and molarity of the Ce^{4+} solution, we can determine the number of moles that, using the balanced equation, can be converted to moles of the Sn^{2+} solution. With moles and volume of Sn^{2+}, we can compute the concentration in terms of molarity.

The unbalanced equation for the titration reaction is

$$Ce^{4+}(aq) + Sn^{2+}(aq) \longrightarrow Ce^{3+}(aq) + Sn^{4+}(aq)$$

The balanced equation is

$$2Ce^{4+}(aq) + Sn^{2+}(aq) \longrightarrow 2Ce^{3+}(aq) + Sn^{4+}(aq)$$

We can obtain the number of moles of Ce^{4+} ions from the volume and molarity of the Ce^{4+} solution used as the titrant:

$$46.45 \text{ mL} \times \frac{1 \text{ L}}{1000 \text{ mL}} \times \frac{0.1050 \text{ mol } Ce^{4+}}{\text{L}} = 4.877 \times 10^{-3} \text{ mol } Ce^{4+}$$

The number of moles of Sn^{2+} ions can be obtained by applying the appropriate mole ratio from the balanced equation:

$$4.877 \times 10^{-3} \text{ mol } Ce^{4+} \times \frac{1 \text{ mol } Sn^{2+}}{2 \text{ mol } Ce^{4+}} = 2.439 \times 10^{-3} \text{ mol } Sn^{2+}$$

This value represents the quantity of Sn^{2+} ions in 1.00 L of solution. Thus the concentration of Sn^{2+} in the unknown solution is

$$\text{Molarity} = \frac{\text{mol } Sn^{2+}}{\text{L solution}} = \frac{2.439 \times 10^{-3} \text{ mol } Sn^{2+}}{1.00 \text{ L}} = 2.44 \times 10^{-3} \text{ M}$$

■ Is the answer reasonable?

The volume of the Sn^{2+} solution is much greater (factor of ~20) than the volume of the Ce^{4+} solution. It makes sense that the concentration of the Sn^{2+} solution is much lower than the concentration of the Ce^{4+} solution.

4.12 Simple Oxidation–Reduction Titrations

Oxidation–reduction reactions are commonly used as a basis for volumetric analytical procedures. For example, a reducing substance can be titrated with a solution of a strong oxidizing agent, or vice versa. Three of the most frequently used oxidizing agents are aqueous solutions of *potassium permanganate* ($KMnO_4$), *potassium dichromate* ($K_2Cr_2O_7$), and *cerium hydrogen sulfate* [$Ce(HSO_4)_4$].

The strong oxidizing agent, the permanganate ion (MnO_4^-), can undergo several different reactions. The reaction that occurs in acidic solution is the one most commonly used:

$$MnO_4^-(aq) + 8H^+(aq) + 5e^- \longrightarrow Mn^{2+}(aq) + 4H_2O(l)$$

Permanganate has the advantage of being its own indicator—the MnO_4^- ion is intensely purple, and the Mn^{2+} ion is almost colorless. As long as some reducing agent remains in the solution being titrated, the solution remains colorless (assuming all other species present are colorless), since the purple MnO_4^- ion being added is converted to the essentially colorless Mn^{2+} ion. However, when all the reducing agent has been consumed, the next drop of permanganate titrant will turn the solution being titrated light purple (pink). Thus the endpoint (where the color change indicates the titration should stop) occurs approximately one drop beyond the stoichiometric point (the actual point at which all the reducing agent has been consumed).

Example 4.17 describes a typical volumetric analysis using permanganate.

EXAMPLE 4.17

Iron ores often involve a mixture of oxides and contain both Fe^{2+} and Fe^{3+} ions. Such an ore can be analyzed for its iron content by dissolving it in acidic solution, reducing all the iron to Fe^{2+} ions, and then titrating with a standard solution of potassium permanganate. In the resulting solution, MnO_4^- is reduced to Mn^{2+}, and Fe^{2+} is oxidized to Fe^{3+}. A sample of iron ore weighing 0.3500 g was dissolved in acidic solution, and all the iron was reduced to Fe^{2+}. Then the solution was titrated with a 1.621×10^{-2} *M* $KMnO_4$ solution. The titration required 41.56 mL of the permanganate solution to reach the light purple (pink) endpoint. Determine the mass percent of iron in the iron ore.

Solution

- What are we trying to solve?

We are asked to determine the mass percent of iron in an iron ore.

- What does this mean?

$$\text{Mass percent of iron} = \frac{\text{mass of iron}}{\text{mass of iron ore}} \times 100\%$$

We know that the mass of the mixture is 0.3500 g, so we change the question to "*What is the mass of the iron?*"

All of the iron metal is converted to Fe^{2+}, which is reacted with a known volume and molarity of MnO_4^-. From volume and molarity we can get moles, and by using the mole ratio in a balanced equation, we can determine the moles of iron. We convert from moles to mass using the atomic mass of iron.

From the problem it is obvious that this is a redox reaction, so we will need to balance the equation accordingly.

First, we write the unbalanced equation for the reaction:

$$H^+(aq) + MnO_4^-(aq) + Fe^{2+}(aq) \longrightarrow Fe^{3+}(aq) + Mn^{2+}(aq) + H_2O(l)$$

Using the half-reaction method, we balance the equation:

$$8H^+(aq) + MnO_4^-(aq) + 5Fe^{2+}(aq) \longrightarrow 5Fe^{3+}(aq) + Mn^{2+}(aq) + 4H_2O(l)$$

The number of moles of MnO_4^- ion required in the titration is found from the volume and concentration of permanganate solution used:

$$41.56 \text{ mL} \times \frac{1 \text{ L}}{1000 \text{ mL}} \times \frac{1.621 \times 10^{-2} \text{ mol } MnO_4^-}{\text{L}} = 6.737 \times 10^{-4} \text{ mol } MnO_4^-$$

The balanced equation shows that five times as much Fe^{2+} as MnO_4^- is required:

$$6.737 \times 10^{-4} \text{ mol } MnO_4^- \times \frac{5 \text{ mol } Fe^{2+}}{1 \text{ mol } MnO_4^-} = 3.368 \times 10^{-3} \text{ mol } Fe^{2+}$$

Thus the 0.3500-g sample of iron ore contained 3.368×10^{-3} mol of iron. The mass of iron present is

$$3.368 \times 10^{-3} \text{ mol Fe} \times \frac{55.85 \text{ g Fe}}{1 \text{ mol Fe}} = 0.1881 \text{ g Fe}$$

The mass percent of iron in the iron ore is

$$\frac{0.1881 \text{ g}}{0.3500 \text{ g}} \times 100\% = 53.74\%$$

Key Terms

aqueous solutions

Section 4.1
polar molecule
hydration

Section 4.2
solute
solvent
electrical conductivity
strong electrolyte
weak electrolyte
nonelectrolyte
solubility
acid
strong acid
strong base
weak acid
weak base

Section 4.3
molarity
standard solution
dilution

Section 4.5
precipitation reaction
precipitate

Section 4.6
molecular equation
complete ionic equation
spectator ion
net ionic equation

Section 4.7
selective precipitation
qualitative analysis

Section 4.9
neutralization reaction
volumetric analysis
titrant
equivalence (stoichiometric) point
indicator, endpoint

Section 4.10
oxidation-reduction (redox) reaction
oxidation state (oxidation number)
oxidation
reduction
oxidizing agent (electron acceptor)
reducing agent (electron donor)

Section 4.11
half-reaction

For Review

Chemical reactions in solution are very important in everyday life.

Water is a polar solvent that dissolves many ionic and polar substances.

- Many ionic substances dissolve in water, although solubility varies greatly.
- Many polar substances dissolve in water.

Electrolytes

- Strong electrolyte: 100% dissociated to produce separate ions; strongly conducts an electric current
- Weak electrolyte: Only a small percentage of dissolved molecules produce ions; weakly conducts an electric current
- Nonelectrolyte: Dissolved substance produces no ions; does not conduct an electric current

Acids and bases

- Arrhenius model
  - Acid: produces H^+
  - Base: produces OH^-
- Brønsted–Lowry model
  - Acid: proton donor
  - Base: proton acceptor
- Strong acid: completely dissociates into separated H^+ and anions
- Strong base: completely dissociates into separated OH^- and cation
- Weak acid: dissociates to a slight extent
- Weak base: results in a solution that is a weak electrolyte and contains OH^- ions

Molarity

- One way to describe solution composition
- Molarity $(M) = \dfrac{\text{moles of solute}}{\text{volume of solution (L)}}$
- Standard solution: Molarity is accurately known.

Dilution

- Solvent is added to reduce the molarity.
- Moles of solute after dilution = moles of solute before dilution
- $M_1V_1 = M_2V_2$

Types of equations that describe solution reactions

- Molecular equation: All reactants and products are written as complete formulas.
- Complete ionic equation: All reactants and products that are strong electrolytes are written as separate ions.
- Net ionic equation: Only those compounds that undergo a change are written; spectator ions are not included.

Solubility rules

- Based on experiment observation
- Help predict the outcomes of precipitation reactions

Qualitative analysis

- A mixture of ions can be separated by selective precipitation

Important types of solution reactions
- Acid–base reactions: involve a transfer of H^+ ions
- Precipitation reactions: formation of a solid occurs
- Oxidation–reduction reactions: involve electron transfer

Titrations
- Measures the volume of a standard solution (titrant) needed to react with a substance in solution
- Stoichiometric (equivalence) point: the point at which the required amount of titrant has been added to exactly react with the substance being analyzed
- Endpoint: the point at which a chemical indicator changes color

Oxidation–reduction reactions
- Oxidation states are assigned using a set of rules to keep track of electron flow
- Oxidation: increase in oxidation state (a loss of electrons)
- Reduction: decrease in oxidation state (a gain of electrons)
- Oxidizing agent: gains electrons (is reduced)
- Reducing agent: loses electrons (is oxidized)
- Balancing oxidation–reduction reactions:
  - Oxidation state method
  - Half-reaction method
    - In acidic solutions
    - In basic solutions
- Can be used for volumetric analytical procedures
  - Titrations

Discussion Questions

These questions are designed to be considered by groups of students in class. Often these questions work well for introducing a particular topic in class.

1. Assume you have a highly magnified view of a solution of HCl that allows you to "see" the HCl. Draw this magnified view. If you dropped in a piece of magnesium, the magnesium would disappear, and hydrogen gas would be released. Represent this change using symbols for the elements, and write out the balanced equation.
2. You have a solution of table salt in water. What happens to the salt concentration (increases, decreases, or stays the same) as the solution boils? Draw pictures to explain your answer.
3. You have a sugar solution (solution A) with concentration x. You pour one-third of this solution into a beaker and add an equivalent volume of water (solution B).
   a. What is the ratio of sugar in solutions A and B?
   b. Compare the volumes of solutions A and B.
   c. What is the ratio of the concentrations of sugar in solutions A and B?
4. You add an aqueous solution of lead nitrate to an aqueous solution of potassium iodide. Draw highly magnified views of each solution individually and the mixed solution, including any product that forms. Write the balanced equation for the reaction.
5. You need to make 150.0 mL of a 0.10 M NaCl solution. You have solid NaCl and your lab partner has a 2.5 M NaCl solution. Explain how you each make the 0.10 M NaCl solution.
6. The exposed electrodes of a light bulb are placed in a solution of H_2SO_4 in an electrical circuit such that the light bulb is glowing. You add a dilute salt solution, and the bulb dims. Which of the following could be the salt in the solution?
   a. $Ba(NO_3)_2$
   b. $NaNO_3$
   c. K_2SO_4
   d. $Ca(NO_3)_2$

   Justify your choices. For those you did not choose, explain why they are incorrect.
7. You have two solutions of chemical A. To determine which has the highest concentration of A (molarity), which of the following must you know (there may be more than one answer)?
   a. the mass in grams of A in each solution
   b. the molar mass of A
   c. the volume of water added to each solution
   d. the total volume of the solution

   Explain.

8. Which of the following must be known to calculate the molarity of a salt solution (there may be more than one answer)?
   a. the mass of salt added
   b. the molar mass of the salt
   c. the volume of water added
   d. the total volume of the solution

   Explain.

9. Consider separate aqueous solutions of HCl and H_2SO_4, each with the same molar concentration. An aqueous solution of NaOH is added to each solution to neutralize the acid. Which acid solution requires the largest volume of NaOH solution to react completely with the acid present? Explain.

Exercises

OWL Interactive versions of these problems may be assigned in OWL.

A blue exercise number indicates that the answer to that exercise appears at the back of this book and a solution appears in the *Solutions Guide.*

Aqueous Solutions: Strong and Weak Electrolytes

10. Characterize strong electrolytes versus weak electrolytes versus nonelectrolytes. Give examples of each. How do you experimentally determine whether a soluble substance is a strong electrolyte, weak electrolyte, or nonelectrolyte.

11. The figures below are molecular-level representations of four aqueous solutions of the same solute. Arrange the solutions from most to least concentrated.

Solution A (1.0 L)

Solution B (4.0 L)

Solution C (2.0 L)

Solution D (2.0 L)

12. Which of the following statements is (are) true? Correct the false statements.
    a. A concentrated solution in water will always contain a strong or weak electrolyte.
    b. A strong electrolyte will break up into ions when dissolved in water.
    c. An acid is a strong electrolyte.
    d. All ionic compounds are strong electrolytes in water.

13. Differentiate between what happens when the following are dissolved in water.
    a. polar solute versus nonpolar solute
    b. KF versus $C_6H_{12}O_6$
    c. RbCl versus AgCl
    d. HNO_3 versus CO

14. Commercial cold packs and hot packs are available for treating athletic injuries. Both types contain a pouch of water and a dry chemical. When the pack is struck, the pouch of water breaks, dissolving the chemical, and the solution becomes either hot or cold. Many hot packs use magnesium sulfate, and many cold packs use ammonium nitrate. Write reaction equations to show how these strong electrolytes break apart in water.

15. Match each name below with the following microscopic pictures of that compound in aqueous solution.

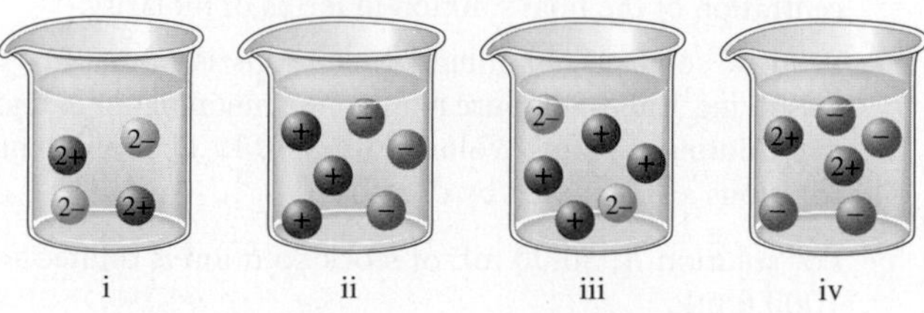

    a. barium nitrate
    b. sodium chloride
    c. potassium carbonate
    d. magnesium sulfate

Solution Concentration: Molarity

16. A solution of ethanol (C_2H_5OH) in water is prepared by dissolving 75.0 mL of ethanol (density = 0.79 g/cm^3) in enough water to make 250.0 mL of solution. What is the molarity of the ethanol in this solution?

17. Describe how you would prepare 2.00 L of each of the following solutions.
    a. 0.250 *M* NaOH from solid NaOH
    b. 0.250 *M* NaOH from 1.00 *M* NaOH stock solution
    c. 0.100 *M* K_2CrO_4 from solid K_2CrO_4
    d. 0.100 *M* K_2CrO_4 from 1.75 *M* K_2CrO_4 stock solution

18. How would you prepare 1.00 L of a 0.50 *M* solution of each of the following?
    a. H_2SO_4 from "concentrated" (18 *M*) sulfuric acid
    b. HCl from "concentrated" (12 *M*) reagent
    c. $NiCl_2$ from the salt $NiCl_2 \cdot 6H_2O$
    d. HNO_3 from "concentrated" (16 *M*) reagent
    e. Sodium carbonate from the pure solid

19. What mass of NaOH is contained in 250.0 mL of a 0.400 *M* sodium hydroxide solution?

20. If 10. g of $AgNO_3$ is available, what volume of 0.25 *M* $AgNO_3$ solution can be prepared?

21. Which of the following solutions of strong electrolytes contains the largest number of moles of chloride ions: 100.0 mL of 0.30 *M* $AlCl_3$, 50.0 mL of 0.60 *M* $MgCl_2$, or 200.0 mL of 0.40 *M* NaCl?

22. Calculate the concentration of all ions present in each of the following solutions of strong electrolytes.
    a. 0.100 mole of $Ca(NO_3)_2$ in 100.0 mL of solution
    b. 2.5 moles of Na_2SO_4 in 1.25 L of solution
    c. 5.00 g of NH_4Cl in 500.0 mL of solution
    d. 1.00 g of K_3PO_4 in 250.0 mL of solution

23. Calculate the sodium ion concentration when 70.0 mL of 3.0 *M* sodium carbonate is added to 30.0 mL of 1.0 *M* sodium bicarbonate.

24. A solution is prepared by dissolving 25.0 g of ammonium sulfate in enough water to make 100.0 mL of stock solution. A 10.00-mL sample of this stock solution is added to 50.00 mL of water. Calculate the concentration of ammonium ions and sulfate ions in the final solution.

25. A standard solution is prepared for the analysis of fluoxymesterone ($C_{20}H_{29}FO_3$), an anabolic steroid. A stock solution is first prepared by dissolving 10.0 mg of fluoxymesterone in enough water to give a total volume of 500.0 mL. A 100.0-μL aliquot (portion) of this solution is diluted to a final volume of 100.0 mL. Calculate the concentration of the final solution in terms of molarity.

26. A stock solution containing Mn^{2+} ions is prepared by dissolving 1.584 g of pure manganese metal in nitric acid and diluting to a final volume of 1.000 L. The following solutions are prepared by dilution.

For solution A, 50.00 mL of stock solution is diluted to 1000.0 mL.

For solution B, 10.00 mL of A is diluted to 250.0 mL.

For solution C, 10.00 mL of B is diluted to 500.0 mL.

Calculate the molar concentrations of the stock solution and solutions A, B, and C.

27. The units of parts per million (ppm) and parts per billion (ppb) are commonly used by environmental chemists. In general, 1 ppm means 1 part of solute for every 10^6 parts of solution. (Both solute and solution are measured using the same units.) Mathematically, by mass:

$$\text{ppm} = \frac{\mu\text{g solute}}{\text{g solution}} = \frac{\text{mg solute}}{\text{kg solution}}$$

In the case of very dilute aqueous solutions, a concentration of 1.0 ppm is equal to 1.0 μg of solute per 1.0 mL of solution, which equals 1.0 g of solution. Parts per billion is defined in a similar fashion. Calculate the molarity of each of the following aqueous solutions.
a. 5.0 ppb Hg in H_2O
b. 1.0 ppb $CHCl_3$ in H_2O
c. 10.0 ppm As in H_2O
d. 0.10 ppm DDT ($C_{14}H_9Cl_5$) in H_2O

28. In the spectroscopic analysis of many substances, a series of standard solutions of known concentration are measured to generate a calibration curve. How would you prepare standard solutions containing 10.0, 25.0, 50.0, 75.0, and 100. ppm of copper from a commercially produced 1000.0-ppm solution? Assume each solution has a final volume of 100.0 mL. (See Exercise 27 for definitions.)

Precipitation Reactions

29. List the formulas of three soluble bromide salts and three insoluble bromide salts. Do the same exercise for sulfate salts, hydroxide salts, and phosphate salts (list three soluble salts and three insoluble salts). List the formulas for six insoluble Pb^{2+} salts and one soluble Pb^{2+} salt.

30. When 1.0 mole of solid lead nitrate is added to 2.0 moles of aqueous potassium iodide, a yellow precipitate forms. After the precipitate settles to the bottom, does the solution above the precipitate conduct electricity? Explain. Write the complete ionic equation to help you answer this question.

31. When the following solutions are mixed together, what precipitate (if any) will form?
a. $Hg_2(NO_3)_2(aq) + CuSO_4(aq)$
b. $Ni(NO_3)_2(aq) + CaCl_2(aq)$
c. $K_2CO_3(aq) + MgI_2(aq)$
d. $Na_2CrO_4(aq) + AlBr_3(aq)$

32. For the reactions in Exercise 31, write the balanced molecular equation, complete ionic equation, and net ionic equation. If no precipitate forms, write "No reaction."

33. Write the balanced molecular, complete, and net ionic equations for the reaction, if any, that occurs when aqueous solutions of the following are mixed.
a. ammonium sulfate and barium nitrate
b. lead(II) nitrate and sodium chloride
c. sodium phosphate and potassium nitrate
d. sodium bromide and rubidium chloride
e. copper(II) chloride and sodium hydroxide

34. How would you separate the following ions in aqueous solution by selective precipitation?
a. Ag^+, Ba^{2+}, and Cr^{3+}
b. Ag^+, Pb^{2+}, and Cu^{2+}
c. Hg_2^{2+} and Ni^{2+}

35. Write the balanced molecular and net ionic equations for the reaction that occurs when the contents of the two beakers are added together. What colors represent the spectator ions in each reaction?

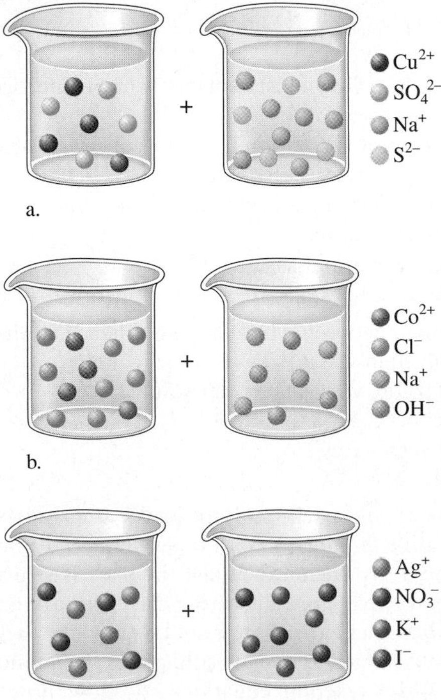

36. Give an example of how each of the following insoluble ionic compounds could be produced using a precipitation reaction. Write the balanced molecular equation for each reaction.
a. $Fe(OH)_3(s)$
b. $Hg_2Cl_2(s)$
c. $PbSO_4(s)$
d. $BaCrO_4(s)$

37. Separate samples of a solution of an unknown soluble ionic compound are treated with KCl, Na_2SO_4, and NaOH. A precipitate forms only when Na_2SO_4 is added. Which cations could be present in the unknown soluble ionic compound?

38. What volume of 0.100 *M* Na_3PO_4 is required to precipitate all of the lead(II) ions from 150.0 mL of 0.250 *M* $Pb(NO_3)_2$?

39. How many grams of silver chloride can be prepared by the reaction of 100.0 mL of 0.20 *M* silver nitrate with 100.0 mL of 0.15 *M* calcium chloride? Calculate the concentrations of each ion remaining in solution after precipitation is complete.

40. The following drawings represent aqueous solutions. Solution A is 2.00 L of a 2.00 *M* aqueous solution of copper(II) nitrate. Solution B is 2.00 L of a 3.00 *M* aqueous solution of potassium hydroxide.

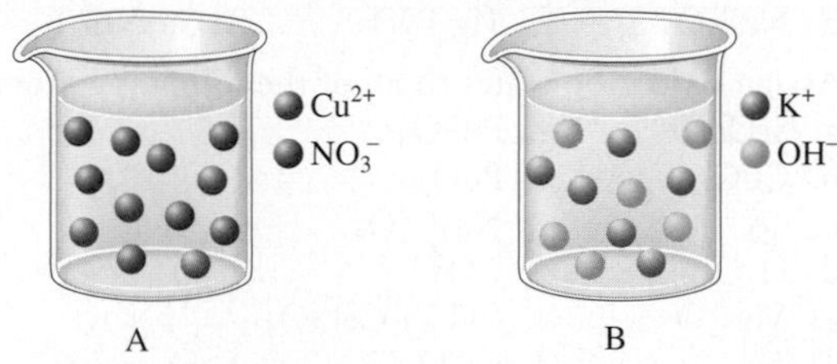

a. Draw a picture of the solution made by mixing solutions A and B together after the precipitation reaction takes place. Make sure this picture shows the correct relative volume compared with solutions A and B and the correct relative number of ions, along with the correct relative amount of solid formed.
b. Determine the concentrations (in *M*) of all ions left in solution (from part a) and the mass of solid formed.

41. What mass of Na_2CrO_4 is required to precipitate all of the silver ions from 75.0 mL of a 0.100 *M* solution of $AgNO_3$?

42. A 1.00-g sample of an alkaline earth metal chloride is treated with excess silver nitrate. All of the chloride is recovered as 1.38 g of silver chloride. Identify the metal.

43. A mixture contains only NaCl and $Al_2(SO_4)_3$. A 1.45-g sample of the mixture is dissolved in water, and an excess of NaOH is added, producing a precipitate of $Al(OH)_3$. The precipitate is filtered, dried, and weighed. The mass of the precipitate is 0.107 g. What is the mass percent of $Al_2(SO_4)_3$ in the sample?

44. The thallium (present as Tl_2SO_4) in a 9.486-g pesticide sample was precipitated as thallium(I) iodide. Calculate the mass percent of Tl_2SO_4 in the sample if 0.1824 g of TlI was recovered.

45. Saccharin ($C_7H_5NO_3S$) is sometimes dispensed in tablet form. Ten tablets with a total mass of 0.5894 g were dissolved in water. This solution was then oxidized to convert all the sulfur to sulfate ion, which was precipitated by adding an excess of barium chloride solution. The mass of $BaSO_4$ obtained was 0.5032 g. What is the average mass of saccharin per tablet? What is the average mass percent of saccharin in the tablets?

46. Douglasite is a mineral with the formula $2KCl \cdot FeCl_2 \cdot 2H_2O$. Calculate the mass percent of douglasite in a 455.0-mg sample if it took 37.20 mL of a 0.1000 *M* $AgNO_3$ solution to precipitate all the Cl^- as AgCl. Assume the douglasite is the only source of chloride ion.

47. A 1.42-g sample of a pure compound with formula M_2SO_4 was dissolved in water and treated with an excess of aqueous calcium chloride, resulting in the precipitation of all the sulfate ions as calcium sulfate. The precipitate was collected, dried, and found to weigh 1.36 g. Determine the atomic mass of M and identify M.

Acid–Base Reactions

48. Write balanced equations (all three types) for the reactions that occur when the following aqueous solutions are mixed.
a. ammonia (aqueous) and nitric acid
b. barium hydroxide (aqueous) and hydrochloric acid
c. perchloric acid [$HClO_4(aq)$] and solid iron(III) hydroxide
d. solid silver hydroxide and hydrobromic acid

49. What acid and what base would react in aqueous solution so that the following salts appear as products in the molecular equation? Write the balanced molecular equation for each reaction.
a. potassium perchlorate
b. cesium nitrate
c. calcium iodide

50. Carminic acid, a naturally occurring red pigment extracted from the cochineal insect, contains only carbon, hydrogen, and oxygen. It was commonly used as a dye in the first half of the nineteenth century. It is 53.66% C and 4.09% H by mass. A titration required 18.02 mL of 0.0406 *M* NaOH to neutralize 0.3602 g of carminic acid. Assuming that there is only one acidic hydrogen per molecule, what is the molecular formula of carminic acid?

51. What volume of each of the following acids will react completely with 50.00 mL of 0.100 *M* NaOH?
a. 0.100 *M* HCl
b. 0.100 *M* H_2SO_3 (two acidic hydrogens)
c. 0.200 *M* H_3PO_4 (three acidic hydrogens)
d. 0.150 *M* HNO_3
e. 0.200 *M* $HC_2H_3O_2$ (one acidic hydrogen)
f. 0.300 *M* H_2SO_4 (two acidic hydrogens)

52. A 30.0-mL sample of an unknown strong base is neutralized after the addition of 12.0 mL of a 0.150 *M* HNO_3 solution. If the unknown base concentration is 0.0300 *M*, give some possible identities for the unknown base.

53. A student had 1.00 L of a 1.00 *M* acid solution. Much to the surprise of the student, it took 2.00 L of 1.00 *M* NaOH solution to react completely with the acid. Explain why it took twice as much NaOH to react with all of the acid.

In a different experiment, a student had 10.0 mL of 0.020 *M* HCl. Again, much to the surprise of the student, it took only 5.00 mL of 0.020 *M* strong base to react completely with the HCl. Explain why it took only half as much strong base to react with all of the HCl.

54. Sodium hydroxide solution is usually standardized by titrating a pure sample of potassium hydrogen phthalate ($KHC_8H_4O_4$, often abbreviated KHP), an acid with one acidic hydrogen and a molar mass of 204.22 g/mol. It takes 34.67 mL of a sodium hydroxide solution to titrate a 0.1082-g sample of KHP. What is the molarity of the sodium hydroxide?

55. A 0.500-L sample of H_2SO_4 solution was analyzed by taking a 100.0-mL aliquot and adding 50.0 mL of 0.213 *M* NaOH. After the reaction occurred, an excess of OH^- ions remained in the solution. The excess base required 13.21 mL of 0.103 *M* HCl for neutralization. Calculate the molarity of the original sample of H_2SO_4. (Sulfuric acid has two acidic hydrogens.)

56. What volume of 0.0521 *M* $Ba(OH)_2$ is required to neutralize exactly 14.20 mL of 0.141 *M* H_3PO_4? Phosphoric acid contains three acidic hydrogens.

57. A 10.00-mL sample of vinegar, an aqueous solution of acetic acid ($HC_2H_3O_2$), is titrated with 0.5062 *M* NaOH, and 16.58 mL is required to reach the endpoint.
    a. What is the molarity of the acetic acid?
    b. If the density of the vinegar is 1.006 g/cm^3, what is the mass percent of acetic acid in the vinegar?

58. A student titrates an unknown amount of potassium hydrogen phthalate (KHP) with 20.46 mL of a 0.1000 *M* NaOH solution. KHP (molar mass = 204.22 g/mol) has one acidic hydrogen. How many grams of KHP were titrated (reacted completely) by the sodium hydroxide solution?

59. A student mixes four reagents together, thinking that the solutions will neutralize each other. The solutions mixed together are 50.0 mL of 0.100 *M* hydrochloric acid, 100.0 mL of 0.200 *M* of nitric acid, 500.0 mL of 0.0100 *M* calcium hydroxide, and 200.0 mL of 0.100 *M* rubidium hydroxide. Is the resulting solution neutral? If not, calculate the concentration of excess H^+ or OH^- ions left in solution.

60. A 50.00-mL sample of an ammonia solution is analyzed by titration with HCl. The reaction is

$$NH_3(aq) + H^+(aq) \longrightarrow NH_4^+(aq)$$

It took 39.47 mL of 0.0984 *M* HCl to titrate (react completely with) the ammonia. What is the concentration of the original ammonia solution?

61. Hydrochloric acid (75.0 mL of 0.250 *M*) is added to 225.0 mL of 0.0550 *M* $Ba(OH)_2$ solution. What is the concentration of the excess H^+ or OH^- left in this solution?

62. A 2.20-g sample of an unknown acid (empirical formula = $C_3H_4O_3$) is dissolved in 1.0 L of water. A titration required 25.0 mL of 0.500 *M* NaOH to react completely with all the acid present. Assuming that the unknown acid has one acidic proton per molecule, what is the molecular formula of the unknown acid?

Oxidation–Reduction Reactions

63. Differentiate between the following terms.
    a. species reduced versus the reducing agent
    b. species oxidized versus the oxidizing agent
    c. oxidation state versus actual charge

64. How do you balance redox reactions by the oxidation states method?

65. Assign oxidation states to all atoms in each compound.
    a. $KMnO_4$
    b. NiO_2
    c. $K_4Fe(CN)_6$ (Fe only)
    d. $(NH_4)_2HPO_4$
    e. P_4O_6
    f. Fe_3O_4
    g. $XeOF_4$
    h. SF_4
    i. CO
    j. $C_6H_{12}O_6$

66. Assign oxidation states to all of the following atoms.
    a. UO_2^{2+}
    b. As_2O_3
    c. $NaBiO_3$
    d. As_4
    e. $HAsO_2$
    f. $Mg_2P_2O_7$
    g. $Na_2S_2O_3$
    h. Hg_2Cl_2
    i. $Ca(NO_3)_2$

67. Assign oxidation states to all of the following atoms.
    a. $SrCr_2O_7$
    b. $CuCl_2$
    c. O_2
    d. H_2O_2
    e. $MgCO_3$
    f. Ag
    g. $PbSO_3$
    h. PbO_2
    i. $Na_2C_2O_4$
    j. CO_2
    k. $(NH_4)_2Ce(SO_4)_3$
    l. Cr_2O_3

68. Tell which of the following are oxidation–reduction reactions. For those that are, identify the oxidizing agent, the reducing agent, the substance being oxidized, and the substance being reduced.
    a. $CH_4(g) + 2O_2(g) \longrightarrow CO_2(g) + 2H_2O(g)$
    b. $Zn(s) + 2HCl(aq) \longrightarrow ZnCl_2(aq) + H_2(g)$
    c. $Cr_2O_7^{2-}(aq) + 2OH^-(aq) \longrightarrow 2CrO_4^{2-}(aq) + H_2O(l)$
    d. $O_3(g) + NO(g) \longrightarrow O_2(g) + NO_2(g)$
    e. $2H_2O_2(l) \longrightarrow 2H_2O(l) + O_2(g)$
    f. $2CuCl(aq) \longrightarrow CuCl_2(aq) + Cu(s)$
    g. $HCl(g) + NH_3(g) \longrightarrow NH_4Cl(s)$
    h. $SiCl_4(l) + 2H_2O(l) \longrightarrow 4HCl(aq) + SiO_2(s)$
    i. $SiCl_4(l) + 2Mg(s) \longrightarrow 2MgCl_2(s) + Si(s)$

69. Many oxidation–reduction reactions can be balanced by inspection. Try to balance the following reactions by inspection. In each reaction, identify the substance reduced and the substance oxidized.
    a. $Al(s) + HCl(aq) \longrightarrow AlCl_3(aq) + H_2(g)$
    b. $CH_4(g) + S(s) \longrightarrow CS_2(l) + H_2S(g)$
    c. $C_3H_8(g) + O_2(g) \longrightarrow CO_2(g) + H_2O(l)$
    d. $Cu(s) + Ag^+(aq) \longrightarrow Ag(s) + Cu^{2+}(aq)$

70. Balance each of the following oxidation–reduction reactions by using the oxidation states method.
    a. $C_2H_6(g) + O_2(g) \longrightarrow CO_2(g) + H_2O(g)$
    b. $Mg(s) + HCl(aq) \longrightarrow Mg^{2+}(aq) + Cl^-(aq) + H_2(g)$
    c. $Cu(s) + Ag^+(aq) \longrightarrow Cu^{2+}(aq) + Ag(s)$
    d. $Zn(s) + H_2SO_4(aq) \longrightarrow ZnSO_4(aq) + H_2(g)$

71. Balance the following oxidation–reduction reactions, which occur in acidic solution, using the half-reaction method.
a. $Cu(s) + NO_3^-(aq) \longrightarrow Cu^{2+}(aq) + NO(g)$
b. $Cr_2O_7^{2-}(aq) + Cl^-(aq) \longrightarrow Cr^{3+}(aq) + Cl_2(g)$
c. $Pb(s) + PbO_2(s) + H_2SO_4(aq) \longrightarrow PbSO_4(s)$
d. $Mn^{2+}(aq) + NaBiO_3(s) \longrightarrow Bi^{3+}(aq) + MnO_4^-(aq)$
e. $H_3AsO_4(aq) + Zn(s) \longrightarrow AsH_3(g) + Zn^{2+}(aq)$
f. $As_2O_3(s) + NO_3^-(aq) \longrightarrow H_3AsO_4(aq) + NO(g)$
g. $Br^-(aq) + MnO_4^-(aq) \longrightarrow Br_2(l) + Mn^{2+}(aq)$
h. $CH_3OH(aq) + Cr_2O_7^{2-}(aq) \longrightarrow CH_2O(aq) + Cr^{3+}(aq)$

72. Balance the following oxidation–reduction reactions, which occur in basic solution, using the half-reaction method.
a. $Al(s) + MnO_4^-(aq) \longrightarrow MnO_2(s) + Al(OH)_4^-(aq)$
b. $Cl_2(g) \longrightarrow Cl^-(aq) + ClO^-(aq)$
c. $NO_2^-(aq) + Al(s) \longrightarrow NH_3(g) + AlO_2^-(aq)$
d. $MnO_4^-(aq) + S^{2-}(aq) \longrightarrow MnS(s) + S(s)$
e. $CN^-(aq) + MnO_4^-(aq) \longrightarrow CNO^-(aq) + MnO_2(s)$

73. Balance the following equations by the half-reaction method.
a. $Fe(s) + HCl(aq) \longrightarrow HFeCl_4(aq) + H_2(g)$
b. $IO_3^-(aq) + I^-(aq) \xrightarrow{\text{Acidic}} I_3^-(aq)$
c. $Cr(NCS)_6^{4-}(aq) + Ce^{4+}(aq) \xrightarrow{\text{Acidic}} Cr^{3+}(aq) + Ce^{3+}(aq) + NO_3^-(aq) + CO_2(g) + SO_4^{2-}(aq)$
d. $CrI_3(s) + Cl_2(g) \xrightarrow{\text{Basic}} CrO_4^{2-}(aq) + IO_4^-(aq) + Cl^-(aq)$
e. $Fe(CN)_6^{4-}(aq) + Ce^{4+}(aq) \xrightarrow{\text{Basic}} Ce(OH)_3(s) + Fe(OH)_3(s) + CO_3^{2-}(aq) + NO_3^-(aq)$

74. One of the classic methods for the determination of the manganese content in steel involves converting all the manganese to the deeply colored permanganate ion and then measuring the absorption of light. The steel is first dissolved in nitric acid, producing the manganese(II) ion and nitrogen dioxide gas. This solution is then reacted with an acidic solution containing periodate ion; the products are the permanganate and iodate ions. Write balanced chemical equations for both of these steps.

75. A solution of permanganate is standardized by titration with oxalic acid ($H_2C_2O_4$). It required 28.97 mL of the permanganate solution to react completely with 0.1058 g of oxalic acid. The unbalanced equation for the reaction is

$$MnO_4^-(aq) + H_2C_2O_4(aq) \xrightarrow{\text{Acidic}} Mn^{2+}(aq) + CO_2(g)$$

What is the molarity of the permanganate solution?

76. A 50.00-mL sample of solution containing Fe^{2+} ions is titrated with a 0.0216 M $KMnO_4$ solution. It required 20.62 mL of $KMnO_4$ solution to oxidize all the Fe^{2+} ions to Fe^{3+} ions by the reaction

$$MnO_4^-(aq) + Fe^{2+}(aq) \xrightarrow{\text{Acidic}} Mn^{2+}(aq) + Fe^{3+}(aq)$$
(Unbalanced)

a. What was the concentration of Fe^{2+} ions in the sample solution?
b. What volume of 0.0150 M $K_2Cr_2O_7$ solution would it take to do the same titration? The reaction is

$$Cr_2O_7^{2-}(aq) + Fe^{2+}(aq) \xrightarrow{\text{Acidic}} Cr^{3+}(aq) + Fe^{3+}(aq)$$
(Unbalanced)

77. The iron content of iron ore can be determined by titration with a standard $KMnO_4$ solution. The iron ore is dissolved in HCl, and all the iron is reduced to Fe^{2+} ions. This solution is then titrated with $KMnO_4$ solution, producing Fe^{3+} and Mn^{2+} ions in acidic solution. If it required 38.37 mL of 0.0198 M $KMnO_4$ to titrate a solution made from 0.6128 g of iron ore, what is the mass percent of iron in the iron ore?

78. The vanadium in a sample of ore is converted to VO^{2+}. The VO^{2+} ion is subsequently titrated with MnO_4^- in acidic solution to form $V(OH)_4^+$ and manganese(II) ion. To titrate the solution, 26.45 mL of 0.02250 M MnO_4^- was required. If the mass percent of vanadium in the ore was 58.1%, what was the mass of the ore sample?

79. When hydrochloric acid reacts with magnesium metal, hydrogen gas and aqueous magnesium chloride are produced. What volume of 5.0 M HCl is required to react completely with 3.00 g of magnesium?

80. Triiodide ions are generated in solution by the following (unbalanced) reaction in acidic solution:

$$IO_3^-(aq) + I^-(aq) \longrightarrow I_3^-(aq)$$

Triiodide ion is determined by titration with a sodium thiosulfate ($Na_2S_2O_3$) solution. The products are iodide ion and tetrathionate ion ($S_4O_6^{2-}$).
a. Balance the equation for the reaction of IO_3^- with I^- ions.
b. A sample of 0.6013 g of potassium iodate was dissolved in water. Hydrochloric acid and solid potassium iodide were then added in excess. What is the minimum mass of solid KI and the minimum volume of 3.00 M HCl required to convert all of the IO_3^- ions to I_3^- ions?
c. Write and balance the equation for the reaction of $S_2O_3^{2-}$ with I_3^- in acidic solution.
d. A 25.00-mL sample of a 0.0100 M solution of KIO_3 is reacted with an excess of KI. It requires 32.04 mL of $Na_2S_2O_3$ solution to titrate the I_3^- ions present. What is the molarity of the $Na_2S_2O_3$ solution?
e. How would you prepare 500.0 mL of the KIO_3 solution in part d, using pure, dry KIO_3?

Additional Exercises

81. A 230.-mL sample of a 0.275 *M* $CaCl_2$ solution is left on a hot plate overnight; the following morning, the solution is 1.10 *M*. What volume of water evaporated from the 0.275 *M* $CaCl_2$ solution?

82. Using the general solubility rules given in Table 4.1, name three reagents that would form precipitates with each of the following ions in aqueous solution. Write the net ionic equation for each of your suggestions.
    a. chloride ion
    b. calcium ion
    c. iron(III) ion
    d. sulfate ion
    e. mercury(I) ion, Hg_2^{2+}
    f. silver ion

83. Consider a 1.50-g mixture of magnesium nitrate and magnesium chloride. After dissolving this mixture in water, 0.500 *M* silver nitrate is added dropwise until precipitate formation is complete. This mass of the white precipitate formed is 0.641 g.
    a. Calculate the mass percent of magnesium chloride in the mixture.
    b. Determine the minimum volume of silver nitrate that must have been added to ensure complete formation of the precipitate.

84. What mass of solid aluminum hydroxide can be produced when 50.0 mL of 0.200 *M* $Al(NO_3)_3$ is added to 200.0 mL of 0.100 *M* KOH?

85. In most of its ionic compounds, cobalt is either Co(II) or Co(III). One such compound, containing chloride ion and waters of hydration, was analyzed, and the following results were obtained. A 0.256-g sample of the compound was dissolved in water, and excess silver nitrate was added. The silver chloride was filtered, dried, and weighed, and it had a mass of 0.308 g. A second sample of 0.416 g of the compound was dissolved in water, and an excess of sodium hydroxide was added. The hydroxide salt was filtered and heated in a flame, forming cobalt(III) oxide. The mass of the cobalt(III) oxide formed was 0.145 g.
    a. What is the percent composition, by mass, of the compound?
    b. Assuming the compound contains one cobalt ion per formula unit, what is the formula?
    c. Write balanced equations for the three reactions described.

86. A mixture contains only NaCl and $Fe(NO_3)_3$. A 0.456-g sample of the mixture is dissolved in water, and an excess of NaOH is added, producing a precipitate of $Fe(OH)_3$. The precipitate is filtered, dried, and weighed. Its mass is 0.107 g. Calculate the following.
    a. the mass of iron in the sample
    b. the mass of $Fe(NO_3)_3$ in the sample
    c. the mass percent of $Fe(NO_3)_3$ in the sample

87. A mixture contains only sodium chloride and potassium chloride. A 0.1586-g sample of the mixture was dissolved in water. It took 22.90 mL of 0.1000 *M* $AgNO_3$ to completely precipitate all the chloride present. What is the composition (by mass percent) of the mixture?

88. Tris(pentafluorophenyl)borane, commonly known by its acronym BARF, is frequently used to initiate polymerization of ethylene or propylene in the presence of a catalytic transition metal compound. It is composed solely of C, F, and B; it is 42.23% C and 55.66% F by mass.
    a. What is the empirical formula of BARF?
    b. A 2.251-g sample of BARF dissolved in 347.0 mL of solution produces a 0.01267 *M* solution. What is the molecular formula of BARF?

89. A student added 50.0 mL of an NaOH solution to 100.0 mL of 0.400 *M* HCl. The solution was then treated with an excess of aqueous chromium(III) nitrate, resulting in formation of 2.06 g of precipitate. Determine the concentration of the NaOH solution.

90. In a 1-L beaker, 203 mL of 0.307 *M* ammonium chromate was mixed with 137 mL of 0.269 *M* chromium(III) nitrite to produce ammonium nitrite and chromium(III) chromate. Write the balanced chemical equation for the reaction occurring here. If the percent yield of the reaction was 88.0%, how much chromium(III) chromate was isolated?

91. It took 25.06 ± 0.05 mL of a sodium hydroxide solution to titrate a 0.4016-g sample of KHP (see Exercise 54). Calculate the concentration and uncertainty in the concentration of the sodium hydroxide solution. (See Appendix Section A1.5.) Neglect any uncertainty in the mass.

92. You wish to prepare 1 L of a 0.02 *M* potassium iodate solution. You require that the final concentration be within 1% of 0.02 *M* and that the concentration must be known accurately to the fourth decimal place. How would you prepare this solution? Specify the glassware you would use, the accuracy needed for the balance, and the ranges of acceptable masses of KIO_3 that can be used.

93. Citric acid, which can be obtained from lemon juice, has the molecular formula $C_6H_8O_7$. A 0.250-g sample of citric acid dissolved in 25.0 mL of water requires 37.2 mL of 0.105 *M* NaOH for complete neutralization. How many acidic hydrogens per molecule does citric acid have?

94. Acetylsalicylic acid is the active ingredient in aspirin. It took 35.17 mL of 0.5065 *M* sodium hydroxide to react completely with 3.210 g of acetylsalicylic acid. Acetylsalicylic acid has one acidic hydrogen. What is the molar mass of acetylsalicylic acid?

95. When organic compounds containing sulfur are burned, sulfur dioxide is produced. The amount of SO_2 formed can be determined by reaction with hydrogen peroxide:

$$H_2O_2(aq) + SO_2(g) \longrightarrow H_2SO_4(aq)$$

The resulting sulfuric acid is then titrated with a standard NaOH solution. A 1.325-g sample of coal is burned and the SO_2 collected in a solution of hydrogen peroxide. It took 28.44 mL of 0.1000 *M* NaOH to neutralize the resulting sulfuric acid. Calculate the mass percent of sulfur in the coal sample. Sulfuric acid has two acidic hydrogens.

Challenge Problems

96. The blood alcohol (C_2H_5OH) level can be determined by titrating a sample of blood plasma with an acidic potassium dichromate solution, resulting in the production of $Cr^{3+}(aq)$ and carbon dioxide. The reaction can be monitored because the dichromate ion ($Cr_2O_7^{2-}$) is orange in solution, and the Cr^{3+} ion is green. The unbalanced redox equation is

$$Cr_2O_7^{2-}(aq) + C_2H_5OH(aq) \longrightarrow Cr^{3+}(aq) + CO_2(g)$$

If 31.05 mL of 0.0600 *M* potassium dichromate solution is required to titrate 30.0 g of blood plasma, determine the mass percent of alcohol in the blood.

97. Zinc and magnesium metal each react with hydrochloric acid according to the following equations:

$$Zn(s) + 2HCl(aq) \longrightarrow ZnCl_2(aq) + H_2(g)$$
$$Mg(s) + 2HCl(aq) \longrightarrow MgCl_2(aq) + H_2(g)$$

A 10.00-g mixture of zinc and magnesium is reacted with the stoichiometric amount of hydrochloric acid. The reaction mixture is then reacted with 156 mL of 3.00 *M* silver nitrate to produce the maximum possible amount of silver chloride.
a. Determine the percent magnesium by mass in the original mixture.
b. If 78.0 mL of HCl was added, what was the concentration of the HCl?

98. A 10.00-g sample consisting of a mixture of sodium chloride and potassium sulfate is dissolved in water. This aqueous mixture then reacts with excess aqueous lead(II) nitrate to form 21.75 g of solid. Determine the mass percent of sodium chloride in the original mixture.

99. Consider the reaction of 19.0 g of zinc with excess silver nitrite to produce silver metal and zinc nitrite. The reaction is stopped before all the zinc metal has reacted and 29.0 g of solid metal is present. Calculate the mass of each metal in the 29.0-g mixture.

100. Consider an experiment in which two burets, Y and Z, are simultaneously draining into a beaker that initially contained 275.0 mL of 0.300 *M* HCl. Buret Y contains 0.150 *M* NaOH and buret Z contains 0.250 *M* KOH. The stoichiometric point in the titration is reached 60.65 minutes after Y and Z were started simultaneously. The total volume in the beaker at the stoichiometric point is 655 mL. Calculate the flow rates of burets Y and Z. Assume the flow rates remain constant during the experiment.

101. A sample is a mixture of KCl and KBr. When 0.1024 g of the sample is dissolved in water and reacted with excess silver nitrate, 0.1889 g of solid is obtained. What is the composition by mass percent of the mixture?

102. You made 100.0 mL of a lead(II) nitrate solution for lab but forgot to cap it. The next lab session you noticed that there was only 80.0 mL left (the rest had evaporated). In addition, you forgot the initial concentration of the solution. You decide to take 2.00 mL of the solution and add an excess of a concentrated sodium chloride solution. You obtain a solid with a mass of 3.407 g. What was the concentration of the original lead(II) nitrate solution?

103. Polychlorinated biphenyls (PCBs) have been used extensively as dielectric materials in electrical transformers. Because PCBs have been shown to be potentially harmful, analysis for their presence in the environment has become very important. PCBs are manufactured according to the following generic reaction:

$$C_{12}H_{10} + nCl_2 \xrightarrow[\text{catalyst}]{\text{Fe}} C_{12}H_{10-n}Cl_n + nHCl$$

This reaction results in a mixture of PCB products. The mixture is analyzed by decomposing the PCBs and then precipitating the resulting Cl^- as AgCl.
a. Develop a general equation that relates the average value of *n* to the mass of a given mixture of PCBs and the mass of AgCl produced.
b. A 0.1947-g sample of a commercial PCB yielded 0.4971 g of AgCl. What is the average value of *n* for this sample?

104. Consider reacting copper(II) sulfate with iron. Two possible reactions can occur, as represented by the following equations.

copper(II) sulfate(aq) + iron(s) $\longrightarrow$ copper(s) + iron(II) sulfate(aq)

copper(II) sulfate(aq) + iron(s) $\longrightarrow$ copper(s) + iron(III) sulfate(aq)

You place 87.7 mL of a 0.500 *M* solution of copper(II) sulfate in a beaker. You then add 2.00 g of iron filings to the copper(II) sulfate solution. After the reaction occurs, you isolate 2.27 g of copper. Which equation above describes the reaction that occurred? Support your answer.

105. A stream flows at a rate of 5.00×10^4 liters per second (L/s) upstream of a manufacturing plant. The plant discharges 3.50×10^3 L/s of water that contains 65.0 ppm HCl into the stream. (See Exercise 27 for definitions.)
a. Calculate the stream's total flow rate downstream from this plant.
b. Calculate the concentration of HCl in ppm downstream from this plant.
c. Further downstream, another manufacturing plant diverts 1.80×10^4 L/s of water from the stream for its own use. This plant must first neutralize the acid and does so by adding lime:

$$CaO(s) + 2H^+(aq) \longrightarrow Ca^{2+}(aq) + H_2O(l)$$

What mass of CaO is consumed in an 8.00-h work day by this plant?
d. The original stream water contained 10.2 ppm Ca^{2+}. Although no calcium was in the waste water from the first plant, the waste water of the second plant contains Ca^{2+} from the neutralization process. If 90.0% of the water used by the second plant is returned to the stream, calculate the concentration of Ca^{2+} in ppm downstream of the second plant.

106. Chromium has been investigated as a coating for steel cans. The thickness of the chromium film is determined by dissolving a sample of a can in acid and oxidizing the resulting Cr^{3+} to $Cr_2O_7^{2-}$ with the peroxydisulfate ion:

$$S_2O_8^{2-}(aq) + Cr^{3+}(aq) + H_2O(l) \longrightarrow Cr_2O_7^{2-}(aq) + SO_4^{2-}(aq) + H^+(aq) \text{ (Unbalanced)}$$

After removal of unreacted $S_2O_8^{2-}$, an excess of ferrous ammonium sulfate [$Fe(NH_4)_2(SO_4)_2 \cdot 6H_2O$] is added, reacting with $Cr_2O_7^{2-}$ produced from the first reaction. The unreacted Fe^{2+} from the excess ferrous ammonium sulfate is titrated with a separate $K_2Cr_2O_7$ solution. The reaction is:

$$H^+(aq) + Fe^{2+}(aq) + Cr_2O_7^{2-}(aq) \longrightarrow Fe^{3+}(aq) + Cr^{3+}(aq) + H_2O(l) \text{ (Unbalanced)}$$

a. Write balanced chemical equations for the two reactions.
b. In one analysis, a 40.0-cm^2 sample of a chromium-plated can was treated according to this procedure. After dissolution and removal of excess $S_2O_8^{2-}$, 3.000 g of $Fe(NH_4)_2(SO_4)_2 \cdot 6H_2O$ was added. It took 8.58 mL of 0.0520 *M* $K_2Cr_2O_7$ solution to completely react with the excess Fe^{2+}. Calculate the thickness of the chromium film on the can. (The density of chromium is 7.19 g/cm^3.)

107. One high-temperature superconductor has the general formula $YBa_2Cu_3O_x$. The copper is a mixture of Cu(II) and Cu(III) oxidation states. This mixture of oxidation states appears vital for high-temperature superconductivity to occur. A simple method for determining the average copper oxidation state has been reported [D. C. Harris, M. E. Hillis, and T. A. Hewston, *J. Chem. Educ.* 64, 847(1987)]. The described analysis takes place in two steps:

i. One superconductor sample is treated directly with I^-:

$$Cu^{2+}(aq) + I^-(aq) \longrightarrow CuI(s) + I_3^-(aq) \text{ (Unbalanced)}$$

$$Cu^{3+}(aq) + I^-(aq) \longrightarrow CuI(s) + I_3^-(aq) \text{ (Unbalanced)}$$

ii. A second superconductor sample is dissolved in acid, converting all copper to Cu(II). This solution is then treated with I^-:

$$Cu^{2+}(aq) + I^-(aq) \longrightarrow CuI(s) + I_3^-(aq) \text{ (Unbalanced)}$$

In both steps the I_3^- is determined by titrating with a standard sodium thiosulfate ($Na_2S_2O_3$) solution:

$$I_3^-(aq) + S_2O_3^{2-}(aq) \longrightarrow S_4O_6^{2-}(aq) + I^-(aq) \text{ (Unbalanced)}$$

a. Calculate the average copper oxidation states for materials with the formulas $YBa_2Cu_3O_{6.5}$, $YBa_2Cu_3O_7$, and $YBa_2Cu_3O_8$. Interpret your results in terms of a mixture of Cu(II) and Cu(III) ions, assuming that only Y^{3+}, Ba^{2+}, and O^{2-} are present in addition to the copper ions.
b. Balance the equations involved in the copper analysis.
c. A superconductor sample was analyzed by the above procedure. In step i, it took 37.77 mL of 0.1000 *M* $Na_2S_2O_3$ to react completely with the I_3^- generated from a 562.5-mg sample. In step ii, it took 22.57 mL of 0.1000 *M* $Na_2S_2O_3$ to react with the I_3^- generated by a 504.2-mg sample. Determine the formula of this superconductor sample (that is, find the value of x in $YBa_2Cu_3O_x$). Calculate the average oxidation state of copper in this material.

108. You are given a solid that is a mixture of Na_2SO_4 and K_2SO_4. A 0.205-g sample of the mixture is dissolved in water. An excess of an aqueous solution of $BaCl_2$ is added. The $BaSO_4$ that is formed is filtered, dried, and weighed. Its mass is 0.298 g. What mass of SO_4^{2-} ion is in the sample? What is the mass percent of SO_4^{2-} ion in the sample? What are the percent compositions by mass of Na_2SO_4 and K_2SO_4 in the sample?

109. A sample is a mixture of $AgNO_3$, $CuCl_2$, and $FeCl_3$. When a 1.0000-g sample of the mixture is dissolved in water and reacted with excess silver nitrate, 1.7809 g of precipitate forms. When a separate 1.0000-g sample of the mixture is treated with a reducing agent, all the metal ions in the mixture are reduced to pure metals. The total mass of pure metals produced is 0.4684 g. Calculate the mass percent of $AgNO_3$, $CuCl_2$, and $FeCl_3$ in the original mixture.

110. Three students were asked to find the identity of the metal in a particular sulfate salt. They dissolved a 0.1472-g sample of the salt in water and treated it with excess barium chloride, resulting in the precipitation of barium sulfate. After the precipitate had been filtered and dried, it weighed 0.2327 g.

Each student analyzed the data independently and came to different conclusions. Pat decided that the metal was titanium. Chris thought it was sodium. Randy reported that it was gallium. What formula did each student assign to the sulfate salt?

Look for information on the sulfates of gallium, sodium, and titanium in this text and reference books such as the *CRC Handbook of Chemistry and Physics*. What further tests would you suggest to determine which student is most likely correct?

Marathon Problems*

111. The formate ion, CHO_2^-, forms ionic compounds with many metal ions. Assume that 9.7416 g $M(CHO_2)_2$ (where M represents the atomic symbol for a particular metal) is dissolved in water. When a solution of 0.200 *M* sodium sulfate is added, a white precipitate forms. The sodium sulfate solution is added until no more precipitate forms; then a few milliliters are added in excess. The precipitate is filtered, dried, and weighed. It has a mass of 9.9392 g. The filtrate is saved for further use.

    A potassium permanganate solution is standardized by dissolving 0.9234 g sodium oxalate in dilute sulfuric acid and then titrating with the potassium permanganate solution. The principal products of the reaction are manganese(II) ion and carbon dioxide gas. The titration requires 18.55 mL of the potassium permanganate solution to reach the endpoint, which is indicated by the first permanent, but barely perceptible, pink color of the permanganate ion.

    The filtrate from the original reaction is diluted by pouring it into a 250-mL volumetric flask, diluting to the mark with water, and then mixing thoroughly. An aliquot consisting of 10.00 mL of this diluted solution is pipetted into a 125-mL Erlenmeyer flask, approximately 25 mL of water is added, and the solution is made basic. What volume of the standard permanganate solution will be needed to titrate this solution to the equivalence point? The principal products of the reaction are carbonate ion and manganese(IV) oxide. Identify M.

112. You have two 500.0-mL aqueous solutions. Solution A is a solution of a metal nitrate that is 8.246% nitrogen by mass. The ionic compound in solution B consists of potassium, chromium, and oxygen; chromium has an oxidation state of +6, and there are 2 potassiums and 1 chromium in the formula. The masses of the solutes in each of the solutions are the same. When the solutions are added together, a blood-red precipitate forms. After the reaction has gone to completion, you dry the solid and find that it has a mass of 331.8 g.
    a. Identify the ionic compounds in solution A and solution B.
    b. Identify the blood-red precipitate.
    c. Calculate the concentration (molarity) of all ions in the original solutions.
    d. Calculate the concentration (molarity) of all ions in the final solution.

*From James H. Burness, "The Use of "Marathon" Problems as Effective Vehicles for the Presentation of General Chemistry Lectures," Journal of Chemical Education, 68(11).

5 Gases

chapter

Hot air balloon taking off from the ski resort of Chateau d'Oex in the Swiss Alps.

Carlos Caetano/Shutterstock.com #20537510

OWL
Sign in to OWL at www.cengage.com/owl to view tutorials and simulations, develop problem-solving skills, and complete online homework assigned by your professor.

Download mini lecture videos for key concept review and exam prep from OWL or purchase them from www.cengagebrain.com.

Matter exists in three distinct physical states: gas, liquid, and solid. Of these, the gaseous state is the easiest to describe both experimentally and theoretically. In particular, the study of gases provides an excellent example of the scientific method in action. It illustrates how observations lead to natural laws, which in turn can be accounted for by models. Then, as more accurate measurements become available, the models are modified.

In addition to providing a good illustration of the scientific method, gases are important in their own right. For example, gases are often produced in chemical reactions and thus must be dealt with in stoichiometric calculations. Also, the earth's atmosphere is a mixture of gases, primarily elemental nitrogen and oxygen; it both supports life and acts as a waste receptacle for the exhaust gases that accompany many industrial processes.

For these reasons, it is important to understand the behavior of gases. We will pursue this goal by considering the properties of gases, the laws and models that describe the behavior of gases, and finally the reactions that occur among the gases in the atmosphere.

5.1 Early Experiments

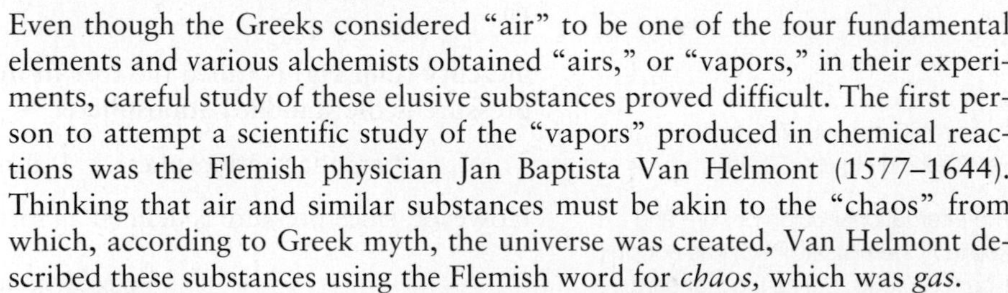

Even though the Greeks considered "air" to be one of the four fundamental elements and various alchemists obtained "airs," or "vapors," in their experiments, careful study of these elusive substances proved difficult. The first person to attempt a scientific study of the "vapors" produced in chemical reactions was the Flemish physician Jan Baptista Van Helmont (1577–1644). Thinking that air and similar substances must be akin to the "chaos" from which, according to Greek myth, the universe was created, Van Helmont described these substances using the Flemish word for *chaos,* which was *gas.*

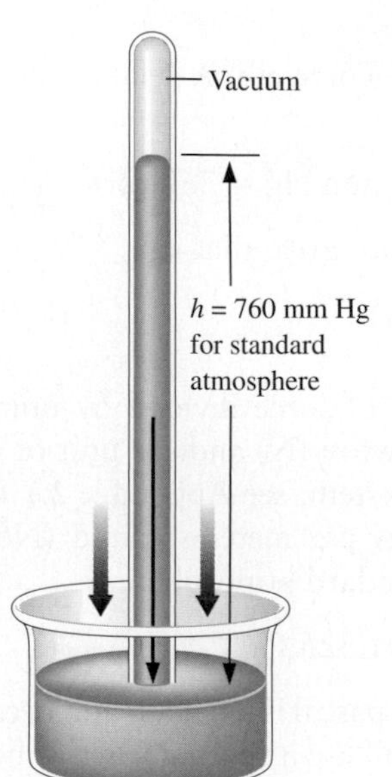

Figure 5.1
A torricellian barometer. The tube, completely filled with mercury, is inverted in a dish of mercury. Mercury flows out of the tube until the pressure of the column of mercury (shown by black arrow) "standing on the surface" of the mercury in the dish is equal to the pressure of the air (shown by purple arrows) on the rest of the surface of the mercury in the dish.

Van Helmont extensively studied a gas he obtained from burning wood, which he called "gas sylvestre" and which we now know as carbon dioxide, and noted that this substance was similar in many ways but not identical to air. By the end of his life, the importance of gases, especially air, was becoming more apparent. In 1643 the Italian physicist Evangelista Torricelli (1608–1647), who had been a student of Galileo, performed experiments that showed that *the air in the atmosphere exerts pressure.* (In fact, as we will see, all gases exert pressure.) Torricelli designed the first **barometer** by filling a tube that was closed at one end with mercury and then inverting it in a dish of mercury (Fig. 5.1). He observed that a column of mercury approximately 760 millimeters long always remained in the tube as a result of the pressure of the atmosphere.

A few years later Otto von Guericke, a German physicist, invented an air pump, often called a vacuum pump, that he used in a famous demonstration for the king of Prussia in 1654. Guericke placed two hemispheres together and pumped the air out of the resulting sphere through a valve, which was subsequently closed. He then dramatically showed that teams of horses could not pull the hemispheres apart. However, after secretly opening the valve to let air in, Guericke was able to separate the hemispheres easily by hand. The king of Prussia was so impressed by Guericke's cleverness that he awarded him a lifetime pension.

Units of Pressure

Because instruments used for measuring pressure, such as the **manometer** (Fig. 5.2), often use columns of mercury because of its high density, the most commonly used units for pressure are based on the height of the mercury column (in millimeters) the gas pressure can support. The unit **millimeters of**

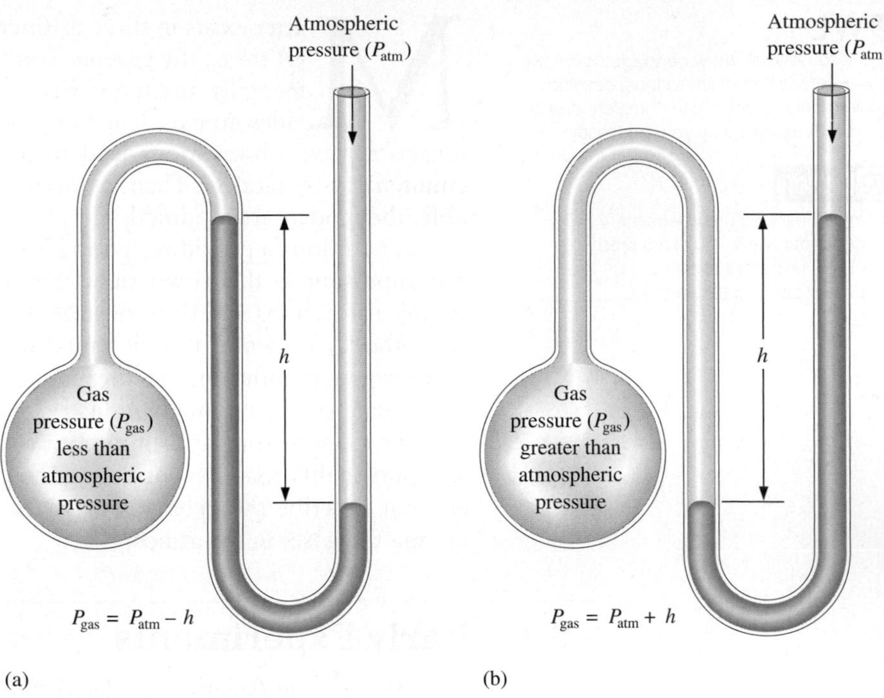

Figure 5.2
A simple manometer, a device for measuring the pressure of a gas in a container. The pressure of the gas is given by h (the difference in mercury levels) in units of torr (equivalent to mm Hg). (a) Gas pressure = atmospheric pressure − h. (b) Gas pressure = atmospheric pressure + h.

mercury (mm Hg) is called the **torr** in honor of Torricelli. A related unit for pressure is the **standard atmosphere:**

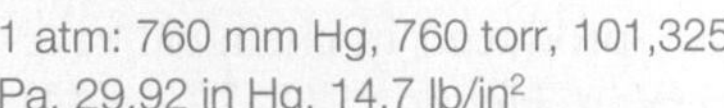

1 atm: 760 mm Hg, 760 torr, 101,325 Pa, 29.92 in Hg, 14.7 lb/in^2

$$1 \text{ standard atmosphere} = 1 \text{ atm} = 760 \text{ mm Hg} = 760 \text{ torr}$$

The International Union of Pure and Applied Chemists (IUPAC) has adopted 1 bar (100,000. Pa) as the standard pressure instead of 1 atm (101,325 Pa). Both standards are now widely used.

However, since pressure is defined as force per unit area, that is,

$$\text{Pressure} = \frac{\text{force}}{\text{area}}$$

the fundamental units of pressure involve units of force divided by units of area. In the SI system, the unit of force is the newton (N) and the unit of area is meters squared (m^2). (For a review of the SI system, see Appendix 2.) Thus the unit of pressure in the SI system is newtons per meter squared (N/m^2), called the **pascal** (Pa). In terms of pascals the standard atmosphere is

$$1 \text{ standard atmosphere} = 101{,}325 \text{ Pa}$$

Thus 1 atm is approximately 10^5 pascals. Since the pascal is so small, and because it is not commonly used in the United States, we will use it sparingly in this book. However, converting from torrs or atmospheres to pascals is straightforward.

5.2 The Gas Laws of Boyle, Charles, and Avogadro

Boyle's Law

The first quantitative experiments on gases were performed by the Irish chemist Robert Boyle (1627–1691). Using a J-shaped tube closed at one end (Fig. 5.3), which he reportedly set up in the multistory entryway of his house, Boyle studied the relationship between the pressure of the trapped gas and its volume. Representative values from Boyle's experiments are given in Table 5.1. These data show that the product of the pressure and volume for the trapped air sample is constant within the accuracies of Boyle's measurements (note the third column in Table 5.1). This behavior can be represented by the equation

$$PV = k$$

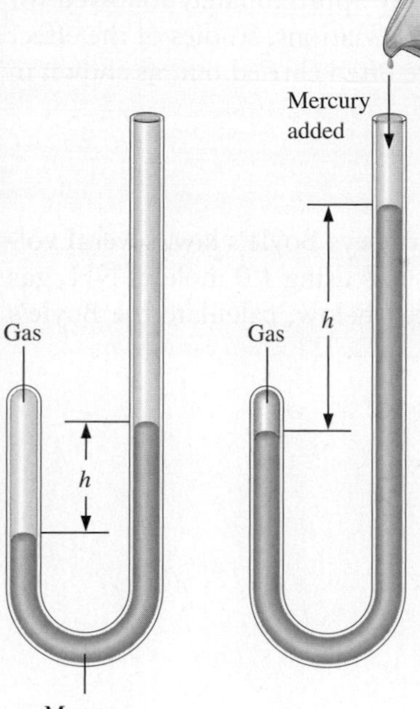

Figure 5.3
A J-tube similar to the one used by Boyle.

Table 5.1
Actual Data from Boyle's Experiments

Volume (in^3)	Pressure (in Hg)	Pressure × Volume (in Hg × in^3)
48.0	29.1	14.0×10^2
40.0	35.3	14.1×10^2
32.0	44.2	14.1×10^2
24.0	58.8	14.1×10^2
20.0	70.7	14.1×10^2
16.0	87.2	14.0×10^2
12.0	117.5	14.1×10^2

which is called **Boyle's law,** where k is a constant at a specific temperature for a given sample of air.

It is convenient to represent the data in Table 5.1 by using two different plots. Figure 5.4(a) shows a plot of P versus V, which produces a hyperbola. Notice that as the pressure drops by half, the volume doubles. Thus there is an *inverse relationship* between pressure and volume. The second type of plot can be obtained by rearranging Boyle's law to give

$$V = \frac{k}{P}$$

which is the equation for a straight line of the type

$$y = mx + b$$

Graphing is reviewed in Appendix A1.3.

where m represents the slope and b is the intercept of the straight line. In this case, $y = V$, $x = 1/P$, $m = k$, and $b = 0$. Thus a plot of V versus $1/P$ using Boyle's data gives a straight line with an intercept of zero, as shown in Fig. 5.4(b).

Boyle's law: $V \propto 1/P$ at constant temperature.

Boyle's law only approximately describes the relationship between pressure and volume for a gas. Highly accurate measurements on various gases at a constant temperature have shown that the product PV is not quite constant but changes with pressure. Results for several gases are shown in Fig. 5.5. Note the small changes that occur in the product PV as the pressure is varied. Such changes become very significant at pressures much higher than normal atmospheric pressure. We will discuss these deviations and the reasons for them in detail in Section 5.10. *A gas that obeys Boyle's law is called an* **ideal gas.** We will describe the characteristics of an ideal gas more completely in Section 5.3.

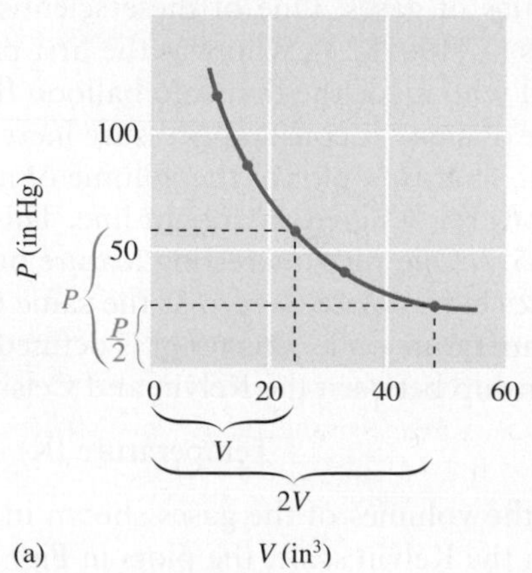

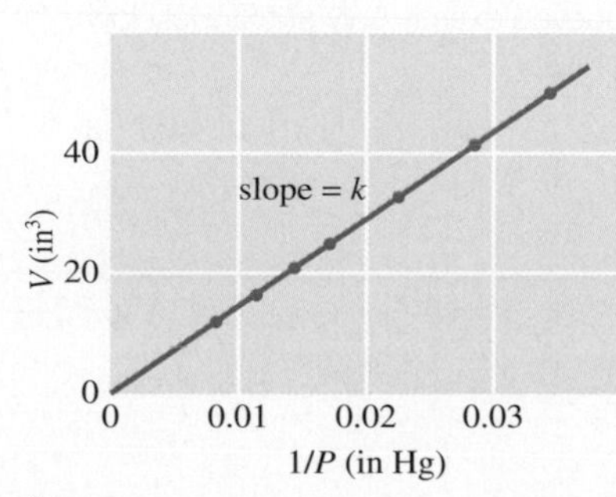

Figure 5.4
Plotting Boyle's data from Table 5.1. (a) A plot of P versus V shows that the volume doubles as the pressure is halved. (b) A plot of V versus $1/P$ gives a straight line. The slope of this line equals the value of the constant k.

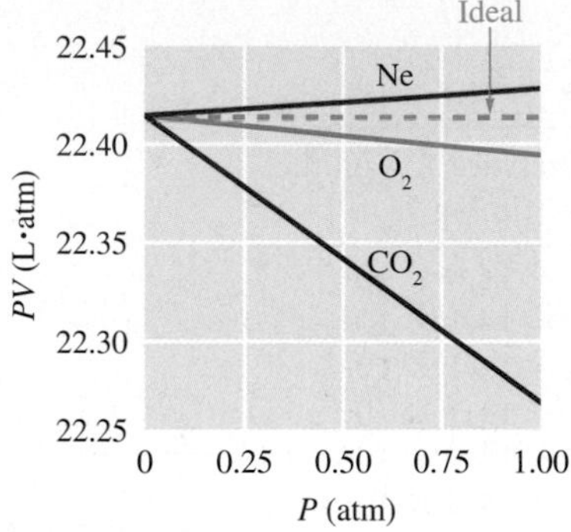

Figure 5.5
A plot of *PV* versus *P* for several gases. An ideal gas is expected to have a constant value of *PV*, as shown by the dashed line. Carbon dioxide shows the largest change in *PV*, and this change is actually quite small: *PV* changes from approximately 22.39 L atm at 0.25 atm to 22.26 L atm at 1.00 atm. Thus Boyle's law is a good approximation at these relatively low pressures.

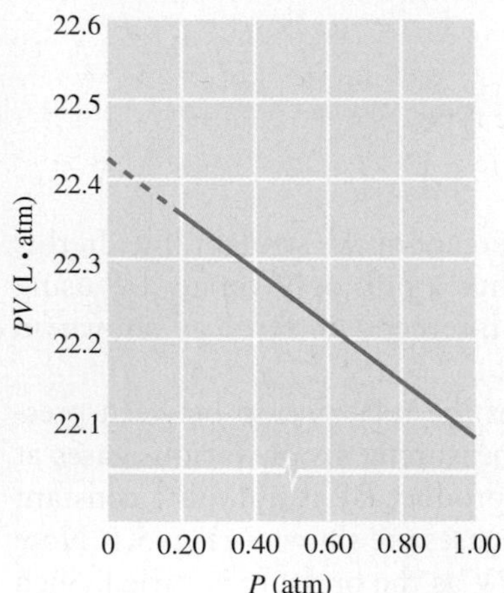

Figure 5.6
A plot of *PV* versus *P* for 1 mole of ammonia. The dashed line shows the extrapolation of the data to zero pressure to give the "ideal" value of *PV* of 22.41 L atm.

As with Boyle's law, Charles's law is obeyed exactly only at relatively low pressures.

One common use of Boyle's law is to predict the new volume of a gas when the pressure is changed (at constant temperature), or vice versa.

We mentioned earlier that Boyle's law is only approximately followed for real gases. To determine the significance of the deviations, studies of the effect of changing pressure on the volume of a gas are often carried out, as shown in Example 5.1.

EXAMPLE 5.1

In a study to see how closely gaseous ammonia obeys Boyle's law, several volume measurements were made at various pressures using 1.0 mole of NH_3 gas at a temperature of 0°C. Using the results listed below, calculate the Boyle's law constant for NH_3 at the various pressures.

Experiment	Pressure (atm)	Volume (L)
1	0.1300	172.1
2	0.2500	89.28
3	0.3000	74.35
4	0.5000	44.49
5	0.7500	29.55
6	1.000	22.08

Solution To determine how closely NH_3 gas follows Boyle's law under these conditions, we calculate the value of *k* (in L atm) for each set of values:

Experiment	1	2	3	4	5	6
$k = PV$	22.37	22.32	22.31	22.25	22.16	22.08

Although the deviations from true Boyle's law behavior are quite small at these low pressures, the value of *k* changes regularly in one direction as the pressure is increased. Thus, to calculate the "ideal" value of *k* for NH_3, plot *PV* versus *P*, as shown in Fig. 5.6, and extrapolate (extend the line beyond the experimental points) back to zero pressure, where, for reasons we will discuss later, a gas behaves most ideally. The value of *k* obtained by this extrapolation is 22.41 L atm. This is the same value obtained from similar plots for the gases CO_2, O_2, and Ne at 0°C, as shown in Fig. 5.5.

Charles's Law

In the century following Boyle's findings, scientists continued to study the properties of gases. One of these scientists was the French physicist Jacques Charles (1746–1823), who was the first person to fill a balloon with hydrogen gas and who made the first solo balloon flight. In 1787 Charles found that the volume of a gas at constant pressure increases *linearly* with the temperature of the gas. That is, a plot of the volume of a gas (at constant pressure) versus its temperature (°C) gives a straight line. This behavior is shown for several gases in Fig. 5.7. One very interesting feature of these plots is that the volumes of all the gases extrapolate to zero at the same temperature, −273.2°C. On the Kelvin temperature scale, this point is defined as 0 K, which leads to the following relationship between the Kelvin and Celsius scales:

$$\text{Temperature (K)} = 0°\text{C} + 273$$

When the volumes of the gases shown in Fig. 5.7 are plotted versus temperature on the Kelvin scale, the plots in Fig. 5.8 result. In this case the volume of

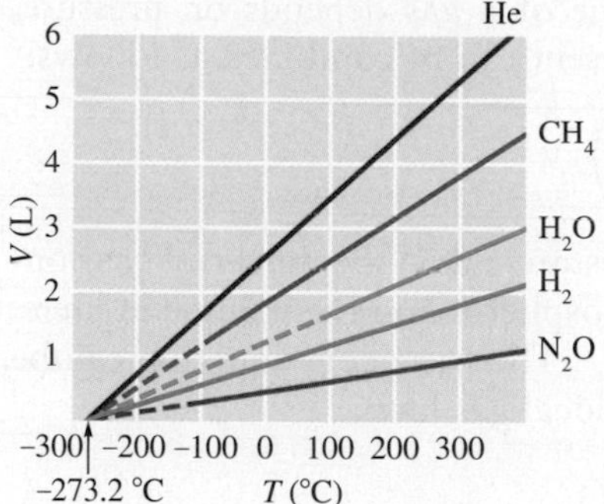

Figure 5.8
Plots of *V* versus *T* as in Fig. 5.7, except that here the Kelvin scale is used for temperature.

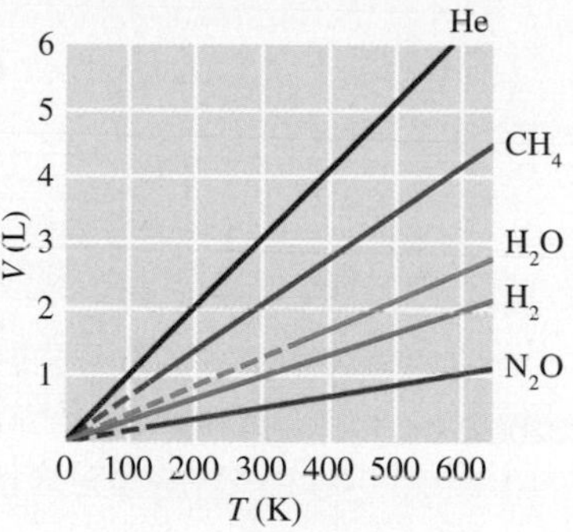

Figure 5.7
Plots of *V* versus *T* (°C) for several gases. The solid lines represent experimental measurements on gases. The dashed lines represent extrapolation of the data into regions where these gases would become liquids or solids. Note that the samples of the various gases contain different numbers of moles.

each gas is *directly proportional to temperature* and extrapolates to zero when the temperature is 0 K. This behavior is represented by the equation known as **Charles's law,**

$$V = bT$$

where T is the temperature (in kelvins) and b is a proportionality constant.

Before we illustrate the uses of Charles's law, let's consider the importance of 0 K. At temperatures below this point, the extrapolated volumes would become negative. The fact that a gas cannot have a negative volume suggests that 0 K has a special significance. In fact, 0 K is called **absolute zero,** and much evidence suggests that this temperature cannot be attained. Temperatures of approximately 10^{-6} K have been produced in laboratories, but 0 K has never been reached.

Avogadro's Law

In Chapter 2 we noted that in 1811 the Italian chemist Avogadro postulated that equal volumes of gases at the same temperature and pressure contain the same number of "particles." This observation is called **Avogadro's law** (or **hypothesis**), which can be stated mathematically as

$$V = an$$

where V is the volume of the gas, n is the number of moles, and a is a proportionality constant. This equation states that *for a gas at constant temperature and pressure, the volume is directly proportional to the number of moles of gas.* This relationship is obeyed closely by gases at low pressures.

5.3 The Ideal Gas Law

We have considered three laws that describe the behavior of gases as revealed by experimental observations:

Boyle's law:	$V = \frac{k}{P}$	(at constant T and n)
Charles's law:	$V = bT$	(at constant P and n)
Avogadro's law:	$V = an$	(at constant T and P)

These relationships showing how the volume of a gas depends on pressure, temperature, and number of moles of gas present can be combined as follows:

$$V = R\left(\frac{Tn}{P}\right)$$

$R = 0.08206$ L atm K^{-1} mol^{-1}

where R is the combined proportionality constant called the **universal gas constant.** When the pressure is expressed in atmospheres and the volume in liters, R has the value of 0.08206 L atm K^{-1} mol^{-1}. The preceding equation can be rearranged to the more familiar form of the **ideal gas law:**

$$PV = nRT$$

The ideal gas law is an *equation of state* for a gas, where the state of the gas is its condition at a given time. A particular *state* of a gas is described by its pressure, volume, temperature, and number of moles. Knowledge of any three of these properties is enough to completely define the state of a gas since the fourth property can then be determined from the equation for the ideal gas law.

It is important to recognize that the ideal gas law is an empirical equation—it is based on experimental measurements of the properties of gases. A gas that obeys this equation is said to behave *ideally*. That is, this equation defines the behavior of an ideal gas, which is a hypothetical substance. The ideal gas equation is best regarded as a limiting law—it expresses behavior that real gases *approach* at low pressures and high temperatures. Most gases obey this equation closely enough at pressures below 1 atm that only minimal errors result from assuming ideal behavior. Unless you are given information to the contrary, you should assume ideal gas behavior when solving problems involving gases in this text.

The ideal gas law applies best at pressures below 1 atm.

OWL INTERACTIVE EXAMPLE 5.2

A sample of hydrogen gas (H_2) has a volume of 8.56 L at a temperature of 0°C and a pressure of 1.5 atm. Calculate the moles of H_2 present in this gas sample.

Solution Solving the ideal gas law for n gives

$$n = \frac{PV}{RT}$$

In this case $P = 1.5$ atm, $V = 8.56$ L, $T = 0°\text{C} + 273 = 273$ K, and $R = 0.08206$ L atm K^{-1} mol^{-1}. Thus

$$n = \frac{(1.5 \text{ atm})(8.56 \text{ L})}{\left(0.08206 \frac{\text{L atm}}{\text{K mol}}\right)(273 \text{ K})} = 0.57 \text{ mol}$$

The ideal gas law is often used to calculate the changes that will occur when the conditions of a gas are changed, as described below.

OWL INTERACTIVE EXAMPLE 5.3

Suppose we have a sample of ammonia gas with a volume of 3.5 L at a pressure of 1.68 atm. The gas is compressed to a volume of 1.35 L at a constant temperature. Use the ideal gas law to calculate the final pressure.

Solution The basic assumption we make when using the ideal gas law to describe a change in state for a gas is that the equation applies equally well to both the initial and the final states. In dealing with a change in state, we always *place the variables on one side of the equals sign and the constants on the other.* In this case the pressure and volume change, whereas the temperature and the number of moles remain constant (as does R, by definition). Thus we write the ideal gas law as

$$PV = nRT$$

Change ↗ ↖ Remain constant

Since n and T remain the same in this case, we can write $P_1V_1 = nRT$ and $P_2V_2 = nRT$. Combining these equations gives

$$P_1V_1 = nRT = P_2V_2 \quad \text{or} \quad P_1V_1 = P_2V_2$$

We are given $P_1 = 1.68$ atm, $V_1 = 3.5$ L, $V_2 = 1.35$ L. Solving for P_2 gives

$$P_2 = \left(\frac{V_1}{V_2}\right)P_1 = \left(\frac{3.5\text{ L}}{1.35\text{ L}}\right)1.68\text{ atm} = 4.4\text{ atm}$$

Check: Does this answer make sense? The volume decreased (at constant temperature), so the pressure should increase, as the result of the calculation indicates. Note that the calculated final pressure is 4.4 atm. Because most gases do not behave ideally above 1 atm, we might find that if we *measured* the pressure of this gas sample, the observed pressure would differ slightly from 4.4 atm.

OWL INTERACTIVE EXAMPLE 5.4

A sample of methane gas that has a volume of 3.8 L at 5°C is heated to 86°C at constant pressure. Calculate its new volume.

Solution To solve this problem, we take the ideal gas law and segregate the changing variables and the constants by placing them on opposite sides of the equation. In this case volume and temperature change, and number of moles and pressure (and of course R) remain constant. Thus $PV = nRT$ becomes

$$\frac{V}{T} = \frac{nR}{P}$$

which leads to

$$\frac{V_1}{T_1} = \frac{nR}{P} \quad \text{and} \quad \frac{V_2}{T_2} = \frac{nR}{P}$$

Combining these equations gives

$$\frac{V_1}{T_1} = \frac{nR}{P} = \frac{V_2}{T_2} \quad \text{or} \quad \frac{V_1}{T_1} = \frac{V_2}{T_2}$$

We are given

$$T_1 = 5°\text{C} + 273 = 278\text{ K} \qquad T_2 = 86°\text{C} + 273 = 359\text{ K}$$

$$V_1 = 3.8\text{ L} \qquad V_2 = ?$$

Thus $$V_2 = \frac{T_2V_1}{T_1} = \frac{(359\text{ K})(3.8\text{ L})}{278\text{ K}} = 4.9\text{ L}$$

Check: Is the answer sensible? In this case the temperature was increased (at constant pressure), so the volume should increase. Thus the answer makes sense.

The problem in Example 5.4 can be described as a Charles's law problem, whereas the problem in Example 5.3 can be said to be a Boyle's law problem. In both cases, however, we started with the ideal gas law. The real advantage of using the ideal gas law is that it applies to virtually any problem dealing with gases and is easy to remember.

OWL INTERACTIVE EXAMPLE 5.5

A sample of diborane gas (B_2H_6), a substance that bursts into flames when exposed to air, has a pressure of 345 torr at a temperature of −15°C and a volume of 3.48 L. If conditions are changed so that the temperature is 36°C and the pressure is 468 torr, what will be the volume of the sample?

Solution Since, for this sample, pressure, temperature, and volume all change while the number of moles remains constant, we use the ideal gas law in the form

$$\frac{PV}{T} = \text{nR}$$

which leads to

$$\frac{P_1V_1}{T_1} = nR = \frac{P_2V_2}{T_2} \quad \text{or} \quad \frac{P_1V_1}{T_1} = \frac{P_2V_2}{T_2}$$

Then

$$V_2 = \frac{T_2P_1V_1}{T_1P_2}$$

We have

$$P_1 = 345 \text{ torr} \qquad P_2 = 468 \text{ torr}$$

$$T_1 = -15°\text{C} + 273 = 258 \text{ K} \qquad T_2 = 36°\text{C} + 273 = 309 \text{ K}$$

$$V_1 = 3.48 \text{ L} \qquad V_2 = ?$$

Thus

$$V_2 = \frac{(309 \text{ K})(345 \text{ torr})(3.48 \text{ L})}{(258 \text{ K})(468 \text{ torr})} = 3.07 \text{ L}$$

Since the equation used in Example 5.5 involved a *ratio* of pressures, it was unnecessary to convert pressures to units of atmospheres. The units of torr cancel. (You will obtain the same answer by inserting $P_1 = \frac{345}{760}$ and $P_2 = \frac{468}{760}$ into the equation.) However, temperature *must always* be converted to the Kelvin scale; since this conversion involves *addition* of 273, the conversion factor does not cancel. Be careful.

Always convert the temperature to the Kelvin scale when applying the ideal gas law.

5.4 Gas Stoichiometry

STP: 0°C and 1 atm

Suppose we have 1 mole of an ideal gas at 0°C (273.2 K) and 1 atm. From the ideal gas law, the volume of the gas is given by

$$V = \frac{nRT}{P} = \frac{(1.000 \text{ mol})(0.08206 \text{ L atm K}^{-1} \text{ mol}^{-1})(273.2 \text{ K})}{1.000 \text{ atm}} = 22.42 \text{ L}$$

This volume of 22.42 liters is called the **molar volume** of an ideal gas. The measured molar volumes of several gases are listed in Table 5.2. Note that the molar volumes of some of the gases are very close to the ideal value, but others deviate significantly. Later in this chapter we will discuss some of the reasons for the deviations.

The conditions 0°C and 1 atm, called **standard temperature and pressure** (abbreviated **STP**), are common reference conditions for the properties of gases. For example, the molar volume of an ideal gas is 22.42 L at STP.

Table 5.2

Molar Volumes for Various Gases at 0°C and 1 atm

Gas	Molar Volume (L)
Oxygen (O_2)	22.397
Nitrogen (N_2)	22.402
Hydrogen (H_2)	22.433
Helium (He)	22.434
Argon (Ar)	22.397
Carbon dioxide (CO_2)	22.260
Ammonia (NH_3)	22.079

Many chemical reactions involve gases. By assuming ideal behavior for these gases, we can carry out stoichiometric calculations if the pressure, volume, and temperature of the gases are known.

OWL INTERACTIVE EXAMPLE 5.6

Quicklime (CaO) is produced by the thermal decomposition of calcium carbonate ($CaCO_3$). Calculate the volume of CO_2 produced at STP from the decomposition of 152 g of $CaCO_3$ according to the reaction

$$CaCO_3(s) \longrightarrow CaO(s) + CO_2(g)$$

Solution

- What are we trying to solve?

We are asked to solve for the volume of $CO_2(g)$ produced at STP. We are given the pressure and temperature, so to determine the volume we will need to determine the number of moles of gas produced.

We use the same strategy we used in the stoichiometry problems earlier in the book. That is, we compute the number of moles of $CaCO_3$ consumed and the number of moles of CO_2 produced. The moles of CO_2 can then be converted to volume by using the molar volume of an ideal gas.

Using the molar mass of $CaCO_3$, we can calculate the number of moles of $CaCO_3$:

$$152 \text{ g } CaCO_3 \times \frac{1 \text{ mol } CaCO_3}{100.1 \text{ g } CaCO_3} = 1.52 \text{ mol } CaCO_3$$

Since each mole of $CaCO_3$ produces 1 mole of CO_2, 1.52 moles of CO_2 will be formed. We can compute the volume of CO_2 at STP by using the molar volume:

$$1.52 \text{ mol } CO_2 \times \frac{22.42 \text{ L } CO_2}{1 \text{ mol } CO_2} = 34.1 \text{ L } CO_2$$

Thus the decomposition of 152 g of $CaCO_3$ will produce 34.1 L of CO_2 at STP.

Remember that the molar volume of an ideal gas is 22.42 L at STP.

Note that in Example 5.6 the final step involved calculation of the volume of gas from the number of moles. Since the conditions were specified as STP, we were able to use the molar volume of a gas at STP. If the conditions of a problem are different from STP, the ideal gas law must be used to calculate the volume.

Molar Mass

One very important use of the ideal gas law is in the calculation of the molar mass (molecular weight) of a gas from its measured density. To understand the relationship between gas density and molar mass, note that the number of moles of gas n can be expressed as

$$n = \frac{\text{grams of gas}}{\text{molar mass}} = \frac{\text{mass}}{\text{molar mass}} = \frac{m}{\text{molar mass}}$$

Substitution into the ideal gas equation gives

$$P = \frac{nRT}{V} = \frac{(m/\text{molar mass})RT}{V} = \frac{m(RT)}{V(\text{molar mass})}$$

But m/V is the gas density d in units of grams per liter. Thus

$$P = \frac{dRT}{\text{molar mass}}$$

or

$$\text{Molar mass} = \frac{dRT}{P} \qquad (5.1)$$

Thus, if the density of a gas at a given temperature and pressure is known, its molar mass can be calculated.

You can memorize the equation involving gas density and molar mass, but it is better simply to remember the ideal gas equation, the definition of density, and the relationship between number of moles and molar mass. You can then derive this equation when you need it. This approach proves that you understand the concepts and means one less equation to memorize.

5.5 Dalton's Law of Partial Pressures

Among the experiments that led John Dalton to propose the atomic theory were his studies of mixtures of gases. In 1803 Dalton summarized his observations as follows: *For a mixture of gases in a container, the total pressure exerted is the sum of the pressures that each gas would exert if it were alone.* This statement, known as **Dalton's law of partial pressures,** can be expressed as follows:

$$P_{\text{Total}} = P_1 + P_2 + P_3 + \cdots$$

where the subscripts refer to the individual gases (gas 1, gas 2, and so on). The pressures P_1, P_2, P_3, and so on are called **partial pressures;** that is, each one is the pressure that gas would exert if it were alone in the container.

Assuming that each gas behaves ideally, the partial pressure of each gas can be calculated from the ideal gas law:

$$P_1 = \frac{n_1RT}{V}, \qquad P_2 = \frac{n_2RT}{V}, \qquad P_3 = \frac{n_3RT}{V}, \qquad \cdots$$

The total pressure of the mixture P_{Total} can be represented as

$$\begin{aligned} P_{\text{Total}} = P_1 + P_2 + P_3 + \cdots &= \frac{n_1RT}{V} + \frac{n_2RT}{V} + \frac{n_3RT}{V} + \cdots \\ &= (n_1 + n_2 + n_3 + \cdots)\left(\frac{RT}{V}\right) = n_{\text{Total}}\left(\frac{RT}{V}\right) \end{aligned}$$

where n_{Total} is the sum of the numbers of moles of the various gases. Thus, for a mixture of ideal gases, it is the *total number of moles of particles* that is im-

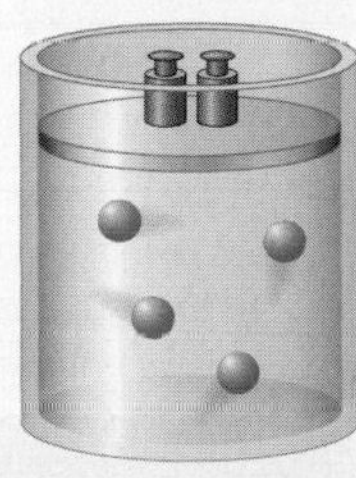

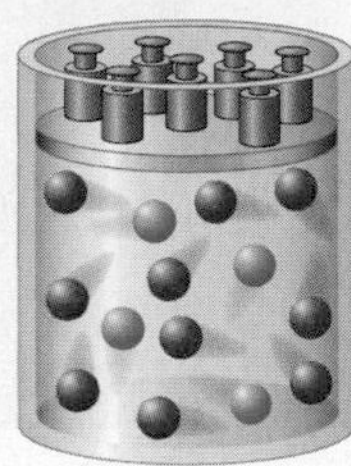

Figure 5.9
The partial pressure of each gas in a mixture of gases depends on the number of moles of that gas. The total pressure is the sum of the partial pressures and depends on the total moles of gas particles present, no matter what their identities.

portant, not the identity or composition of the individual gas particles. This idea is illustrated in Fig. 5.9.

This important result indicates some fundamental characteristics of an ideal gas. The fact that the pressure exerted by an ideal gas is not affected by the identity (structure) of the gas particles reveals two things about ideal gases: (1) the volume of the individual gas particle must not be important, and (2) the forces among the particles must not be important. If these factors were important, the pressure exerted by the gas would depend on the nature of the individual particles. These observations will strongly influence the model that we will eventually construct to explain ideal gas behavior.

At this point we need to define the **mole fraction:** *the ratio of the number of moles of a given component in a mixture to the total number of moles in the mixture.* The Greek letter chi (χ) is used to symbolize the mole fraction. For a given component in a mixture, the mole fraction χ_1 is

$$\chi_1 = \frac{n_1}{n_{\text{Total}}} = \frac{n_1}{n_1 + n_2 + n_3 + \cdots}$$

From the ideal gas equation, we know that the number of moles of a gas is directly proportional to the pressure of the gas, since

$$n = P\left(\frac{V}{RT}\right)$$

That is, for each component in the mixture,

$$n_1 = P_1\left(\frac{V}{RT}\right), \quad n_2 = P_2\left(\frac{V}{RT}\right), \quad \ldots$$

Therefore, we can represent the mole fraction in terms of pressures:

$$\chi_1 = \frac{n_1}{n_{\text{Total}}} = \frac{\overbrace{P_1(V/RT)}^{n_1}}{\underbrace{P_1(V/RT)}_{n_1} + \underbrace{P_2(V/RT)}_{n_2} + \underbrace{P_3(V/RT)}_{n_3} + \cdots}$$

$$= \frac{(V/RT)P_1}{(V/RT)(P_1 + P_2 + P_3 + \cdots)}$$

$$= \frac{P_1}{P_1 + P_2 + P_3 + \cdots} = \frac{P_1}{P_{\text{Total}}}$$

Similarly, $$\chi_2 = \frac{n_2}{n_{\text{Total}}} = \frac{P_2}{P_{\text{Total}}}$$

and so on. Thus the mole fraction of a particular component in a mixture of ideal gases is directly related to its partial pressure.

The expression for the mole fraction,

$$\chi_1 = \frac{P_1}{P_{\text{Total}}}$$

can be rearranged: $$P_1 = \chi_1 \times P_{\text{Total}}$$

That is, *the partial pressure of a particular component of a gaseous mixture is equal to the mole fraction of that component times the total pressure.*

A mixture of gases occurs whenever a gas is collected by displacement of water. For example, Fig. 5.10 shows the collection of oxygen gas produced by

Chemical Insights The Chemistry of Air Bags

Most experts agree that air bags represent a very important advance in automobile safety. First patented by American inventor John W. Hetrick in 1953, air bags are now required in all cars and trucks in the United States. These bags, which are stored in the auto's steering wheel or dash, are designed to inflate rapidly (within about 40 ms) in the event of a crash, cushioning the front-seat occupants against impact. The bags then deflate immediately to allow vision and movement after the crash. Air bags are activated when a severe deceleration (an impact) causes a steel ball to compress a spring and electrically ignite a detonator cap, which, in turn, causes sodium azide (NaN_3) to decompose explosively, forming sodium and nitrogen gas:

$$2NaN_3(s) \longrightarrow 2Na(s) + 3N_2(g)$$

This system works very well and requires only a relatively small amount of sodium azide [100 g yields 56 L of $N_2(g)$ at 25°C and 1 atm].

In addition to being located in the steering wheel and dash, air bags are now found in many other sites in motor vehicles. Air bags to protect against side impacts are located above the windows (called *curtain air bags* to protect against head injuries) and in the doors (called *torso air bags*). Some vehicles also have bags to prevent knee injuries. Because the explosive deployment of air bags can cause serious injuries, especially to children, variable force air bags have been developed that depend on the weight of the person occupying the front seat.

Inflated dual air bags.

Ford Motor Company

When a vehicle containing air bags reaches the end of its useful life, the sodium azide present in the activators must be given proper disposal. Besides being explosive, sodium azide has a toxicity roughly equal to that of sodium cyanide. It also forms hydrazoic acid (HN_3), a toxic and explosive liquid, when treated with acid.

The air bag represents an application of chemistry that has already saved thousands of lives.

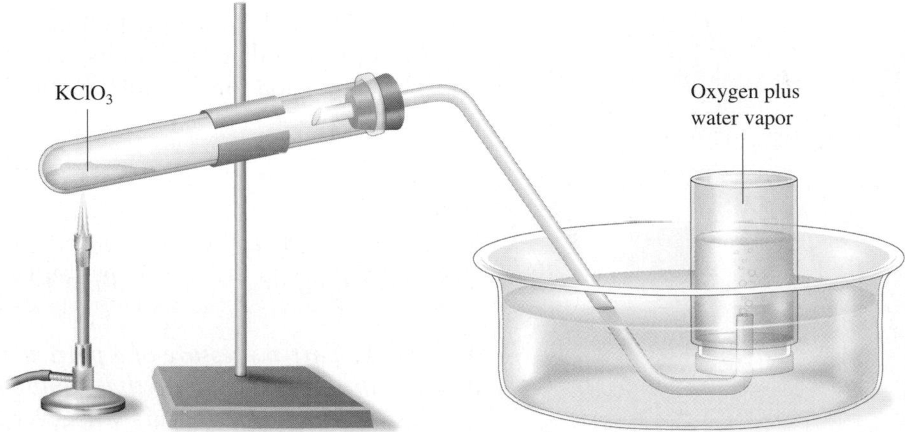

Figure 5.10
The production of oxygen by thermal decomposition of $KClO_3$. The MnO_2 catalyst is mixed with the $KClO_3$ to make the reaction faster.

Vapor pressure will be discussed in detail in Chapter 16.

the decomposition of solid potassium chlorate. In this situation the gas in the bottle is a mixture of water vapor and the gas being collected. Water vapor is present because molecules of water escape from the surface of the liquid and collect in the space above the liquid. Molecules of water also return to the liquid. When the rate of escape equals the rate of return, the number of water molecules in the vapor state remains constant, and thus the pressure of water vapor remains constant. This pressure, which depends on temperature, is called the *vapor pressure of water.*

OWL INTERACTIVE EXAMPLE 5.7

The mole fraction of nitrogen in air is 0.7808. Calculate the partial pressure of N_2 in air when the atmospheric pressure is 760. torr.

Solution The partial pressure of N_2 can be calculated as follows:

$$P_{N_2} = \chi_{N_2} \times P_{Total} = 0.7808 \times 760.\text{ torr} = 593\text{ torr}$$

OWL INTERACTIVE EXAMPLE 5.8

A sample of solid potassium chlorate ($KClO_3$) was heated in a test tube (Fig. 5.10) and decomposed according to the following reaction:

$$2KClO_3(s) \longrightarrow 2KCl(s) + 3O_2(g)$$

The oxygen produced was collected by displacement of water at 22°C at a total pressure of 754 torr. The volume of the gas collected was 0.650 L, and the vapor pressure of water at 22°C is 21 torr. Calculate the partial pressure of O_2 in the gas collected and the mass of $KClO_3$ in the sample that was decomposed.

Solution

- What are we trying to solve?

We are asked to find the partial pressure of O_2 in the gas collected and the mass of reactant ($KClO_3$) in the original sample.

We have the balanced equation and are given the volume, temperature, total pressure of the gas mixture, and vapor pressure of the water at that temperature. Since oxygen and water vapor are the only gases in the mixture, we can determine the partial pressure of the oxygen gas from Dalton's law of partial pressures:

$$P_{Total} = P_{O_2} + P_{H_2O} = P_{O_2} + 21\text{ torr} = 754\text{ torr}$$

Thus

$$P_{O_2} = 754\text{ torr} - 21\text{ torr} = 733\text{ torr}$$

We now have to determine the mass of $KClO_3$ from the partial pressure of oxygen gas. Recall our strategy used in stoichiometry problems. That is, we can determine the mass of $KClO_3$ from the number of moles of $KClO_3$, which we can determine from the number of moles of O_2. We know the partial pressure of O_2. Along with volume and temperature, we can use the ideal gas law to find the number of moles of O_2:

$$n_{O_2} = \frac{P_{O_2}V}{RT}$$

In this case

$$P_{O_2} = 733 \text{ torr} = \frac{733 \text{ torr}}{760 \text{ torr/atm}} = 0.964 \text{ atm}$$

$$V = 0.650 \text{ L}$$

$$T = 22°\text{C} + 273 = 295 \text{ K}$$

$$R = 0.08206 \text{ L atm K}^{-1} \text{ mol}^{-1}$$

Thus

$$n_{O_2} = \frac{(0.964 \text{ atm})(0.650 \text{ L})}{(0.08206 \text{ L atm K}^{-1} \text{ mol}^{-1})(295 \text{ K})} = 2.59 \times 10^{-2} \text{ mol}$$

Next, we calculate the moles of $KClO_3$ needed to produce this quantity of O_2 using the mole ratio from the balanced equation for the decomposition of $KClO_3$:

$$2.59 \times 10^{-2} \text{ mol } O_2 \times \frac{2 \text{ mol } KClO_3}{3 \text{ mol } O_2} = 1.73 \times 10^{-2} \text{ mol } KClO_3$$

Using the molar mass of $KClO_3$, we calculate the grams of $KClO_3$:

$$1.73 \times 10^{-2} \text{ mol } KClO_3 \times \frac{122.6 \text{ g } KClO_3}{1 \text{ mol } KClO_3} = 2.12 \text{ g } KClO_3$$

Thus the original sample contained 2.12 g of $KClO_3$.

5.6 The Kinetic Molecular Theory of Gases

So far we have considered the behavior of gases from an experimental point of view. On the basis of observations from different types of experiments, we know that at pressure less than 1 atm most gases closely approach the behavior described by the ideal gas law. Now we want to construct a model to explain this behavior.

Before we construct the model, we will briefly review the scientific method. Recall that a law is a way of generalizing behavior that has been observed in many experiments. Laws are very useful since they allow us to predict the behavior of similar systems. For example, if a chemist prepares a new gaseous compound, a measurement of the gas density at known pressure and temperature can provide a reliable value for the compound's molar mass.

However, although laws summarize observed behavior, they do not tell us *why* nature behaves in the observed fashion. This is the central question for scientists. To try to answer this question, we construct theories (build models). The models in chemistry consist of speculations about what the individual atoms or molecules (microscopic particles) might be doing to cause the observed behavior of the macroscopic systems (collections of very large numbers of atoms and molecules).

A model is considered successful if it explains the observed behavior in question and predicts correctly the results of future experiments. Note that a model can never be proved to be absolutely true. In fact, *any model is an approximation* by its very nature and is bound to fail at some point. Models range from the simple to the extraordinarily complex. We use simple models to predict approximate behavior and more complicated models to account very precisely for observed quantitative behavior. In this text we will stress simple models that provide an approximate picture of what might be happening and that fit the most important experimental results.

Separating Gases

Chemical Insights

Assume you work for an oil company that owns a huge natural gas reservoir containing a mixture of methane and nitrogen gases. In fact, the gas mixture contains so much nitrogen that it is unusable as a fuel. Your job is to separate the nitrogen (N_2) from the methane (CH_4). How might you accomplish this task? You clearly need some sort of "molecular filter" that will stop the slightly larger methane molecules (size ≈430 pm) and allow the nitrogen molecules (size ≈410 pm) to pass through. To accomplish the separation of molecules so similar in size will require a very precise "filter."

The good news is that such a filter exists. Recent work by Steven Kuznicki and Valerie Bell at Engelhard Corporation in New Jersey and Michael Tsapatsis at the University of Massachusetts has produced a "molecular sieve" in which the pore (passage) sizes can be adjusted precisely enough to separate N_2 molecules from CH_4 molecules. The material involved is a special hydrated titanosilicate (contains H_2O, Ti, Si, O, and Sr) compound patented by Engelhard and known as ETS-4 (Engelhard TitanoSilicate-4). When sodium ions are substituted for the strontium ions in ETS-4 and the new material is carefully dehydrated, a uniform and controllable pore-size reduction occurs (see figure). The researchers have shown that the material can be used to separate N_2 (≈410 pm) from O_2 (≈390 pm). They have also shown that it is possible to reduce the nitrogen content of natural gas from 18% to less than 5% with a 90% recovery of methane.

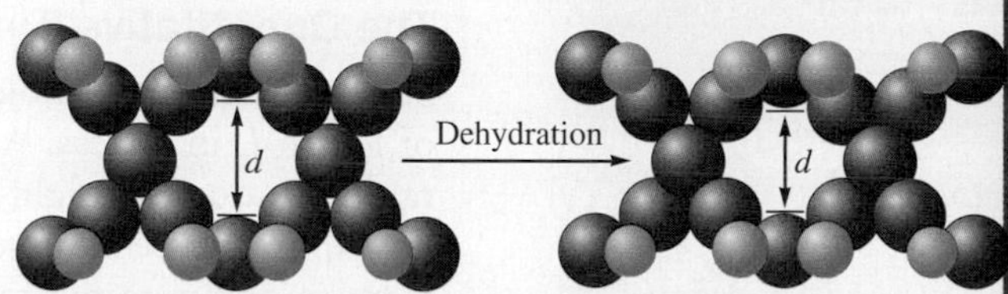

Molecular sieve framework of titanium (blue), silicon (green), and oxygen (red) atoms contracts on heating—at room temperature (left), $d = 4.27$ Å; at 250°C (right), $d = 3.94$ Å.

An example of this type of model is the **kinetic molecular theory,** a simple model that attempts to explain the properties of an ideal gas. This model is based on speculations about the behavior of the individual gas particles (atoms or molecules). The postulates of the kinetic molecular theory can be stated as follows:

Kinetic Molecular Theory

- The particles are so small compared with the distances between them that *the volume of the individual particles can be assumed to be negligible* (zero).
- *The particles are in constant motion. The collisions of the particles with the walls of the container are the cause of the pressure exerted by the gas.*
- *The particles are assumed to exert no forces on each other;* they are assumed to neither attract nor repel each other.
- *The average kinetic energy of a collection of gas particles is assumed to be directly proportional to the Kelvin temperature of the gas.*

Of course, real gas particles do have a finite volume and do exert forces on each other. Thus they do not conform exactly to these assumptions. But we will see that these postulates do indeed explain *ideal* gas behavior.

The true test of a model is how well its predictions fit the experimental observations. The postulates of the kinetic molecular model picture an ideal gas as consisting of particles having no volume and no attraction for each other, and the model assumes that the gas produces pressure on its container by collisions with the walls. To test the validity of this model, we need to consider the question: "When we apply the principles of physics to a collection of these gas particles, can we derive an expression for pressure that agrees with the ideal gas law?" The answer is, "Yes, we can." We will now consider this derivation in detail.

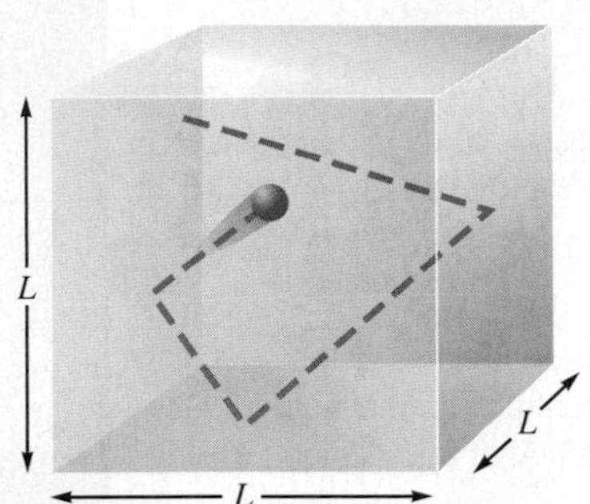

Figure 5.11
An ideal gas particle in a cube whose sides are of length L (in meters). The particle collides elastically with the walls in a random, straight-line motion.

The Quantitative Kinetic Molecular Model

Suppose there are n moles of an ideal gas in a cubical container with sides each of length L in meters. Assume each gas particle has a mass m and that it is in rapid, random, straight-line motion colliding with the walls (Fig. 5.11). The collisions will be assumed to be *elastic*—no loss of kinetic energy occurs. We want to compute the force on the walls from the colliding gas particles and then, since pressure is force per unit area, to obtain an expression for the pressure of the gas.

Before we can derive the expression for the pressure of a gas, we must first discuss some characteristics of velocity. Each particle in the gas has a particular velocity u, which can be broken into components u_x, u_y, and u_z (Fig. 5.12). First, using u_x and u_y and the Pythagorean theorem, we can obtain u_{xy} (Fig. 5.12):

$$u_{xy}^2 = u_x^2 + u_y^2$$

Hypotenuse of right triangle (u_{xy}^2); Sides of right triangle (u_x^2, u_y^2)

Then, constructing another triangle as shown in Fig. 5.12, we find

$$u^2 = u_{xy}^2 + u_z^2$$

or

$$u^2 = u_x^2 + u_y^2 + u_z^2$$

Now let's consider how an individual gas particle moves. For example, how often does this particle strike the two walls of the box that are perpendicular to the x axis? Note that only the x component of the velocity affects the particle's impacts on these two walls (Fig. 5.13). The larger the x component of the velocity, the faster the particle travels between these two walls, thus producing more impacts per unit of time on these walls. Remember that the pressure of the gas is caused by these collisions with the walls.

The collision frequency (collisions per unit of time) with the two walls that are perpendicular to the x axis is given by

$$(\text{Collision frequency})_x = \frac{\text{velocity in the } x \text{ direction}}{\text{distance between the walls}} = \frac{u_x}{L}$$

Figure 5.12
(a) The Cartesian coordinate axes.
(b) The velocity u of any gas particle can be broken down into three mutually perpendicular components, u_x, u_y, and u_z. This can be represented as a rectangular solid with sides u_x, u_y, and u_z and body diagonal u.
(c) In the xy plane,

$$u_x^2 + u_y^2 = u_{xy}^2$$

by the Pythagorean theorem. Since u_{xy} and u_z are also perpendicular,

$$u^2 = u_{xy}^2 + u_z^2 = u_x^2 + u_y^2 + u_z^2$$

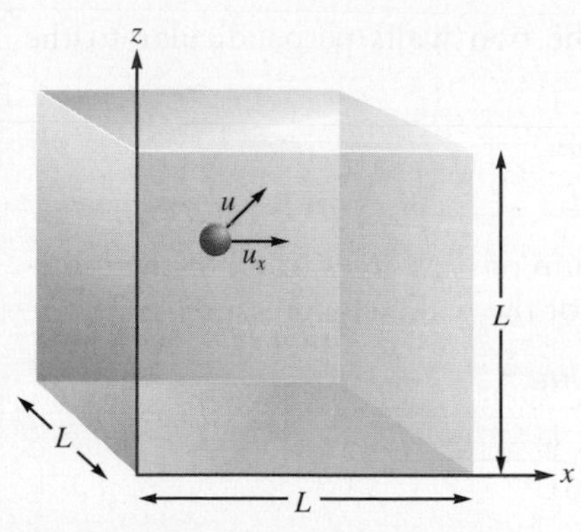

(a)

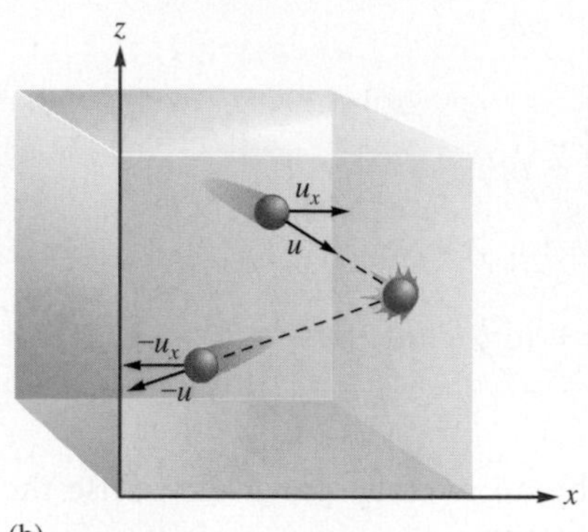

(b)

Figure 5.13
(a) Only the x component of the gas particle's velocity affects the frequency of impacts on the shaded walls, the walls that are perpendicular to the x axis. (b) For an elastic collision, there is an exact reversal of the x component of the velocity and of the total velocity. The change in momentum (final − initial) is then

$$-mu_x - mu_x = -2mu_x$$

Next, what is the force of a collision? Force is defined as mass times acceleration (change in velocity per unit of time):

$$F = ma = m\left(\frac{\Delta u}{\Delta t}\right)$$

where F represents force, a represents the acceleration, Δu represents a change in velocity, and Δt represents a given length of time.

Since we assume that the particle has constant mass, we can write

$$F = \frac{m\Delta u}{\Delta t} = \frac{\Delta(mu)}{\Delta t}$$

The quantity mu is the momentum of the particle (momentum is the product of mass and velocity), and the expression $F = \Delta(mu)/\Delta t$ means that force is the change in momentum per unit of time. When a particle hits a wall perpendicular to the x axis, as shown in Fig. 5.13, an elastic collision occurs, resulting in an *exact reversal* of the x component of velocity. That is, the *sign,* or direction, of u_x reverses when the particle collides with one of the walls perpendicular to the x axis. Thus the final momentum is the *negative,* or opposite, of the initial momentum. Remember that an elastic collision means that there is no change in the *magnitude* of the velocity. The change in momentum in the x direction is

$$\begin{aligned}\text{Change in momentum} &= \Delta(mu_x)\\ &= \text{final momentum} - \text{initial momentum}\\ &= -mu_x - mu_x\end{aligned}$$

↗ Final momentum in x direction ↖ Initial momentum in x direction

$$= -2mu_x$$

We are interested in the magnitude of the force the gas particle exerts on the walls of the box. Since we know that every action produces an equal but opposite reaction, the change in momentum with respect to the wall on impact is $-(-2mu_x)$, or $2mu_x$.

Recall that since force is the change in momentum per unit of time, then

$$\text{Force}_x = \frac{\Delta(mu_x)}{\Delta t}$$

for the walls perpendicular to the x axis.

This expression can be obtained by multiplying the change in momentum per impact by the number of impacts per unit of time:

$$\text{Force}_x = (2mu_x)\left(\frac{u_x}{L}\right) = \text{change in momentum per unit of time}$$

↗ Change in momentum per impact ↖ Impacts per unit of time

That is,

$$\text{Force}_x = \frac{2mu_x^{\,2}}{L}$$

So far we have considered only the two walls of the box perpendicular to the x axis. We can assume that the magnitude of the force on the two walls perpendicular to the y axis is given by

$$\text{Force}_y = \frac{2mu_y^{\,2}}{L}$$

and that the magnitude of the force on the two walls perpendicular to the z axis is given by

$$\text{Force}_z = \frac{2mu_z^2}{L}$$

Pressure is force per unit area, or the sum of the forces of all of the molecules striking the walls divided by the area of the wall. The pressure is

$$\text{Pressure} = \frac{\dfrac{2mu_x^2}{L} + \dfrac{2mu_y^2}{L} + \dfrac{2mu_z^2}{L}}{6L^2}$$

The 6 sides of the cube ↗ ↖ Area of each side

Since we have shown that

$$u^2 = u_x^2 + u_y^2 + u_z^2$$

the pressure is equal to

$$\text{Pressure} = \frac{\dfrac{2m}{L}(u_x^2 + u_y^2 + u_z^2)}{6L^2} = \frac{\dfrac{2m}{L}(u^2)}{6L^2}$$

Now, since we want the pressure caused by an average particle, we use the average of the square of the velocity $\overline{u^2}$ to obtain

$$\text{Pressure caused by "average" particle} = \frac{2m\overline{u^2}/L}{6L^2} = \frac{m\overline{u^2}}{3L^2}$$

Since the volume V of the cube is equal to L^3, we can write

$$\text{Pressure} = P = \frac{m\overline{u^2}}{3V}$$

So far we have considered the pressure on the walls caused by a single, "average" particle. Of course, we want the pressure caused by the entire gas

A balloon filled with air at room temperature.

The balloon is dipped into liquid nitrogen at 77 K.

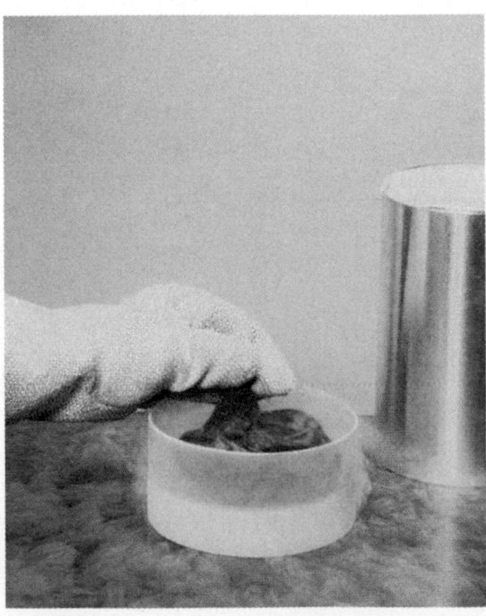
The balloon collapses as the molecules inside slow down because of the decreased temperature. Slower molecules produce a lower pressure.

Photos Ken O'Donoghue

sample. The number of particles in a given gas sample can be expressed as follows:

$$\text{Number of gas particles} = nN_A$$

where n is the number of moles and N_A is Avogadro's number.

The total pressure on the box caused by n moles of a gas is therefore

$$P = nN_A \frac{m\overline{u^2}}{3V}$$

Next, we want to express the pressure in terms of the kinetic energy of the gas molecules. Kinetic energy (the energy caused by motion) is given by $\frac{1}{2}mu^2$, where m is the mass and u is the velocity. Since we are using the average of the velocity squared ($\overline{u^2}$), and since $m\overline{u^2} = 2(\frac{1}{2}m\overline{u^2})$, we have

$$P = \frac{2}{3}\left[\frac{nN_A(\frac{1}{2}m\overline{u^2})}{V}\right]$$

Recall that P is the pressure of the gas, n is the number of moles of gas, N_A is Avogadro's number, m is the mass of each particle, $\overline{u^2}$ is the average of the squares of the velocities of the particles, and V is the volume of the container.

KE = $\frac{1}{2}mu^2$, the energy caused by the motion of a particle.

The quantity $\frac{1}{2}m\overline{u^2}$ represents the average kinetic energy of a gas particle. If the average kinetic energy of an individual particle is multiplied by N_A, the number of particles in a mole, we get the average kinetic energy for a mole of gas particles:

$$(\text{KE})_{\text{avg}} = N_A(\tfrac{1}{2}m\overline{u^2})$$

Using this definition, we can rewrite the expression for pressure as

$$P = \frac{2}{3}\left[\frac{n(\text{KE})_{\text{avg}}}{V}\right] \quad \text{or} \quad \frac{PV}{n} = \frac{2}{3}(\text{KE})_{\text{avg}}$$

The fourth postulate of the kinetic molecular theory is that the average kinetic energy of the particles in the gas sample is directly proportional to the temperature in Kelvins. Thus, since $(\text{KE})_{\text{avg}} \propto T$, we can write

$$\frac{PV}{n} = \frac{2}{3}(\text{KE})_{\text{avg}} \propto T \quad \text{or} \quad \frac{PV}{n} \propto T$$

Note that this expression, has been *derived* from the assumptions of the kinetic molecular theory. How does it compare with the ideal gas law—the equation obtained from experiment? Compare the ideal gas law,

$$\frac{PV}{n} = RT \qquad \text{From experiment}$$

with the result from the kinetic molecular theory,

$$\frac{PV}{n} \propto T \qquad \text{From theory}$$

These expressions have exactly the same form if R, the universal gas constant, is considered the proportionality constant in the second case.

The agreement between the ideal gas, law and the kinetic molecular theory gives us confidence in the validity of the model. The characteristics we have assumed for ideal gas particles must agree, at least under certain conditions, with their actual behavior.

The Meaning of Temperature

We have seen from the kinetic molecular theory that the Kelvin temperature is a measure of the average kinetic energy of the gas particles. The exact relationship between temperature and average kinetic energy can be obtained by combining the equations

$$\frac{PV}{n} = RT = \frac{2}{3}(\text{KE})_{\text{avg}}$$

which yields the expression

$$(\text{KE})_{\text{avg}} = \tfrac{3}{2}RT$$

This is a very important relationship. It summarizes the meaning of the Kelvin temperature of a gas: The Kelvin temperature is an index of the random motions of the particles of a gas, with higher temperature meaning greater motion.

Root Mean Square Velocity

In the equation from the kinetic molecular theory, the average velocity of the gas particles is a special kind of average. The symbol $\overline{u^2}$ means the average of the *squares* of the particle velocities. The square root of $\overline{u^2}$ is called the **root mean square velocity** and is symbolized by u_{rms}:

$$u_{\text{rms}} = \sqrt{\overline{u^2}}$$

We can obtain an expression for u_{rms} from the equations

$$(\text{KE})_{\text{avg}} = N_A(\tfrac{1}{2}m\overline{u^2}) \qquad \text{and} \qquad (\text{KE})_{\text{avg}} = \tfrac{3}{2}RT$$

Combination of these equations gives

$$N_A(\tfrac{1}{2}m\overline{u^2}) = \tfrac{3}{2}RT \qquad \text{or} \qquad \overline{u^2} = \frac{3RT}{N_A m}$$

Taking the square root of both sides of the last equation produces

$$\sqrt{\overline{u^2}} = u_{\text{rms}} = \sqrt{\frac{3RT}{N_A m}}$$

In this expression, m represents the mass in kilograms of a single gas particle. When N_A, the number of particles in a mole, is multiplied by m, the product is the mass of a *mole* of gas particles in *kilograms*. We will call this quantity M. Substituting M for $N_A m$ in the equation for u_{rms}, we obtain

$$u_{\text{rms}} = \sqrt{\frac{3RT}{M}}$$

Before we can use this equation, we need to consider the units for R. So far we have used 0.08206 L atm K^{-1} mol^{-1} as the value of R. But to obtain the desired units (meters per second) for u_{rms}, R must be expressed in different units. As we will see in more detail in Chapter 9, the energy unit most often used in the SI system is the joule (J). A **joule** is defined as a kilogram meter squared per second squared (kg m^2/s^2). When R is converted from liter atmospheres to joules, it has the value 8.3145 J K^{-1} mol^{-1}. When R with these units is used in the expression $\sqrt{3RT/M}$, u_{rms} has units of meters per second, as desired.

So far we have said nothing about the range of velocities actually found in a gas sample. In a real gas, there are large numbers of collisions between particles. For example, when an odorous gas such as ammonia is released in a room, it takes some time for the odor to permeate the air, as we will see in Section 5.7. This delay results from collisions between the NH_3 molecules and O_2 and N_2 molecules in the air, which greatly slow the mixing process.

$R = 0.08206 \text{ L atm K}^{-1} \text{ mol}^{-1}$
$R = 8.3145 \text{ J K}^{-1} \text{ mol}^{-1}$

If the path of a particular gas particle could be monitored, it would probably look very erratic, something like that shown in Fig. 5.14. The average distance a particle travels between collisions in a particular gas sample is called the **mean free path.** It is typically a very small distance (1×10^{-7} m for O_2 at STP). One effect of the many collisions among gas particles is to produce a large range of velocities as the particles collide and exchange kinetic energy. Although u_{rms} for oxygen gas at STP is approximately 500 m/s, the majority of O_2 molecules do not have this velocity. The actual distribution of molecular velocities for oxygen gas at STP is shown in Fig. 5.15. This figure shows the relative number of gas molecules having each particular velocity.

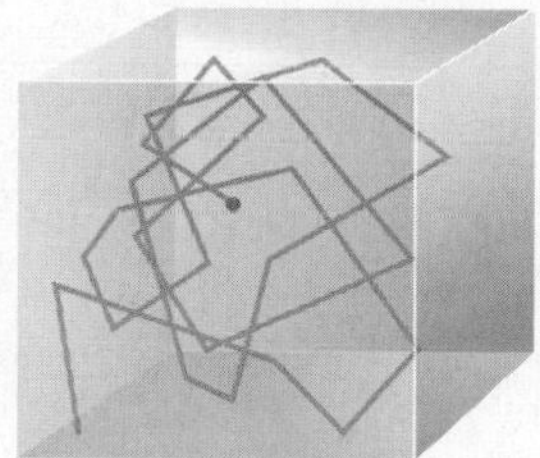

Figure 5.14
Path of one particle in a gas. Any given particle will continuously change its course as a result of collisions with other particles as well as with the walls of the container.

We are also interested in the effect of *temperature* on the velocity distribution in a gas. Figure 5.16 shows the velocity distribution for nitrogen gas at three temperatures. Note that as the temperature is increased, the curve maximum, which reflects the average velocity, moves toward higher values and the range of velocities becomes much larger.

The distribution of velocities of the particles in an ideal gas is described by the Maxwell–Boltzmann distribution law:

$$f(u) = 4\pi\left(\frac{m}{2k_BT}\right)^{3/2} u^2 e^{-mu^2/2k_BT}$$

where

$$u = \text{velocity in m/s}$$
$$m = \text{mass of a gas particle in kg}$$
$$k_B = \text{Boltzmann's constant} = 1.38066 \times 10^{-23} \text{ J/K}$$
$$T = \text{temperature in K}$$

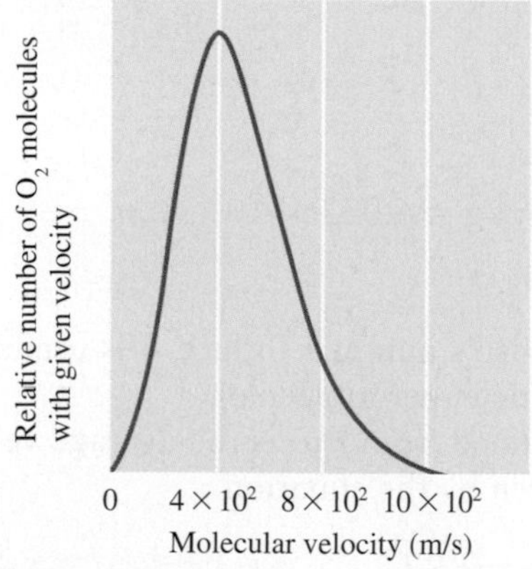

Figure 5.15
A plot of the relative number of O_2 molecules that have a given velocity at STP.

This equation was derived independently by James C. Maxwell, a Scottish physicist, and Ludwig E. Boltzmann, an Austrian physicist who did much of the fundamental theoretical work on the kinetic molecular description of an ideal gas. The product of $f(u)du$ represents the fraction of gas molecules with velocities between u and $u + du$, where du represents an infinitesimal velocity increment. This function is the one plotted in Figs. 5.15 and 5.16.

Analysis of the expression for $f(u)$ yields the following equation for the most probable velocity u_{mp} (the velocity possessed by the greatest number of gas particles):

$$u_{mp} = \sqrt{\frac{2k_BT}{m}} = \sqrt{\frac{2RT}{M}}$$

Figure 5.16
A plot of the relative number of N_2 molecules that have a given velocity at three temperatures. Note that as the temperature increases, both the average velocity (reflected by the curve's peak) and the spread of velocities increase.

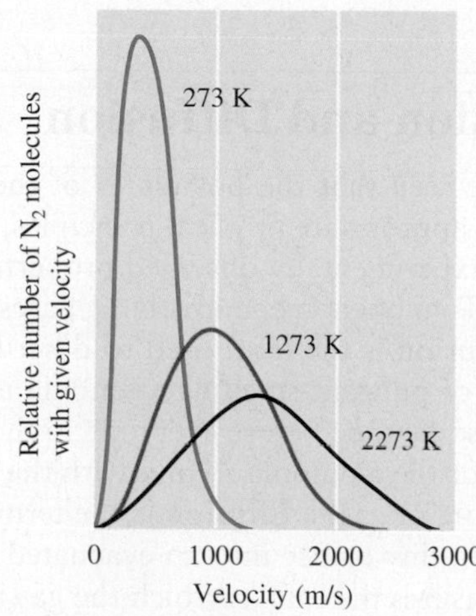

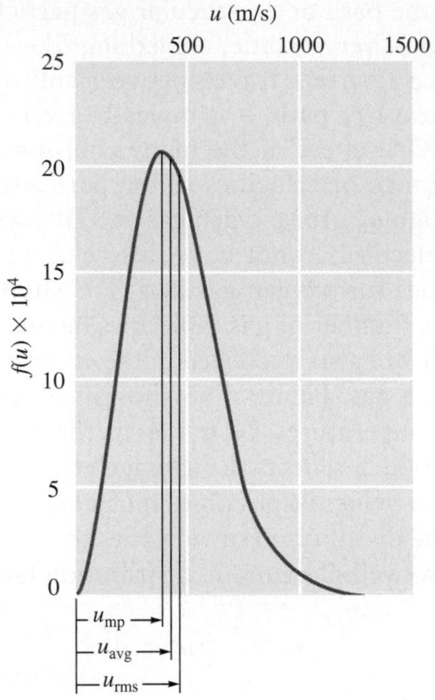

Figure 5.17
The velocity distribution for nitrogen gas at 273 K, with the values of most probable velocity u_{mp} (the velocity at the curve maximum), the average velocity u_{avg}, and the root mean square velocity u_{rms} indicated.

where

$$M = \text{molar mass of the gas particles in kg} = 6.022 \times 10^{23} \times m$$

$$R = \text{gas constant} = 6.022 \times 10^{23} \times k_B$$

Note that R and k_B are related by Avogadro's number. In fact, it is useful to think of k_B as the gas law constant per particle (per molecule).

Another type of velocity that can be obtained from $f(u)$ is the average velocity u_{avg} (sometimes written $\bar{u}$), which is given by the equation

$$u_{avg} = \bar{u} = \sqrt{\frac{8k_BT}{\pi m}} = \sqrt{\frac{8RT}{\pi M}}$$

Thus we have three ways to describe a "typical" velocity for the particles in an ideal gas: the root mean square velocity, the most probable velocity, and the average velocity. As can be seen from the equations for u_{rms}, u_{mp}, and u_{avg}, these velocities are not the same. In fact, they stand in the ratios

$$u_{mp} : u_{avg} : u_{rms} = 1.000 : 1.128 : 1.225$$

This relationship is shown for nitrogen gas at 0°C in Fig. 5.17.

5.7 Effusion and Diffusion

We have seen that the postulates of the kinetic molecular theory, combined with the appropriate physical principles, produce an equation that successfully fits the experimentally observed properties of gases as they approach ideal behavior. Two phenomena involving gases provide further tests of this model.

Diffusion is the term used to describe the mixing of gases. When a small amount of pungent-smelling ammonia is released at the front of a classroom, it takes some time before everyone in the room can smell it because time is required for the ammonia to mix with the air. The rate of diffusion is the rate of the mixing of gases. **Effusion** is the term used to describe the passage of a gas through a tiny orifice into an evacuated chamber (Fig. 5.18). The rate of effusion measures the rate at which the gas is transferred into the chamber.

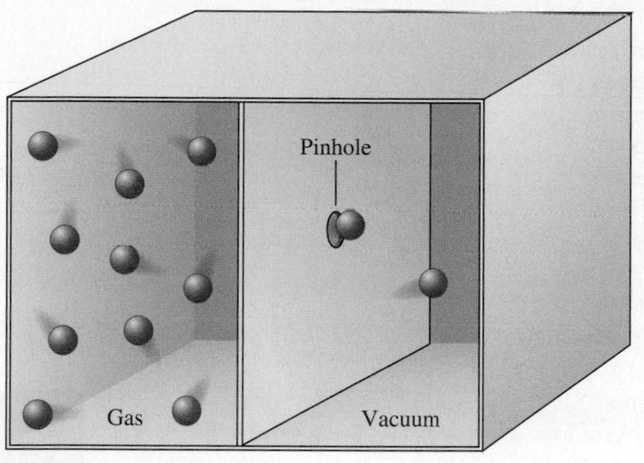

Figure 5.18
The effusion of a gas into an evacuated chamber. The rate of effusion (the rate at which the gas is transferred across the barrier through the pin hole) is inversely proportional to the square root of the mass of the gas molecules.

Effusion

Thomas Graham (1805–1869), a Scottish chemist, found experimentally that the rate of effusion of a gas is inversely proportional to the square root of the mass of its particles. Stated in another way, the relative rates of effusion of two gases at the same temperature and pressure are given by the inverse ratio of the square roots of the masses of the gas particles:

$$\frac{\text{Rate of effusion for gas 1}}{\text{Rate of effusion for gas 2}} = \frac{\sqrt{M_2}}{\sqrt{M_1}}$$

In Graham's law, the units for molar mass can be g/mol or kg/mol, since the units cancel in the ratio $\sqrt{M_2}/\sqrt{M_1}$.

where M_1 and M_2 represent the molar masses of the gases. This equation is called **Graham's law of effusion.**

Does the kinetic molecular model for gases correctly predict the relative effusion rates of gases summarized by Graham's law? To answer this question, we must recognize that the effusion rate for a gas depends directly on the average velocity of its particles. The faster the gas particles are moving, the more likely they are to pass through the effusion orifice. This reasoning leads to the following *prediction* for two gases at the same temperature T:

$$\frac{\text{Effusion rate for gas 1}}{\text{Effusion rate for gas 2}} = \frac{u_{\text{avg}} \text{ for gas 1}}{u_{\text{avg}} \text{ for gas 2}} = \frac{\sqrt{8RT/\pi M_1}}{\sqrt{8RT/\pi M_2}} = \frac{\sqrt{M_2}}{\sqrt{M_1}}$$

This equation is Graham's law, and thus the kinetic molecular model fits the experimental results for the effusion of gases.

Diffusion

Diffusion is frequently illustrated by the lecture demonstration represented in Fig. 5.19, in which two cotton plugs, one soaked in ammonia and the other in hydrochloric acid, are simultaneously placed at the ends of a long tube. A white ring of ammonium chloride (NH_4Cl) forms where the NH_3 and HCl molecules meet several minutes later:

$$NH_3(g) + HCl(g) \longrightarrow \underset{\text{White solid}}{NH_4Cl(s)}$$

The progress of the gases through the tube is surprisingly slow in light of the fact that the velocities of the HCl and NH_3 molecules at 25°C are approximately 450 and 660 m/s, respectively. Why does it take several minutes for the NH_3 and HCl molecules to meet? The answer is that the tube contains air and thus the NH_3 and HCl molecules undergo many collisions with O_2 and N_2 molecules as they travel through the tube. Although these collisions greatly slow their progress through the tube, it still seems reasonable to expect the

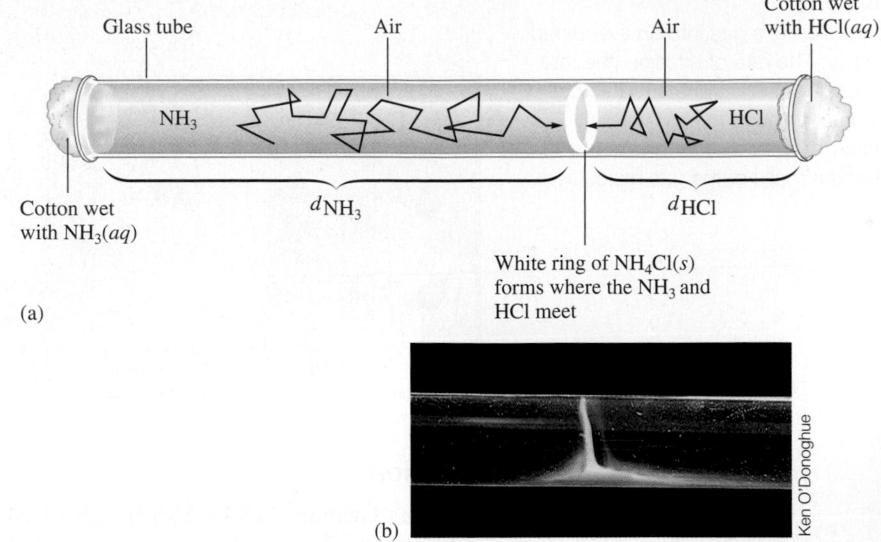

Figure 5.19
(a) A demonstration of the relative diffusion rates of NH_3 and HCl molecules through air. Two cotton plugs, one dipped in HCl(*aq*) and one dipped in NH_3(*aq*), are simultaneously inserted into the ends of the tube. Gaseous NH_3 and HCl vaporizing from the cotton plugs diffuse toward each other and, where they meet, react to form NH_4Cl(*s*).
(b) When HCl(*g*) and NH_3(*g*) meet in the tube, a white ring of NH_4Cl(*s*) forms.

relative distances traveled by the NH_3 and HCl molecules to be related to their velocities:

$$\frac{d_{NH_3}}{d_{HCl}} = \frac{\text{distance traveled by } NH_3}{\text{distance traveled by HCl}} = \frac{u_{avg(NH_3)}}{u_{avg(HCl)}} = \sqrt{\frac{M_{HCl}}{M_{NH_3}}} = \sqrt{\frac{36.5}{17}} = 1.5$$

However, careful experiments show that this prediction is not borne out—the observed ratio of distances is 1.3, not 1.5 as predicted by Graham's law. This discrepancy is not due to a failure of the kinetic molecular theory or of Graham's law; it exists because this "diffusion" experiment does not involve a simple diffusion process. Rather, it involves a *flow* of ammonia and hydrogen chloride gases through the air in the tube. Because the NH_3 and HCl molecules suffer many collisions with the N_2 and O_2 molecules in the tube, the flow rates of NH_3 and HCl are not directly proportional to their molecular velocities. Higher velocities lead to a higher number of intermolecular collisions, which in turn impedes the flow of the gas. Because of its smaller mass (and thus higher average velocity), the flow of the ammonia gas is impeded more than the flow of the hydrogen chloride gas. Therefore, the NH_3(*g*) travels a smaller distance to meet the HCl(*g*) than is expected from Graham's law (the distance ratio is smaller than 1.5).

If no air were present in the tube, the ratio of distances would be 1.5 as predicted from Graham's law.

Although we have given only a qualitative treatment here, the phenomena accompanying the mixing of gases are well understood, and the results of this experiment can be described very accurately by quantitative theories.

Although other technologies are now coming into use for this purpose, gaseous diffusion has played an important role in the enrichment of uranium for use in nuclear reactors. Natural uranium is mostly $^{238}_{92}U$, which cannot be fissioned to produce energy. It contains only about 0.7% of the fissionable nuclide $^{235}_{92}U$. For uranium to be useful as a nuclear fuel, the relative amount of $^{235}_{92}U$ must be increased to about 3%. In the gas diffusion enrichment process, the natural uranium (containing $^{238}_{92}U$ and a small amount of $^{235}_{92}U$) reacts with fluorine to form a mixture of $^{238}UF_6$ and $^{235}UF_6$. Because these molecules have slightly different masses, they will have slightly different velocities at a given temperature, which allows them to be separated by a multistage diffusion process. To understand how this process works, imagine a series of chambers separated by semiporous walls that allow passage of some UF_6 molecules but prevent bulk flow of gas. In effect, each porous wall acts much like a tiny hole in an effusion cell. Assume that the UF_6 from natural uranium is placed in chamber 1. Thus chamber 1 contains 99.3% $^{238}UF_6$ and 0.7% $^{235}UF_6$ (that is, 993 molecules of $^{238}UF_6$ for every 7 molecules of $^{235}UF_6$). Some molecules of this UF_6 diffuse through the semiporous barrier into chamber 2, which was initially empty. Because of its smaller mass, $^{235}UF_6$, which has a slightly greater velocity than $^{238}UF_6$, diffuses at a slightly greater rate. Thus chamber 2 will contain a ratio of $^{235}UF_6$ to $^{238}UF_6$ that is slightly greater than 7 to 993.

Although the process is called *gaseous diffusion* because the chambers are separated by barriers that effectively allow only individual UF_6 molecules to pass through, it behaves like an effusion process. Thus we can find the actual ratio of the two types of UF_6 in chamber 2 from Graham's law:

$$\frac{\text{Diffusion rate for } ^{235}UF_6}{\text{Diffusion rate for } ^{238}UF_6} = \sqrt{\frac{\text{mass}(^{238}UF_6)}{\text{mass}(^{235}UF_6)}}$$

$$= \sqrt{\frac{352.05 \text{ g/mol}}{349.03 \text{ g/mol}}}$$

$$= 1.0043$$

We can use this factor to calculate the ratio of $^{235}UF_6/^{238}UF_6$ in chamber 2:

$$\underset{\text{Chamber 2}}{\underset{\uparrow}{\frac{^{235}UF_6}{^{238}UF_6}}} = 1.0043 \times \underset{\text{Chamber 1}}{\underset{\uparrow}{\frac{^{235}UF_6}{^{238}UF_6}}} = 1.0043\left(\frac{7}{993}\right)$$

$$= 1.0043(7.0493 \times 10^{-3})$$

$$= 7.0797 \times 10^{-3}$$

This very slight increase represents a change from the ratio of 70,493 $^{235}UF_6$ molecules per 10,000,000 $^{238}UF_6$ molecules in chamber 1 to the ratio of 70,797 $^{235}UF_6$ molecules per 10,000,000 $^{238}UF_6$ molecules in chamber 2.

This enrichment process (in $^{235}UF_6$) continues as the slightly enriched gas in chamber 2 diffuses into chamber 3 and is again enriched by a factor of 1.0043. The same process is repeated until sufficient enrichment occurs. Obviously, this process will take many stages. For example, to calculate the number of steps required to enrich from 0.700% ^{235}U to 3.00% ^{235}U, we have the following equation:

$$\underset{\text{Original ratio}}{\underset{\uparrow}{\frac{0.700\ ^{235}UF_6}{99.3\ ^{238}UF_6}}} \times (1.0043)^N = \underset{\text{Desired ratio}}{\underset{\uparrow}{\frac{3.00\ ^{235}UF_6}{97.0\ ^{238}UF_6}}}$$

where N represents the number of stages. This equation follows from the fact that each stage produces an enrichment by the factor 1.0043. Thus

$$\text{Original ratio} \times \underset{\text{First stage}}{\underset{\uparrow}{1.0043}} \times \underset{\text{Second stage}}{\underset{\uparrow}{1.0043}} \times \underset{\text{Third stage}}{\underset{\uparrow}{1.0043}} \times \cdots = \text{final ratio}$$

Solving this equation for N yields 345. Thus we predict that 345 stages are required to obtain the desired enrichment.

Although we have greatly oversimplified* the actual enrichment process here, this discussion gives you an idea of how it is accomplished. A photo of actual diffusion cells is shown in Fig. 5.20.

U.S. Department of Energy

Figure 5.20
Uranium-enrichment converters from the Paducah gaseous diffusion plant in Kentucky.

*For a more detailed description, see W. Spindel and T. Ishida, "Isotope Separation," *J. Chem. Ed.* 68 (1991): 312.

Enrichment of uranium by gaseous diffusion has become obsolete. Increasingly, a process using gas centrifuges has become the method of choice. Such a process uses a large number of rotating cylinders (centrifuges) that cause the more massive $^{238}UF_6$ to move to the outside of each cylinder relative to the $^{235}UF_6$, which remains closer to the center. Gas centrifuge technology requires much less energy than gaseous diffusion, and each step has a 1.3 separation factor compared to 1.0043 for gaseous diffusion. Other technologies are also being explored for uranium enrichment, but we will not discuss them here.

5.8 Collisions of Gas Particles with the Container Walls

In the analysis of the kinetic molecular model that led to the ideal gas equation, we assumed that the pressure a gas exerts is caused by the collisions of its particles with the walls of its container. In this section we will consider the details of that phenomenon.

Our goal is to obtain an equation that describes the number of particles that collide per second with a given area of the wall. Although a rigorous derivation of such an equation can be carried out from the details of the kinetic molecular theory, we will not do that. Instead, we will pursue a qualitative strategy, trying to obtain the fundamental relationships from our conceptual understanding of how an ideal gas is expected to behave. We will define the quantity we are looking for as Z_A, the collision rate (per second) of the gas particles with a section of wall that has an area A (in m^2). We expect Z_A to depend on the following factors:

1. The average velocity of the gas particles
2. The size of the area being considered
3. The number of particles in the container

How is Z_A expected to depend on the average velocity of the gas particles? For example, if we double the average velocity, we double the number of wall impacts, so Z_A should double. Thus Z_A depends directly on u_{avg}:

$$Z_A \propto u_{avg}$$

Similarly, Z_A depends directly on A, the area of the wall under consideration. That is, if we double the area being considered, we will double the number of impacts per second that occur within that section of the wall. Thus $Z_A \propto A$.

Likewise, if the number of particles in the container is doubled, the impacts with the wall will double. For a general case, we need to consider not the absolute number of particles but the number of particles per unit volume (the number density of particles), which can be represented by N/V, the number of particles N divided by the volume V (in m^3). Thus Z_A is expected to depend directly on N/V. That is, $Z_A \propto N/V$.

In summary, Z_A should be directly proportional to u_{avg}, A, and N/V:

$$Z_A \propto u_{avg} \times A \times \frac{N}{V}$$

Note that the units for Z_A expected from this relationship are

$$\frac{\text{m}}{\text{s}} \times \text{m}^2 \times \frac{\text{(particles)}}{\text{m}^3} \longrightarrow \frac{\text{(particles)}}{\text{s}} \quad \text{or} \quad \frac{\text{(collisions)}}{\text{s}}$$

The parentheses are used here because particles and collisions are understood and are not actual units. The correct units for Z_A are 1/s, or s^{-1}. The fact that the product $u_{avg} \times A \times N/V$ gives the units expected for Z_A indicates that we are considering all the gas properties that influence Z_A. Substituting the expression for u_{avg} gives

$$Z_A \propto \frac{N}{V} A \sqrt{\frac{8RT}{\pi M}}$$

A more detailed analysis of the situation shows that the proportionality constant is $\frac{1}{4}$. Thus the exact equation for Z_A is

$$Z_A = \frac{1}{4}\frac{N}{V} A \sqrt{\frac{8RT}{\pi M}} = A\frac{N}{V}\sqrt{\frac{RT}{2\pi M}}$$

OWL INTERACTIVE EXAMPLE 5.9

Calculate the impact rate on a 1.00-cm² section of a vessel containing oxygen gas at a pressure of 1.00 atm and 27°C.

Solution To calculate Z_A, we must identify the values of the variables in the equation

$$Z_A = A\frac{N}{V}\sqrt{\frac{RT}{2\pi M}}$$

In this case, A is given as 1.00 cm². However, to be inserted into the expression for Z_A, A must have the units m². The appropriate conversion gives $A = 1.00 \times 10^{-4}$ m².

The quantity N/V can be obtained from the ideal gas law by solving for n/V and then converting to the appropriate units:

$$\frac{n}{V} = \frac{P}{RT} = \frac{1.00 \text{ atm}}{\left(0.08206 \frac{\text{L atm}}{\text{K mol}}\right)(300.\text{ K})} = 4.06 \times 10^{-2} \text{ mol/L}$$

To obtain N/V, which has the units (molecules)/m³, from n/V, we make the following conversion:

$$\frac{N}{V} = 4.06 \times 10^{-2}\frac{\text{mol}}{\text{L}} \times 6.022 \times 10^{23}\frac{\text{(molecules)}}{\text{mol}} \times \frac{1000 \text{ L}}{\text{m}^3}$$
$$= 2.44 \times 10^{25} \text{ (molecules)/m}^3$$

The quantity M represents the molar mass of O_2 in kg. Thus

$$M = 32.0\frac{\text{g}}{\text{mol}} \times \frac{1 \text{ kg}}{1000 \text{ g}} = 3.20 \times 10^{-2} \text{ kg/mol}$$

Next, we insert these quantities into the expression for Z_A:

$$Z_A = A\frac{N}{V}\sqrt{\frac{RT}{2\pi M}} = (1.00 \times 10^{-4} \text{ m}^2)(2.44 \times 10^{25} \text{ m}^{-3})$$
$$\times \sqrt{\frac{\left(8.3145\frac{\text{J}}{\text{K mol}}\right)(300.\text{ K})}{(2)(3.14)\left(3.20 \times 10^{-2}\frac{\text{kg}}{\text{mol}}\right)}} = 2.72 \times 10^{23} \text{ s}^{-1}$$

That is, in this gas 2.72×10^{23} collisions per second occur on each 1.00-cm² area of the container.

5.9 Intermolecular Collisions

Recall that the postulates of the kinetic molecular model do not take into account collisions between gas particles. Since this model correctly fits ideal gas behavior (that is, the behavior approached by real gases at high T and low P), our conclusion is that intermolecular collisions apparently do not have an important influence on the pressure, volume, or temperature of a gas behaving ideally. That is, the effects of the collisions must somehow "cancel out" relative to the properties P, V, and T of an ideal gas. However, there is much evidence to suggest that collisions do occur among the gas particles in a real gas. For example, a gas that is somehow disturbed from a Maxwell–Boltzmann distribution of velocities will rapidly change until it again reaches a Maxwell–Boltzmann distribution. This behavior must be caused by energy exchanges through collisions.

In this section we will consider the collision frequency of the particles in a gas. We will start by considering a single spherical gas particle with diameter d (in meters) that is moving with velocity u_{avg}. As this particle moves through the gas in a straight line, it will collide with another particle only if the other particle has its center in a cylinder with radius d, as shown in Fig. 5.21.

Any particle with its center outside this cylinder will not be hit by our particle. Thus our particle "sweeps out" a cylinder of radius d and length $u_{avg} \times 1$ second during every second of its flight. Therefore, the volume of the cylinder swept out per second is

$$V = \text{volume} = \underbrace{(\pi d^2)}_{\substack{\text{Area of} \\ \text{cylinder} \\ \text{slice}}} \underbrace{(u_{avg})(1\text{ s})}_{\substack{\text{Length of} \\ \text{cylinder}}}$$

As the particle travels through this cylinder, the number of collisions depends on the number of gas particles in that volume. To specify the number of gas particles, we use the number density of the gas N/V, which indicates the number of gas particles per unit volume. Thus we can write

$$\begin{aligned}\text{Number of collisions per second} &= \begin{pmatrix}\text{volume} \\ \text{swept out}\end{pmatrix} \times \frac{N}{V} = \pi d^2 (u_{avg})\left(\frac{N}{V}\right) \\ &= \pi d^2\left(\sqrt{\frac{8RT}{\pi M}}\right)\left(\frac{N}{V}\right) = \frac{N}{V}\, d^2\sqrt{\frac{8\pi RT}{M}}\end{aligned}$$

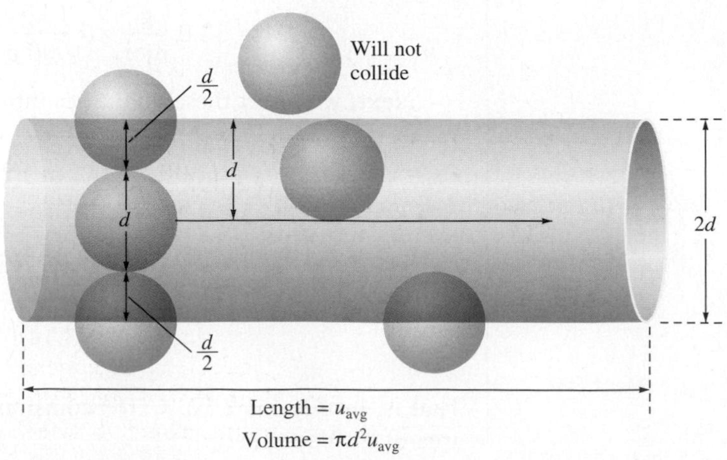

Figure 5.21
The cylinder swept out by a gas particle of diameter *d*.

This equation is not quite correct. If you are thinking carefully about this situation, you may be asking yourself the question, "What about the motions of the other particles?" That is, we have said that the primary particle has velocity u_{avg}, but we have assumed that the other particles are stationary. Of course, they are not really stationary. They are moving in various directions with various velocities. When the motions of the other particles are accounted for (a derivation we will not show here), the *relative velocity* of the primary particle becomes $\sqrt{2}\, u_{avg}$ rather than the value u_{avg} that we have been using. Thus the expression for the collision rate becomes

$$\text{Collision rate (per second)} = Z = \sqrt{2}\frac{N}{V}d^2\sqrt{\frac{8\pi RT}{M}} = 4\frac{N}{V}d^2\sqrt{\frac{\pi RT}{M}}$$

OWL INTERACTIVE EXAMPLE 5.10

Calculate the collision frequency for an oxygen molecule in a sample of pure oxygen gas at 27°C and 1.0 atm. Assume that the diameter of an O_2 molecule is 300 pm.

Solution To obtain the collision frequency, we must identify the quantities in the expression

$$Z = 4\frac{N}{V}d^2\sqrt{\frac{\pi RT}{M}}$$

that are appropriate to this case. We can obtain the value of N/V for this sample of oxygen by assuming ideal behavior. From the ideal gas law,

$$\frac{n}{V} = \frac{P}{RT} = \frac{1.0 \text{ atm}}{\left(0.08206 \dfrac{\text{L atm}}{\text{K mol}}\right)(300.\text{ K})} = 4.1 \times 10^{-2} \text{ mol/L}$$

Thus

$$\frac{N}{V} = \left(4.1 \times 10^{-2}\frac{\text{mol}}{\text{L}}\right)\left(6.022 \times 10^{23}\frac{\text{molecules}}{\text{mol}}\right)\left(\frac{1000 \text{ L}}{\text{m}^3}\right)$$

$$= 2.5 \times 10^{25} \text{ (molecules)/m}^3$$

From the given information, we know that

$$d = 300 \text{ pm} = 300 \times 10^{-12} \text{ m or } 3 \times 10^{-10} \text{ m}$$

Also, for O_2, $M = 3.20 \times 10^{-2}$ kg/mol. Thus

$$Z = 4(2.5 \times 10^{25} \text{ m}^{-3})(3 \times 10^{-10} \text{ m})^2 \times \sqrt{\frac{\pi(8.3145 \text{ J K}^{-1}\text{ mol}^{-1})(300 \text{ K})}{3.20 \times 10^{-2} \text{ kg/mol}}}$$

$$= 4 \times 10^9 \text{ (collisions)/s} = 4 \times 10^9 \text{ s}^{-1}$$

Notice how large this number is. Each O_2 molecule undergoes approximately 4 billion collisions per second in this gas sample.

Mean Free Path

As we saw earlier, the collision frequency Z represents the number of collisions per second that occur in a given gas sample. On the other hand, the reciprocal of Z gives the time (in seconds) between collisions. Thus, if $Z = 4 \times 10^9$ (collisions) per second, then $1/Z = 2.5 \times 10^{-10}$ seconds between collisions. Now if we multiply $1/Z$ by the average velocity, we obtain the **mean free path λ:**

$$\lambda = \underset{\substack{\nearrow \\ \text{Time between} \\ \text{collisions (s)}}}{\frac{1}{Z}} \times \underset{\substack{\uparrow \\ \text{Distance traveled} \\ \text{per second}}}{u_{\text{avg}}} = \text{distance between collisions}$$

Substituting the expressions for $1/Z$ and u_{avg} gives

$$\lambda = \left[\frac{1}{4(N/V)(d^2)\sqrt{RT/M}}\right]\left(\sqrt{\frac{8RT}{\pi M}}\right) = \frac{1}{\sqrt{2}(N/V)(\pi d^2)}$$

EXAMPLE 5.11

Calculate the mean free path in a sample of oxygen gas at 27°C and 1.0 atm.

Solution Using data from the preceding example, we have

$$\lambda = \frac{1}{\sqrt{2}(2.5 \times 10^{25}\ \text{m}^{-3})(\pi)(3 \times 10^{-10}\ \text{m})^2} = 1 \times 10^{-7}\ \text{m}$$

Note that an O_2 molecule travels only a very short distance before it collides with another O_2 molecule. This produces a path for a given O_2 molecule like the one represented in Fig. 5.14, where the length of each straight line is $\sim 10^{-7}$ m.

5.10 Real Gases

An ideal gas is a hypothetical concept. No gas *exactly* follows the ideal gas law, although many gases come very close at low pressures and/or high temperatures. Thus ideal gas behavior can best be thought of as the behavior *approached by real gases* under certain conditions.

We have seen that a very simple model, the kinetic molecular theory, by making some rather drastic assumptions (no interparticle interactions and zero volume for the gas particles), successfully explains ideal behavior. However, it is important that we examine real gas behavior to see how it differs from that predicted by the ideal gas law and to determine what modifications of the kinetic molecular theory are needed to explain the observed behavior. Since a model is an approximation and will inevitably fail, we must be ready to learn from such failures. In fact, we often learn more about nature from the failures of our models than from their successes.

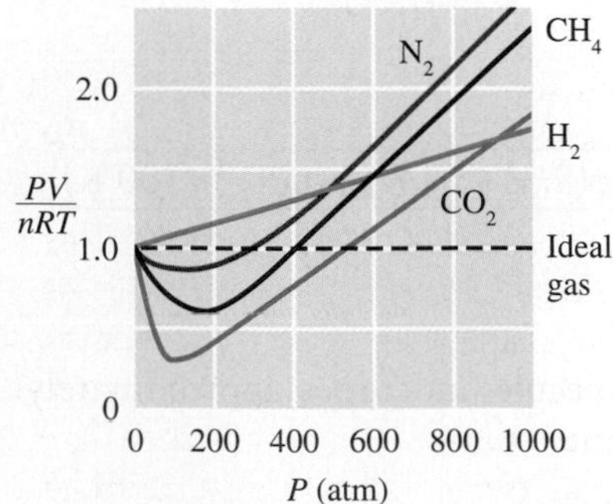

Figure 5.22
Plots of PV/nRT versus P for several gases (200 K). Note the significant deviations from ideal behavior ($PV/nRT = 1$). The behavior is close to ideal only at low pressures (less than 1 atm).

We will examine the experimentally observed behavior of real gases by measuring the pressure, volume, temperature, and number of moles for a gas and noting how the quantity PV/nRT depends on pressure. Plots of PV/nRT versus P are shown for several gases in Fig. 5.22. For an ideal gas, PV/nRT equals 1 under all conditions, but notice that for real gases, PV/nRT approaches 1 only at low pressures (typically 1 atm). To illustrate the effect of temperature, we have plotted PV/nRT versus P for nitrogen gas at several temperatures in Fig. 5.23. Notice that the behavior of the gas appears to become more nearly ideal as the temperature is increased. The most important conclusion to be drawn from these plots is that a real gas typically exhibits behavior that is closest to ideal behavior at *low pressures* and *high temperatures.*

How can we modify the assumptions of the kinetic molecular theory to fit the behavior of real gases? An equation for real gases was developed in 1873 by Johannes van der Waals, a physics professor at the University of Amster-

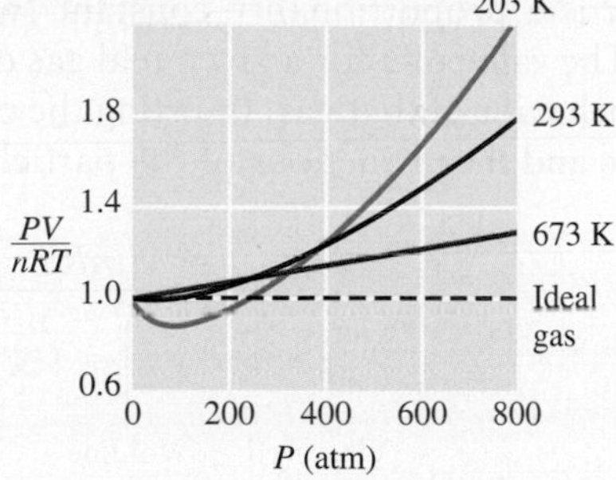

Figure 5.23
Plots of PV/nRT versus P for nitrogen gas at three temperatures. Note that although nonideal behavior is evident in each case, the deviations are smaller at the higher temperatures.

PV/nRT is also 1 at high pressures for many gases because of a canceling of nonideal effects.

P' is corrected for the finite volume of the particles. The attractive forces have not yet been taken into account.

P_{obs} is usually called just P.

We have now corrected for both the finite volume and the attractive forces of the particles.

dam who in 1910 received a Nobel Prize for his work. To follow his analyses, we start with the ideal gas law,

$$P = \frac{nRT}{V}$$

Remember that this equation describes the behavior of a hypothetical gas consisting of volumeless entities that do not interact with each other. In contrast, a real gas consists of atoms or molecules that have finite volumes. Thus the volume available to a given particle in a real gas is less than the volume of the container because the gas particles themselves take up some of the space. To account for this discrepancy, van der Waals represented the actual volume as the volume of the container V minus a correction factor for the volume of the molecules nb, where n is the number of moles of gas and b is an empirical constant (one determined by fitting the equation to the experimental results). Thus the volume *actually available* to a given gas molecule is given by the difference $V - nb$.

This modification of the ideal gas equation leads to the expression

$$P' = \frac{nRT}{(V - nb)}$$

The volume of the gas particles has now been taken into account.

The next step is to account for the attractions that occur among the particles in a real gas. The effect of these attractions is to make the observed pressure P_{obs} smaller than it would be if the gas particles did not interact:

$$P_{obs} = (P' - \text{correction factor}) = \left(\frac{nRT}{V - nb} - \text{correction factor}\right)$$

This effect can be understood by using the following model. When gas particles come close together, attractive forces occur, which cause the particles to hit the wall slightly less often than they would in the absence of these interactions (Fig. 5.24).

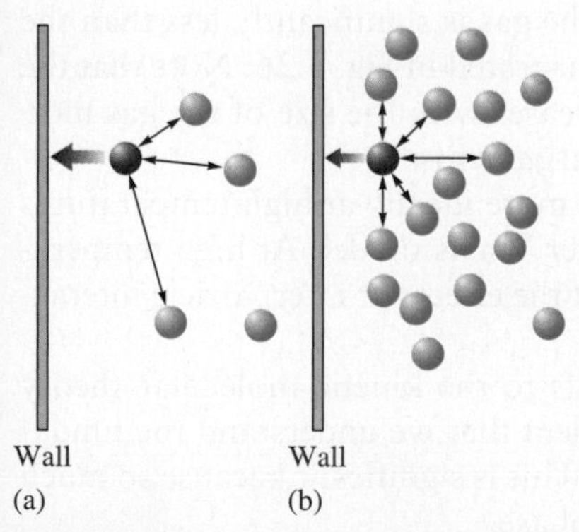

Figure 5.24
(a) Gas at low concentration—relatively few interactions between particles. The indicated gas particle exerts a pressure on the wall close to that predicted for an ideal gas.
(b) Gas at high concentration—many more interactions between particles. Because of these interactions the collision frequency with the walls is lowered, thus causing the observed pressure to be smaller than if the gas were behaving ideally.

The size of the correction factor depends on the concentration of gas molecules defined in terms of moles of gas particles per liter (n/V). The higher the concentration, the more likely a pair of gas particles will be close enough to attract each other. For large numbers of particles, the number of interacting *pairs* of particles depends on the square of the number of particles and thus on the square of the concentration, or $(n/V)^2$. This reasoning can be justified as follows: In a gas sample containing N particles, there are $N - 1$ partners available for each particle, as shown in Fig. 5.25. Since the $1 \cdots 2$ pair is the same as the $2 \cdots 1$ pair, this analysis counts each pair twice. Thus for N particles there are $N(N - 1)/2$ pairs. If N is a very large number, $N - 1$ approximately equals N, giving $N^2/2$ possible pairs. Thus the correction to the ideal pressure for the attractions of the particles has the form

$$P_{obs} = P' - a\left(\frac{n}{V}\right)^2$$

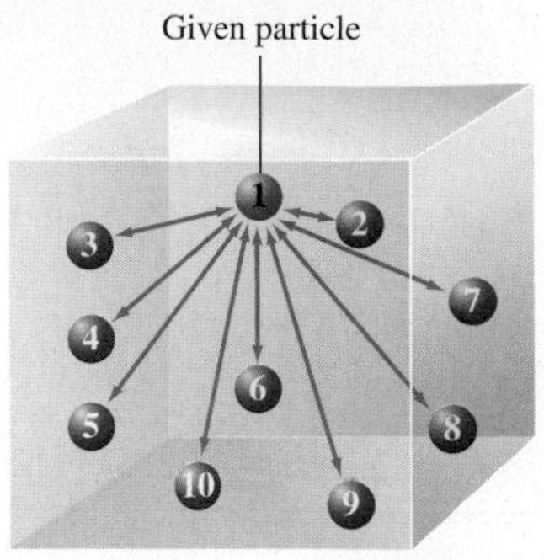

Figure 5.25
Illustration of pairwise interactions among gas particles. In a sample with 10 particles, each particle has 9 possible partners, to give 10(9)/2 = 45 distinct pairs. The factor of $\frac{1}{2}$ arises because when particle 1 is the particle of interest, we count the 1···2 pair, and when particle 2 is the particle of interest, we count the 2···1 pair. However, 1···2 and 2···1 are the same pair, which we thus have counted twice. Therefore, we must divide by 2 to get the correct number of pairs.

where a is a proportionality constant (which includes the factor of $1\frac{1}{2}$ from $N^2/2$). The value of a for a given real gas can be determined from observing the actual behavior of that gas. Inserting the corrections for both the volume of the particles and the attractions of the particles gives the equation

$$\underbrace{P_{\text{obs}}}_{\text{Observed pressure}} = \frac{nRT}{\underbrace{V}_{\text{Volume of the container}} - \underbrace{nb}_{\text{Volume correction}}} - \underbrace{a\left(\frac{n}{V}\right)^2}_{\text{Pressure correction}}$$

This equation can be rearranged to give the **van der Waals equation:**

$$\underbrace{\underbrace{\left[P_{\text{obs}} + a\left(\frac{n}{V}\right)^2\right]}_{\text{Corrected pressure}}}_{P_{\text{ideal}}} \underbrace{\underbrace{(V - nb)}_{\text{Corrected volume}}}_{V_{\text{ideal}}} = nRT$$

The values of the weighting factors, a and b, are determined for a given gas by fitting experimental behavior. That is, a and b are varied until the best fit of the observed pressure is obtained under all conditions. The values of a and b for various gases are given in Table 5.3.

Experimental studies indicate that the changes van der Waals made in the basic assumptions of the kinetic molecular theory corrected the major flaws in the model. First, consider the effects of volume. For a gas at low pressure (large volume), the volume of the container is very large compared with the volumes of the gas particles. That is, the volume available to the gas is essentially equal to the volume of the container, so the gas behaves ideally. On the other hand, for a gas at high pressure (small volume), the volume of the particles becomes significant so that the volume available to the gas is significantly less than the container volume. These observations are illustrated in Fig. 5.26. Note that the volume-correction constant b generally increases with the size of the gas molecule, which gives further support to these arguments.

The fact that a real gas tends to behave more ideally at high temperatures can also be explained in terms of the van der Waals model. At high temperatures the particles are moving so rapidly that the effects of interparticle interactions are not very important.

The corrections made by van der Waals to the kinetic molecular theory make physical sense, which makes us confident that we understand the fundamentals of gas behavior at the particle level. This is significant because so much important chemistry takes place in the gas phase.

Table 5.3
Values of van der Waals Constants for Some Common Gases

Gas	$a\left(\frac{\text{atm L}^2}{\text{mol}^2}\right)$	$b\left(\frac{\text{L}}{\text{mol}}\right)$
He	0.034	0.0237
Ne	0.211	0.0171
Ar	1.35	0.0322
Kr	2.32	0.0398
Xe	4.19	0.0511
H_2	0.244	0.0266
N_2	1.39	0.0391
O_2	1.36	0.0318
Cl_2	6.49	0.0562
CO_2	3.59	0.0427
CH_4	2.25	0.0428
NH_3	4.17	0.0371
H_2O	5.46	0.0305

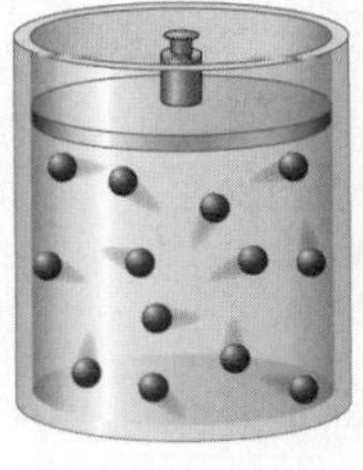

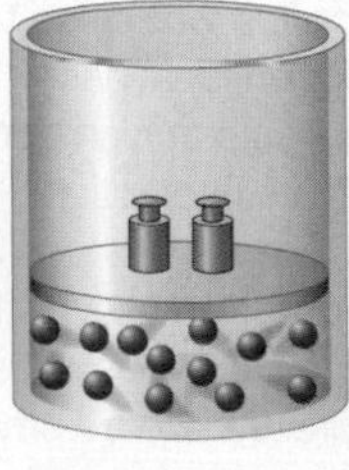

Figure 5.26
The volume occupied by the gas particles themselves is less important at (a) large container volumes (low pressure) than at (b) small container volumes (high pressure).

Kenneth Suslick Practices Sound Chemistry

Chemistry Explorers

Professor Kenneth S. Suslick, who received his B.S. degree from the California Institute of Technology and his Ph.D. from Stanford University, has spent his entire academic career at the University of Illinois at Urbana-Champaign. Although his research interests have spanned the traditional areas of chemistry, Professor Suslick and his group have been especially interested in sonochemistry, the chemical effects of ultrasound in which sound waves (pitched above human hearing) are applied to solutions.

The effects of high-intensity sound waves on solutions come from cavitation: the formation, growth, and implosive collapse of bubbles in a liquid. Cavitational collapse produces very high pressures that lead to local heating so intense that they cause reactions requiring high energies to occur, often accompanied by the emission of light.

In fact, Suslick's research has just shown that as the bubble implodes, the interior can reach temperatures higher than 15,000 K—about three times the temperature of the surface of the sun. At these temperatures atoms come apart to form a plasma, which contains ions and electrons. Thus cavitation can create extraordinarily hot spots in an otherwise cold liquid.

Besides its use for studying high-energy reactions, ultrasound has also proved valuable in the synthesis of nanostructured materials. One example is the formation of liquid-containing protein microspheres that could be injected into the body's circulatory system to deliver drugs. Another application involves surface chemistry. When cavitation occurs near a solid surface, the high-speed jets of liquid and the associated sound waves can alter the surface properties of the solid. This has proved useful in activating the surfaces of metals used as catalysts.

Sonochemistry is indeed sound chemistry.

Jim Gray/Courtesy of Kenneth S. Suslick

A humorous photograph of Professor Kenneth S. Suslick. The fog apparently emanating from his head is produced by a very cold vapor from liquid nitrogen, which freezes moisture from the air.

5.11 Characteristics of Several Real Gases

We can understand gas behavior more completely if we examine the characteristics of several common gases. Note from Fig. 5.22 that the gases H_2, N_2, CH_4, and CO_2 show different behavior when the compressibility PV/nRT is plotted versus P. For example, notice that the plot for $H_2(g)$ never drops below the ideal value (1.0) in contrast to all the other gases. What is special about H_2 compared to these other gases? Recall from Section 5.8 that the reason that the compressibility of a real gas falls below 1.0 is that the actual (observed) pressure is lower than the pressure expected for an ideal gas due to the intermolecular attractions that occur in real gases. This must mean that H_2 molecules have very low attractive forces for each other. This idea is borne out by looking at the van der Waals a value for H_2 in Table 5.3. Note that H_2 has the lowest value among the gases H_2, N_2, CH_4, and CO_2. Remember that the value of a reflects how much of a correction must be made to adjust the observed pressure up to the expected ideal pressure:

$$P_{\text{ideal}} = P_{\text{obs}} + a\left(\frac{n}{V}\right)^2$$

A low value for a reflects weak intermolecular forces among the gas molecules.

Also notice that although the compressibility for N_2 dips below 1.0, it does not show as much deviation as that for CH_4, which in turn does not show as much deviation as the compressibility for CO_2. Based on this behavior, we can surmise that the importance of intermolecular interactions increases in this order:

$$H_2 < N_2 < CH_4 < CO_2$$

This order is reflected by the relative *a* values for these gases in Table 5.3. In Section 16.1, we will see how these variations in intermolecular interactions can be explained. The main point to be made here is that real gas behavior can tell us about the relative importance of intermolecular attractions among gas molecules.

5.12 Chemistry in the Atmosphere

Table 5.4

Atmospheric Composition Near Sea Level (dry air)*

Component	Mole Fraction
N_2	0.78084
O_2	0.20946
Ar	0.00934
CO_2	0.000345
Ne	0.00001818
He	0.00000524
CH_4	0.00000168
Kr	0.00000114
H_2	0.0000005
NO	0.0000005
Xe	0.000000087

*The atmosphere contains various amounts of water vapor, depending on conditions.

The gases that are most important to us are located in the **atmosphere** that surrounds the earth's surface. The principal components are N_2 and O_2, but many other important gases, such as H_2O and CO_2, are also present. The average composition of the earth's atmosphere near sea level, with the water vapor removed, is shown in Table 5.4. Because of gravitational effects, the composition of the earth's atmosphere is not constant: Heavier molecules tend to be near the earth's surface, and light molecules tend to migrate to higher altitudes and eventually to escape into space. The atmosphere is a highly complex and dynamic system, but for convenience, we divide it into several layers based on the way the temperature changes with altitude. (The lowest layer, called the *troposphere,* is shown in Fig. 5.27.) Note that in contrast to the complex temperature profile of the atmosphere in general, the pressure decreases in a regular way with increasing altitude in the troposphere.

The chemistry occurring in the higher levels of the atmosphere is mostly determined by the effects of high-energy radiation and particles from the sun and other sources in space. In fact, the upper atmosphere serves as an important shield to prevent this high-energy radiation from reaching the earth, where it would damage the relatively fragile molecules sustaining life. In particular, the ozone in the upper atmosphere helps prevent high-energy ultraviolet radiation from penetrating to the earth. Intensive research is in progress to determine the natural factors that control the ozone concentration and to understand how it is affected by chemicals released into the atmosphere.

The chemistry occurring in the troposphere is strongly influenced by human activities. Millions of tons of gases and particulates are released into the tropo-

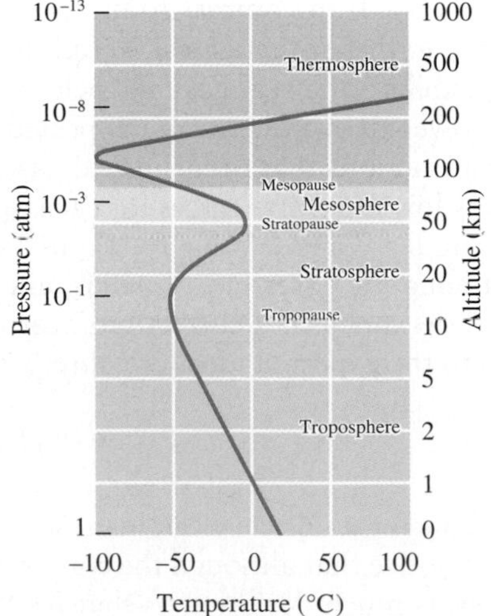

Figure 5.27
The variation of temperature and pressure with altitude. Note that the pressure steadily decreases with increasing altitude but that the temperature does not change monotonically.

sphere by our highly industrial civilization. Actually, it is amazing that the atmosphere can absorb so much material with relatively small permanent changes.

Significant changes, however, are occurring. Severe **air pollution** is found around many large cities, and it is probable that long-range changes in the planet's weather are taking place. We will deal only with the short-term, localized effects of pollution.

The two main sources of pollution are transportation and the production of electricity. The combustion of petroleum in vehicles produces CO, CO_2, NO, and NO_2, along with unburned molecules from petroleum. When this mixture is trapped close to the ground in stagnant air, reactions occur, producing chemicals that are potentially irritating and harmful to living systems.

Although represented here as O_2, the actual oxidant is an organic peroxide such as CH_3COO, formed by reaction of O_2 with organic pollutants.

The complex chemistry of polluted air appears to center on ozone and the nitrogen oxides (NO_x). At the high temperatures in the gasoline and diesel engines of cars and trucks, N_2 and O_2 react to form a small quantity of NO, which is emitted into the air with the exhaust gases (Fig. 5.28). This NO is oxidized in air to NO_2, which in turn absorbs energy from sunlight and breaks up into nitric oxide and free oxygen atoms:

$$NO_2(g) \xrightarrow{\text{Radiant energy}} NO(g) + O(g)$$

Oxygen atoms are very reactive and can combine with O_2 to form *ozone:*

$$O(g) + O_2(g) \longrightarrow O_3(g)$$

Ozone is also very reactive. It can react with the unburned hydrocarbons in the polluted air to produce chemicals that cause the eyes to water and burn and are harmful to the respiratory system.

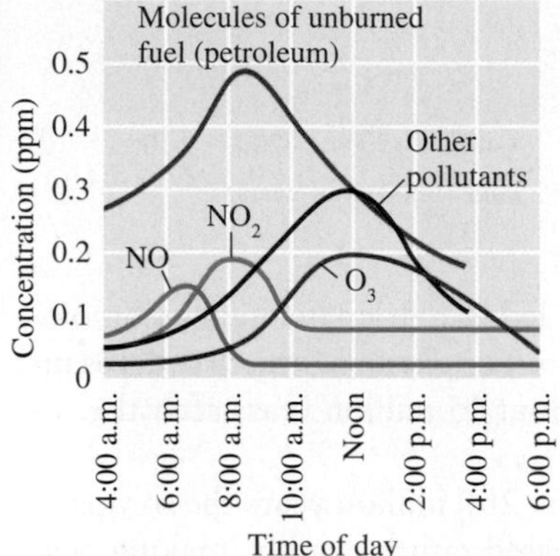

Figure 5.28
Concentration (in molecules per million molecules of "air") of some smog components versus time of day. After P. A. Leighton's classic experiment, "Photochemistry of Air Pollution," in *Physical Chemistry: A Series of Monographs,* ed. Eric Hutchinson and P. Van Rysselberghe, Vol. IX. New York: Academic Press, 1961.

The end product of this whole process is often referred to as **photochemical smog,** so called because light is required to initiate some of the reactions. The production of photochemical smog can be more clearly understood by examining as a group the preceding reactions:

$$NO_2(g) \longrightarrow NO(g) + O(g)$$
$$O(g) + O_2(g) \longrightarrow O_3(g)$$
$$NO(g) + \tfrac{1}{2}O_2(g) \longrightarrow NO_2(g)$$
$$\text{Net reaction:} \quad \tfrac{3}{2}O_2(g) \longrightarrow O_3(g)$$

Note that the NO_2 molecules assist in the formation of ozone without being consumed themselves. The ozone then produces other pollutants.

We can observe this process by analyzing polluted air at various times during a day (Fig. 5.28). As people drive to work between 6 and 8 a.m., the amounts of NO, NO_2, and unburned molecules from petroleum increase. Later, as the decomposition of NO_2 occurs, the concentration of ozone and other pollutants builds up. Current efforts to combat the formation of photochemical smog are focused on cutting down the amounts of molecules from unburned fuel in automobile exhaust and designing engines that produce less nitric oxide (Fig. 5.29).

John Lawlor

Figure 5.29
Our various modes of transportation produce large amounts of nitrogen oxides, which facilitate the formation of photochemical smog.

The other major source of pollution results from burning coal to produce electricity. Much of the coal found in the Midwest contains significant quantities of sulfur, which, when burned, produces sulfur dioxide:

$$S\,(\text{In coal}) + O_2(g) \longrightarrow SO_2(g)$$

A further oxidation reaction occurs when sulfur dioxide is changed to sulfur trioxide in the air:

$$2SO_2(g) + O_2(g) \longrightarrow 2SO_3(g)$$

Chemical Insights

The Importance of Oxygen

Oxygen has been present only for the last half of the earth's history—appearing about 2.5 billion years ago in what is called *The Great Oxidation Event.* Before this time the earth's atmosphere contained large quantities of methane, which reacted with oxygen and prevented its buildup. Now there is geological evidence that about 2.7 billion years ago the amount of dissolved nickel in the oceans began to decrease. This was important because the organisms that produced methane required nickel ions to exist. As the methane concentrations in the atmosphere decreased, oxygen produced by chlorophyll-containing organisms began to build up. In contrast, oxygen was removed from the atmosphere by mountain building and erosion as freshly exposed rocks combined with oxygen to form oxygen-containing minerals.

The concentration of oxygen in the atmosphere has varied greatly over the last 600 million years, as shown in the accompanying graph. Note that 300 million years ago (at the end of the Carboniferous period) the air consisted of about 35% oxygen. The fossil record indicates that during this time insects and other arthropods that absorb oxygen through holes in their exoskeletons were extraordinarily large. It is thought that mayflies as big as today's robins and dragonflies as big as modern hawks were commonplace in this period.

About 255 million years ago, the oxygen concentration in the atmosphere was about 30%, but for some reason the oxygen content plunged to about 13% (about the concentration at an elevation of 15,000 feet in today's world) in the relatively short geological time span of 10 million years. Die-offs during this period claimed as many as 95% of the species living in the ocean and about 70% of those living on land. The oxygen content then began to rebound (to about 16%) 200 million years ago, which led to a dramatic increase in biological innovation. For example, the first dinosaurs appeared only about 15 million years after the mass die-offs.

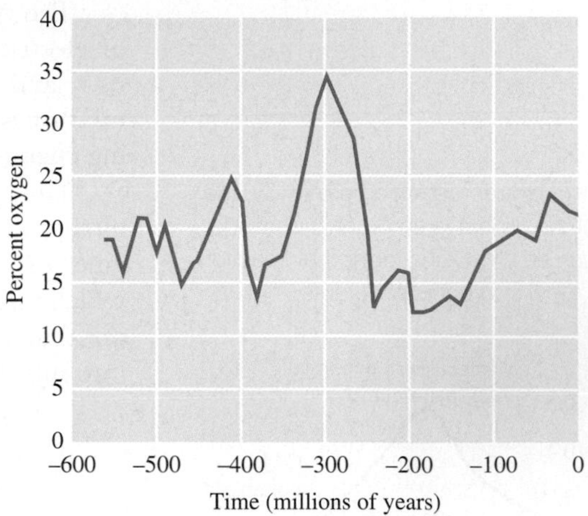

During the last 200 million years the oxygen content has increased rather steadily, making possible the existence of fuel-intense species such as mammals. In fact about 25 million years ago when oxygen concentration maximized at 23%, many mammals had become gigantic. For example, the relatives of today's rhino stood almost 5 m tall and weighed 15 metric tons—the largest ever land mammals. After peaking at 23%, the oxygen levels dropped to today's level of 21% and the "megamammals" disappeared. If history is any indication, the oxygen levels in the atmosphere will continue to change significantly over time, but this is obviously not a high-priority problem for us in the twenty-first century.

This equation describes only the overall stoichiometry of the process; many different oxidants actually participate in the oxidation of sulfur dioxide (see Chapter 15 for a further discussion). The production of sulfur trioxide is significant because it can combine with droplets of water in the air to form sulfuric acid:

$$SO_3(g) + H_2O(l) \longrightarrow H_2SO_4(aq)$$

Chemistry Explorers

Kristie A. Boering and Ronald C. Cohen Study the Earth's Atmosphere

One of the most important areas of research is the study of the chemistry of the earth's atmosphere and how human activities are changing it. Two researchers who are exploring these issues are Kristie A. Boering and Ronald C. Cohen, both faculty members at the University of California at Berkeley. Professor Boering and her research group are studying the earth's atmospheric chemistry through observations from aircraft, balloons, and ground-based platforms; computer simulations; and laboratory experiments. Dr. Boering is particularly interested in the exchange of gases between the biosphere and the atmosphere in modern times and over the past millennium.

Professor Cohen's overall goal is to develop a model for the ways human activity can cause global changes in the atmosphere. His group is particularly interested in what chemical reactions control ozone formation and depletion.

Photo by Michael Barnes/University of California at Berkeley

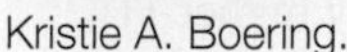

Kristie A. Boering.

Photo by Michael Barnes/University of California at Berkeley

Ronald C. Cohen.

Professors Boering and Cohen hope their efforts to understand the changes in atmospheric chemistry will lead to solutions to problems such as global warming.

Sulfuric acid is very corrosive to both living things and building materials. Another result of this type of pollution is **acid rain** (Fig. 5.30). In many parts of the northeastern United States and southeastern Canada, acid rain has caused some freshwater lakes to become too acidic for fish to live.

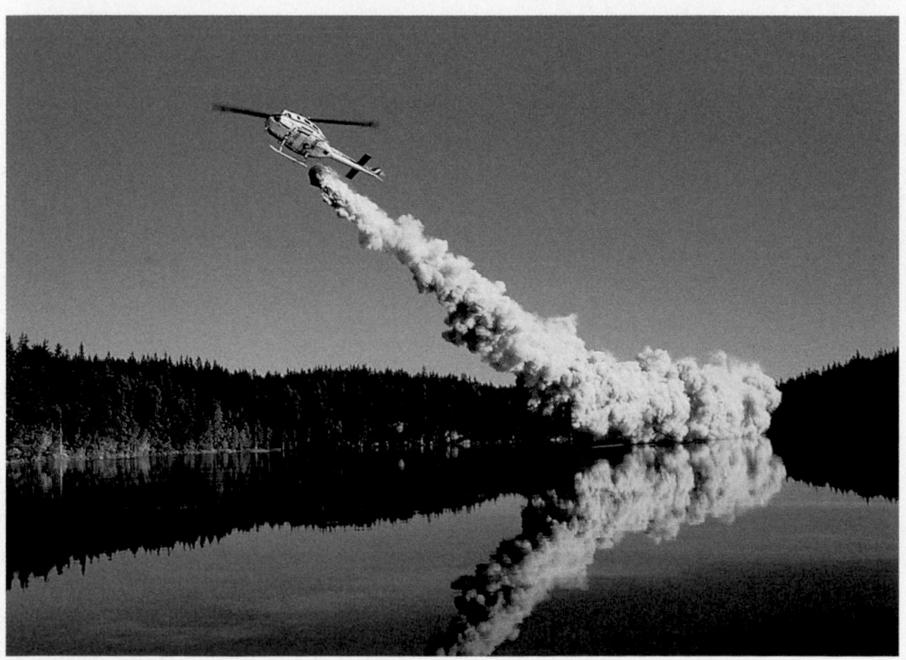

M. Edwards/Peter Arnold, Inc.

Figure 5.30
A helicopter dropping lime in a lake in Sweden to neutralize excess acid from acid rain.

Chemical Insights Acid Rain: An Expensive Problem

Rainwater, even in pristine wilderness areas, is slightly acidic because some of the carbon dioxide present in the atmosphere dissolves in the raindrops to produce H^+ ions by the following reaction:

$$H_2O(l) + CO_2(g) \longrightarrow H^+(aq) + HCO_3^-(aq)$$

This process produces only very small concentrations of H^+ ions in the rainwater. However, gases such as NO_2 and SO_2, which are by-products of energy use, can produce significantly higher H^+ concentrations. Nitrogen dioxide reacts with water to give a mixture of nitrous acid and nitric acid:

$$2NO_2(g) + H_2O(l) \longrightarrow HNO_2(aq) + HNO_3(aq)$$

Sulfur dioxide is oxidized to sulfur trioxide, which then reacts with water to form sulfuric acid:

$$2SO_2(g) + O_2(g) \longrightarrow 2SO_3(g)$$

$$SO_3(g) + H_2O(l) \longrightarrow H_2SO_4(aq)$$

The damage caused by the acid formed in polluted air is a growing worldwide problem. Lakes are dying in Norway, the forests are sick in Germany, and buildings and statues are deteriorating all over the world.

For example, the Field Museum in Chicago contains more white Georgia marble than any other structure in the world. But more than 70 years of exposure to the elements has taken such a toll on it that the building underwent a multimillion-dollar renovation to replace the damaged marble with freshly quarried material.

What is the chemistry of the deterioration of marble by sulfuric acid? Marble is produced by geological processes at high temperatures and pressures from limestone, a sedimentary rock formed by slow deposition of calcium carbonate from the shells of marine organisms. Limestone and marble are chemically identical ($CaCO_3$) but differ in physical properties because limestone is composed of smaller particles of calcium carbonate and is thus more porous and more workable. Although both limestone and marble are used for buildings, marble can be polished to a higher sheen and is often preferred for decorative purposes.

Both marble and limestone react with sulfuric acid to form calcium sulfate. The process can be represented most simply as

$$CaCO_3(s) + H_2SO_4(aq) \longrightarrow Ca^{2+}(aq) + SO_4^{2-}(aq) + H_2O(l) + CO_2(g)$$

The problem of sulfur dioxide pollution is further complicated by the energy crisis. As petroleum supplies dwindle and the price increases, our dependence on coal will grow. As supplies of low-sulfur coal are used up, high-sulfur coal will be used. One way to use high-sulfur coal without further harming the air quality is to remove the sulfur dioxide from the exhaust gas by means of a system called a *scrubber* before it is emitted from the power plant stack. A common method of *scrubbing* involves blowing powdered limestone ($CaCO_3$) into the combustion chamber, where it is decomposed to lime and carbon dioxide:

$$CaCO_3(s) \longrightarrow CaO(s) + CO_2(g)$$

The lime then combines with the sulfur dioxide to form calcium sulfite:

$$CaO(s) + SO_2(g) \longrightarrow CaSO_3(s)$$

The calcium sulfite and any remaining unreacted sulfur dioxide are removed by injecting an aqueous suspension of lime into the combustion chamber and the stack, producing a *slurry* (a thick suspension), as shown in Fig. 5.31.

Unfortunately, there are many problems associated with scrubbing. The systems are complicated and expensive and consume a great deal of energy. The large quantities of calcium sulfite produced in the process present a disposal problem. For a typical scrubber approximately 1 ton of calcium sulfite

In this equation the calcium sulfate is represented by separate hydrated ions because calcium sulfate dissolves in rainwater. Thus in areas bathed in rainwater, the marble slowly dissolves away.

In areas of the building protected from the rain, the calcium sulfate can form the mineral gypsum, $CaSO_4 \cdot 2H_2O$. The $\cdot\ 2H_2O$ in the formula of gypsum indicates the presence of two water molecules (called waters of hydration) for each $CaSO_4$ formula unit in the solid. The smooth surface of the marble is thus replaced by a thin layer of gypsum, a more porous material that binds soot and dust.

What can be done to protect limestone and marble structures from this kind of damage? Of course, one approach is to lower sulfur dioxide and nitrogen oxide emissions from power plants (Fig. 5.31). In addition, scientists are experimenting with coatings to protect marble from the acidic atmosphere. However, a coating can do more harm than good unless it "breathes." If moisture trapped beneath the coating freezes, the expanding ice can fracture the marble. Needless to say, it is difficult to find a coating that will allow water to pass but not allow acid to pass, so the search continues.

Photos Field Museum, Chicago #CSGN40263 and #GN83213_6C.

The damaging effects of acid rain can be seen by comparing these photos of a decorative statue at the Field Museum in Chicago. The photo on the left was taken c. 1920; the photo on the right was taken in 1990. Recent renovation has since replaced the deteriorating marble.

Figure 5.31
Schematic diagram of the process for scrubbing sulfur dioxide from stack gases in power plants.

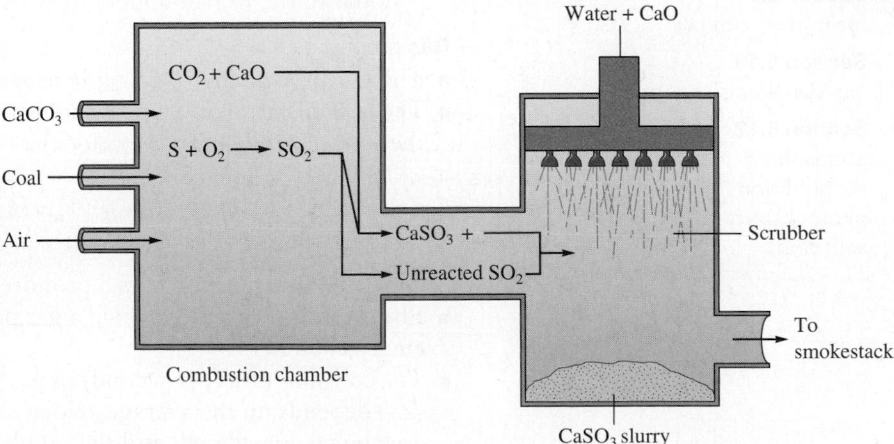

per year is produced per person served by the power plant. Since no use has yet been found for this calcium sulfite, it is usually buried in a landfill. As a result of these difficulties, air pollution by sulfur dioxide continues to be a major problem, one that is expensive in terms of damage to the environment and to human health, as well as in monetary terms.

Key Terms

Section 5.1
barometer
manometer
mm Hg
torr
standard atmosphere
pascal

Section 5.2
Boyle's law
ideal gas
Charles's law
absolute zero
Avogadro's law

Section 5.3
universal gas constant
ideal gas law

Section 5.4
molar volume
standard temperature and pressure (STP)

Section 5.5
Dalton's law of partial pressures
partial pressure
mole fraction

Section 5.6
kinetic molecular theory
root mean square velocity
joule
mean free path

Section 5.7
diffusion
effusion
Graham's law of effusion

Section 5.9
mean free path (λ)

Section 5.10
van der Waals equation

Section 5.12
atmosphere
air pollution
photochemical smog
acid rain

For Review

OWL and go Chemistry

Sign in at **www.cengage.com/owl** to:

- View tutorials and simulations, develop problem-solving skills, and complete online homework assigned by your professor.
- Download Go Chemistry mini lecture modules for quick review and exam prep from OWL (or purchase them at **www.cengagebrain.com**)

State of a gas

- The state of a gas can be described completely by specifying its pressure (P), volume (V), temperature (T), and the amount (moles) of gas present (n).
- Pressure
  - Common units
    - 1 torr = 1 mm Hg
    - 1 atm = 760 torr
  - SI unit: pascal
    - 1 atm = 101,325 Pa

Gas laws

- Discovered by observing the properties of gases
- Boyle's law: $PV = k$
- Charles's law: $V = bT$
- Avogadro's law: $V = an$
- Ideal gas law: $PV = nRT$
- Dalton's law of partial pressures: $P_{\text{Total}} = P_1 + P_2 + P_3 + \cdots$, where P_n represents the partial pressure of component n in a mixture of gases

Kinetic molecular theory (KMT)

- Model that accounts for ideal gas behavior
- Postulates of the KMT:
  - Volume of gas particles is negligible (zero)
  - No particle interactions
  - Particles are in constant motion, colliding with the container walls to produce pressure
  - The average kinetic energy of the gas particles is directly proportional to the Kelvin temperature of the gas

Gas properties

- The particles in any gas sample have a range of velocities
- The root mean square (rms) velocity for a gas represents the average of the squares of the particle velocities

$$\mu_{\text{rms}} = \sqrt{\frac{3RT}{M}}$$

- Diffusion: the mixing of two or more gases
- Effusion: the process in which a gas passes through a small hole into an empty chamber
- The collision rate (per second) of gas particles with the container walls (Z_A) depends on the average velocity of the gas particles, the size of the area being considered, and the number of particles in the container

$$Z_A = A\frac{N}{V}\sqrt{\frac{RT}{1\pi M}}$$

- The intermolecular collision rate (per second) of gas particles (Z) depends on the average velocity of the gas particles, the size of the gas particles, and the number of particles in the container

$$Z = 4\frac{N}{V}d^2\sqrt{\frac{\pi RT}{M}}$$

Real gas behavior

- Real gases approach ideal behavior at high temperatures and low pressures
- Understanding how the ideal gas law must be modified to account for real gas behavior helps us understand how gases behave on a molecular level
- Van der Waals found that to describe real gas behavior we must consider particle interactions and particle volumes

Discussion Questions

These questions are designed to be considered by groups of students in class. Often these questions work well for introducing a particular topic in class.

1. Consider the following apparatus: a test tube covered with a nonpermeable elastic membrane inside a container that is closed with a cork. A syringe goes through the cork.

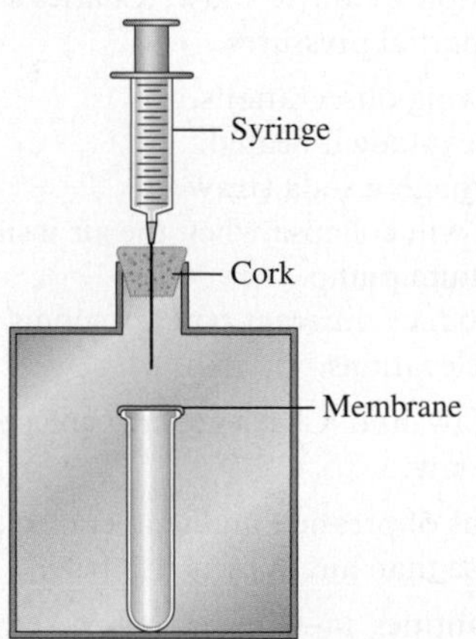

   a. As you push down on the syringe, how does the membrane covering the test tube change?
   b. You stop pushing the syringe but continue to hold it down. In a few seconds, what happens to the membrane?

2. Figure 5.1 shows a picture of a barometer. Which of the following statements is the best explanation of how this barometer works?
   a. Air pressure outside the tube causes the mercury to move in the tube until the air pressure inside and outside the tube is equal.
   b. Air pressure inside the tube causes the mercury to move in the tube until the air pressure inside and outside the tube is equal.
   c. Air pressure outside the tube counterbalances the weight of the mercury in the tube.
   d. Capillary action of the mercury causes the mercury to go up the tube.
   e. The vacuum that is formed at the top of the tube holds up the mercury.

   Justify your choice. For choices that you did not pick, explain why they are incorrect. Pictures help!

3. The barometer on the left in the following diagram shows the level of mercury at a given atmospheric pressure. Fill all the other barometers with mercury for that same atmospheric pressure. Explain your answer.

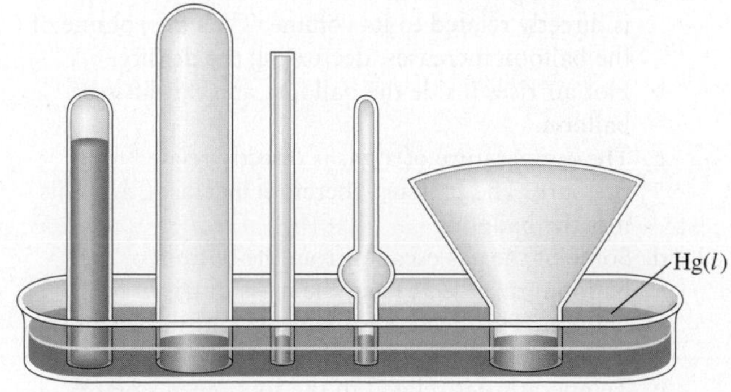

4. As you increase the temperature of a gas in a sealed, rigid container, what happens to the density of the gas? Would the results be the same if you did the same experiment in a container with a piston at constant pressure? Explain.

5. A diagram in a chemistry book shows a magnified view of a flask of air as follows:

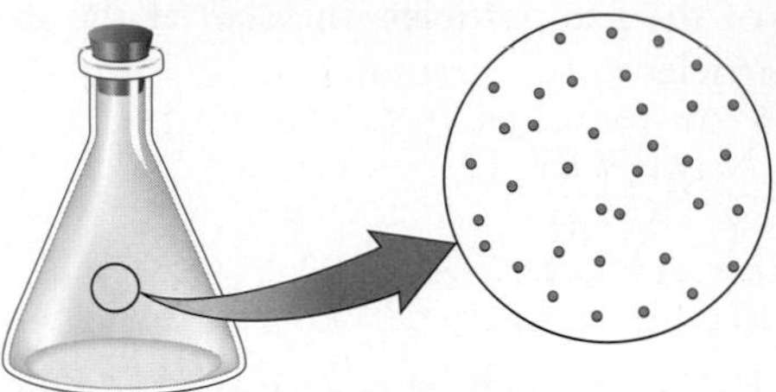

What do you suppose is between the dots (the dots represent air molecules)?
a. air
b. dust
c. pollutants
d. oxygen
e. nothing

6. If you put a drinking straw in water, place your finger over the opening, and lift the straw out of the water, some water stays in the straw. Explain.

7. A chemistry student relates the following story: "I noticed my tires were a bit low and went to the gas station. As I was filling the tires, I thought about the kinetic molecular theory (KMT), and I realized that I was increasing both the pressure and volume of the tires as I filled the tires with air. 'Hmmm,' I thought, 'that goes against what I learned in chemistry, where I was told pressure and volume are inversely proportional.'" What is the fault of the logic of the chemistry student in this situation? Explain *why* we think pressure and volume to be inversely related (draw pictures and use the KMT).

8. Chemicals X and Y (both gases) react to form the gas XY, but it takes a bit of time for the reaction to occur. Both X and Y are placed in a container with a piston (free to move), and you note the volume. As the reaction occurs, what happens to the volume of the container? Explain.

9. Which statement best explains why a hot-air balloon rises when the air in the balloon is heated?
a. According to Charles's law, the temperature of a gas is directly related to its volume. Thus the volume of the balloon increases, decreasing the density.
b. Hot air rises inside the balloon, and this lifts the balloon.
c. The temperature of a gas is directly related to its pressure. The pressure therefore increases, and this lifts the balloon.
d. Some of the gas escapes from the bottom of the balloon, thus decreasing the mass of gas in the balloon. This decreases the density of the gas in the balloon, and this lifts the balloon.
e. Temperature is related to the root mean square velocity of the gas molecules. Thus the molecules are moving faster, hitting the balloon more often, and thus lifting the balloon.

Justify your choice. For those you did not choose, explain why they are incorrect.

10. Draw a highly magnified view of a sealed, rigid container filled with a gas. Then draw what it would look like if you cooled the gas significantly, but kept the temperature above the boiling point of the substance in the container. Also draw what it would look like if you heated the gas significantly. Finally, draw what each situation would look like if you evacuated enough of the gas to decrease the pressure by a factor of 2.

11. If you release a helium balloon, it soars upward and eventually pops. Explain.

12. If you have any two gases in different containers that are the same size at the same pressure and same temperature, what is true about the moles of each gas? Why is this true?

13. Explain the following seeming contradiction: You have two gases, A and B, in two separate containers of equal volume and at equal pressure and temperature. Therefore, you must have the same number of moles of each gas. Because the two temperatures are equal, the average kinetic energies of the two samples are equal. Therefore, since the energy of such a system corresponds to translational motion, the root mean square velocities of the two are equal, and thus the particles in each sample move, on average, with the same relative speed. Since A and B are different gases, each must have a different molar mass. If A has a higher molar mass than B, the particles of A must be hitting the sides of the container with more force. Thus the pressure in the container of gas A must be higher than that in the container with gas B. However, one of our initial assumptions was that the pressures were equal. Explain.

14. Using postulates of the kinetic molecular theory, give a molecular interpretation of Boyle's law, Charles's law, and Dalton's law of partial pressures.

15. Rationalize the following observations.
a. Aerosol cans will explode if heated.
b. You can drink through a soda straw.
c. A thin-walled can will collapse when the air inside is removed by a vacuum pump.
d. Manufacturers produce different types of tennis balls for high and low elevations.

16. Show how Boyle's law and Charles's law are special cases of the ideal gas law.

17. At the same conditions of pressure and temperature, ammonia gas is less dense than air. Why is this true?

18. For each of the quantities (a–f) listed below, explain which of the following properties (mass of the molecule, density of the gas sample, temperature of the gas sample, size of the molecule, and number of moles of gas) must be known to calculate the quantity.
a. average kinetic energy
b. average number of collisions per second with other gas molecules
c. average force of each impact with the wall of the container
d. root mean square velocity
e. average number of collisions with a given area of the container
f. distance between collisions

19. You have two containers each with 1 mole of xenon gas at 15°C. Container A has a volume of 3.0 L, and container B has a volume of 1.0 L. Explain how the following quantities compare between the two containers.
    a. the average kinetic energy of the Xe atoms
    b. the force with which the Xe atoms collide with the container walls
    c. the root mean square velocity of the Xe atoms
    d. the collision frequency of the Xe atoms (with other atoms)
    e. the pressure of the Xe sample

20. You have a balloon covering the mouth of a flask filled with air at 1 atm. You apply heat to the bottom of the flask until the volume of the balloon is equal to that of the flask.
    a. Which has more air in it—the balloon or the flask? Or do both contain the same amount of air? Explain.
    b. In which is the pressure greater—the balloon or the flask? Or is the pressure the same? Explain.

Exercises

OWL Interactive versions of these problems may be assigned in OWL.

A blue exercise number indicates that the answer to that exercise appears at the back of this book and a solution appears in the *Solutions Guide*.

Pressure

21. A sealed-tube manometer as shown below can be used to measure pressures below atmospheric pressure. The tube above the mercury is evacuated. When there is a vacuum in the flask, the mercury levels in both arms of the U-tube are equal. If a gaseous sample is introduced into the flask, the mercury levels are different. The difference h is a measure of the pressure of the gas inside the flask. If h is equal to 4.75 cm, calculate the pressure in the flask in torr, pascals, and atmospheres.

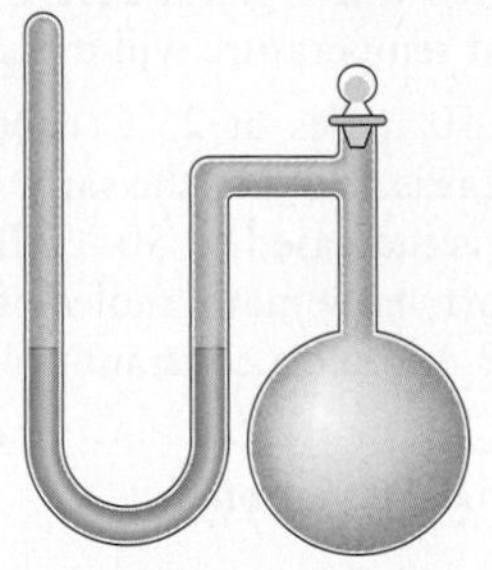

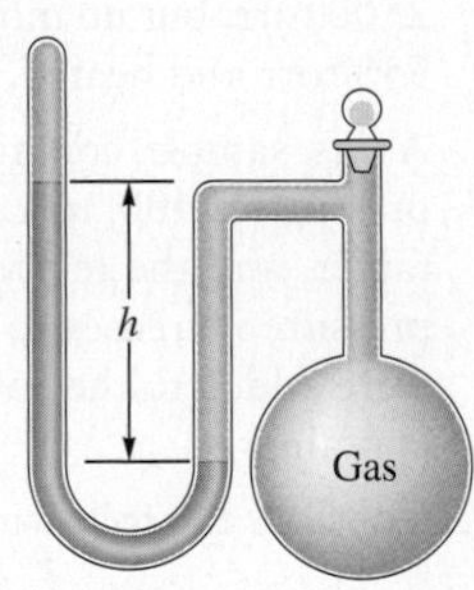

22. A diagram for an open-tube manometer is shown below.

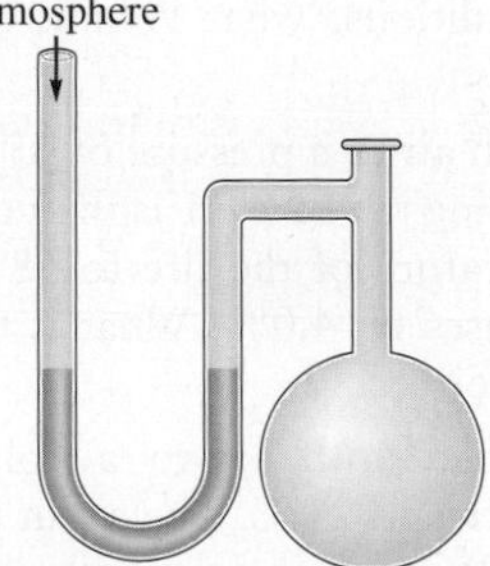

If the flask is open to the atmosphere, the mercury levels are equal. For each of the following situations in which a gas is contained in the flask, calculate the pressure in the flask in torr, atmospheres, and pascals.

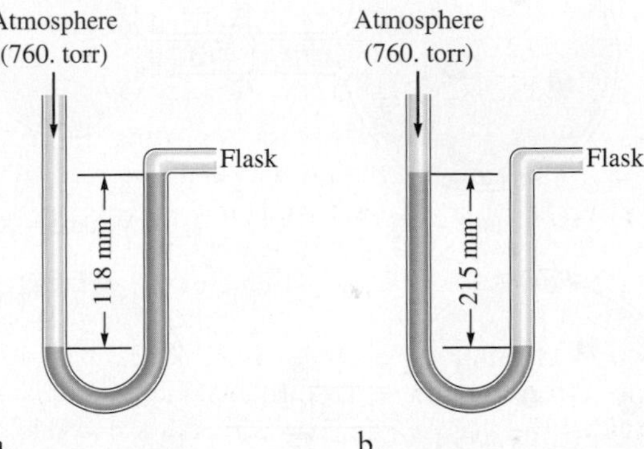

c. Calculate the pressures in the flask in parts a and b (in torr) if the atmospheric pressure is 635 torr.

23. The gravitational force exerted by an object is given by

$$F = mg$$

where F is the force in newtons, m is the mass in kilograms, and g is the acceleration due to gravity, 9.81 m/s^2. Calculate the force exerted per unit of area by a column of mercury (density = 13.59 g/cm^3) that is 76.0 cm high. How high would a column of water (density = 1.00 g/cm^3) have to be to exert the same force?

24. a. If the open-tube manometer in Exercise 22 contains a nonvolatile silicone oil (density = 1.30 g/cm^3) instead of mercury (density = 13.6 g/cm^3), what are the pressures in the flask as shown in parts a and b in torr, atmospheres, and pascals?
    b. What advantage would there be in using a less dense fluid than mercury in a manometer used to measure relatively small differences in pressure?

25. Freon-12 (CF_2Cl_2) is commonly used as the refrigerant in central home air conditioners. The system is initially charged to a pressure of 4.8 atm. Express this pressure in each of the following units (1 atm = 14.7 psi).
    a. mm Hg b. torr c. Pa d. psi

Gas Laws

26. Draw a qualitative graph to show how the first property varies with the second in each of the following (assume 1 mole of an ideal gas and T in kelvins).
    a. PV versus V with constant T
    b. P versus T with constant V

c. T versus V with constant P
d. P versus V with constant T
e. P versus $1/V$ with constant T
f. PV/T versus P

27. As weather balloons rise from the earth's surface, the pressure of the atmosphere becomes less, tending to cause the volume of the balloons to expand. However, the temperature is much lower in the upper atmosphere than at sea level. Would this temperature effect tend to make such a balloon expand or contract? Weather balloons do, in fact, expand as they rise. What does this tell you?

28. Consider the flasks in the following diagrams.

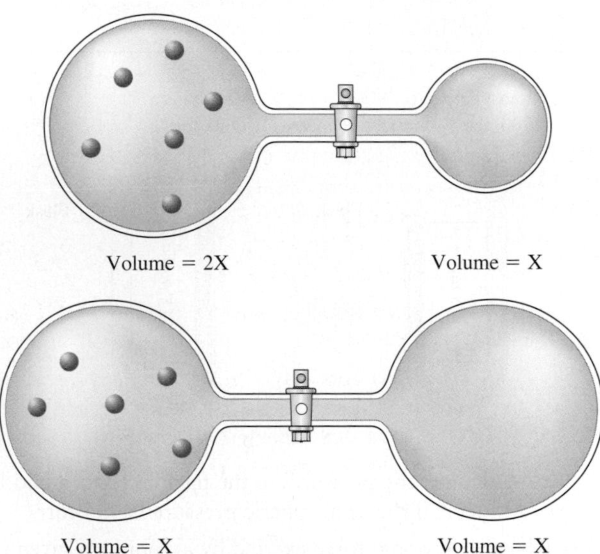

Assuming the connecting tube has negligible volume, draw what each diagram will look like after the stopcock between the two flasks is opened. Also, solve for the final pressure in each case, in terms of the original pressure. Assume temperature is constant.

29. Consider the flask diagramed below. What are the final partial pressures of H_2 and N_2 after the stopcock between the two flasks is opened? (Assume the final volume is 3.00 L.) What is the total pressure (in torr)?

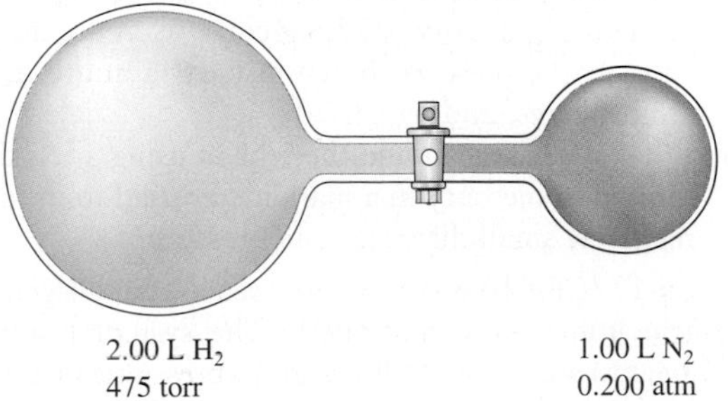

30. Consider the flask apparatus in Exercise 29, which contains 2.00 L of H_2 at a pressure of 360. torr and 1.00 L of N_2 at an unknown pressure. If the total pressure in the flasks is 320. torr after the stopcock is opened, determine the initial pressure of N_2 in the 1.00-L flask.

31. A compressed-gas cylinder contains 1.00×10^3 g of argon gas. The pressure inside the cylinder is 2050. psi (pounds per square inch) at a temperature of 18°C. How much gas remains in the cylinder if the pressure is decreased to 650. psi at a temperature of 26°C?

32. A sealed balloon is filled with 1.00 L of helium at 23°C and 1.00 atm. The balloon rises to a point in the atmosphere where the pressure is 220. torr and the temperature is −31°C. What is the change in the volume of the balloon as it ascends from 1.00 atm to a pressure of 220. torr?

33. A piece of solid carbon dioxide, with a mass of 22.0 g, is placed in an otherwise empty 4.00-L container at 27°C. What is the pressure in the container after all the carbon dioxide vaporizes? If 22.0 g of solid carbon dioxide was placed in a similar container already containing air at 740. torr, what would be the partial pressure of carbon dioxide and the total pressure in the container after the carbon dioxide had vaporized?

34. An ideal gas is in a cylinder with a volume of 5.0×10^2 mL at a temperature of 30.°C and a pressure of 710 torr. The gas is compressed to a volume of 25 mL, and the temperature is raised to 820°C. What is the new pressure?

35. Suppose two 200.0-L tanks are to be filled separately with the gases helium and hydrogen. What mass of each gas is needed to produce a pressure of 135 atm in its respective tank at 24°C?

36. An ideal gas at 7°C is in a spherical flexible container having a radius of 1.00 cm. The gas is heated at constant pressure to 88°C. Determine the radius of the spherical container after the gas is heated. (Volume of a sphere = $4/3\pi r^3$.)

37. A flask that can withstand an internal pressure of 2500 torr, but no more, is filled with a gas at 21.0°C and 758 torr and heated. At what temperature will it burst?

38. A gas sample containing 1.50 moles at 25°C exerts a pressure of 400. torr. Some gas is *added* to the same container, and the temperature is increased to 50.°C. If the pressure increases to 800. torr, how many moles of gas were added to the container? Assume a constant-volume container.

39. Consider the following chemical equation:

$$2NO_2(g) \longrightarrow N_2O_4(g)$$

If 25.0 mL of NO_2 gas is completely converted to N_2O_4 gas under the same conditions, what volume will the N_2O_4 occupy?

40. A bicycle tire is filled with air to a pressure of 75 psi at a temperature of 19°C. Riding the bike on asphalt on a hot day increases the temperature of the tire to 58°C. The volume of the tire increases by 4.0%. What is the new pressure in the bicycle tire?

41. A hot-air balloon is filled with air to a volume of 4.00×10^3 m^3 at 745 torr and 21°C. The air in the balloon is then heated to 62°C, causing the balloon to expand to a volume of 4.20×10^3 m^3. What is the ratio of the number of moles of air in the heated balloon to the original number of moles of air in the balloon? (*Hint:* Openings in the balloon allow air to flow in and out. Thus the pressure in the balloon is always the same as that of the atmosphere.)

42. Determine the partial pressure of each gas as shown in the figure below. *Note:* The relative numbers of each type of gas are depicted in the figure.

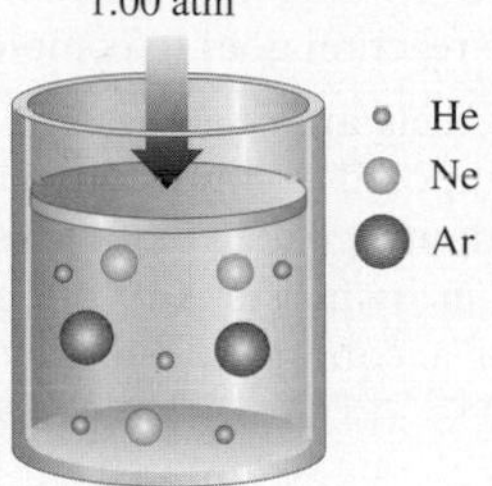

43. Consider the flasks in the following diagrams.

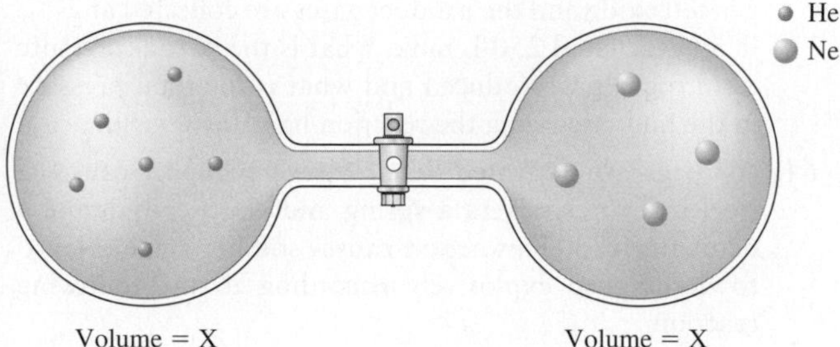

a. Which is greater, the initial pressure of helium or initial pressure of neon? How much greater?
b. Assuming the connecting tube has negligible volume, draw what each diagram will look like after the stopcock between the two flasks is opened.
c. Solve for the final pressure in terms of the original pressures of helium and neon. Assume temperature is constant.
d. Solve for the final partial pressures of helium and neon in terms of their original pressures. Assume the temperature is constant.

44. A sample of nitrogen gas was collected over water at 20.°C and a total pressure of 1.00 atm. A total volume of 2.50×10^2 mL was collected. What mass of nitrogen was collected? (At 20.°C the vapor pressure of water is 17.5 torr.)

45. Helium is collected over water at 25°C and 1.00 atm total pressure. What total volume of gas must be collected to obtain 0.586 g of helium? (At 25°C the vapor pressure of water is 23.8 torr.)

46. A 2.00-L sample of $O_2(g)$ was collected over water at a total pressure of 785 torr and 25°C. When the $O_2(g)$ was dried (water vapor removed), the gas had a volume of 1.94 L at 25°C and 785 torr. Calculate the vapor pressure of water at 25°C.

47. In a mixture of the two gases, the partial pressures of $CH_4(g)$ and $O_2(g)$ are 0.175 atm and 0.250 atm, respectively.
a. What is the mole fraction of each gas in the mixture?
b. If the mixture occupies a volume of 10.5 L at 65°C, calculate the total number of moles of gas in the mixture.
c. Calculate the number of grams of each gas in the mixture.

48. A 1.00-L gas sample at 100.°C and 600. torr contains 50.0% helium and 50.0% xenon by mass. What are the partial pressures of the individual gases?

49. At 0°C a 1.0 L flask contains 5.0×10^{-2} mole of N_2, 1.5×10^2 mg O_2, and 5.0×10^{21} molecules of NH_3. What is the partial pressure of each gas, and what is the total pressure in the flask?

Gas Density, Molar Mass, and Reaction Stoichiometry

50. Given that a sample of air is made up of nitrogen, oxygen, and argon in the mole fractions 78% N_2, 21% O_2, and 1.0% Ar, what is the density of air at standard temperature and pressure?

51. Consider two different containers, each filled with 2 moles of Ne(*g*). One of the containers is rigid and has constant volume. The other container is flexible (like a balloon) and is capable of changing its volume to keep the external pressure and internal pressure equal to each other. If you raise the temperature in both containers, what happens to the pressure and density of the gas inside each container? Assume a constant external pressure.

52. An unknown diatomic gas has a density of 3.164 g/L at STP. What is the identity of the gas?

53. A compound contains only nitrogen and hydrogen and is 87.4% nitrogen by mass. A gaseous sample of the compound has a density of 0.977 g/L at 710. torr and 100.°C. What is the molecular formula of the compound?

54. A compound has the empirical formula CHCl. A 256-mL flask, at 373 K and 750. torr, contains 0.800 g of the gaseous compound. Give the molecular formula.

55. One of the chemical controversies of the nineteenth century concerned the element beryllium (Be). Berzelius originally claimed that beryllium was a trivalent element (forming Be^{3+} ions) and that it formed an oxide with the formula Be_2O_3. This assumption resulted in a calculated atomic mass of 13.5 for beryllium. In formulating his periodic table, Mendeleev proposed that beryllium was divalent (forming Be^{2+} ions) and that it gave an oxide with the formula BeO. This assumption gives an atomic mass of 9.0. In 1894 A. Combes (*Comptes Rendes*, 1894, p. 1221) reacted beryllium with the anion $C_5H_7O_2^-$ and measured the density of the gaseous product. Combes's data for two different experiments are as follows:

	I	II
Mass	0.2022 g	0.2224 g
Volume	22.6 cm^3	26.0 cm^3
Temperature	13°C	17°C
Pressure	765.2 torr	764.6 torr

If beryllium is a divalent metal, the molecular formula of the product will be $Be(C_5H_7O_2)_2$; if it is trivalent, the formula will be $Be(C_5H_7O_2)_3$. Show how Combes's data help to confirm that beryllium is a divalent metal.

56. Discrepancies in the experimental values of the molar mass of nitrogen provided some of the first evidence for

the existence of the noble gases. If pure nitrogen is collected from the decomposition of ammonium nitrite,

$$NH_4NO_2(s) \xrightarrow{\text{Heat}} N_2(g) + 2H_2O(g)$$

its measured molar mass is 28.01. If O_2, CO_2, and H_2O are removed from air, the remaining gas has an average molar mass of 28.15. Assuming this discrepancy is solely a result of contamination with argon (atomic mass = 39.95), calculate the ratio of moles of Ar to moles of N_2 in air.

57. A sample of methane (CH_4) gas contains a small amount of helium. Calculate the volume percentage of helium if the density of the sample is 0.70902 g/L at 0.0°C and 1.000 atm.

58. Metallic molybdenum can be produced from the mineral molybdenite (MoS_2). The mineral is first oxidized in air to molybdenum trioxide and sulfur dioxide. Molybdenum trioxide is then reduced to metallic molybdenum using hydrogen gas. The balanced equations are

$$MoS_2(s) + 7/2O_2(g) \longrightarrow MoO_3(s) + 2SO_2(g)$$

$$MoO_3(s) + 3H_2(g) \longrightarrow Mo(s) + 3H_2O(l)$$

Calculate the volumes of air and hydrogen gas at 17°C and 1.00 atm that are necessary to produce 1.00×10^3 kg of pure molybdenum from MoS_2. Assume air contains 21% oxygen by volume and assume 100% yield for each reaction.

59. In 1897 the Swedish explorer Andreé tried to reach the North Pole in a balloon. The balloon was filled with hydrogen gas. The hydrogen gas was prepared from iron splints and diluted sulfuric acid. The reaction is

$$Fe(s) + H_2SO_4(aq) \longrightarrow FeSO_4(aq) + H_2(g)$$

The volume of the balloon was 4800 m^3, and the loss of hydrogen gas during filling was estimated at 20.%. What mass of iron splints and 98% (by mass) H_2SO_4 were needed to ensure the complete filling of the balloon? Assume a temperature at 0°C, a pressure of 1.0 atm during filling, and 100% yield.

60. Urea (H_2NCONH_2) is used extensively as a nitrogen source in fertilizers. It is produced commercially from the reaction of ammonia and carbon dioxide:

$$2NH_3(g) + CO_2(g) \xrightarrow[\text{Pressure}]{\text{Heat}} H_2NCONH_2(s) + H_2O(g)$$

Ammonia gas at 223°C and 90. atm flows into a reactor at a rate of 500. L/min. Carbon dioxide at 223°C and 45 atm flows into the reactor at a rate of 600. L/min. What mass of urea is produced per minute by this reaction assuming 100% yield?

61. Methanol (CH_3OH) can be produced by the following reaction:

$$CO(g) + 2H_2(g) \longrightarrow CH_3OH(g)$$

Hydrogen at STP flows into a reactor at a rate of 16.0 L/min. Carbon monoxide at STP flows into the reactor at a rate of 25.0 L/min. If 5.30 g of methanol is produced per minute, what is the percent yield of the reaction?

62. Consider the reaction between 50.0 mL of liquid methanol (CH_3OH; density = 0.850 g/mL) and 22.8 L of O_2 at 27°C and a pressure of 2.00 atm. The products of the reaction are $CO_2(g)$ and $H_2O(g)$. Calculate the number of moles of H_2O formed if the reaction goes to completion.

63. Some very effective rocket fuels are composed of lightweight liquids. The fuel composed of dimethylhydrazine [$(CH_3)_2N_2H_2$] mixed with dinitrogen tetroxide was used to power the lunar lander in its missions to the moon. The two components react according to the following equation:

$$(CH_3)_2N_2H_2(l) + 2N_2O_4(l) \longrightarrow 3N_2(g) + 4H_2O(g) + 2CO_2(g)$$

If 150 g of dimethylhydrazine reacts with excess dinitrogen tetroxide and the product gases are collected at 27°C in an evacuated 250-L tank, what is the partial pressure of nitrogen gas produced and what is the total pressure in the tank assuming the reaction has 100% yield?

64. Air bags are activated when a severe impact causes a steel ball to compress a spring and electrically ignite a detonator cap. This action causes sodium azide (NaN_3) to decompose explosively according to the following reaction:

$$2NaN_3(s) \longrightarrow 2Na(s) + 3N_2(g)$$

What mass of $NaN_3(s)$ must be reacted to inflate an air bag to 70.0 L at STP?

65. At elevated temperatures, sodium chlorate decomposes to produce sodium chloride and oxygen gas. A 0.8765-g sample of impure sodium chlorate was heated until the production of oxygen gas ceased. The oxygen gas collected over water occupied 57.2 mL at a temperature of 22°C and a pressure of 734 torr. Calculate the mass percent of $NaClO_3$ in the original sample. (At 22°C the vapor pressure of water is 19.8 torr.)

66. Xenon and fluorine will react to form binary compounds when a mixture of these two gases is heated to 400°C in a nickel reaction vessel. A 100.0-mL nickel container is filled with xenon and fluorine giving partial pressures of 1.24 atm and 10.10 atm, respectively, at a temperature of 25°C. The reaction vessel is heated to 400°C to cause a reaction to occur and then cooled to a temperature at which F_2 is a gas and the xenon fluoride is a nonvolatile solid. The remaining F_2 gas is transferred to another 100.0-mL nickel container where the pressure of F_2 at 25°C is 7.62 atm. Assuming all of the xenon has reacted, what is the formula of the product?

67. The nitrogen content of organic compounds can be determined by the Dumas method. The compound in question is first reacted by passage over hot $CuO(s)$:

$$\text{Compound} \xrightarrow[CuO(s)]{\text{Hot}} N_2(g) + CO_2(g) + H_2O(g)$$

The gaseous products are then passed through a concentrated solution of KOH to remove the CO_2. After passage through the KOH solution, the gas contains N_2 and is saturated with water vapor. In a given experiment, a 0.253-g sample of a compound produced 31.8 mL of N_2 saturated with water vapor at 25°C and 726 torr. What is the mass percent of nitrogen in the compound? (The vapor pressure of water at 25°C is 23.8 torr.)

68. An organic compound contains C, H, N, and O. Combustion of 0.1023 g of the compound in excess oxygen yielded 0.2766 g of CO_2 and 0.0991 g of H_2O. A sample of 0.4831 g of the compound was analyzed for nitrogen by the Dumas method (see Exercise 67). At STP, 27.6 mL of dry N_2 was obtained. In a third experiment, the density of the compound as a gas was found to be 4.02 g/L at 127°C and 256 torr. What are the empirical formula and the molecular formula of the compound?

69. Nitric acid is produced commercially by the Ostwald process. In the first step, ammonia is oxidized to nitric oxide:

$$4NH_3(g) + 5O_2(g) \longrightarrow 4NO(g) + 6H_2O(g)$$

Assume this reaction is carried out in the apparatus diagramed below.

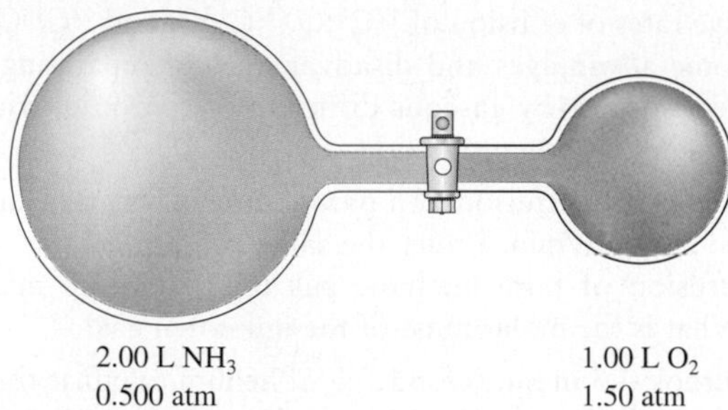

The stopcock between the two reaction containers is opened, and the reaction proceeds using proper catalysts. Calculate the partial pressure of NO after the reaction is complete. Assume 100% yield for the reaction, assume the final container volume is 3.00 L, and assume the temperature is constant.

70. Consider the following balanced equation in which gas X forms gas X_2:

$$2X(g) \longrightarrow X_2(g)$$

Equal moles of X are placed in two separate containers. One container is rigid, so the volume cannot change; the other container is flexible, so the volume changes to keep the internal pressure equal to the external pressure. The above reaction is run in each container. What happens to the pressure and density of the gas inside each container as reactants are converted to products?

71. As $NH_3(g)$ is decomposed into nitrogen gas and hydrogen gas at constant pressure and temperature, the volume of the product gases collected is twice the volume of NH_3 reacted. Explain. As $NH_3(g)$ is decomposed into nitrogen gas and hydrogen gas at constant volume and temperature, the total pressure increases by some factor. Why does the increase in pressure occur, and by what factor does the total pressure increase when reactants are completely converted into products? How do the partial pressures of the product gases compare to each other and to the initial pressure of NH_3?

Kinetic Molecular Theory and Real Gases

72. Use the postulates of the kinetic molecular theory (KMT) to explain why Boyle's law, Charles's law, Avogadro's law, and Dalton's law of partial pressures hold true for ideal gases. Use the KMT to explain the P versus n (at constant V and T) relationship and the P versus T (at constant V and n) relationship.

73. You have a gas in a container fitted with a piston and you change one of the conditions of the gas such that a change takes place, as shown below:

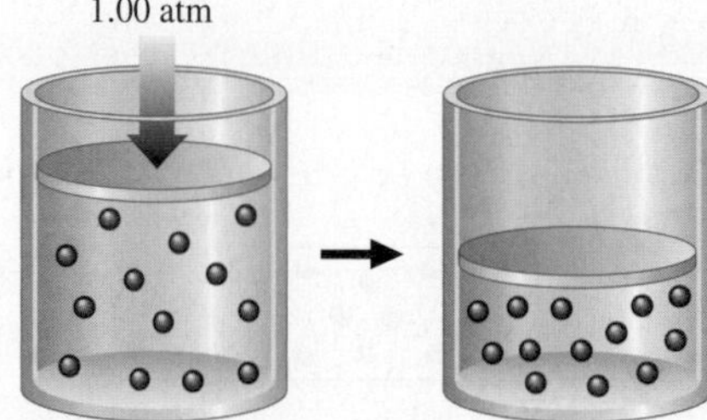

State two distinct changes you can make to accomplish this, and explain why each would work.

74. You have a gas in a container fitted with a piston and you change one of the conditions of the gas such that a change takes place, as shown below:

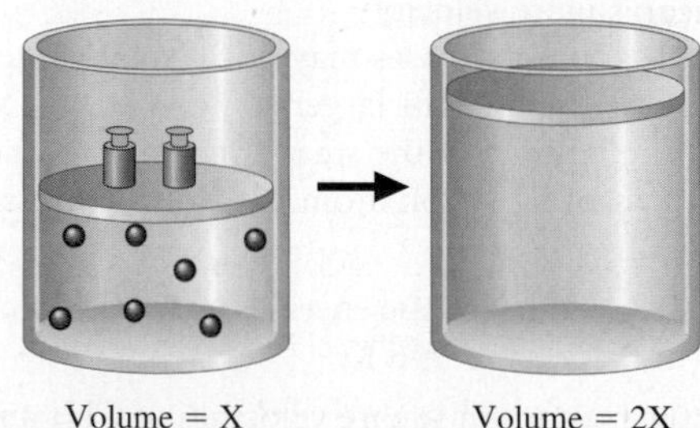

State three distinct changes you can make to accomplish this, and explain why each would work.

75. Consider two gases, A and B, each in a 1.0-L container with both gases at the same temperature and pressure. The mass of gas A in the container is 0.34 g, and the mass of gas B in the container is 0.48 g.

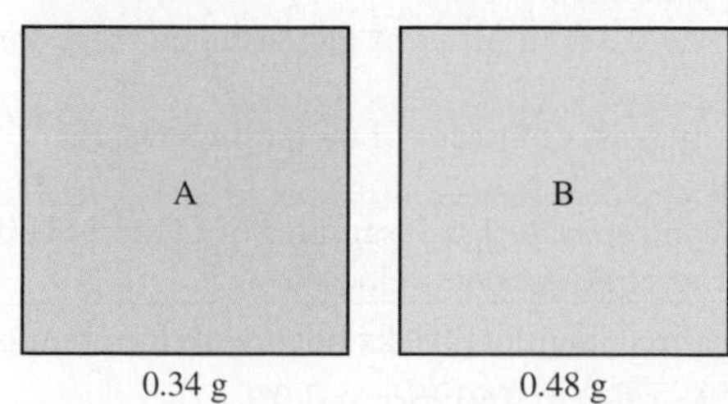

a. Which gas sample has the most molecules present? Explain.
b. Which gas sample has the largest average kinetic energy? Explain.
c. Which gas sample has the fastest average velocity? Explain.

d. How can the pressure in the two containers be equal to each other since the larger gas B molecules collide with the container walls more forcefully?

76. Consider the following samples of gases at the same temperature.

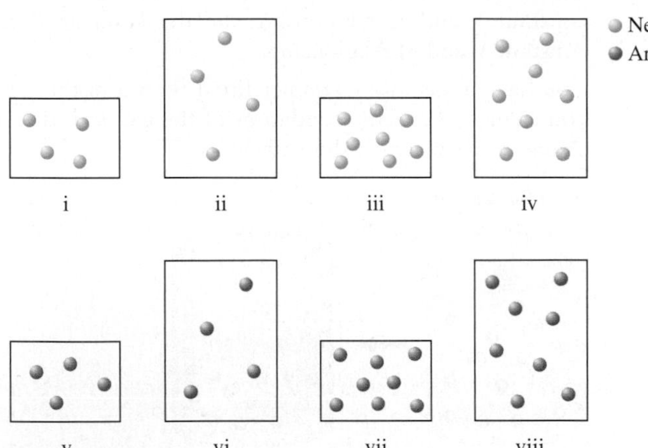

Arrange each of these samples in order from lowest to highest.

a. pressure
b. average kinetic energy
c. density
d. root mean square velocity

Note: Some samples of gases may have equal values for these attributes. Assume the larger containers have a volume twice the volume of the smaller containers and assume the mass of an argon atom is twice the mass of a neon atom.

77. Calculate the average kinetic energies of the CH_4 and N_2 molecules at 273 K and 546 K.

78. Calculate the root mean square velocities of CH_4 and N_2 molecules at 273 K and 546 K.

79. Do all the molecules in a 1-mole sample of $CH_4(g)$ have the same kinetic energy at 273 K? Do all the molecules in a 1-mole sample of $N_2(g)$ have the same velocity at 546 K? Explain.

80. Consider separate 1.0-L gaseous samples of H_2, Xe, Cl_2, and O_2, all at STP.

a. Rank the gases in order of increasing average kinetic energy.
b. Rank the gases in order of increasing average velocity.
c. How can separate 1.0-L samples of O_2 and H_2 both have the same average velocity?

81. Consider three identical flasks filled with different gases.

Flask A: CO at 760 torr and 0°C

Flask B: N_2 at 250 torr and 0°C

Flask C: H_2 at 100 torr and 0°C

a. In which flask will the molecules have the greatest average kinetic energy?
b. In which flask will the molecules have the greatest root mean square velocity?
c. Which flask will have the greatest number of collisions per second with the walls of the container?

82. Consider a 1.0-L container of neon gas at STP. Will the average kinetic energy, root mean square velocity, frequency of collisions of gas molecules with each other, frequency of collisions of gas molecules with the walls of the container, and energy of impact of gas molecules with the container increase, decrease, or remain the same under each of the following conditions?

a. The temperature is increased to 100°C.
b. The temperature is decreased to −50°C.
c. The volume is decreased to 0.5 L.
d. The number of moles of neon is doubled.

83. Freon-12 is used as a refrigerant in central home air conditioners. The rate of effusion of Freon-12 to Freon-11 (molar mass = 137.4 g/mol) is 1.07:1. The formula of Freon-12 is one of the following: CF_4, CF_3Cl, CF_2Cl_2, $CFCl_3$, or CCl_4. Which formula is correct for Freon-12?

84. One way of separating oxygen isotopes is by gaseous diffusion of carbon monoxide. The gaseous diffusion process behaves like an effusion process. Calculate the relative rates of effusion of $^{12}C^{16}O$, $^{12}C^{17}O$, and $^{12}C^{18}O$. List some advantages and disadvantages of separating oxygen isotopes by gaseous diffusion of carbon dioxide instead of carbon monoxide.

85. The rate of effusion of a particular gas was measured to be 24.0 mL/min. Under the same conditions, the rate of effusion of pure methane gas (CH_4) is 47.8 mL/min. What is the molar mass of the unknown gas?

86. It took 4.5 minutes for 1.0 L of helium to effuse through a porous barrier. How long will it take for 1.0 L of Cl_2 gas to effuse under identical conditions?

87. Calculate the pressure exerted by 0.5000 mole of N_2 in a 1.0000-L container at 25.0°C. (See Table 5.3.)

a. Use the ideal gas law.
b. Use the van der Waals equation.
c. Compare the results from parts a and b.

88. Calculate the pressure exerted by 0.5000 mole of N_2 in a 10.000-L container at 25.0°C. (See Table 5.3.)

a. Use the ideal gas law.
b. Use the van der Waals equation.
c. Compare the results from parts a and b.
d. Compare the results with those in Exercise 87.

89. Why do real gases not always behave ideally? Under what conditions does a real gas behave most ideally? Why?

90. Consider the following velocity distribution curves *A* and *B*.

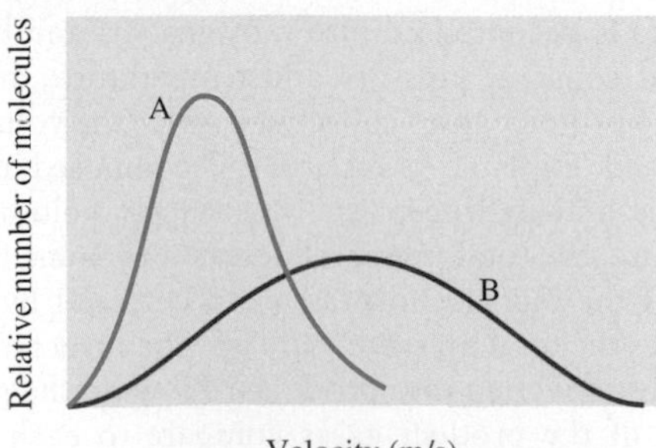

a. If the plots represent the velocity distribution of 1.0 L of He(*g*) at STP versus 1.0 L of $Cl_2(g)$ at STP, which plot corresponds to each gas? Explain your reasoning.

b. If the plots represent the velocity distribution of 1.0 L of $O_2(g)$ at temperatures of 273 K versus 1273 K, which plot corresponds to each temperature? Explain your reasoning. Under which temperature condition would the $O_2(g)$ sample behave most ideally? Explain.

91. In the van der Waals equation, why is a term added to the observed pressure and why is a term subtracted from the container volume to correct for nonideal gas behavior?

92. Without looking at tables of values, which of the following gases would you expect to have the largest value of the van der Waals constant b: H_2, N_2, CH_4, C_2H_6, or C_3H_8?

93. From the values in Table 5.3 for the van der Waals constant a for the gases H_2, CO_2, N_2, and CH_4, predict which molecule shows the strongest intermolecular attractions.

94. The Maxwell–Boltzmann distribution function $f(u)$ increases at small values of u and decreases at large values of u. Identify the parts of the function responsible for this behavior.

95. Calculate the root mean square, the most probable, and the average velocities for $N_2(g)$ at 227°C.

96. Calculate the kinetic energy possessed by 1.00×10^{20} molecules of methane gas (CH_4) at $T = 27°C$, assuming ideal behavior.

97. A flask contains $\frac{1}{3}$ mole of H_2 and $\frac{2}{3}$ mole of He. Compare the force on the wall per impact of H_2 relative to that for He.

98. A certain sample of uranium is reacted with fluorine to form a mixture of $^{235}UF_6(g)$ and $^{238}UF_6(g)$. After 100 diffusion steps, the gas contains 1526 $^{235}UF_6$ molecules per 1.000×10^5 total number of molecules in the gas ($^{235}UF_6 + {}^{238}UF_6$). What is the ratio of ^{235}U to ^{238}U atoms in the original sample of uranium?

99. Consider separate 1.0-L samples of $O_2(g)$ and He(g), both at 25°C and the same pressure. Compare the change in momentum per impact and the number of impacts per second in the two samples.

100. Consider separate 1.00-L samples of Ar(g), both containing the same number of moles, one at 27°C and the other at 77°C. Compare the change in momentum per impact and the number of impacts per second in the two samples.

101. Calculate the intermolecular collision frequency and the mean free path in a sample of helium gas with a volume of 5.0 L at 27°C and 3.0 atm. Assume that the diameter of a helium atom is 50. pm.

Atmosphere Chemistry

102. Use the data in Table 5.4 to calculate the partial pressure of He in dry air assuming that the total pressure is 1.0 atm. Assuming a temperature of 25°C, calculate the number of He atoms per cubic centimeter.

103. Atmospheric scientists often use mixing ratios to express the concentrations of trace compounds in air. Mixing ratios are often expressed as ppmv (parts per million volume):

$$\text{ppmv of } X = \frac{\text{vol of X at STP}}{\text{total vol of air at STP}} \times 10^6$$

On a certain November day, the concentration of carbon monoxide in the air in downtown Denver, Colorado, reached 3.0×10^2 ppmv. The atmospheric pressure at that time was 628 torr and the temperature was 0°C.

a. What was the partial pressure of CO?

b. What was the concentration of CO in molecules per cubic meter?

c. What was the concentration of CO in molecules per cubic centimeter?

104. Write reactions to show how nitric and sulfuric acids are produced in the atmosphere. Write reactions to show how the nitric and sulfuric acids in acid rain react with marble and limestone. (Both marble and limestone are primarily calcium carbonate.)

105. Trace organic compounds in the atmosphere are first concentrated and then measured by gas chromatography. In the concentration step, several liters of air are pumped through a tube containing a porous substance that traps organic compounds. The tube is then connected to a gas chromatograph and heated to release the trapped compounds. The organic compounds are separated in the column and the amounts are measured. In an analysis for benzene and toluene in air, a 3.00-L sample of air at 748 torr and 23°C was passed through the trap. The gas chromatography analysis showed that this air sample contained 89.6 ng of benzene (C_6H_6) and 153 ng of toluene (C_7H_8). Calculate the mixing ratio (see Exercise 103) and number of molecules per cubic centimeter for both benzene and toluene.

Additional Exercises

106. A form of Boyle's law is $PV = k$ (at constant T and n). Table 5.1 contains actual data from pressure–volume experiments conducted by Robert Boyle. The value of k in most experiments is 14.1×10^2 in Hg · in^3. Express k in units of atm · L. In Example 5.1, k was determined for NH_3 at various pressures and volumes. Give some reasons why the k values differ so dramatically between Example 5.1 and Table 5.1.

107. A glass vessel contains 28 g nitrogen gas. Assuming ideal behavior, which of the processes listed below would double the pressure exerted on the walls of the vessel?

a. Adding enough mercury to fill one-half the container.

b. Raising the temperature of the container from 30.°C to 60.°C.

c. Raising the temperature of the container from −73°C to 127°C.

d. Adding 28 g nitrogen gas.

108. Which of the following statements is(are) true? For the false statements, correct them.
  a. At constant temperature, the lighter the gas molecules, the faster the average velocity of the gas molecules.
  b. At constant temperature, the heavier the gas molecules, the larger the average kinetic energy of the gas molecules.
  c. A real gas behaves most ideally when the container volume is relatively large and the gas molecules are moving relatively quickly.
  d. As temperature increases, the effect of interparticle interactions on gas behavior is increased.
  e. At constant V and T, as gas molecules are added into a container, the number of collisions per unit area increases, resulting in a higher pressure.
  f. The kinetic molecular theory predicts that pressure is inversely proportional to temperature at constant volume and moles of gas.

109. A person accidentally swallows a drop of liquid oxygen, $O_2(l)$, which has a density of 1.149 g/mL. Assuming the drop has a volume of 0.050 mL, what volume of gas will be produced in the person's stomach at body temperature (37°C) and a pressure of 1.0 atm?

110. Hydrogen azide, HN_3, decomposes on heating by the following *unbalanced* reaction:

$$HN_3(g) \longrightarrow N_2(g) + H_2(g)$$

If 3.0 atm of pure $HN_3(g)$ is decomposed initially, what is the final total pressure in the reaction container? What are the partial pressures of nitrogen and hydrogen gas? Assume the volume and temperature of the reaction container are constant.

111. A 20.0 L stainless steel container at 25°C was charged with 2.00 atm of hydrogen gas and 3.00 atm of oxygen gas. A spark ignited the mixture, producing water. What is the pressure in the tank at 25°C? If the same experiment were performed, but the temperature was 125°C instead of 25°C, what would be the pressure in the tank?

112. In the "Méthode Champenoise," grape juice is fermented in a wine bottle to produce sparkling wine. The reaction is

$$C_6H_{12}O_6(aq) \longrightarrow 2C_2H_5OH(aq) + 2CO_2(g)$$

Fermentation of 750. mL of grape juice (density = 1.0 g/cm^3) is allowed to take place in a bottle with a total volume of 825 mL until 12% by volume is ethanol (C_2H_5OH). Assuming that the CO_2 is insoluble in H_2O (actually a wrong assumption), what would be the pressure of CO_2 inside the wine bottle at 25°C? (The density of ethanol is 0.79 g/cm^3.)

113. A 2.747-g sample of manganese metal is reacted with excess HCl gas to produce 3.22 L of $H_2(g)$ at 373 K and 0.951 atm and a manganese chloride compound ($MnCl_x$). What is the formula of the manganese chloride compound produced in the reaction?

114. The total mass that can be lifted by a balloon is given by the difference between the mass of air displaced by the balloon and the mass of the gas inside the balloon. Consider a hot-air balloon that approximates a sphere 5.00 m in diameter and contains air heated to 65°C. The surrounding air temperature is 21°C. The pressure in the balloon is equal to the atmospheric pressure, which is 745 torr.
  a. What total mass can the balloon lift? Assume the average molar mass of air is 29.0 g/mol. (*Hint:* Heated air is less dense than cool air.)
  b. If the balloon is filled with enough helium at 21°C and 745 torr to achieve the same volume as in part a, what total mass can the balloon lift?
  c. What mass could the hot-air balloon (from part a) lift if it were on the ground in Denver, Colorado, where a typical atmospheric pressure is 630. torr?
  d. What mass could the hot-air balloon (from part a) lift if it were a cold day with a temperature of −8°C?

115. At STP, 1.0 L Br_2 reacts completely with 3.0 L F_2, producing 2.0 L of a product. What is the formula of the product? (All substances are gases.)

116. Natural gas is a mixture of hydrocarbons, primarily methane (CH_4) and ethane (C_2H_6). A typical mixture might have $\chi_{methane} = 0.915$ and $\chi_{ethane} = 0.085$. What are the partial pressures of the two gases in a 15.00-L container of natural gas at 20.°C and 1.44 atm? Assuming complete combustion of both gases in the natural gas sample, what is the total mass of water formed?

117. An important process for the production of acrylonitrile (C_3H_3N) (annual U.S. production is greater than 10^9 lb) is given by the following equation:

$$2C_3H_6(g) + 2NH_3(g) + 3O_2(g) \longrightarrow 2C_3H_3N(g) + 6H_2O(g)$$

A 150.-L reactor is charged to the following partial pressures at 25°C:

$$P_{C_3H_6} = 0.500 \text{ MPa}$$
$$P_{NH_3} = 0.800 \text{ MPa}$$
$$P_{O_2} = 1.500 \text{ MPa}$$

What mass of acrylonitrile can be produced from this mixture (MPa = 10^6 Pa)?

118. The oxides of Group 2A metals (symbolized by M here) react with carbon dioxide according to the following reaction:

$$MO(s) + CO_2(g) \longrightarrow MCO_3(s)$$

A 2.85-g sample containing only MgO and CuO is placed in a 3.00-L container. The container is filled with CO_2 to a pressure of 740. torr at 20.°C. After the reaction has gone to completion, the pressure inside the flask is 390. torr at 20.°C. What is the mass percent of MgO in the mixture? Assume that only the MgO reacts with CO_2.

119. Small quantities of hydrogen gas can be prepared in the laboratory by the addition of aqueous hydrochloric acid to metallic zinc.

$$Zn(s) + 2HCl(aq) \longrightarrow ZnCl_2(aq) + H_2(g)$$

Typically, the hydrogen gas is bubbled through water for collection and becomes saturated with water vapor. Suppose 240. mL of hydrogen gas is collected at 30.°C and has a total pressure of 1.032 atm by this process. What is the partial pressure of hydrogen gas in the sample? How many grams of zinc must have reacted to produce this quantity of hydrogen? (The vapor pressure of water is 32 torr at 30°C.)

120. Nitrogen gas (N_2) reacts with hydrogen gas (H_2) to form ammonia gas (NH_3). You have nitrogen and hydrogen gases in a 15.0-L container fitted with a movable piston (the piston allows the container volume to change so as to keep the pressure constant inside the container). Initially, the partial pressure of each reactant gas is 1.00 atm. Assume the temperature is constant and the reaction goes to completion.
   a. Calculate the partial pressure of ammonia in the container after the reaction has reached completion.
   b. Calculate the volume of the container after the reaction has reached completion.

121. Consider the three flasks in the diagram below. Assuming the connecting tubes have negligible volume, what is the partial pressure of each gas and the total pressure after all the stopcocks are opened?

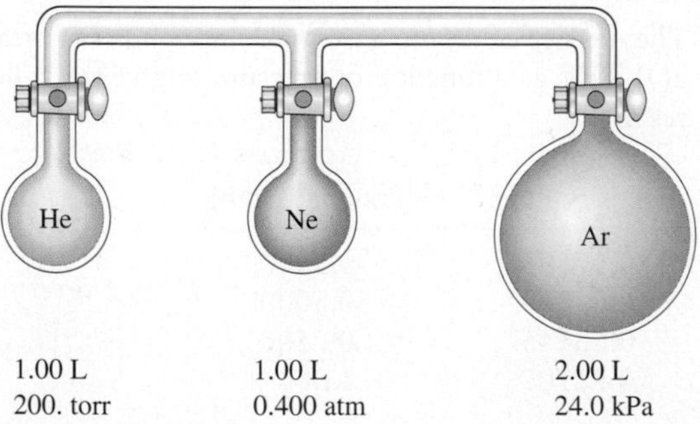

122. Equal moles of sulfur dioxide gas and oxygen gas are mixed in a flexible reaction vessel and then sparked to initiate the formation of gaseous sulfur trioxide. Assuming that the reaction goes to completion, what is the ratio of the final volume of the gas mixture to the initial volume of the gas mixture if both volumes are measured at the same temperature and pressure?

123. Silane (SiH_4) is the silicon analogue of methane (CH_4). It is prepared industrially according to the following equations:

$$Si(s) + 3HCl(g) \longrightarrow HSiCl_3(l) + H_2(g)$$

$$4HSiCl_3(l) \longrightarrow SiH_4(g) + 3SiCl_4(l)$$

   a. If 156 mL of $HSiCl_3$ (d = 1.34 g/mL) is isolated when 15.0 L of HCl at 10.0 atm and 35°C is used, what is the percent yield of $HSiCl_3$?
   b. When 156 mL of $HSiCl_3$ is heated, what volume of SiH_4 at 10.0 atm and 35°C will be obtained if the percent yield of the reaction is 93.1%?

124. A compound containing only C, H, and N yields the following data.
   i. Complete combustion of 35.0 mg of the compound produced 33.5 mg of CO_2 and 41.1 mg of H_2O.
   ii. A 65.2-mg sample of the compound was analyzed for nitrogen by the Dumas method (see Exercise 67), giving 35.6 mL of dry N_2 at 740. torr and 25°C.
   iii. The effusion rate of the compound as a gas was measured and found to be 24.6 mL/min. The effusion rate of argon gas, under identical conditions, is 26.4 mL/min.

   What is the formula of the compound?

125. A 15.0-L tank is filled with H_2 to a pressure of 2.00×10^2 atm. How many balloons (each 2.00 L) can be inflated to a pressure of 1.00 atm from the tank? Assume that there is no temperature change and that the tank cannot be emptied below 1.00 atm pressure.

126. Consider the following diagram.

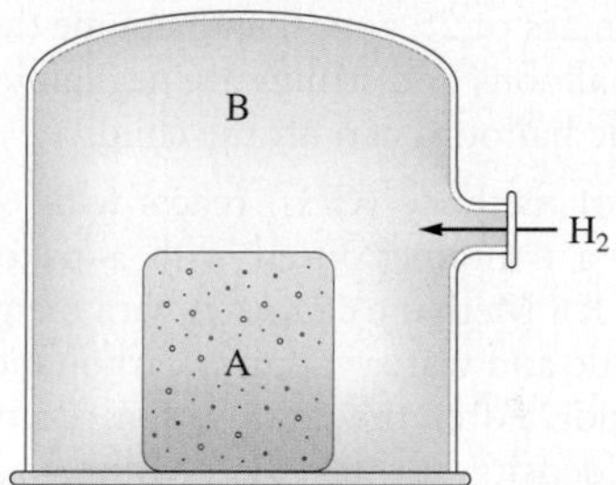

A porous container (A), filled with air at STP, is contained in a large enclosed container (B), which is flushed with $H_2(g)$. What will happen to the pressure inside container A? Explain your answer.

127. A 100.-L flask contains a mixture of methane (CH_4) and argon at 25°C. The mass of argon present is 228 g and the mole fraction of methane in the mixture is 0.650. Calculate the total kinetic energy of the gaseous mixture.

128. Represent the following plots.
   a. PV/n (y axis) versus P (x axis) for a real gas that obeys the equation $PV/n = \alpha + \beta P$
   b. change in momentum per impact versus mass of an individual gas particle for a series of ideal gases all at the same temperature
   c. P versus T (°C) for an ideal gas where n and V are constant

129. A spherical glass container of unknown volume contains helium gas at 25°C and 1.960 atm. When a portion of the helium is withdrawn and adjusted to 1.00 atm at 25°C, it is found to have a volume of 1.75 cm^3. The gas remaining in the first container shows a pressure of 1.710 atm. Calculate the volume of the spherical container.

130. A compound Z is known to have a composition of 34.38% Ni, 28.13% C, and 37.48% O. In an experiment 1.00 L of gaseous Z is mixed with 1.00 L of argon, where each gas is at P = 2.00 atm and T = 25°C. When this mixture of gases is put in an effusion chamber, the ratio of Z molecules to Ar molecules in the effused mixture is 0.4837. Using these data, calculate the following.
   a. the empirical formula for Z
   b. the molar mass for Z
   c. the molecular formula for Z
   d. the mole ratio of Z to argon in a sample of gas obtained by five effusion steps (starting with the original mixture)

131. Hydrogen cyanide gas is commercially prepared by the reaction of methane [$CH_4(g)$], ammonia [$NH_3(g)$], and oxygen [$O_2(g)$] at a high temperature. The other product is gaseous water.
   a. Write a balanced chemical equation for the reaction.
   b. Methane and ammonia gases flow into a reactor at a rate of 20.0 L/s. Oxygen gas is introduced at a flow rate of 40.0 L/s. All the reactant gases are at 1.00 atm and 150.°C. What mass of HCN is produced per second by this reaction assuming 100% yield?

Challenge Problems

132. Consider a children's cartoon illustrating a child holding the strings of several helium balloons and being lifted into the sky.
   a. Estimate the minimum number of 10.-L balloons it would take to lift a 50.-lb child. Assume air has an average molar mass of 29 g/mol, and assume the masses of the balloons and strings are negligible.
   b. Explain why the balloons can lift the child.

133. A 16.0-g sample of methane (CH_4) reacts with 64.0 g of oxygen gas in a container fitted with a piston (at 1.00 atm and 425 K). Methane can react with oxygen to form carbon dioxide and water vapor or carbon monoxide and water vapor. After the combustion reaction is complete, the gas density at the given conditions is observed to be 0.7282 g/L. Calculate the mole fraction of methane that reacts to form carbon monoxide rather than carbon dioxide.

134. You have two samples of helium gas at the same pressure in separate steel containers of the same volume. You want the number of collisions of helium atoms with the walls of container 1 to be twice the number of collisions of helium atoms with the walls of container 2. Assume ideal behavior.
   a. How does the temperature in container 1 compare to the temperature in container 2? That is, which temperature is larger and by what factor? Explain your answer and support it mathematically.
   b. If the number of collisions is different in each container, how can the pressure be the same? Provide a written explanation with mathematical support.

135. A mixture of chromium and zinc weighing 0.362 g was reacted with an excess of hydrochloric acid. After all the metals in the mixture reacted, 225 mL of dry hydrogen gas was collected at 27°C and 750. torr. Determine the mass percent of Zn in the metal sample. [Zinc reacts with hydrochloric acid to produce zinc chloride and hydrogen gas; chromium reacts with hydrochloric acid to produce chromium(III) chloride and hydrogen gas.]

136. You have a sealed, flexible balloon filled with argon gas. The atmospheric pressure is 1.00 atm and the temperature is 25°C. The air has a mole fraction of nitrogen of 0.79, the rest being oxygen.
   a. Explain why the balloon would float when heated. Make sure to discuss which factors change and which remain constant, and why this matters. Be complete.
   b. Above what temperature would you heat the balloon so that it would float?

137. Derive a linear relationship between gas density and temperature, and use it to estimate the value of absolute zero temperature (in °C to the nearest 0.1°C) from an air sample whose density is 1.2930 g/L at 0.0°C and 0.9460 g/L at 100.0°C. Assume air obeys the ideal gas law and that the pressure is held constant.

138. A chemist weighed out 5.14 g of a mixture containing unknown amounts of $BaO(s)$ and $CaO(s)$ and placed the sample in a 1.50-L flask containing $CO_2(g)$ at 30.0°C and 750. torr. After the reaction to form $BaCO_3(s)$ and $CaCO_3(s)$ was completed, the pressure of $CO_2(g)$ remaining was 230. torr. Calculate the mass percents of $CaO(s)$ and $BaO(s)$ in the mixture.

139. The density of a pure gaseous compound was measured at 0.00°C as a function of pressure to give the following results:

Density (g/L)	Pressure (atm)
0.17893	0.2500
0.35808	0.5000
0.53745	0.7500
0.71707	1.000

Calculate the molar mass of this compound, corrected for any nonideal behavior of the gas. Assume the nonideal gas obeys the equation $PV/nRT = 1 + \beta P$. (*Hint:* Derive an equation for P/d and plot P/d versus P.)

140. Consider separate 1.0-L samples of $He(g)$ and $UF_6(g)$, both at 1.00 atm and containing the same number of moles. What ratio of temperatures for the two samples would produce the same collision frequency with the vessel walls?

141. The most probable velocity u_{mp} is the velocity possessed by the greatest number of gas particles. At a certain temperature, the probability that a gas particle has the most probable velocity is equal to one-half the probability that the same gas particle has the most probable velocity at 300. K. Is the temperature higher or lower than 300. K? Calculate the temperature.

142. Derive Dalton's law of partial pressures from the kinetic molecular theory of gases. What assumptions are necessary?

143. One of the assumptions of the kinetic molecular theory is that the volume of a gas particle is negligible. If this were the case, the ratio of the number of collisions of gas particles with the walls of the container compared to the

number of collisions a given gas particle experiences with other gas particles should be quite high. Determine the volume of a cube (in L) filled with helium such that the ratio of the number of collisions of helium atoms with the container walls to the number of intermolecular collisions for a given helium atom is 1 quintillion (1 quintillion = 1.00×10^{18}). The atomic radius of helium is 3.2×10^{-11} m.

144. Consider a sample of a hydrocarbon (a compound consisting of only carbon and hydrogen) at 0.959 atm and 298 K. Upon combusting the entire sample in oxygen, you collect a mixture of gaseous carbon dioxide and water vapor at 1.51 atm and 375 K. This mixture has a density of 1.391 g/L and occupies a volume four times as large as that of the pure hydrocarbon. Determine the molecular formula of the hydrocarbon.

145. A steel cylinder contains 5.00 moles of graphite (pure carbon) and 5.00 moles of O_2. The mixture is ignited and all the graphite reacts. Combustion produces a mixture of CO gas and CO_2 gas. After the cylinder has cooled to its original temperature, it is found that the pressure of the cylinder has increased by 17.0%. Calculate the mole fractions of CO, CO_2, and O_2 in the final gaseous mixture.

146. You have an equimolar mixture of the gases SO_2 and O_2, along with some He, in a container fitted with a piston. The density of this mixture at STP is 1.924 g/L. Assume ideal behavior and constant temperature.
   a. What is the mole fraction of He in the original mixture?
   b. The SO_2 and O_2 react to completion to form SO_3. What is the density of the gas mixture after the reaction is complete?

147. Methane (CH_4) gas flows into a combustion chamber at a rate of 200. L/min at 1.50 atm and ambient temperature. Air is added to the chamber at 1.00 atm and the same temperature, and the gases are ignited.
   a. To ensure complete combustion of CH_4 to $CO_2(g)$ and $H_2O(g)$, three times as much oxygen as is necessary is reacted. Assuming air is 21 mole percent O_2 and 79 mole percent N_2, calculate the flow rate of air necessary to deliver the required amount of oxygen.
   b. Under the conditions in part a, combustion of methane was not complete as a mixture of $CO_2(g)$ and $CO(g)$ was produced. It was determined that 95.0% of the carbon in the exhaust gas was present in the CO_2. The remainder was present as carbon in the CO. Calculate the composition of the exhaust gas in terms of mole fractions of CO, CO_2, O_2, N_2, and H_2O. Assume CH_4 is completely reacted and N_2 is unreacted.
   c. Assuming a total pressure of the exhaust gas of 1.00 atm, calculate the partial pressures of the gases in part b.

148. A spherical vessel with a volume of 1.00 L was evacuated and sealed. Twenty-four hours later the pressure of air in the vessel was found to be 1.20×10^{-6} atm. During this 24-h period, the vessel had been surrounded by air at 27°C and 1.00 atm. Assuming that air is 78 mole percent nitrogen and that the remainder is oxygen, calculate the diameter of the tiny circular hole in the vessel that allowed the air to leak in.

149. Calculate the number of stages needed to change a mixture of $^{13}CO_2$ and $^{12}CO_2$ that is originally 0.10% (by moles) $^{13}CO_2$ to a mixture that is 0.010% $^{13}CO_2$ by a gaseous diffusion process. (The mass of ^{13}C is 13.003355 amu.)

150. Two samples of gas are separated in two rectangular 1.00-L chambers by a thin metal wall. One sample is pure helium and the other is pure radon. Both samples are at 27°C and show a pressure of 2.00×10^{-6} atm. Assuming that the metal wall separating the gases suddenly develops a circular hole of radius 1.00×10^{-6} m, calculate the pressure in each chamber after 10.0 h have passed.

151. You have a helium balloon at 1.00 atm and 25°C. You want to make a hot-air balloon with the same volume and same lift as the helium balloon. Assume air is 79.0% nitrogen and 21.0% oxygen by volume. The "lift" of a balloon is given by the difference between the mass of air displaced by the balloon and the mass of gas inside the balloon.
   a. Will the temperature in the hot-air balloon have to be higher or lower than 25°C? Explain.
   b. Calculate the temperature of the air required for the hot-air balloon to provide the same lift as the helium balloon at 1.00 atm and 25°C. Assume atmospheric conditions are 1.00 atm and 25°C.

152. Consider an equimolar mixture (equal number of moles) of two diatomic gases (A_2 and B_2) in a container fitted with a piston. The gases react to form one product (which is also a gas) with the formula A_xB_y. The density of the sample after the reaction is complete (and the temperature returns to its original state) is 1.50 times greater than the density of the reactant mixture.
   a. Specify the formula of the product, and explain if more than one answer is possible based on the given data.
   b. Can you determine the molecular formula of the product with the information given or only the empirical formula?

153. You are given an unknown gaseous binary compound (that is, a compound consisting of two different elements). When 10.0 g of the compound is burned in excess oxygen, 16.3 g of water is produced. The compound has a density 1.38 times that of oxygen gas at the same conditions of temperature and pressure. Give a possible identity for the unknown compound.

Marathon Problem

154.* Use the following information to identify element A and compound B, then answer questions a and b.

An empty glass container has a mass of 658.572 g. It has a mass of 659.452 g after it has been filled with nitrogen gas at a pressure of 790. torr and a temperature of 15°C. When the container is evacuated and refilled with a certain element (A) at a pressure of 745 torr and a temperature of 26°C, it has a mass of 660.59 g.

Compound B, a gaseous organic compound that consists of 85.6% carbon and 14.4% hydrogen by mass, is placed in a stainless steel vessel (10.68 L) with excess oxygen gas. The vessel is placed in a constant-temperature bath at 22°C. The pressure in the vessel is 11.98 atm. In the bottom of the vessel is a container that is packed with Ascarite and a desiccant. Ascarite is asbestos impregnated with sodium hydroxide; it quantitatively absorbs carbon dioxide:

$$2NaOH(s) + CO_2(g) \longrightarrow Na_2CO_3(s) + H_2O(l)$$

The desiccant is anhydrous magnesium perchlorate, which quantitatively absorbs the water produced by the combustion reaction as well as the water produced by the preceding reaction. Neither the Ascarite nor the desiccant reacts with compound B or oxygen. The total mass of the container with the Ascarite and desiccant is 765.3 g.

The combustion reaction of compound B is initiated by a spark. The pressure immediately rises, then begins to decrease, and finally reaches a steady value of 6.02 atm. The stainless steel vessel is carefully opened, and the mass of the container inside the vessel is found to be 846.7 g.

A and B react quantitatively in a 1:1 mole ratio to form 1 mole of gas C.

a. How many grams of C will be produced if 10.0 L of A and 8.60 L of B (each at STP) are reacted by opening a stopcock connecting the two samples?
b. What will be the total pressure in the system?

*From James H. Burness, "The Use of "Marathon" Problems as Effective Vehicles for the Presentation of General Chemistry Lectures," Journal of Chemical Education, 68(11).

Chemical Equilibrium

6

chapter

Black sea nettle in the Monterey Bay Aquarium in California. Jellyfish use statocysts to maintain their physical equilibrium. A statocyst consists of a fluid-filled sac containing statoliths that stimulate sensory cells and help indicate position when the animal moves.

In doing stoichiometry calculations, we assume that reactions proceed to completion—that is, until one of the reactants is consumed. Many reactions *do* proceed essentially to completion. For such reactions it can be assumed that the reactants are quantitatively converted to products and that the amount of limiting reactant that remains is negligible. On the other hand, there are many chemical reactions that stop far short of completion. An example is the dimerization of nitrogen dioxide:

$$2NO_2(g) \longrightarrow N_2O_4(g)$$

The reactant NO_2 is a reddish brown gas, and the product N_2O_4 is a colorless gas. When NO_2 is placed in an evacuated, sealed glass vessel at 25°C, the initial dark brown color decreases in intensity as the NO_2 is converted to colorless N_2O_4. However, even over a long period of time, the contents of the reaction vessel do not become colorless. Instead, the intensity of the brown color eventually becomes constant, which means that the concentration of NO_2 is no longer changing. This is illustrated on the molecular level in Fig. 6.1. This observation is a clear indication that the reaction has stopped short of completion. In fact, the system has reached **chemical equilibrium,** *the state in which the concentrations of all reactants and products remain constant with time.*

Any chemical reaction carried out in a closed vessel will reach equilibrium. For some reactions the equilibrium position so favors the products that the reaction appears to have gone to completion. We say that the equilibrium position for such a reaction lies *far to the right,* in the direction of the products. For example, when gaseous hydrogen and oxygen are mixed in stoichiometric quantities and react to form water vapor, the reaction proceeds essentially to completion. The amounts of the reactants that remain when the system reaches equilibrium are so tiny that they are negligible. In contrast, some reactions occur only to a slight extent. For example, when solid CaO is placed in a closed vessel at 25°C, the decomposition to solid Ca and gaseous O_2 is virtually undetectable. In cases like this, the equilibrium position is said to lie *far to the left,* in the direction of the reactants.

In this chapter we will discuss how and why a chemical system comes to equilibrium and the characteristics of a system at equilibrium. In particular, we will discuss how to calculate the concentrations of the reactants and products present for a given system at equilibrium.

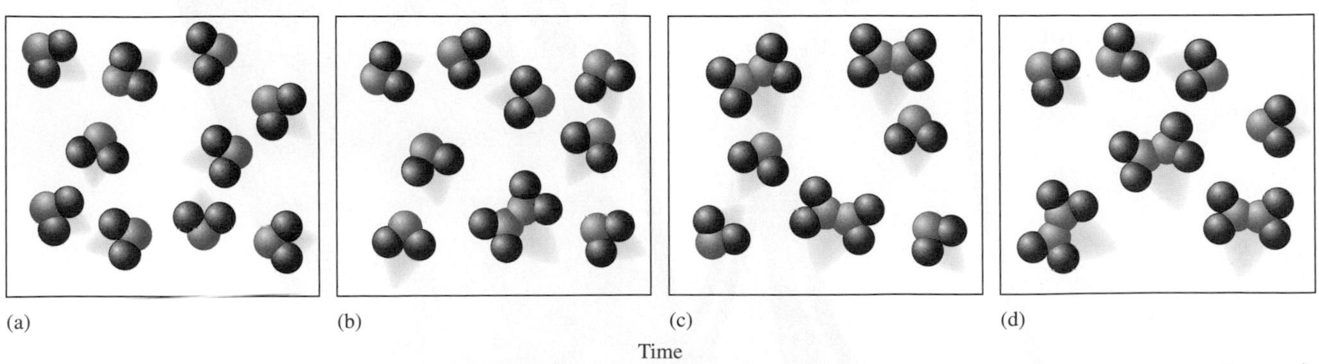

Figure 6.1
A molecular representation of the reaction $2NO_2(g) \longrightarrow N_2O_4(g)$ over time in a closed vessel. Note that the numbers of NO_2 and N_2O_4 in the container become constant (c) and (d) after sufficient time has passed.

6.1 The Equilibrium Condition

Since no changes occur in the concentrations of reactants or products in a reaction system at equilibrium, it may appear that everything has stopped. However, this is not the case. On the molecular level, there is frenetic activity. Equilibrium is not static; it is a highly *dynamic* situation. The concept of chemical equilibrium is analogous to two island cities connected by a bridge. Suppose the traffic flow on the bridge is the same in both directions. It is obvious that there is motion, since one can see the cars traveling across the bridge, but the number of cars in each city is not changing because equal numbers are entering and leaving. The result is no *net* change in the car population.

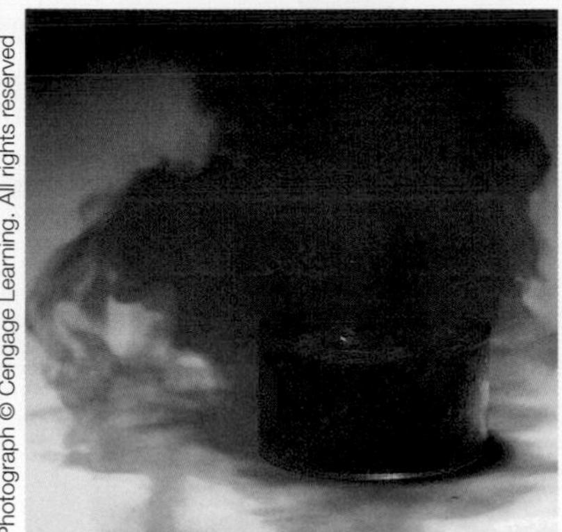

Reddish brown nitrogen dioxide gas streaming from a flask where copper is reacting with concentrated nitric acid.

To see how this concept applies to chemical reactions, consider the reaction between steam and carbon monoxide in a closed vessel at a high temperature, where the reaction takes place rapidly:

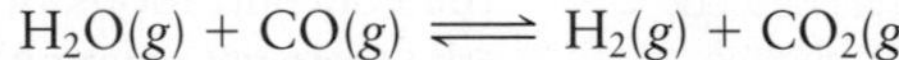

$$H_2O(g) + CO(g) \rightleftharpoons H_2(g) + CO_2(g)$$

Assume that the same number of moles of gaseous CO and gaseous H_2O are placed in a closed vessel and allowed to react. The plots of the concentrations of reactants and products versus time are shown in Fig. 6.2. Note that since CO and H_2O were originally present in equal molar quantities, and since they react in a 1:1 ratio, the concentrations of the two gases are always equal. Also, since H_2 and CO_2 are formed in equal amounts, they are always present at the same concentrations.

Figure 6.2 is a profile of the progress of the reaction. When CO and H_2O are mixed, they immediately begin reacting to form H_2 and CO_2. This leads to a decrease in the concentrations of the reactants, but the concentrations of the products, which were initially at zero, are increasing. Beyond a certain time, indicated by the dashed line in Fig. 6.2, the concentrations of reactants and products no longer change—equilibrium has been reached. Unless the system is somehow disturbed, no further changes in concentrations will occur. Note that although the equilibrium position lies far to the right, the concentrations of reactants never reach zero; the reactants will always be present in small but constant concentrations. This is shown on the microscopic level in Fig. 6.3.

Equilibrium is a dynamic situation.

Why does equilibrium occur? As we will see in much more detail in Chapter 15, chemical reactions occur via collisions of the reacting molecules. The energy associated with a collision can break bonds in the reactant molecules, allowing them to rearrange to form the products. Since the collision rate of the molecules in a gas depends on the concentration of molecules present, the rate of a reaction depends on the concentrations of the reactants. Thus, as reactants collide and react to form products

$$H_2O(g) + CO(g) \longrightarrow H_2(g) + CO_2(g)$$

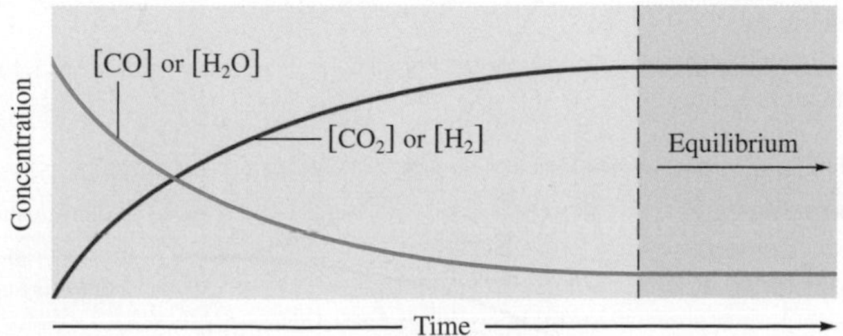

Figure 6.2
The changes in concentrations with time for the reaction $H_2O(g) + CO(g) \rightleftharpoons H_2(g) + CO_2(g)$ when equal molar quantities of $H_2O(g)$ and $CO(g)$ are mixed.

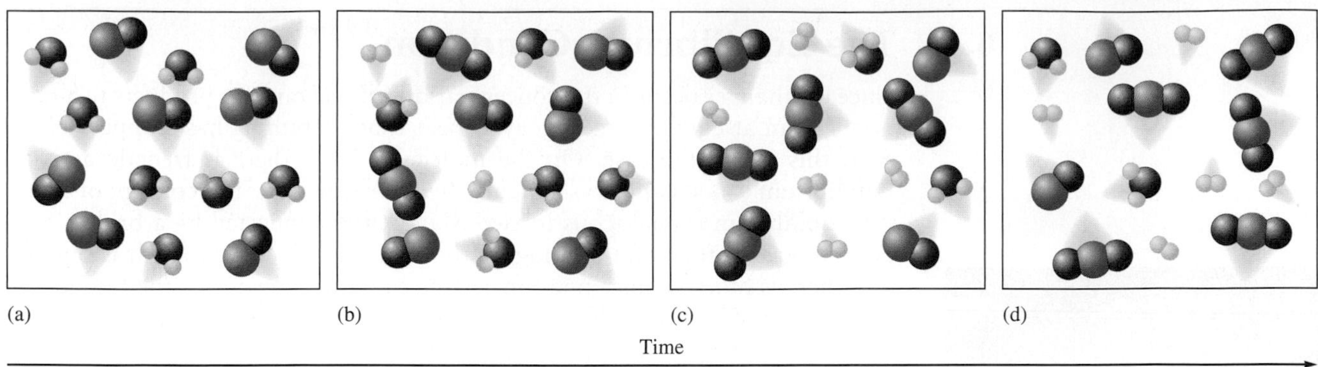

Figure 6.3
(a) H_2O and CO are mixed in equal numbers and begin to react (b) to form CO_2 and H_2. After time has passed, equilibrium is reached (c), and the numbers of reactant and product molecules then remain constant over time (d).

the concentrations of the reactants decrease, causing the rate of this reaction (the *forward* reaction) to decrease—that is, the reaction slows down (Fig. 6.4).

As in the bridge-traffic analogy, there is also a reverse direction:

$$H_2(g) + CO_2(g) \longrightarrow H_2O(g) + CO(g)$$

Initially in this experiment no H_2 and CO_2 were present, and this reverse reaction could not occur. However, as the forward reaction proceeds, the concentrations of H_2 and CO_2 build up, and the rate of the reverse reaction increases (Fig. 6.4) as the forward reaction slows down. Eventually, the concentrations reach levels where the rate of the forward reaction equals the rate of the reverse reaction. That is, the concentrations of the reactants and products achieve values such that H_2O and CO are being consumed by the forward reaction at exactly the same rate as they are being produced by the reverse reaction. The system has reached equilibrium.

What would happen to the gaseous equilibrium mixture of reactants and products represented in Fig. 6.3, parts (c) and (d), if we injected some $H_2O(g)$ into the box? To answer this question, we need to be sure we understand the equilibrium condition: The concentrations of reactants and products remain constant at equilibrium because the forward and reverse reaction rates are equal. If we inject some H_2O molecules, what will happen to the forward reaction: $H_2O + CO \rightarrow H_2 + CO_2$? It will speed up because when there are more H_2O molecules there will be more collisions between H_2O and CO molecules. This in turn will form more products and will cause the reverse reaction $H_2O + CO \leftarrow H_2 + CO_2$ to speed up. Thus the system will change until the forward and reverse reaction rates again become equal. Will this new equilibrium position contain more or fewer product molecules than are shown in Fig. 6.3(c) and (d)? Think about this carefully. If you are not sure of the answer

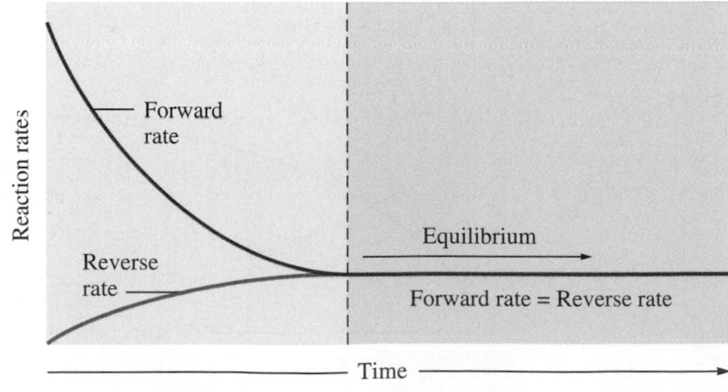

Figure 6.4
The changes with time in the rates of forward and reverse reactions for $H_2O(g) + CO(g) \rightleftharpoons H_2(g) + CO_2(g)$ when equal molar quantities of $H_2O(g)$ and $CO(g)$ are mixed. Note that the rates for the forward and reverse reactions do not change in the same way with time. We will not be concerned with the reasons for this difference at this point.

now, keep reading. We will consider this type of situation in more detail later in this chapter.

The equilibrium position of a reaction—left, right, or somewhere in between—is determined by many factors: the initial concentrations, the relative energies of the reactants and products, and the relative "degree of organization" of the reactants and products. Energy and organization come into play because nature tries to achieve minimum energy and maximum disorder. For now, we will simply view the equilibrium phenomenon as an experimentally verified fact. The theoretical origins of equilibrium will be explored in detail in Chapter 10.

The relationship between equilibrium and thermodynamics is explored in Section 10.11.

The Characteristics of Chemical Equilibrium

To explore the important characteristics of chemical equilibrium, we will consider the synthesis of ammonia from elemental nitrogen and hydrogen:

$$N_2(g) + 3H_2(g) \rightleftharpoons 2NH_3(g)$$

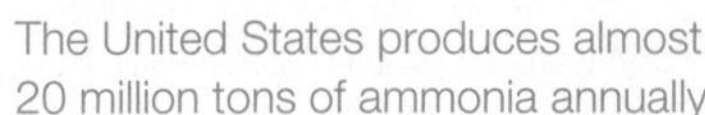

The United States produces almost 20 million tons of ammonia annually.

This process (called the Haber process) is of great commercial value because ammonia is an important fertilizer for the growth of corn and other crops. Ironically, this beneficial process was discovered in Germany just before World War I in a search for ways to produce nitrogen-based explosives. In the course of this work, German chemist Fritz Haber (1868–1934) pioneered the large-scale production of ammonia.

When gaseous nitrogen, hydrogen, and ammonia are mixed in a closed vessel at 25°C, no apparent change in the concentrations occurs over time, regardless of the original amounts of the gases. It would seem that equilibrium has been attained. However, this is not necessarily true.

There are two possible reasons why the concentrations of the reactants and products of a given chemical reaction remain unchanged when mixed:

1. The system is at chemical equilibrium.
2. The forward and reverse reactions are so slow that the system moves toward equilibrium at an undetectable rate.

The second reason applies to the nitrogen, hydrogen, and ammonia mixture at 25°C. Because the molecules involved have strong chemical bonds, mixtures of N_2, H_2, and NH_3 at 25°C can exist with no apparent change over long periods of time. However, under appropriate conditions the system does reach equilibrium, as shown in Fig. 6.5. Note that because of the reaction stoichiometry, H_2 disappears three times as fast as N_2 does, and NH_3 forms twice as fast as N_2 disappears.

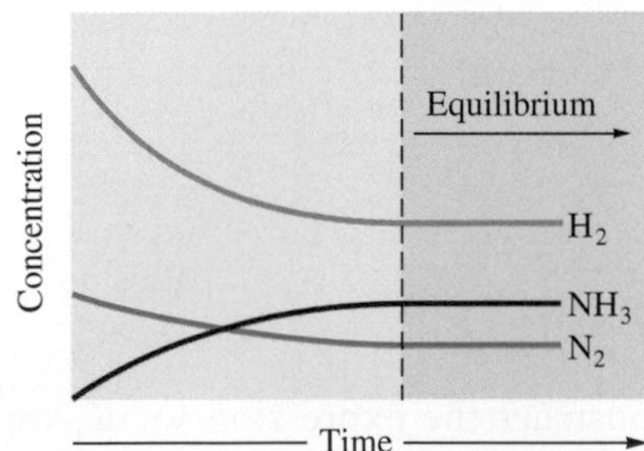

Figure 6.5
A concentration profile for the reaction $N_2(g) + 3H_2(g) \rightleftharpoons 2NH_3(g)$ when only $N_2(g)$ and $H_2(g)$ are mixed initially.

6.2 The Equilibrium Constant

Science is fundamentally empirical—it is based on experiment. The development of the equilibrium concept is typical. From observations of many chemical reactions, two Norwegian chemists, Cato Maximilian Guldberg (1836–1902) and Peter Waage (1833–1900), proposed the **law of mass action** in 1864 as a general description of the equilibrium condition. For a reaction of the type

The law of mass action is based on experimental observations.

$$jA + kB \rightleftharpoons lC + mD$$

where A, B, C, and D represent chemical species and j, k, l, and m are their coefficients in the balanced equation, the law of mass action is represented by the following **equilibrium expression:**

$$K = \frac{[C]^l[D]^m}{[A]^j[B]^k}$$

The square brackets indicate the concentrations of the chemical species *at equilibrium,* and K is a constant called the **equilibrium constant.**

Guldberg and Waage found that the equilibrium concentrations for every reaction system that they studied obeyed this relationship. That is, when the observed equilibrium concentrations are inserted into the equilibrium expression constructed from the law of mass action for a given reaction, the result is a constant (at a given temperature and assuming ideal behavior). Thus the value of the equilibrium constant for a given reaction system can be calculated from the measured concentrations of reactants and products present at equilibrium, a procedure illustrated in Example 6.1.

The K's used in this section might best be called K^{observed} since they are calculated from "observed" concentrations that are not corrected for the effects of nonideality. Only K^{obs} values have units.

OWL INTERACTIVE EXAMPLE 6.1

The following equilibrium concentrations were observed for the Haber process at 127°C:

$$[NH_3] = 3.1 \times 10^{-2} \text{ mol/L}$$
$$[N_2] = 8.5 \times 10^{-1} \text{ mol/L}$$
$$[H_2] = 3.1 \times 10^{-3} \text{ mol/L}$$

a. Calculate the value of K at 127°C for this reaction.

b. Calculate the value of the equilibrium constant at 127°C for the reaction

$$2NH_3(g) \rightleftharpoons N_2(g) + 3H_2(g)$$

c. Calculate the value of the equilibrium constant at 127°C for the reaction given by the equation

$$\tfrac{1}{2}N_2(g) + \tfrac{3}{2}H_2(g) \rightleftharpoons NH_3(g)$$

Solution

a. The balanced equation for the Haber process is

$$N_2(g) + 3H_2(g) \rightleftharpoons 2NH_3(g)$$

Thus, using the law of mass action to construct the expression for K, we have

$$K = \frac{[NH_3]^2}{[N_2][H_2]^3} = \frac{(3.1 \times 10^{-2} \text{ mol/L})^2}{(8.5 \times 10^{-1} \text{ mol/L})(3.1 \times 10^{-3} \text{ mol/L})^3}$$
$$= 3.8 \times 10^4 \text{ L}^2/\text{mol}^2$$

b. This reaction is written in the reverse order of the equation given in part a. This leads to the equilibrium expression

$$K' = \frac{[N_2][H_2]^3}{[NH_3]^2}$$

which is the reciprocal of the expression used in part a. So

$$K' = \frac{[N_2][H_2]^3}{[NH_3]^2} = \frac{1}{K} = \frac{1}{3.8 \times 10^4 \text{ L}^2/\text{mol}^2} = 2.6 \times 10^{-5} \text{ mol}^2/\text{L}^2$$

c. We use the law of mass action: $K'' = \dfrac{[NH_3]}{[N_2]^{1/2}[H_2]^{3/2}}$

If we compare this expression with the one obtained in part a, we see that since

$$\frac{[NH_3]}{[N_2]^{1/2}[H_2]^{3/2}} = \left(\frac{[NH_3]^2}{[N_2][H_2]^3}\right)^{1/2}$$

then

$$K'' = K^{1/2}$$

Thus

$$K'' = K^{1/2} = (3.8 \times 10^4 \text{ L}^2/\text{mol}^2)^{1/2} = 1.9 \times 10^2 \text{ L/mol}$$

We can draw some important conclusions from the results of Example 6.1. For a reaction of the form

$$jA + kB \rightleftharpoons lC + mD$$

the equilibrium expression is

$$K = \frac{[C]^l[D]^m}{[A]^j[B]^k}$$

If this reaction is reversed, the new equilibrium expression is

$$K' = \frac{[A]^j[B]^k}{[C]^l[D]^m} = \frac{1}{K}$$

If the original reaction is multiplied by some factor n to give

$$njA + nkB \rightleftharpoons nlC + nmD$$

the equilibrium expression becomes

$$K'' = \frac{[C]^{nl}[D]^{nm}}{[A]^{nj}[B]^{nk}} = K^n$$

Some Characteristics of the Equilibrium Expression

1. The equilibrium expression for a reaction written in reverse is the reciprocal of that for the original reaction.
2. When the balanced equation for a reaction is multiplied by a factor n, the equilibrium expression for the new reaction is the original expression raised to the nth power. Thus $K_{new} = (K_{original})^n$.
3. The apparent units for K are determined by the powers of the various concentration terms. The (apparent) units for K therefore depend on the reaction being considered. We will have more to say about the units for K in Section 6.4.

The K's referred to here are K^{obs} values.

The law of mass action applies to solution and gaseous equilibria.

The law of mass action is widely applicable. It correctly describes the equilibrium behavior of all chemical reaction systems whether they occur in solution or in the gas phase. Although, as we will see later, corrections for nonideal behavior must be applied in certain cases, such as for concentrated aqueous solutions and for gases at high pressures, the law of mass action provides a remarkably accurate description of all types of chemical equilibria. For example, consider again the ammonia synthesis reaction. At 500°C the value of K for this reaction is 6.0×10^{-2} L^2/mol^2. Whenever N_2, H_2, and NH_3 are mixed together at this temperature, the system will always come to an equilibrium position such that

$$\frac{[NH_3]^2}{[N_2][H_2]^3} = 6.0 \times 10^{-2} \text{ L}^2/\text{mol}^2$$

This expression has the same value at 500°C, *regardless of the amounts of the gases that are mixed together initially.*

Danny Eilers/Alamy

Applying anhydrous ammonia to soybean stubble prior to planting corn.

Although the special ratio of products to reactants defined by the equilibrium expression is constant for a given reaction system at a given temperature, the *equilibrium concentrations will not always be the same.* Table 6.1 gives

Table 6.1

Results of Three Experiments for the Reaction $N_2(g) + 3H_2(g) \rightleftharpoons 2NH_3(g)$

Experiment	Initial Concentrations	Equilibrium Concentrations	$K = \frac{[NH_3]^2}{[N_2][H_2]^3}$
I	$[N_2]_0 = 1.000\ M$ $[H_2]_0 = 1.000\ M$ $[NH_3]_0 = 0$	$[N_2] = 0.921\ M$ $[H_2] = 0.763\ M$ $[NH_3] = 0.157\ M$	$K = 6.02 \times 10^{-2}\ L^2/mol^2$
II	$[N_2]_0 = 0$ $[H_2]_0 = 0$ $[NH_3]_0 = 1.000\ M$	$[N_2] = 0.399\ M$ $[H_2] = 1.197\ M$ $[NH_3] = 0.203\ M$	$K = 6.02 \times 10^{-2}\ L^2/mol^2$
III	$[N_2]_0 = 2.00\ M$ $[H_2]_0 = 1.00\ M$ $[NH_3]_0 = 3.00\ M$	$[N_2] = 2.59\ M$ $[H_2] = 2.77\ M$ $[NH_3] = 1.82\ M$	$K = 6.02 \times 10^{-2}\ L^2/mol^2$

three sets of data for the synthesis of ammonia, showing that even though the individual sets of equilibrium concentrations are quite different for the different situations, the *equilibrium constant, which depends on the ratio of the concentrations, remains the same* (within experimental error). Note that subscripts of zero indicate initial concentrations.

Each *set of equilibrium concentrations* is called an **equilibrium position.** It is essential to distinguish between the equilibrium constant and the equilibrium positions for a given reaction system. There is only *one* equilibrium constant for a particular system at a particular temperature, but there are an *infinite* number of equilibrium positions. The specific equilibrium position adopted by a system depends on the initial concentrations, but the equilibrium constant does not.

For a reaction at a given temperature, there are many equilibrium positions but only one value for *K*.

6.3 Equilibrium Expressions Involving Pressures

So far we have been describing equilibria involving gases in terms of concentrations. Equilibria involving gases can also be described in terms of pressures. The relationship between the pressure and the concentration of a gas can be seen from the ideal gas equation:

$$PV = nRT \qquad \text{or} \qquad P = \left(\frac{n}{V}\right)RT = CRT$$

where C equals n/V, or the number of moles of gas n per unit volume V. Thus C represents the *molar concentration of the gas.*

For the ammonia synthesis reaction, the equilibrium expression can be written in terms of concentrations,

$$K = \frac{[NH_3]^2}{[N_2][H_2]^3} = \frac{C_{NH_3}{}^2}{(C_{N_2})(C_{H_2}{}^3)}$$

or in terms of the *equilibrium partial pressures of the gases,*

$$K_p = \frac{P_{NH_3}{}^2}{(P_{N_2})(P_{H_2}{}^3)}$$

K involves concentrations; K_p involves pressures.

In this book K denotes an equilibrium constant in terms of concentrations, and K_p represents an equilibrium constant in terms of partial pressures.

The relationship between K and K_p for a particular reaction follows from the fact that for an ideal gas, $C = P/RT$. For example, for the ammonia synthesis reaction,

$$K = \frac{[NH_3]^2}{[N_2][H_2]^3} = \frac{C_{NH_3}{}^2}{(C_{N_2})(C_{H_2}{}^3)}$$

$$= \frac{\left(\frac{P_{NH_3}}{RT}\right)^2}{\left(\frac{P_{N_2}}{RT}\right)\left(\frac{P_{H_2}}{RT}\right)^3} = \frac{P_{NH_3}{}^2}{(P_{N_2})(P_{H_2}{}^3)} \times \frac{\left(\frac{1}{RT}\right)^2}{\left(\frac{1}{RT}\right)^4}$$

$$= \frac{P_{NH_3}{}^2}{(P_{N_2})(P_{H_2}{}^3)}(RT)^2 = K_p(RT)^2$$

However, for the synthesis of hydrogen fluoride from its elements,

$$H_2(g) + F_2(g) \rightleftharpoons 2HF(g)$$

the relationship between K and K_p is

$$K = \frac{[HF]^2}{[H_2][F_2]} = \frac{C_{HF}{}^2}{(C_{H_2})(C_{F_2})} = \frac{\left(\frac{P_{HF}}{RT}\right)^2}{\left(\frac{P_{H_2}}{RT}\right)\left(\frac{P_{F_2}}{RT}\right)} = \frac{P_{HF}{}^2}{(P_{H_2})(P_{F_2})} = K_p$$

Thus for this reaction K is equal to K_p. This equality occurs because the sum of the coefficients on either side of the balanced equation is identical, so the terms in RT cancel. In the equilibrium expression for the ammonia synthesis reaction, the sum of the powers in the numerator is different from that in the denominator, so K does not equal K_p.

For the general reaction

$$jA + kB \rightleftharpoons lC + mD$$

the relationship between K and K_p is

$$K_p = K(RT)^{\Delta n}$$

where Δn is the sum of the coefficients of the *gaseous* products minus the sum of the coefficients of the *gaseous* reactants. This equation is easy to derive from the definitions of K and K_p and the relationship between pressure and concentration. For the preceding general reaction,

$$K_p = \frac{(P_C{}^l)(P_D{}^m)}{(P_A{}^j)(P_B{}^k)} = \frac{(C_C \times RT)^l(C_D \times RT)^m}{(C_A \times RT)^j(C_B \times RT)^k}$$

$$= \frac{(C_C{}^l)(C_D{}^m)}{(C_A{}^j)(C_B{}^k)} \times \frac{(RT)^{l+m}}{(RT)^{j+k}} = K(RT)^{(l+m)-(j+k)} = K(RT)^{\Delta n}$$

Δn always involves products minus reactants.

where $\Delta n = (l + m) - (j + k)$, the difference in the sums of the coefficients for the gaseous products and reactants.

We have seen that the (apparent) units of the equilibrium constant depend on the specific reaction. For example, for the reaction

$$H_2(g) + F_2(g) \rightleftharpoons 2HF(g)$$

the units for K and K_p can be found as follows:

$$K = \frac{C_{HF}{}^2}{(C_{H_2})(C_{F_2})} = \frac{(\text{mol/L})^2}{(\text{mol/L})(\text{mol/L})} \Rightarrow \text{no units}$$

$$K_p = \frac{P_{HF}{}^2}{(P_{H_2})(P_{F_2})} = \frac{(\text{atm})^2}{(\text{atm})(\text{atm})} \Rightarrow \text{no units}$$

For this reaction, neither K nor K_p has units, and K is equal to K_p. Because there are identical powers in the numerator and denominator, the units cancel. For equilibrium expressions in which the powers in the numerator and denominator are not the same, the equilibrium constants will have (apparent) units and K will not equal K_p.

Note that in the preceding discussion we used the term "apparent units" when referring to equilibrium constants. This term was used because the theoretical foundation for the concept of equilibrium based on thermodynamics includes a *reference state* for each substance, which always causes the units of concentration or pressure to cancel. We will explore this situation thoroughly in Chapter 10, but we will introduce this concept in Section 6.4.

6.4 The Concept of Activity

As we will see in Chapter 10, the "true" equilibrium constant expression does not simply involve the observed equilibrium pressure or the concentration for a substance but involves the *ratio* of the equilibrium pressure (or concentration) for a given substance to a *reference* pressure (or concentration) for that substance. This ratio is defined as the **activity** of the substance, which in terms of pressures is defined as

In 1982, the International Union of Pure and Applied Chemists (IUPAC) set the standard pressure as 1 bar (exactly). Both conventions are now used, although most thermodynamic data are now referenced to 1 bar instead of 1 atm.

$$\text{Activity } (i\text{th component}) = a_i = \frac{P_i}{P_{\text{reference}}}$$

where P_i = partial pressure of the ith gaseous component

$P_{\text{reference}}$ = 1 atm (exactly)

and where ideal behavior is assumed.

Using the concept of activities, the equilibrium expression for the reaction

$$j\text{A}(g) + k\text{B}(g) \rightleftharpoons l\text{C}(g) + m\text{D}(g)$$

is written as

$$K = \frac{(a_C)^l(a_D)^m}{(a_A)^j(a_B)^k} = \frac{\left(\frac{P_C}{P_{ref}}\right)^l\left(\frac{P_D}{P_{ref}}\right)^m}{\left(\frac{P_A}{P_{ref}}\right)^j\left(\frac{P_B}{P_{ref}}\right)^k}$$

With all the pressures expressed in atmospheres, we have

$$K_p = \frac{\left(\frac{P_C\ \cancel{(atm)}}{1\ \cancel{atm}}\right)^l\left(\frac{P_D\ \cancel{(atm)}}{1\ \cancel{atm}}\right)^m}{\left(\frac{P_A\ \cancel{(atm)}}{1\ \cancel{atm}}\right)^j\left(\frac{P_B\ \cancel{(atm)}}{1\ \cancel{atm}}\right)^k} = \frac{P_C{}^l P_D{}^m}{P_A{}^j P_B{}^k}$$

where K_p is unitless as shown.

When the equilibrium composition of a system is expressed in units of moles per liter, the reference state is (exactly) 1 mol/L.

Because of the difference in reference states, in general,

$$K \neq K_p$$

Equilibrium composition expressed in concentration units (K)

Equilibrium composition expressed as pressures (K_p)

The only exception to this principle occurs when the sum of the powers in the numerator and the denominator are the same (as discussed previously for $H_2 + F_2 \rightleftharpoons 2HF$). In such a case $K = K_p$.

Because of the ideas discussed in this section, it is customary to give the values of equilibrium constants without units. This is the practice we will follow in the remainder of the text.

6.5 Heterogeneous Equilibria

So far we have discussed equilibria only for systems in the gas phase, where all reactants and products are gases. These situations represent **homogeneous equilibria.** However, many equilibria involve more than one phase and are called **heterogeneous equilibria.** For example, the thermal decomposition of calcium carbonate in the commercial preparation of lime occurs by a reaction involving both solid and gas phases:

Lime is among the top six chemicals manufactured in the United States in terms of amount produced.

$$CaCO_3(s) \rightleftharpoons \underset{\text{Lime}}{\underset{\uparrow}{CaO(s)}} + CO_2(g)$$

Larry Andre Maslennikov/Peter Arnold/PhotoLibrary

Helicopter liming acidic wetland in Sweden.

Straightforward application of the law of mass action leads to the equilibrium expression

$$K' = \frac{[CO_2][CaO]}{[CaCO_3]}$$

However, experimental results show that the *position of a heterogeneous equilibrium does not depend on the amounts of pure solids or liquids present* (Fig. 6.6). This result makes sense when the meaning of an activity for a pure liquid or solid is understood. For a pure liquid or solid, the reference state is the pure liquid or solid. Thus, for the composition of $CaCO_3$ considered above, we do not insert $[CaCO_3]$ or $[CaO]$ into the equilibrium expression but rather into the activity of each:

$$a_{CaCO_3} = \frac{\overset{\text{Pure solid}}{[CaCO_3]}}{\underset{\text{Pure solid (reference state)}}{[CaCO_3]}} = 1$$

and

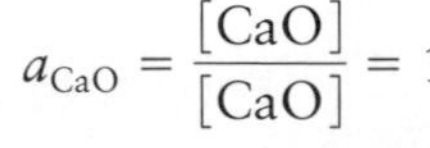

$$a_{CaO} = \frac{[CaO]}{[CaO]} = 1$$

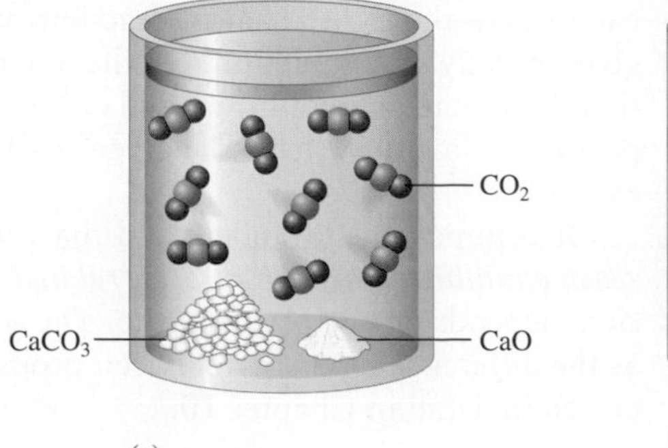

Figure 6.6
The position of the equilibrium $CaCO_3(s) \rightleftharpoons CaO(s) + CO_2(g)$ does not depend on the amounts of $CaCO_3(s)$ and $CaO(s)$ present.

Thus the equilibrium expressions for the decomposition of solid $CaCO_3$ are

$$K = \frac{[CO_2](1)}{1} = [CO_2] \quad \text{and} \quad K_p = \frac{P_{CO_2}(1)}{1} = P_{CO_2}$$

In summary, we can make the following general statement: *The activity of a pure solid or liquid is always 1.*

Note that the net effect of inserting an activity of 1 into the equilibrium expression for each pure solid or liquid in the reaction has the same effect as simply disregarding them. If pure solids or pure liquids are involved in a chemical reaction, their concentrations *are not included in the equilibrium expression* for the reaction. This simplification occurs *only* with pure solids or liquids, not with solutions or gases, because in these last two cases the activity cannot be assumed to be 1.

For example, in the decomposition of liquid water to gaseous hydrogen and oxygen,

$$2H_2O(l) \rightleftharpoons 2H_2(g) + O_2(g)$$

where

$$K = [H_2]^2[O_2] \quad \text{and} \quad K_p = (P_{H_2}{}^2)(P_{O_2})$$

water is not included in either equilibrium expression because it is present as a pure liquid ($a_{H_2O(l)} = 1$). However, if the reaction were carried out under conditions in which the water is a gas rather than a liquid,

$$2H_2O(g) \rightleftharpoons 2H_2(g) + O_2(g)$$

then

$$K = \frac{[H_2]^2[O_2]}{[H_2O]^2} \quad \text{and} \quad K_p = \frac{(P_{H_2}{}^2)(P_{O_2})}{P_{H_2O}{}^2}$$

because the concentration or pressure of water vapor can assume different values, depending on the conditions. That is, we cannot assume an activity of 1 in such an instance.

6.6 Applications of the Equilibrium Constant

Knowing the equilibrium constant for a reaction allows us to predict several important features of the reaction: the tendency of the reaction to occur (but not the speed of the reaction), whether a given set of concentrations represents an equilibrium condition, and the equilibrium position that will be achieved from a given set of initial concentrations.

The Extent of a Reaction

The inherent tendency for a reaction to occur is indicated by the magnitude of the equilibrium constant. A value of K that is much larger than 1 means that at equilibrium the reaction system will consist of mostly products—the equilibrium lies to the right. That is, reactions with very large equilibrium constants go essentially to completion. On the other hand, a very small value of K means that the system at equilibrium will consist of mostly reactants—the equilibrium position is far to the left. The given reaction does not occur to any significant extent.

It is important to understand that *the size of K and the time required to reach equilibrium are not directly related.* The time required to achieve equilibrium depends on the reaction rate. The size of K is determined by factors such as the difference in energy between products and reactants, which will be discussed in detail in Chapter 10.

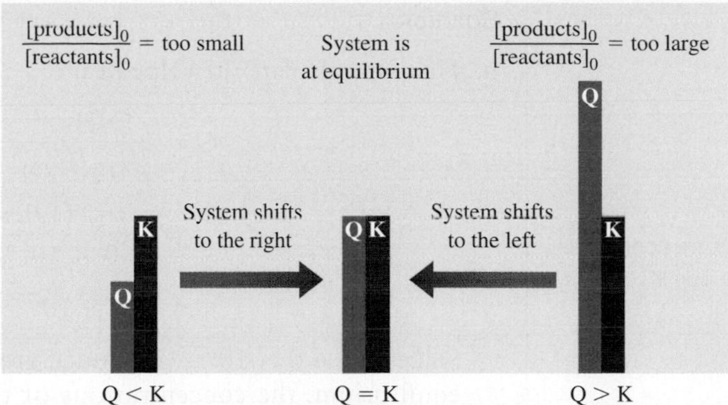

Figure 6.7
Comparing the values of Q and K allows us to determine the direction the system will shift to reach equilibrium.

Reaction Quotient

When the reactants and products of a given chemical reaction are mixed, it is useful to know whether the mixture is at equilibrium and, if it is not, in which direction the system will shift to reach equilibrium. If the concentration of one of the reactants or products is zero, the system will shift in the direction that produces the missing component. However, if all the initial concentrations are not zero, it is more difficult to determine the direction of the move toward equilibrium. To determine the shift in such cases, we use the **reaction quotient,** Q. The reaction quotient is obtained by applying the law of mass action, but using *initial concentrations* instead of equilibrium concentrations. For example, for the synthesis of ammonia,

$$N_2(g) + 3H_2(g) \rightleftharpoons 2NH_3(g)$$

the expression for the reaction quotient is

$$Q = \frac{[NH_3]_0^{\,2}}{[N_2]_0[H_2]_0^{\,3}}$$

where the zero subscripts indicate initial concentrations.

To determine in which direction a system will shift to reach equilibrium, we compare the values of Q and K (Fig. 6.7). There are three possible situations:

1. *Q is equal to K.* The system is at equilibrium; no shift will occur.
2. *Q is greater than K.* In this case the ratio of initial concentrations of products to initial concentrations of reactants is too large. For the system to reach equilibrium, a net change of products to reactants must occur. The system *shifts to the left,* consuming products and forming reactants, until equilibrium is achieved.
3. *Q is less than K.* In this case the ratio of initial concentrations of products to initial concentrations of reactants is too small. The system *must shift to the right,* consuming reactants and forming products, to attain equilibrium.

OWL INTERACTIVE EXAMPLE 6.2

For the synthesis of ammonia at 500°C, the equilibrium constant is 6.0×10^{-2}. Predict the direction in which the system will shift to reach equilibrium in each of the following cases.

a. $[NH_3]_0 = 1.0 \times 10^{-3}\,M$; $[N_2]_0 = 1.0 \times 10^{-5}\,M$; $[H_2]_0 = 2.0 \times 10^{-3}\,M$
b. $[NH_3]_0 = 2.00 \times 10^{-4}\,M$; $[N_2]_0 = 1.50 \times 10^{-5}\,M$; $[H_2]_0 = 3.54 \times 10^{-1}\,M$
c. $[NH_3]_0 = 1.0 \times 10^{-4}\,M$; $[N_2]_0 = 5.0\,M$; $[H_2]_0 = 1.0 \times 10^{-2}\,M$

We will not include units for concentrations that are in the equilibrium expression or reaction quotient.

Solution

a. First we calculate the value of Q:

$$Q = \frac{[NH_3]_0^2}{[N_2]_0[H_2]_0^3}$$

$$= \frac{(1.0 \times 10^{-3})^2}{(1.0 \times 10^{-5})(2.0 \times 10^{-3})^3}$$

$$= 1.3 \times 10^7$$

Since $K = 6.0 \times 10^{-2}$, Q is much greater than K. For the system to attain equilibrium, the concentrations of the products must be decreased and the concentrations of the reactants increased. The system will shift to the left:

$$N_2 + 3H_2 \longleftarrow 2NH_3$$

b. We calculate the value of Q:

$$Q = \frac{[NH_3]_0^2}{[N_2]_0[H_2]_0^3} = \frac{(2.00 \times 10^{-4})^2}{(1.50 \times 10^{-5})(3.54 \times 10^{-1})^3}$$

$$= 6.01 \times 10^{-2}$$

In this case $Q = K$, so the system is at equilibrium. No shift will occur.

c. The value of Q is

$$Q = \frac{[NH_3]_0^2}{[N_2]_0[H_2]_0^3} = \frac{(1.0 \times 10^{-4})^2}{(5.0)(1.0 \times 10^{-2})^3}$$

$$= 2.0 \times 10^{-3}$$

Here Q is less than K, so the system will shift to the right, attaining equilibrium by increasing the concentration of the product and decreasing the concentrations of the reactants:

$$N_2 + 3H_2 \longrightarrow 2NH_3$$

Calculating Equilibrium Pressures and Concentrations

A typical equilibrium problem involves finding the equilibrium concentrations (or pressures) of reactants and products given the value of the equilibrium constant and the initial concentrations (or pressures).

OWL INTERACTIVE EXAMPLE 6.3

Assume that the reaction for the formation of gaseous hydrogen fluoride from hydrogen and fluorine has an equilibrium constant of 1.15×10^2 at a certain temperature. In a particular experiment at this temperature 3.000 moles of each component was added to a 1.500-liter flask. Calculate the equilibrium concentrations of all species.

Solution The balanced equation for the reaction is

$$H_2(g) + F_2(g) \rightleftharpoons 2HF(g)$$

The equilibrium expression is

$$K = 1.15 \times 10^2 = \frac{[HF]^2}{[H_2][F_2]}$$

We first calculate the initial concentrations:

$$[HF]_0 = [H_2]_0 = [F_2]_0 = \frac{3.000 \text{ mol}}{1.500 \text{ L}} = 2.000\ M$$

From the value of Q,

$$Q = \frac{[HF]_0^2}{[H_2]_0[F_2]_0} = \frac{(2.000)^2}{(2.000)(2.000)} = 1.000$$

which is much less than K, we know that the system must shift to the right to reach equilibrium.

What change in the concentrations is necessary? Since the answer to this question is presently unknown, we will define the change needed in terms of x. Let x equal the number of moles per liter of H_2 consumed to reach equilibrium. The stoichiometry of the reaction shows that x mol/L of F_2 will also be consumed and that $2x$ mol/L of HF will be formed:

$$H_2(g) + F_2(g) \longrightarrow 2HF(g)$$

$$x \text{ mol/L} + x \text{ mol/L} \longrightarrow 2x \text{ mol/L}$$

Now the equilibrium concentrations can be expressed in terms of x:

Initial Concentration (mol/L)	Change (mol/L)	Equilibrium Concentration (mol/L)
$[H_2]_0 = 2.000$	$-x$	$[H_2] = 2.000 - x$
$[F_2]_0 = 2.000$	$-x$	$[F_2] = 2.000 - x$
$[HF]_0 = 2.000$	$+2x$	$[HF] = 2.000 + 2x$

These concentrations can be represented in a shorthand table as follows:

This shorthand representation is sometimes called an *ICE table* from the first letters of the labels.

	$H_2(g)$	+	$F_2(g)$	$\rightleftharpoons$	$2HF(g)$
Initial:	2.000		2.000		2.000
Change:	$-x$		$-x$		$+2x$
Equilibrium:	$2.000 - x$		$2.000 - x$		$2.000 + 2x$

To solve for x, we substitute the equilibrium concentrations into the equilibrium expression:

$$K = 1.15 \times 10^2 = \frac{[HF]^2}{[H_2][F_2]} = \frac{(2.000 + 2x)^2}{(2.000 - x)^2}$$

The right side of this equation is a perfect square, so taking the square root of both sides gives

$$\sqrt{1.15 \times 10^2} = \frac{2.000 + 2x}{2.000 - x}$$

which yields $x = 1.528$. The equilibrium concentrations can now be calculated:

$$[H_2] = [F_2] = 2.000\ M - x = 0.472\ M$$

$$[HF] = 2.000\ M + 2x = 5.056\ M$$

Check: Checking these values by substituting them into the equilibrium expression gives

$$\frac{[HF]^2}{[H_2][F_2]} = \frac{(5.056)^2}{(0.472)^2} = 1.15 \times 10^2$$

which agrees with the given value of K.

6.7 Solving Equilibrium Problems

We have already considered most of the strategies needed to solve equilibrium problems. The typical procedure for analyzing a chemical equilibrium problem can be summarized as shown below.

STEPS

Solving Equilibrium Problems

1 Write the balanced equation for the reaction.
2 Write the equilibrium expression using the law of mass action.
3 List the initial concentrations.
4 Calculate Q, and determine the direction of the shift to equilibrium.
5 Define the change needed to reach equilibrium, and define the equilibrium concentrations by applying the change to the initial concentrations.
6 Substitute the equilibrium concentrations into the equilibrium expression, and solve for the unknown.
7 Check your calculated equilibrium concentrations by making sure that they give the correct value of K.

In Example 6.3 we were able to solve for the unknown by taking the square root of both sides of the equation. However, this situation is not very common, so we must now consider a more typical problem. Suppose that for a synthesis of hydrogen fluoride from hydrogen and fluorine, 3.000 moles of H_2 and 6.000 moles of F_2 are mixed in a 3.000-L flask. The equilibrium constant for the synthesis reaction at this temperature is 1.15×10^2. We calculate the equilibrium concentration of each component as follows:

- We begin as usual by writing the balanced equation for the reaction:

$$H_2(g) + F_2(g) \rightleftharpoons 2HF(g)$$

- The equilibrium expression is

$$K = 1.15 \times 10^2 = \frac{[HF]^2}{[H_2][F_2]}$$

- The initial concentrations are

$$[H_2]_0 = \frac{3.000\text{ mol}}{3.000\text{ L}} = 1.000\ M$$

$$[F_2]_0 = \frac{6.000\text{ mol}}{3.000\text{ L}} = 2.000\ M$$

$$[HF]_0 = 0$$

- There is no need to calculate Q; since no HF is initially present, we know that the system must shift to the right to reach equilibrium.
- If we let x represent the number of moles per liter of H_2 consumed to reach equilibrium, we can represent the concentrations as follows:

Initial Concentration (mol/L)	Change (mol/L)	Equilibrium Concentration (mol/L)
$[H_2]_0 = 1.000$	$-x$	$[H_2] = 1.000 - x$
$[F_2]_0 = 2.000$	$-x$	$[F_2] = 2.000 - x$
$[HF]_0 = 0$	$+2x$	$[HF] = 0 + 2x$

Or in shorthand form:

	$H_2(g)$	+	$F_2(g)$	$\rightleftharpoons$	$2HF(g)$
Initial:	1.000		2.000		0
Change:	$-x$		$-x$		$+2x$
Equilibrium:	$1.000 - x$		$2.000 - x$		$2x$

- Substituting the equilibrium concentrations into the equilibrium expression gives

$$K = 1.15 \times 10^2 = \frac{[HF]^2}{[H_2][F_2]} = \frac{(2x)^2}{(1.000 - x)(2.000 - x)}$$

To solve for x, we perform the indicated multiplication,

$$(1.000 - x)(2.000 - x)(1.15 \times 10^2) = (2x)^2$$

to give

$$(1.15 \times 10^2)x^2 - 3.000(1.15 \times 10^2)x + 2.000(1.15 \times 10^2) = 4x^2$$

and collect terms,

$$(1.11 \times 10^2)x^2 - (3.45 \times 10^2)x + 2.30 \times 10^2 = 0$$

This expression is a quadratic equation of the general form

$$ax^2 + bx + c = 0$$

where the roots can be obtained from the quadratic formula:

$$x = \frac{-b \pm \sqrt{b^2 - 4ac}}{2a}$$

In this example $a = 1.11 \times 10^2$, $b = -3.45 \times 10^2$, and $c = 2.30 \times 10^2$. Substituting these values into the quadratic formula gives two values for x:

$$x = 2.14 \text{ mol/L} \quad \text{and} \quad x = 0.968 \text{ mol/L}$$

Both of these results cannot be valid (because a *given* set of initial concentrations leads to only *one* equilibrium position). How can we choose between them? Since the expression for the equilibrium concentration of H_2 is

$$[H_2] = 1.000\ M - x$$

the value of x cannot be 2.14 mol/L (because subtracting 2.14 M from 1.000 M gives a negative concentration for H_2, which is physically impossible). Thus the correct value for x is 0.968 mol/L, and the equilibrium concentrations are as follows:

$$[H_2] = 1.000\ M - 0.968\ M = 3.2 \times 10^{-2}\ M$$

$$[F_2] = 2.000\ M - 0.968\ M = 1.032\ M$$

$$[HF] = 2(0.968\ M) = 1.936\ M$$

- We can check these concentrations by substituting them into the equilibrium expression:

$$\frac{[HF]^2}{[H_2][F_2]} = \frac{(1.936)^2}{(3.2 \times 10^{-2})(1.032)} = 1.13 \times 10^2$$

This value is in close agreement with the given value for K (1.15×10^2), so the calculated equilibrium concentrations are correct.

Note that although we used the quadratic formula to solve for x in this problem, other methods are also available. For example, trial and error is always a possibility. However, use of successive approximations (see Appendix A1.4) is often preferable. For example, in this case successive approximations can be carried out conveniently by starting with the quadratic equation

$$(1.11 \times 10^2)x^2 - (3.45 \times 10^2)x + 2.30 \times 10^2 = 0$$

and dividing it by 1.11×10^2 to give

$$x^2 - 3.11x + 2.07 = 0$$

which can then be rearranged to

$$x^2 = 3.11x - 2.07$$

or

$$x = \sqrt{3.11x - 2.07}$$

Now we can proceed by guessing a value of x, which is then inserted into the square root expression. Next, we calculate a "new" value of x from the expression

$$x = \sqrt{3.11x - 2.07}$$

"New" value calculated (↗ x) — Guessed value of x inserted (↖ x under the root)

When the calculated value (the new value) of x agrees with the guessed value, the equation has been solved.

To solve the algebraic equations you encounter when doing chemistry problems, use whatever method is convenient and comfortable for you.

Treating Systems That Have Small Equilibrium Constants

We have seen that fairly complicated calculations are often necessary to solve equilibrium problems. However, under certain conditions we can make simplifications that greatly reduce the mathematical difficulties. For example, consider gaseous NOCl, which decomposes to form the gases NO and Cl_2. At 35°C the equilibrium constant is 1.6×10^{-5} mol/L. In an experiment in which 1.0 mole of NOCl is placed in a 2.0-L flask, what are the equilibrium concentrations?

The balanced equation is

$$2NOCl(g) \rightleftharpoons 2NO(g) + Cl_2(g)$$

and

$$K = \frac{[NO]^2[Cl_2]}{[NOCl]^2} = 1.6 \times 10^{-5}$$

The initial concentrations are

$$[NOCl]_0 = \frac{1.0\text{ mol}}{2.0\text{ L}} = 0.50\ M, \qquad [NO]_0 = 0, \qquad \text{and} \qquad [Cl_2]_0 = 0$$

Since there are no products initially, the system will move to the right to reach equilibrium. We will define x as the change in concentration of Cl_2 needed to reach equilibrium. The changes in the concentrations of NOCl and NO can then be obtained from the balanced equation:

$$2NOCl(g) \longrightarrow 2NO(g) + Cl_2(g)$$

$$2x \longrightarrow 2x + x$$

The concentrations can be summarized as follows:

Initial Concentration (mol/L)	Change (mol/L)	Equilibrium Concentration (mol/L)
$[NOCl]_0 = 0.50$	$-2x$	$[NOCl] = 0.50 - 2x$
$[NO]_0 = 0$	$+2x$	$[NO] = 0 + 2x = 2x$
$[Cl_2]_0 = 0$	$+x$	$[Cl_2] = 0 + x = x$

Or in shorthand form:

	$2NOCl(g)$	$\rightleftharpoons$	$2NO(g)$	+	$Cl_2(g)$
Initial:	0.50		0		0
Change:	$-2x$		$+2x$		$+x$
Equilibrium:	$0.50 - 2x$		$2x$		x

The equilibrium concentrations must satisfy the equilibrium expression:

$$K = 1.6 \times 10^{-5} = \frac{[NO]^2[Cl_2]}{[NOCl]^2} = \frac{(2x)^2(x)}{(0.50 - 2x)^2}$$

Multiplying and collecting terms results in an equation that requires complicated methods to solve directly. However, we can avoid this situation by recognizing that since K is so small (1.6×10^{-5} mol/L), the system will not proceed far to the right to reach equilibrium. That is, *x represents a relatively small number*. Consequently, the term $(0.50 - 2x)$ can be approximated by 0.50. That is, when x is small,

$$0.50 - 2x \approx 0.50$$

Approximations can simplify complicated math, but their validity should be carefully checked.

Making this approximation allows us to simplify the equilibrium expression:

$$1.6 \times 10^{-5} = \frac{(2x)^2(x)}{(0.50 - 2x)^2} \approx \frac{(2x)^2(x)}{(0.50)^2} = \frac{4x^3}{(0.50)^2}$$

Solving for x^3 gives

$$x^3 = \frac{(1.6 \times 10^{-5})(0.50)^2}{4} = 1.0 \times 10^{-6}$$

and $x = 1.0 \times 10^{-2}$ mol/L.

Next, we must check the validity of the approximation. If $x = 1.0 \times 10^{-2}$, then

$$0.50 - 2x = 0.50 - 2(1.0 \times 10^{-2}) = 0.48$$

A good way to assess whether a 4% error is acceptable here is to examine the precision of the data given. For example, note that the value of K is 1.6×10^{-5}, which can be interpreted as $(1.6 \pm 0.1) \times 10^{-5}$. Thus the uncertainty in K is at least 1 part in 16, or about 6%. Therefore, a 4% error in [NOCl] is acceptable.

The difference between 0.50 and 0.48 is 0.02, or 4% of the initial concentration of NOCl, a relatively small discrepancy that will have little effect on the outcome. That is, since $2x$ is very small compared with 0.50, the value of x obtained in the approximate solution should be very close to the exact value. We use this approximate value of x to calculate the equilibrium concentrations:

$$[NOCl] = 0.50 - 2x = 0.48\ M \approx 0.50\ M$$

$$[NO] = 2x = 2(1.0 \times 10^{-2}\ M) = 2.0 \times 10^{-2}\ M$$

$$[Cl_2] = x = 1.0 \times 10^{-2}\ M$$

Check: $\dfrac{[NO]^2[Cl_2]}{[NOCl]^2} = \dfrac{(2.0 \times 10^{-2})^2(1.0 \times 10^{-2})}{(0.50)^2} = 1.6 \times 10^{-5}$

Since the given value of K is 1.6×10^{-5}, these calculated concentrations are correct.

This problem turned out to be relatively easy to solve because the *small value of K and the resulting small shift to the right to reach equilibrium allowed simplification.*

6.8 Le Châtelier's Principle

It is important to understand the factors that control the *position* of a chemical equilibrium. For example, when a chemical is manufactured, the chemists and chemical engineers in charge of production want to choose conditions that favor the desired product as much as possible. In other words, they want the equilibrium to lie far to the right. When Fritz Haber was developing the process for the synthesis of ammonia, he did extensive studies on how the temperature and pressure affect the equilibrium concentration of ammonia. Some of his results are given in Table 6.2. Note that the amount of NH_3 at equilibrium increases with an increase in pressure but decreases with an increase in temperature. Thus the amount of NH_3 present at equilibrium is favored by conditions of low temperature and high pressure.

However, this is not the whole story. Carrying out the process at low temperatures is not feasible because then the reaction is too slow. Even though the equilibrium tends to shift to the right as the temperature is lowered, the attainment of equilibrium is much too slow at low temperatures to be practical. This observation emphasizes once again that we must study both the thermodynamics (Chapter 10) and the kinetics (Chapter 15) of a reaction before we really understand the factors that control it.

We can qualitatively predict the effects of changes in concentration, pressure, and temperature on a system at equilibrium by using **Le Châtelier's principle,** which states that *if a change in conditions (a "stress") is imposed on a system at equilibrium, the equilibrium position will shift in a direction that tends to reduce that change in conditions.* Although this rule, put forth by Henri Le Châtelier in 1884, sometimes oversimplifies the situation, it works remarkably well.

Science Photo Library/Photo Researchers

Henri Louis Le Châtelier (1850–1936), the French physical chemist and metallurgist, seen here while a student at the École Polytechnique.

The Effect of a Change in Concentration

To see how we can predict the effects of a change in concentration on a system at equilibrium, we will consider the ammonia synthesis reaction. Suppose there is an equilibrium position described by these concentrations:

$$[N_2] = 0.399\ M, \qquad [H_2] = 1.197\ M, \qquad \text{and} \qquad [NH_3] = 0.202\ M$$

Table 6.2

Percent by Mass of NH_3 at Equilibrium in a Mixture of N_2, H_2, and NH_3 as a Function of Temperature and Total Pressure*

	Total Pressure		
Temperature (°C)	300 atm	400 atm	500 atm
400	48% NH_3	55% NH_3	61% NH_3
500	26% NH_3	32% NH_3	38% NH_3
600	13% NH_3	17% NH_3	21% NH_3

*Each experiment was begun with a 3:1 mixture of H_2 and N_2.

What will happen if 1.000 mole per liter of N_2 is suddenly injected into the system at constant volume? We can answer this question by calculating the value of Q. The concentrations before the system adjusts are

$$[N_2]_0 = 0.399\ M + \underset{\text{Added } N_2}{\underset{\uparrow}{1.000\ M}} = 1.399\ M$$

$$[H_2]_0 = 1.197\ M$$

$$[NH_3]_0 = 0.202\ M$$

Note that we label these as "initial concentrations" because the system is no longer at equilibrium. Then

$$Q = \frac{[NH_3]_0^{\,2}}{[N_2]_0[H_2]_0^{\,3}} = \frac{(0.202)^2}{(1.399)(1.197)^3} = 1.70 \times 10^{-2}$$

Since we are not given the value of K, we must calculate it from the first set of equilibrium concentrations:

$$K = \frac{[NH_3]^2}{[N_2][H_2]^3} = \frac{(0.202)^2}{(0.399)(1.197)^3} = 5.96 \times 10^{-2}$$

Blue anhydrous cobalt(II) chloride and pink hydrated cobalt(II) chloride. Since the reaction $CoCl_2(s) + 6H_2O(g) \longrightarrow CoCl_2 \cdot 6H_2O(s)$ is shifted to the right by water vapor, $CoCl_2$ is often used in novelty devices to detect humidity.

As we might have expected, because the concentration of N_2 was increased, Q is less than K. The system will shift to the right to arrive at the new equilibrium position. Rather than do the calculations, we simply summarize the results:

Equilibrium Position I		Equilibrium Position II
$[N_2] = 0.399\ M$ $[H_2] = 1.197\ M$ $[NH_3] = 0.202\ M$	$\xrightarrow[\text{of } N_2 \text{ added}]{1.000\ \text{mol/L}}$	$[N_2] = 1.348\ M$ $[H_2] = 1.044\ M$ $[NH_3] = 0.304\ M$

These data reveal that the equilibrium position does in fact shift to the right: The concentration of H_2 decreases; the concentration of NH_3 increases; and, of course, since nitrogen is added, the concentration of N_2 shows an increase relative to the amount present at the original equilibrium position. (However, note that the nitrogen decreased from the amount present immediately after addition of the 1.000 mole of N_2 because the reaction shifted to the right.)

We can predict this shift qualitatively by using Le Châtelier's principle. Since the stress imposed is the addition of nitrogen, Le Châtelier's principle predicts that the system will shift in a direction that consumes nitrogen. This reduces the effect of the addition. Thus Le Châtelier's principle correctly predicts that adding nitrogen causes the equilibrium to shift to the right (Fig. 6.8).

The system shifts in the direction that compensates for the imposed change in conditions.

If ammonia had been added instead of nitrogen, the system would have shifted to the left to consume ammonia. So we can paraphrase Le Châtelier's principle for this case as follows: *If a gaseous reactant or product is added to a system at equilibrium, the system will shift away from the added component. If a gaseous reactant or product is removed, the system will shift toward the removed component.*

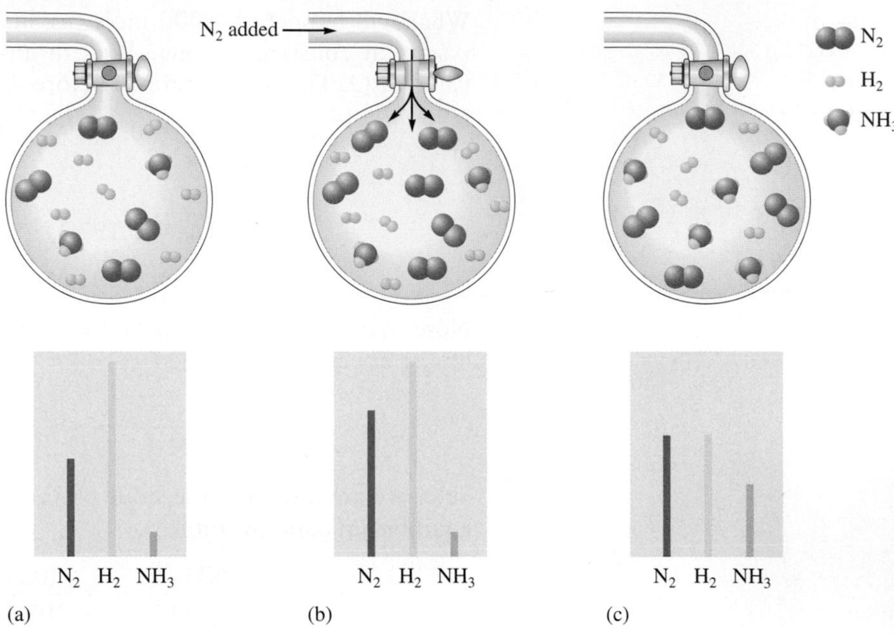

Figure 6.8
(a) The initial equilibrium mixture of N_2, H_2, and NH_3. (b) Addition of N_2. (c) The new equilibrium position for the system containing more N_2 (due to addition of N_2), less H_2, and more NH_3 than the mixture in (a).

OWL INTERACTIVE EXAMPLE 6.4

Arsenic can be extracted from its ores by first reacting the ore with oxygen (a process called *roasting*) to form solid As_4O_6, which is then reduced with carbon:

$$As_4O_6(s) + 6C(s) \rightleftharpoons As_4(g) + 6CO(g)$$

Predict the direction of the shift of the equilibrium position for this reaction in response to each of the following changes in conditions.

a. Addition of CO

b. Addition or removal of C or As_4O_6

c. Removal of As_4

Solution

a. Le Châtelier's principle predicts that the shift will be away from the substance whose concentration is increased. The equilibrium position will shift to the left when CO is added.

b. Since the amount of a pure solid has no effect on the equilibrium position, changing the amount of C or As_4O_6 will have no effect.

c. If gaseous As_4 is removed, the equilibrium position will shift to the right to form more products. In industrial processes the desired product is often continuously removed from the reaction system to increase the yield.

The Effect of a Change in Pressure

Basically, there are three ways to change the pressure of a reaction system involving gaseous components at a given temperature:

1. Add or remove a gaseous reactant or product at constant volume.
2. Add an inert gas (one not involved in the reaction) at constant volume.
3. Change the volume of the container.

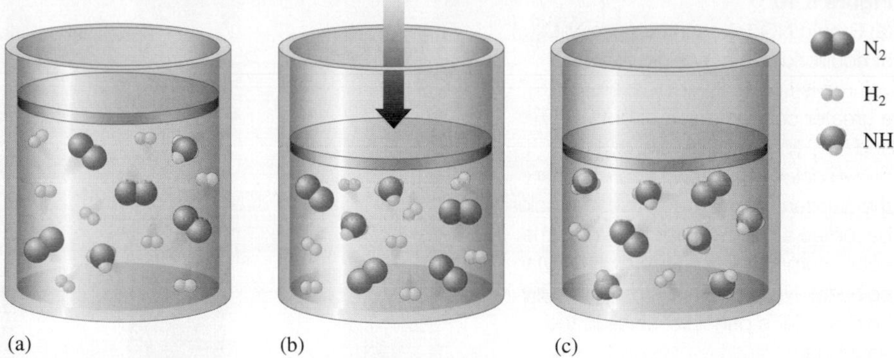

Figure 6.9
(a) A mixture of $NH_3(g)$, $N_2(g)$, and $H_2(g)$ at equilibrium. (b) The volume is suddenly decreased. (c) The new equilibrium position for the system containing more NH_3, less N_2, and less H_2. The reaction $N_2(g) + 3H_2(g) \rightleftharpoons 2NH_3(g)$ shifts to the right (toward the side with fewer molecules) when the container volume is decreased.

We have already considered the addition or removal of a reactant or product. When an inert gas is added at constant volume, there is no effect on the equilibrium position. *The addition of an inert gas increases the total pressure but has no effect on the concentrations or partial pressures of the reactants or products (assuming ideal gas behavior).* Thus the system remains at the original equilibrium position.

When the volume of the container is changed, the concentrations (and thus the partial pressures) of both reactants and products are changed. We could calculate Q and predict the direction of the shift. However, for systems involving gaseous components, there is an easier way: We focus on the volume. The central idea is that *when the volume of the container holding a gaseous system is reduced, the system responds by reducing its own volume. This is done by decreasing the total number of gaseous molecules in the system.*

To see how this works, we can rearrange the ideal gas law to give

$$V = \left(\frac{RT}{P}\right)n$$

or at constant T and P

$$V \propto n$$

That is, at constant temperature and pressure, the volume of a gas is directly proportional to the number of moles of gas present.

Suppose we have a mixture of gaseous nitrogen, hydrogen, and ammonia at equilibrium (Fig. 6.9). If we suddenly reduce the volume, what will happen to the equilibrium position? The reaction system can reduce its volume by reducing the number of molecules present. Consequently, the reaction

$$N_2(g) + 3H_2(g) \rightleftharpoons 2NH_3(g)$$

will shift to the right, since in this direction four molecules (one of nitrogen and three of hydrogen) react to produce two molecules (of ammonia), thus *reducing the total number of gaseous molecules present.* The new equilibrium position will be further to the right than the original one. That is, the equilibrium position will shift toward the side of the reaction involving the smaller number of gaseous molecules in the balanced equation. This phenomenon is illustrated in Fig. 6.10.

The opposite is also true. When the container volume is increased, the system will shift in the direction that increases its volume. An increase in volume in the ammonia synthesis system will produce a shift to the left to increase the total number of gaseous molecules present.

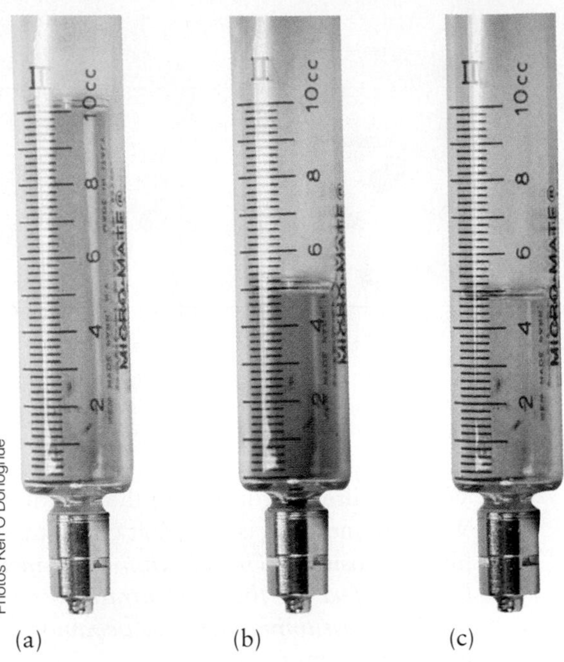

Figure 6.10
(a) Brown $NO_2(g)$ and colorless $N_2O_4(g)$ at equilibrium in a syringe. (b) The volume is suddenly decreased, giving a greater concentration of both N_2O_4 and NO_2 (indicated by the darker brown color). (c) A few seconds after the sudden volume decrease, the color becomes a much lighter brown as the equilibrium shifts from brown $NO_2(g)$ to colorless $N_2O_4(g)$. This is predicted by Le Châtelier's principle, since in the equilibrium

$$2NO_2(g) \rightleftharpoons N_2O_4(g)$$

the product side has the smaller number of molecules.

OWL INTERACTIVE EXAMPLE 6.5

Predict the shift in equilibrium position that will occur for each of the following processes when the volume is reduced.

a. The preparation of liquid phosphorus trichloride:

$$P_4(s) + 6Cl_2(g) \rightleftharpoons 4PCl_3(l)$$

b. The preparation of gaseous phosphorus pentachloride:

$$PCl_3(g) + Cl_2(g) \rightleftharpoons PCl_5(g)$$

c. The reaction of phosphorus trichloride with ammonia:

$$PCl_3(g) + 3NH_3(g) \rightleftharpoons P(NH_2)_3(g) + 3HCl(g)$$

Solution

a. Since P_4 and PCl_3 are a pure solid and a pure liquid, respectively, we need to consider only the effect of the decrease in volume on Cl_2. The position of the equilibrium will shift to the right, since the reactant side contains six gaseous molecules and the product side has none.

b. Decreasing the volume will shift the given reaction to the right, since the product side contains only one gaseous molecule and the reactant side has two.

c. Both sides of the balanced reaction equation have four gaseous molecules. A change in volume will have no effect on the equilibrium position. There is no shift in this case.

The Effect of a Change in Temperature

It is important to recognize that although the changes we have just discussed may alter the equilibrium *position,* they do not alter the equilibrium *constant* (assuming ideal behavior). For example, the addition of a reactant shifts the equilibrium position to the right but has no effect on the value of the equilib-

Table 6.3

Observed Value of K for the Ammonia Synthesis Reaction as a Function of Temperature*

Temperature (K)	K
500	90
600	3
700	0.3
800	0.04

*For this exothermic reaction, the value of K decreases as the temperature increases, as predicted by Le Châtelier's principle.

rium constant; the new equilibrium concentrations satisfy the original equilibrium constant.

The effect of temperature on equilibrium is different, however, because *the value of K changes with temperature.* We can use Le Châtelier's principle to predict the direction of the change.

The synthesis of ammonia from nitrogen and hydrogen releases energy (is *exothermic*). We can represent this situation by treating energy as a product:

$$N_2(g) + 3H_2(g) \rightleftharpoons 2NH_3(g) + \text{energy}$$

If energy in the form of heat is added to this system at equilibrium, Le Châtelier's principle predicts that the shift will be in the direction that consumes energy, in this case to the left. Note that this shift decreases the concentration of NH_3 and increases the concentrations of N_2 and H_2, thus *decreasing the value of K*. The experimentally observed change in K with temperature for this reaction is indicated in Table 6.3. The value of K decreases with increased temperature, as predicted.

On the other hand, for a reaction that consumes energy (an *endothermic* reaction), such as the decomposition of calcium carbonate,

$$\text{Energy} + CaCO_3(s) \rightleftharpoons CaO(s) + CO_2(g)$$

an increase in temperature will cause the equilibrium to shift to the right and the value of K to increase.

In summary, to use Le Châtelier's principle to describe the effect of a temperature change on a system at equilibrium, treat energy as a reactant (in an endothermic process) or as a product (in an exothermic process), and predict the direction of the shift as if an actual reactant or product is added or removed. Although Le Châtelier's principle cannot predict the size of the change in K, it can correctly predict the direction of the change.

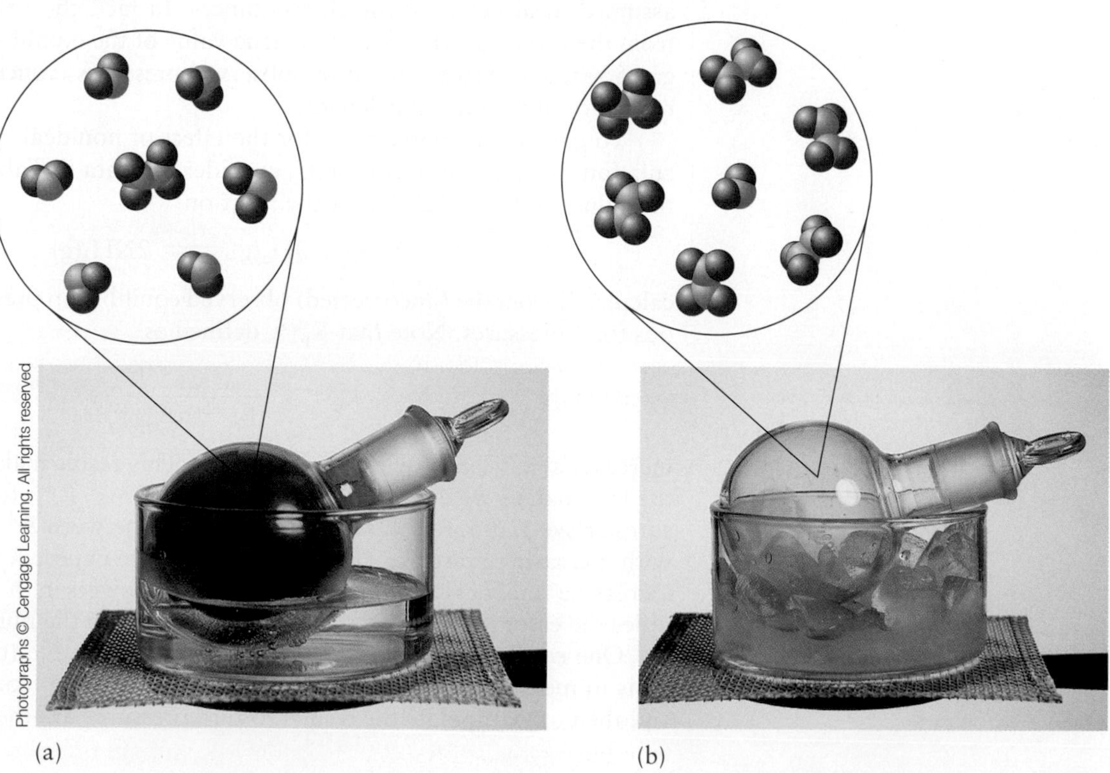

Shifting the $N_2O_4(g) \longrightarrow 2NO_2(g)$ equilibrium by changing the temperature. (a) At 100°C the flask is definitely reddish brown due to a large amount of NO_2 present. (b) At 0°C the equilibrium is shifted toward colorless $N_2O_4(g)$.

Table 6.4

Shifts in the Equilibrium Position for the Reaction $N_2O_4(g) \rightleftharpoons 2NO_2(g)$

Change	Shift
Addition of $N_2O_4(g)$	Right
Addition of $NO_2(g)$	Left
Removal of $N_2O_4(g)$	Left
Removal of $NO_2(g)$	Right
Addition of He(g)	None
Decrease in container volume	Left
Increase in container volume	Right
Increase in temperature	Right
Decrease in temperature	Left

We have seen how Le Châtelier's principle can be used to predict the effect of several types of changes on a system at equilibrium. As a summary of these ideas, Table 6.4 shows how various changes affect the equilibrium position of the endothermic reaction

$$N_2O_4(g) \rightleftharpoons 2NO_2(g)$$

6.9 Equilibria Involving Real Gases

Up to this point in our discussion of the equilibrium phenomenon, we have assumed ideal behavior for all substances. In fact, the value of K calculated from the law of mass action is the true value of the equilibrium constant for a given reaction system only if the observed pressures (concentrations) are corrected for any nonideal behavior.

To gain some appreciation for the effect of nonideal behavior on the calculation of equilibrium constants, consider the data in Table 6.5, which show the values of K_p (at 723 K) for the reaction

$$N_2(g) + 3H_2(g) \rightleftharpoons 2NH_3(g)$$

calculated from the (uncorrected) observed equilibrium pressures (P^{obs}) at various total pressures. Note that K_p^{obs}, defined as

$$K_p^{obs} = \frac{(P_{NH_3}^{obs})^2}{(P_{N_2}^{obs})(P_{H_2}^{obs})^3}$$

increases significantly with total pressure. This result makes sense in view of the fact that, as we discussed in Section 5.10, $P^{obs} < P^{ideal}$ for a real gas at pressures above 1 atm. Recall that the discrepancy between P^{obs} and P^{ideal} increases with increasing pressure. Thus, for this case, we expect K_p^{obs} to increase with increasing total pressure because the excess of powers in the denominator magnifies the error in pressures there as compared with the numerator.

One common method for finding the limiting value (the "true" value) of K_p is to measure K_p at various values of total pressure (constant temperature) and then to extrapolate the results to zero pressure. Another way to obtain the true value of K_p is to correct the observed equilibrium pressures for any nonideal behavior. For example, we might represent the activity of the ith gaseous component as

$$a_i = \frac{\gamma_i P_i^{obs}}{P_{ref}}$$

where γ_i is called the activity coefficient for correcting P_i^{obs} to the ideal value. Obtaining the values of the activity coefficients is a complex process, which will not be treated here.

In general, for equilibrium pressures of 1 atm or less, the value of K_p calculated from the observed equilibrium pressures is expected to be within about 1% of the true value. However, at high pressures the deviations can be quite severe, as illustrated by the data in Table 6.5.

Table 6.5

Values of K_p^{obs} at 723 K for the Reaction $N_2(g) + 3H_2(g) \rightleftharpoons 2NH_3(g)$ as a Function of Total Pressure (at equilibrium)

Total Pressure (atm)	K_p^{obs}
10	4.4×10^{-5}
50	4.6×10^{-5}
100	5.2×10^{-5}
300	7.7×10^{-5}
600	1.7×10^{-4}
1000	5.3×10^{-4}

Key Terms

chemical equilibrium

Section 6.1
law of mass action
equilibrium expression
equilibrium constant
equilibrium position

Section 6.4
activity

Section 6.5
homogeneous equilibria
heterogeneous equilibria

Section 6.6
reaction quotient, Q

Section 6.8
LeChâtelier's principle

For Review

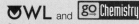

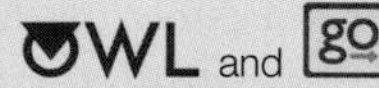

Chemical equilibrium

- When a reaction takes place in a closed system, it reaches a condition where the concentrations of the reactants and products remain constant over time
- Dynamic state: reactants and products are interconverted continually
  - Forward rate = reverse rate
- The law of mass action: for the reaction

$$\text{jA} + \text{kB} \rightleftharpoons \text{mC} + \text{nD}$$

$$K = \frac{[C]^m[D]^n}{[A]^j[B]^k} = \text{equilibrium constant}$$

- A pure liquid or solid is never included in the equilibrium expression
- For a gas-phase reaction the reactants and products can be described in terms of their partial pressures and the equilibrium constant called K_p:

$$K_p = K(RT)^{\Delta n}$$

where Δn is the sum of the coefficients of the gaseous products minus the sum of the coefficients of the gaseous reactants.

Activity

- An equilibrium constant expression involves the ratio of the equilibrium concentration (pressure) to a reference concentration (pressure) for that substance
  - Equilibrium constants are therefore unitless

Equilibrium position

- A set of reactant and product concentrations that satisfies the equilibrium constant expression
  - There is one value of K for a given system at a given temperature
  - There are an infinite number of equilibrium positions at a given temperature depending on the initial concentrations
- A small value of K means the equilibrium lies to the left; a large value of K means the equilibrium lies to the right.
  - The magnitude of K has no relationship to the speed at which equilibrium is achieved
- Q, the reaction quotient, applies the law of mass action to initial concentrations rather than equilibrium concentrations
  - If $Q > K$, the system will shift to the left to achieve equilibrium.
  - If $Q < K$, the system will shift to the right to achieve equilibrium.
- Finding the concentrations that characterize a given equilibrium position:
  - Start with the given initial concentrations (pressures)
  - Define the change needed to reach equilibrium
  - Apply the change to the initial concentrations (pressures) and solve for the equilibrium concentrations (pressures)

LeChâtelier's principle

- Enables qualitative prediction of the effects of changes in concentration, pressure, and temperature on a system at equilibrium
- If a change in conditions is imposed on a system at equilibrium, the system will shift in a direction that compensates for the imposed change

Discussion Questions

These questions are designed to be considered by groups of students in class. Often these questions work well for introducing a particular topic in class.

1. Consider an equilibrium mixture of four chemicals (A, B, C, and D, all gases) reacting in a closed flask according to the equation

$$A + B \rightleftharpoons C + D$$

   a. You add more A to the flask. How does the concentration of each chemical compare with its original concentration after equilibrium is reestablished? Justify your answer.
   b. You have the original setup at equilibrium, and add more D to the flask. How does the concentration of each chemical compare with its original concentration after equilibrium is reestablished? Justify your answer.

2. The boxes shown below represent a set of initial conditions for the reaction:

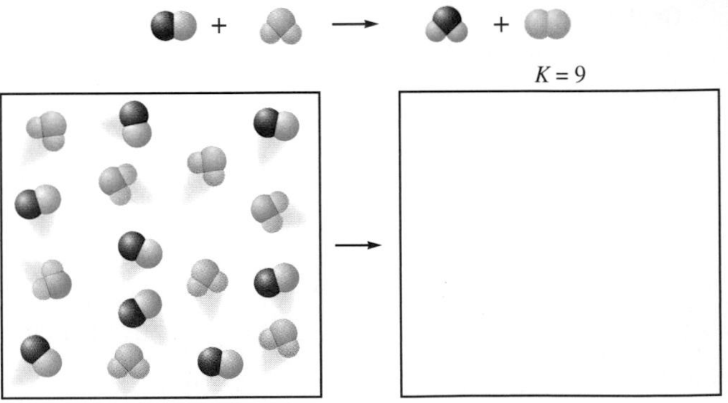

Draw a quantitative molecular picture that shows what this system looks like after the reactants are mixed in one of the boxes and the system reaches equilibrium. Support your answer with calculations.

3. For the reaction $H_2(g) + I_2(g) \rightleftharpoons 2HI(g)$, consider two possibilities using the same-sized, rigid container: (a) you add 0.5 mole of each reactant, allow the system to come

to equilibrium, then add another mole of H_2, and allow the system to reach equilibrium again, or (b) you add 1.5 moles of H_2 and 0.5 mole of I_2 and allow the system to come to equilibrium. Will the final equilibrium mixture be different for the two procedures? Explain.

4. Given the reaction $A(g) + B(g) \rightleftharpoons C(g) + D(g)$, consider the following situations:
   i. You have 1.3 *M* A and 0.8 *M* B initially.
   ii. You have 1.3 *M* A, 0.8 *M* B, and 0.2 *M* C initially.
   iii. You have 2.0 *M* A and 0.8 *M* B initially.

   After equilibrium has been reached, order i–iii in terms of increasing equilibrium concentrations of D. Explain your sequence. Then give the order in terms of increasing equilibrium concentration of B and explain.

5. Consider the reaction $A(g) + 2B(g) \rightleftharpoons C(g) + D(g)$ in a 1.0-L rigid flask. Answer the following questions for each situation (a–d):
   i. Estimate a range (as small as possible) for the requested substance. For example, [A] could be between 95 *M* and 100 *M*.
   ii. Explain how you decided on the limits for the estimated range.
   iii. Indicate what other information would enable you to narrow your estimated range.
   iv. Compare the estimated concentrations for a through d, and explain any differences.

   a. If at equilibrium [A] = 1 *M*, and then 1 mole of C is added, estimate the value for [A] once equilibrium is reestablished.
   b. If at equilibrium [B] = 1 *M*, and then 1 mole of C is added, estimate the value for [B] once equilibrium is reestablished.
   c. If at equilibrium [C] = 1 *M*, and then 1 mole of C is added, estimate the value for [C] once equilibrium is reestablished.
   d. If at equilibrium [D] = 1 *M*, and then 1 mole of C is added, estimate the value for [D] once equilibrium is reestablished.

6. Consider the reaction $A(g) + B(g) \rightleftharpoons C(g) + D(g)$. A friend asks the following: "I know we have been told that if a mixture of A, B, C, and D is at equilibrium and more of A is added, more C and D will form. But how can more C and D form if we do not add more B?" What do you tell your friend?

7. Consider the following statements: "Consider the reaction $A(g) + B(g) \rightleftharpoons C(g)$, at equilibrium in a 1-L container, with [A] = 2 *M*, [B] = 1 *M*, and [C] = 4 *M*. To this 1-L container you add 3 moles of B. A possible new equilibrium condition is [A] = 1 *M*, [B] = 3 *M*, and [C] = 6 *M* because in both cases $K = 2$." Indicate everything you think is correct in these statements and everything that is incorrect. Correct the incorrect statements, and explain.

8. Le Châtelier's principle is stated (Section 6.8) as "If a gaseous reactant or product is added to a system at equilibrium, the system will shift away from the added component." The system $N_2(g) + 3H_2(g) \rightleftharpoons 2NH_3(g)$ is used as an example in which the addition of nitrogen gas at equilibrium results in a decrease in H_2 concentration and an increase in NH_3 concentration as equilibrium is reestablished. In this experiment the volume is assumed to be constant. On the other hand, if N_2 is added to the reaction system in a container with a piston so that the pressure can be held constant, the concentration of NH_3 could actually *decrease* and the concentration of H_2 would *increase* as equilibrium is reestablished. Explain how this is possible. Also, if you consider this same system at equilibrium, the addition of an inert gas, at constant pressure, *does* affect the equilibrium position. How is the equilibrium position affected? Explain.

9. The value of the equilibrium constant *K* depends on which of the following (there may be more than one answer)?
   a. the initial concentrations of the reactants
   b. the initial concentrations of the products
   c. the temperature of the system
   d. the nature of the reactants and products

   Explain.

Exercises

OWL Interactive versions of these problems may be assigned in OWL.

A blue exercise number indicates that the answer to that exercise appears at the back of this book and a solution appears in the *Solutions Guide*.

Characteristics of Chemical Equilibrium

10. Consider an initial mixture of N_2 and H_2 gases that can be represented as follows.

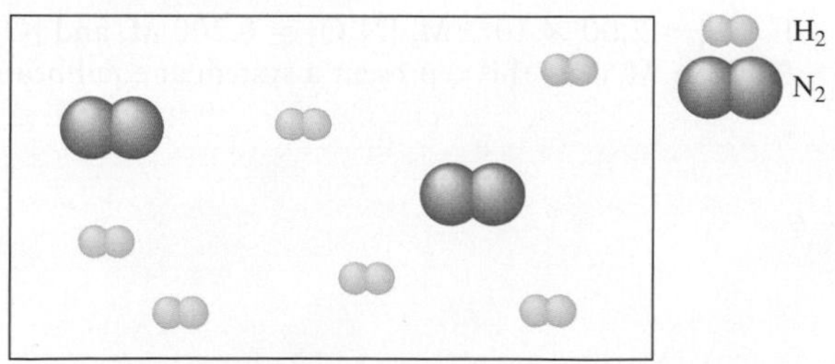

The gases react to form ammonia gas (NH_3) as represented by the following concentration profile.

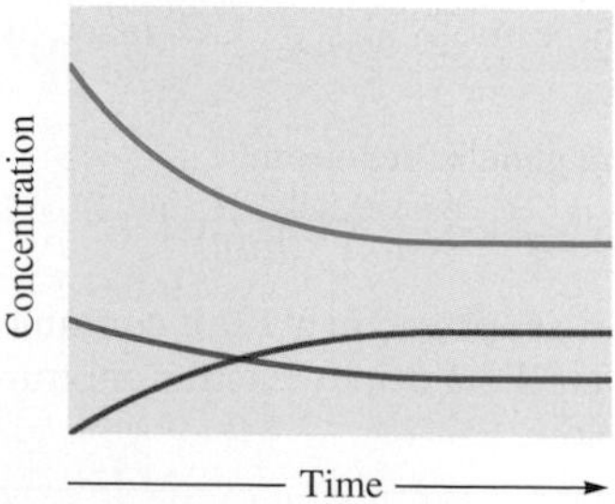

a. Label each plot on the graph as N_2, H_2, or NH_3 and explain your answers.
b. Explain the relative shapes of the plots.
c. When is equilibrium reached? How do you know?

11. Consider the following reactions at some temperature:

$$2NOCl(g) \rightleftharpoons 2NO(g) + Cl_2(g) \qquad K = 1.6 \times 10^{-5}$$

$$2NO(g) \rightleftharpoons N_2(g) + O_2(g) \qquad K = 1 \times 10^{31}$$

For each reaction some quantities of the reactants were placed in separate containers and allowed to come to equilibrium. Describe the relative amounts of reactants and products that are present at equilibrium. At equilibrium, which is faster, the forward or reverse reaction in each case?

12. Consider the following reaction:

$$H_2O(g) + CO(g) \rightleftharpoons H_2(g) + CO_2(g)$$

Amounts of H_2O, CO, H_2, and CO_2 are put into a flask so that the composition corresponds to an equilibrium position. If the CO placed in the flask is labeled with radioactive ^{14}C, will ^{14}C be found only in CO molecules for an indefinite period of time? Why or why not?

13. Consider the same reaction as in Exercise 12. In a particular experiment 1.0 mole of $H_2O(g)$ and 1.0 mole of $CO(g)$ are put into a flask and heated to 350°C. In another experiment 1.0 mole of $H_2(g)$ and 1.0 mole of $CO_2(g)$ are put into a different flask with the same volume as the first. This mixture is also heated to 350°C. After equilibrium is reached, will there be any difference in the composition of the mixtures in the two flasks?

14. Consider the following reaction at some temperature:

$$H_2O(g) + CO(g) \rightleftharpoons H_2(g) + CO_2(g) \qquad K = 2.0$$

Some molecules of H_2O and CO are placed in a 1.0-L container as shown below.

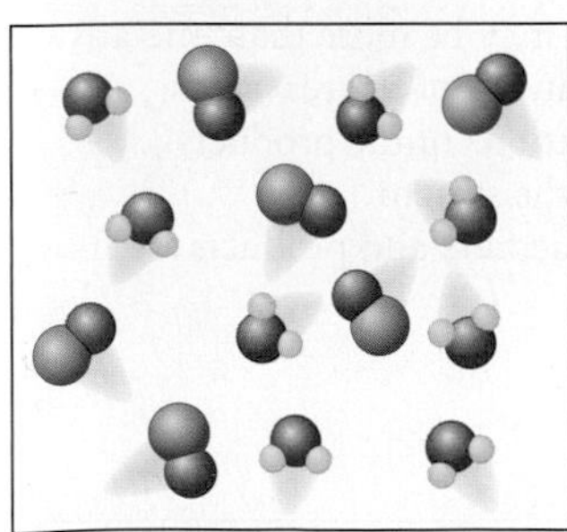

When equilibrium is reached, how many molecules of H_2O, CO, H_2, and CO_2 are present? Do this problem by trial and error—that is, if two molecules of CO react, is this equilibrium; if three molecules of CO react, is this equilibrium; and so on.

15. Consider the following generic reaction:

$$2A_2B(g) \rightleftharpoons 2A_2(g) + B_2(g)$$

Some molecules of A_2B are placed in a 1.0-L container. As time passes, several snapshots of the reaction mixture are taken as illustrated below.

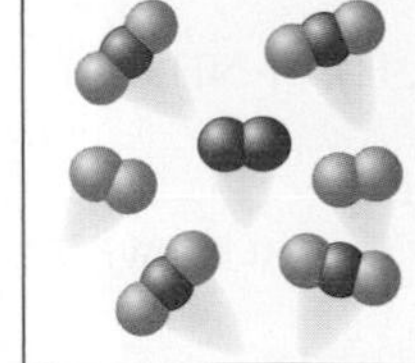

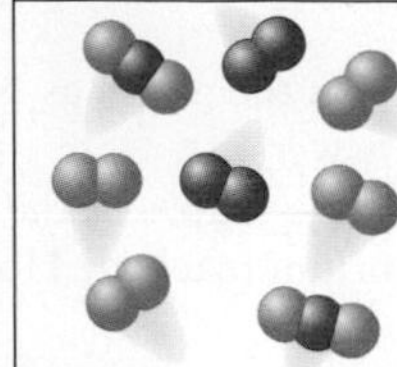

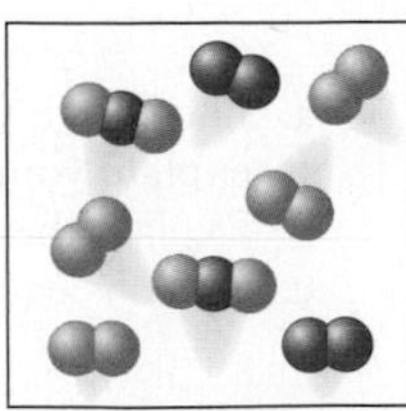

Which illustration is the first to represent an equilibrium mixture? Explain. How many molecules of A_2B were initially placed in the container?

The Equilibrium Constant

16. There is only one value of the equilibrium constant for a particular system at a particular temperature, but there are an infinite number of equilibrium positions. Explain.

17. Explain the difference between K, K_p, and Q.

18. What are homogeneous equilibria? Heterogeneous equilibria? What is the difference in writing K expressions for homogeneous versus heterogeneous reactions? Summarize which species are included in K expressions and which species are not included.

19. Write expressions for K and K_p for the following reactions.
    a. $2NH_3(g) + CO_2(g) \rightleftharpoons N_2CH_4O(s) + H_2O(g)$
    b. $2NBr_3(s) \rightleftharpoons N_2(g) + 3Br_2(g)$
    c. $2KClO_3(s) \rightleftharpoons 2KCl(s) + 3O_2(g)$
    d. $CuO(s) + H_2(g) \rightleftharpoons Cu(l) + H_2O(g)$

20. For which reactions in Exercise 19 is K_p equal to K?

21. At a particular temperature, a 3.0-L flask contains 2.4 moles of Cl_2, 1.0 mole of NOCl, and 4.5×10^{-3} mole of NO. Calculate K at this temperature for the following reaction.

$$2NOCl(g) \rightleftharpoons 2NO(g) + Cl_2(g)$$

22. At 1100 K, $K_p = 0.25$ for the reaction

$$2SO_2(g) + O_2(g) \rightleftharpoons 2SO_3(g)$$

What is the value of K at this temperature?

23. At 327°C, the equilibrium concentrations are $[CH_3OH] = 0.15\ M$, $[CO] = 0.24\ M$, and $[H_2] = 1.1\ M$ for the reaction

$$CH_3OH(g) \rightleftharpoons CO(g) + 2H_2(g)$$

Calculate K_p at this temperature.

24. For the reaction

$$H_2(g) + Br_2(g) \rightleftharpoons 2HBr(g)$$

$K_p = 3.5 \times 10^4$ at 1495 K. What is the value of K_p for the following reactions at 1495 K?
    a. $HBr(g) \rightleftharpoons \frac{1}{2}H_2(g) + \frac{1}{2}Br_2(g)$
    b. $2HBr(g) \rightleftharpoons H_2(g) + Br_2(g)$
    c. $\frac{1}{2}H_2(g) + \frac{1}{2}Br_2(g) \rightleftharpoons HBr(g)$

25. At a particular temperature, a 2.00-L flask at equilibrium contains 2.80×10^{-4} mole of N_2, 2.50×10^{-5} mole of O_2, and 2.00×10^{-2} mole of N_2O. Calculate K at this temperature for the reaction

$$2N_2(g) + O_2(g) \rightleftharpoons 2N_2O(g)$$

If $[N_2] = 2.00 \times 10^{-4}\ M$, $[N_2O] = 0.200\ M$, and $[O_2] = 0.00245\ M$, does this represent a system at equilibrium?

26. The following equilibrium pressures were observed at a certain temperature for the reaction

$$N_2(g) + 3H_2(g) \rightleftharpoons 2NH_3(g)$$

$$P_{NH_3} = 3.1 \times 10^{-2} \text{ atm}$$

$$P_{N_2} = 8.5 \times 10^{-1} \text{ atm}$$

$$P_{H_2} = 3.1 \times 10^{-3} \text{ atm}$$

Calculate the value for the equilibrium constant K_p at this temperature. If $P_{N_2} = 0.525$ atm, $P_{NH_3} = 0.0167$ atm, and $P_{H_2} = 0.00761$ atm, does this represent a system at equilibrium?

27. For the reaction

$$2H_2O(g) \rightleftharpoons 2H_2(g) + O_2(g)$$

$K = 2.4 \times 10^{-3}$ at a given temperature. At equilibrium in a 2.0-L container, it is found that $[H_2O(g)] = 1.1 \times 10^{-1}$ M and $[H_2(g)] = 1.9 \times 10^{-2}$ M. Calculate the moles of $O_2(g)$ present under these conditions.

28. The reaction

$$2NO(g) + Br_2(g) \rightleftharpoons 2NOBr(g)$$

as $K_p = 109$ at 25°C. If the equilibrium partial pressure of Br_2 is 0.0159 atm and the equilibrium partial pressure of NOBr is 0.0768 atm, calculate the partial pressure of NO at equilibrium.

29. In a study of the reaction

$$3Fe(s) + 4H_2O(g) \rightleftharpoons Fe_3O_4(s) + 4H_2(g)$$

at 1200 K, it was observed that when the equilibrium partial pressure of water vapor is 15.0 torr, the total pressure at equilibrium is 36.3 torr. Calculate K_p for this reaction at 1200 K.

30. Nitrogen gas (N_2) reacts with hydrogen gas (H_2) to form ammonia (NH_3). At 200°C in a closed container, 1.00 atm of nitrogen gas is mixed with 2.00 atm of hydrogen gas. At equilibrium, the total pressure is 2.00 atm. Calculate the partial pressure of hydrogen gas at equilibrium, and calculate the value of K_p for this reaction.

31. A sample of gaseous PCl_5 was introduced into an evacuated flask so that the pressure of pure PCl_5 would be 0.50 atm at 523 K. However, PCl_5 decomposes to gaseous PCl_3 and Cl_2, and the actual pressure in the flask was found to be 0.84 atm. Calculate K_p for the decomposition reaction

$$PCl_5(g) \rightleftharpoons PCl_3(g) + Cl_2(g)$$

at 523 K. Also calculate K at this temperature.

32. A sample of $S_8(g)$ is placed in an otherwise empty, rigid container at 1325 K at an initial pressure of 1.00 atm, where it decomposes to $S_2(g)$ by the reaction

$$S_8(g) \rightleftharpoons 4S_2(g)$$

At equilibrium, the partial pressure of S_8 is 0.25 atm. Calculate K_p for this reaction at 1325 K.

33. At a particular temperature, 12.0 moles of SO_3 is placed into a 3.0-L rigid container, and the SO_3 dissociates by the reaction

$$2SO_3(g) \rightleftharpoons 2SO_2(g) + O_2(g)$$

At equilibrium, 3.0 moles of SO_2 is present. Calculate K for this reaction.

34. At a particular temperature, 8.0 moles of NO_2 is placed into a 1.0-L container and the NO_2 dissociates by the reaction

$$2NO_2(g) \rightleftharpoons 2NO(g) + O_2(g)$$

At equilibrium the concentration of NO(g) is 2.0 M. Calculate K for this reaction.

Equilibrium Calculations

35. The equilibrium constant is 0.0900 at 25°C for the reaction

$$H_2O(g) + Cl_2O(g) \rightleftharpoons 2HOCl(g)$$

For which of the following sets of conditions is the system at equilibrium? For those which are not at equilibrium, in which direction will the system shift?
   a. A 1.0-L flask contains 1.0 mole of HOCl, 0.10 mole of Cl_2O, and 0.10 mole of H_2O.
   b. A 2.0-L flask contains 0.084 mole of HOCl, 0.080 mole of Cl_2O, and 0.98 mole of H_2O.
   c. A 3.0-L flask contains 0.25 mole of HOCl, 0.0010 mole of Cl_2O, and 0.56 mole of H_2O.

36. The equilibrium constant is 0.0900 at 25°C for the reaction

$$H_2O(g) + Cl_2O(g) \rightleftharpoons 2HOCl(g)$$

For which of the following sets of conditions is the system at equilibrium? For those which are not at equilibrium, in which direction will the system shift?
   a. $P_{H_2O} = 1.00$ atm, $P_{Cl_2O} = 1.00$ atm, $P_{HOCl} = 1.00$ atm
   b. $P_{H_2O} = 200.$ torr, $P_{Cl_2O} = 49.8$ torr, $P_{HOCl} = 21.0$ torr
   c. $P_{H_2O} = 296$ torr, $P_{Cl_2O} = 15.0$ torr, $P_{HOCl} = 20.0$ torr

37. At 900.°C, $K_p = 1.04$ for the reaction

$$CaCO_3(s) \rightleftharpoons CaO(s) + CO_2(g)$$

At a low temperature dry ice (solid CO_2), calcium oxide, and calcium carbonate are introduced into a 50.0-L reaction chamber. The temperature is raised to 900.°C. For the following mixtures, will the initial amount of calcium oxide increase, decrease, or remain the same as the system moves toward equilibrium?
   a. 655 g of $CaCO_3$, 95.0 g of CaO, 58.4 g of CO_2
   b. 780 g of $CaCO_3$, 1.00 g of CaO, 23.76 g of CO_2
   c. 0.14 g of $CaCO_3$, 5000 g of CaO, 23.76 g of CO_2
   d. 715 g of $CaCO_3$, 813 g of CaO, 4.82 g of CO_2

38. At a particular temperature, $K = 3.75$ for the reaction

$$SO_2(g) + NO_2(g) \rightleftharpoons SO_3(g) + NO(g)$$

If all four gases had initial concentrations of 0.800 M, calculate the equilibrium concentrations of the gases.

39. At 25°C, $K = 0.090$ for the reaction

$$H_2O(g) + Cl_2O(g) \rightleftharpoons 2HOCl(g)$$

Calculate the concentrations of all species at equilibrium for each of the following cases.

a. 1.0 g of H_2O and 2.0 g of Cl_2O are mixed in a 1.0-L flask.
b. 1.0 mole of pure HOCl is placed in a 2.0-L flask.

40. For the reaction below at a certain temperature, it is found that the equilibrium concentrations in a 5.00-L rigid container are $[H_2] = 0.0500\ M$, $[F_2] = 0.0100\ M$, and $[HF] = 0.400\ M$.

$$H_2(g) + F_2(g) \rightleftharpoons 2HF(g)$$

If 0.200 mole of F_2 is added to this equilibrium mixture, calculate the concentrations of all gases once equilibrium is reestablished.

41. At 1100 K, $K_p = 0.25$ for the following reaction:

$$2SO_2(g) + O_2(g) \rightleftharpoons 2SO_3(g)$$

Calculate the equilibrium partial pressures of SO_2, O_2, and SO_3 produced from an initial mixture in which $P_{SO_2} = P_{O_2} = 0.50$ atm and $P_{SO_3} = 0$.

42. At 2200°C, $K = 0.050$ for the reaction

$$N_2(g) + O_2(g) \rightleftharpoons 2NO(g)$$

What is the partial pressure of NO at equilibrium assuming the N_2 and O_2 had initial pressures of 0.80 atm and 0.20 atm, respectively?

43. A type of reaction we will study is that having a very small K value ($K << 1$). Solving for equilibrium concentrations in an equilibrium problem usually requires many mathematical operations to be performed. However, the math involved in solving equilibrium problems for reactions having small K values ($K << 1$) is simplified. What assumption is made when solving equilibrium concentrations for reactions having small K values? Whenever assumptions are made, they must be checked for validity. In general, the "5% rule" is used to check the validity of assuming that x (or $2x$, $3x$, and so on) is very small compared to some number. When x (or $2x$, $3x$, and so on) is less than 5% of the number the assumption was made against, then the assumption is said to be valid. If the 5% rule fails, what do you do to solve for the equilibrium concentrations?

44. At 35°C, $K = 1.6 \times 10^{-5}$ for the reaction

$$2NOCl(g) \rightleftharpoons 2NO(g) + Cl_2(g)$$

Calculate the concentrations of all species at equilibrium for each of the following original mixtures.

a. 2.0 moles of pure NOCl in a 2.0-L flask
b. 2.0 moles of NO and 1.0 mole of Cl_2 in a 1.0-L flask
c. 1.0 mole of NOCl and 1.0 mole of NO in a 1.0-L flask
d. 3.0 moles of NO and 1.0 mole of Cl_2 in a 1.0-L flask
e. 2.0 moles of NOCl, 2.0 moles of NO, and 1.0 mole of Cl_2 in a 1.0-L flask
f. 1.00 mol/L concentration of all three gases

45. At a particular temperature, $K = 2.0 \times 10^{-6}$ for the reaction

$$2CO_2(g) \rightleftharpoons 2CO(g) + O_2(g)$$

If 2.0 moles of CO_2 is initially placed into a 5.0-L vessel, calculate the equilibrium concentrations of all species.

46. At a particular temperature, $K_p = 0.25$ for the reaction

$$N_2O_4(g) \rightleftharpoons 2NO_2(g)$$

a. A flask containing only N_2O_4 at an initial pressure of 4.5 atm is allowed to reach equilibrium. Calculate the equilibrium partial pressures of the gases.
b. A flask containing only NO_2 at an initial pressure of 9.0 atm is allowed to reach equilibrium. Calculate the equilibrium partial pressures of the gases.
c. From your answers to parts a and b, does it matter from which direction an equilibrium position is reached?
d. The volume of the container in part a is decreased to one-half the original volume. Calculate the new equilibrium partial pressures.

47. For the reaction below, $K_p = 1.16$ at 800.°C.

$$CaCO_3(s) \rightleftharpoons CaO(s) + CO_2(g)$$

If a 20.0-g sample of $CaCO_3$ is put into a 10.0-L container and heated to 800.°C, what percentage by mass of the $CaCO_3$ will react to reach equilibrium?

48. At 25°C, $K_p = 2.9 \times 10^{-3}$ for the reaction

$$NH_4OCONH_2(s) \rightleftharpoons 2NH_3(g) + CO_2(g)$$

In an experiment carried out at 25°C, a certain amount of NH_4OCONH_2 is placed in an evacuated rigid container and allowed to come to equilibrium. Calculate the total pressure in the container at equilibrium.

49. Lexan is a plastic used to make compact discs, eyeglass lenses, and bullet-proof glass. One of the compounds used to make Lexan is phosgene ($COCl_2$), a poisonous gas. Phosgene is produced by the reaction

$$CO(g) + Cl_2(g) \rightleftharpoons COCl_2(g)$$

for which $K = 4.5 \times 10^9$ at 100.°C.

a. Calculate K_p at 100.°C.
b. Equal moles of CO and Cl_2 are reacted at 100.°C. If the total pressure at equilibrium is 5.0 atm, calculate the equilibrium partial pressures of all the gases.

50. At a certain temperature, $K = 1.1 \times 10^3$ for the reaction

$$Fe^{3+}(aq) + SCN^-(aq) \rightleftharpoons FeSCN^{2+}(aq)$$

Calculate the concentrations of Fe^{3+}, SCN^-, and $FeSCN^{2+}$ at equilibrium if 0.020 mole of $Fe(NO_3)_3$ is added to 1.0 L of 0.10 M KSCN. (Neglect any volume change.)

Le Châtelier's Principle

51. Which of the following statements is(are) true? Correct the false statement(s).

a. When a reactant is added to a system at equilibrium at a given temperature, the reaction will shift right to reestablish equilibrium.
b. When a product is added to a system at equilibrium at a given temperature, the value of K for the reaction will increase when equilibrium is reestablished.

c. When temperature is increased for a reaction at equilibrium, the value of K for the reaction will increase.
d. Addition of a catalyst (a substance that increases the speed of the reaction) has no effect on the equilibrium position.

52. How will the equilibrium position of a gas-phase reaction be affected if the volume of the reaction vessel changes? Are there reactions that will not have their equilibria shifted by a change in volume? Explain. Why does changing the pressure in a rigid container by adding an inert gas not shift the equilibrium position for a gas-phase reaction?

53. Suppose the reaction system

$$UO_2(s) + 4HF(g) \rightleftharpoons UF_4(g) + 2H_2O(g)$$

has already reached equilibrium. Predict the effect that each of the following changes will have on the equilibrium position. Tell whether the equilibrium will shift to the right, will shift to the left, or will not be affected.
a. More $UO_2(s)$ is added to the system.
b. The reaction is performed in a glass reaction vessel; $HF(g)$ attacks and reacts with glass.
c. Water vapor is removed.

54. Consider the reaction

$$Fe^{3+}(aq) + SCN^-(aq) \rightleftharpoons FeSCN^{2+}(aq)$$

How will the equilibrium position shift if
a. water is added, doubling the volume?
b. $AgNO_3(aq)$ is added? (AgSCN is insoluble.)
c. $NaOH(aq)$ is added? [$Fe(OH)_3$ is insoluble.]
d. $Fe(NO_3)_3(aq)$ is added?

55. Chromium(VI) forms two different oxyanions, the orange dichromate ion ($Cr_2O_7^{2-}$), and the yellow chromate ion (CrO_4^{2-}). (See the photos below.) The equilibrium reaction between the two ions is

$$Cr_2O_7^{2-}(aq) + H_2O(l) \rightleftharpoons 2CrO_4^{2-}(aq) + 2H^+(aq)$$

Explain why orange dichromate solutions turn yellow when sodium hydroxide is added.

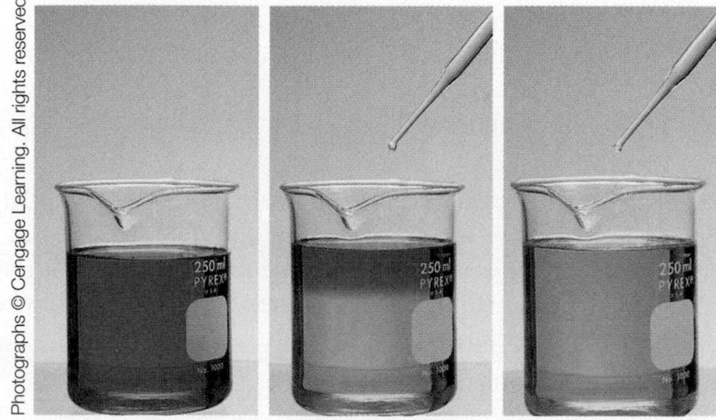

56. What will happen to the number of moles of SO_3 in equilibrium with SO_2 and O_2 in the reaction

$$2SO_3(g) \rightleftharpoons 2SO_2(g) + O_2(g)$$

in each of the following cases?
a. Oxygen gas is added.
b. The pressure is increased by decreasing the volume of the reaction container.
c. In a rigid reaction container, the pressure is increased by adding argon gas.
d. The temperature is decreased (the reaction is endothermic).
e. Gaseous sulfur dioxide is removed.

57. An important reaction in the commercial production of hydrogen is

$$CO(g) + H_2O(g) \rightleftharpoons H_2(g) + CO_2(g)$$

How will this system at equilibrium shift in each of the five following cases?
a. Gaseous carbon dioxide is removed.
b. Water vapor is added.
c. In a rigid reaction container, the pressure is increased by adding helium gas.
d. The temperature is increased (the reaction is exothermic).
e. The pressure is increased by decreasing the volume of the reaction container.

58. Hydrogen for use in ammonia production is produced by the reaction

$$CH_4(g) + H_2O(g) \xrightleftharpoons[750^\circ C]{\text{Ni catalyst}} CO(g) + 3H_2(g)$$

What will happen to a reaction mixture at equilibrium if
a. $H_2O(g)$ is removed?
b. the temperature is increased (the reaction is endothermic)?
c. an inert gas is added to a rigid reaction container?
d. $CO(g)$ is removed?
e. the volume of the container is tripled?

59. In which direction will the position of the equilibrium

$$2HI(g) \rightleftharpoons H_2(g) + I_2(g)$$

be shifted for each of the following changes?
a. $H_2(g)$ is added.
b. $I_2(g)$ is removed.
c. $HI(g)$ is removed.
d. In a rigid reaction container, some $Ar(g)$ is added.
e. The volume of the container is doubled.
f. The temperature is decreased (the reaction is exothermic).

60. Predict the shift in the equilibrium position that will occur for each of the following reactions when the volume of the reaction container is increased.
a. $N_2(g) + 3H_2(g) \rightleftharpoons 2NH_3(g)$
b. $PCl_5(g) \rightleftharpoons PCl_3(g) + Cl_2(g)$
c. $H_2(g) + F_2(g) \rightleftharpoons 2HF(g)$
d. $COCl_2(g) \rightleftharpoons CO(g) + Cl_2(g)$
e. $CaCO_3(s) \rightleftharpoons CaO(s) + CO_2(g)$

61. Old-fashioned "smelling salts" consist of ammonium carbonate [$(NH_4)_2CO_3$]. The reaction for the decomposition of ammonium carbonate

$$(NH_4)_2CO_3(s) \rightleftharpoons 2NH_3(g) + CO_2(g) + H_2O(g)$$

is endothermic. Would the smell of ammonia increase or decrease as the temperature is increased?

62. Ammonia is produced by the Haber process, in which nitrogen and hydrogen are reacted directly using an iron mesh impregnated with oxides as a catalyst. For the reaction

$$N_2(g) + 3H_2(g) \rightleftharpoons 2NH_3(g)$$

equilibrium constants as a function of temperature are

300°C, 4.34×10^{-3}

500°C, 1.45×10^{-5}

600°C, 2.25×10^{-6}

Is the reaction exothermic or endothermic? Explain.

Additional Exercises

63. At 25°C, $K_p \approx 1 \times 10^{-31}$ for the reaction

$$N_2(g) + O_2(g) \rightleftharpoons 2NO(g)$$

a. Calculate the concentration of NO (in molecules/cm^3) that can exist in equilibrium in air at 25°C. In air $P_{N_2} = 0.8$ atm and $P_{O_2} = 0.2$ atm.
b. Typical concentrations of NO in relatively pristine environments range from 10^8 molecules/cm^3 to 10^{10} molecules/cm^3. Why is there a discrepancy between these values and your answer to part a?

64. Given the following equilibrium constants at 427°C,

$$Na_2O(s) \rightleftharpoons 2Na(l) + \tfrac{1}{2}O_2(g) \qquad K_1 = 2 \times 10^{-25}$$

$$NaO(g) \rightleftharpoons Na(l) + \tfrac{1}{2}O_2(g) \qquad K_2 = 2 \times 10^{-5}$$

$$Na_2O_2(s) \rightleftharpoons 2Na(l) + O_2(g) \qquad K_3 = 5 \times 10^{-29}$$

$$NaO_2(s) \rightleftharpoons Na(l) + O_2(g) \qquad K_4 = 3 \times 10^{-14}$$

determine the values for the equilibrium constants for the following reactions.
a. $Na_2O(s) + \frac{1}{2}O_2(g) \rightleftharpoons Na_2O_2(s)$
b. $NaO(g) + Na_2O(s) \rightleftharpoons Na_2O_2(s) + Na(l)$
c. $2NaO(g) \rightleftharpoons Na_2O_2(s)$
(*Hint:* When reaction equations are added, the equilibrium expressions are multiplied.)

65. Calculate a value for the equilibrium constant for the reaction

$$O_2(g) + O(g) \rightleftharpoons O_3(g)$$

given that

$$NO_2(g) \overset{h\nu}{\rightleftharpoons} NO(g) + O(g) \qquad K = 6.8 \times 10^{-49}$$

$$O_3(g) + NO(g) \rightleftharpoons NO_2(g) + O_2(g) \qquad K = 5.8 \times 10^{-34}$$

(See the hint in Exercise 64.)

66. Given $K = 3.50$ at 45°C for the reaction

$$A(g) + B(g) \rightleftharpoons C(g)$$

and $K = 7.10$ at 45°C for the reaction

$$2A(g) + D(g) \rightleftharpoons C(g)$$

what is the value of K at the same temperature for the reaction

$$C(g) + D(g) \rightleftharpoons 2B(g)$$

What is the value of K_p at 45°C for the reaction? Starting with 1.50 atm partial pressures of both C and D, what is the mole fraction of B once equilibrium is reached?

67. An initial mixture of nitrogen gas and hydrogen gas is reacted in a rigid container at a certain temperature as follows:

$$3H_2(g) + N_2(g) \rightleftharpoons 2NH_3(g)$$

At equilibrium, the concentrations are $[H_2] = 5.0\ M$, $[N_2] = 8.0\ M$, and $[NH_3] = 4.0\ M$. What were the concentrations of nitrogen gas and hydrogen gas that were reacted initially?

68. At 25°C, $K_p = 5.3 \times 10^5$ for the reaction

$$N_2(g) + 3H_2(g) \rightleftharpoons 2NH_3(g)$$

When a certain partial pressure of $NH_3(g)$ is put into an otherwise empty rigid vessel at 25°C, equilibrium is reached when 50.0% of the original ammonia has decomposed. What was the original partial pressure of ammonia before any decomposition occurred?

69. A 2.4156-g sample of PCl_5 was placed in an empty 2.000-L flask and allowed to decompose to PCl_3 and Cl_2 at 250.0°C:

$$PCl_5(g) \rightleftharpoons PCl_3(g) + Cl_2(g)$$

At equilibrium the total pressure inside the flask was observed to be 358.7 torr.
a. Calculate the partial pressure of each gas at equilibrium and the value of K_p at 250.0°C.
b. What are the new equilibrium pressures if 0.250 mole of Cl_2 gas is added to the flask?

70. At 25°C, gaseous SO_2Cl_2 decomposes to $SO_2(g)$ and $Cl_2(g)$ to the extent that 12.5% of the original SO_2Cl_2 (by moles) has decomposed to reach equilibrium. The total pressure (at equilibrium) is 0.900 atm. Calculate the value of K_p for this system.

71. The partial pressures of an equilibrium mixture of $N_2O_4(g)$ and $NO_2(g)$ are $P_{N_2O_4} = 0.34$ atm and $P_{NO_2} = 1.20$ atm at a certain temperature. The volume of the container is doubled. Calculate the partial pressures of the two gases when a new equilibrium is established.

72. For the reaction

$$PCl_5(g) \rightleftharpoons PCl_3(g) + Cl_2(g)$$

at 600. K, the equilibrium constant is 11.5. Suppose that 2.450 g of PCl_5 is placed in an evacuated 500.-mL bulb, which is then heated to 600. K.
a. What would the pressure of PCl_5 be if it did not dissociate?
b. What is the partial pressure of PCl_5 at equilibrium?

c. What is the total pressure in the bulb at equilibrium?
d. What is the degree of dissociation of PCl_5 at equilibrium?

73. At 125°C, $K_p = 0.25$ for the reaction

$$2NaHCO_3(s) \rightleftharpoons Na_2CO_3(s) + CO_2(g) + H_2O(g)$$

A 1.00-L flask containing 10.0 g of $NaHCO_3$ is evacuated and heated to 125°C.
a. Calculate the partial pressures of CO_2 and H_2O after equilibrium is established.
b. Calculate the masses of $NaHCO_3$ and Na_2CO_3 present at equilibrium.
c. Calculate the minimum container volume necessary for all the $NaHCO_3$ to decompose.

74. The gas arsine (AsH_3) decomposes as follows:

$$2AsH_3(g) \rightleftharpoons 2As(s) + 3H_2(g)$$

In an experiment pure $AsH_3(g)$ was placed in an empty, rigid, sealed flask at a pressure of 392.0 torr. After 48 h the pressure in the flask was observed to be constant at 488.0 torr.
a. Calculate the equilibrium pressure of $H_2(g)$.
b. Calculate K_p for this reaction.

75. For the reaction

$$NH_3(g) + H_2S(g) \rightleftharpoons NH_4HS(s)$$

$K = 400.$ at 35.0°C. If 2.00 moles each of NH_3, H_2S, and NH_4HS are placed in a 5.00-L vessel, what mass of NH_4HS will be present at equilibrium? What is the pressure of H_2S at equilibrium?

76. The hydrocarbon naphthalene was frequently used in mothballs until recently, when it was discovered that human inhalation of naphthalene vapors can lead to hemolytic anemia. Naphthalene is 93.71% carbon by mass, and a 0.256-mole sample of naphthalene has a mass of 32.8 g. What is the molecular formula of naphthalene? This compound works as a pesticide in mothballs by sublimation of the solid so that it fumigates enclosed spaces with its vapors according to the equation

$$\text{Naphthalene}(s) \rightleftharpoons \text{naphthalene}(g) \qquad K = 4.29 \times 10^{-6} \text{ (at 298 K)}$$

If 3.00 g of solid naphthalene is placed in an enclosed space with a volume of 5.00 L at 25°C, what percentage of the naphthalene will have sublimed once equilibrium has been established?

77. Consider the decomposition of the compound $C_5H_6O_3$ as follows:

$$C_5H_6O_3(g) \longrightarrow C_2H_6(g) + 3CO(g)$$

When a 5.63-g sample of pure $C_5H_6O_3(g)$ was sealed in an otherwise empty 2.50-L flask and heated to 200.°C, the pressure in the flask gradually rose to 1.63 atm and remained at that value. Calculate K for this reaction.

Challenge Problems

78. A sample of $N_2O_4(g)$ is placed in an empty cylinder at 25°C. After equilibrium is reached, the total pressure is 1.5 atm, and 16% (by moles) of the original $N_2O_4(g)$ has dissociated to $NO_2(g)$.
a. Calculate the value of K_p for this dissociation reaction at 25°C.
b. If the volume of the cylinder is increased until the total pressure is 1.0 atm (the temperature of the system remains constant), calculate the equilibrium pressure of $N_2O_4(g)$ and $NO_2(g)$.
c. What percentage (by moles) of the original $N_2O_4(g)$ is dissociated at the new equilibrium position (total pressure = 1.00 atm)?

79. Nitric oxide and bromine at initial partial pressures of 98.4 torr and 41.3 torr, respectively, were allowed to react at 300. K. At equilibrium the total pressure was 110.5 torr. The reaction is

$$2NO(g) + Br_2(g) \rightleftharpoons 2NOBr(g)$$

a. Calculate the value of K_p.
b. What would be the partial pressures of all species if NO and Br_2, both at an initial partial pressure of 0.30 atm, were allowed to come to equilibrium at this temperature?

80. Consider the decomposition equilibrium for dinitrogen pentoxide:

$$2N_2O_5(g) \rightleftharpoons 4NO_2(g) + O_2(g)$$

At a certain temperature and a total pressure of 1.00 atm, the N_2O_5 is 0.50% decomposed (by moles) at equilibrium.
a. If the volume is increased by a factor of 10.0, will the mole percent of N_2O_5 decomposed at equilibrium be greater than, less than, or equal to 0.50%? Explain your answer.
b. Calculate the mole percent of N_2O_5 that will be decomposed at equilibrium if the volume is increased by a factor of 10.0.

81. Consider the reaction

$$P_4(g) \longrightarrow 2P_2(g)$$

where $K_p = 1.00 \times 10^{-1}$ at 1325 K. In an experiment where $P_4(g)$ was placed in a container at 1325 K, the equilibrium mixture of $P_4(g)$ and $P_2(g)$ has a total pressure of 1.00 atm. Calculate the equilibrium pressures of $P_4(g)$ and $P_2(g)$. Calculate the fraction (by moles) of $P_4(g)$ that has dissociated to reach equilibrium.

82. Suppose 1.50 atm of $CH_4(g)$, 2.50 atm of $C_2H_6(g)$, and 15.00 atm of $O_2(g)$ are placed in a flask at a given temperature. The reactions are

$$CH_4(g) + 2O_2(g) \rightleftharpoons CO_2(g) + 2H_2O(g) \quad K_p = 1.0 \times 10^4$$

$$2C_2H_6(g) + 7O_2(g) \rightleftharpoons 4CO_2(g) + 6H_2O(g) \quad K_p = 1.0 \times 10^8$$

Calculate the equilibrium pressures of all gases.

83. Consider the reaction

$$3O_2(g) \rightleftharpoons 2O_3(g)$$

At 175°C and a pressure of 128 torr, an equilibrium mixture of O_2 and O_3 has a density of 0.168 g/L. Calculate K_p for the above reaction at 175°C.

84. A mixture of N_2, H_2 and NH_3 is at equilibrium according to the equation $N_2(g) + 3H_2(g) \rightleftharpoons 2NH_3(g)$ as depicted below.

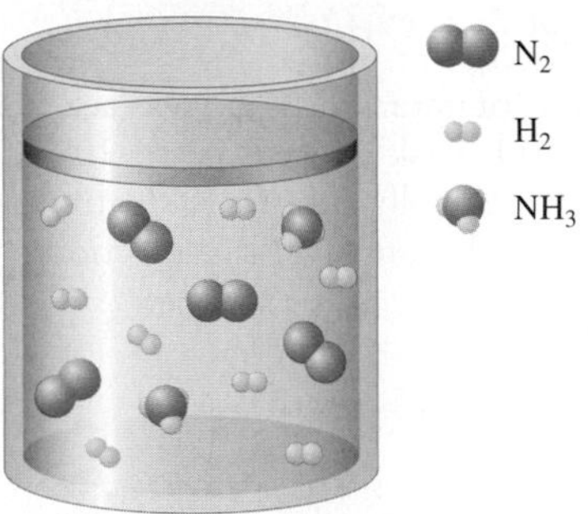

The volume is suddenly decreased (by increasing the external pressure), and a new equilibrium is established as depicted below.

a. If the volume of the final equilibrium mixture is 1.00 L, determine the value of the equilibrium constant K for the reaction. Assume temperature is constant.
b. Determine the volume of the initial equilibrium mixture assuming a final equilibrium volume of 1.00 L and assuming a constant temperature.

85. A 4.72-g sample of methanol (CH_3OH) was placed in an otherwise empty 1.00-L flask and heated to 250.°C to vaporize the methanol. Over time the methanol vapor decomposed by the following reaction:

$$CH_3OH(g) \rightleftharpoons CO(g) + 2H_2(g)$$

After the system has reached equilibrium, a tiny hole is drilled in the side of the flask allowing gaseous compounds to effuse out of the flask. Measurements of the effusing gas show that it contains 33.0 times as much $H_2(g)$ as $CH_3OH(g)$. Calculate K for this reaction at 250.°C.

86. The compound $SbCl_5(g)$ decomposes at high temperatures to gaseous antimony trichloride and chlorine gas. When 89.7 g of $SbCl_5(g)$ is placed in a 15.0-L container at 180°C, the $SbCl_5(g)$ is 29.2% decomposed (by moles) after the system has reached equilibrium.
a. Calculate the value of K for this reaction at 180°C.
b. Determine the number of moles of chlorine gas that must be injected into the flask to make the new equilibrium pressure of antimony trichloride half that of the original equilibrium pressure of antimony trichloride in the original experiment.

87. At 207°C, $K_p = 0.267$ for the reaction

$$PCl_5(g) \rightleftharpoons PCl_3(g) + Cl_2(g)$$

a. If 0.100 mole of $PCl_5(g)$ is placed in an otherwise empty 12.0-L vessel at 207°C, calculate the partial pressures of $PCl_5(g)$, $PCl_3(g)$, and $Cl_2(g)$ at equilibrium.
b. In another experiment the total pressure of an equilibrium mixture is 2.00 atm at 207°C. What mass of PCl_5 was introduced into a 5.00-L vessel to reach this equilibrium position?

88. A 1.604-g sample of methane (CH_4) gas and 6.400 g of oxygen gas are sealed in a 2.50-L vessel at 411°C and are allowed to reach equilibrium. Methane can react with oxygen to form gaseous carbon dioxide and water vapor, or methane can react with oxygen to form gaseous carbon monoxide and water vapor. At equilibrium the pressure of oxygen is 0.326 atm, and the pressure of water vapor is 4.45 atm. Calculate the pressures of carbon monoxide and carbon dioxide present at equilibrium.

89. At 1000 K the $N_2(g)$ and $O_2(g)$ in air (78% N_2, 21% O_2, by moles) react to form a mixture of $NO(g)$ and $NO_2(g)$. The values of the equilibrium constants are 1.5×10^{-4} and 1.0×10^{-5} for the formation of $NO(g)$ and $NO_2(g)$, respectively. At what total pressure will the partial pressures of $NO(g)$ and $NO_2(g)$ be equal in an equilibrium mixture of $N_2(g)$, $O_2(g)$, $NO(g)$, and $NO_2(g)$?

90. The equilibrium constant K_p for the reaction

$$CCl_4(g) \rightleftharpoons C(s) + 2Cl_2(g)$$

at 700°C is 0.76. Determine the initial pressure of carbon tetrachloride that will produce a total equilibrium pressure of 1.20 atm at 700°C.

91. An 8.00-g sample of SO_3 was placed in an evacuated container, where it decomposed at 600.°C according to the following reaction:

$$SO_3(g) \rightleftharpoons SO_2(g) + \tfrac{1}{2}O_2(g)$$

At equilibrium the total pressure and the density of the gaseous mixture were 1.80 atm and 1.60 g/L, respectively. Calculate K_p for this reaction.

92. A sample of iron(II) sulfate was heated in an evacuated container to 920 K, where the following reactions occurred:

$$2FeSO_4(s) \rightleftharpoons Fe_2O_3(s) + SO_3(g) + SO_2(g)$$

$$SO_3(g) \rightleftharpoons SO_2(g) + \tfrac{1}{2}O_2(g)$$

After equilibrium was reached, the total pressure was 0.836 atm, and the partial pressure of oxygen was 0.0275 atm. Calculate K_p for each of the above reactions.

93. At 450°C, $K_p = 6.5 \times 10^{-3}$ for the ammonia synthesis reaction. Assume that a reaction vessel with a movable piston initially contains 3.0 moles of $H_2(g)$ and 1.0 mole of $N_2(g)$. Make a plot to show how the partial pressure of $NH_3(g)$ present at equilibrium varies for the total pressures of 1.0 atm, 10.0 atm, 100. atm, and 1000. atm (assuming that K_p remains constant). [*Note:* Assume these total pressures represent the initial total pressure of $H_2(g)$ plus $N_2(g)$, where $P_{NH_3} = 0$.]

94. A sample of gaseous nitrosyl bromide (NOBr) was placed in a container fitted with a frictionless, massless piston, where it decomposed at 25°C according to the following equation:

$$2NOBr(g) \rightleftharpoons 2NO(g) + Br_2(g)$$

The initial density of the system was recorded as 4.495 g/L. After equilibrium was reached, the density was noted to be 4.086 g/L.

a. Determine the value of the equilibrium constant *K* for the reaction.
b. If Ar(*g*) is added to the system at equilibrium at constant temperature, what will happen to the equilibrium position? What happens to the value of *K*? Explain each answer.

95. A gaseous material XY(*g*) dissociates to some extent to produce X(*g*) and Y(*g*):

$$XY(g) \rightleftharpoons X(g) + Y(g)$$

A 2.00-g sample of XY (molar mass = 165 g/mol) is placed in a container with a movable piston at 25°C. The pressure is held constant at 0.967 atm. As XY begins to dissociate, the piston moves until 35.0 mole percent of the original XY has dissociated and then remains at a constant position. Assuming ideal behavior, calculate the density of the gas in the container after the piston has stopped moving, and determine the value of *K* for this reaction at 25°C.

Marathon Problem

96.* Consider the reaction

$$A(g) + B(g) \rightleftharpoons C(g)$$

for which $K = 1.30 \times 10^2$. Assume that 0.406 mole of C(*g*) is placed in the cylinder represented here. The temperature is 300.0 K, and the barometric pressure on the piston (which is assumed to be massless and frictionless) is constant at 1.00 atm. The original volume [before the 0.406 mole of C(*g*) begins to decompose] is 10.00 L. What is the volume in the cylinder at equilibrium?

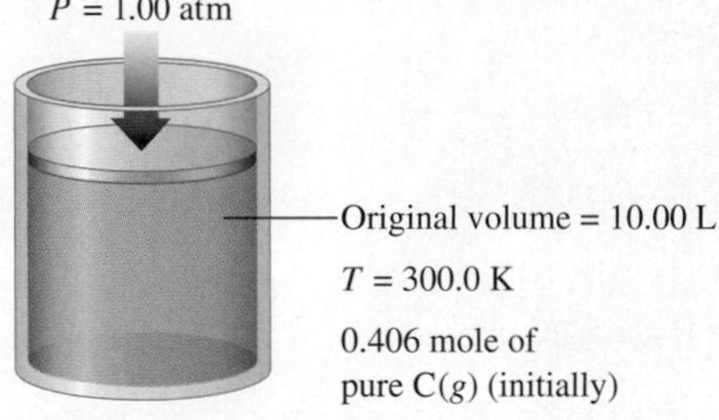

*From James H. Burness, "The Use of "Marathon" Problems as Effective Vehicles for the Presentation of General Chemistry Lectures," Journal of Chemical Education, 68(11).

7 Acids and Bases

chapter

A polarized light micrograph of tartaric acid crystals. Tartaric acid is found in grapes as well as other fruits.

OWL
Sign in to OWL at www.cengage.com/owl to view tutorials and simulations, develop problem-solving skills, and complete online homework assigned by your professor.

go Chemistry
Download mini lecture videos for key concept review and exam prep from OWL or purchase them from www.cengagebrain.com.

In this chapter we reencounter two very important classes of compounds, acids and bases. We will explore their interactions and apply the fundamentals of chemical equilibria discussed in Chapter 6 to systems involving proton transfer reactions.

Acid–base chemistry is important in a wide variety of everyday applications. There are complex systems in our bodies that carefully control the acidity of our blood, and even small deviations may lead to serious illness and death. The same sensitivity exists in other life forms. If you have ever owned tropical fish or goldfish, you know how important it is to monitor and control the acidity of the water in the aquarium.

Acids and bases are also important industrially. For example, the vast quantity of sulfuric acid manufactured in the United States each year is needed to produce fertilizers, polymers, steel, and many other materials.

The influence of acids on living things has assumed special importance in the United States, Canada, and Europe in recent years as a result of the phenomenon of acid rain. This problem is complex, and its diplomatic and economic overtones make it all the more difficult to solve.

7.1 The Nature of Acids and Bases

Acids were first recognized as a class of substances that taste sour. Vinegar tastes sour because it is a dilute solution of acetic acid; citric acid is responsible for the sour taste of a lemon. Bases, sometimes called *alkalis,* are characterized by their bitter taste and slippery feel. Commercial preparations for unclogging drains are highly basic.

The first person to recognize the essential nature of acids and bases was Svante Arrhenius. Based on his experiments with electrolytes, Arrhenius postulated that *acids produce hydrogen ions in aqueous solution, and bases produce hydroxide ions.* At the time of its discovery, the **Arrhenius concept** of acids and bases was a major step forward in quantifying acid–base chemistry, but this concept is limited because it applies only to aqueous solutions and allows for only one kind of base—the hydroxide ion. A more general definition of acids and bases was suggested independently by Danish chemist Johannes N. Brønsted (1879–1947) and English chemist Thomas M. Lowry (1874–1936) in 1923. In terms of the **Brønsted–Lowry definition,** *an acid is a proton (H^+) donor, and a base is a proton acceptor.* For example, when gaseous HCl dissolves in water, each HCl molecule donates a proton to a water molecule, and so HCl qualifies as a Brønsted–Lowry acid. The molecule that accepts the proton—water in this case—is a Brønsted–Lowry base.

To understand how water can act as a base, we need to recognize that the oxygen of the water molecule has two unshared electron pairs, either of which can form a covalent bond with an H^+ ion. When gaseous HCl dissolves, the following reaction occurs:

$$\mathrm{H{-}\underset{\underset{\displaystyle H}{|}}{\ddot{O}}{:}} + \mathrm{H{-}Cl} \longrightarrow \left[\mathrm{H{-}\underset{\underset{\displaystyle H}{|}}{\ddot{O}}{-}H}\right]^+ + \mathrm{Cl^-}$$

Note that the proton is transferred from the HCl molecule to the water molecule to form H_3O^+, which is called the **hydronium ion.**

The general reaction that occurs when an acid is dissolved in water can best be represented as

Recall that (*aq*) means the substance is hydrated.

$$\underset{\text{Acid}}{\mathrm{HA}(aq)} + \underset{\text{Base}}{\mathrm{H_2O}(l)} \rightleftharpoons \underset{\text{Conjugate acid}}{\mathrm{H_3O^+}(aq)} + \underset{\text{Conjugate base}}{\mathrm{A^-}(aq)} \quad (7.1)$$

This representation emphasizes the significant role of the polar water molecule in pulling the proton from the acid. Note that the **conjugate base** is everything that remains of the acid molecule after a proton is lost. The **conjugate acid** is formed when the proton is transferred to the base. A **conjugate acid–base pair** consists of two substances related to each other by the donating and accepting of a single proton. In Equation (7.1) there are two conjugate acid–base pairs: HA and A^-, and H_2O and H_3O^+.

It is important to note that Equation (7.1) really represents *a competition for the proton between the two bases* H_2O *and* A^-. If H_2O is a much stronger base than A^-—that is, if H_2O has a much greater affinity for H^+ than A^- does—the equilibrium position will be far to the right; most of the acid dissolved will be in the ionized form. Conversely, if A^- is a much stronger base than H_2O, the equilibrium position will lie far to the left. In this instance most of the acid dissolved will be present at equilibrium as HA.

The equilibrium expression for the reaction given in Equation (7.1) is

$$K_a = \frac{[H_3O^+][A^-]}{[HA]} = \frac{[H^+][A^-]}{[HA]} \qquad (7.2)$$

In this chapter we will always represent an acid as simply dissociating. This does not mean we are using the Arrhenius model for acids. Since water does not affect the equilibrium position, we leave it out of the acid dissociation reaction for simplicity.

where K_a is called the **acid dissociation constant.** Both $H_3O^+(aq)$ and $H^+(aq)$ are commonly used to represent the hydrated proton. In this book we will often use simply H^+, but you should remember that it is hydrated in aqueous solutions.

In Chapter 6 we saw that pure solids and liquids are always omitted from the equilibrium expression because they have unit activities. In a dilute solution containing an acid, we can assume that the activity of water is 1. Thus the term $[H_2O]$ is not included in Equation (7.2), and the equilibrium expression for K_a has the same form as that for the simple dissociation

$$HA(aq) \rightleftharpoons H^+(aq) + A^-(aq)$$

You should not forget, however, that water plays an important role in causing the acid to dissociate, as represented below.

Note that K_a is the equilibrium constant for the reaction in which a proton is removed from HA to form the conjugate base A^-. We use K_a to represent *only* this type of reaction. With this information you can write the K_a expression for any acid, even one that is totally unfamiliar to you.

The Brønsted–Lowry definition is not limited to aqueous solutions; it can be extended to reactions in the gas phase. For example, consider the reaction between gaseous hydrogen chloride and ammonia that we discussed when we studied diffusion (Chapter 5):

$$NH_3(g) + HCl(g) \rightleftharpoons NH_4Cl(s)$$

Lewis structures, which represent the electron arrangements in molecules, will be discussed fully in Chapter 13.

In this reaction a proton is donated by the hydrogen chloride to the ammonia, as shown by the following Lewis structures:

$$\mathrm{H{-}\overset{\displaystyle H}{\underset{\displaystyle H}{\overset{|}{\underset{|}{N}}}}\!:} \quad \mathrm{H{-}\ddot{\underset{..}{Cl}}\!:} \rightleftharpoons \left[\mathrm{H{-}\overset{\displaystyle H}{\underset{\displaystyle H}{\overset{|}{\underset{|}{N}}}}{-}H}\right]^+ + \left[:\ddot{\underset{..}{Cl}}:\right]^-$$

Note that this reaction is not considered an acid–base reaction according to the Arrhenius concept.

7.2 Acid Strength

The strength of an acid is defined by the equilibrium position of its dissociation reaction:

$$HA(aq) + H_2O(l) \rightleftharpoons H_3O^+(aq) + A^-(aq)$$

A **strong acid** is one for which *this equilibrium lies far to the right.* This means that almost all the original HA is dissociated at equilibrium [Fig. 7.1(a)]. There is an important connection between the strength of an acid and that of its conjugate base. *A strong acid yields a weak conjugate base*—one that has a low affinity for a proton. A strong acid can also be described as an acid whose conjugate base is a much weaker base than water (Fig. 7.2). In this case the water molecules win the competition for the H^+ ions.

Conversely, a **weak acid** is one for which *the equilibrium lies far to the left.* Most of the acid originally placed in the solution is still present as HA at equilibrium. That is, a weak acid dissociates only to a very small extent in aqueous solution [Fig. 7.1(b)]. In contrast to a strong acid, a weak acid has a conjugate base that is a much stronger base than water. In this case a water molecule is not very successful in pulling an H^+ ion from the conjugate base. *A weak acid yields a relatively strong conjugate base.*

The various ways of describing the strength of an acid are summarized in Table 7.1.

The common strong acids are sulfuric acid [$H_2SO_4(aq)$], hydrochloric acid [$HCl(aq)$], nitric acid [$HNO_3(aq)$], and perchloric acid [$HClO_4(aq)$]. Sulfuric

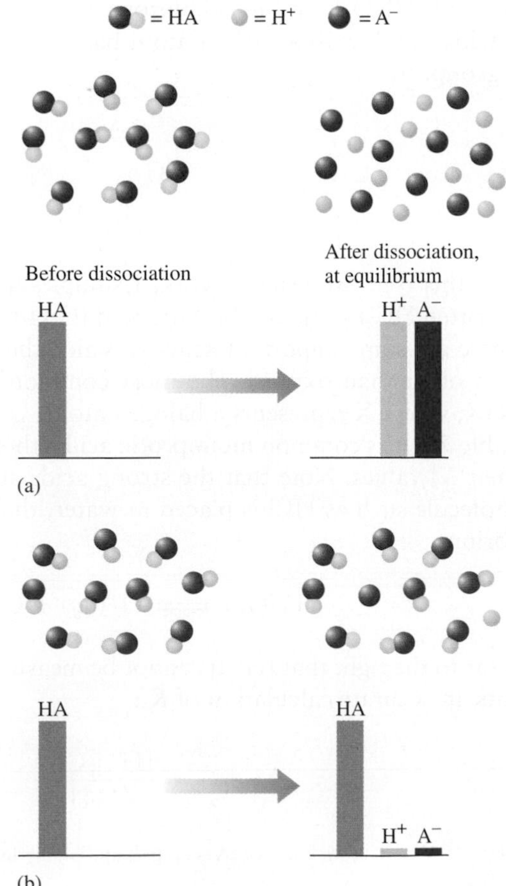

Figure 7.1 Graphical representation of the behavior of acids of different strengths in aqueous solution. (a) A strong acid. (b) A weak acid.

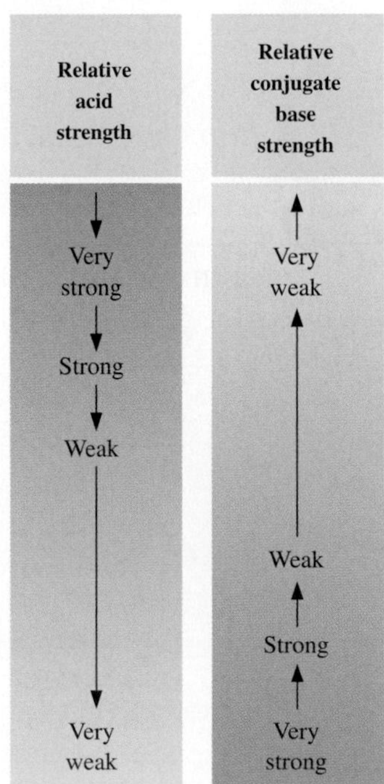

Figure 7.2 The relationship of acid strength and conjugate base strength for the reaction

$$\underset{\text{Acid}}{HA(aq)} + H_2O(l) \rightleftharpoons H_3O^+(aq) + \underset{\text{Conjugate base}}{A^-(aq)}$$

Table 7.1

Various Ways to Describe Acid Strength

Property	Strong Acid	Weak Acid
K_a value	K_a is large	K_a is small
Position of the dissociation equilibrium	Far to the right	Far to the left
Equilibrium concentration of H^+ compared with original concentration of HA	$[H^+] \approx [HA]_0$	$[H^+] \ll [HA]_0$
Strength of conjugate base compared with that of water	A^- much weaker base than H_2O	A^- much stronger base than H_2O

Perchloric acid can explode if handled improperly.

acid is actually a **diprotic acid,** an acid having two acidic protons. The acid H_2SO_4 is a strong acid, virtually 100% dissociated in water:

$$H_2SO_4(aq) \longrightarrow H^+(aq) + HSO_4^-(aq)$$

The HSO_4^- ion is a weak acid:

$$HSO_4^-(aq) \rightleftharpoons H^+(aq) + SO_4^{2-}(aq)$$

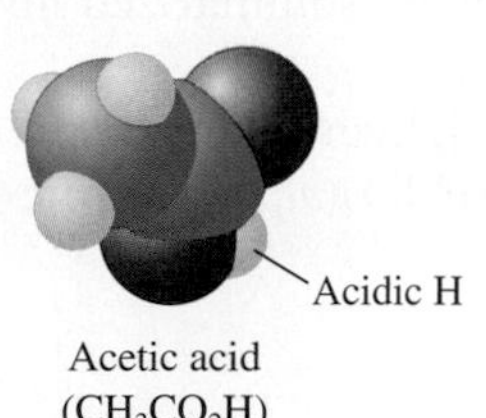

Acetic acid (CH_3CO_2H)

Most acids are **oxyacids,** in which the acidic proton is attached to an oxygen atom. The strong acids mentioned above, except hydrochloric acid, are typical examples. Many common weak acids, such as phosphoric acid (H_3PO_4), nitrous acid (HNO_2), and hypochlorous acid (HOCl), are also oxyacids. **Organic acids,** those with a carbon atom backbone, commonly contain the **carboxyl group:**

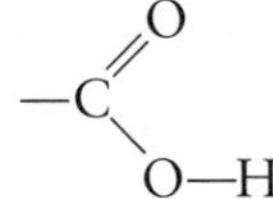

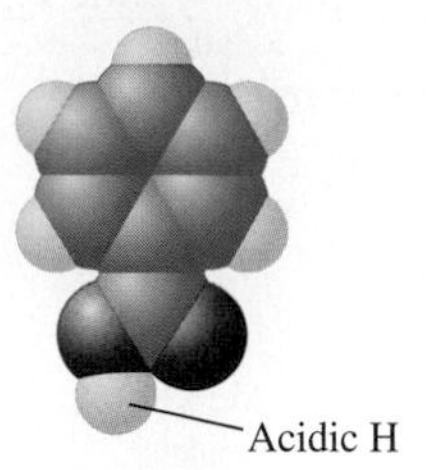

Benzoic acid ($C_6H_5CO_2H$)

Acids of this type are usually weak. Examples are acetic acid (CH_3COOH), often written $HC_2H_3O_2$, and benzoic acid (C_6H_5COOH).

There are some important acids in which the acidic proton is attached to an atom other than oxygen. The most common of these are the hydrohalic acids HX, where X represents a halogen atom.

Table 7.2 lists common **monoprotic acids** (those having *one* acidic proton) and their K_a values. Note that the strong acids are not listed. When a strong acid molecule such as HCl is placed in water, the position of the dissociation equilibrium

$$HCl(aq) \rightleftharpoons H^+(aq) + Cl^-(aq)$$

lies so far to the right that [HCl] cannot be measured accurately. This situation prevents an accurate calculation of K_a:

$$K_a = \frac{[H^+][Cl^-]}{\underset{\substack{\uparrow \\ \text{Very small and highly uncertain}}}{[HCl]}}$$

Appendix Table A5.1 contains K_a values.

Table 7.2

Values of K_a for Some Common Monoprotic Acids

Formula	Name	Value of K_a
HSO_4^-	Hydrogen sulfate ion	1.2×10^{-2}
$HClO_2$	Chlorous acid	1.2×10^{-2}
$HC_2H_2ClO_2$	Monochloracetic acid	1.35×10^{-3}
HF	Hydrofluoric acid	7.2×10^{-4}
HNO_2	Nitrous acid	4.0×10^{-4}
$HC_2H_3O_2$	Acetic acid	1.8×10^{-5}
$[Al(H_2O)_6]^{3+}$	Hydrated aluminum(III) ion	1.4×10^{-5}
$HOCl$	Hypochlorous acid	3.5×10^{-8}
HCN	Hydrocyanic acid	6.2×10^{-10}
NH_4^+	Ammonium ion	5.6×10^{-10}
HOC_6H_5	Phenol	1.6×10^{-10}

↑ Increasing acid strength

OWL INTERACTIVE EXAMPLE 7.1

Using Table 7.2, arrange the following species according to their strength as bases: H_2O, F^-, Cl^-, NO_2^-, and CN^-.

Solution Remember that water is a stronger base than the conjugate base of a strong acid but a weaker base than the conjugate base of a weak acid. This rule leads to the following order:

$$Cl^- < H_2O < \text{conjugate bases of weak acids}$$

Weakest bases ⟶ Strongest bases

We can order the remaining conjugate bases by recognizing that the strength of an acid is *inversely related* to the strength of its conjugate base. From Table 7.2 we have

$$K_a \text{ for HF} > K_a \text{ for } HNO_2 > K_a \text{ for HCN}$$

Thus the base strengths increase as follows:

$$F^- < NO_2^- < CN^-$$

The combined order of increasing base strength is

$$Cl^- < H_2O < F^- < NO_2^- < CN^-$$

Water as an Acid and a Base

A substance is said to be *amphoteric* if it can behave either as an acid or as a base. Water is the most common **amphoteric substance.** We see this behavior in the **autoionization** of water, which involves the transfer of a proton from one water molecule to another to produce a hydroxide ion and a hydronium ion:

$$\mathrm{H{-}\ddot{O}{-}H} + \mathrm{H{-}\ddot{O}{-}H} \rightleftharpoons \left[\mathrm{H{-}\ddot{O}(H){-}H}\right]^+ + \left[:\ddot{O}{-}H\right]^-$$

In this reaction one water molecule acts as an acid by furnishing a proton, and the other acts as a base by accepting the proton. This reaction also can be represented as follows:

Sulfuric acid (H_2SO_4)

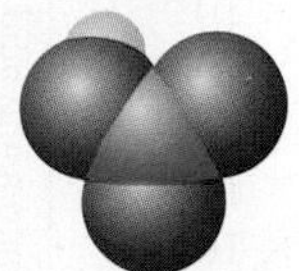

Nitric acid (HNO_3)

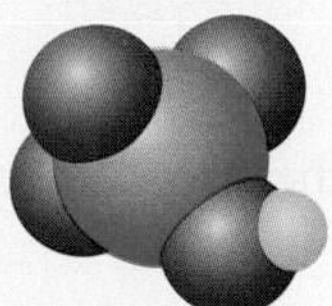

Perchloric acid ($HClO_4$)

Phosphoric acid (H_3PO_4)

Nitrous acid (HNO_2)

Hypochlorous acid (HOCl)

Autoionization can occur in other liquids as well. For example, in liquid ammonia the autoionization reaction is

$$\mathrm{H{-}\ddot{N}H{-}H} + \mathrm{H{-}\ddot{N}H{-}H} \rightleftharpoons \left[\mathrm{NH_4}\right]^+ + \left[\mathrm{H{-}\ddot{\underset{..}{N}}{-}H}\right]^-$$

The autoionization reaction for water

$$2H_2O(l) \rightleftharpoons H_3O^+(aq) + OH^-(aq)$$

leads to the equilibrium expression

$$K_w = [H_3O^+][OH^-] = [H^+][OH^-]$$

where K_w, called the **ion-product constant** (or the *dissociation constant*), always refers to the autoionization of water.

Experiment shows that at 25°C

$$[H^+] = [OH^-] = 1.0 \times 10^{-7}\ M$$

which means that at 25°C

$$K_w = [H^+][OH^-] = (1.0 \times 10^{-7}\ \text{mol/L})(1.0 \times 10^{-7}\ \text{mol/L})$$
$$= 1.0 \times 10^{-14}\ \text{mol}^2/\text{L}^2$$

The units are customarily omitted, for reasons discussed in Section 6.3.

It is important to recognize the meaning of K_w. In any aqueous solution at 25°C, *no matter what it contains,* the product of $[H^+]$ and $[OH^-]$ must always equal 1.0×10^{-14}. There are three possible situations:

1. A neutral solution, where $[H^+] = [OH^-]$
2. An acidic solution, where $[H^+] > [OH^-]$
3. A basic solution, where $[OH^-] > [H^+]$

In each case, however, at 25°C

$$K_w = [H^+][OH^-] = 1.0 \times 10^{-14}$$

EXAMPLE 7.2

At 60°C the value of K_w is 1×10^{-13}.

a. Using Le Châtelier's principle, predict whether the reaction

$$2H_2O(l) \rightleftharpoons H_3O^+(aq) + OH^-(aq)$$

is exothermic (releases energy) or endothermic (absorbs energy).

b. Calculate $[H^+]$ and $[OH^-]$ in a neutral solution at 60°C.

Solution

a. K_w *increases* from 1×10^{-14} at 25°C to 1×10^{-13} at 60°C. Le Châtelier's principle states that if a system at equilibrium is heated, it will adjust to consume energy. Since the value of K_w increases with temperature, we think of energy as a reactant, and so the process must be endothermic.

b. At 60°C $\qquad [H^+][OH^-] = 1 \times 10^{-13}$

For a neutral solution

$$[H^+] = [OH^-] = \sqrt{1 \times 10^{-13}} = 3 \times 10^{-7}\ M$$

7.3 The pH Scale

Because $[H^+]$ in an aqueous solution is typically quite small, the pH scale provides a convenient way to represent solution acidity. The pH is a log scale based on 10, where

$$pH = -\log[H^+]$$

Thus, for a solution in which

$$[H^+] = 1.0 \times 10^{-7}\ M$$

then

$$pH = -(-7.00) = 7.00$$

The pH scale is a compact way to represent solution acidity. It involves base-10 logs, not natural logs (ln).

The definition of pH in terms of $[H^+]$ neglects any correction for nonideality of the solutions.

At this point we need to discuss significant figures for logarithms. The rule is that *the number of decimal places in the log is equal to the number of significant figures in the original number.* Thus

$$\underbrace{[H^+] = 1.0 \times 10^{-9}\ M}_{\text{2 significant figures}}$$

$$\underbrace{pH = 9.00}_{\text{2 decimal places}}$$

Similar log scales are used for representing other quantities. For example,

$$pOH = -\log[OH^-]$$

$$pK = -\log K$$

Since pH is a log scale based on 10, *the pH changes by 1 for every power of 10 change in $[H^+]$.* For example, a solution of pH 3 has an H^+ concentration 10 times that of a solution of pH 4 and 100 times that of a solution of pH 5. Also note that because pH is defined as $-\log[H^+]$, *the pH decreases as $[H^+]$ increases.* The pH scale and the pH values for several common substances are shown in Fig. 7.3.

The pH of a solution is usually measured by using a pH meter, an electronic device with a probe that is inserted into a solution of unknown pH. The probe contains an acidic aqueous solution enclosed by a special glass membrane that allows migration of H^+ ions. If the unknown solution has a different pH from that of the solution in the probe, an electrical potential results, which is registered on the meter (Fig. 7.4).

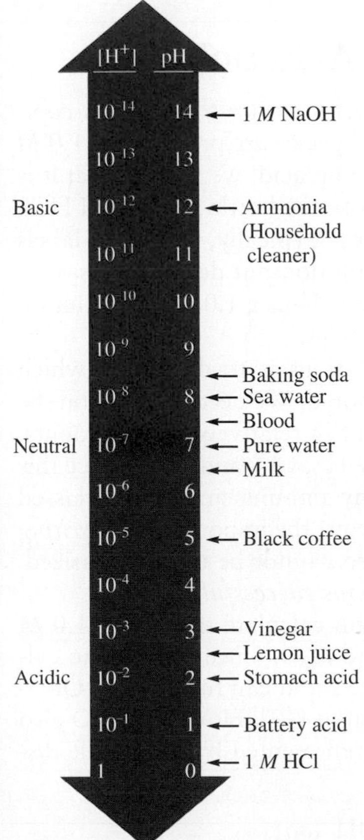

Figure 7.3
The pH scale and pH values of some common substances.

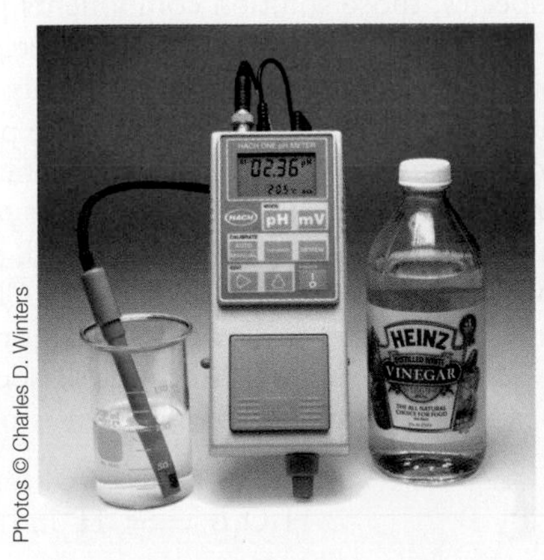

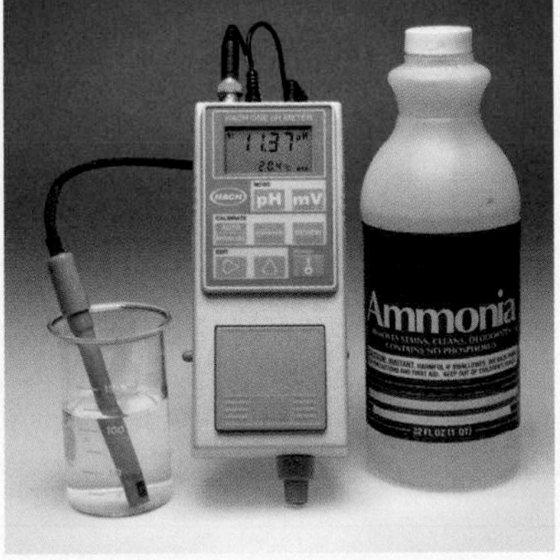

Photos © Charles D. Winters

(a) (b)

Figure 7.4
(a) Measuring the pH of vinegar. (b) Measuring the pH of aqueous ammonia.

Now that we have considered all the fundamental definitions relevant to acid–base solutions, we can proceed to a quantitative description of the equilibria present in these solutions. The main reason that acid–base problems sometimes seem difficult is that because a typical aqueous solution contains many components, the problems tend to be complicated. However, you can deal with these problems successfully if you use the following general strategies.

General Strategies for Solving Acid–Base Problems

1. *Think chemistry.* Focus on the solution components and their reactions. It will almost always be possible to choose one reaction that is the most important.
2. *Be systematic.* Acid–base problems require a step-by-step approach.
3. *Be flexible.* Although all acid–base problems are similar in many ways, important differences do occur. Treat each problem as a separate entity. Do not try to force a given problem to match any you have solved before. Look for both the similarities and the differences.
4. *Be patient.* The complete solution to a complicated problem cannot be seen immediately in all its detail. Pick the problem apart into workable steps.
5. *Be confident.* Look within the problem for the solution, and let the problem guide you. Assume that you can think it out. Do not rely on memorizing solutions to problems. In fact, memorizing solutions is usually detrimental because you tend to try to force a new problem to be the same as one you have seen before. *Understand and think; don't just memorize.*

7.4 Calculating the pH of Strong Acid Solutions

When we deal with acid–base equilibria, *we must focus on the solution components and their chemistry.* For example, what species are present in a 1.0 *M* solution of HCl? Since hydrochloric acid is a strong acid, we assume that it is completely dissociated. Thus, although the label on the bottle says 1.0 *M* HCl, the solution contains virtually no HCl molecules. Typically, container labels indicate the substance(s) used to make up the solution but do not necessarily describe the solution components after dissolution. Thus a 1.0 *M* HCl solution contains H^+ and Cl^- ions rather than HCl molecules.

The next step in dealing with aqueous solutions is to determine which components are significant and which can be ignored. We need to focus on the **major species,** those solution components present in relatively large amounts. In 1.0 *M* HCl, for example, the major species are H^+, Cl^-, and H_2O. Since this solution is very acidic, OH^- is present only in tiny amounts and thus is classed as a minor species. In attacking acid–base problems, the importance of *writing the major species in the solution* as the first step cannot be overemphasized. *This single step is the key to solving these problems successfully.*

Always write the major species present in the solution.

To illustrate the main ideas involved, we will calculate the pH of 1.0 *M* HCl. We first list the major species: H^+, Cl^-, and H_2O. Since we want to calculate the pH, we will focus on those major species that can furnish H^+. Obviously, we must consider H^+ from the dissociation of HCl. However, H_2O also furnishes H^+ by autoionization, which is often represented by the simple dissociation reaction

$$H_2O(l) \rightleftharpoons H^+(aq) + OH^-(aq)$$

The H^+ from the strong acid drives the equilibrium $H_2O \rightleftharpoons H^+ + OH^-$ to the left.

But is autoionization an important source of H^+ ions? In pure water at 25°C, $[H^+]$ is 10^{-7} *M*. In 1.0 *M* HCl the water will produce even less than 10^{-7} *M* H^+, since by Le Châtelier's principle the H^+ from the dissociated HCl will drive the position of the water equilibrium to the left. Thus the amount of H^+ contributed by water is negligible compared with the 1.0 M H^+ from the dissociation of HCl. Therefore we can say that $[H^+]$ in the solution is 1.0 M and that

$$\text{pH} = -\log[H^+] = -\log(1.0) = 0.00$$

7.5 Calculating the pH of Weak Acid Solutions

Since a weak acid dissolved in water can be viewed as a prototype of almost any equilibrium occurring in aqueous solution, we will proceed carefully and systematically. Although some of the procedures we develop here may seem superfluous, they will become essential as the problems become more complicated. We will develop the necessary strategies by calculating the pH of a 1.00 M solution of HF ($K_a = 7.2 \times 10^{-4}$).

First, as always, write the major species present in the solution.

The first step, as always, is to *write the major species in the solution.* From its small K_a value, we know that hydrofluoric acid is a weak acid and will be dissociated only to a slight extent. Thus when we write the major species, the hydrofluoric acid will be represented in its dominant form, as HF. The major species in solution are HF and H_2O.

Major Species

 HF

H_2O

The next step is to decide which of the major species can furnish H^+ ions. Actually, both major species can do so:

$$HF(aq) \rightleftharpoons H^+(aq) + F^-(aq) \qquad K_a = 7.2 \times 10^{-4}$$

$$H_2O(l) \rightleftharpoons H^+(aq) + OH^-(aq) \qquad K_w = 1.0 \times 10^{-14}$$

In aqueous solutions typically one source of H^+ can be singled out as dominant. By comparing K_a for HF with K_w for H_2O, we see that hydrofluoric acid, although weak, is still a much stronger acid than water. Thus we will assume that hydrofluoric acid will be the dominant source of H^+. We will ignore the tiny contribution expected from water.

Just as with gas-phase equilibria, the equilibrium constant expressions for reactions in solution actually require activities. In all our calculations, we will assume that $a_x = [x]$, where x represents a species in solution.

Therefore, it is the dissociation of HF that will determine the equilibrium concentration of H^+ and hence the pH:

$$HF(aq) \rightleftharpoons H^+(aq) + F^-(aq)$$

The equilibrium expression is

$$K_a = 7.2 \times 10^{-4} = \frac{[H^+][F^-]}{[HF]}$$

To solve the equilibrium problem, we follow the procedures developed in Chapter 6 for gas-phase equilibria. First, we list the initial concentrations, the *concentrations before the reaction of interest has proceeded to equilibrium.* Before any HF dissociates, the concentrations of the species in the equilibrium are

$$[HF]_0 = 1.00\ M, \qquad [F^-]_0 = 0, \qquad \text{and} \qquad [H^+]_0 = 10^{-7}\ M \approx 0$$

(Note that the zero value for $[H^+]_0$ is an approximation, since we are neglecting the H^+ ions from the autoionization of water.)

The next step is to determine the change required to reach equilibrium. Since some HF will dissociate to come to equilibrium (but that amount is presently unknown), we let x be the change in the concentration of HF that is required to achieve equilibrium. That is, we assume that x moles per liter of HF will dissociate to produce x moles per liter of H^+ and x moles per liter of F^- as the system adjusts to its equilibrium position. Now the equilibrium concentrations can be defined in terms of x:

$$[HF] = [HF]_0 - x = 1.00 - x$$

$$[F^-] = [F^-]_0 + x = 0 + x = x$$

$$[H^+] = [H^+]_0 + x \approx 0 + x = x$$

Substituting these equilibrium concentrations into the equilibrium expression gives

$$K_a = 7.2 \times 10^{-4} = \frac{[H^+][F^-]}{[HF]} = \frac{(x)(x)}{1.00 - x}$$

This expression produces a quadratic equation that can be solved by using the quadratic formula, as for the gas-phase systems in Chapter 6. However, since K_a for HF is so small, HF will dissociate only slightly; thus x is expected to be small. This will allow us to simplify the calculation. If x is very small compared with 1.00, the term in the denominator can be approximated as follows:

$$1.00 - x \approx 1.00$$

The equilibrium expression then becomes

$$7.2 \times 10^{-4} = \frac{(x)(x)}{1.00 - x} \approx \frac{(x)(x)}{1.00}$$

which yields

$$x^2 \approx (7.2 \times 10^{-4})(1.00) = 7.2 \times 10^{-4}$$

$$x \approx \sqrt{7.2 \times 10^{-4}} = 2.7 \times 10^{-2}$$

The validity of an approximation should always be checked.

How valid is the approximation that $[HF] = 1.00\ M$? Because this question will arise often in connection with acid–base equilibrium calculations, we will consider it carefully. *The validity of the approximation depends on how much accuracy we demand for the calculated value of [H⁺].* Typically, the K_a values for acids are known to an accuracy of only about ±5%. Therefore, it is reasonable to apply this figure when determining the validity of the approximation

Note that although the 5% rule is an arbitrary choice, it makes sense because of the typical uncertainty in K_a values. Be aware that the precision of the data for a particular situation should be used to evaluate which approximations are reasonable.

$$[HA]_0 - x \approx [HA]_0$$

We will use the following test.

First calculate the value of x by making the approximation

$$K_a = \frac{x^2}{[HA]_0 - x} \approx \frac{x^2}{[HA]_0}$$

where

$$x^2 \approx K_a[HA]_0 \quad \text{and} \quad x \approx \sqrt{K_a[HA]_0}$$

Then compare the sizes of x and $[HA]_0$. If the expression

$$\frac{x}{[HA]_0} \times 100\%$$

is less than or equal to 5%, the value of x is small enough for the approximation

$$[HA]_0 - x \approx [HA]_0$$

to be considered valid.

In our example

$$x = 2.7 \times 10^{-2}\ \text{mol/L}$$

$$[HA]_0 = [HF]_0 = 1.00\ \text{mol/L}$$

and

$$\frac{x}{[HA]_0} \times 100\% = \frac{2.7 \times 10^{-2}}{1.00} \times 100\% = 2.7\%$$

The approximation we made is considered valid, so the value of x calculated by using that approximation is acceptable. Thus

$$x = [H^+] = 2.7 \times 10^{-2}\,M \qquad \text{and} \qquad pH = -\log(2.7 \times 10^{-2}) = 1.57$$

This problem illustrates all the important steps required for solving a typical equilibrium problem involving a weak acid. These steps are summarized below.

STEPS

Solving Weak Acid Equilibrium Problems

1. List the major species in the solution.
2. Choose the species that can produce H^+, and write balanced equations for the reactions producing H^+.
3. Comparing the values of the equilibrium constants for the reactions you have written, decide which reaction will dominate in the production of H^+.
4. Write the equilibrium expression for the dominant reaction.
5. List the initial concentrations of the species participating in the dominant reaction.
6. Define the change needed to achieve equilibrium; that is, define x.
7. Write the equilibrium concentrations in terms of x.
8. Substitute the equilibrium concentrations into the equilibrium expression.
9. Solve for x the "easy" way—that is, by assuming that $[HA]_0 - x \approx [HA]_0$.
10. Verify whether the approximation is valid (the 5% rule is the test in this case).
11. Calculate $[H^+]$ and pH.

The pH of a Mixture of Weak Acids

A table of K_a values for various weak acids is given in Appendix Table A5.1.

Sometimes a solution contains two weak acids of very different strengths. This situation is considered in Example 7.3. Note that the usual steps are followed (although not labeled).

EXAMPLE 7.3

Calculate the pH of a solution that contains 1.00 M HCN ($K_a = 6.2 \times 10^{-10}$) and 5.00 M HNO_2 ($K_a = 4.0 \times 10^{-4}$). Also calculate the concentration of cyanide ion (CN^-) in this solution at equilibrium.

Major Species

HCN

HNO_2

H_2O

Solution Since HCN and HNO_2 are both weak acids and are thus primarily undissociated, the major species in the solution are

$$HCN, \qquad HNO_2, \qquad \text{and} \qquad H_2O$$

All three components produce H^+:

$$HCN(aq) \rightleftharpoons H^+(aq) + CN^-(aq) \qquad K_a = 6.2 \times 10^{-10}$$

$$HNO_2(aq) \rightleftharpoons H^+(aq) + NO_2^-(aq) \qquad K_a = 4.0 \times 10^{-4}$$

$$H_2O(l) \rightleftharpoons H^+(aq) + OH^-(aq) \qquad K_w = 1.0 \times 10^{-14}$$

A mixture of three acids might lead to a very complicated problem. However, the situation is greatly simplified by the fact that even though HNO_2 is a weak acid, it is much stronger than the other two acids present (as revealed by the K values). Thus HNO_2 can be assumed to be the dominant producer of H^+, so we will focus on the equilibrium expression:

$$K_a = 4.0 \times 10^{-4} = \frac{[H^+][NO_2^-]}{[HNO_2]}$$

The initial concentrations, the definition of x, and the equilibrium concentrations are as follows:

Initial Concentration (mol/L)		Equilibrium Concentration (mol/L)
$[HNO_2]_0 = 5.00$ $[NO_2^-]_0 = 0$ $[H^+]_0 \approx 0$	$\xrightarrow[\text{dissociates}]{x \text{ mol/L } HNO_2}$	$[HNO_2] = 5.00 - x$ $[NO_2^-] = x$ $[H^+] = x$

It is often convenient to represent these concentrations in the following shorthand form:

	$HNO_2(aq)$	$\rightleftharpoons$	$H^+(aq)$	+	$NO_2^-(aq)$
Initial:	5.00		0		0
Change:	$-x$		$+x$		$+x$
Equilibrium:	$5.00 - x$		x		x

Substituting the equilibrium concentrations into the equilibrium expression and making the approximation that $5.00 - x = 5.00$ gives

$$K_a = 4.0 \times 10^{-4} = \frac{(x)(x)}{5.00 - x} \approx \frac{x^2}{5.00}$$

We solve for x: $$x = 4.5 \times 10^{-2}$$

Using the 5% rule we show that the approximation is valid:

$$\frac{x}{[HNO_2]_0} \times 100\% = \frac{4.5 \times 10^{-2}}{5.00} \times 100\% = 0.90\%$$

Therefore,

$$[H^+] = x = 4.5 \times 10^{-2}\ M \qquad \text{and} \qquad \text{pH} = 1.35$$

We also want to calculate the equilibrium concentration of cyanide ion in this solution. The CN^- ions in this solution come from the dissociation of HCN:

$$HCN(aq) \rightleftharpoons H^+(aq) + CN^-(aq)$$

Although the position of this equilibrium lies far to the left and does not contribute *significantly* to $[H^+]$, HCN is the *only source* of CN^-. Thus we must consider the extent of the dissociation of HCN to calculate $[CN^-]$. The equilibrium expression for the preceding reaction is

$$K_a = 6.2 \times 10^{-10} = \frac{[H^+][CN^-]}{[HCN]}$$

We know $[H^+]$ for this solution from the results for the first part of this problem. Note that *there is only one kind of H^+ in this solution.* It does not matter from which acid the H^+ ions originate. The equilibrium value of $[H^+]$ for the HCN dissociation is $4.5 \times 10^{-2}\ M$, even though the H^+ was contributed almost entirely by the dissociation of HNO_2. What is [HCN] at equilibrium? We know $[HCN]_0 = 1.00\ M$, and since K_a for HCN is so small, a negligible amount of HCN will dissociate.

Thus
$$[HCN] = [HCN]_0 - \text{amount of HCN dissociated}$$
$$\approx [HCN]_0 = 1.00\ M$$

Since $[H^+]$ and [HCN] are known, we can find $[CN^-]$ from the equilibrium expression:

$$K_a = 6.2 \times 10^{-10} = \frac{[H^+][CN^-]}{[HCN]} = \frac{(4.5 \times 10^{-2})[CN^-]}{1.00}$$

$$[CN^-] = \frac{(6.2 \times 10^{-10})(1.00)}{4.5 \times 10^{-2}} = 1.4 \times 10^{-8}\ M$$

Note the significance of this result. Since $[CN^-] = 1.4 \times 10^{-8}\ M$, and since HCN is the only source of CN^-, only 1.4×10^{-8} mol/L of HCN has dissociated. This is a very small amount compared with the initial concentration of HCN, which is exactly what we would expect from its very small K_a value. Thus $[HCN] = 1.00\ M$ as assumed. Also, this result confirms that HNO_2 is the only significant source of H^+.

Percent Dissociation

It is often useful to specify the amount of weak acid that has dissociated in achieving equilibrium in an aqueous solution. The **percent dissociation** is defined as follows:

$$\text{Percent dissociation} = \frac{\text{amount dissociated (mol/L)}}{\text{initial concentration (mol/L)}} \times 100\% \qquad (7.3)$$

For example, we found earlier that in a 1.00 *M* solution of HF, $[H^+] = 2.7 \times 10^{-2}\ M$. For the system to reach equilibrium, 2.7×10^{-2} moles per liter of the original 1.00 *M* HF dissociates, so

$$\text{Percent dissociation} = \frac{2.7 \times 10^{-2}\ \text{mol/L}}{1.00\ \text{mol/L}} \times 100\% = 2.7\%$$

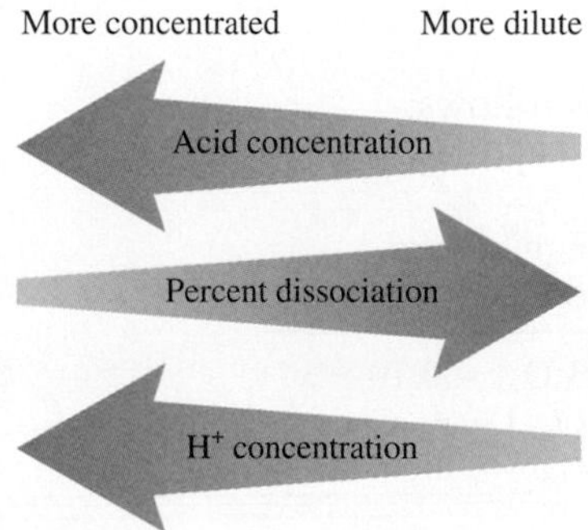

Figure 7.5
The effect of dilution on the percent dissociation and $[H^+]$ of a weak acid solution.

For a given weak acid, the percent dissociation increases as the acid becomes more dilute. For example, the percent dissociation of acetic acid ($HC_2H_3O_2$, $K_a = 1.8 \times 10^{-5}$) is significantly greater in a 0.10 *M* solution than in a 1.0 *M* solution.

Demonstrate for yourself (by doing the calculations) that even though the concentration of H^+ ion at equilibrium is smaller in the 0.10 *M* acetic acid solution than in the 1.0 *M* acetic acid solution, the percent dissociation is significantly greater in the 0.10 *M* solution (1.3%) than in the 1.0 *M* solution (0.42%). This is a general result. *For solutions of any weak acid HA, $[H^+]$ decreases as $[HA]_0$ decreases, but the percent dissociation increases as $[HA]_0$ decreases.*

This phenomenon can be explained in the following way. Consider the weak acid HA with the initial concentration $[HA]_0$. At equilibrium

$$[HA] = [HA]_0 - x \approx [HA]_0$$
$$[H^+] = [A^-] = x$$

Thus
$$K_a = \frac{[H^+][A^-]}{[HA]} \approx \frac{(x)(x)}{[HA_0]}$$

The more dilute the weak acid solution, the greater the percent dissociation.

Now suppose enough water is added to dilute the solution by a factor of 10. The new concentrations before any adjustment occurs are

$$[A^-]_{new} = [H^+]_{new} = \frac{x}{10}$$

$$[HA]_{new} = \frac{[HA]_0}{10}$$

and Q, the reaction quotient, is

$$Q = \frac{(x/10)(x/10)}{[HA]_0/10} = \frac{1(x)(x)}{10[HA]_0} = \frac{1}{10}K_a$$

Since Q is less than K_a, the system must adjust to the right to reach the new equilibrium position. Thus the percent dissociation increases as the acid becomes more dilute. This behavior is summarized in Fig. 7.5. In Example 7.4 we see how the percent dissociation can be used to calculate the K_a value for a weak acid.

Patrick Ward/Corbis

A runner struggles to the top of a hill during a cross-country race in the hills near Wasdale Head, England.

OWL INTERACTIVE EXAMPLE 7.4

Lactic acid ($HC_3H_5O_3$) is a waste product that accumulates in muscle tissue during exertion, leading to pain and a feeling of fatigue. In a 0.100 *M* aqueous solution, lactic acid is 3.7% dissociated. Calculate the value of K_a for this acid.

Solution The small value for the percent dissociation clearly indicates that $HC_3H_5O_3$ is a weak acid. Thus the major species in the solution are the undissociated acid and water:

$$HC_3H_5O_3 \quad \text{and} \quad H_2O$$

Major Species

$HC_3H_5O_3$

H_2O

Although $HC_3H_5O_3$ is a weak acid, it is much stronger than water and thus will be the dominant source of H^+ in the solution. The dissociation reaction is

$$HC_3H_5O_3(aq) \rightleftharpoons H^+(aq) + C_3H_5O_3^-(aq)$$

and the equilibrium expression is

$$K_a = \frac{[H^+][C_3H_5O_3^-]}{[HC_3H_5O_3]}$$

The initial and equilibrium concentrations are as follows:

Initial Concentration (mol/L)		Equilibrium Concentration (mol/L)
$[HC_3H_5O_3]_0 = 0.10$ $[C_3H_5O_3^-]_0 = 0$ $[H^+]_0 \approx 0$	$\xrightarrow[\text{dissociates}]{x \text{ mol/L } HC_3H_5O_3}$	$[HC_3H_5O_3] = 0.10 - x$ $[C_3H_5O_3^-] = x$ $[H^+] = x$

The change needed to reach equilibrium can be obtained from the percent dissociation and Equation (7.3). For this acid

$$\text{Percent dissociation} = 3.7\% = \frac{x}{[HC_3H_5O_3]_0} \times 100\% = \frac{x}{0.10} \times 100\%$$

and

$$x = \frac{3.7}{100}(0.10) = 3.7 \times 10^{-3} \text{ mol/L}$$

Now we can calculate the equilibrium concentrations:

$$[HC_3H_5O_3] = 0.10 - x = 0.10\ M \quad \text{(to the correct number of significant figures)}$$

$$[C_3H_5O_3^-] = [H^+] = x = 3.7 \times 10^{-3}\ M$$

These concentrations can now be used to calculate the value of K_a for lactic acid:

$$K_a = \frac{[H^+][C_3H_5O_3^-]}{[HC_3H_5O_3]} = \frac{(3.7 \times 10^{-3})(3.7 \times 10^{-3})}{0.10} = 1.4 \times 10^{-4}$$

7.6 Bases

In a basic solution pH > 7.

According to the Arrhenius concept, a base is a substance that produces OH^- ions in aqueous solution. According to the Brønsted–Lowry definition, a base is a proton acceptor. The bases sodium hydroxide (NaOH) and potassium hydroxide (KOH) fulfill both criteria. They contain OH^- ions in the solid lattice and behave as strong electrolytes, dissociating completely when dissolving in water:

$$NaOH(s) \xrightarrow{H_2O} Na^+(aq) + OH^-(aq)$$

Thus a 1.0 *M* NaOH solution actually contains 1.0 *M* Na^+ and 1.0 *M* OH^-. Because of their complete dissociation, NaOH and KOH are called **strong bases** in the same sense as we defined strong acids.

All the hydroxides of the Group 1A elements (LiOH, NaOH, KOH, RbOH, and CsOH) are strong bases, but only NaOH and KOH are common laboratory reagents because the lithium, rubidium, and cesium compounds are expensive. The alkaline earth (Group 2A) hydroxides—$Ca(OH)_2$, $Ba(OH)_2$, and $Sr(OH)_2$—are also strong bases. For these compounds, 2 moles of hydroxide ion are produced for every 1 mole of metal hydroxide dissolved in aqueous solution.

The alkaline earth hydroxides are not very soluble and are used only when the solubility factor is not important. In fact, the low solubility of these bases

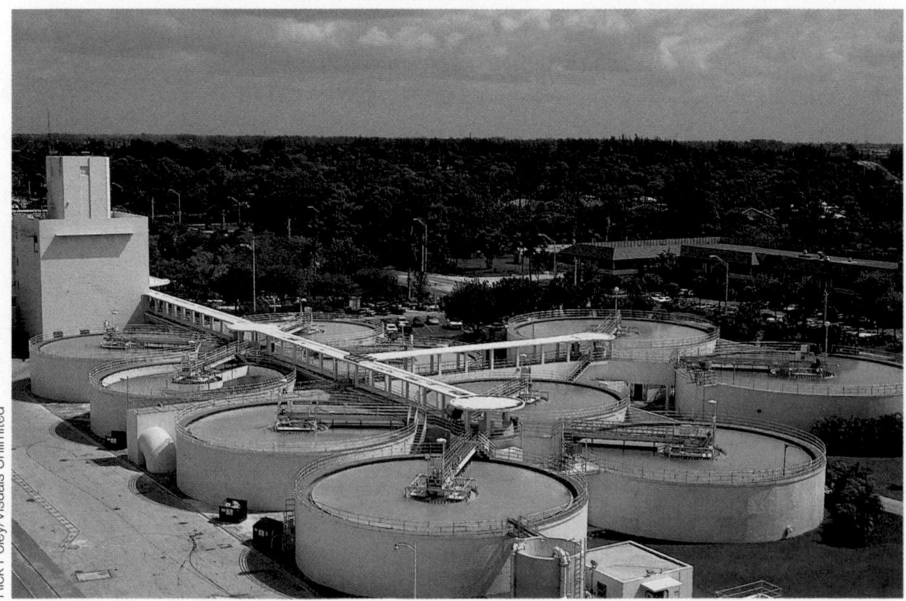

Rick Poley/Visuals Unlimited

Tanks in Miami, Florida, used to soften, filter, and disinfect the public water supply.

can be an advantage. For example, many antacids are suspensions of metal hydroxides such as aluminum hydroxide and magnesium hydroxide. The low solubility of these compounds prevents the formation of a large hydroxide ion concentration that would harm the tissues of the mouth, esophagus, and stomach. Yet these suspensions furnish plenty of hydroxide ion to react with stomach acid, since the salts dissolve as this reaction proceeds.

Calcium hydroxide [$Ca(OH)_2$], often called **slaked lime,** is widely used in industry because it is inexpensive and plentiful. For example, slaked lime is used in scrubbing stack gases to remove sulfur dioxide from the exhaust of power plants and factories. In the scrubbing process, a suspension of slaked lime is sprayed into the stack gases to react with sulfur dioxide gas according to the following equations:

$$SO_2(g) + H_2O(l) \rightleftharpoons H_2SO_3(aq)$$

$$Ca(OH)_2(aq) + H_2SO_3(aq) \rightleftharpoons CaSO_3(s) + 2H_2O(l)$$

Hard water contains Ca^{2+} and Mg^{2+} ions, among others, which are detrimental to detergent action.

Slaked lime is also widely used in water treatment plants for softening hard water, which involves the removal of ions such as Ca^{2+} and Mg^{2+}, ions that hamper the action of detergents. The softening method most often used in water treatment plants is the **lime–soda process,** in which *lime* (CaO) and *soda ash* (Na_2CO_3) are added to the water. As we will see in more detail later in this chapter, the CO_3^{2-} ion from soda ash reacts with water to produce the HCO_3^- ion. When lime is added to hard water, it forms slaked lime,

$$CaO(s) + H_2O(l) \longrightarrow Ca(OH)_2(aq)$$

which then reacts with the HCO_3^- ion and a Ca^{2+} ion to produce calcium carbonate:

$$Ca(OH)_2(aq) + \underset{\text{From hard water}}{\underset{\nearrow}{Ca^{2+}(aq)}} + 2HCO_3^-(aq) \longrightarrow 2CaCO_3(s) + 2H_2O(l)$$

Thus, for every mole of $Ca(OH)_2$ consumed, 1 mole of Ca^{2+} is removed from the hard water, thereby softening it. Some hard water naturally contains bicarbonate ions. In this case no soda ash is needed—simply adding lime accomplishes the softening.

Calculating the pH of a strong base solution is relatively simple, as illustrated in Example 7.5.

OWL INTERACTIVE EXAMPLE 7.5

Calculate the pH of a 5.0×10^{-2} *M* NaOH solution.

Major Species

Na^+

OH^-

H_2O

Solution The major species in this solution are

$$\underbrace{Na^+, \quad OH^-}_{\text{From NaOH}}, \quad \text{and} \quad H_2O$$

Although the autoionization of water also produces OH^- ions, the pH will be determined by the OH^- ions from the dissolved NaOH. Thus in the solution

$$[OH^-] = 5.0 \times 10^{-2}\ M$$

The concentration of H^+ can be calculated from K_w:

$$[H^+] = \frac{K_w}{[OH^-]} = \frac{1.0 \times 10^{-14}}{5.0 \times 10^{-2}} = 2.0 \times 10^{-13}\ M$$

$$pH = 12.70$$

Note that this solution is basic:

$$[OH^-] > [H^+] \quad \text{and} \quad pH > 7$$

The added OH^- from the salt has shifted the water autoionization equilibrium

$$H_2O(l) \rightleftharpoons H^+(aq) + OH^-(aq)$$

to the left, significantly lowering the $[H^+]$ compared with that in pure water.

A base does not have to contain the hydroxide ion.

Many types of proton acceptors (bases) do not contain the hydroxide ion. However, when dissolved in water, these substances increase the concentration of hydroxide ion by reacting with water. For example, ammonia reacts with water as follows:

$$NH_3(aq) + H_2O(l) \rightleftharpoons NH_4^+(aq) + OH^-(aq)$$

The ammonia molecule accepts a proton and thus functions as a base. Water is the acid in this reaction. Note that even though the base ammonia contains no hydroxide ion, it still increases the concentration of hydroxide ion to yield a basic solution.

Bases like ammonia typically have at least one unshared pair of electrons that is capable of forming a bond with a proton. The reaction of an ammonia molecule with a water molecule can be represented as follows:

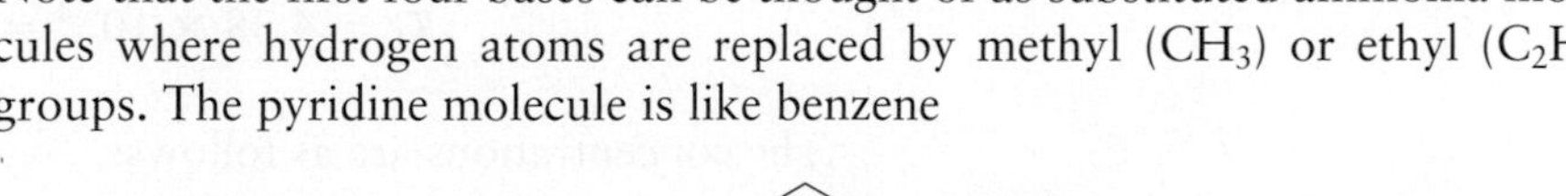

There are many bases like ammonia that produce hydroxide ions by reaction with water. In most of these bases, the lone pair is located on a nitrogen atom. Some examples are

Note that the first four bases can be thought of as substituted ammonia molecules where hydrogen atoms are replaced by methyl (CH_3) or ethyl (C_2H_5) groups. The pyridine molecule is like benzene

Benzene (C_6H_6) is often represented by the symbol

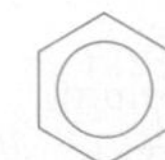

where each vertex represents a carbon atom. The hydrogen atoms are not shown.

except that a nitrogen atom has replaced one of the carbon atoms in the ring.

The general reaction between a base (B) and water is given by

$$\underset{\text{Base}}{B(aq)} + \underset{\text{Acid}}{H_2O(l)} \rightleftharpoons \underset{\substack{\text{Conjugate}\\\text{acid}}}{BH^+(aq)} + \underset{\substack{\text{Conjugate}\\\text{base}}}{OH^-(aq)} \tag{7.4}$$

Appendix Table A5.3 contains K_b values.

The equilibrium reaction for this general solution is

$$K_b = \frac{[BH^+][OH^-]}{[B]}$$

where K_b *always refers to the reaction of a base with water to form the conjugate acid and the hydroxide ion.*

Table 7.3

Values of K_b for Some Common Weak Bases

Name	Formula	Conjugate Acid	K_b
Ammonia	NH_3	NH_4^+	1.8×10^{-5}
Methylamine	CH_3NH_2	$CH_3NH_3^+$	4.38×10^{-4}
Ethylamine	$C_2H_5NH_2$	$C_2H_5NH_3^+$	5.6×10^{-4}
Aniline	$C_6H_5NH_2$	$C_6H_5NH_3^+$	3.8×10^{-10}
Pyridine	C_5H_5N	$C_5H_5NH^+$	1.7×10^{-9}

Bases of the type represented by B in Equation (7.4) compete with OH^-, a very strong base, for the H^+ ion. Thus their K_b values tend to be small (for example, for ammonia $K_b = 1.8 \times 10^{-5}$), and they are called **weak bases.** The K_b values for some common weak bases are listed in Table 7.3.

Typically, pH calculations for solutions of weak bases are very similar to those for weak acids.

OWL INTERACTIVE EXAMPLE 7.6

Major Species

CH_3NH_2

H_2O

Calculate the pH of a 1.0 *M* solution of methylamine ($K_b = 4.38 \times 10^{-4}$).

Solution Since methylamine (CH_3NH_2) is a weak base, the major species in solution are

$$CH_3NH_2 \quad \text{and} \quad H_2O$$

Both are bases; however, since water can be neglected as a source of OH^-, the dominant equilibrium is

$$CH_3NH_2(aq) + H_2O(l) \rightleftharpoons CH_3NH_3^+(aq) + OH^-(aq)$$

and

$$K_b = 4.38 \times 10^{-4} = \frac{[CH_3NH_3^+][OH^-]}{[CH_3NH_2]}$$

The concentrations are as follows:

Initial Concentration (mol/L)		Equilibrium Concentration (mol/L)
$[CH_3NH_2]_0 = 1.0$	*x* mol/L CH_3NH_2 reacts with H_2O to reach equilibrium →	$[CH_3NH_2] = 1.0 - x$
$[CH_3NH_3^+]_0 = 0$		$[CH_3NH_3^+] = x$
$[OH^-]_0 \approx 0$		$[OH^-] = x$

Or in shorthand form:

	$CH_3NH_2(aq)$	+	$H_2O(l)$	$\rightleftharpoons$	$CH_3NH_3^+(aq)$	+	$OH^-(aq)$
Initial:	1.0		—		0		0
Change:	$-x$		—		$+x$		$+x$
Equilibrium:	$1.0 - x$		—		x		x

Amines

Chemical Insights

We have seen that many bases have nitrogen atoms with one lone pair of electrons. These bases can be viewed as substituted ammonia molecules, with the general formula $R_xNH_{(3-x)}$. Compounds of this type are called **amines.**

Amines are widely distributed in animals and plants, often serving as messengers or regulators. For example, in the human nervous system there are two amine stimulants, *norepinephrine* and *adrenaline:*

Norepinephrine: (HO)$_2C_6H_3$–CH(OH)CH_2NH_2

Norepinephrine

Adrenaline: (HO)$_2C_6H_3$–CH(OH)CH_2NHCH_3

Adrenaline

Ephedrine, widely used as a decongestant, was a known drug in China over 2000 years ago. People from cultures in Mexico and the Southwest have used the hallucinogen *mescaline,* extracted from peyote cactus, for centuries.

A peyote cactus in bloom.

C_6H_5–CH(O–H)–CH(CH_3)–N(H)–CH_3

Ephedrine

$CH_2CH_2NH_2$ on a benzene ring bearing three O–CH_3 groups

Mescaline

Many other drugs, such as codeine and quinine, are amines, but they are rarely used in their pure amine forms. Instead, they are treated with an acid to become acid salts. An example of an acid salt is ammonium chloride, obtained by the reaction

$$NH_3 + HCl \longrightarrow NH_4Cl$$

Amines can also be protonated in this way. The resulting acid salt, written as AHCl (where A represents the amine), contains AH^+ and Cl^-. In general, the acid salts are more stable and more soluble in water than the parent amines. For instance, the parent amine of the well-known local anaesthetic *novocaine* is water-insoluble, but the acid salt is much more soluble.

H_2N–C_6H_4–C(=O)–O–CH_2–CH_2–$N^+H(CH_2CH_3)_2$ Cl^-

Novocaine hydrochloride

Substituting the equilibrium concentrations into the equilibrium expression and making the usual approximation gives

$$K_b = 4.38 \times 10^{-4} = \frac{[CH_3NH_3^+][OH^-]}{[CH_3NH_2]} = \frac{(x)(x)}{1.0 - x} \approx \frac{x^2}{1.0}$$

$$x \approx 2.1 \times 10^{-2}$$

The approximation is valid by the 5% rule, so

$$[OH^-] = x = 2.1 \times 10^{-2}\ M \text{ and pOH} = 1.68$$

Note that since $[H^+][OH^-] = 1.0 \times 10^{-14}$, pH + pOH = 14. Thus pH = 14.00 − 1.68 = 12.32.

7.7 Polyprotic Acids

Some important acids, such as sulfuric acid (H_2SO_4) and phosphoric acid (H_3PO_4), can furnish more than one proton per molecule and are called **polyprotic acids.** A polyprotic acid always dissociates in a *stepwise* manner, one proton at a time.

Carbonic Acid

The diprotic (two-proton) *carbonic acid* (H_2CO_3), which is vital for maintaining a constant pH in human blood, dissociates in the following steps:

$$H_2CO_3(aq) \rightleftharpoons H^+(aq) + HCO_3^-(aq) \qquad K_{a_1} = \frac{[H^+][HCO_3^-]}{[H_2CO_3]} = 4.3 \times 10^{-7}$$

$$HCO_3^-(aq) \rightleftharpoons H^+(aq) + CO_3^{2-}(aq) \qquad K_{a_2} = \frac{[H^+][CO_3^{2-}]}{[HCO_3^-]} = 4.8 \times 10^{-11}$$

The successive K_a values for the dissociation equilibria are designated K_{a_1} and K_{a_2}. Note that the conjugate base HCO_3^- of the first dissociation equilibrium becomes the acid in the second step.

Carbonic acid is formed when carbon dioxide gas is dissolved in water. In fact, the first dissociation step for carbonic acid is best represented by the reaction

$$CO_2(aq) + H_2O(l) \rightleftharpoons H^+(aq) + HCO_3^-(aq)$$

since relatively little H_2CO_3 actually exists in solution. However, it is convenient to consider CO_2 in water as H_2CO_3 so that we can treat such solutions by using the familiar dissociation reactions for weak acids.

Any solution of carbonic acid contains various amounts of all three species—$H_2CO_3(CO_2, H_2O)$, HCO_3^-, and CO_3^{2-}—depending on the pH of the solution. At a given pH, the fractions of the various species can be calculated from the dissociation equilibrium constants as shown in Example 7.7.

OWL INTERACTIVE EXAMPLE 7.7

Calculate the fractions of H_2CO_3, HCO_3^-, and CO_3^{2-} at pH 9.00.

Solution The fraction of each species present is the concentration of that species divided by the total concentrations of all three species. For example, for HCO_3^- we have

$$\text{Fraction } HCO_3^- = \frac{[HCO_3^-]}{[H_2CO_3] + [HCO_3^-] + [CO_3^{2-}]} = f_{HCO_3^-}$$

Dividing the numerator and denominator by $[HCO_3^-]$ gives

$$f_{HCO_3^-} = \frac{1}{\frac{[H_2CO_3]}{[HCO_3^-]} + 1 + \frac{[CO_3^{2-}]}{[HCO_3^-]}}$$

We can calculate the $[H_2CO_3]/[HCO_3^-]$ ratio from K_{a_1}:

$$K_{a_1} = \frac{[H^+][HCO_3^-]}{[H_2CO_3]}$$

or

$$\frac{[H_2CO_3]}{[HCO_3^-]} = \frac{[H^+]}{K_{a_1}}$$

Since $K_{a_1} = 4.3 \times 10^{-7}$ and pH $= 9.00$ ($[H^+] = 1.00 \times 10^{-9}$),

$$\frac{[H_2CO_3]}{[HCO_3^-]} = \frac{1.00 \times 10^{-9}}{4.3 \times 10^{-7}} = 2.3 \times 10^{-3}$$

We can use K_{a_2} to calculate the $[CO_3^{2-}]/[HCO_3^-]$ ratio:

$$K_{a_2} = \frac{[H^+][CO_3^{2-}]}{[HCO_3^-]} = 4.8 \times 10^{-11}$$

so

$$\frac{[CO_3^{2-}]}{[HCO_3^-]} = \frac{K_{a_2}}{[H^+]} = \frac{4.8 \times 10^{-11}}{1.00 \times 10^{-9}} = 4.8 \times 10^{-2}$$

Now we can calculate the fraction of $[HCO_3^-]$ present:

$$f_{HCO_3^-} = \frac{1}{\frac{[H_2CO_3]}{[HCO_3^-]} + 1 + \frac{[CO_3^{2-}]}{[HCO_3^-]}} = \frac{1}{2.3 \times 10^{-3} + 1 + 4.8 \times 10^{-2}}$$

$$= \frac{1}{1.05} = 0.95$$

Note that at pH 9, HCO_3^- represents 95% of the carbonate-containing species in the solution.

Similar calculations can be used to find the fraction of each species over the entire pH range. A graph of the results of these calculations is shown in Fig. 7.6.

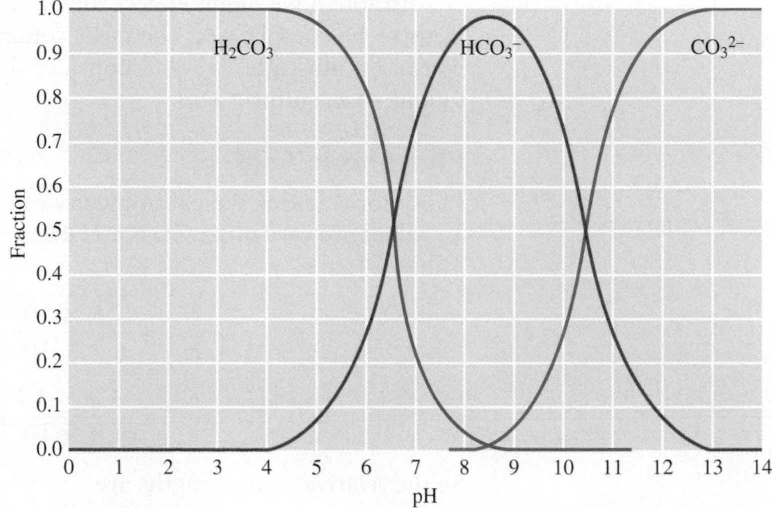

Figure 7.6
A plot of the fractions of H_2CO_3, HCO_3^-, and CO_3^{2-} in aqueous solution as a function of pH.

Table 7.4

Stepwise Dissociation Constants for Several Common Polyprotic Acids

Name	Formula	K_{a_1}	K_{a_2}	K_{a_3}
Phosphoric acid	H_3PO_4	7.5×10^{-3}	6.2×10^{-8}	4.8×10^{-13}
Arsenic acid	H_3AsO_4	5×10^{-3}	8×10^{-8}	6×10^{-10}
Carbonic acid*	H_2CO_3	4.3×10^{-7}	4.8×10^{-11}	
Sulfuric acid	H_2SO_4	Large	1.2×10^{-2}	
Sulfurous acid	H_2SO_3	1.5×10^{-2}	1.0×10^{-7}	
Hydrosulfuric acid†	H_2S	1.0×10^{-7}	$\approx 10^{-19}$	
Oxalic acid	$H_2C_2O_4$	6.5×10^{-2}	6.1×10^{-5}	
Ascorbic acid (vitamin C)	$H_2C_6H_6O_6$	7.9×10^{-5}	1.6×10^{-12}	

*This is really $CO_2(aq)$.
†The K_{a_2} value for H_2S is quite uncertain. Its small size makes it very difficult to measure.

Phosphoric acid is a **triprotic acid** (three protons) that dissociates in the following steps:

$$H_3PO_4(aq) \rightleftharpoons H^+(aq) + H_2PO_4^{2-}(aq) \qquad K_{a_1} = \frac{[H^+][H_2PO_4^-]}{[H_3PO_4]} = 7.5 \times 10^{-3}$$

$$H_2PO_4^{2-}(aq) \rightleftharpoons H^+(aq) + HPO_4^{2-}(aq) \qquad K_{a_2} = \frac{[H^+][HPO_4^{2-}]}{[H_2PO_4^-]} = 6.2 \times 10^{-8}$$

$$HPO_4^{2-}(aq) \rightleftharpoons H^+(aq) + PO_4^{3-}(aq) \qquad K_{a_3} = \frac{[H^+][PO_4^{3-}]}{[HPO_4^{2-}]} = 4.8 \times 10^{-13}$$

For a typical, weak polyprotic acid,

$$K_{a_1} > K_{a_2} > K_{a_3}$$

That is, the acid involved in each successive step of the dissociation is weaker. This is shown by the stepwise dissociation constants given in Table 7.4. These values indicate that the loss of a second or third proton occurs less readily than loss of the first proton. This result is not surprising; the greater the negative charge on the acid, the more difficult it becomes to remove the positively charged proton.

Although we might expect the pH calculations for solutions of polyprotic acids to be complicated, the most common cases are surprisingly straightforward. To illustrate, we will consider a typical case, phosphoric acid, and a unique case, sulfuric acid.

Phosphoric Acid

Phosphoric acid is typical of most weak polyprotic acids in that its successive K_a values are very different. For H_3PO_4, the ratios of successive K_a values (from Table 7.4) are

$$\frac{K_{a_1}}{K_{a_2}} = \frac{7.5 \times 10^{-3}}{6.2 \times 10^{-8}} = 1.2 \times 10^5$$

$$\frac{K_{a_2}}{K_{a_3}} = \frac{6.2 \times 10^{-8}}{4.8 \times 10^{-13}} = 1.3 \times 10^5$$

So the relative acid strengths are

$$H_3PO_4 \gg H_2PO_4^- \gg HPO_4^{2-}$$

For a typical polyprotic acid in water, only the first dissociation step is important in determining the pH.

This means that in a solution prepared by dissolving H_3PO_4 in water, *only the first dissociation step makes an important contribution to [H^+]*. This greatly simplifies the pH calculations for phosphoric acid solutions, as is illustrated in Example 7.8.

EXAMPLE 7.8

Major Species

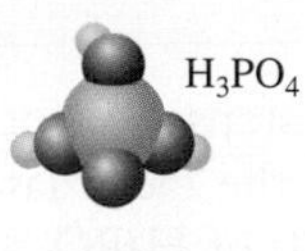

Calculate the pH of a 5.0 *M* H_3PO_4 solution and determine equilibrium concentrations of the species H_3PO_4, $H_2PO_4^-$, HPO_4^{2-}, and PO_4^{3-}.

Solution The major species in solution are

$$H_3PO_4 \quad \text{and} \quad H_2O$$

None of the dissociation products of H_3PO_4 is written, since the K_a values are all so small that they will be minor species. The dominant equilibrium will be the dissociation of H_3PO_4:

$$H_3PO_4(aq) \rightleftharpoons H^+(aq) + H_2PO_4^-(aq)$$

where $K_{a_1} = 7.5 \times 10^{-3} = \dfrac{[H^+][H_2PO_4^-]}{[H_3PO_4]}$

The concentrations are as follows:

Initial Concentration (mol/L)		Equilibrium Concentration (mol/L)
$[H_3PO_4]_0 = 5.0$	x mol/L H_3PO_4	$[H_3PO_4] = 5.0 - x$
$[H_2PO_4^-]_0 = 0$	$\longrightarrow$	$[H_2PO_4^-] = x$
$[H^+]_0 \approx 0$	dissociates	$[H^+] = x$

Or in shorthand form:

	$H_3PO_4(aq)$	$\rightleftharpoons$	$H^+(aq)$	+	$H_2PO_4^-(aq)$
Initial:	5.0		0		0
Change:	$-x$		$+x$		$+x$
Equilibrium:	$5.0 - x$		x		x

Substituting the equilibrium concentrations into the expression for K_{a_1} and making the usual approximation gives

$$K_{a_1} = 7.5 \times 10^{-3} = \frac{[H^+][H_2PO_4^-]}{[H_3PO_4]} = \frac{(x)(x)}{5.0 - x} \approx \frac{x^2}{5.0}$$

Thus $x \approx 1.9 \times 10^{-1}$

Since 1.9×10^{-1} is less than 5% of 5.0, the approximation is acceptable, and

$$[H^+] = x = 0.19\ M \quad \text{and} \quad \text{pH} = 0.72$$

So far we have determined that

$$[H^+] = [H_2PO_4^-] = 0.19\ M$$

and $[H_3PO_4] = 5.0 - x = 4.8\ M$

The concentration of HPO_4^{2-} can be obtained by using the expression for K_{a_2}:

$$K_{a_2} = 6.2 \times 10^{-8} = \frac{[H^+][HPO_4^{2-}]}{[H_2PO_4^-]}$$

where $[H^+] = [H_2PO_4^-] = 0.19\ M$

Thus $$[HPO_4^{2-}] = K_{a_2} = 6.2 \times 10^{-8}\ M$$

To calculate $[PO_4^{3-}]$, we use the expression for K_{a_3} and the values of $[H^+]$ and $[HPO_4^{2-}]$ calculated previously:

$$K_{a_3} = \frac{[H^+][PO_4^{3-}]}{[HPO_4^{2-}]} = 4.8 \times 10^{-13} = \frac{0.19[PO_4^{3-}]}{6.2 \times 10^{-8}}$$

$$[PO_4^{3-}] = \frac{(4.8 \times 10^{-13})(6.2 \times 10^{-8})}{0.19} = 1.6 \times 10^{-19}\ M$$

These results show that the second and third dissociation steps do not make an important contribution to $[H^+]$. This is apparent from the fact that $[HPO_4^{2-}]$ is $6.2 \times 10^{-8}\ M$, indicating that only 6.2×10^{-8} mol/L of $H_2PO_4^-$ has dissociated. The value of $[PO_4^{3-}]$ shows that the dissociation of HPO_4^{2-} is even smaller. But we must use the second and third dissociation steps to calculate $[HPO_4^{2-}]$ and $[PO_4^{3-}]$, since these steps are the only sources of these ions.

EXAMPLE 7.9

A 0.200-mole sample of sodium phosphate is dissolved in water, and hydrochloric acid is added to give a total volume of 1.00 L and a final pH of 4.630. Calculate the concentrations of all phosphate-containing species in this solution.

Solution Before we do the complete calculation, we can determine the ratios of the various phosphate-containing species from the various K_a expressions:

$$\frac{[H_3PO_4]}{[H_2PO_4^-]} = \frac{[H^+]}{K_{a_1}} = \frac{2.34 \times 10^{-5}}{7.5 \times 10^{-3}} = 3.1 \times 10^{-3}$$

The inverse ratio is

$$\frac{[H_2PO_4^-]}{[H_3PO_4]} = \frac{1}{3.1 \times 10^{-3}} = 3.2 \times 10^2$$

$$\frac{[H_2PO_4^-]}{[HPO_4^{2-}]} = \frac{[H^+]}{K_{a_2}} = \frac{2.34 \times 10^{-5}}{6.2 \times 10^{-8}} = 3.8 \times 10^2$$

$$\frac{[HPO_4^{2-}]}{[PO_4^{3-}]} = \frac{[H^+]}{K_{a_3}} = \frac{2.34 \times 10^{-5}}{4.8 \times 10^{-13}} = 4.9 \times 10^7$$

These ratios show that $H_2PO_4^-$ is the dominant species at a pH of 4.630. Notice that this is exactly what is predicted by the plot shown in Fig. 7.7. This

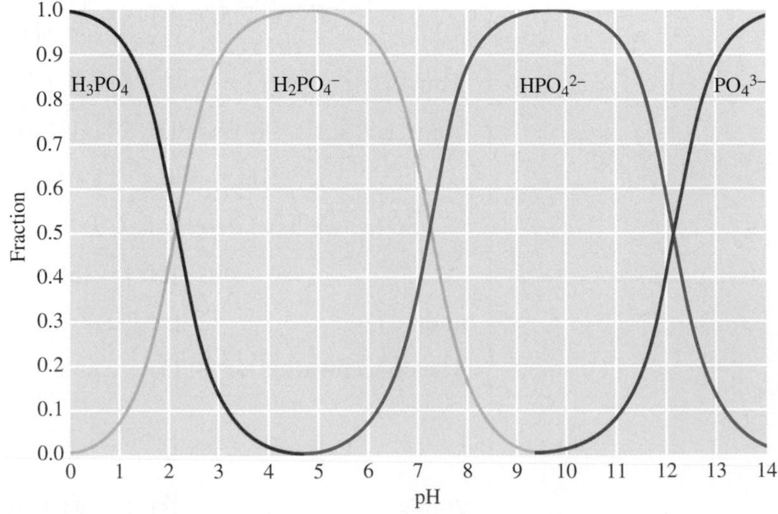

Figure 7.7
A plot of the fractions of H_3PO_4, $H_2PO_4^-$, HPO_4^{2-}, and PO_4^{3-} in aqueous solution as a function of pH.

plot shows the fractions of phosphate-containing species as a function of pH. Note that the fraction of $H_2PO_4^-$ is maximum at about pH 5.

Now we will proceed to determine the concentrations of H_3PO_4, $H_2PO_4^-$, HPO_4^{2-}, and PO_4^{3-}. We know that the total concentrations of these species must be 0.200 *M*, since this represents the concentration of PO_4^{3-} originally added to the solution.

Thus

$$[PO_4^{3-}] + [HPO_4^{2-}] + [H_2PO_4^-] + [H_3PO_4] = 0.200\ M$$

Also note that a pH of 4.630 means that $[H^+] = 2.34 \times 10^{-5}$.

To solve this problem we need to reduce the equation to one variable. For example, we can use the K_{a_1}, K_{a_2}, and K_{a_3} expressions to represent each species in terms of $[H_3PO_4]$ as follows:

$$[H_2PO_4^-] = \frac{[H_3PO_4]K_{a_1}}{[H^+]} = \frac{[H_3PO_4]7.5 \times 10^{-3}}{2.34 \times 10^{-5}} = 3.21 \times 10^2[H_3PO_4]$$

$$[HPO_4^{2-}] = \frac{[H_2PO_4^-]K_{a_2}}{[H^+]} = \frac{3.21 \times 10^2[H_3PO_4]K_{a_2}}{[H^+]} = 8.49 \times 10^{-1}[H_3PO_4]$$

Since $K_{a_1} \times K_{a_2} \times K_{a_3} = \dfrac{[H^+]^3[PO_4^{3-}]}{[H_3PO_4]}$,

$$[PO_4^{3-}] = \frac{(K_{a_1} \times K_{a_2} \times K_{a_3})[H_3PO_4]}{[H^+]^3} = 1.74 \times 10^{-8}[H_3PO_4]$$

Substituting these expressions into the equation

$$[PO_4^{3-}] + [HPO_4^{2-}] + [H_2PO_4^-] + [H_3PO_4] = 0.200\ M$$

gives

$$1.74 \times 10^{-8}[H_3PO_4] + 8.49 \times 10^{-1}[H_3PO_4] + 3.21 \times 10^2[H_3PO_4] + [H_3PO_4] = 0.200\ M$$

$$[H_3PO_4] = \frac{0.200\ M}{322.8} = 6.20 \times 10^{-4}\ M$$

$$[H_2PO_4^-] = (3.21 \times 10^2)(6.20 \times 10^{-4}\ M) = 0.199\ M$$

$$[HPO_4^{2-}] = (8.49 \times 10^{-1})(6.20 \times 10^{-4}\ M) = 5.26 \times 10^{-4}\ M$$

$$[PO_4^{3-}] = (1.74 \times 10^{-8})(6.20 \times 10^{-4}\ M) = 1.08 \times 10^{-11}\ M$$

Notice that at this pH the dominant species by far is $H_2PO_4^-$, as we predicted earlier.

Sulfuric Acid

Sulfuric acid is unique among the common acids because it is *a strong acid in its first dissociation step and a weak acid in its second step:*

$$H_2SO_4(aq) \longrightarrow H^+(aq) + HSO_4^-(aq) \qquad K_{a_1} \text{ is very large}$$

$$HSO_4^-(aq) \rightleftharpoons H^+(aq) + SO_4^{2-}(aq) \qquad K_{a_2} = 1.2 \times 10^{-2}$$

Example 7.10 illustrates how to calculate the pH for sulfuric acid solutions.

Major Species

H^+

HSO_4^-

H_2O

EXAMPLE 7.10

Calculate the pH of a 1.0 M H_2SO_4 solution.

Solution The major species in the solution are

$$H^+, \quad HSO_4^-, \quad \text{and} \quad H_2O$$

where the first two ions are produced by the complete first dissociation step of H_2SO_4. The concentration of H^+ in this solution will be at least 1.0 M, since this amount is produced by the first dissociation step of H_2SO_4. We must now answer this question: "Does the HSO_4^- ion dissociate enough to make a significant contribution to the concentration of H^+?" This question can be answered by calculating the equilibrium concentrations for the dissociation reaction of HSO_4^-:

$$HSO_4^-(aq) \rightleftharpoons H^+(aq) + SO_4^{2-}(aq)$$

where

$$K_{a_2} = 1.2 \times 10^{-2} = \frac{[H^+][SO_4^{2-}]}{[HSO_4^-]}$$

The concentrations are as follows:

Initial Concentration (mol/L)		Equilibrium Concentration (mol/L)
$[HSO_4^-]_0 = 1.0$	x mol/L HSO_4^- dissociates	$[HSO_4^-] = 1.0 - x$
$[SO_4^{2-}]_0 = 0$	$\longrightarrow$	$[SO_4^{2-}] = x$
$[H^+]_0 = 1.0$	to reach equilibrium	$[H^+] = 1.0 + x$

Or in shorthand form:

	$HSO_4^-(aq)$	$\rightleftharpoons$	$H^+(aq)$	+	$SO_4^{2-}(aq)$
Initial:	1.0		1.0		0
Change:	$-x$		$+x$		$+x$
Equilibrium:	$1.0 - x$		$1.0 + x$		x

Note that $[H^+]_0$ is not equal to zero, as is usually the case for a weak acid, because the first dissociation step has already produced some H^+.

Substituting the equilibrium concentrations into the expression for K_{a_2} and making the usual approximation gives

$$K_{a_2} = 1.2 \times 10^{-2} = \frac{[H^+][SO_4^{2-}]}{[HSO_4^-]} = \frac{(1.0 + x)(x)}{1.0 - x} \approx \frac{(1.0)(x)}{(1.0)}$$

Thus

$$x \approx 1.2 \times 10^{-2}$$

Since 1.2×10^{-2} is 1.2% of 1.0, the approximation is valid according to the 5% rule. Note that x is not equal to $[H^+]$ in this case. Instead,

$$[H^+] = 1.0\ M + x = 1.0\ M + (1.2 \times 10^{-2})\ M$$

$$= 1.0\ M \quad \text{(to the correct number of significant figures)}$$

Thus, since the dissociation of HSO_4^- does not make a significant contribution to the concentration of H^+,

$$[H^+] = 1.0\ M \quad \text{and} \quad \text{pH} = 0.00$$

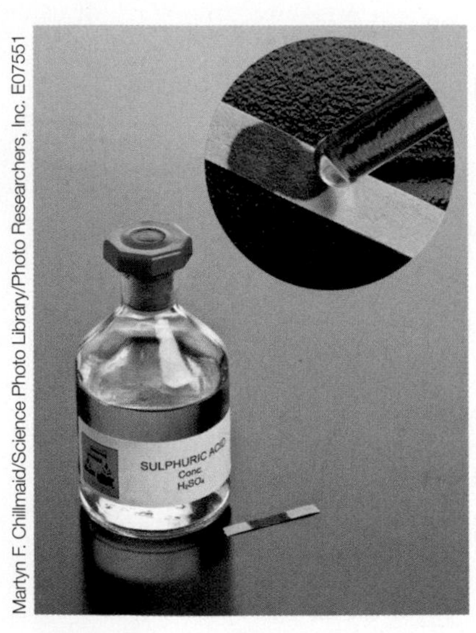

Martyn F. Chillmaid/Science Photo Library/Photo Researchers, Inc. E07551

A bottle of sulfuric acid. A drop of sulfuric acid turns Universal indicator paper bright red, showing it is very acidic.

Only in dilute H_2SO_4 solutions does the second dissociation step contribute significantly to $[H^+]$.

Example 7.10 illustrates the most common case for sulfuric acid in which only the first dissociation makes an important contribution to the concentration of H^+. In solutions more dilute than 1.0 *M* (for example, 0.10 *M* H_2SO_4), the dissociation of HSO_4^- is important. Solving this type of problem requires use of the quadratic formula, as shown in Example 7.11.

EXAMPLE 7.11

Calculate the pH of a 1.00×10^{-2} *M* H_2SO_4 solution.

Solution The major species in solution are

$$H^+, \quad HSO_4^-, \quad \text{and} \quad H_2O$$

Proceeding as in Example 7.10, we consider the dissociation of HSO_4^-, which leads to the following concentrations:

Initial Concentration (mol/L)		Equilibrium Concentration (mol/L)
$[HSO_4^-]_0 = 0.0100$ $[SO_4^{2-}]_0 = 0$ $[H^+]_0 = 0.0100$ ↗ From dissociation of H_2SO_4	x mol/L HSO_4^- dissociates → to reach equilibrium	$[HSO_4^-] = 0.0100 - x$ $[SO_4^{2-}] = x$ $[H^+] = 0.0100 + x$

Substituting the equilibrium concentrations into the expression for K_{a_2} gives

$$1.2 \times 10^{-2} = K_{a_2} = \frac{[H^+][SO_4^{2-}]}{[HSO_4^-]} = \frac{(0.0100 + x)(x)}{(0.0100 - x)}$$

If we make the usual approximation, then $0.010 + x \approx 0.010$ and $0.010 - x \approx 0.010$, and we have

$$1.2 \times 10^{-2} = \frac{(0.0100 + x)(x)}{(0.0100 - x)} \approx \frac{(0.0100)x}{(0.0100)}$$

The calculated value of x is

$$x = 1.2 \times 10^{-2} = 0.012$$

This value is larger than 0.010, clearly a ridiculous result. Thus we cannot make the usual approximation and must instead solve the quadratic equation. The expression

$$1.2 \times 10^{-2} = \frac{(0.0100 + x)(x)}{(0.0100 - x)}$$

leads to

$$(1.2 \times 10^{-2})(0.0100 - x) = (0.0100 + x)(x)$$

$$(1.2 \times 10^{-4}) - (1.2 \times 10^{-2})x = (1.0 \times 10^{-2})x + x^2$$

$$x^2 + (2.2 \times 10^{-2})x - (1.2 \times 10^{-4}) = 0$$

This equation can be solved by using the quadratic formula,

$$x = \frac{-b \pm \sqrt{b^2 - 4ac}}{2a}$$

where $a = 1$, $b = 2.2 \times 10^{-2}$, and $c = -1.2 \times 10^{-4}$. Use of the quadratic formula gives one negative root (which cannot be correct) and one positive root,

$$x = 4.5 \times 10^{-3}$$

Thus $$[H^+] = 0.0100 + x = 0.0100 + 0.0045 = 0.0145$$

and $$pH = 1.84$$

Note that in this case the second dissociation step produces about half as many H^+ ions as the initial step does.

This problem can also be solved by successive approximations, a method illustrated in Appendix A1.4.

Characteristics of Weak Polyprotic Acids

1. Typically, successive K_a values are so much smaller than the first value that only the first dissociation step makes a significant contribution to the equilibrium concentration of H^+. This means that the calculation of the pH for a solution of a weak polyprotic acid is identical to that for a solution of a weak monoprotic acid.
2. Sulfuric acid is unique in being a strong acid in its first dissociation step and a weak acid in its second step. For relatively concentrated solutions of sulfuric acid (1.0 *M* or higher), the large concentration of H^+ from the first dissociation step represses the second step, which can be neglected as a contributor of H^+ ions. For dilute solutions of sulfuric acid, the second step does make a significant contribution and must be considered in obtaining the total H^+ concentration.

7.8 Acid–Base Properties of Salts

The term **salt** is often used by chemists as simply another name for *ionic compound*. When a salt dissolves in water, we assume that it breaks up into its ions, which move about independently, at least in dilute solutions. Under certain conditions these ions can behave as acids or bases. In this section we explore such reactions.

Salts That Produce Neutral Solutions

Recall that the conjugate base of a strong acid has virtually no affinity for protons as compared with that of the water molecule. For this reason strong acids completely dissociate in aqueous solution. Thus, when anions such as Cl^- and NO_3^- are placed in water, they do not combine with H^+ and therefore have no effect on the pH. Cations such as K^+ and Na^+ from strong bases have no affinity for H^+ and no ability to produce H^+, so they too have no effect on the pH of an aqueous solution. *Salts that consist of the cations of strong bases and the anions of strong acids have no effect on [H^+] when dissolved in water.* This means that aqueous solutions of salts such as KCl, NaCl, $NaNO_3$, and KNO_3 are neutral (have a pH of 7).

The salt of a strong acid and a strong base gives a neutral solution.

Salts That Produce Basic Solutions

In an aqueous solution of sodium acetate ($NaC_2H_3O_2$), the major species are

$$Na^+, \quad C_2H_3O_2^-, \quad \text{and} \quad H_2O$$

Major Species

Na^+

$C_2H_3O_2^-$

H_2O

What are the acid–base properties of each component? The Na^+ ion has neither acid nor base properties. The $C_2H_3O_2^-$ ion is the conjugate base of acetic acid, a weak acid. This means that $C_2H_3O_2^-$ has a significant affinity for a proton and acts as a base. Finally, water is neither a strong enough acid nor a strong enough base to affect [H^+].

Thus the pH of this solution will be controlled by the $C_2H_3O_2^-$ ion. Since $C_2H_3O_2^-$ is a base, it will react with the best proton donor available. In this case water is the *only* source of protons, and the reaction is

$$C_2H_3O_2^-(aq) + H_2O(l) \rightleftharpoons HC_2H_3O_2(aq) + OH^-(aq) \qquad (7.5)$$

Note that this reaction, which yields a basic solution, involves a *base reacting with water to produce the hydroxide ion and a conjugate acid.* We have defined K_b as the equilibrium constant for such a reaction. In this instance

$$K_b = \frac{[HC_2H_3O_2][OH^-]}{[C_2H_3O_2^-]}$$

The value of K_a for acetic acid is well known (1.8×10^{-5}). But how can we obtain the K_b value for the acetate ion? The answer lies in the relationships among K_a, K_b, and K_w. Note that when the K_a expression for acetic acid is multiplied by the K_b expression for the acetate ion, the result is K_w:

$$K_a \times K_b = \frac{[H^+][C_2H_3O_2^-]}{[HC_2H_3O_2]} \times \frac{[HC_2H_3O_2][OH^-]}{[C_2H_3O_2^-]} = [H^+][OH^-] = K_w$$

This is a very important result. For any weak acid and its conjugate base,

$$K_a \times K_b = K_w$$

Thus, when either K_a or K_b is known, the other constant can be calculated. For the acetate ion,

$$K_b = \frac{K_w}{K_a \text{ (for } HC_2H_3O_2)} = \frac{1.0 \times 10^{-14}}{1.8 \times 10^{-5}} = 5.6 \times 10^{-10}$$

This is the K_b value for the reaction described by Equation (7.5). Note that it is obtained from the K_a value of the parent weak acid, in this case acetic acid.

A basic solution is formed if the anion of the salt is the conjugate base of a weak acid.

The sodium acetate solution is an example of an important general case. *For any salt whose cation has neutral properties (such as Na^+ or K^+) and whose anion is the conjugate base of a weak acid, the aqueous solution will be basic.* The K_b value for the anion can be obtained from the relationship $K_b = K_w/K_a$. Equilibrium calculations of this type are illustrated in Example 7.12.

OWL INTERACTIVE EXAMPLE 7.12

Calculate the pH of a 0.30 *M* NaF solution. The K_a value for HF is 7.2×10^{-4}.

Major Species

Na^+

F^-

H_2O

Solution The major species in solution are

$$Na^+, \quad F^-, \quad \text{and} \quad H_2O$$

Since HF is a weak acid, the F^- ion must have a significant affinity for protons. Therefore the dominant reaction will be

$$F^-(aq) + H_2O(l) \rightleftharpoons HF(aq) + OH^-(aq)$$

which yields the K_b expression

$$K_b = \frac{[HF][OH^-]}{[F^-]}$$

The value of K_b can be calculated from K_w and the K_a value for HF:

$$K_b = \frac{K_w}{K_a \text{ (for HF)}} = \frac{1.0 \times 10^{-14}}{7.2 \times 10^{-4}} = 1.4 \times 10^{-11}$$

The concentrations are as follows:

Initial Concentration (mol/L)		Equilibrium Concentration (mol/L)
$[F^-]_0 = 0.30$ $[HF]_0 = 0$ $[OH^-]_0 \approx 0$	x mol/L F^- reacts with H_2O to reach equilibrium $\longrightarrow$	$[F^-] = 0.30 - x$ $[HF] = x$ $[OH^-] = x$

Thus

$$K_b = 1.4 \times 10^{-11} = \frac{[HF][OH^-]}{[F^-]} = \frac{(x)(x)}{0.30 - x} \approx \frac{x^2}{0.30}$$

$$x \approx 2.0 \times 10^{-6}$$

The approximation is valid by the 5% rule, so

$$[OH^-] = x = 2.0 \times 10^{-6}\ M$$

$$pOH = 5.69$$

$$pH = 14.00 - 5.69 = 8.31$$

As expected, the solution is basic.

Base Strength in Aqueous Solution

To emphasize the concept of base strength, consider the basic properties of the cyanide ion. One relevant reaction is the dissociation of hydrocyanic acid in water:

$$HCN(aq) + H_2O(l) \rightleftharpoons H_3O^+(aq) + CN^-(aq) \qquad K_a = 6.2 \times 10^{-10}$$

Since HCN is such a weak acid, CN^- appears to be a *strong* base, showing a very high affinity for H^+ *compared with* H_2O, with which it is competing. However, we also need to look at the reaction in which cyanide ion reacts with water:

$$CN^-(aq) + H_2O(l) \rightleftharpoons HCN(aq) + OH^-(aq)$$

where

$$K_b = \frac{K_w}{K_a} = \frac{1.0 \times 10^{-14}}{6.2 \times 10^{-10}} = 1.6 \times 10^{-5}$$

In this reaction CN^- appears to be a weak base; the K_b value is only 1.6×10^{-5}. What accounts for this apparent difference in base strength? The key idea is that in the reaction of CN^- with H_2O, *CN^- is competing with OH^- for H^+, instead of competing with H_2O,* as it does in the HCN dissociation reaction. These equilibria show the following relative base strengths:

$$OH^- > CN^- > H_2O$$

Similar arguments can be made for other "weak" bases, such as ammonia, the acetate ion, and the fluoride ion.

Salts That Produce Acidic Solutions

Some salts produce acidic solutions when dissolved in water. For example, when solid NH_4Cl is dissolved in water, NH_4^+ and Cl^- ions are released, with NH_4^+ behaving as a weak acid:

$$NH_4^+(aq) \rightleftharpoons NH_3(aq) + H^+(aq)$$

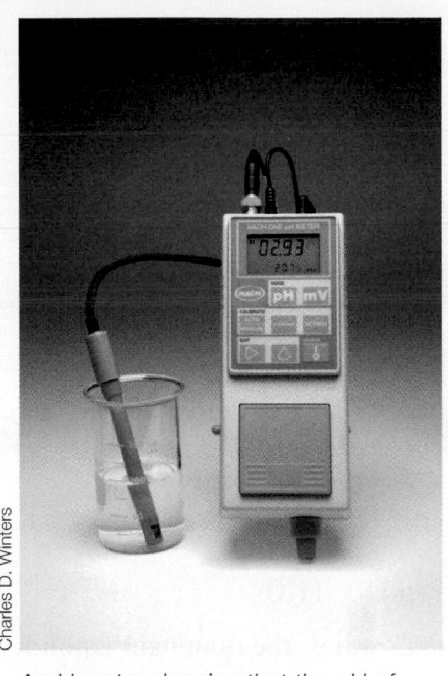
Charles D. Winters

A pH meter showing that the pH of 0.1 *M* $AlCl_3$ is 2.93.

The Cl^- ion, having virtually no affinity for H^+ in water, does not affect the pH of the solution.

In general, *a salt whose cation is the conjugate acid of a weak base produces an acidic solution.*

A second type of salt that produces an acidic solution is one that contains a *highly charged metal ion.* For example, when solid aluminum chloride ($AlCl_3$) is dissolved in water, the resulting solution is significantly acidic. Although the Al^{3+} ion is not itself a Brønsted–Lowry acid, the hydrated ion $Al(H_2O)_6^{3+}$ formed in water is a weak acid:

$$Al(H_2O)_6^{3+}(aq) \rightleftharpoons Al(OH)(H_2O)_5^{2+}(aq) + H^+(aq)$$

The high charge on the metal ion polarizes the O—H bonds in the attached water molecules, making the hydrogens in these water molecules more acidic than those in free water molecules. Typically, the higher the charge on the metal ion, the stronger is the acidity of the hydrated ion.

OWL INTERACTIVE EXAMPLE 7.13

Calculate the pH of a 0.10 *M* NH_4Cl solution. The K_b value for NH_3 is 1.8×10^{-5}.

Major Species

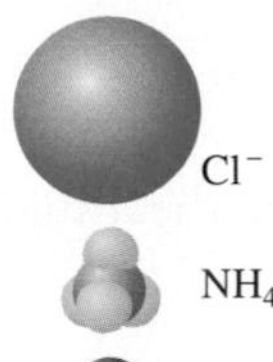

Solution The major species in solution are

$$NH_4^+, \quad Cl^-, \quad \text{and} \quad H_2O$$

Note that both NH_4^+ and H_2O can produce H^+. The dissociation reaction for the NH_4^+ ion is

$$NH_4^+(aq) \rightleftharpoons NH_3(aq) + H^+(aq)$$

for which

$$K_a = \frac{[NH_3][H^+]}{[NH_4^+]}$$

Note that although the K_b value for NH_3 is given, the reaction corresponding to K_b is not appropriate here, since NH_3 is not a major species in the solution. Instead, the given value of K_b is used to calculate K_a for NH_4^+ from the relationship

$$K_a \times K_b = K_w$$

Thus

$$K_a \text{ (for } NH_4^+) = \frac{K_w}{K_b \text{ (for } NH_3)} = \frac{1.0 \times 10^{-14}}{1.8 \times 10^{-5}} = 5.6 \times 10^{-10}$$

Although NH_4^+ is a very weak acid, as indicated by its K_a value, it is stronger than H_2O and thus will dominate in the production of H^+. Therefore, we will focus on the dissociation reaction of NH_4^+ to calculate the pH of this solution.

We solve the weak acid problem in the usual way:

Initial Concentration (mol/L)		Equilibrium Concentration (mol/L)
$[NH_4^+]_0 = 0.10$ $[NH_3]_0 = 0$ $[H^+]_0 \approx 0$	x mol/L NH_4^+ dissociates $\longrightarrow$ to reach equilibrium	$[NH_4^+] = 0.10 - x$ $[NH_3] = x$ $[H^+] = x$

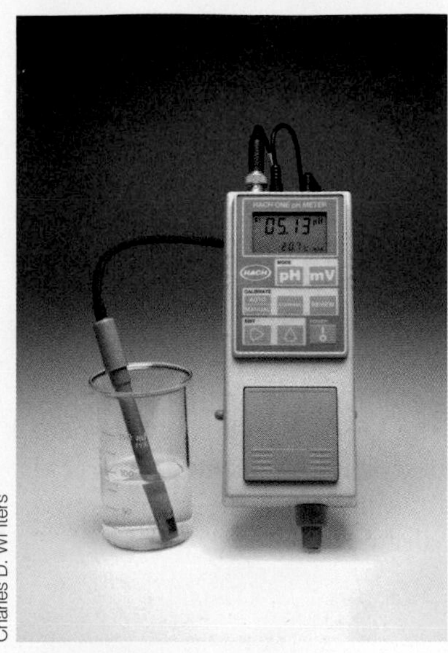

Charles D. Winters

A pH meter showing that the pH of 0.1 *M* NH_4Cl is 5.13.

Thus

$$5.6 \times 10^{-10} = K_a = \frac{[H^+][NH_3]}{[NH_4^+]} = \frac{(x)(x)}{0.10 - x} = \frac{x^2}{0.10}$$

$$x \approx 7.5 \times 10^{-6}$$

The approximation is valid by the 5% rule, so

$$[H^+] = x = 7.5 \times 10^{-6}\ M \qquad \text{and} \qquad pH = 5.13$$

EXAMPLE 7.14

Calculate the pH of a 0.010 *M* $AlCl_3$ solution. The K_a value for $Al(H_2O)_6^{3+}$ is 1.4×10^{-5}.

Solution The major species in solution are

$$Al(H_2O)_6^{3+}, \qquad Cl^-, \qquad \text{and} \qquad H_2O$$

Major Species

Cl^-

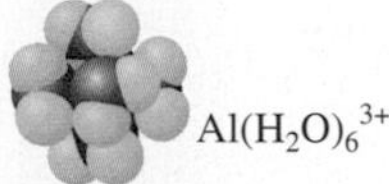

$Al(H_2O)_6^{3+}$

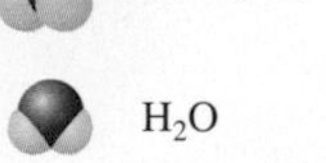

H_2O

Since the $Al(H_2O)_6^{3+}$ ion is a stronger acid than water, the dominant equilibrium is

$$Al(H_2O)_6^{3+}(aq) \rightleftharpoons Al(OH)(H_2O)_5^{2+}(aq) + H^+(aq)$$

and

$$1.4 \times 10^{-5} = K_a = \frac{[Al(OH)(H_2O)_5^{2+}][H^+]}{[Al(H_2O)_6^{3+}]}$$

This is a typical weak acid problem, which we can solve with the usual procedures.

Initial Concentration (mol/L)		Equilibrium Concentration (mol/L)
$[Al(H_2O)_6^{3+}]_0 = 0.010$ $[Al(OH)(H_2O)_5^{2+}]_0 = 0$ $[H^+]_0 \approx 0$	$\xrightarrow{x \text{ mol/L}}$ $Al(H_2O)_6^{3+}$ dissociates to reach equilibrium	$[Al(H_2O)_6^{3+}] = 0.010 - x$ $[Al(OH)(H_2O)_5^{2+}] = x$ $[H^+] = x$

Thus

$$1.4 \times 10^{-5} = K_a = \frac{[Al(OH)(H_2O)_5^{2+}][H^+]}{[Al(H_2O)_6^{3+}]} = \frac{(x)(x)}{0.010 - x} \approx \frac{x^2}{0.010}$$

$$x \approx 3.7 \times 10^{-4}$$

Since the approximation is valid by the 5% rule,

$$[H^-] = x = 3.7 \times 10^{-4}\ M \qquad \text{and} \qquad pH = 3.43$$

So far we have considered salts containing only one ion that has acidic or basic properties. For many salts, such as ammonium acetate ($NH_4C_2H_3O_2$), both ions affect the pH of the aqueous solution. First, we will consider the qualitative aspects of such problems. We can predict whether the solution will be basic, acidic, or neutral by comparing the K_a value for the acidic ion with the K_b value for the basic ion. If the K_a value for the acidic ion is larger than the K_b value for the basic ion, the solution will be acidic. If the K_b value is larger than the K_a value, the solution is basic. When the K_a and K_b values are equal, the solution is neutral. These facts are summarized in Table 7.5. Table 7.6 summarizes the acid–base properties of aqueous solutions of various salts.

Table 7.5

Qualitative Prediction of pH for Solutions of Salts for Which Both Cation and Anion Have Acidic or Basic Properties

$K_a > K_b$	pH $<$ 7 (acidic)
$K_b > K_a$	pH $>$ 7 (basic)
$K_a = K_b$	pH = 7 (neutral)

Table 7.6

Acid–Base Properties of Aqueous Solutions of Various Types of Salts

Type of Salt	Examples	Comments	pH of Solution
Cation is from strong base; anion is from strong acid	KCl, KNO_3, NaCl, $NaNO_3$	Acts as neither an acid nor a base	Neutral
Cation is from strong base; anion is from weak acid	$NaC_2H_3O_2$, KCN, NaF	Anion acts as a base; cation has no effect on pH	Basic
Cation is conjugate acid of weak base; anion is from strong acid	NH_4Cl, NH_4NO_3	Cation acts as an acid; anion has no effect on pH	Acidic
Cation is conjugate acid of weak base; anion is conjugate base of weak acid	$NH_4C_2H_3O_2$, NH_4CN	Cation acts as an acid; anion acts as a base	Acidic if $K_a > K_b$, basic if $K_b > K_a$, neutral if $K_a = K_b$
Cation is highly charged metal ion; anion is from strong acid	$Al(NO_3)_3$, $FeCl_3$	Hydrated cation acts as an acid; anion has no effect on pH	Acidic

OWL INTERACTIVE EXAMPLE 7.15

Predict whether an aqueous solution of each of the following salts will be acidic, basic, or neutral.

a. $NH_4C_2H_3O_2$ b. NH_4CN c. $Al_2(SO_4)_3$

Solution

a. The ions in solution are NH_4^+ and $C_2H_3O_2^-$. As we mentioned previously, K_a for NH_4^+ is 5.6×10^{-10}, and K_b for $C_2H_3O_2^-$ is 5.6×10^{-10}. Thus, since K_a for NH_4^+ is equal to K_b for $C_2H_3O_2^-$, the solution will be neutral (pH = 7).

b. The solution will contain NH_4^+ and CN^- ions. The K_a value for NH_4^+ is 5.6×10^{-10}, and

$$K_b\ (\text{for } CN^-) = \frac{K_w}{K_a\ (\text{for HCN})} = 1.6 \times 10^{-5}$$

Since K_b for CN^- is much larger than K_a for NH_4^+, this solution will be basic.

c. The solution will contain $Al(H_2O)_6^{3+}$ and SO_4^{2-} ions. The K_a value for $Al(H_2O)_6^{3+}$ is 1.4×10^{-5}, as given in Example 7.14. We must calculate K_b for SO_4^{2-}. The HSO_4^- ion is the conjugate acid of SO_4^{2-}, and its K_a value is K_{a_2} for sulfuric acid, or 1.2×10^{-2}. Therefore,

$$K_b\ (\text{for } SO_4^{2-}) = \frac{K_w}{K_{a_2}\ (\text{for sulfuric acid})} = \frac{1.0 \times 10^{-14}}{1.2 \times 10^{-2}} = 8.3 \times 10^{-13}$$

This solution will be acidic, since K_a for $Al(H_2O)_6^{3+}$ is much greater than K_b for SO_4^{2-}.

We have seen that it is possible to make a qualitative prediction of the acidity or basicity of an aqueous solution containing a dissolved salt. We also can give a quantitative description of these solutions by using the procedures we have developed for treating acid–base equilibria. Example 7.16 illustrates this technique.

EXAMPLE 7.16

Calculate the pH of a 0.100 *M* solution of NH_4CN.

Solution The major species in solution are

$$NH_4^+, \quad CN^-, \quad \text{and} \quad H_2O$$

The familiar reactions involving these species are

$$NH_4^+(aq) \rightleftharpoons NH_3(aq) + H^+(aq) \qquad K_a = 5.6 \times 10^{-10}$$

$$CN^-(aq) + H_2O(l) \rightleftharpoons HCN(aq) + OH^-(aq) \qquad K_b = 1.6 \times 10^{-5}$$

$$H_2O(l) + H_2O(l) \rightleftharpoons H_3O^+(aq) + OH^-(aq) \qquad K_w = 1.0 \times 10^{-14}$$

However, noting that NH_4^+ is an acid and CN^- is a base, it is also sensible to consider the reaction

$$NH_4^+(aq) + CN^-(aq) \rightleftharpoons HCN(aq) + NH_3(aq)$$

To evaluate the importance of this reaction, we need the value of its equilibrium constant. Note that

$$K = \frac{[NH_3][HCN]}{[NH_4^+][CN^-]} = \frac{[H^+][NH_3]}{[NH_4^+]} \times \frac{[HCN]}{[H^+][CN^-]}$$

$$= K_a(NH_4^+) \times \frac{1}{K_a\,(HCN)}$$

Thus the value of the equilibrium constant we need is

$$K = \frac{K_a\,(NH_4^+)}{K_a\,(HCN)} = \frac{5.6 \times 10^{-10}}{6.2 \times 10^{-10}} = 0.90$$

Notice that this equilibrium constant is much larger than those for the other possible reactions. Thus we expect this reaction to be dominant in this solution.

Following the usual procedures, we have the concentrations listed below.

Initial Concentration (mol/L)	Equilibrium Concentration (mol/L)
$[NH_4^+]_0 = 0.100$	$[NH_4^+] = 0.100 - x$
$[CN^-]_0 = 0.100$	$[CN^-] = 0.100 - x$
$[NH_3]_0 = 0$	$[NH_3] = x$
$[HCN]_0 = 0$	$[HCN] = x$

Then

$$K = 0.90 = \frac{x^2}{(0.100 - x)^2}$$

Taking the square root of both sides yields

$$0.95 = \frac{x}{0.100 - x}$$

and

$$x = 4.9 \times 10^{-2}\ M = [NH_3] = [HCN]$$

Notice that the reaction under consideration does not involve H^+ or OH^- directly. Thus, to obtain the pH, we must consider the position of the HCN or NH_4^+ dissociation equilibrium. For example, for HCN

$$K_a = 6.2 \times 10^{-10} = \frac{[H^+][CN^-]}{[HCN]}$$

From the preceding calculations,

$$[CN^-] = 0.100 - x = 0.100 - 0.049 = 0.051\ M$$

$$[HCN] = x = 4.9 \times 10^{-2}\ M$$

Substituting these values into the K_a expression for HCN gives

$$[H^+] = 6.0 \times 10^{-10}\ M$$

and

$$pH = 9.22$$

Note that this solution is basic, just as we predicted in Example 7.15.

7.9 Acid Solutions in Which Water Contributes to the H^+ Concentration

In the typical case involving a weak acid HA in water, the $[H^+]$ produced by the acid is much greater than that produced by water, so

$$[H^+] = [H^+]_{HA} + [H^+]_{H_2O} = [H^+]_{HA}$$

The HA and H_2O are simultaneously in equilibrium, but in this case we can ignore water as a source of H^+.

In most solutions containing an acid, we can assume that the acid dominates in the production of H^+ ions. That is, we typically can assume that the acid produces so much H^+ in comparison with the amount of H^+ produced by water that water can be ignored as a source of H^+. However, in certain cases water must be taken into account when the pH of an aqueous solution is calculated. For example, consider a $1.0 \times 10^{-4}\ M$ solution of a very weak acid HA ($K_a = 1.0 \times 10^{-10}$). A quick calculation shows that if water is ignored, the $[H^+]$ produced by this acid is $1.0 \times 10^{-7}\ M$. This value cannot be the correct $[H^+]$ in this solution at equilibrium because in pure water $[H^+] = 1.0 \times 10^{-7}\ M$. In this instance perhaps the thing to do to get the total $[H^+]$ is to add the two H^+ concentrations:

$$\underset{\substack{\uparrow \\ \text{From} \\ 10^{-4}\ M\ \text{HA}}}{1.0 \times 10^{-7}\ M} + \underset{\substack{\uparrow \\ \text{From} \\ H_2O}}{1.0 \times 10^{-7}\ M} = 2.0 \times 10^{-7}\ M$$

However, this procedure is not correct because the two sources of H^+ will affect each other. That is, because both of the reactions

$$H_2O(l) \rightleftharpoons H^+(aq) + OH^-(aq)$$

$$HA(aq) \rightleftharpoons H^+(aq) + A^-(aq)$$

involve H^+, the equilibrium position of each will be affected by the other. Thus we must solve these equilibria simultaneously. This procedure will lead to a concentration of H^+ such that

$$1.0 \times 10^{-7}\ M < [H^+] < 2.0 \times 10^{-7}\ M$$

Note that in these two equilibria there are four unknown concentrations:

$$[H^+], \quad [OH^-], \quad [HA], \quad \text{and} \quad [A^-]$$

To solve for these concentrations, we need four independent equations that relate them. Two of these equations are provided by the two equilibrium expressions:

$$K_w = [H^+][OH^-] \quad \text{and} \quad K_a = \frac{[H^+][A^-]}{[HA]}$$

A third equation can be derived from the principle of **charge balance:** The positive and negative charges carried by the ions in an aqueous solution must balance. That is, the "concentration of positive charge" must equal the "concentration of negative charge." In this case H^+ is the only positive ion, and the negative ions are A^- and OH^-. Thus the *charge balance* expression is

$$[H^+] = [A^-] + [OH^-]$$

Another relationship can be obtained by recognizing that all the HA originally dissolved must be present at equilibrium as either A^- or HA. This observation leads to the equation

This expression conserves A.

$$[HA]_0 = [HA] + [A^-]$$

↑ Original concentration of HA dissolved

which is called the **material balance equation.**

These four equations can be used to derive an equation involving only $[H^+]$. We will start with the K_a expression,

$$K_a = \frac{[H^+][A^-]}{[HA]}$$

and use the other relationships to express $[A^-]$ and [HA] in terms of $[H^+]$. Recall that the charge balance equation is

$$[H^+] = [A^-] + [OH^-]$$

Using the K_w expression, we have

$$[OH^-] = \frac{K_w}{[H^+]}$$

and the charge balance equation becomes

$$[H^+] = [A^-] + \frac{K_w}{[H^+]} \quad \text{or} \quad [A^-] = [H^+] - \frac{K_w}{[H^+]}$$

This equation gives $[A^-]$ in terms of $[H^+]$.

The material balance equation is

$$[HA]_0 = [HA] + [A^-] \quad \text{or} \quad [HA] = [HA]_0 - [A^-]$$

Since

$$[A^-] = [H^+] - \frac{K_w}{[H^+]}$$

we have

$$[HA] = [HA]_0 - \left([H^+] - \frac{K_w}{[H^+]}\right)$$

Now we substitute the expressions for $[A^-]$ and [HA] into the K_a expression:

$$K_a = \frac{[H^+][A^-]}{[HA]} = \frac{[H^+]\left([H^+] - \frac{K_w}{[H^+]}\right)}{[HA]_0 - \left([H^+] - \frac{K_w}{[H^+]}\right)} = \frac{[H^+]^2 - K_w}{[HA]_0 - \frac{[H^+]^2 - K_w}{[H^+]}}$$

This expression permits the calculation of the $[H^+]$ in a solution containing a weak acid. That is, it gives the correct $[H^+]$ for any solution made by dissolving a weak acid in pure water.

See Appendix A1.4 for information on using successive approximations.

The equation can be solved by simple trial and error or by the more systematic method of successive approximations. Recall that the usual way of doing successive approximations is to substitute a guessed value of the variable of interest ($[H^+]$ in this case) into the equation everywhere it appears except in one place. The equation is then solved to obtain a new value of the variable, which becomes the "guessed value" in the next round. The process is continued until the calculated value equals the guessed value.

Even though the full equation can be solved in this manner, the process is tedious and time-consuming. We would certainly like to use the simpler method (ignoring the contribution of water to the $[H^+]$) whenever possible. Thus a key question arises: "Under what conditions can problems involving a weak acid be done in the simple way?"

Notice that the term $[H^+]^2 - K_w$ appears twice in the full equation:

$$K_a = \frac{[H^+]^2 - K_w}{[HA]_0 - \dfrac{[H^+]^2 - K_w}{[H^+]}}$$

Now, assume that the condition

$$[H^+]^2 \gg K_w$$

applies, which means that

$$[H^+]^2 - K_w \approx [H^+]^2$$

Under this condition the full equation can be simplified as follows:

$$K_a = \frac{[H^+]^2 - K_w}{[HA]_0 - \dfrac{[H^+]^2 - K_w}{[H^+]}} \approx \frac{[H^+]^2}{[HA]_0 - \dfrac{[H^+]^2}{[H^+]}} = \frac{[H^+]^2}{[HA]_0 - [H^+]}$$

$$= \frac{x^2}{[HA]_0 - x}$$

where $x = [H^+]$ at equilibrium.

This is an important result: If $[H^+]^2 \gg K_w$, the full equation reduces to the typical expression for a weak acid, which originates from ignoring water as a source of H^+. Because uncertainties in K_a values are typically greater than 1%, we can safely assume that "much greater than" means at least 100 times greater. Then since $K_w = 1.0 \times 10^{-14}$, the $[H^+]^2$ must be at least 100×10^{-14}, or 10^{-12}, which corresponds to $[H^+] = 10^{-6}$. Thus, if $[H^+]$ is greater than or equal to 10^{-6} *M*, the complicated question reduces to the simple equation—that is, you get the *same answer* by using either equation.

How do we decide when we must use the complicated equation? The best way to proceed is as follows: Calculate the $[H^+]$ in the normal way, ignoring any contribution from H_2O. If $[H^+]$ from this calculation is greater than or equal to 10^{-6} *M*, the answer is correct—that is, the complicated equation will give the same answer. If the $[H^+]$ calculated from the simple equation is less than 10^{-6} *M*, you must use the full equation—that is, water must be considered as a source of H^+.

EXAMPLE 7.17

Calculate the $[H^+]$ in

a. 1.0 *M* HCN ($K_a = 6.2 \times 10^{-10}$).

b. 1.0×10^{-4} *M* HCN ($K_a = 6.2 \times 10^{-10}$).

Solution

a. First, do the weak acid problem the "normal" way. This technique leads to the expression

$$\frac{x^2}{1.0 - x} = 6.2 \times 10^{-10} \approx \frac{x^2}{1.0}$$

$$x = 2.5 \times 10^{-5}\,M = [H^+]$$

Note that the $[H^+]$ from the dissociation of HCN is greater than $10^{-6}\,M$, so we are finished. Water makes no important contribution to the $[H^+]$ in this solution.

b. First, do the weak acid problem the "normal" way. This procedure leads to the expression

$$K_a = 6.2 \times 10^{-10} = \frac{x^2}{1.0 \times 10^{-4} - x} \approx \frac{x^2}{1.0 \times 10^{-4}}$$

$$x = 2.5 \times 10^{-7}\,M$$

In this very dilute solution of HCN, the $[H^+]$ from HCN alone is less than $10^{-6}\,M$, so the full equation must be used to obtain the correct $[H^+]$ in the solution:

$$6.2 \times 10^{-10} = K_a = \frac{[H^+]^2 - 10^{-14}}{1.0 \times 10^{-4} - \dfrac{[H^+]^2 - 10^{-14}}{[H^+]}}$$

We will now solve for $[H^+]$ by use of successive approximations. First we must determine a reasonable guess for $[H^+]$. Note from the preceding simple calculation that $[H^+]$, ignoring the contribution from water, is $2.5 \times 10^{-7}\,M$. Will the actual $[H^+]$ be larger or smaller than this value? It will be a little larger because of the contribution from H_2O. So a reasonable guess for $[H^+]$ is $3.0 \times 10^{-7}\,M$.

We now substitute this value for $[H^+]$ into the denominator of the equation, to give

$$K_a = 6.2 \times 10^{-10} = \frac{[H^+]^2 - 1.0 \times 10^{-14}}{1.0 \times 10^{-4} - \dfrac{(3.0 \times 10^{-7})^2 - 1.0 \times 10^{-14}}{3.0 \times 10^{-7}}}$$

$$6.2 \times 10^{-10} = \frac{[H^+]^2 - 1.0 \times 10^{-14}}{1.0 \times 10^{-4} - 2.67 \times 10^{-7}}$$

Now, rearrange this equation so that a value for $[H^+]$ can be calculated:

$$[H^+]^2 = 6.2 \times 10^{-14} - 1.66 \times 10^{-16} + 1.0 + 10^{-14}$$

$$= 7.2 \times 10^{-14}$$

$$[H^+] = \sqrt{7.2 \times 10^{-14}} = 2.68 \times 10^{-7}$$

Recall that the original guessed value of $[H^+]$ was 3.0×10^{-7}. Since the calculated value and the guessed value do not agree, use 2.68×10^{-7} as the new guessed value:

$$K_a = \frac{[H^+]^2 - 1.0 \times 10^{-14}}{1.0 \times 10^{-4} - \dfrac{(2.68 \times 10^{-7})^2 - 1.0 \times 10^{-14}}{2.68 \times 10^{-7}}}$$

Solving for $[H^+]$, we have

$$[H^+] = 2.68 \times 10^{-7} = 2.7 \times 10^{-7}\ M$$

Since the guessed value and the newly calculated value agree, this answer is correct, and it takes into account both contributors to $[H^+]$ (water and HCN). Thus for this solution,

$$pH = -\log(2.7 \times 10^{-7}) = 6.57$$

As you followed the preceding procedure, you may have noticed that there was an opportunity to simplify the math, but we did not take advantage of it. Note that the term

$$[HA]_0 - \frac{[H^+]^2 - K_w}{[H^+]}$$

occurs in the denominator of the overall equation. Because $[H^+]$ will be between 10^{-6} and 10^{-7} (otherwise, we would be using the simple equation), we can see that the value of the term

$$\frac{[H^+]^2 - K_w}{[H^+]}$$

will be between 0 (if $[H^+] = 10^{-7}\ M$) and 10^{-6} (if $[H^+] = 10^{-6}\ M$). Thus, if $[HA]_0 > 2 \times 10^{-5}\ M$ in a given acid solution, then

$$[HA]_0 - \frac{[H^+]^2 - K_w}{[H^+]} \approx [HA]_0$$

within the limits of the 5% rule. Under these conditions the equation

$$K_a = \frac{[H^+]^2 - K_w}{[HA]_0 - \dfrac{[H^+]^2 - K_w}{[H^+]}}$$

becomes

$$K_a \approx \frac{[H^+]^2 - K_w}{[HA]_0}$$

which can be readily solved for $[H^+]$:

Note that this equation gives the same $[H^+]$ for $1.0 \times 10^{-4}\ M$ HCN as the full equation.

$$[H^+] \approx \sqrt{K_a[HA]_0 + K_w}$$

This simplified equation applies to all cases except for very dilute weak acid solutions.

We will now summarize the conclusions of this section.

The pH Calculations for an Aqueous Solution of a Weak Acid HA (Major Species HA and H_2O)

1. The full equation for this case is

$$K_a = \frac{[H^+]^2 - K_w}{[HA]_0 - \dfrac{[H^+]^2 - K_w}{H^+}}$$

2. When the weak acid by itself produces $[H^+] \geq 10^{-6}\ M$, the full equation becomes

$$K_a = \frac{[H^+]^2}{[HA]_0 - [H^+]}$$

This corresponds to the typical weak acid case.

Continued

3. When

$$[HA]_0 \gg \frac{[H^+]^2 - K_w}{[H^+]}$$

the full equation becomes

$$K_a = \frac{[H^+]^2 - K_w}{[HA]_0}$$

which gives

$$[H^+] = \sqrt{K_a[HA]_0 + K_w}$$

7.10 Strong Acid Solutions in Which Water Contributes to the H^+ Concentration

Although in a typical strong acid solution (for example, 0.1 *M* HCl) the $[H^+]$ is determined by the amount of strong acid present, there are circumstances in which the contribution of water must be taken into account. For example, consider a 1.0×10^{-7} *M* HNO_3 solution. For this very dilute solution, the strong acid and the water make comparable contributions to $[H^+]$ at equilibrium. Because the H^+ from HNO_3 will affect the position of the water equilibrium, the total $[H^+]$ in this solution will not be simply 1.0×10^{-7} *M* + 1.0×10^{-7} *M* – 2.0×10^{-7} *M*. Rather, $[H^+]$ will be between 1.0×10^{-7} *M* and 2.0×10^{-7} *M*. We can calculate the exact $[H^+]$ by using the principle of charge balance:

$$[\text{Positive charge}] = [\text{negative charge}]$$

In this case we have

$$[H^+] = [NO_3^-] + [OH^-]$$

which, from $K_w = [H^+][OH^-]$, can be written as

$$[H^+] = [NO_3^-] + \frac{K_w}{[H^+]} \quad \text{or} \quad \frac{[H^+]^2 - K_w}{[H^+]} = [NO_3^-]$$

The fact that the solution contains 1.0×10^{-7} *M* HNO_3 means that $[NO_3^-] = 1.0 \times 10^{-7}$ *M*. Inserting this value, we can solve the preceding equation to give $[H^+] = 1.6 \times 10^{-7}$ *M*.

This approach applies for any strong acid (although it is unnecessary for more typical concentrations). It can also be adapted to calculate the pH of a very dilute strong base solution. (Try your hand at this problem by calculating the pH of a 5.0×10^{-8} *M* KOH solution.)

7.11 Strategy for Solving Acid–Base Problems: A Summary

In this chapter we have encountered many different situations involving aqueous solutions of acids and bases, and in the next chapter we will encounter still more. In solving for the equilibrium concentrations in these aqueous solutions, you may be tempted to create a pigeonhole for each possible situation and to memorize the procedures necessary to deal with each particular situation. This approach is just not practical and usually leads to frustration: Too many pigeonholes are required, because there seems to be an infinite number of cases. But you can handle any case successfully by taking a systematic, patient, and thoughtful approach. When analyzing an acid–base equilibrium problem, do *not* ask yourself how a memorized solution can be used to solve the problem. Instead, ask yourself this question: "*What are the major species in the solution, and how does each behave chemically?*"

The most important part of doing a complicated acid–base equilibrium problem is the analysis you do at the beginning of a problem:

Which major species are present?
Does a reaction occur that can be assumed to go to completion?
Which equilibrium dominates the solution?

Let the problem guide you. Be patient.

The following steps outline a general strategy for solving problems involving acid–base equilibria.

STEPS

Solving Acid–Base Equilibria Problems

1 List the major species in solution.

2 Look for reactions that can be assumed to go to completion, such as a strong acid dissociating or H^+ reacting with OH^-.

3 For a reaction that can be assumed to go to completion:
   a. Determine the concentrations of the products.
   b. Write down the major species in solution after the reaction.

4 Look at each major component of the solution, and decide whether it is an acid or a base.

5 Pick the equilibrium that will control the pH. Use known values of the dissociation constants for the various species to determine the dominant equilibrium.
   a. Write the equation for the reaction and the equilibrium expression.
   b. Compute the initial concentrations (assuming that the dominant equilibrium has not yet occurred—for example, there has been no acid dissociation).
   c. Define x.
   d. Compute the equilibrium concentrations in terms of x.
   e. Substitute the concentrations into the equilibrium expression, and solve for x.
   f. Check the validity of the approximation.
   g. Calculate the pH and other concentrations as required.

Although these procedures may seem somewhat cumbersome, especially for simpler problems, they will become increasingly helpful as the aqueous solutions become more complicated. If you develop the habit of approaching acid–base problems systematically, the more complex cases will be much easier to manage.

Key Terms

Section 7.1
Arrhenius concept
Brønsted–Lowry model
hydronium ion
conjugate base
conjugate acid
conjugate acid–base pair
acid dissociation constant

Section 7.2
strong acid
weak acid
diprotic acid
oxyacid
organic acid
carboxyl group
monoprotic acid
amphoteric substance
autoionization
ion-product (dissociating) constant

Section 7.4
major species

Section 7.5
percent dissociation

Section 7.6
strong bases
slaked lime
lime-soda process
weak bases
amine

Section 7.7
polyprotic acid
triprotic acid

Section 7.8
salt

Section 7.9
charge balance
material balance equation

For Review

Models for acids and bases
- Arrhenius model
  - Acids produce H^+ in solution
  - Bases produce OH^- in solution
- Brønsted–Lowry model
  - An acid is a proton donor
  - A base is a proton acceptor
  - In this model an acid molecule reacts with a water molecule, which behaves as a base:

$$\underset{\text{Acid}}{HA(aq)} + \underset{\text{Base}}{H_2O(l)} \rightleftharpoons \underset{\text{Conjugate acid}}{H_3O^+(aq)} + \underset{\text{Conjugate base}}{A^-(aq)}$$

to form a new acid (conjugate acid) and a new base (conjugate base).
- Lewis model
  - A Lewis acid is an electron-pair acceptor
  - A Lewis base is an electron-pair donor

Acid–base equilibrium
- The equilibrium constant for an acid dissociating (ionizing) in water is called K_a
- The K_a expression is

$$K_a = \frac{[H_3O^+][A^-]}{[HA]}$$

which is often simplified as

$$K_a = \frac{[H^+][A^-]}{[HA]}$$

  - $[H_2O]$ is never included because it is assumed to be constant

Acid strength
- A strong acid has a very large K_a value
  - The acid completely dissociates (ionizes) in water
  - The dissociation (ionization) equilibrium position lies all the way to the right
  - Strong acids have very weak conjugate bases
  - The common strong acids are nitric acid [$HNO_3(aq)$], hydrochloric acid [$HCl(aq)$], sulfuric acid [$H_2SO(aq)$], and perchloric acid [$HClO_4(aq)$]
- A weak acid has a small K_a value
  - The acid dissociates (ionizes) to only a slight extent
  - The dissociation (ionization) equilibrium position lies far to the left
  - Weak acids have relatively strong conjugate bases
  - Percent dissociation of a weak acid

$$\%\ \text{dissociation} = \frac{\text{amount dissociated (mol/L)}}{\text{initial concentration (mol/L)}} \times 100\%$$

  - The smaller the percent dissociation, the weaker the acid
  - Dilution of a weak acid increases its percent dissociation

Autoionization of water

- Water is an amphoteric substance: it behaves as both an acid and a base
- Water reacts with itself in an acid–base reaction

$$H_2O(l) + H_2O(l) \rightleftharpoons H_3O^+(aq) + OH^-(aq)$$

which leads to the equilibrium expression

$$K_w = [H_3O^+][OH^-] \quad \text{or} \quad [H^+][OH^-] = K_w$$

  - K_w is the ion-product constant for water
  - At 25°C in pure water $[H^+] = [OH^-] = 1.0 \times 10^{-7}$, so $K_w = 1.0 \times 10^{-14}$
- Acidic solution: $[H^+] > [OH^-]$
- Basic solution: $[OH^-] > [H^+]$
- Neutral solution: $[H^+] = [OH^-]$

The pH scale

- $pH = -\log [H^+]$
- Since pH is a log scale, the pH changes by 1 for every 10-fold change in $[H^+]$
- The log scale is also used for $[OH^-]$ and for K_a values

$$pOH = -\log[OH^-]$$

$$pK_a = -\log K_a$$

Bases

- Strong bases are hydroxide salts, such as NaOH and KOH
- Weak bases react with water to produce OH^-

$$B(aq) + H_2O(l) \rightleftharpoons BH^+(aq) + OH^-(aq)$$

  - The equilibrium constant for this reaction is called K_b where

$$K_b = \frac{[BH^+][OH^-]}{[B]}$$

  - In water a base B is always competing with OH^- for a proton (H^+), so K_b values tend to be very small, thus making B a weak base (compared to OH^-)

Polyprotic acids

- A polyprotic acid has more than one acidic proton
- Polyprotic acids dissociate one proton at a time
  - Each step has a characteristic K_a value
  - Typically for a weak polyprotic acid, $K_{a_1} > K_{a_2} > K_{a_3}$
- Sulfuric acid is unique
  - It is a strong acid in the first dissociation step (K_{a_1} is very large)
  - It is a weak acid in the second step

Acid–base properties of salts

- Can produce acidic, basic, or neutral solutions
- Salts that contain:
  - Cations of strong bases and anions of strong acids produce neutral solutions
  - Cations of strong bases and anions of weak acids produce basic solutions
  - Cations of weak bases and anions of strong acids produce acidic solutions
- Acidic solutions are produced by salts containing a highly charged metal cation—for example, Al^{3+} and Fe^{3+}

Solutions for which water contributes significantly to the H^+ concentration

- Weak acid solutions
  - $$K_a = \frac{[H^+]^2 - K_w}{[HA]_0 - \frac{[H^+]^2 - K_w}{[H^+]}}$$
- Strong acid solutions
  - Charge balance
  - $[H^+] = [A^-] + [OH^-]$

Discussion Questions

These questions are designed to be considered by groups of students in class. Often these questions work well for introducing a particular topic in class.

1. Consider two beakers of pure water at different temperatures. How do their pH values compare? Which is more acidic? More basic? Explain.
2. Differentiate between the terms *strength* and *concentration* as they apply to acids and bases. When is HCl strong? Weak? Concentrated? Dilute? Answer the same questions for ammonia.
3. Sketch two graphs: (a) percent dissociation of weak acid HA versus initial concentration of HA ($[HA]_0$), and (b) H^+ concentration versus $[HA]_0$. Explain both.
4. Consider a solution prepared by mixing a weak acid HA and HCl. What are the major species? Explain what is occurring in solution. How would you calculate the pH? What if you added NaA to this solution? Then added NaOH?
5. Explain why salts can be acidic, basic, or neutral, and show examples. Do so without specific numbers.
6. Consider two separate aqueous solutions: one of a weak acid HA and one of HCl. Assuming you started with 10 molecules of each:
   a. Draw a picture of what each looks like at equilibrium.
   b. What are the major species in each beaker?
   c. From your pictures, calculate the K_a values of each acid.
   d. Order the following from strongest to weakest base: H_2O, A^-, and Cl^-. Explain your sequence.
7. You are asked for the H^+ concentration in a solution of NaOH(*aq*). Because sodium hydroxide is a strong base, can we say there is no H^+, since having H^+ would imply that the solution is acidic?
8. Consider a solution prepared by mixing equal moles of a weak acid HA, HCl, and NaA. Which of the following best describes what happens?
   a. The H^+ from the HCl reacts completely with the A^- from the NaA. Then the HA dissociates to some extent.
   b. The H^+ from the HCl reacts with the A^- from the NaA to make HA, whereas the HA is dissociating. Eventually you have equal amounts of everything.
   c. The H^+ from the HCl reacts with the A^- from the NaA to make HA, whereas the HA is dissociating. Eventually all the reactions have equal rates.
   d. The H^+ from the HCl reacts completely with the A^- from the NaA. Then the HA dissociates until "too much" H^+ and A^- are formed, so the H^+ and A^- react to form HA, and so on. Eventually equilibrium is reached.

   Justify the best choice. For those you did not choose, explain why they are incorrect.
9. Consider a solution formed by mixing 100.0 mL of 0.10 *M* HA ($K_a = 1.0 \times 10^{-6}$), 100.0 mL of 0.10 *M* NaA, and 100.0 mL of 0.05 *M* HCl. In calculating the pH for the final solution, you would make some assumptions about the order in which various reactions occur to simplify the calculations. State these assumptions. Does it matter whether the reactions actually occur in the assumed order? Relate this to Question 8. Explain.
10. A certain sodium compound is dissolved in water to liberate Na^+ ions and a particular negative ion. What evidence would you look for to determine whether the anion is behaving as an acid or a base (without measuring the pH of the solution)? Explain how the anion could behave simultaneously as an acid and a base.
11. Acids and bases can be thought of as chemical opposites (acids are proton donors, and bases are proton acceptors). Therefore, one might think that $K_a = 1/K_b$. Why isn't this the case? What is the relationship between K_a and K_b? Prove it with a derivation.
12. You have two solutions of the salts NaX(*aq*) and NaY(*aq*) at equal concentrations. What would you need to know to determine which solution has the higher pH? Explain how you would decide (perhaps even provide a sample calculation).
13. Is the conjugate base of a weak acid a strong base? Explain. Explain why Cl^- does not affect the pH of an aqueous solution.

14. Match the following pH values: 1, 2, 5, 6, 6.5, 8, 11, 11, and 13 with the following chemicals (of equal concentration): HBr, NaOH, NaF, NaCN, NH_4F, CH_3NH_3F, HF, HCN, and NH_3. Answer this question without performing calculations.

15. The salt BX, when dissolved in water, produces an acidic solution. Which of the following could be true? (There may be more than one correct answer.)
    a. The acid HX is a weak acid.
    b. The acid HX is a strong acid.
    c. The cation B^+ is a weak acid.
    Explain.

Exercises

OWL Interactive versions of these problems may be assigned in OWL.

A blue exercise number indicates that the answer to that exercise appears at the back of this book and a solution appears in the *Solutions Guide*.

Nature of Acids and Bases

16. Consider the autoionization of liquid ammonia:

Label each of the species in the equation as an acid or a base and explain your answer.

17. The following are representations of acid–base reactions:

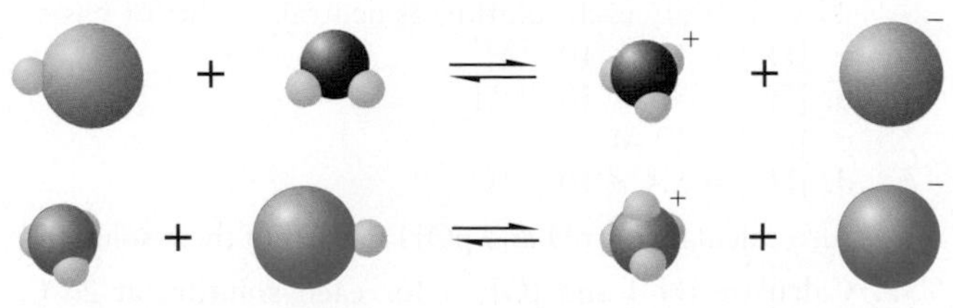

a. Label each of the species in both equations as an acid or a base and explain.
b. For those species that are acids, which labels apply: Arrhenius acid and/or Brønsted-Lowery acid? What about the bases?

18. Consider the following statements. Write out an example reaction and *K* expression that are associated with each statement.
    a. The autoionization of water.
    b. An acid reacts with water to produce the conjugate base of the acid and the hydronium ion.
    c. A base reacts with water to produce the conjugate acid of the base and the hydroxide ion.

19. For each of the following aqueous reactions, identify the acid, the base, the conjugate base, and the conjugate acid.
    a. $H_2O + H_2CO_3 \rightleftharpoons H_3O^+ + HCO_3^-$
    b. $C_5H_5NH^+ + H_2O \rightleftharpoons C_5H_5N + H_3O^+$
    c. $HCO_3^- + C_5H_5NH^+ \rightleftharpoons H_2CO_3 + C_5H_5N$

20. Write balanced equations that describe the following reactions.
    a. The dissociation of perchloric acid in water.
    b. The dissociation of propanoic acid ($CH_3CH_2CO_2H$) in water.
    c. The dissociation of ammonium ion in water.

21. Write the dissociation reaction and the corresponding K_a equilibrium expression for each of the following acids in water.
    a. $HC_2H_3O_2$ b. $Co(H_2O)_6^{3+}$ c. $CH_3NH_3^+$

22. Classify each of the following as a strong acid or a weak acid.

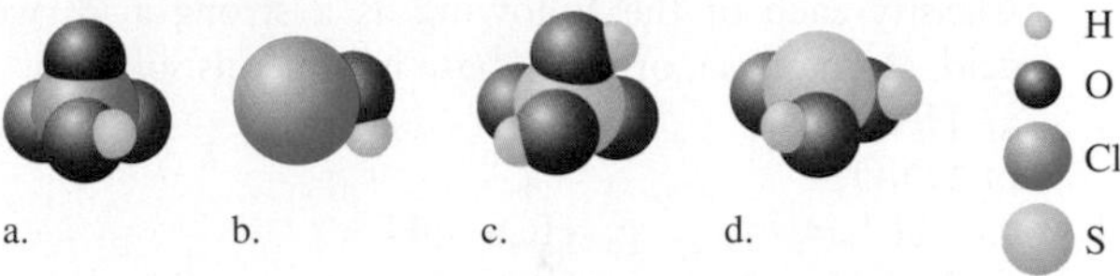

23. Consider the following illustrations:

Which beaker best illustrates what happens when the following acids are dissolved in water?
    a. HNO_2
    b. HNO_3
    c. HCl
    d. HF
    e. $HC_2H_3O_2$

24. Write the reaction and the corresponding K_b equilibrium expression for each of the following substances (acting as bases in water).
    a. NH_3
    b. CN^-
    c. pyridine, C_5H_5N
    d. aniline, $C_6H_5NH_2$

25. Use Table 7.2 to order the following from the strongest to the weakest acid.

$$HClO_2,\ H_2O,\ NH_4^+,\ HClO_4$$

26. Use Table 7.2 to order the following from the strongest to the weakest base.

$$ClO_2^-,\ H_2O,\ NH_3,\ ClO_4^-$$

27. You may need Table 7.2 to answer the following questions.
    a. Which is the stronger acid, HCl or H_2O?
    b. Which is the stronger acid, H_2O or HNO_2?
    c. Which is the stronger acid, HCN or HOC_6H_5?

28. You may need Table 7.2 to answer the following questions.
    a. Which is the stronger base, Cl^- or H_2O?
    b. Which is the stronger base, H_2O or NO_2^-?
    c. Which is the stronger base, CN^- or $OC_6H_5^-$?
29. Consider the reaction of acetic acid in water

$$CH_3CO_2H(aq) + H_2O(l) \rightleftharpoons CH_3CO_2^-(aq) + H_3O^+(aq)$$

where $K_a = 1.8 \times 10^{-5}$.
    a. Which two bases are competing for the proton?
    b. Which is the stronger base?
    c. In light of your answer to part b, why do we classify the acetate ion ($CH_3CO_2^-$) as a weak base? Use an appropriate reaction to justify your answer.
30. In general, as base strength increases, conjugate acid strength decreases. Explain why the conjugate acid of the weak base NH_3 is a weak acid.
31. Classify each of the following as a strong acid, weak acid, strong base, or weak base in aqueous solution.
    a. HNO_2
    b. HNO_3
    c. CH_3NH_2
    d. NaOH
    e. NH_3
    f. HF
    g. $HC(=O)-OH$
    h. $Ca(OH)_2$
    i. H_2SO_4

Autoionization of Water and pH Scale

32. Values of K_w as a function of temperature are as follows:

Temp (°C)	K_w
0	1.14×10^{-15}
25	1.00×10^{-14}
35	2.09×10^{-14}
40.	2.92×10^{-14}
50.	5.47×10^{-14}

    a. Is the autoionization of water exothermic or endothermic?
    b. What is the pH of pure water at 50.°C?
    c. From a plot of $\ln(K_w)$ versus $1/T$ (using the Kelvin scale), estimate K_w at 37°C, normal physiological temperature.
    d. What is the pH of a neutral solution at 37°C?
33. At 40.°C the value of K_w is 2.92×10^{-14}.
    a. Calculate the [H^+] and [OH^-] in pure water at 40.°C.
    b. What is the pH of pure water at 40.°C?
    c. If the hydroxide ion concentration in a solution is 0.10 *M*, what is the pH at 40.°C?
34. Give the conditions for a neutral aqueous solution at 25°C, in terms of [H^+], pH, and the relationship between [H^+] and [OH^-]. Do the same for an acidic solution and for a basic solution. As a solution becomes more acidic, what happens to pH, pOH, [H^+], and [OH^-]? As a solution becomes more basic, what happens to pH, pOH, [H^+], and [OH^-]?
35. Calculate the [H^+] of each of the following solutions at 25°C. Identify each solution as neutral, acidic, or basic.
    a. [OH^-] = 1.5 *M*
    b. [OH^-] = 3.6×10^{-15} *M*
    c. [OH^-] = 1.0×10^{-7} *M*
    d. [OH^-] = 7.3×10^{-4} *M*

    Also calculate the pH and pOH of each of these solutions.
36. Calculate the [OH^-] of each of the following solutions at 25°C. Identify each solution as neutral, acidic, or basic.
    a. [H^+] = 1.0×10^{-7} *M*
    b. [H^+] = 8.3×10^{-16} *M*
    c. [H^+] = 12 *M*
    d. [H^+] = 5.4×10^{-5} *M*

    Also calculate the pH and pOH of each of these solutions.
37. Calculate [H^+] and [OH^-] for each solution at 25°C. Identify each solution as neutral, acidic, or basic.
    a. pH = 7.40 (the normal pH of blood)
    b. pH = 15.3
    c. pH = −1.0
    d. pH = 3.20
    e. pOH = 5.0
    f. pOH = 9.60
38. Fill in the missing information in the following table.

	pH	pOH	[H^+]	[OH^-]	Acidic, Basic, or Neutral?
Solution a	9.63	____	____	____	____
Solution b	____	____	____	3.9×10^{-6} *M*	____
Solution c	____	____	0.027 *M*	____	____
Solution d	____	12.2	____	____	____

Solutions of Acids

39. Calculate the pH of each of the following solutions of a strong acid in water.
    a. 0.10 *M* HCl
    b. 5.0 *M* $HClO_4$
    c. 1.0×10^{-11} *M* HI
40. A solution is prepared by adding 50.0 mL of 0.050 *M* HBr to 150.0 mL of 0.10 *M* HI. Calculate [H^+] and the pH of this solution. HBr and HI are both considered strong acids.
41. How would you prepare 1600 mL of a pH = 1.50 solution using concentrated (12 *M*) HCl?

42. What mass of HNO_3 is present in 250.0 mL of a nitric acid solution having a pH = 5.10?

43. What are the major species present in 0.250 *M* solutions of each of the following acids? Calculate the pH of each of these solutions.
a. HNO_2 b. CH_3CO_2H ($HC_2H_3O_2$)

44. What are the major species present in 0.250 *M* solutions of each of the following acids? Calculate the pH of each of these solutions.
a. HOC_6H_5 b. HCN

45. Calculate the concentration of all species present and the pH of a 0.020 *M* HF solution.

46. Calculate the percent dissociation for a 0.22 *M* solution of chlorous acid ($HClO_2$, $K_a = 1.2 \times 10^{-2}$).

47. The following illustration displays the relative number of species when an acid, HA, is added to water.

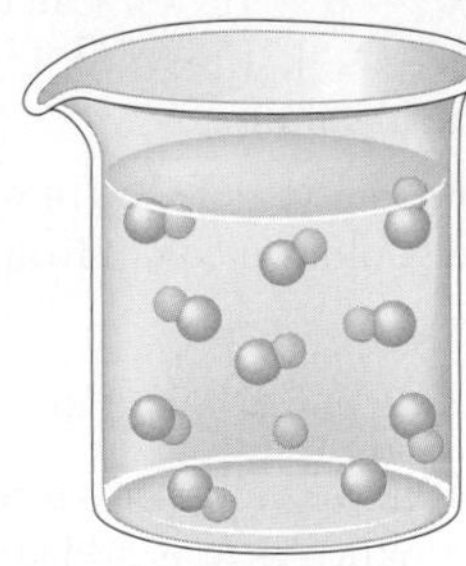

a. Is HA a weak or strong acid? How can you tell?
b. Using the relative numbers given in the illustration, determine the value for K_a and the percent dissociation of the acid. Assume the initial acid concentration is 0.20 *M*.

48. Monochloroacetic acid ($HC_2H_2ClO_2$) is a skin irritant that is used in "chemical peels" intended to remove the top layer of dead skin from the face and ultimately improve the complexion. The value of K_a for monochloroacetic acid is 1.35×10^{-3}. Calculate the pH of a 0.10 *M* solution of monochloroacetic acid.

49. Calculate the pH of a 0.010 *M* solution of iodic acid (HIO_3, $K_a = 0.17$).

50. For propanoic acid ($HC_3H_5O_2$, $K_a = 1.3 \times 10^{-5}$), determine the concentration of all species present, the pH, and the percent dissociation of a 0.100 *M* solution.

51. A solution is prepared by dissolving 0.56 g of benzoic acid ($C_6H_5CO_2H$, $K_a = 6.4 \times 10^{-5}$) in enough water to make 1.0 L of solution. Calculate [$C_6H_5CO_2H$], [$C_6H_5CO_2^-$], [H^+], [OH^-], and the pH of this solution.

52. At 25°C a saturated solution of benzoic acid (see Exercise 51) has a pH of 2.80. Calculate the water solubility of benzoic acid in moles per liter and grams per 100. mL.

53. A typical aspirin tablet contains 325 mg of acetylsalicylic acid ($HC_9H_7O_4$). Calculate the pH of a solution that is prepared by dissolving two aspirin tablets in one cup (237 mL) of solution. Assume the aspirin tablets are pure acetylsalicylic acid, $K_a = 3.3 \times 10^{-4}$.

54. Calculate the pH of a solution that contains 1.0 *M* HF and 1.0 *M* HOC_6H_5. Also calculate the concentration of $OC_6H_5^-$ in this solution at equilibrium.

55. Calculate the pH of each of the following.
a. a solution containing 0.10 *M* HCl and 0.10 *M* HOCl
b. a solution containing 0.050 *M* HNO_3 and 0.50 *M* $HC_2H_3O_2$

56. A 0.15 *M* solution of a weak acid is 3.0% dissociated. Calculate K_a.

57. An acid HX is 25% dissociated in water. If the equilibrium concentration of HX is 0.30 *M*, calculate the K_a value for HX.

58. Calculate the percent dissociation of the acid in each of the following solutions.
a. 0.50 *M* acetic acid
b. 0.050 *M* acetic acid
c. 0.0050 *M* acetic acid
d. Use Le Châtelier's principle to explain why percent dissociation increases as the concentration of a weak acid decreases.
e. Even though the percent dissociation increases from solutions a to c, the [H^+] decreases. Explain.

59. The pH of a 1.00×10^{-2} *M* solution of cyanic acid (HOCN) is 2.77 at 25°C. Calculate K_a for HOCN from this result.

60. Trichloroacetic acid (CCl_3CO_2H) is a corrosive acid that is used to precipitate proteins. The pH of a 0.050 *M* solution of trichloroacetic acid is the same as the pH of a 0.040 *M* $HClO_4$ solution. Calculate K_a for trichloroacetic acid.

61. A typical sample of vinegar has a pH of 3.0. Assuming that vinegar is only an aqueous solution of acetic acid ($K_a = 1.8 \times 10^{-5}$), calculate the concentration of acetic acid in vinegar.

62. You have 100.0 g of saccharin, a sugar substitute, and you want to prepare a pH = 5.75 solution. What volume of solution can be prepared? For saccharin ($HC_7H_4NSO_3$), $pK_a = 11.70$ ($pK_a = -\log K_a$).

Solutions of Bases

63. Using Table 7.3, order the following bases from strongest to weakest.

NO_3^-, H_2O, NH_3, and C_5H_5N

64. Using Table 7.3, order the following acids from strongest to weakest.

HNO_3, H_2O, NH_4^+, and $C_5H_5NH^+$

65. Use Table 7.3 to help answer the following questions.
a. Which is the stronger base, ClO_4^- or $C_6H_5NH_2$?
b. Which is the stronger base, H_2O or $C_6H_5NH_2$?
c. Which is the stronger base, OH^- or $C_6H_5NH_2$?
d. Which is the stronger base, $C_6H_5NH_2$ or CH_3NH_2?

66. Use Table 7.3 to help answer the following questions.
a. Which is the stronger acid, $HClO_4$ or $C_6H_5NH_3^+$?
b. Which is the stronger acid, H_2O or $C_6H_5NH_3^+$?
c. Which is the stronger acid, $C_6H_5NH_3^+$ or $CH_3NH_3^+$?

67. Calculate the pH of the following solutions.
    a. 0.10 M NaOH
    b. 1.0×10^{-10} M NaOH
    c. 2.0 M NaOH

68. Calculate $[OH^-]$, pOH, and pH for each of the following.
    a. 0.00040 M $Ca(OH)_2$
    b. a solution containing 25 g of KOH per liter
    c. a solution containing 150.0 g of NaOH per liter

69. Calculate the concentration of an aqueous $Ba(OH)_2$ solution that has pH = 10.50.

70. What mass of KOH is necessary to prepare 800.0 mL of a solution having a pH = 11.56?

71. For the reaction of hydrazine (N_2H_4) in water.

$$H_2NNH_2(aq) + H_2O(l) \rightleftharpoons H_2NNH_3^+(aq) + OH^-(aq)$$

K_b is 3.0×10^{-6}. Calculate the concentrations of all species and the pH of a 2.0 M solution of hydrazine in water.

72. Calculate the percentage of pyridine (C_5H_5N) that forms pyridinium ion, $C_5H_5NH^+$, in a 0.10 M aqueous solution of pyridine ($K_b = 1.7 \times 10^{-9}$).

73. The presence of what element most commonly results in basic properties for an organic compound? What is present on this element in compounds that allows it to accept a proton?

74. Calculate $[OH^-]$, $[H^+]$, and the pH of 0.40 M solutions of each of the following amines (the K_b values are found in Table 7.3).
    a. aniline
    b. methylamine

75. Calculate the pH of a 0.20 M $C_2H_5NH_2$ solution ($K_b = 5.6 \times 10^{-4}$).

76. Calculate the pH of a 0.050 M $(C_2H_5)_2NH$ solution ($K_b = 1.3 \times 10^{-3}$).

77. Codeine is a derivative of morphine that is used as an analgesic, narcotic, or antitussive. It was once commonly used in cough syrups but is now available only by prescription because of its addictive properties. The formula of codeine is $C_{18}H_{21}NO_3$, and the pK_b is 6.05. Calculate the pH of a 10.0-mL solution containing 5.0 mg of codeine (p$K_b = -\log K_b$).

78. A codeine-containing cough syrup lists codeine sulfate as a major ingredient instead of codeine. *The Merck Index* gives $C_{36}H_{44}N_2O_{10}S$ as the formula for codeine sulfate. Describe the composition of codeine sulfate (see Exercise 77). Why is codeine sulfate used instead of codeine?

79. What is the percent ionization in each of the following solutions?
    a. 0.10 M NH_3
    b. 0.010 M NH_3
    c. 0.10 M CH_3NH_2

80. Quinine ($C_{20}H_{24}N_2O_2$) is the most important alkaloid derived from cinchona bark. It is used as an antimalarial drug. For quinine pK_{b_1} = 5.1 and pK_{b_2} = 9.7 (pK_b = $-\log K_b$). Only 1.0 g of quinine will dissolve in 1900.0 mL of solution. Calculate the pH of a saturated aqueous solution of quinine. Consider only the reaction $Q + H_2O \rightleftharpoons QH^+ + OH^-$ described by pK_{b_1}, where Q = quinine.

81. The pH of a 0.016 M aqueous solution of *p*-toluidine ($CH_3C_6H_4NH_2$) is 8.60. Calculate K_b.

82. Calculate the mass of $HONH_2$ required to dissolve in enough water to make 250.0 mL of solution having a pH of 10.00 ($K_b = 1.1 \times 10^{-8}$).

Polyprotic Acids

83. Write out the stepwise K_a reactions for citric acid ($H_3C_6H_5O_7$), a triprotic acid.

84. Consider a 0.10 M H_2CO_3 solution and a 0.10 M H_2SO_4 solution. Without doing any detailed calculations, choose one of the following statements that best describes the $[H^+]$ of each solution and explain your answer.
    a. The $[H^+]$ is less than 0.10 M.
    b. The $[H^+]$ is 0.10 M.
    c. The $[H^+]$ is between 0.10 M and 0.20 M.
    d. The $[H^+]$ is 0.20 M.

85. Arsenic acid (H_3AsO_4) is a triprotic acid with $K_{a_1} = 5 \times 10^{-3}$, $K_{a_2} = 8 \times 10^{-8}$, and $K_{a_3} = 6 \times 10^{-10}$. Calculate $[H^+]$, $[OH^-]$, $[H_3AsO_4]$, $[H_2AsO_4^-]$, $[HAsO_4^{2-}]$, and $[AsO_4^{3-}]$ in a 0.20 M arsenic acid solution.

86. Calculate $[CO_3^{2-}]$ in a 0.010 M solution of CO_2 in water (H_2CO_3). If all the CO_3^{2-} in this solution comes from the reaction

$$HCO_3^-(aq) \rightleftharpoons H^+(aq) + CO_3^{2-}(aq)$$

what percentage of the H^+ ions in the solution is a result of the dissociation of HCO_3^-? When acid is added to a solution of sodium hydrogen carbonate ($NaHCO_3$), vigorous bubbling occurs. How is this reaction related to the existence of carbonic acid (H_2CO_3) molecules in aqueous solution?

87. A typical vitamin C tablet (containing pure ascorbic acid, $H_2C_6H_6O_6$) weighs 500. mg. One vitamin C tablet is dissolved in enough water to make 200.0 mL of solution. Calculate the pH of this solution. Ascorbic acid is a diprotic acid.

88. Calculate the pH and $[S^{2-}]$ in a 0.10 M H_2S solution. Assume $K_{a_1} = 1.0 \times 10^{-7}$; $K_{a_2} = 1.0 \times 10^{-19}$.

89. Calculate the pH of a 2.0 M solution of H_2SO_4.

90. Calculate the pH of a 5.0×10^{-3} M solution of H_2SO_4.

Acid–Base Properties of Salts

91. Give three example solutions that fit each of the following descriptions.
    a. a strong electrolyte solution that is very acidic
    b. a strong electrolyte solution that is slightly acidic
    c. a strong electrolyte solution that is very basic
    d. a strong electrolyte solution that is slightly basic
    e. a strong electrolyte solution that is neutral

92. Derive an expression for the relationship between pK_a and pK_b for a conjugate acid–base pair.

93. Rank the following 0.10 M solutions in order of increasing pH.
    a. HI, HF, NaF, NaI
    b. NH_4Br, HBr, KBr, NH_3
    c. $C_6H_5NH_3NO_3$, $NaNO_3$, NaOH, HOC_6H_5, KOC_6H_5, $C_6H_5NH_2$, HNO_3

94. Arrange the following 0.10 *M* solutions in order from most acidic to most basic.

$CaBr_2$, KNO_2, $HClO_4$, HNO_2, $HONH_3ClO_4$, and NH_4NO_2

95. Are solutions of the following salts acidic, basic, or neutral? For those that are not neutral, explain why the solution is acidic or basic. The relevant K_a and K_b values are found in Tables 7.2, 7.3, and 7.4.
a. $Sr(NO_3)_2$
b. $C_2H_5NH_3CN$
c. C_5H_5NHF
d. $NH_4C_2H_3O_2$
e. $NaHCO_3$

96. Is an aqueous solution of $NaHSO_4$ acidic, basic, or neutral? What reaction occurs with water? Calculate the pH of a 0.10 *M* solution of $NaHSO_4$.

97. Determine $[OH^-]$, $[H^+]$, and the pH of each of the following solutions.
a. 1.0 *M* KCl
b. 1.0 *M* KF

98. Calculate the concentrations of all species present in a 0.25 *M* solution of ethylammonium chloride ($C_2H_5NH_3Cl$).

99. A 0.050 *M* solution of the salt NaB has a pH of 9.00. Calculate the pH of a 0.010 *M* solution of HB.

100. Calculate the pH of each of the following solutions.
a. 0.10 *M* CH_3NH_3Cl
b. 0.050 *M* NaCN

101. Calculate the pH of each of the following solutions.
a. 0.12 *M* KNO_2
b. 0.45 *M* NaOCl
c. 0.40 *M* NH_4ClO_4

102. Sodium azide (NaN_3) is sometimes added to water to kill bacteria. Calculate the concentration of all species in a 0.010 *M* solution of NaN_3. The K_a value for hydrazoic acid (HN_3) is 1.9×10^{-5}.

103. An unknown salt is either NaCN, $NaC_2H_3O_2$, NaF, NaCl, or NaOCl. When 0.100 mole of the salt is dissolved in 1.00 L of solution, the pH of the solution is 8.07. What is the identity of the salt?

104. Consider a solution of an unknown salt having the general formula BHCl, where B is one of the weak bases in Table 7.3. A 0.10 *M* solution of the unknown salt has a pH of 5.82. What is the actual formula of the salt?

105. Calculate the pH of a 0.10 *M* solution of $CoCl_3$. The K_a value for $Co(H_2O)_6^{3+}$ is 1.0×10^{-5}.

106. Calculate the pH of a 0.200 *M* solution of C_5H_5NHF.

107. Determine the pH of a 0.50 *M* solution of NH_4OCl.

108. Calculate the pH of a 0.10 *M* solution of sodium phosphate.

Solutions of Dilute Acids and Bases

109. Using the assumptions we ordinarily make in calculating the pH of an aqueous solution of a weak acid, calculate the pH of a 1.0×10^{-6} *M* solution of hypobromous acid (HBrO, $K_a = 2 \times 10^{-9}$). What is wrong with your answer? Why is it wrong? Without trying to solve the problem, tell what has to be included to solve the problem correctly.

110. Calculate the pH of 4.0×10^{-5} *M* phenol ($K_a = 1.6 \times 10^{-10}$).

111. Calculate the pH of 5.0×10^{-4} *M* HCN.

112. Calculate the pH of 5.0×10^{-8} *M* HNO_3.

113. Calculate the pH of a 7.0×10^{-7} *M* HCl solution.

114. Calculate the pH of a 1.0×10^{-7} *M* solution of NaOH in water.

Additional Exercises

115. Calculate the value for the equilibrium constant for each of the following aqueous reactions.
a. $NH_3 + H_3O^+ \rightleftharpoons NH_4^+ + H_2O$
b. $NO_2^- + H_3O^+ \rightleftharpoons HNO_2 + H_2O$
c. $NH_4^+ + CH_3CO_2^- \rightleftharpoons NH_3 + CH_3CO_2H$
d. $H_3O^+ + OH^- \rightleftharpoons 2H_2O$
e. $NH_4^+ + OH^- \rightleftharpoons NH_3 + H_2O$
f. $HNO_2 + OH^- \rightleftharpoons H_2O + NO_2^-$

116. A solution is prepared by adding 50.0 mL concentrated hydrochloric acid and 20.0 mL concentrated nitric acid to 300 mL water. More water is added until the final volume is 1.00 L. Calcuate $[H^+]$, $[OH^-]$, and the pH for this solution. [*Hint:* Concentrated HCl is 38% HCl (by mass) and has a density of 1.19 g/mL; concentrated HNO_3 is 70.% HNO_3 (by mass) and has a density of 1.42 g/mL.]

117. A 10.0-mL sample of an HCl solution has a pH of 2.000. What volume of water must be added to change the pH to 4.000?

118. Phosphoric acid is a common ingredient in traditional cola drinks. It is added to provide the drinks with a pleasantly tart taste. Although phosphoric acid is a triprotic acid, its protons are lost one at a time. Assuming that in cola drinks the concentration of phosphoric acid is 0.007 *M*, calculate the pH in this solution.

119. Hemoglobin (abbreviated Hb) is a protein that is responsible for the transport of oxygen in the blood of mammals. Each hemoglobin molecule contains four iron atoms that are the binding sites for O_2 molecules. The oxygen binding is pH-dependent. The relevant equilibrium reaction is

$$HbH_4^{4+}(aq) + 4O_2(g) \rightleftharpoons Hb(O_2)_4(aq) + 4H^+(aq)$$

Use Le Châtelier's principle to answer the following.
a. What form of hemoglobin, HbH_4^{4+} or $Hb(O_2)_4$, is favored in the lungs? What form is favored in the cells?
b. When a person hyperventilates, the concentration of CO_2 in the blood is decreased. How does this affect the oxygen-binding equilibrium? How does breathing into a paper bag help to counteract this effect? (See Exercise 120.)

c. When a person has suffered a cardiac arrest, injection of a sodium bicarbonate solution is given. Why is this necessary? (*Hint:* CO_2 blood levels increase during cardiac arrest.)

120. The pH of human blood is steady at a value of approximately 7.4 owing to the following equilbrium reactions:

$$CO_2(aq) + H_2O(l) \rightleftharpoons H_2CO_3(aq) \rightleftharpoons HCO_3^-(aq) + H^+(aq)$$

Acids formed during normal celluar respiration react with the HCO_3^- to form carbonic acid, which is in equilibrium with $CO_2(aq)$ and $H_2O(l)$. During vigorous exercise, a person's H_2CO_3 blood levels were 26.3 m*M*, whereas his CO_2 levels were 1.63 m*M*. On resting, the H_2CO_3 levels declined to 24.9. What was the CO_2 blood level at rest?

121. A solution is tested for pH and conductivity as pictured below:

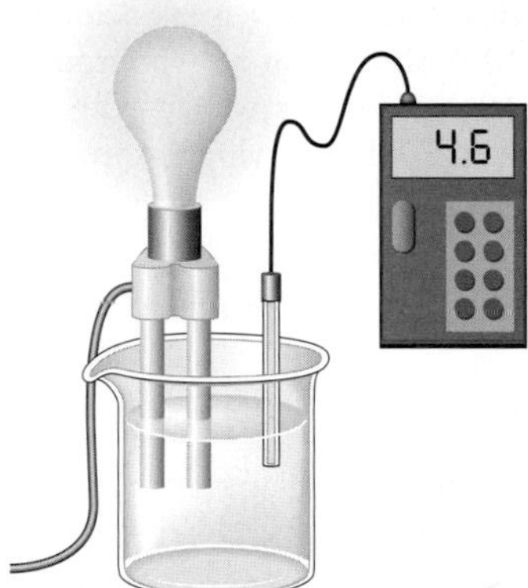

The solution contains one of the following substances: HCl, NaOH, NH_4Cl, HCN, NH_3, HF, or NaCN. If the solute concentration is about 1.0 *M*, what is the identity of the solute?

122. A 0.20 *M* sodium chlorobenzoate ($NaC_7H_4ClO_2$) solution has a pH of 8.65. Calculate the pH of a 0.20 *M* chlorobenzoic acid ($HC_7H_4ClO_2$) solution.

123. A 0.25-g sample of lime (CaO) is dissolved in enough water to make 1500 mL of solution. Calculate the pH of the solution.

124. Isocyanic acid (HNCO) can be prepared by heating sodium cyanate in the presence of solid oxalic acid according to the equation

$$2NaOCN(s) + H_2C_2O_4(s) \longrightarrow 2HNCO(l) + Na_2C_2O_4(s)$$

Upon isolating pure HNCO(*l*), an aqueous solution of HNCO can be prepared by dissolving the liquid HNCO in water. What is the pH of a 100.-mL solution of HNCO prepared from the reaction of 10.0 g each of NaOCN and $H_2C_2O_4$, assuming all of the HNCO produced is dissolved in solution? (K_a of HNCO = 1.2×10^{-4}.)

125. Papaverine hydrochloride (abbreviated papH$^+$Cl$^-$; molar mass = 378.85 g/mol) is a drug that belongs to a group of medicines called vasodilators, which cause blood vessels to expand, thereby increasing blood flow. This drug is the conjugate acid of the weak base papaverine (abbreviated pap; $K_b = 8.33 \times 10^{-9}$ at 35.0°C). Calculate the pH of a 30.0 mg/mL aqueous dose of papH$^+$Cl$^-$ prepared at 35.0°C. (K_w at 35.0°C is 2.1×10^{-14}.)

126. Acrylic acid ($CH_2{=}CHCO_2H$) is a precursor for many important plastics. (K_a for acrylic acid is 5.6×10^{-5}.)
   a. Calculate the pH of a 0.10 *M* solution of acrylic acid.
   b. Calculate the percent dissociation of a 0.10 *M* solution of acrylic acid.
   c. Calculate the [H$^+$] necessary to ensure that the percent dissociation of a 0.10 *M* solution of acrylic acid is less than 0.010%.
   d. Calculate the pH of a 0.050 *M* solution of sodium acrylate ($NaC_3H_3O_2$).

127. The equilibrium constant K_a for the reaction

$$Fe(H_2O)_6^{3+}(aq) + H_2O(l) \rightleftharpoons Fe(H_2O)_5(OH)^{2+}(aq) + H_3O^+(aq)$$

is 6.0×10^{-3}.
   a. Calculate the pH of a 0.10 *M* solution of $Fe(H_2O)_6^{3+}$.
   b. Calculate the pH necessary for 99.90% of the iron(III) to be in the form $Fe(H_2O)_6^{3+}$.
   c. Will a 1.0 *M* solution of iron(II) nitrate have a higher or lower pH than a 1.0 *M* solution of iron(III) nitrate? Explain.

128. How many moles of HCl(*g*) must be added to 1.0 L of 2.0 *M* NaOH to achieve a pH of 0.00? (Neglect any volume changes.)

129. A solution contains a mixture of acids: 0.50 *M* HA ($K_a = 1.0 \times 10^{-3}$), 0.20 *M* HB ($K_a = 1.0 \times 10^{-10}$), and 0.10 *M* HC ($K_a = 1.0 \times 10^{-12}$). Calculate the [H$^+$] in this solution.

130. One mole of a weak acid HA was dissolved in 2.0 L of solution. After the system had come to equilibrium, the concentration of HA was found to be 0.45 *M*. Calculate K_a for HA.

131. Calculate [OH$^-$] in a solution obtained by adding 0.0100 mole of solid NaOH to 1.00 L of 15.0 *M* NH_3.

132. Calculate the pH of an aqueous solution containing 1.0×10^{-2} *M* HCl, 1.0×10^{-2} *M* H_2SO_4, and 1.0×10^{-2} *M* HCN.

133. A solution is made by adding 50.0 mL of 0.200 *M* acetic acid ($K_a = 1.8 \times 10^{-5}$) to 50.0 mL of 1.00×10^{-3} *M* HCl.
   a. Calculate the pH of the solution.
   b. Calculate the acetate ion concentration.

134. Will 0.10 *M* solutions of the following salts be acidic, basic, or neutral? See Appendix 5 for K_a values.
   a. ammonium bicarbonate
   b. sodium dihydrogen phosphate
   c. sodium hydrogen phosphate
   d. ammonium dihydrogen phosphate
   e. ammonium formate

135. Citric acid ($H_3C_6H_5O_7$) is a triprotic acid with $K_{a_1} = 8.4 \times 10^{-4}$, $K_{a_2} = 1.8 \times 10^{-5}$, and $K_{a_3} = 4.0 \times 10^{-6}$. Calculate the pH of 0.15 *M* citric acid.

Challenge Problems

136. Consider 1000. mL of a 1.00×10^{-4} *M* solution of a certain acid HA that has a K_a value equal to 1.00×10^{-4}. How much water must be added or removed (by evaporation) so that a solution remains in which 25.0% of HA is dissociated at equilibrium? Assume that HA is nonvolatile.

137. a. The principal equilibrium in a solution of $NaHCO_3$ is

$$HCO_3^-(aq) + HCO_3^-(aq) \rightleftharpoons H_2CO_3(aq) + CO_3^{2-}(aq)$$

Calculate the value of the equilibrium constant for this reaction.

b. At equilibrium, what is the relationship between $[H_2CO_3]$ and $[CO_3^{2-}]$?

c. Using the equilibrium

$$H_2CO_3(aq) \rightleftharpoons 2H^+(aq) + CO_3^{2-}(aq)$$

and the result from part b, derive an expression for the pH of the solution in terms of K_{a_1} and K_{a_2}.

d. What is the pH of the solution of $NaHCO_3$?

138. A typical solution of baking soda (sodium bicarbonate, $NaHCO_3$) has a pH that is independent of concentration. The pH of a solution of sodium bisulfate ($NaHSO_4$) does depend on the concentration.

a. Explain *why* the pH of a typical solution of sodium bicarbonate is concentration-independent, whereas the pH of a solution of sodium bisulfate is concentration-dependent.

b. What is the pH of a solution of $NaHCO_3$?

c. Determine the pH of a solution of 0.010 *M* $NaHSO_4$.

139. Calculate the mass of sodium hydroxide that must be added to 1.00 L of 1.00 *M* $HC_2H_3O_2$ to double the pH of the solution (assume that the added NaOH does not change the volume of the solution).

140. A certain acid, HA, has a vapor density of 5.11 g/L when in the gas phase at a temperature of 25°C and a pressure of 1.00 atm. When 1.50 g of this acid is dissolved in enough water to make 100.0 mL of solution, the pH is found to be 1.80. Calculate K_a for HA.

141. A 0.100 *M* solution of the salt BHX has a pH of 8.00, where B is a weak base and X^- is the anion of the weak acid HX. Calculate the K_a value for HX if the K_b value for B is 1.0×10^{-3}.

142. Determine the pH of a 0.100 *M* solution of $(NH_4)_2C_2O_4$.

143. An aqueous solution contains a mixture of 0.0500 *M* HCOOH ($K_a = 1.77 \times 10^{-4}$) and 0.150 *M* CH_3CH_2COOH ($K_a = 1.34 \times 10^{-5}$). Calculate the pH of this solution.

144. Consider 50.0 mL of a solution of weak acid HA ($K_a = 1.00 \times 10^{-6}$), which has a pH of 4.000. What volume of water must be added to make the pH = 5.000?

145. A 50.00-mL solution of a weak acid HA ($K_a = 5.00 \times 10^{-10}$) in water has a pH = 5.650. Calculate the amount of water that must be added to reach a pH value of 6.650.

146. Calculate the pH of a solution initially with 0.10 *M* $NaHSO_4$ and 0.10 *M* NH_3.

147. A chemist dissolves 0.135 mole of $CO_2(g)$ in 2.50 L of 0.105 *M* Na_2CO_3. Calculate the pH of the resulting solution.

148. Derive an equation to solve for the pH for a dilute weak base in which water is a significant contributor to the pH. Use this formula to calculate the pH of a 100.0-mL sample of 2.0×10^{-5} *M* B (where B is a weak base with a K_b value of 6.1×10^{-11}).

149. Calculate the pH of 6.0×10^{-4} *M* $NaNO_2$.

150. Calculate the resulting pH when 1.00 L of 1.00 *M* H_2SO_4 is added to a tank containing 1.00×10^7 L of pure water.

151. Calculate the pH of a solution prepared by mixing equal volumes of 1.0×10^{-4} *M* NH_3 and 1.0×10^{-4} *M* HCl.

152. Calculate $[OH^-]$ in a 3.0×10^{-7} *M* solution of $Ca(OH)_2$.

Marathon Problems

153.* Captain Kirk, of the Starship *Enterprise,* has been told by his superiors that only a chemist can be trusted with the combination to the safe containing the dilithium crystals that power the ship. The combination is the pH of solution A described below, followed by the pH of solution C. (Example: If the pH of solution A is 3.47 and that of solution C is 8.15, then the combination to the safe is 3-47-8-15). The chemist must determine the combination using only the information below (all solutions are at 25°C):

Solution A is 50.0 mL of a 0.100 *M* solution of the weak monoprotic acid HX.

Solution B is a 0.0500 *M* solution of the salt NaX. It has a pH of 10.02.

Solution C is made by adding 15.0 mL of 0.250 *M* KOH to solution A.

What is the combination to the safe?

154. Mix equal volumes of one solution from Group I with one solution from Group II to achieve the results below. Calculate the pH of each solution.

Group I: 0.20 *M* NH_4Cl, 0.20 *M* HCl, 0.20 *M* $C_6H_5NH_3Cl$, 0.20 *M* $(C_2H_5)_3NHCl$

Group II: 0.20 *M* KOI, 0.20 *M* NaCN, 0.20 *M* KOCl, 0.20 *M* $NaNO_2$

a. the solution with the lowest pH

b. the solution with the highest pH

c. the solution with the pH closest to 7.00

*From James H. Burness, "The Use of "Marathon" Problems as Effective Vehicles for the Presentation of General Chemistry Lectures," Journal of Chemical Education, 68(11).

8 Applications of Aqueous Equilibria

chapter

Stalactites and stalagmites in Carlsbad Caverns, New Mexico.

OWL
Sign in to OWL at www.cengage.com/owl to view tutorials and simulations, develop problem-solving skills, and complete online homework assigned by your professor.

go Chemistry
Download mini lecture videos for key concept review and exam prep from OWL or purchase them from www.cengagebrain.com.

Much important chemistry, including most of the chemistry of the natural world, occurs in aqueous solution. We have already introduced one very significant class of aqueous equilibria, acid–base reactions. In this chapter we consider more applications of acid–base chemistry and introduce two additional types of aqueous equilibria, those involving the solubility of salts and the formation of complex ions.

The interplay of acid–base, solubility, and complex ion equilibria is often important in natural processes, such as the weathering of minerals, the uptake of nutrients by plants, and tooth decay. For example, limestone ($CaCO_3$) will dissolve in water made acidic by dissolved carbon dioxide:

$$CO_2(aq) + H_2O(l) \rightleftharpoons H^+(aq) + HCO_3^-(aq)$$
$$H^+(aq) + CaCO_3(s) \rightleftharpoons Ca^{2+}(aq) + HCO_3^-(aq)$$

This process and its reverse account for the formation of limestone caves and the stalactites and stalagmites found there. The acidic water (containing carbon dioxide) dissolves the underground limestone deposits, thereby forming a cavern. As the water drips from the ceiling of the cave, the carbon dioxide is lost to the air, and solid calcium carbonate forms by the reverse of the preceding process to produce stalactites on the ceiling and stalagmites where the drops hit the cave floor.

Before we consider the other types of aqueous equilibria, we will deal with acid–base equilibria in more detail.

8.1 Solutions of Acids or Bases Containing a Common Ion

In Chapter 7 we were concerned with calculating the equilibrium concentrations of species (particularly H^+ ions) in solutions containing an acid or a base. In this section we discuss solutions that contain not only the weak acid HA but also its salt NaA. Although this case appears to be a new type of problem, it can be handled rather easily by using the procedures developed in Chapter 7.

Suppose we have a solution containing weak-acid hydrofluoric acid (HF, $K_a = 7.2 \times 10^{-4}$) and its salt, sodium fluoride (NaF). Recall that when a salt dissolves in water, it breaks up completely into its ions—it is a strong electrolyte:

$$NaF(s) \xrightarrow{H_2O(l)} Na^+(aq) + F^-(aq)$$

Since hydrofluoric acid is a weak acid and only slightly dissociated, the major species in the solution are HF, Na^+, F^-, and H_2O. The **common ion** in this solution is F^-, since it is produced by both hydrofluoric acid and sodium fluoride. What effect does the presence of the dissolved sodium fluoride have on the dissociation equilibrium of hydrofluoric acid?

To answer this question, we compare the extent of dissociation of hydrofluoric acid in two different solutions, the first containing 1.0 *M* HF and the second containing 1.0 *M* HF and 1.0 *M* NaF. According to Le Châtelier's principle, the dissociation equilibrium for HF

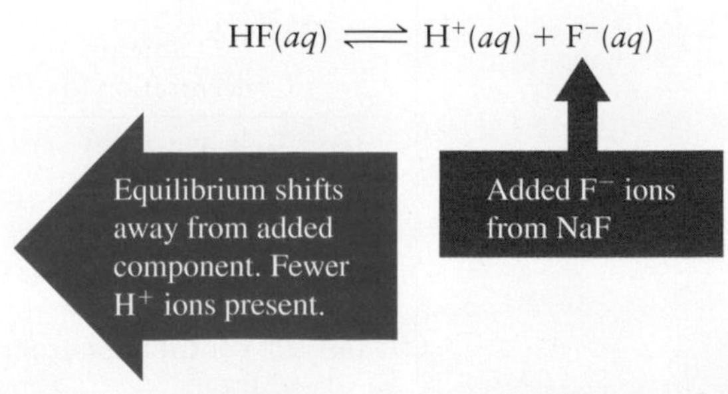
HF(aq) ⇌ H+(aq) + F−(aq)
Equilibrium shifts away from added component. Fewer H+ ions present.
Added F− ions from NaF

in the second solution will be *driven to the left by the presence of the F^- ions from the NaF.* Thus the extent of dissociation of HF will be less in the presence of dissolved NaF: The shift in equilibrium position that occurs because of the addition of an ion already involved in the equilibrium reaction is called the **common ion effect.** This effect makes a solution of NaF and HF less acidic than a solution of HF alone.

The common ion effect is quite general. For example, when solid NH_4Cl is dissolved in a 1.0 *M* NH_3 solution

$$NH_4Cl(s) \longrightarrow NH_4^+(aq) + Cl^-(aq)$$

the added ammonium ions cause the position of the ammonia–water equilibrium

$$NH_3(aq) + H_2O(l) \rightleftharpoons NH_4^+(aq) + OH^-(aq)$$

to shift to the left, reducing the concentration of OH^- ions.

The common ion effect is also important in solutions of polyprotic acids. The production of protons by the first dissociation step greatly inhibits the succeeding dissociation steps, which also produce protons, the common ion in this case. We will see later in this chapter that the common ion effect is also important in dealing with the solubility of salts.

OWL INTERACTIVE EXAMPLE 8.1

In Section 7.5 we found that the equilibrium concentration of H^+ in a 1.0 *M* HF solution is 2.7×10^{-2} *M* and the percent dissociation of HF is 2.7%. Calculate $[H^+]$ and the percent dissociation of HF in a solution containing both 1.0 *M* HF ($K_a = 7.2 \times 10^{-4}$) and 1.0 *M* NaF.

Major Species

H_2O

Solution As the aqueous solutions we consider become more complex, it becomes increasingly important to be systematic and to *focus on the chemistry* occurring in the solution before thinking about mathematical procedures. *Always* write the major species first and consider the chemical properties of each component.

In a solution containing 1.0 *M* HF and 1.0 *M* NaF, the major species are

$$HF, \quad F^-, \quad Na^+, \quad \text{and} \quad H_2O$$

Since Na^+ ions have neither acidic nor basic properties, and since water is such a weak acid or base, the important species are HF and F^-; they participate in the acid dissociation equilibrium that controls $[H^+]$ in this solution. That is, the position of the equilibrium

$$HF(aq) \rightleftharpoons H^+(aq) + F^-(aq)$$

will determine $[H^+]$ in the solution. The equilibrium expression is

$$K_a = \frac{[H^+][F^-]}{[HF]} = 7.2 \times 10^{-4}$$

The important concentrations are listed in the following table.

Initial Concentration (mol/L)		Equilibrium Concentration (mol/L)
$[HF]_0 = 1.0$ (from dissolved HF)		$[HF] = 1.0 - x$
$[F^-]_0 = 1.0$ (from dissolved NaF)	x mol/L HF dissociates $\longrightarrow$ to reach equilibrium	$[F^-] = 1.0 + x$
$[H^+]_0 = 0$ (neglect contribution from H_2O)		$[H^+] = x$

Note that $[F^-]_0 = 1.0\ M$ from the dissolved sodium fluoride and that the equilibrium $[F^-] > 1.0\ M$ because when the acid dissociates, it produces F^- as well as H^+. Then

$$K_a = 7.2 \times 10^{-4} = \frac{[H^+][F^-]}{[HF]} = \frac{(x)(1.0 + x)}{1.0 - x} \approx \frac{(x)(1.0)}{1.0}$$

since x is expected to be small.

Solving for x gives

$$x = \frac{1.0}{1.0}(7.2 \times 10^{-4}) = 7.2 \times 10^{-4}$$

Noting that x is small compared with 1.0, we conclude that this result is acceptable. Thus

$$[H^+] = x = 7.2 \times 10^{-4}\ M \qquad \text{(The pH is 3.14.)}$$

The percent dissociation of HF in this solution is

$$\frac{[H^+]}{[HF]_0} \times 100\% = \frac{7.2 \times 10^{-4}\ M}{1.0\ M} \times 100\% = 0.072\%$$

Compare these values for $[H^+]$ and percent dissociation of HF with those for a 1.0 M HF solution, where $[H^+] = 2.7 \times 10^{-2}\ M$ and the percent dissociation is 2.7%. The large difference clearly shows that the presence of the F^- ions from the dissolved NaF greatly inhibits the dissociation of HF. The position of the acid dissociation equilibrium has been shifted to the left by the presence of F^- ions from NaF.

8.2 Buffered Solutions

The most important buffering system in the blood involves HCO_3^- and H_2CO_3.

The most important application of acid–base solutions containing a common ion is buffering. A **buffered solution** is one that *resists a change in pH* when either hydroxide ions or protons are added. The most important practical example of a buffered solution is human blood, which can absorb the acids and bases produced by biological reactions without changing its pH. A constant pH for blood is vital because cells can survive only in a very narrow pH range around 7.4.

A buffered solution may contain a weak acid and its salt (for example, HF and NaF) or a weak base and its salt (for example, NH_3 and NH_4Cl). By choosing the appropriate components, a solution can be buffered at virtually any pH.

In treating buffered solutions in this chapter, we will start by considering the equilibrium calculations. We will then use these results to show how buffering works. That is, we will answer the question: "How does a buffered solution resist changes in pH when an acid or base is added?"

As you do the calculations associated with buffered solutions, keep in mind that they are merely solutions containing weak acids or bases and that the procedures required are the same ones we have already developed. Be sure to use the systematic approach introduced in Chapter 7.

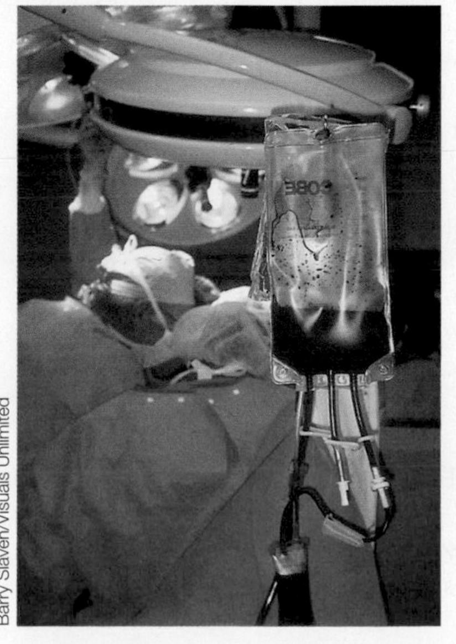
Barry Slaven/Visuals Unlimited

Human blood is a buffered solution.

OWL INTERACTIVE EXAMPLE 8.2

A buffered solution contains 0.50 M acetic acid ($HC_2H_3O_2$, $K_a = 1.8 \times 10^{-5}$) and 0.50 M sodium acetate ($NaC_2H_3O_2$).

a. Calculate the pH of this solution.

Major Species

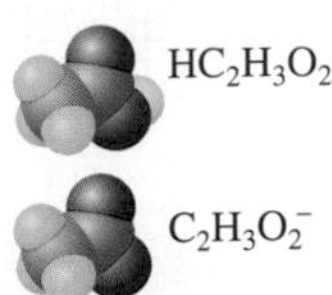
$HC_2H_3O_2$

$C_2H_3O_2^-$

Na⁺

H_2O

Solution The major species in the solution are

$HC_2H_3O_2$,	Na^+,	$C_2H_3O_2^-$,	and	H_2O
↑ Weak acid	↑ Neither acid nor base	↑ Base (conjugate base of $HC_2H_3O_2$)		↑ Very weak acid or base

Examination of the solution components leads to the conclusion that the acetic acid dissociation equilibrium, which involves both $HC_2H_3O_2$ and $C_2H_3O_2^-$, will control the pH of the solution:

$$HC_2H_3O_2(aq) \rightleftharpoons H^+(aq) + C_2H_3O_2^-(aq)$$

$$K_a = 1.8 \times 10^{-5} = \frac{[H^+][C_2H_3O_2^-]}{[HC_2H_3O_2]}$$

The concentrations are as follows:

Initial Concentration (mol/L)		Equilibrium Concentration (mol/L)
$[HC_2H_3O_2]_0 = 0.50$ $[C_2H_3O_2^-]_0 = 0.50$ $[H^+]_0 \approx 0$	x mol/L of $HC_2H_3O_2$ dissociates to reach equilibrium ⟶	$[HC_2H_3O_2] = 0.50 - x$ $[C_2H_3O_2^-] = 0.50 + x$ $[H^+] = x$

Then

$$K_a = 1.8 \times 10^{-5} = \frac{[H^+][C_2H_3O_2^-]}{[HC_2H_3O_2]} = \frac{(x)(0.50 + x)}{0.50 - x} \approx \frac{(x)(0.50)}{0.50}$$

and

$$x = 1.8 \times 10^{-5}$$

The approximation is valid (by the 5% rule), so

$$[H^+] = x = 1.8 \times 10^{-5}\ M \qquad \text{and} \qquad pH = 4.74$$

A digital pH meter shows the pH of the buffered solution to be 4.74.

b. Calculate the change in pH that occurs when 0.010 mole of solid NaOH is added to 1.0 L of the buffered solution. Compare this pH change with the change that occurs when 0.010 mole of solid NaOH is added to 1.0 L of water.

Solution Since the added solid NaOH will completely dissociate, the major species in solution *before any reaction occurs* are $HC_2H_3O_2$, Na^+, $C_2H_3O_2^-$, OH^-, and H_2O. Note that the solution contains a relatively large amount of the very strong base, the hydroxide ion, which has a great affinity for protons. The best source of protons is the acetic acid, so the reaction that will occur is

$$OH^- + HC_2H_3O_2 \longrightarrow H_2O + C_2H_3O_2^-$$

Although acetic acid is a weak acid, the hydroxide ion is such a strong base that the preceding reaction will *proceed essentially to completion* (until the OH^- ions are consumed).

The best approach to this problem involves two distinct steps: (1) assume the reaction goes to completion and carry out the stoichiometric calculations, and then (2) carry out the equilibrium calculations.

■ *The stoichiometry problem.* The reaction occurs as shown below.

	$HC_2H_3O_2$	+	OH^-	$\longrightarrow$	$C_2H_3O_2^-$	+ H_2O
Before reaction:	$1.0\text{ L} \times 0.50\ M$ = 0.50 mole		0.010 mole		$1.0\text{ L} \times 0.50\ M$ = 0.50 mole	
After reaction:	$0.50 - 0.01$ = 0.49 mole		$0.010 - 0.010$ = 0 mole		$0.50 + 0.01$ = 0.51 mole	

Note that 0.01 mole of $HC_2H_3O_2$ has been converted to 0.01 mole of $C_2H_3O_2^-$ by the added OH^-.

■ *The equilibrium problem.* After the reaction between OH^- and $HC_2H_3O_2$ has run to completion, the major species in solution are

$$HC_2H_3O_2, \quad Na^+, \quad C_2H_3O_2^-, \quad \text{and} \quad H_2O$$

The dominant equilibrium involves the dissociation of acetic acid.

This problem is very similar to that in part a. The only difference is that the addition of 0.01 mole of OH^- has consumed some $HC_2H_3O_2$ and produced some $C_2H_3O_2^-$, yielding the following concentrations:

Initial Concentration (mol/L)		Equilibrium Concentration (mol/L)
$[HC_2H_3O_2]_0 = 0.49$ $[C_2H_3O_2^-]_0 = 0.51$ $[H^+]_0 \approx 0$	x mol/L of $HC_2H_3O_2$ dissociates to reach equilibrium $\longrightarrow$	$[HC_2H_3O_2] = 0.49 - x$ $[C_2H_3O_2^-] = 0.51 + x$ $[H^+] = x$

Note that the initial concentrations are defined after the reaction with OH^- is complete but before the system adjusts to equilibrium.

Following the usual procedures gives

$$K_a = 1.8 \times 10^{-5} = \frac{[H^+][C_2H_3O_2^-]}{[HC_2H_3O_2]} = \frac{(x)(0.51 + x)}{0.49 - x} \approx \frac{(x)(0.51)}{0.49}$$

$$x \approx 1.7 \times 10^{-5}$$

The approximations are valid (by the 5% rule), so

$$[H^+] = x = 1.7 \times 10^{-5} \quad \text{and} \quad \text{pH} = 4.76$$

The change in pH produced by the addition of 0.01 mole of OH^- to this buffered solution is then

$$\underset{\text{New solution}}{\underset{\uparrow}{4.76}} - \underset{\text{Original solution}}{\underset{\uparrow}{4.74}} = +0.02$$

The pH has increased by 0.02 pH units.

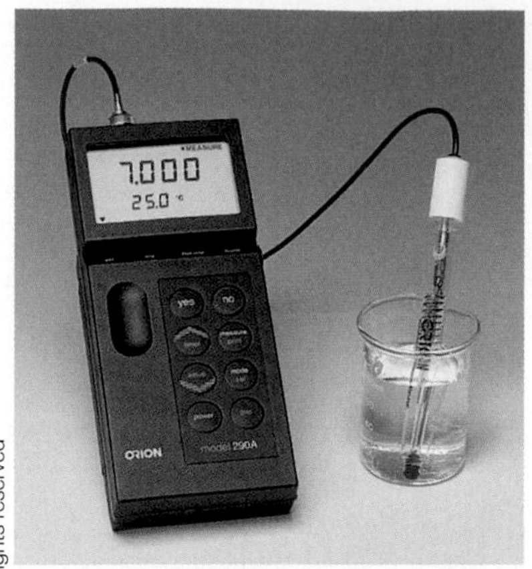

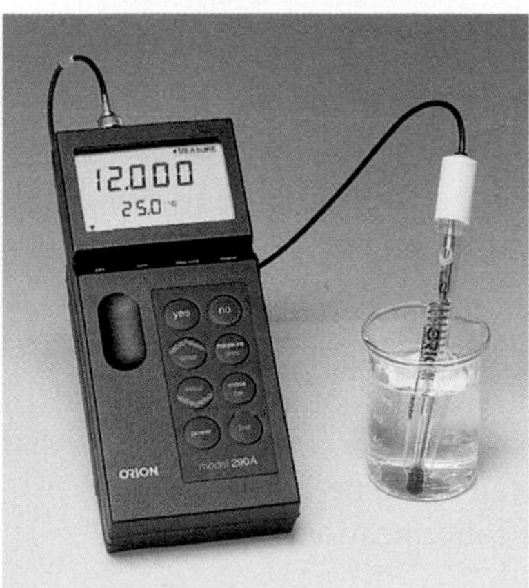

(top) Pure water at pH 7.00.
(bottom) When 0.01 mole of NaOH is added to 1.0 L of pure water, the pH jumps to 12.00.

Now compare this result with what happens when 0.01 mole of solid NaOH is added to 1.0 L of water to give 0.01 *M* NaOH. In this case, $[OH^-] = 0.01\ M$ and

$$[H^+] = \frac{K_w}{[OH^-]} = \frac{1.0 \times 10^{-14}}{1.0 \times 10^{-2}} = 1.0 \times 10^{-12}$$

$$pH = 12.00$$

Thus the change in pH is

$$\underset{\text{New solution}}{12.00} - \underset{\text{Pure water}}{7.00} = +5.00$$

The increase is 5.00 pH units. Note how well the buffered solution resists a change in pH compared with pure water.

Example 8.2 is a typical buffer problem. It contains all the concepts necessary for handling the calculations for buffered solutions containing weak acids. Pay special attention to the following points:

1. Buffered solutions are simply solutions of weak acids or bases containing a common ion. The pH calculations for buffered solutions require exactly the same procedures previously introduced in Chapter 7. *This is not a new type of problem.*
2. When a strong acid or base is added to a buffered solution, it is best to deal with the stoichiometry of the resulting reaction first. After the stoichiometric calculations are completed, then consider the equilibrium calculations. This procedure can be represented as follows:

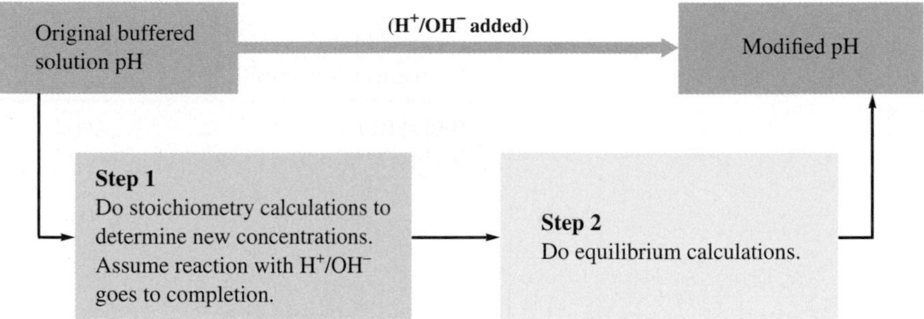

Buffering: How Does It Work?

Example 8.2 demonstrates the ability of a buffered solution to absorb hydroxide ions without a significant change in pH. *But how does a buffer work?* Suppose a buffered solution contains relatively large quantities of a weak acid HA and its conjugate base A^-. Since the weak acid represents the best source of protons, the following reaction occurs when hydroxide ions are added to the solution:

$$OH^- + HA \longrightarrow A^- + H_2O$$

The net result is that OH^- ions are not allowed to accumulate but are replaced by A^- ions.

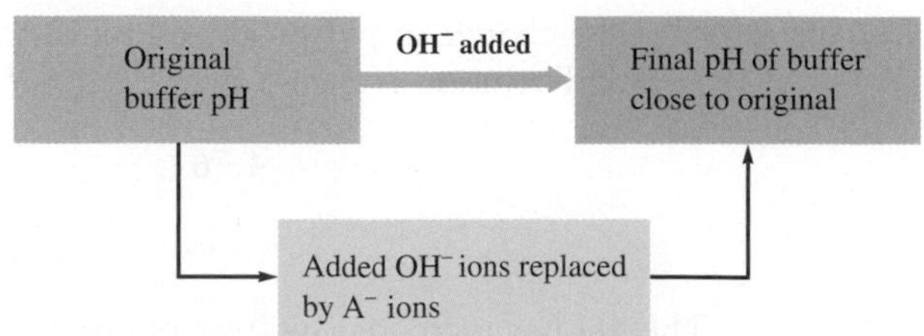

The stability of the pH under these conditions can be understood by examining the equilibrium expression for the dissociation of HA:

$$K_a = \frac{[H^+][A^-]}{[HA]} \qquad \text{or rearranging,} \qquad [H^+] = K_a\frac{[HA]}{[A^-]}$$

In a buffered solution the pH is governed by the ratio [HA]/[A⁻].

In other words, the *equilibrium concentration of H^+ and thus the pH are determined by the ratio [HA]/[A⁻].* When OH^- ions are added, HA is converted to A^-, causing the ratio [HA]/[A⁻] to decrease. However, *if the amounts of HA and A^- originally present are very large compared with the amount of OH^- added,* the change in the [HA]/[A⁻] ratio is small.

In Example 8.2

$$\frac{[HA]}{[A^-]} = \frac{0.50}{0.50} = 1.0 \qquad \text{Initially}$$

$$\frac{[HA]}{[A^-]} = \frac{0.49}{0.51} = 0.96 \qquad \text{After adding 0.01 mol/L of } OH^-$$

The change in the ratio [HA]/[A⁻] is very small. Thus the [H⁺] and the pH remain essentially constant.

The essence of buffering, then, is that [HA] and [A⁻] are large compared with the amount of OH^- added. Thus, when the OH^- is added, the concentrations of HA and A^- change, but only by small amounts. Under these conditions, the [HA]/[A⁻] ratio and thus the [H⁺] stay virtually constant.

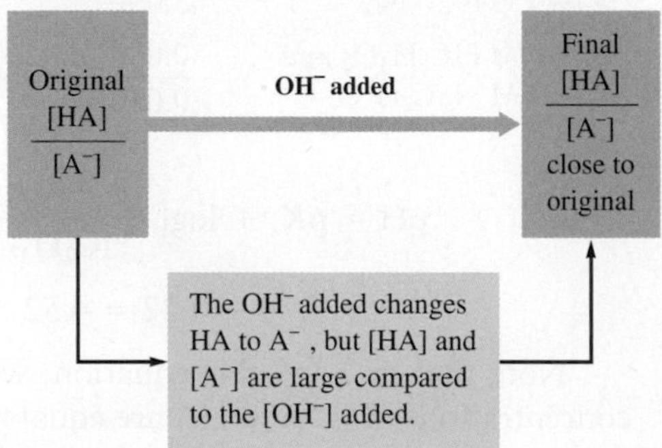

Similar reasoning applies when protons are added to a buffered solution containing a weak acid and a salt of its conjugate base. Because the A^- ion has a high affinity of H^+, the added H^+ ions react with A^- to form the weak acid:

$$H^+ + A^- \longrightarrow HA$$

Thus free H^+ ions do not accumulate. In this case there will be a net change of A^- to HA. However, if [A⁻] and [HA] are large compared with the [H⁺] added, only a slight change in the pH occurs.

An alternative form of the acid dissociation equilibrium expression,

$$[H^+] = K_a\frac{[HA]}{[A^-]} \tag{8.1}$$

is often useful for calculating [H⁺] in buffered solutions, since [HA] and [A⁻] are usually known. For example, to calculate [H⁺] in a buffered solution containing 0.10 *M* HF ($K_a = 7.2 \times 10^{-4}$) and 0.30 *M* NaF, we simply substitute the respective concentrations into Equation (8.1):

$$[H^+] = \underbrace{(7.2 \times 10^{-4})}_{K_a}\frac{\overset{[HF]}{0.10}}{\underset{[F^-]}{0.30}} = 2.4 \times 10^{-4}\ M$$

Another useful form of Equation (8.1) can be obtained by taking the negative log of both sides:

$$-\log[\mathrm{H^+}] = -\log(K_a) - \log\left(\frac{[\mathrm{HA}]}{[\mathrm{A^-}]}\right)$$

That is,

$$\mathrm{pH} = \mathrm{p}K_a - \log\left(\frac{[\mathrm{HA}]}{[\mathrm{A^-}]}\right)$$

or inverting the log term and reversing the sign,

$$\mathrm{pH} = \mathrm{p}K_a + \log\left(\frac{[\mathrm{A^-}]}{[\mathrm{HA}]}\right) = \mathrm{p}K_a + \log\left(\frac{[\mathrm{base}]}{[\mathrm{acid}]}\right) \tag{8.2}$$

This log form of the expression for K_a is called the **Henderson–Hasselbalch equation** and is useful for calculating the pH of solutions when the ratio $[\mathrm{HA}]/[\mathrm{A^-}]$ is known.

For a particular buffering system (acid–conjugate base pair), all solutions that have the same ratio of $[A^-]/[HA]$ have the same pH. For example, a buffered solution containing 5.0 M $HC_2H_3O_2$ and 3.0 M $NaC_2H_3O_2$ has the same pH as one containing 0.050 M $HC_2H_3O_2$ and 0.030 M $NaC_2H_3O_2$. This result can be shown as follows:

System	$[A^-]/[HA]$
5.0 *M* $HC_2H_3O_2$ and 3.0 *M* $NaC_2H_3O_2$	$\frac{3.0\ M}{5.0\ M} = 0.60$
0.050 *M* $HC_2H_3O_2$ and 0.030 *M* $NaC_2H_3O_2$	$\frac{0.030\ M}{0.050\ M} = 0.60$

Thus

$$\mathrm{pH} = \mathrm{p}K_a + \log\left(\frac{[\mathrm{C_2H_3O_2^-}]}{[\mathrm{HC_2H_3O_2}]}\right) = 4.74 + \log(0.60)$$

$$= 4.74 - 0.22 = 4.52$$

Note that in using this equation, we have assumed that the equilibrium concentrations of A^- and HA are equal to their initial concentrations. That is, we are assuming the validity of the approximations

$$[\mathrm{A^-}] = [\mathrm{A^-}]_0 + x \approx [\mathrm{A^-}]_0 \quad \text{and} \quad [\mathrm{HA}] = [\mathrm{HA}]_0 - x \approx [\mathrm{HA}]_0$$

where x represents the amount of acid that dissociates. Since the initial concentrations of HA and A^- are expected to be relatively large in a buffered solution, this assumption is generally acceptable.

OWL INTERACTIVE EXAMPLE 8.3

A buffered solution contains 0.25 *M* NH_3 ($K_b = 1.8 \times 10^{-5}$) and 0.40 *M* NH_4Cl.

a. Calculate the pH of this solution.

Solution The major species in the solution are

$$\mathrm{NH_3}, \quad \underbrace{\mathrm{NH_4^+}, \quad \mathrm{Cl^-},}_{\text{From the dissolved NH}_4\text{Cl}} \quad \text{and} \quad \mathrm{H_2O}$$

Major Species

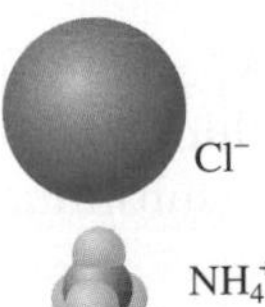

Since Cl^- is such a weak base and water is a weak acid or base, the important equilibrium is

$$\mathrm{NH_3}(aq) + \mathrm{H_2O}(l) \rightleftharpoons \mathrm{NH_4^+}(aq) + \mathrm{OH^-}(aq)$$

and

$$K_b = 1.8 \times 10^{-5} = \frac{[\mathrm{NH_4^+}][\mathrm{OH^-}]}{[\mathrm{NH_3}]}$$

The appropriate concentrations are as follows:

Initial Concentration (mol/L)		Equilibrium Concentration (mol/L)
$[NH_3]_0 = 0.25$ $[NH_4^+]_0 = 0.40$ $[OH^-] \approx 0$	$\xrightarrow[\text{reacts with } H_2O]{x \text{ mol/L } NH_3}$	$[NH_3] = 0.25 - x$ $[NH_4^+] = 0.40 + x$ $[OH^-] = x$

Thus

$$K_b = 1.8 \times 10^{-5} = \frac{[NH_4^+][OH^-]}{[NH_3]} = \frac{(0.40 + x)(x)}{0.25 - x} \approx \frac{(0.40)(x)}{0.25}$$

$$x = 1.1 \times 10^{-5}$$

The approximations are valid (by the 5% rule), so

$$[OH^-] = x = 1.1 \times 10^{-5}$$

$$pOH = 4.95$$

$$pH = 14.00 - 4.95 = 9.05$$

This case is typical of a buffered solution in that the initial and equilibrium concentrations of buffering materials are essentially the same.

Alternative Solution. There is another way to solve this problem. Since the solution contains relatively large quantities of *both* NH_4^+ and NH_3, we can use the equilibrium

$$NH_3(aq) + H_2O(l) \rightleftharpoons NH_4^+(aq) + OH^-(aq)$$

to calculate $[OH^-]$ and then calculate $[H^+]$ from K_w, as we have just done. Or we can use the dissociation equilibrium for NH_4^+,

$$NH_4^+(aq) \rightleftharpoons NH_3(aq) + H^+(aq)$$

to calculate $[H^+]$ directly. *Either choice will give the same answer,* since the same equilibrium concentrations of NH_3 and NH_4^+ must satisfy both equilibria.

We can obtain the K_a value for NH_4^+ from the given K_b value for NH_3, since $K_a \times K_b = K_w$:

$$K_a = \frac{K_w}{K_b} = \frac{1.0 \times 10^{-14}}{1.8 \times 10^{-5}} = 5.6 \times 10^{-10}$$

Then using the Henderson–Hasselbalch equation, we have

$$pH = pK_a + \log\left(\frac{[\text{base}]}{[\text{acid}]}\right)$$

$$= 9.25 + \log\left(\frac{0.25\ M}{0.40\ M}\right) = 9.25 - 0.20 = 9.05$$

b. Calculate the pH of the solution that results when 0.10 mole of gaseous HCl is added to 1.0 L of the buffered solution from part a.

Solution *Before any reaction occurs,* the solution contains the following major species:

$$NH_3, \quad NH_4^+, \quad Cl^-, \quad H^+, \quad \text{and} \quad H_2O$$

Remember: Think about the chemistry first. Ask yourself if a reaction will occur among the major species.

What reaction can occur? We know that H^+ will not react with Cl^- to form HCl. In contrast to Cl^-, the NH_3 molecule has a great affinity for protons [this is demonstrated by the fact that NH_4^+ is such a weak acid ($K_a = 5.6 \times 10^{-10}$)]. Thus NH_3 will react with H^+ to form NH_4^+:

$$NH_3(aq) + H^+(aq) \longrightarrow NH_4^+(aq)$$

Since we can assume that this reaction goes essentially to completion, forming the very weak acid NH_4^+, we will do the stoichiometric calculations before we consider the equilibrium calculations. That is, we will let the reaction run to completion and then consider the equilibrium.

The stoichiometric calculations for this process are shown below.

	NH_3	+	H^+	$\longrightarrow$	NH_4^+
Before reaction:	(1.0 L)(0.25 *M*) = 0.25 mole		0.10 mole ↑ Limiting reactant		(1.0 L)(0.40 *M*) = 0.40 mole
After reaction:	0.25 − 0.10 = 0.15 mole		0		0.40 + 0.10 = 0.50 mole

After the reaction goes to completion, the solution contains the major species

$$NH_3, \quad NH_4^+, \quad Cl^-, \quad \text{and} \quad H_2O$$

and

$$[NH_3]_0 = \frac{0.15 \text{ mol}}{1.0 \text{ L}} = 0.15\ M$$

$$[NH_4^+]_0 = \frac{0.50 \text{ mol}}{1.0 \text{ L}} = 0.50\ M$$

We can use the Henderson–Hasselbalch equation, where

$$[\text{Base}] = [NH_3] \approx [NH_3]_0 = 0.15\ M$$

$$[\text{Acid}] = [NH_4^+] \approx [NH_4^+]_0 = 0.50\ M$$

Then

$$\text{pH} = \text{p}K_a + \log\left(\frac{[NH_3]}{[NH_4^+]}\right) = 9.25 + \log\left(\frac{0.15\ M}{0.50\ M}\right)$$

$$= 9.25 - 0.52 = 8.73$$

Note that the addition of HCl only slightly decreases the pH (from 9.05 to 8.73), as we would expect in a buffered solution.

We can now summarize the most important characteristics of buffered solutions.

Characteristics of Buffered Solutions

1. Buffered solutions contain relatively large concentrations of a weak acid and its corresponding weak base. They can involve a weak acid HA and the conjugate base A^- or a weak base B and the conjugate acid BH^+.
2. When H^+ is added to a buffered solution, it reacts essentially to completion with the weak base present:

$$H^+ + A^- \longrightarrow HA \quad \text{or} \quad H^+ + B \longrightarrow BH^+$$

3. When OH^- is added to a buffered solution, it reacts essentially to completion with the weak acid present:

$$OH^- + HA \longrightarrow A^- + H_2O \quad \text{or} \quad OH^- + BH^+ \longrightarrow B + H_2O$$

4. The pH of the buffered solution is determined by the ratio of the concentrations of the weak base and weak acid. As long as this ratio remains virtually constant, the pH will remain virtually constant. This will be the case as long as the concentrations of the buffering materials (HA and A^- or B and BH^+) are large compared with the amounts of H^+ or OH^- added.

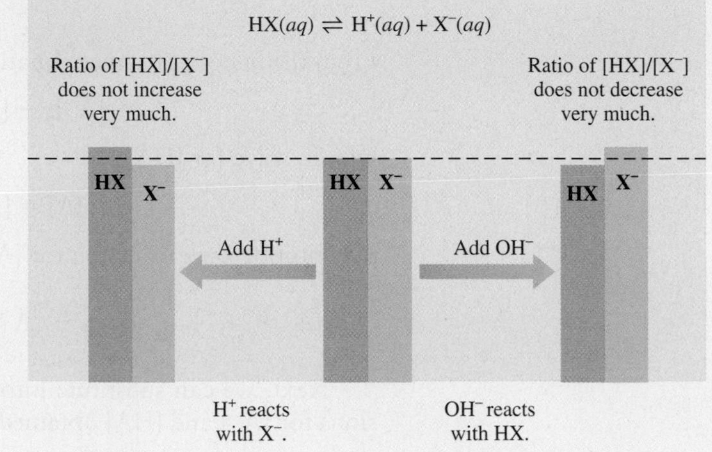
HX(aq) ⇌ H+(aq) + X−(aq)
Ratio of [HX]/[X−] does not increase very much.
Ratio of [HX]/[X−] does not decrease very much.
HX
X−
HX
X−
HX
X−
Add H+
Add OH−
H+ reacts with X−.
OH− reacts with HX.

8.3 Exact Treatment of Buffered Solutions

Because buffered solutions can have a pH value of 7, the question naturally arises about the possible importance of water as a contributor to the $[H^+]$ under these conditions. To derive a general equation for buffered solutions that includes any possible contribution from water, we will use the approach developed in Section 7.9.

In an aqueous buffered solution containing the weak acid HA and its salt NaA, the equilibria of interest are

$$HA(aq) \rightleftharpoons H^+(aq) + A^-(aq)$$

and

$$H_2O(l) \rightleftharpoons H^+(aq) + OH^-(aq)$$

The charge balance relationship for this solution is

$$[Na^+] + [H^+] = [A^-] + [OH^-]$$

in which we must include the Na^+ added to the solution.

The material balance equation based on the conservation of A is

$$\underset{\text{From added NaA}}{[A^-]_0} + \underset{\text{Original HA concentration}}{[HA]_0} = [HA] + [A^-]$$

Since $[A^-]_0 = [Na^+]$, because all of the Na^+ comes from the added salt (NaA), and

$$[OH^-] = \frac{K_w}{[H^+]},$$

we can rewrite the charge balance equation

$$[Na^+] + [H^+] = [A^-] + [OH^-]$$

as follows:

$$[A^-]_0 + [H^+] = [A^-] + \frac{K_w}{[H^+]}$$

We can now solve for $[A^-]$:

$$[A^-] = [A^-]_0 + [H^+] - \frac{K_w}{[H^+]}$$

$$= [A^-]_0 + \frac{[H^+]^2 - K_w}{[H^+]}$$

From the material balance equation

$$[A^-]_0 + [HA]_0 = [HA] + [A^-]$$

we can solve for [HA]:

$$[HA] = [A^-]_0 + [HA]_0 - [A^-]$$

Substituting the expression for $[A^-]$ obtained above, we have

$$[HA] = [A^-]_0 + [HA]_0 - [A^-]_0 - \frac{[H^+]^2 - K_w}{[H^+]} = [HA]_0 - \frac{[H^+]^2 - K_w}{[H^+]}$$

Next, we can substitute into the K_a expression for HA using the expressions for $[A^-]$ and [HA] obtained above:

$$K_a = \frac{[H^+][A^-]}{[HA]} = \frac{[H^+]\left([A^-]_0 + \dfrac{[H^+]^2 - K_w}{[H^+]}\right)}{[HA]_0 - \dfrac{[H^+]^2 - K_w}{[H^+]}}$$

Notice that when $[A^-]_0$ is zero—that is, when no salt is added—this expression turns into the equation obtained in Section 7.9 for a weak acid HA dissolved in water. Thus the strategies useful for solving this equation are the same as those presented in Section 7.9.

OWL INTERACTIVE EXAMPLE 8.4

Calculate the $[H^+]$ of a buffered solution containing 3.0×10^{-4} *M* HOCl ($K_a = 3.5 \times 10^{-8}$) and 1.0×10^{-4} *M* NaOCl.

Solution We recognize that this problem involves a buffered solution containing the weak acid HOCl and its salt NaOCl.

First let's solve this problem using the regular procedures:

$$K_a = \frac{[H^+][OCl^-]}{[HOCl]} = 3.5 \times 10^{-8}$$

If we let $x = [H^+]$, then

$$[OCl^-] = 1.0 \times 10^{-4} + x$$

$$[HOCl] = 3.0 \times 10^{-4} - x$$

and we have

$$3.5 \times 10^{-8} = \frac{[H^+][OCl^-]}{[HOCl]} = \frac{(x)(1.0 \times 10^{-4} + x)}{(3.0 \times 10^{-4} - x)}$$

Assuming x is small compared to 1.0×10^{-4}, we have

$$3.5 \times 10^{-8} \approx \frac{(x)(1.0 \times 10^{-4})}{(3.0 \times 10^{-4})}$$

$$[H^+] = x = \frac{1.05 \times 10^{-11}}{1.0 \times 10^{-4}} = 1.05 \times 10^{-7}\,M = 1.1 \times 10^{-7}\,M$$

Note that the $[H^+]$ value obtained in this way is very close to 1.0×10^{-7} *M*. Since the calculated $[H^+]$ is so close to 10^{-7} *M*, must we consider the contribution of water to the pH?

To answer that question, we will use the complete equation derived earlier, which does include water's contribution to the pH. This equation is

$$K_a = 3.5 \times 10^{-8} = \frac{[H^+]\left([OCl^-]_0 + \dfrac{[H^+]^2 - 1.0 \times 10^{-14}}{[H^+]}\right)}{[HOCl]_0 - \dfrac{[H^+]^2 - 1.0 \times 10^{-14}}{[H^+]}}$$

where

$$[OCl^-]_0 = 1.0 \times 10^{-4}\ M$$

and

$$[HOCl]_0 = 3.0 \times 10^{-4}\ M$$

We expect the final $[H^+]$ to be very close to 1.0×10^{-7}, so the term

$$\frac{[H^+]^2 - 1.0 \times 10^{-14}}{[H^+]}$$

will be very small since $[H^+]^2$ will be very close to 1.0×10^{-14}. Thus, as a first approximation, we will assume that

$$[OCl^-]_0 = 1.0 \times 10^{-4}\ M >>> \frac{[H^+]^2 - 1.0 \times 10^{-14}}{[H^+]}$$

and

$$[HOCl]_0 = 3.0 \times 10^{-4}\ M >>> \frac{[H^+]^2 - 1.0 \times 10^{-14}}{[H^+]}$$

The expression then becomes

$$3.5 \times 10^{-8} = \frac{[H^+][OCl^-]_0}{[HOCl]_0} = \frac{[H^+](1.0 \times 10^{-4})}{(3.0 \times 10^{-4})}$$

and

$$[H^+] = 1.05 \times 10^{-7}\ M = 1.1 \times 10^{-7}\ M$$

as we found before.

Using this result we can check the magnitude of the neglected term

$$\frac{[H^+]^2 - 1.0 \times 10^{-14}}{[H^+]} = \frac{(1.05 \times 10^{-7})^2 - 1.0 \times 10^{-14}}{1.05 \times 10^{-7}} = 9.8 \times 10^{-9}$$

This term is clearly negligible as compared with 1.0×10^{-4} and 3.0×10^{-4}.

In this case water does not have to be explicitly taken into account. Notice that the rigorous equation produces a different result from the normal procedure only when the buffering materials are very dilute (on the order of 10^{-6} *M* or smaller). For buffered solutions with "normal" concentrations of HA and A^-, the simple approach used in this text to treat buffers will suffice. However, the rigorous equation always gives the correct answer and has the advantage of emphasizing explicitly the approximations being made in the simpler approach.

8.4 Buffer Capacity

A buffer with a large capacity contains large concentrations of the buffering components.

The **buffer capacity** of a buffered solution is defined in terms of the amount of protons or hydroxide ions it can absorb without a significant change in pH. A buffer with a large capacity contains large concentrations of buffering components and so can absorb a relatively large amount of protons or hydroxide ions and show little pH change. *The pH of a buffered solution is determined by the ratio* $[A^-]/[HA]$. *The capacity of a buffered solution is determined by the magnitudes of* $[HA]$ *and* $[A^-]$.

EXAMPLE 8.5

Calculate the change in pH that occurs when 0.010 mole of gaseous HCl is added to 1.0 L of each of the following solutions.

Solution A: 5.00 M $HC_2H_3O_2$ and 5.00 M $NaC_2H_3O_2$
Solution B: 0.050 M $HC_2H_3O_2$ and 0.050 M $NaC_2H_3O_2$

For acetic acid, $K_a = 1.8 \times 10^{-5}$.

Solution For both solutions the initial pH can be determined from the Henderson–Hasselbalch equation:

$$pH = pK_a + \log\left(\frac{[C_2H_3O_2^-]}{[HC_2H_3O_2]}\right)$$

In each case $[C_2H_3O_2^-] = [HC_2H_3O_2]$. Thus, for both A and B,

$$pH = pK_a + \log(1) = pK_a = -\log(1.8 \times 10^{-5}) = 4.74$$

After the addition of HCl to each of these solutions, the major species *before any reaction occurs* are

$$HC_2H_3O_2, \quad Na^+, \quad C_2H_3O_2^-, \quad \underbrace{H^+, \quad Cl^-}_{\text{From the added HCl}}, \quad \text{and} \quad H_2O$$

Will any reactions occur among these species? Note that we have a relatively large quantity of H^+ that will readily react with any effective base. We know that Cl^- will not react with H^+ to form HCl in water. However, $C_2H_3O_2^-$ will react with H^+ to form the weak acid $HC_2H_3O_2$:

$$H^+(aq) + C_2H_3O_2^-(aq) \longrightarrow HC_2H_3O_2(aq)$$

Because $HC_2H_3O_2$ is a weak acid, we assume that this reaction runs to completion; the 0.010 mole of added H^+ will convert 0.010 mole of $C_2H_3O_2^-$ to 0.010 mole of $HC_2H_3O_2$.

For solution A (since the solution volume is 1.0 L, the number of moles equals the molarity), we have the following concentrations:

	H^+	+	$C_2H_3O_2^-$	$\longrightarrow$	$HC_2H_3O_2$
Before reaction:	0.010 M		5.00 M		5.00 M
After reaction:	0		4.99 M		5.01 M

Original solution		New solution
$\frac{[A^-]}{[HA]} = \frac{5.00}{5.00} = 1.00$	H^+ added	$\frac{[A^-]}{[HA]} = \frac{4.99}{5.01} = 0.996$

The new pH can be obtained by substituting the new concentrations into the Henderson–Hasselbalch equation:

$$pH = pK_a + \log\left(\frac{[C_2H_3O_2^-]}{[HC_2H_3O_2]}\right) = 4.74 + \log\left(\frac{4.99}{5.01}\right)$$

$$= 4.74 - 0.0017 = 4.74$$

There is virtually no change in pH for solution A when 0.010 mole of gaseous HCl is added.

For solution B we have the following calculations:

	H^+	+	$C_2H_3O_2^-$	$\longrightarrow$	$HC_2H_3O_2$
Before reaction:	0.010 M		0.050 M		0.050 M
After reaction:	0		0.040 M		0.060 M

Original solution: $\frac{[A^-]}{[HA]} = \frac{.050}{.050} = 1.0$ → H^+ added → New solution: $\frac{[A^-]}{[HA]} = \frac{0.040}{0.060} = 0.67$

The new pH is

$$pH = 4.74 + \log\left(\frac{0.040}{0.060}\right) = 4.74 - 0.18 = 4.56$$

Although the pH change for solution B is small, a change did occur, in contrast to the case for solution A.

These results show that solution A, which contains much larger quantities of buffering components, has a much higher buffering capacity than solution B.

We have seen that the pH of a buffered solution depends on the ratio of the concentrations of buffering components. When this ratio is least affected by added protons or hydroxide ions, the solution is the most resistant to a change in pH. To find the ratio that gives optimum buffering, suppose that we have a buffered solution containing a large concentration of acetate ion and only a small concentration of acetic acid. Addition of protons to form acetic acid will produce a relatively large *percentage* change in the concentration of acetic acid and so will produce a relatively large change in the ratio $[C_2H_3O_2^-]/[HC_2H_3O_2]$ (Table 8.1). Similarly, if hydroxide ions are added to remove some acetic acid, the percentage change in the concentration of acetic acid is again large. The same effects are seen if the initial concentration of acetic acid is large and that of acetate ion is small.

Because large changes in the ratio $[A^-]/[HA]$ will produce large changes in pH, we want to avoid this situation for the most effective buffering. This type of reasoning leads us to the general conclusion that optimum buffering will occur when [HA] is equal to $[A^-]$. It is under this condition that the ratio $[A^-]/[HA]$ is most resistant to change when H^+ or OH^- is added. Thus, when choosing the buffering components for a specific application, we want $[A^-]/[HA]$ to equal 1. It follows that since

$$pH = pK_a + \log\left(\frac{[A^-]}{[HA]}\right) = pK_a + \log(1) = pK_a$$

the *pK_a of the weak acid selected for the buffer should be as close as possible to the desired pH*. For example, suppose we need a buffered solution with a pH of 4.00. The most effective buffering will occur when [HA] is equal to $[A^-]$. From the Henderson–Hasselbalch equation,

$$\underset{\substack{\uparrow \\ 4.00}}{pH} = pK_a + \log\underbrace{\left(\frac{[A^-]}{[HA]}\right)}_{\text{Ratio = 1 for most effective buffer}}$$

That is,

$$4.00 = pK_a + \log(1) = pK_a + 0 \qquad \text{and} \qquad pK_a = 4.00$$

Thus in this case the best choice is a weak acid that has $pK_a = 4.00$, or $K_a = 1.0 \times 10^{-4}$.

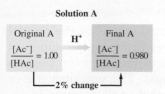

Solution A

Original A: $\frac{[Ac^-]}{[HAc]} = 1.00$ → H^+ → Final A: $\frac{[Ac^-]}{[HAc]} = 0.980$ (2% change)

Solution B

Original B: $\frac{[Ac^-]}{[HAc]} = 100.$ → H^+ → Final B: $\frac{[Ac^-]}{[HAc]} = 49.5$ (50.5% change)

Table 8.1

Change in $[C_2H_3O_2^-]/[HC_2H_3O_2]$ for Two Solutions When 0.01 mole of H^+ Is Added to 1.0 L of Each Solution

Solution	$\left(\frac{[C_2H_3O_2^-]}{[HC_2H_3O_2]}\right)_{orig}$	$\left(\frac{[C_2H_3O_2^-]}{[HC_2H_3O_2]}\right)_{new}$	Change	Percent Change
A	$\frac{1.00\ M}{1.00\ M} = 1.00$	$\frac{0.99\ M}{1.01\ M} = 0.98$	$1.00 \longrightarrow 0.98$	2.00%
B	$\frac{1.00\ M}{0.01\ M} = 100$	$\frac{0.99\ M}{0.02\ M} = 49.5$	$100 \longrightarrow 49.5$	50.5%

OWL INTERACTIVE EXAMPLE 8.6

A chemist needs to prepare a solution buffered at pH 4.30 using one of the following acids (and its sodium salt):

a. chloroacetic acid ($K_a = 1.35 \times 10^{-3}$)
b. propanoic acid ($K_a = 1.3 \times 10^{-5}$)
c. benzoic acid ($K_a = 6.4 \times 10^{-5}$)
d. hypochlorous acid ($K_a = 3.5 \times 10^{-8}$)

Calculate the ratio of [HA]/[A⁻] required for each system to yield a pH of 4.30. Which system will work best?

Solution A pH of 4.30 corresponds to

$$[H^+] = 10^{-4.30} = \text{antilog}(-4.30) = 5.0 \times 10^{-5}\ M$$

Since K_a values rather than pK_a values are given for the various acids, we use Equation (8.1),

$$[H^+] = K_a \frac{[HA]}{[A^-]}$$

instead of the Henderson–Hasselbalch equation. We substitute the required $[H^+]$ and K_a for each acid into Equation (8.1) to calculate each ratio of $[HA]/[A^-]$ needed. The results are as follows:

Acid	$[H^+] = K_a \frac{[HA]}{[A^-]}$	$\frac{[HA]}{[A^-]}$
a. Chloroacetic	$5.0 \times 10^{-5} = 1.35 \times 10^{-3}\left(\frac{[HA]}{[A^-]}\right)$	3.7×10^{-2}
b. Propanoic	$5.0 \times 10^{-5} = 1.3 \times 10^{-5}\left(\frac{[HA]}{[A^-]}\right)$	3.8
c. Benzoic	$5.0 \times 10^{-5} = 6.4 \times 10^{-5}\left(\frac{[HA]}{[A^-]}\right)$	0.78
d. Hypochlorous	$5.0 \times 10^{-5} = 3.5 \times 10^{-8}\left(\frac{[HA]}{[A^-]}\right)$	1.4×10^{-3}

Since $[HA]/[A^-]$ for benzoic acid is closest to 1, the system of benzoic acid and its sodium salt is the best choice among those given for buffering a solution at pH 4.30. This example demonstrates the principle that the optimum buffering system has a pK_a value close to the desired pH. The pK_a for benzoic acid is 4.19.

8.5 Titrations and pH Curves

As we saw in Chapter 4, a titration is commonly used to analyze the amount of acid or base in a solution. This process involves delivering a solution of known concentration (the titrant) from a buret into the unknown solution until the substance being analyzed is just consumed. The stoichiometric or equivalence point is usually signaled by the color change of an indicator. In this section we will discuss the pH changes that occur during an acid–base titration. We will use this information later in this chapter to show how an appropriate indicator can be chosen for a particular titration.

The progress of an acid–base titration is often monitored by plotting the pH of the solution being analyzed as a function of the amount of titrant added. Such a plot is called a **pH curve,** or **titration curve.**

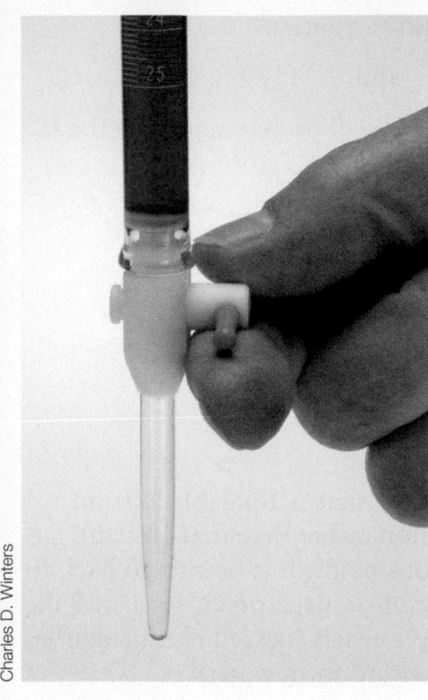

Charles D. Winters

A buret valve.

1 millimole = 1 × 10^{-3} mol

1 mL = 1 × 10^{-3} L

$\frac{\text{mmol}}{\text{mL}} = \frac{\text{mol}}{\text{L}} = M$

Strong Acid–Strong Base Titrations

The reaction for a strong acid–strong base titration is

$$H^+(aq) + OH^-(aq) \longrightarrow H_2O(l)$$

To compute $[H^+]$ at a given point in the titration, we must determine the moles of H^+ remaining at that point and divide by the total volume of the solution. Before we proceed, we need to consider a new unit, which is especially convenient for titrations. Since titrations usually involve small quantities (burets are typically graduated in milliliters), the mole is inconveniently large. Therefore, we will use the **millimole** (abbreviated **mmol**), where

$$1 \text{ mmol} = \frac{1 \text{ mol}}{1000} = 10^{-3} \text{ mol}$$

and

$$\text{Molarity} = \frac{\text{mol of solute}}{\text{L of solution}} = \frac{\frac{\text{mol of solute}}{1000}}{\frac{\text{L of solution}}{1000}} = \frac{\text{mmol of solute}}{\text{mL of solution}}$$

A 1.0 M solution thus contains 1.0 mole of solute per liter of solution or, *equivalently*, 1.0 millimole of solute per milliliter of solution. Just as we obtain the number of moles of solute from the product of the volume in liters and the molarity, we obtain the number of millimoles of solute from the product of the volume in milliliters and the molarity.

We will illustrate the calculations involved in a strong acid–strong base titration by considering the titration of 50.0 mL of 0.200 M HNO_3 with 0.100 M NaOH. We will calculate the pH of the solution at selected points during the course of the titration where specific volumes of 0.100 M NaOH have been added.

A. No NaOH has been added.

Since HNO_3 is a strong acid (is completely dissociated), the solution contains the major species

$$H^+, \quad NO_3^-, \quad \text{and} \quad H_2O$$

The pH is determined by the H^+ from the nitric acid. Since 0.200 M HNO_3 contains 0.200 M H^+,

$$[H^+] = 0.200\ M \quad \text{and} \quad \text{pH} = 0.699$$

B. 10.0 mL of 0.100 *M* NaOH has been added.

In the mixed solution *before any reaction occurs*, the major species are

$$H^+, \quad NO_3^-, \quad Na^+, \quad OH^-, \quad \text{and} \quad H_2O$$

Note that large quantities of both H^+ and OH^- are present. The 1.0 mmol (10.0 mL × 0.10 M) of added OH^- will react with 1.0 mmol of H^+ to form water:

	H^+	+	OH^-	$\longrightarrow$ H_2O
Before reaction:	50.0 mL × 0.200 M = 10.0 mmol		10.0 mL × 0.100 M = 1.00 mmol	
After reaction:	10.0 − 1.00 = 9.0 mmol		1.00 − 1.00 = 0 mmol	

After the reaction is complete, the solution contains

$$H^+, \quad NO_3^-, \quad Na^+, \quad \text{and} \quad H_2O$$

(The OH^- ions have been consumed.) The pH will be determined by the H^+ remaining:

The final solution volume is the sum of the original volume of HNO_3 and the volume of added NaOH.

$$[H^+] = \frac{\text{mmol } H^+ \text{ left}}{\text{volume of solution (mL)}} = \frac{9.0 \text{ mmol}}{(50.0 + 10.0) \text{ mL}} = 0.15\ M$$

(50.0: Original volume of HNO_3 solution; 10.0: Volume of NaOH added)

$$pH = -\log(0.15) = 0.82$$

C. 20.0 mL (total) of 0.100 *M* NaOH has been added.

Go back to the original solution each time you perform a calculation to avoid mistakes.

We consider this point from the perspective that a total of 20.0 mL of NaOH has been added to the *original* solution rather than that 10.0 mL has been added to the solution from the previous point. It is best to go back to the original solution each time a calculation is performed, so a mistake made at an earlier point does not show up in each succeeding calculation. As before, the added OH^- will react with H^+ to form water:

	H^+	+	OH^-	$\longrightarrow$	H_2O
Before reaction:	50.0 mL × 0.200 *M* = 10.0 mmol		20.0 mL × 0.100 *M* = 2.00 mmol		
After reaction:	10.0 − 2.00 = 8.0 mmol		2.00 − 2.00 = 0 mmol		

After the reaction,

$$[H^+] = \frac{8.0 \text{ mmol}}{(50.0 + 20.0) \text{ mL}} = 0.11\ M$$

(8.0 mmol: H^+ remaining)

$$pH = 0.96$$

D. 50.0 mL (total) of 0.100 *M* NaOH has been added.

Proceeding exactly as for the previous two points, we find the pH to be 1.30.

E. 100.0 mL (total) of 0.100 *M* NaOH has been added.

At this point the amount of NaOH that has been added is

$$100.0 \text{ mL} \times 0.100\ M = 10.0 \text{ mmol}$$

The original amount of nitric acid was

$$50.0 \text{ mL} \times 0.200\ M = 10.0 \text{ mmol}$$

Enough OH^- has been added to react exactly with all of the H^+ from the nitric acid. This is the **stoichiometric point,** or **equivalence point,** of the titration. At this point the major species in the solution are

$$Na^+, \quad NO_3^-, \quad \text{and} \quad H_2O$$

Since Na^+ has no acid or base properties and NO_3^- is the anion of the strong acid HNO_3 and is therefore a very weak base, neither NO_3^- nor Na^+ affects the pH. Thus the solution is neutral (the pH is 7.00).

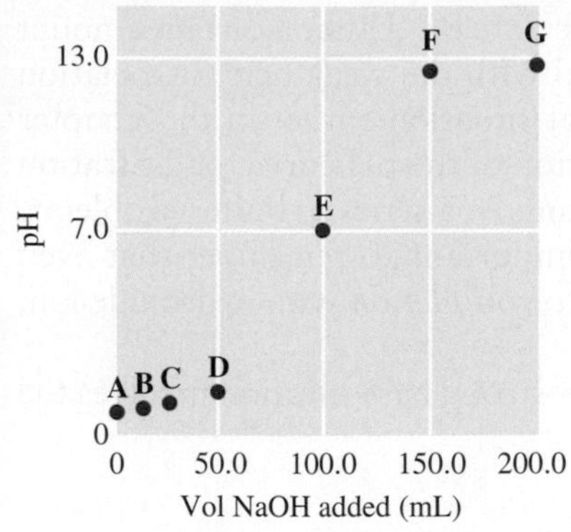

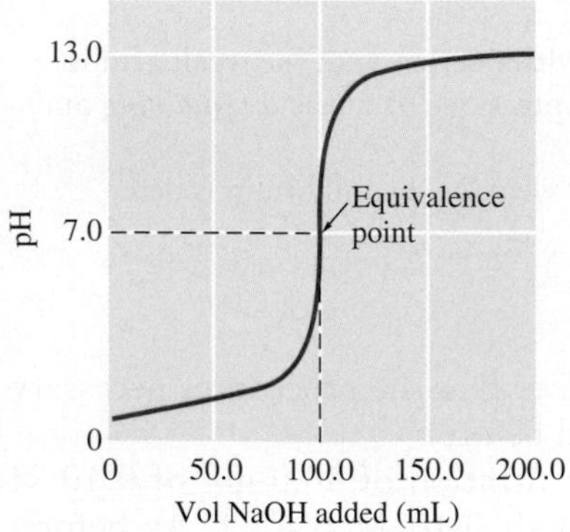

Figure 8.1
The pH curve for the titration of 50.0 mL of 0.200 M HNO_3 with 0.100 M NaOH. Note that the equivalence point occurs when 100.0 mL of NaOH has been added, the point where exactly enough OH^- has been added to react with all the H^+ originally present. The pH of 7 at the equivalence point is characteristic of a strong acid–strong base titration.

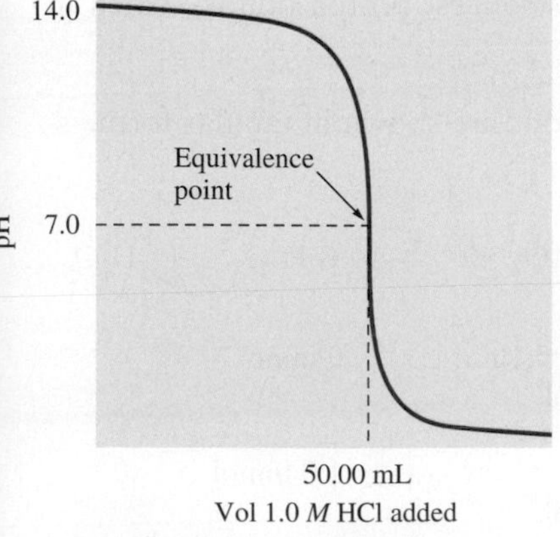

Figure 8.2
The pH curve for the titration of 100.0 mL of 0.50 M NaOH with 1.0 M HCl. The equivalence point occurs when 50.00 mL of HCl has been added, since at this point 5.0 mmol of H^+ ions has been added to react with the original 5.0 mmol of OH^- ions.

F. 150.0 mL (total) of 0.100 *M* NaOH has been added.
The titration reaction is as follows:

	H^+	+	OH^-	$\longrightarrow$	H_2O
Before reaction:	$50.0 \text{ mL} \times 0.200\ M = 10.0 \text{ mmol}$		$150.00 \text{ mL} \times 0.100\ M = 15.0 \text{ mmol}$		
After reaction:	$10.0 - 10.0 = 0 \text{ mmol}$		$15.0 - 10.0 = 5.0 \text{ mmol}$ ↑ Excess OH^- added		

Now the OH^- is *in excess* and thus will determine the pH:

$$[OH^-] = \frac{\text{mmol OH}^- \text{ in excess}}{\text{volume (mL)}} = \frac{5.0 \text{ mmol}}{(50.0 + 150.0) \text{ mL}} = \frac{5.0 \text{ mmol}}{200.0 \text{ mL}}$$

$$= 0.025\ M$$

Since $[H^+][OH^-] = 1.0 \times 10^{-14}$,

$$[H^+] = \frac{1.0 \times 10^{-14}}{2.5 \times 10^{-2}} = 4.0 \times 10^{-13}\ M \quad \text{and} \quad \text{pH} = 12.40$$

G. 200.0 mL (total) of 0.100 *M* NaOH has been added.
Proceeding as for the previous point, we find the pH to be 12.60.

The results of these calculations are summarized by the pH curve shown in Fig. 8.1. Note that the pH changes very gradually until the titration is close to the equivalence point, where a dramatic change occurs. This behavior occurs because early in the titration there is a relatively large amount of H^+ in the solution, and the addition of a given amount of OH^- thus produces only a small change in pH. However, near the equivalence point $[H^+]$ is relatively small, and the addition of a small amount of OH^- produces a large change.

The pH curve in Fig. 8.1, typical of the titration of a strong acid with a strong base, has the following characteristics.

Before the equivalence point, $[H^+]$ (and hence the pH) can be calculated by dividing the number of millimoles of H^+ remaining at that point by the total volume of the solution in milliliters.

At the equivalence point, the pH is 7.00.

After the equivalence point, $[OH^-]$ can be calculated by dividing the number of millimoles of excess OH^- by the total volume of the solution. Then $[H^+]$ is obtained from K_w.

The titration of a strong base with a strong acid requires reasoning very similar to that used above, except, of course, that OH^- is in excess before the equivalence point, and H^+ is in excess after the equivalence point. The pH curve for the titration of 100.0 mL of 0.50 M NaOH with 1.0 M HCl is shown in Fig. 8.2.

Titrations of Weak Acids with Strong Bases

We have seen that since strong acids and strong bases are completely dissociated, the calculations required to obtain the pH curves for titrations involving the two are quite straightforward. However, when the acid being titrated is a weak acid, there is a major difference: To calculate $[H^+]$ after a certain amount of strong base has been added, we must deal with the weak acid dissociation equilibrium. We dealt with this same type of situation earlier in this chapter when we treated buffered solutions. Calculation of the pH curve for a titration of a weak acid with a strong base really amounts to a series of buffer problems. In performing these calculations, it is very important to remember that even though the acid is weak, it *reacts essentially to completion* with hydroxide ion, a very strong base.

Calculating the pH curve for a weak acid–strong base titration involves the following two-step procedure.

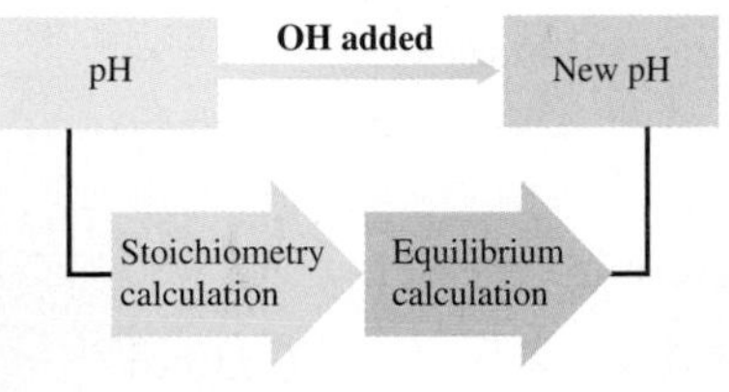

Titration Curve Calculations

1. *A stoichiometry problem.* The reaction of hydroxide ion with the weak acid is assumed to run to completion, and the concentrations of the acid *remaining* and the conjugate base *formed* are determined.
2. *An equilibrium problem.* The position of the weak acid equilibrium is determined, and the pH is calculated.

Treat the stoichiometry and equilibrium problems separately.

It is *essential* to do these steps *separately*. Note that the procedures necessary for solving these problems have all been used before.

As an illustration, we will consider the titration of 50.0 mL of 0.10 *M* acetic acid ($HC_2H_3O_2$, $K_a = 1.8 \times 10^{-5}$) with 0.10 *M* NaOH. As before, we will calculate the pH at various points representing volumes of added NaOH.

- **No NaOH has been added.**

  This is a typical weak acid calculation of the type introduced in Chapter 7. The pH is 2.87. (Check this value yourself.)

- **10.0 mL of 0.10 *M* NaOH has been added.**

  The major species in the mixed solution *before any reaction takes place* are

  $$HC_2H_3O_2, \quad OH^-, \quad Na^+, \quad \text{and} \quad H_2O$$

  The strong base OH^- will react with the strongest proton donor, which in this case is $HC_2H_3O_2$.

  The Stoichiometry Problem. The calculations are shown in tabular form.

	OH^-	+	$HC_2H_3O_2$	$\longrightarrow$	$C_2H_3O_2^-$ + H_2O
Before reaction:	10.0 mL × 0.10 *M* = 1.0 mmol		50.0 mL × 0.10 *M* = 5.0 mmol		0 mmol
After reaction:	1.0 − 1.0 = 0 mmol ↑ Limiting reactant		5.0 − 1.0 = 4.0 mmol		1.0 mmol

  The Equilibrium Problem. We examine the major components left in the solution *after the reaction takes place* to select the dominant equilibrium. The major species are

  $$HC_2H_3O_2, \quad C_2H_3O_2^-, \quad Na^+, \quad \text{and} \quad H_2O$$

Since $HC_2H_3O_2$ is a much stronger acid than H_2O, and since $C_2H_3O_2^-$ is the conjugate base of $HC_2H_3O_2$, the pH will be determined by the position of the acetic acid dissociation equilibrium:

$$HC_2H_3O_2(aq) \rightleftharpoons H^+(aq) + C_2H_3O_2^-(aq)$$

where $$K_a = \frac{[H^+][C_2H_3O_2^-]}{[HC_2H_3O_2]}$$

We follow the usual steps to complete the equilibrium calculations.

The initial concentrations are defined after the reaction with OH^- has gone to completion but before any dissociation of $HC_2H_3O_2$ has occurred.

Initial Concentration		Equilibrium Concentration
$[HC_2H_3O_2]_0 = \frac{4.0 \text{ mmol}}{(50.0 + 10.0) \text{ mL}} = \frac{4.0}{60.0}$	x mmol/mL $HC_2H_3O_2$ dissociates $\longrightarrow$	$[HC_2H_3O_2] = \frac{4.0}{60.0} - x$
$[C_2H_3O_2^-]_0 = \frac{1.0 \text{ mmol}}{(50.0 + 10.0) \text{ mL}} = \frac{1.0}{60.0}$		$[C_2H_3O_2^-] = \frac{1.0}{60.0} + x$
$[H^+]_0 \approx 0$		$[H^+] = x$

Then

$$1.8 \times 10^{-5} = K_a = \frac{[H^+][C_2H_3O_2^-]}{[HC_2H_3O_2]} = \frac{x\left(\frac{1.0}{60.0} + x\right)}{\frac{4.0}{60.0} - x} \approx \frac{x\left(\frac{1.0}{60.0}\right)}{\frac{4.0}{60.0}}$$

$$= \left(\frac{1.0}{4.0}\right)x$$

$$x = \left(\frac{4.0}{1.0}\right)(1.8 \times 10^{-5}) = 7.2 \times 10^{-5} = [H^+]$$

Note that the approximations made are well within 5% uncertainty limits.

and $$pH = 4.14$$

- **25.0 mL (total) of 0.10 M NaOH has been added.**

The procedure here is very similar to that used for the previous point and will be summarized briefly. The stoichiometry problem is as follows:

	OH^-	+	$HC_2H_3O_2$	$\longrightarrow$	$C_2H_3O_2^- + H_2O$
Before reaction:	25.0 mL × 0.10 *M* = 2.5 mmol		50.0 mL × 0.10 *M* = 5.0 mmol		0 mmol
After reaction:	2.5 − 2.5 = 0		50.0 − 2.5 = 2.5 mmol		2.5 mmol

After the reaction the major species in solution are

$$HC_2H_3O_2, \quad C_2H_3O_2^-, \quad Na^+, \quad \text{and} \quad H_2O$$

The equilibrium that will control the pH is

$$HC_2H_3O_2(aq) \rightleftharpoons H^+(aq) + C_2H_3O_2^-(aq)$$

Initial Concentration		Equilibrium Concentration
$[HC_2H_3O_2]_0 = \frac{2.5 \text{ mmol}}{(50.0 + 25.0) \text{ mL}}$	x mmol/mL $HC_2H_3O_2$ dissociates $\longrightarrow$	$[HC_2H_3O_2] = \frac{2.5}{75.0} - x$
$[C_2H_3O_2^-]_0 = \frac{2.5 \text{ mmol}}{(50.0 + 25.0) \text{ mL}}$		$[C_2H_3O_2^-] = \frac{2.5}{75.0} + x$
$[H^+]_0 \approx 0$		$[H^+] = x$

Therefore,

$$1.8 \times 10^{-5} = K_a = \frac{[H^+][C_2H_3O_2^-]}{[HC_2H_3O_2]} = \frac{x\left(\frac{2.5}{75.0} + x\right)}{\frac{2.5}{75.0} - x} \approx \frac{x\left(\frac{2.5}{75.0}\right)}{\frac{2.5}{75.0}}$$

$$x = 1.8 \times 10^{-5} = [H^+] \quad \text{and} \quad pH = 4.74$$

This is a special point in the titration because it is *halfway to the equivalence point.* The original solution, 50.0 mL of 0.10 *M* $HC_2H_3O_2$, contained 5.0 mmol of $HC_2H_3O_2$. Thus 5.0 mmol of OH^- is required to reach the equivalence point. This corresponds to 50.0 mL of NaOH, since

$$(50.0 \text{ mL})(0.10\ M) = 5.0 \text{ mmol}$$

At this point half of the acid has been used up, so $[HC_2H_3O_2] = [C_2H_3O_2^-]$.

After 25.0 mL of NaOH has been added, half of the original $HC_2H_3O_2$ has been converted to $C_2H_3O_2^-$. At this point in the titration, $[HC_2H_3O_2]_0$ is equal to $[C_2H_3O_2^-]_0$. We can neglect the effect of dissociation; that is,

$$[HC_2H_3O_2] = [HC_2H_3O_2]_0 - x \approx [HC_2H_3O_2]_0$$

$$[C_2H_3O_2^-] = [C_2H_3O_2^-]_0 + x \approx [C_2H_3O_2^-]_0$$

The expression for K_a at the halfway point is

$$K_a = \frac{[H^+][C_2H_3O_2^-]}{[HC_2H_3O_2]} = \frac{[H^+][C_2H_3O_2^-]_0}{[HC_2H_3O_2]_0} = [H^+]$$

Equal at the halfway point

Thus, *at the halfway point* in the titration,

$$[H^+] = K_a \quad \text{and} \quad pH = pK_a$$

- **40.0 mL (total) of 0.10 *M* NaOH has been added.**

The procedures required here are the same as those used for the previous two points. The pH is 5.35. (Check this value yourself.)

- **50.0 mL (total) of 0.10 *M* NaOH has been added.**

This point is the equivalence point of the titration; 5.0 mmol of OH^- has been added, which is just enough to react with the 5.0 mmol of $HC_2H_3O_2$ originally present. At this point the solution contains these major species:

$$Na^+, \quad C_2H_3O_2^-, \quad \text{and} \quad H_2O$$

Note that the solution contains $C_2H_3O_2^-$, which is a base. Remember that a base will combine with a proton, and the only source of protons in this solution is water. Thus the reaction will be

$$C_2H_3O_2^-(aq) + H_2O(l) \rightleftharpoons HC_2H_3O_2(aq) + OH^-(aq)$$

This is a *weak base* reaction characterized by K_b:

$$K_b = \frac{[HC_2H_3O_2][OH^-]}{[C_2H_3O_2^-]} = \frac{K_w}{K_a} = \frac{1.0 \times 10^{-14}}{1.8 \times 10^{-5}} = 5.6 \times 10^{-10}$$

The relevant concentrations are

Initial Concentration (before any $C_2H_3O_2^-$ reacts with H_2O)		Equilibrium Concentration
$[C_2H_3O_2^-]_0 = \frac{5.0 \text{ mmol}}{(50.0 + 50.0) \text{ mL}} = 0.050\ M$	x mmol/mL $C_2H_3O_2^-$ reacts with H_2O →	$[C_2H_3O_2^-] = 0.050 - x$
$[OH^-]_0 \approx 0$		$[OH^-] = x$
$[HC_2H_3O_2]_0 = 0$		$[HC_2H_3O_2] = x$

Then

$$5.6 \times 10^{-10} = K_b = \frac{[HC_2H_3O_2][OH^-]}{[C_2H_3O_2^-]} = \frac{(x)(x)}{0.050 - x} \approx \frac{x^2}{0.050}$$

$$x = 5.3 \times 10^{-6}$$

The approximation is valid (by the 5% rule), so

$$[OH^-] = 5.3 \times 10^{-6}\ M$$

and
$$[H^+][OH^-] = K_w = 1.0 \times 10^{-14}$$

$$[H^+] = 1.9 \times 10^{-9}\ M \qquad \text{and} \qquad \text{pH} = 8.72$$

The pH at the equivalence point of a titration of a weak acid with a strong base is always greater than 7.

This is another important result: *The pH at the equivalence point of a titration of a weak acid with a strong base is always greater than 7.* This result occurs because the anion of the acid, which remains in solution at the equivalence point, is a base. In contrast, for the titration of a strong acid with a strong base, the pH at the equivalence point is 7 because the anion remaining in this case is *not* an effective base.

- **60.0 mL (total) of 0.10 *M* NaOH has been added.**

At this point excess OH^- has been added:

	OH^-	+	$HC_2H_3O_2$	$\longrightarrow$	$C_2H_3O_2^- + H_2O$
Before reaction:	60.0 mL × 0.10 *M* = 6.0 mmol		50.0 mL × 0.10 *M* = 5.0 mmol		0 mmol
After reaction:	6.0 − 5.0 = 1.0 mmol in excess		5.0 − 5.0 = 0 mmol		5.0 mmol

After the reaction is complete, the solution contains these major species:

$$Na^+, \quad C_2H_3O_2^-, \quad OH^-, \quad \text{and} \quad H_2O$$

There are two bases in this solution, OH^- and $C_2H_3O_2^-$. However, $C_2H_3O_2^-$ is a weak base compared with OH^-. Therefore, the amount of OH^- produced by the reaction of $C_2H_3O_2^-$ with H_2O will be small compared with the excess OH^- already in solution. You can verify this conclusion by looking at the previous point, where only 5.3×10^{-6} *M* OH^- was produced by $C_2H_3O_2^-$. The amount in this case will be even smaller, since the excess OH^- will push the K_b equilibrium to the left.

Thus the pH is determined by the excess OH^-:

$$[OH^-] = \frac{\text{mmol of OH}^- \text{ in excess}}{\text{volume (in mL)}} = \frac{1.0 \text{ mmol}}{(50.0 + 60.0) \text{ mL}}$$
$$= 9.1 \times 10^{-3}\ M$$

and
$$[H^+] = \frac{1.0 \times 10^{-14}}{9.1 \times 10^{-3}} = 1.1 \times 10^{-12}\ M \quad \text{and} \quad \text{pH} = 11.96$$

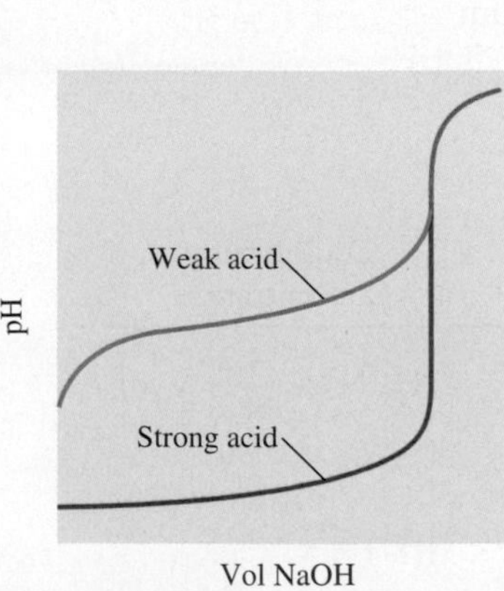

- **75.0 mL (total) of 0.10 *M* NaOH has been added.**

The procedure needed here is very similar to that for the previous point. The pH is 12.30. (Check this value.)

The pH curve for this titration is shown in Fig. 8.3. Note the differences between this curve and the curve in Fig. 8.1. For example, the shapes of the plots are quite different before the equivalence point, but they are very similar after that point. (The shapes of the strong and weak acid curves are the same after the equivalence points because excess OH^- controls the pH in this region in both cases.) Near the beginning of the titration of the weak acid, the pH increases more rapidly than it does in the strong acid case. It levels off near the halfway point and then increases rapidly again. The leveling off near the halfway point is caused by buffering effects. Earlier in this chapter we saw that optimum buffering occurs when [HA] is equal to $[A^-]$. This is exactly the case at the halfway point of the titration. As we can see from the curve, the pH changes least around this point in the titration.

The other notable difference between the curves for strong and weak acids is the value of the pH at the equivalence point. For the titration of a strong acid, the equivalence point occurs at a pH of 7. For the titration of a weak acid, the pH at the equivalence point is greater than 7 because of the basicity of the conjugate base of the weak acid.

The equivalence point is defined by the stoichiometry, not by the pH.

It is important to understand that the equivalence point in an acid–base titration is *defined by the stoichiometry, not by the pH.* The equivalence point occurs when enough titrant has been added to react exactly with all of the acid or base being titrated.

OWL INTERACTIVE EXAMPLE 8.7

Hydrogen cyanide gas (HCN) is a powerful respiratory inhibitor that is highly toxic. It is a very weak acid ($K_a = 6.2 \times 10^{-10}$) when dissolved in water. If a 50.0-mL sample of 0.100 *M* HCN is titrated with 0.100 *M* NaOH, calculate the pH of the solution at the following points.

a. after 8.00 mL of 0.100 *M* NaOH has been added

Solution

The Stoichiometry Problem. After 8.00 mL of 0.100 *M* NaOH has been added, we have the following:

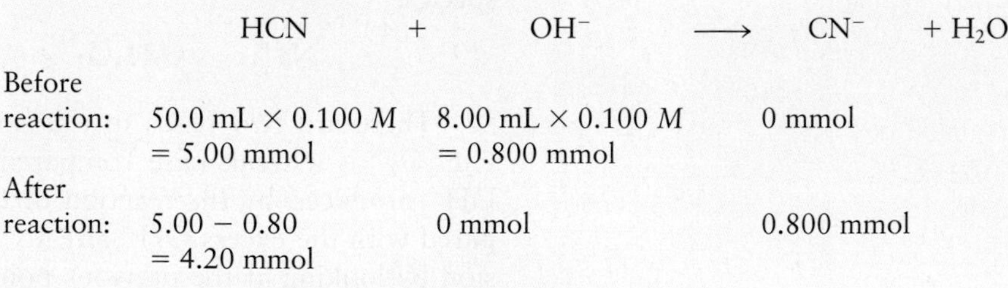

	HCN	+	OH^-	$\longrightarrow$	CN^-	$+ H_2O$
Before reaction:	$50.0\text{ mL} \times 0.100\ M = 5.00\text{ mmol}$		$8.00\text{ mL} \times 0.100\ M = 0.800\text{ mmol}$		0 mmol	
After reaction:	$5.00 - 0.80 = 4.20\text{ mmol}$		0 mmol		0.800 mmol	

The Equilibrium Problem. Since the solution contains the major species

$$HCN, \quad CN^-, \quad Na^+, \quad \text{and} \quad H_2O$$

the position of the acid dissociation equilibrium

$$HCN(aq) \rightleftharpoons H^+(aq) + CN^-(aq)$$

will determine the pH.

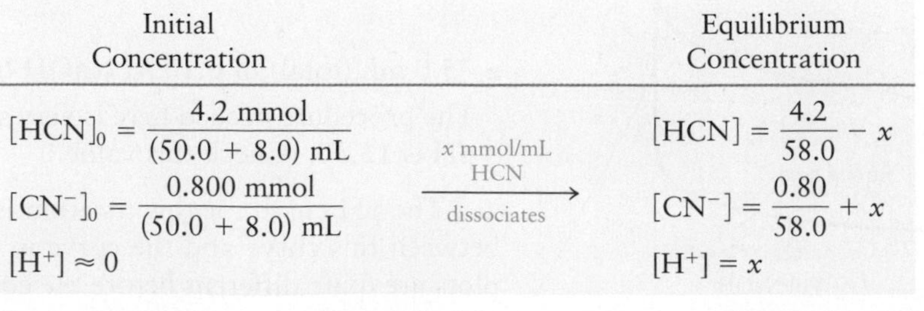

Initial Concentration		Equilibrium Concentration
$[HCN]_0 = \dfrac{4.2\text{ mmol}}{(50.0 + 8.0)\text{ mL}}$	x mmol/mL HCN dissociates $\longrightarrow$	$[HCN] = \dfrac{4.2}{58.0} - x$
$[CN^-]_0 = \dfrac{0.800\text{ mmol}}{(50.0 + 8.0)\text{ mL}}$		$[CN^-] = \dfrac{0.80}{58.0} + x$
$[H^+] \approx 0$		$[H^+] = x$

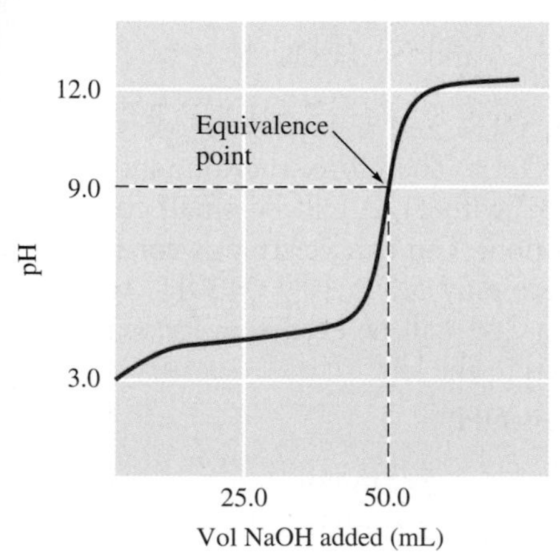

Figure 8.3
The pH curve for the titration of 50.0 mL of 0.10 *M* $HC_2H_3O_2$ with 0.10 *M* NaOH. Note that the equivalence point occurs when 50.0 mL of NaOH has been added, where the amount of added OH^- ions exactly equals the original amount of acid. The pH at the equivalence point is greater than 7 because the $C_2H_3O_2^-$ ion present at this point is a base and reacts with water to produce OH^-.

Substituting into the expression for K_a gives

$$6.2 \times 10^{-10} = K_a = \frac{[H^+][CN^-]}{[HCN]} = \frac{x\left(\frac{0.80}{58.0} + x\right)}{\frac{4.2}{58.0} - x} \approx \frac{x\left(\frac{0.80}{58.0}\right)}{\left(\frac{4.2}{58.0}\right)} = x\left(\frac{0.80}{4.2}\right)$$

The approximations made here are well within 5% uncertainty limits.

$$x = 3.3 \times 10^{-9}\ M = [H^+] \quad \text{and} \quad pH = 8.49$$

b. at the halfway point in the titration

Solution The amount of HCN originally present can be obtained from the original volume and molarity:

$$50.0\ \text{mL} \times 0.100\ M = 5.00\ \text{mmol}$$

Thus the halfway point will occur when 2.50 mmol of OH^- has been added:

$$\text{Volume of NaOH (in mL)} \times 0.100\ M = 2.50\ \text{mmol OH}^-$$

or

$$\text{Volume of NaOH} = 25.0\ \text{mL}$$

As was pointed out previously, at the halfway point [HCN] is equal to $[CN^-]$ and pH is equal to pK_a. Thus, after 25.0 mL of 0.100 *M* NaOH has been added,

$$pH = pK_a = -\log(6.2 \times 10^{-10}) = 9.21$$

c. at the equivalence point

Solution The equivalence point will occur when a total of 5.00 mmol of OH^- has been added. Since the NaOH solution is 0.100 *M*, the equivalence point occurs when 50.0 mL of NaOH has been added. This results in the formation of 5.00 mmol of CN^-. The major species in solution at the equivalence point are

$$CN^-, \quad Na^+, \quad \text{and} \quad H_2O$$

Thus the reaction that will control the pH involves the basic cyanide ion extracting a proton from water:

$$CN^-(aq) + H_2O(l) \rightleftharpoons HCN(aq) + OH^-(aq)$$

and

$$K_b = \frac{K_w}{K_a} = \frac{1.0 \times 10^{-14}}{6.2 \times 10^{-10}} = 1.6 \times 10^{-5} = \frac{[HCN][OH^-]}{[CN^-]}$$

Initial Concentration		Equilibrium Concentration
$[CN^-]_0 = \frac{5.00\ \text{mmol}}{(50.0 + 50.0)\ \text{mL}} = 5.00 \times 10^{-2}\ M$ $[HCN]_0 = 0$ $[OH^-]_0 \approx 0$	x mmol/mL of CN^- reacts with H_2O $\longrightarrow$	$[CN^-] = (5.00 \times 10^{-2}) - x$ $[HCN] = x$ $[OH^-] = x$

Substituting the equilibrium concentrations into the expression for K_b and solving in the usual way gives

$$[OH^-] = x = 8.9 \times 10^{-4}$$

Then from K_w we have

$$[H^+] = 1.1 \times 10^{-11} \quad \text{and} \quad pH = 10.96$$

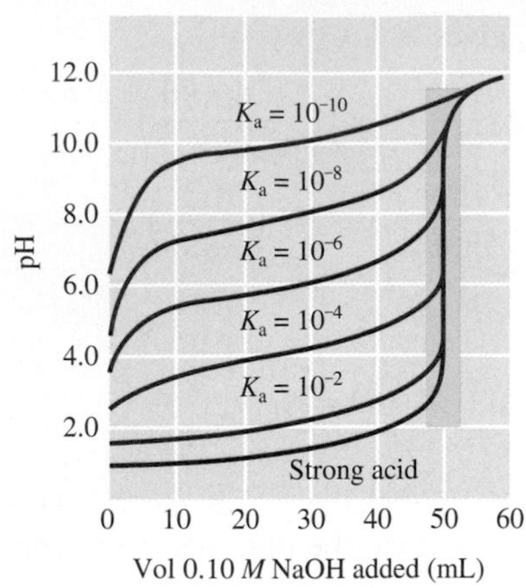

Figure 8.4
The pH curves for the titrations of 50.0-mL samples of 0.10 *M* solutions of various acids with 0.10 *M* NaOH.

Two important conclusions can be drawn from a comparison of the titration of 50.0 mL of 0.1 *M* acetic acid covered earlier in this section with that of 50.0 mL of 0.1 *M* hydrocyanic acid (Example 8.7). First, the same amount of 0.1 *M* NaOH is required to reach the equivalence point in both cases. The fact that HCN is a much weaker acid than $HC_2H_3O_2$ has no bearing on the amount of base required. It is the *amount* of acid, not its strength, that determines the equivalence point. Second, the *pH value* at the equivalence point *is* affected by the acid strength. For the titration of acetic acid, the pH at the equivalence point is 8.72; for the titration of hydrocyanic acid, the pH at the equivalence point is 10.96. This difference occurs because the CN^- ion is a much stronger base than the $C_2H_3O_2^-$ ion. Also, the pH at the halfway point of the titration is much higher for HCN than for $HC_2H_3O_2$, again because of the greater base strength of the CN^- ion (or equivalently, the smaller acid strength of HCN).

The strength of a weak acid has a significant effect on the shape of its pH curve. Figure 8.4 shows pH curves for 50-mL samples of 0.10 *M* solutions of various acids titrated with 0.10 *M* NaOH. Note that the equivalence point occurs at the same volume of 0.10 *M* NaOH for each case but that the shapes of the curves are dramatically different. The weaker the acid, the greater is the pH value at the equivalence point. In particular, note that the vertical region surrounding the equivalence point becomes shorter as the acid being titrated becomes weaker. We will see in the next section how this affects the choice of an indicator for such a titration.

The amount of acid present, not its strength, determines the equivalence point.

In addition to being used to analyze the amount of acid or base in a solution, titrations can be used to determine the values of equilibrium constants, as shown in Example 8.8.

OWL INTERACTIVE EXAMPLE 8.8

A chemist has synthesized a monoprotic weak acid and wants to determine its K_a value. To do so, the chemist dissolves 2.00 mmol of the solid acid in 100.0 mL of water and titrates the resulting solution with 0.0500 *M* NaOH. After 20.0 mL of NaOH has been added, the pH is 6.00. What is the K_a value for the acid?

Solution

The Stoichiometry Problem. We represent the monoprotic acid as HA. The stoichiometry for the titration reaction is shown below.

2.00 mmol HA

↓ add OH^-

1.00 mmol HA
1.00 mmol A^-

	HA	+	OH^-	$\longrightarrow$	A^-	+	H_2O
Before reaction:	2.00 mmol		20.0 mL × 0.0500 *M* = 1.00 mmol		0 mmol		
After reaction:	2.00 − 1.00 = 1.00 mmol		1.00 − 1.00 = 0 mmol		1.00 mmol		

The Equilibrium Problem. After the reaction, the solution contains the major species

$$HA, \quad A^-, \quad Na^+, \quad \text{and} \quad H_2O$$

The pH will be determined by the equilibrium

$$HA(aq) \rightleftharpoons H^+(aq) + A^-(aq)$$

$$K_a = \frac{[H^+][A^-]}{[HA]}$$

Initial Concentration		Equilibrium Concentration
$[HA]_0 = \dfrac{1.00 \text{ mmol}}{(100.0 + 20.0) \text{ mL}} = 8.33 \times 10^{-3} M$		$[HA] = 8.33 \times 10^{-3} - x$
$[A^-]_0 = \dfrac{1.00 \text{ mmol}}{(100.0 + 20.0) \text{ mL}} = 8.33 \times 10^{-3} M$	$\xrightarrow[\text{dissociates}]{x \text{ mmol/mL HA}}$	$[A^-] = 8.33 \times 10^{-3} + x$
$[H^+]_0 \approx 0$		$[H^+] = x$

Note that x is actually known here because the pH at this point is known to be 6.00. Thus

$$x = [H^+] = \text{antilog}(-\text{pH}) = 1.0 \times 10^{-6} M$$

Substituting the equilibrium concentrations into the expression for K_a allows calculation of the K_a value:

$$K_a = \frac{[H^+][A^-]}{[HA]} = \frac{x(8.33 \times 10^{-3} + x)}{(8.33 \times 10^{-3}) - x}$$

$$= \frac{(1.0 \times 10^{-6})(8.33 \times 10^{-3} + 1.0 \times 10^{-6})}{(8.33 \times 10^{-3}) - (1.0 \times 10^{-6})}$$

$$= \frac{(1.0 \times 10^{-6})(8.33 \times 10^{-3})}{8.33 \times 10^{-3}} = 1.0 \times 10^{-6}$$

There is an easier way to think about this problem. The original solution contained 2.00 mmol of HA, and since 20.0 mL of added 0.0500 M NaOH contains 1.00 mmol of OH^-, this is the halfway point in the titration (where [HA] is equal to $[A^-]$). Thus

$$[H^+] = K_a = 1.0 \times 10^{-6}$$

Titrations of Weak Bases with Strong Acids

Titrations of weak bases with strong acids can be treated using the procedures we have introduced previously. As always, you should *first think about the major species in solution* and decide whether a reaction occurs that runs essentially to completion. If such a reaction does occur, let it run to completion and then do the stoichiometric calculations. Finally, choose the dominant equilibrium and calculate the pH.

The calculations for the titration of a weak base with a strong acid are illustrated by the following titration of 100.0 mL of 0.050 M NH_3 with 0.10 M HCl. The strategies needed at several key areas in the titration will be described qualitatively. The actual calculations are summarized in Table 8.2.

- **Before the addition of any HCl.**

1. The major species are

$$NH_3 \quad \text{and} \quad H_2O$$

NH_3 is a base and will seek a source of protons. In this case H_2O is the only available source of protons.

2. No reactions occur that go to completion, since NH_3 cannot readily take a proton from H_2O. This is evidenced by the small K_b value for NH_3.

3. The equilibrium that controls the pH involves the reaction of ammonia with water:

$$NH_3(aq) + H_2O(l) \rightleftharpoons NH_4^+(aq) + OH^-(aq)$$

Table 8.2

Summary of Results for the Titration of 100.0 mL 0.050 M NH_3 with 0.10 M HCl

Volume of 0.10 M HCl Added (mL)	$[NH_3]_0$	$[NH_4^+]_0$	$[H^+]$	pH
0	0.050 M	0	1.1×10^{-11} M	10.96
10.0	$\frac{4.0 \text{ mmol}}{(100 + 10) \text{ mL}}$	$\frac{1.0 \text{ mmol}}{(100 + 10) \text{ mL}}$	1.4×10^{-10} M	9.85
25.0*	$\frac{2.5 \text{ mmol}}{(100 + 25) \text{ mL}}$	$\frac{2.5 \text{ mmol}}{(100 + 25) \text{ mL}}$	5.6×10^{-10} M	9.25
50.0†	0	$\frac{5.0 \text{ mmol}}{(100 + 50) \text{ mL}}$	4.3×10^{-6} M	5.36
60.0‡	0	$\frac{5.0 \text{ mmol}}{(100 + 60) \text{ mL}}$	$\frac{1.0 \text{ mmol}}{160 \text{ mL}} = 6.2 \times 10^{-3}$ M	2.21

*Halfway point.
†Equivalence point.
‡$[H^+]$ determined by the 1.0 mmol of excess H^+.

Use K_b to calculate $[OH^-]$. Although NH_3 is a weak base (compared with OH^-), it produces much more OH^- in this reaction than is produced from the autoionization of H_2O.

- **Before the equivalence point.**

1. The major species (before any reaction occurs) are

$$NH_3, \quad \underbrace{H^+, \quad Cl^-,}_{\text{From added HCl}} \quad \text{and} \quad H_2O$$

2. The NH_3 will react with H^+ from the added HCl:

$$NH_3(aq) + H^+(aq) \rightleftharpoons NH_4^+(aq)$$

This reaction proceeds essentially to completion because the NH_3 readily reacts with a free proton. This case is much different from the previous case, where H_2O was the only source of protons. The stoichiometric calculations are then carried out using the known volume of 0.10 M HCl added.

3. After the reaction of NH_3 with H^+ is run to completion, the solution contains the following major species:

$$NH_3, \quad \underset{\substack{\uparrow \\ \text{Formed in} \\ \text{titration reaction}}}{NH_4^+,} \quad Cl^-, \quad \text{and} \quad H_2O$$

The solution contains NH_3 and NH_4^+; thus the equilibria involving these species will determine $[H^+]$. The $[H^+]$ can be calculated using either the dissociation reaction of NH_4^+,

$$NH_4^+(aq) \rightleftharpoons NH_3(aq) + H^+(aq)$$

or the reaction of NH_3 with H_2O,

$$NH_3(aq) + H_2O(l) \rightleftharpoons NH_4^+(aq) + OH^-(aq)$$

to calculate the pH.

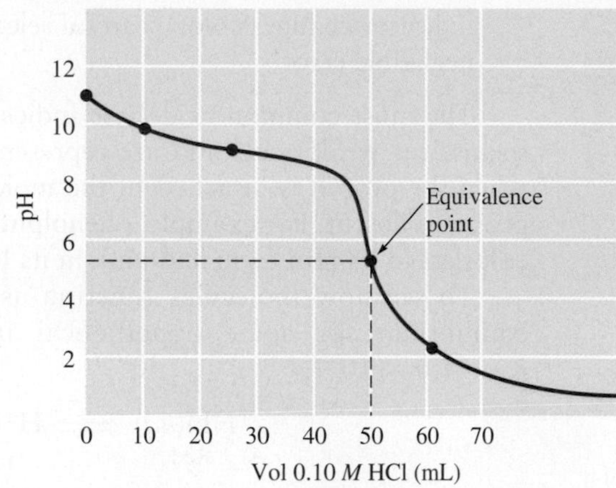

Figure 8.5 The pH curve for the titration of 100.0 mL of 0.050 *M* NH_3 with 0.10 *M* HCl. Note that the pH at the equivalence point is less than 7, since the solution contains the weak acid NH_4^+.

- **At the equivalence point.**
  1. By definition, the equivalence point occurs when all the original NH_3 is converted to NH_4^+. Thus the major species in solution are

     $$NH_4^+, \quad Cl^-, \quad \text{and} \quad H_2O$$

  2. No reaction goes to completion.
  3. The equilibrium that controls $[H^+]$ is the dissociation of the weak acid NH_4^+, for which

     $$K_a = \frac{K_w}{K_b(\text{for } NH_3)}$$

- **Beyond the equivalence point.**
  1. Excess HCl has been added and the major species are

     $$H^+, \quad NH_4^+, \quad Cl^-, \quad \text{and} \quad H_2O$$

  2. No reaction goes to completion.
  3. Although NH_4^+ will dissociate, it is such a weak acid that $[H^+]$ will be determined simply by the excess H^+:

     $$[H^+] = \frac{\text{mmol of } H^+ \text{ in excess}}{\text{mL of solution}}$$

The results of these calculations are shown in Table 8.2. The pH curve is shown in Fig. 8.5.

8.6 Acid–Base Indicators

There are two common methods for determining the equivalence point of an acid–base titration:

1. Use a pH meter to monitor the pH and then plot a titration curve. The center of the vertical region of the pH curve indicates the equivalence point (for example, see Figs. 8.1 through 8.5).
2. Use an **acid–base indicator,** which marks the endpoint of a titration by changing color. Although the *equivalence point of a titration, defined by the stoichiometry, is not necessarily the same as the endpoint* (where the

The *endpoint* is defined by the change in color of the indicator. The *equivalence point* is defined by the reaction stoichiometry.

Photos: Charles D. Winters

Figure 8.6
The indicator phenolphthalein is pink in basic solution (top) and colorless in acidic solution (bottom).

indicator changes color), careful selection of the indicator will ensure only negligible error.

The most common acid–base indicators are complex molecules that are themselves weak acids and are represented by HIn. They exhibit one color when the proton is attached to the molecule and a different color when the proton is absent. For example, **phenolphthalein,** a commonly used indicator, is colorless in its HIn form and pink in its In^-, or basic, form (Fig. 8.6).

To see how molecules function as indicators, consider the following equilibrium for some hypothetical indicator HIn, a weak acid with $K_a = 1.0 \times 10^{-8}$:

$$\underset{\text{Red}}{\mathrm{HIn}(aq)} \rightleftharpoons \mathrm{H^+}(aq) + \underset{\text{Blue}}{\mathrm{In^-}(aq)}$$

$$K_a = \frac{[\mathrm{H^+}][\mathrm{In^-}]}{[\mathrm{HIn}]}$$

By rearranging, we get

$$\frac{K_a}{[\mathrm{H^+}]} = \frac{[\mathrm{In^-}]}{[\mathrm{HIn}]}$$

Suppose we add a few drops of this indicator to an acidic solution whose pH is 1.0 ($[\mathrm{H^+}] = 1.0 \times 10^{-1}$). Then

$$\frac{K_a}{[\mathrm{H^+}]} = \frac{1. \times 10^{-8}}{1.0 \times 10^{-1}} = 10^{-7} = \frac{[\mathrm{In^-}]}{[\mathrm{HIn}]} - \frac{1}{10{,}000{,}000}$$

This ratio shows that the predominant form of the indicator is HIn, resulting in a red solution. As OH^- is added to this solution in a titration, $[H^+]$ decreases, and the equilibrium shifts to the right, changing HIn to In^-. At some point in the titration, enough of the In^- form will be present in the solution so that a purple tint will be noticeable. That is, a color change from red to reddish purple will occur.

How much In^- must be present in the solution for the human eye to detect that the color is different from the original one? For most indicators, about one-tenth of the initial form must be converted to the other form before a new color is apparent. We will assume, then, that in the titration of an acid with a base, the color change will be apparent at a pH where

$$\frac{[\mathrm{In^-}]}{[\mathrm{HIn}]} = \frac{1}{10}$$

EXAMPLE 8.9

Bromthymol blue, an indicator with a K_a value of 1.0×10^{-7}, is yellow in its HIn form and blue in its In^- form. Suppose we put a few drops of this indicator in a strongly acidic solution. If the solution is then titrated with NaOH, at what pH will the indicator color change first be visible?

Solution For bromthymol blue,

$$K_a = 1.0 \times 10^{-7} = \frac{[\mathrm{H^+}][\mathrm{In^-}]}{[\mathrm{HIn}]}$$

We assume the color change is visible when

$$\frac{[\mathrm{In^-}]}{[\mathrm{HIn}]} = \frac{1}{10}$$

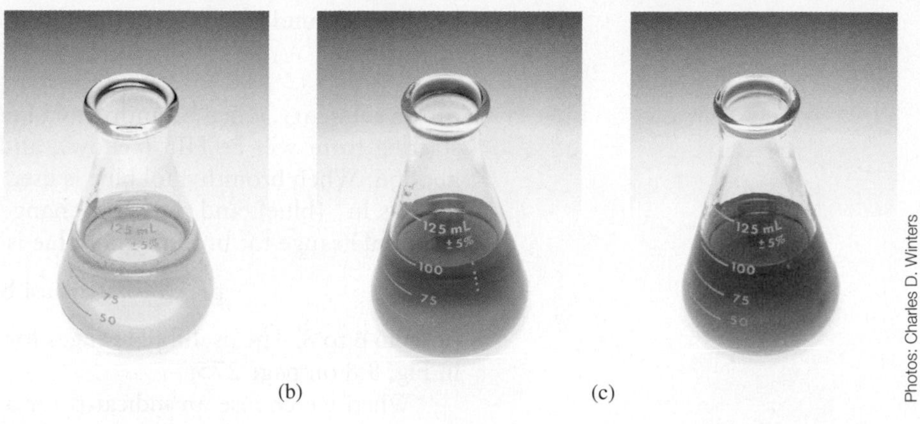

Figure 8.7
(a) Yellow acid form of bromthymol blue; (b) a greenish tint is seen when the solution contains 1 part blue and 10 parts yellow; (c) blue basic form.

That is, we assume we can see the first hint of a greenish tint (yellow plus a little blue) when the solution contains 1 part blue and 10 parts yellow (Fig. 8.7). Thus

$$K_a = 1.0 \times 10^{-7} = \frac{[H^+](1)}{10}$$

$$[H^+] = 1.0 \times 10^{-6} \quad \text{or} \quad pH = 6.0$$

The color change is first visible at a pH of 6.0.

The Henderson–Hasselbalch equation is very useful in determining the pH at which an indicator changes color. For example, application of Equation (8.2) to the K_a expression for the general indicator HIn yields

$$pH = pK_a + \log\left(\frac{[In^-]}{[HIn]}\right)$$

where K_a is the dissociation constant for the acid form [HIn]. Since we assume that the color change is visible when

$$\frac{[In^-]}{[HIn]} = \frac{1}{10}$$

we have the following equation for determining the pH at which the color change occurs:

$$pH = pK_a + \log(\tfrac{1}{10}) = pK_a - 1$$

For bromthymol blue ($K_a = 1 \times 10^{-7}$, or $pK_a = 7$), the pH at the color change is

$$pH = 7 - 1 = 6$$

as we calculated in Example 8.9.

When a basic solution is titrated, the indicator HIn will initially exist as In^- in solution, but as acid is added, more HIn will form. In this case the color change will be visible when there is a mixture of 10 parts In^- to 1 part HIn. That is, a color change from blue to blue-green will occur (Fig. 8.7) because of the presence of some of the yellow HIn molecules. This color change will be first visible when

$$\frac{[In^-]}{[HIn]} = \frac{10}{1}$$

Note that this expression is the reciprocal of the ratio for the titration of an acid. Substituting this ratio into the Henderson–Hasselbalch equation gives

$$pH = pK_a + \log(\tfrac{10}{1}) = pK_a + 1$$

For bromthymol blue ($pK_a = 7$), we have a color change at

$$pH = 7 + 1 = 8$$

In summary, when bromthymol blue is used for the titration of an acid, the starting form will be HIn (yellow), and the color change occurs at a pH of about 6. When bromthymol blue is used for the titration of a base, the starting form is In^- (blue), and the color change occurs at a pH of about 8. Thus the useful pH range for bromthymol blue is

$$pK_a \text{ (bromthymol blue)} \pm 1 = 7 \pm 1$$

or from 6 to 8. The useful pH ranges for several common indicators are shown in Fig. 8.8 on page 275.

When we choose an indicator for a titration, we want the indicator endpoint (where the color changes) and the titration equivalence point to be as close as possible. Choosing an indicator is easier if there is a large change in pH near the equivalence point of the titration. The dramatic change in pH near the equivalence point in a strong acid–strong base titration (Figs. 8.1 and 8.2) produces a sharp endpoint; that is, the complete color change (from the acid-to-base or the base-to-acid colors) usually occurs over one drop of added titrant.

What indicator should we use for the titration of 100.00 mL of 0.100 *M* HCl with 0.100 *M* NaOH? We know that the equivalence point occurs at pH 7.00. In the initially acidic solution, the indicator will exist predominantly in the HIn form. As OH^- ions are added, the pH will increase rather slowly at first (Fig. 8.1) and then will rise rapidly at the equivalence point. This sharp change causes the indicator dissociation equilibrium

$$HIn \rightleftharpoons H^+ + In^-$$

to shift suddenly to the right, producing enough In^- ions to cause a color change. Since we are titrating an acid, the indicator is predominantly in the acid form initially. Therefore the first observable color change will occur at a pH where

$$\frac{[In^-]}{[HIn]} = \frac{1}{10}$$

Thus

$$pH = pK_a + \log(\tfrac{1}{10}) = pK_a - 1$$

If we want an indicator that will change color at pH 7, we can use this relationship to find the pK_a value of a suitable indicator:

$$pH = 7 = pK_a - 1 \quad \text{or} \quad pK_a = 7 + 1 = 8$$

Thus an indicator with a pK_a value of 8 ($K_a = 1 \times 10^{-8}$) will change color at about a pH of 7 and will be ideal to mark the endpoint for a strong acid–strong base titration.

How crucial is it in a strong acid–strong base titration that the indicator change color exactly at a pH of 7? We can answer this question by examining the pH change near the equivalence point of the titration of 100.00 mL of 0.100 *M* HCl with 0.100 *M* NaOH. The data for a few points at or near the equivalence point are shown in Table 8.3. Note that in going from 99.99 mL to 100.01 mL of added NaOH solution (about half of a drop), the pH changes from 5.3 to 8.7—a very dramatic change. This behavior leads to the following general conclusions about indicators for a strong acid–strong base titration:

Indicator color change will be sharp, occurring with the addition of a single drop of titrant.

There is a wide choice of suitable indicators. The results will agree within one drop of titrant, using indicators with endpoints as far apart as pH = 5 and pH = 9 (Fig. 8.9).

Table 8.3

Selected pH Values Near the Equivalence Point in the Titration of 100.0 mL of 0.100 *M* HCl with 0.100 *M* NaOH

NaOH Added (mL)	pH
99.99	5.3
100.00	7.0
100.01	8.7

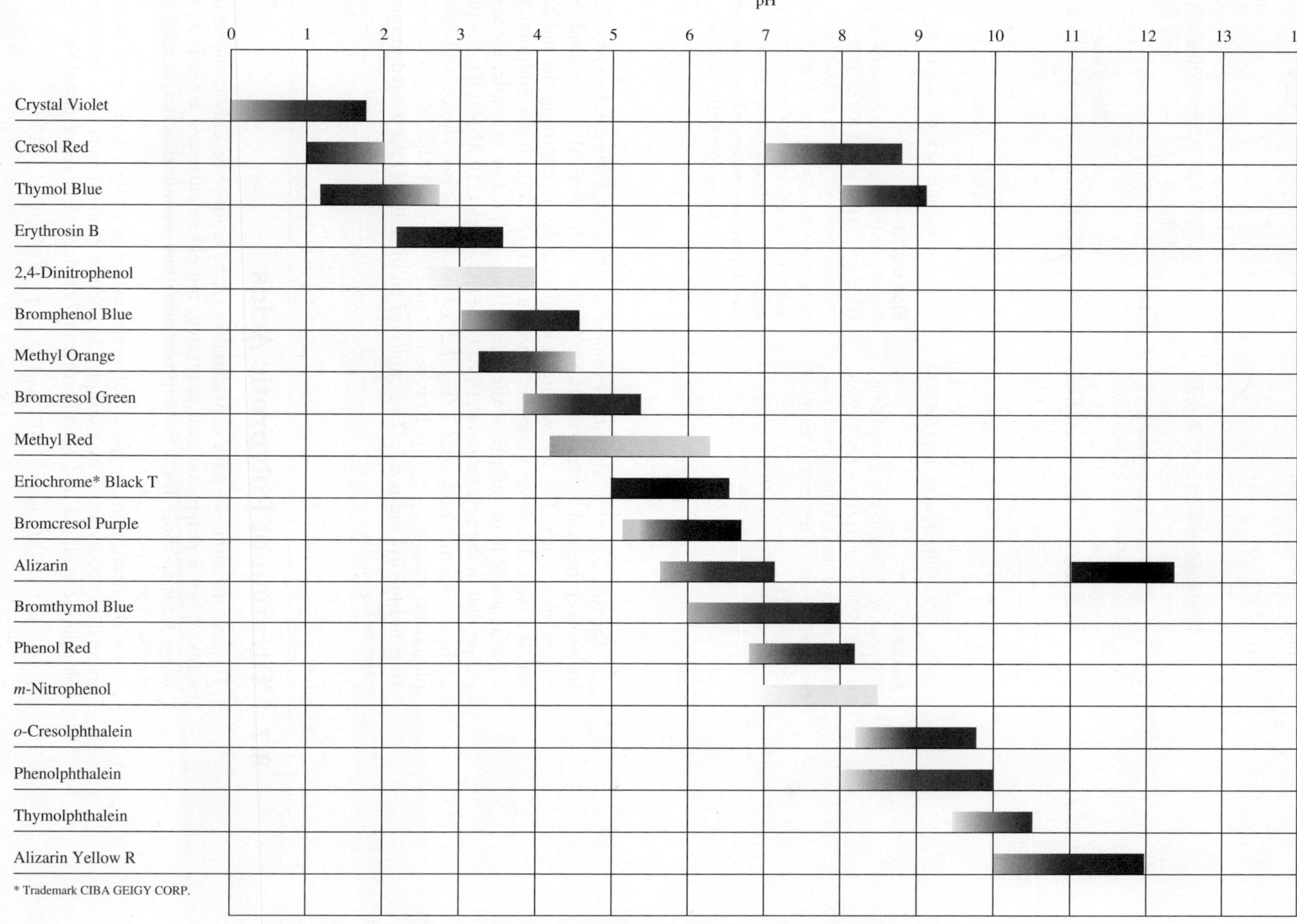

Figure 8.8
The useful pH ranges for several common indicators. Note that most indicators have a useful range of about two pH units, as predicted by the expression $pK_a \pm 1$.

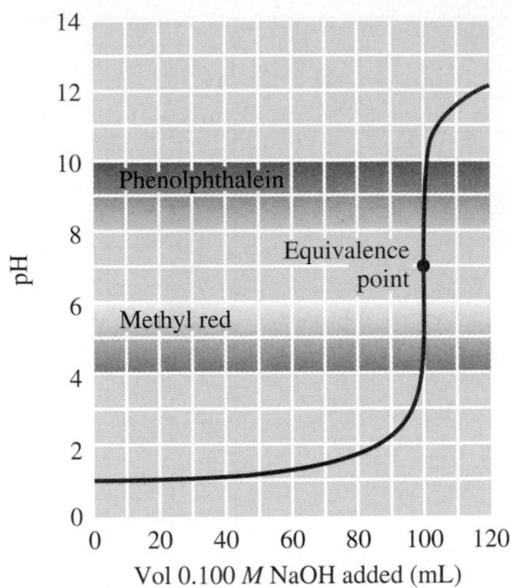

Figure 8.9
The pH curve for the titration of 100.0 mL of 0.100 M HCl with 0.100 M NaOH. Note that phenolphthalein and methyl red have endpoints at virtually the same amounts of added NaOH.

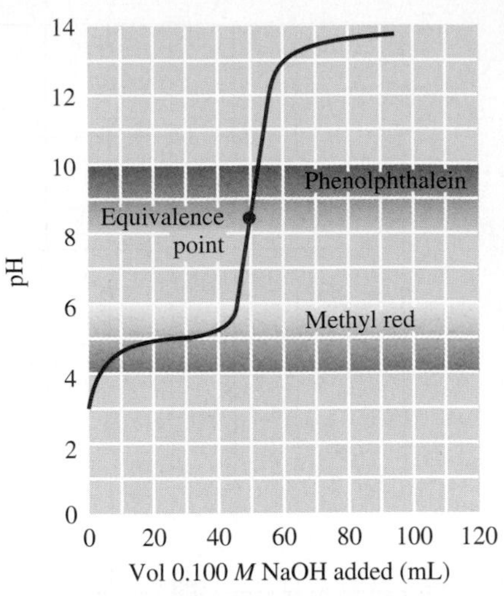

Figure 8.10
The pH curve for the titration of 50 mL of 0.100 M $HC_2H_3O_2$ with 0.100 M NaOH. Phenolphthalein will give an endpoint very close to the equivalence point of the titration. Methyl red will change color well before the equivalence point (so the endpoint will be very different from the equivalence point) and is not a suitable indicator for this titration.

The titration of weak acids is somewhat different. Figure 8.4 shows that the weaker the acid being titrated, the smaller is the vertical area around the equivalence point. This allows much less flexibility in choosing the indicator. We must choose an indicator whose useful pH range has a midpoint as close as possible to the pH at the equivalence point. For example, we saw earlier that in the titration of 0.10 M $HC_2H_3O_2$ with 0.10 M NaOH, the pH at the equivalence point is 8.7 (Fig. 8.3). A good indicator choice is phenolphthalein, since its useful pH range is 8 to 10. Thymol blue is also acceptable, but methyl red is not. The choice of an indicator is illustrated graphically in Fig. 8.10.

8.7 Titration of Polyprotic Acids

The acid titrations we have considered so far have involved only monoprotic acids. When a polyprotic acid is titrated, the pH calculations are similar in many ways to those for a monoprotic acid, but enough differences exist to warrant special coverage.

In the titration of a typical polyprotic acid, the various acidic protons are titrated in succession. For example, as sodium hydroxide is used to titrate phosphoric acid, the first reaction that takes place can be represented as

$$H_3PO_4(aq) + OH^-(aq) \longrightarrow H_2PO_4^-(aq) + H_2O(l)$$

This reaction occurs until the H_3PO_4 is consumed (to reach the first equivalence point). Therefore, at the first equivalence point the solution contains the major species Na^+, $H_2PO_4^-$, and H_2O. Then, as more sodium hydroxide is added, the reaction

$$H_2PO_4^-(aq) + OH^-(aq) \longrightarrow HPO_4^{2-}(aq) + H_2O(l)$$

Table 8.4

A Summary of Various Points in the Titration of a Triprotic Acid

Point in the Titration	Major Species Present	Equilibrium Expression Used to Obtain the pH
No base added	H_3A, H_2O	$K_{a_1} = \frac{[H^+][H_2A^-]}{[H_3A]}$
Base added		
Before the first equivalence point	H_3A, H_2A^-, H_2O	$K_{a_1} = \frac{[H^+][H_2A^-]}{[H_3A]}$
At the first equivalence point	H_2A^-, H_2O	See discussion in text
Between the first and second equivalence points	H_2A^-, HA^{2-}, H_2O	$K_{a_2} = \frac{[H^+][HA^{2-}]}{[H_2A^-]}$
At the second equivalence point	HA^{2-}, H_2O	See discussion in text
Between the second and third equivalence points	HA^{2-}, A^{3-}, H_2O	$K_{a_3} = \frac{[H^+][A^{3-}]}{[HA^{2-}]}$
At the third equivalence point	A^{3-}, H_2O	$K_b = \frac{K_w}{K_{a_3}} = \frac{[HA^{2-}][OH^-]}{[A^{3-}]}$
Beyond the third equivalence point	A^{3-}, OH^-, H_2O	pH determined by excess OH^-

occurs to give a solution that contains Na^+, HPO_4^{2-}, and H_2O as the major species at the second equivalence point. As sodium hydroxide is added beyond the second equivalence point, the reaction that occurs can be represented as

$$HPO_4^{2-}(aq) + OH^-(aq) \longrightarrow PO_4^{3-}(aq) + H_2O(l)$$

As mentioned earlier, the calculations involved in obtaining the pH curve for the titration of a polyprotic acid are closely related to those for a monoprotic acid. The same principles apply, but we must be very careful in identifying which of the various equilibria is appropriate to use in a given case. The secret to success here is, as always, identifying the major species in solution at any given point in the titration. We summarize the various cases in Table 8.4 for a triprotic acid H_3A with dissociation constants K_{a_1}, K_{a_2}, and K_{a_3}.

A point that cannot be overemphasized is that the appropriate equilibrium expression is chosen by knowing what major species are present. Thus, if the solution contains HA^{2-} and A^{3-}, we must use K_{a_3} to determine the pH, and so on. Note that in two instances in Table 8.4 we did not specify the equilibrium expression to be used. These two cases, which need to be considered in more detail, are discussed in the section that follows.

Solutions Containing Amphoteric Anions as the Only Acid–Base Major Species

At the first equivalence point in the titration of the acid H_3A with sodium hydroxide, the major species are H_2A^- and H_2O. What equilibrium will control the $[H^+]$ in such a solution?

The key to answering this question is to recognize that H_2A^- is an amphoteric species: It is both an acid,

$$H_2A^-(aq) \rightleftharpoons H^+(aq) + HA^{2-}(aq)$$

and a base,

$$H_2A^-(aq) + H^+(aq) \rightleftharpoons H_3A(aq)$$

What is the best source of protons for H_2A^- behaving as a base? There are two possible sources: H_2O and other H_2A^- ions in the solution. By now we realize that H_2O is a very weak acid. In a typical case H_2A^- will be a much stronger acid than H_2O. Thus, in a solution containing H_2A^- and H_2O as the major species, we expect the reaction

$$H_2A^-(aq) + H_2A^-(aq) \rightleftharpoons H_3A(aq) + HA^{2-}(aq)$$

to be the most important acid–base reaction. Notice that this reaction expresses both the acidic and basic properties of H_2A^- (in the preceding equation, one H_2A^- is behaving as the acid and the other H_2A^- as the base). This reaction leads to the equilibrium expression

$$K = \frac{[H_3A][HA^{2-}]}{[H_2A^-]^2}$$

We can obtain the value for K by recognizing that

$$\frac{[H_3A][HA^{2-}]}{[H_2A^-][H_2A^-]} = \frac{[H_3A]}{[H^+][H_2A^-]} \times \frac{[H^+][HA^{2-}]}{[H_2A^-]} = \frac{1}{K_{a_1}} \times K_{a_2}$$

Thus $$K = \frac{K_{a_2}}{K_{a_1}}$$

The position of this equilibrium will determine the concentrations of H_3A, H_2A^-, and HA^{2-} in the solution and thus will determine the pH. We can obtain an expression for $[H^+]$ from the equation

$$\frac{K_{a_2}}{K_{a_1}} = \frac{[H_3A][HA^{2-}]}{[H_2A^-]^2}$$

by recognizing that if the reaction

$$H_2A^-(aq) + H_2A^-(aq) \rightleftharpoons H_3A(aq) + HA^{2-}(aq)$$

is the only important reaction involving these species, then

$$[H_3A] = [HA^{2-}]$$

This condition allows us to write

$$\frac{K_{a_2}}{K_{a_1}} = \frac{[H_3A][HA^{2-}]}{[H_2A^-]^2} = \frac{[H_3A]^2}{[H_2A^-]^2}$$

From the expression for K_{a_1} we have

$$\frac{[H^+]}{K_{a_1}} = \frac{[H_3A]}{[H_2A^-]}$$

Thus $$\frac{K_{a_2}}{K_{a_1}} = \frac{[H_3A]^2}{[H_2A^-]^2} = \frac{[H^+]^2}{{K_{a_1}}^2}$$

or $$[H^+]^2 = {K_{a_1}}^2 \times \frac{K_{a_2}}{K_{a_1}} = K_{a_1}K_{a_2}$$

and $$[H^+] = K_{a_1}K_{a_2}$$

In terms of pH, this equation becomes

$$\text{pH} = \frac{\text{p}K_{a_1} + \text{p}K_{a_2}}{2}$$

Note that this equation applies only to a solution containing the major species H_2A^- and H_2O. It does not apply, for example, to a solution that contains the major species H_2A^-, HA^{2-}, and H_2O. In the former case H_2A^- is simultaneously the best acid and the best base, and thus the pH is determined by the reaction of H_2A^- with itself. In the latter case the solution contains the acid H_2A^- and its conjugate base HA^{2-}. In this case H_2A^- is the best acid and HA^{2-} is the best base, and the equilibrium that controls the pH is that described by K_{a_2}:

$$H_2A^-(aq) \rightleftharpoons H^+(aq) + HA^{2-}(aq)$$

Example 8.10 shows how the pH is calculated at the first equivalence point of the titration of phosphoric acid with sodium hydroxide, where the solution contains $H_2PO_4^-$. Note that the pH of the solution does not depend on the concentration of $H_2PO_4^-$ in the solution. Thus the pH is 4.67 at the first equivalence point in any typical titration of H_3PO_4. Likewise, at the second equivalence point, where the major species are HPO_4^{2-} and H_2O, the pH is calculated from the expression

$$\text{pH} = \frac{\text{p}K_{a_2} + \text{p}K_{a_3}}{2}$$

OWL INTERACTIVE EXAMPLE 8.10

Calculate the pH of a 1.0 *M* solution of NaH_2PO_4. (For H_3PO_4, $K_{a_1} = 7.5 \times 10^{-3}$, $K_{a_2} = 6.2 \times 10^{-8}$, and $K_{a_3} = 4.8 \times 10^{-13}$.)

Solution The major species in solution are

$$Na^+, \quad H_2PO_4^-, \quad \text{and} \quad H_2O$$

This is an example of a solution containing the amphoteric anion $H_2PO_4^-$, which is simultaneously the best acid and the best base. Both properties must be considered to calculate the pH correctly. Use the formula involving the average of the pK's:

$$\text{pH} = \frac{\text{p}K_{a_1} + \text{p}K_{a_2}}{2} = \frac{2.12 + 7.21}{2} = 4.67$$

Titration of a Polyprotic Acid with Sodium Hydroxide—A Summary

At this point it is useful to summarize the pH calculations associated with the titration of a triprotic acid H_3A. Figure 8.11 shows which expression should be used for the major species in the solution at a given point in the titration.

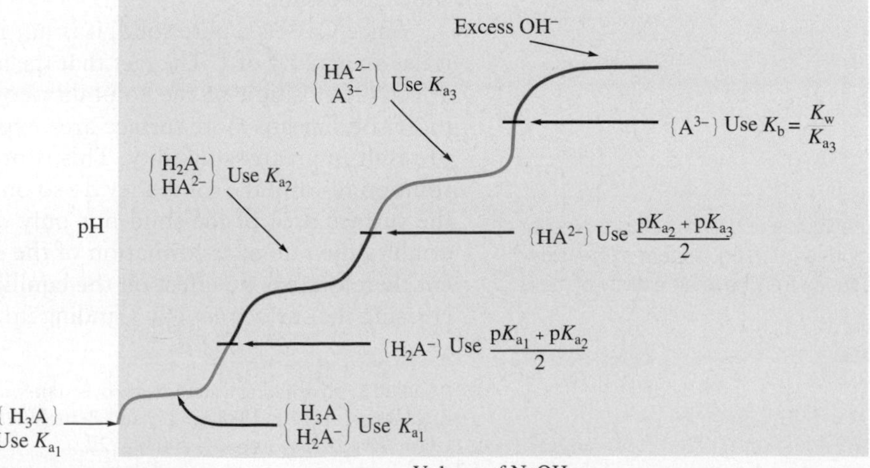

Figure 8.11 A summary of the important equilibria at various points in the titration of a triprotic acid.

8.8 Solubility Equilibria and the Solubility Product

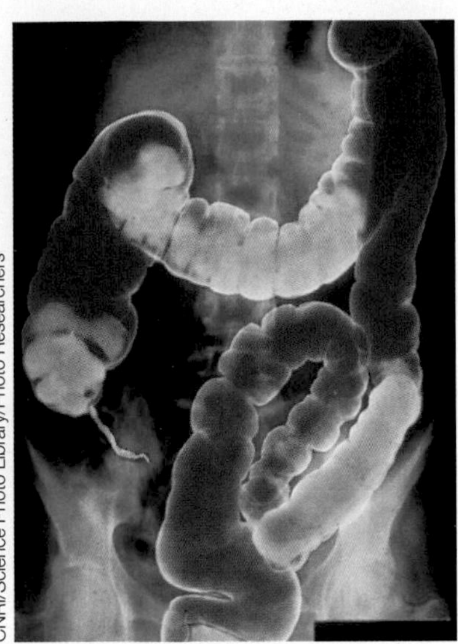
CNRI/Science Photo Library/Photo Researchers

An X ray of the upper gastrointestinal tract clarified by barium sulfate.

Solubility is a very important phenomenon. The fact that substances such as sugar and table salt dissolve in water allows us to flavor foods easily. Because calcium carbonate is less soluble in hot water than in cold water, it coats tubes in boilers, reducing thermal efficiency. Tooth decay involves solubility: When food lodges between the teeth, acids form that dissolve tooth enamel, which contains a mineral called hydroxyapatite [$Ca_5(PO_4)_3OH$]. Tooth decay can be reduced by treating teeth with fluoride.* Fluoride replaces the hydroxide in hydroxyapatite to produce the corresponding fluorapatite [$Ca_5(PO_4)_3F$] and calcium fluoride (CaF_2), both of which are less soluble in acids than the original enamel. Another important consequence of solubility occurs in the use of a suspension of barium sulfate to improve the clarity of X rays of the gastrointestinal tract. The very low solubility of barium sulfate, which contains the toxic ion Ba^{2+}, makes ingestion of the compound safe.

In this section we consider the equilibria associated with solids dissolving in water to form aqueous solutions. When an ionic solid dissolves in water, we typically assume that it dissociates into separate hydrated cations and anions. For example, when calcium fluoride dissolves in water, we typically represent the situation as follows:

$$CaF_2(s) \xrightarrow{H_2O} Ca^{2+}(aq) + 2F^-(aq)$$

When the solid salt is first added to the water, no Ca^{2+} or F^- ions are present. However, as the dissolution proceeds, the concentrations of Ca^{2+} and F^- increase, making it more and more likely that these ions will collide and re-form the solid phase. Thus two competing processes are occurring, the preceding reaction and the reverse reaction:

$$Ca^{2+}(aq) + 2F^-(aq) \longrightarrow CaF_2(s)$$

Ultimately, dynamic equilibrium is reached:

$$CaF_2(s) \rightleftharpoons Ca^{2+}(aq) + 2F^-(aq)$$

At this point, no more solid can dissolve (the solution is said to be *saturated*).

We can write an equilibrium expression for this process according to the law of mass action:

$$K_{sp} = [Ca^{2+}][F^-]^2$$

This analysis ignores the presence of ion pairs such as CaF^-, which may be present in significant amounts.

where $[Ca^{2+}]$ and $[F^-]$ are expressed in mol/L. The constant K_{sp} is called the **solubility product constant,** or simply the **solubility product** for the equilibrium expression.

Since CaF_2 is a pure solid, it is not included in the equilibrium expression; it has an activity of 1. The fact that the amount of excess solid present does not affect the position of the solubility equilibrium might seem strange at first; more solid means more surface area exposed to the solvent, which would seem to result in greater solubility. This is not the case, however. When the ions in solution re-form the solid, they do so on the surface of the solid. Thus doubling the surface area of the solid not only doubles the rate of dissolving but also doubles the rate of re-formation of the solid. The amount of excess solid present therefore has no effect on the equilibrium position. Similarly, although increasing the surface area by grinding up the solid or stirring the solution speeds

Pure liquids and pure solids are never included in an equilibrium expression because they have an activity of 1.

*Adding F^- to drinking water is controversial. See Bette Hileman, "Fluoridation of Water," *Chem. Eng. News,* Aug. 1, 1988, p. 26; and Bette Hileman, "Fluoride Concerns Surface Once Again," *Chem. Eng. News,* Aug. 25, 2003, p. 22.

Table 8.5

K_{sp} Values at 25°C for Common Ionic Solids

Ionic Solid	K_{sp} (at 25°C)	Ionic Solid	K_{sp} (at 25°C)	Ionic Solid	K_{sp} (at 25°C)
Fluorides		Hg_2CrO_4*	2×10^{-9}	$Co(OH)_2$	2.5×10^{-16}
BaF_2	2.4×10^{-5}	$BaCrO_4$	8.5×10^{-11}	$Ni(OH)_2$	1.6×10^{-16}
MgF_2	6.4×10^{-9}	Ag_2CrO_4	9.0×10^{-12}	$Zn(OH)_2$	4.5×10^{-17}
PbF_2	4×10^{-8}	$PbCrO_4$	2×10^{-16}	$Cu(OH)_2$	1.6×10^{-19}
SrF_2	7.9×10^{-10}			$Hg(OH)_2$	3×10^{-26}
CaF_2	4.0×10^{-11}	Carbonates		$Sn(OH)_2$	3×10^{-27}
		$NiCO_3$	1.4×10^{-7}	$Cr(OH)_3$	6.7×10^{-31}
Chlorides		$CaCO_3$	8.7×10^{-9}	$Al(OH)_3$	2×10^{-32}
$PbCl_2$	1.6×10^{-5}	$BaCO_3$	1.6×10^{-9}	$Fe(OH)_3$	4×10^{-38}
$AgCl$	1.6×10^{-10}	$SrCO_3$	7×10^{-10}	$Co(OH)_3$	2.5×10^{-43}
Hg_2Cl_2*	1.1×10^{-18}	$CuCO_3$	2.5×10^{-10}		
		$ZnCO_3$	2×10^{-10}	Sulfides	
Bromides		$MnCO_3$	8.8×10^{-11}	MnS	2.3×10^{-13}
$PbBr_2$	4.6×10^{-6}	$FeCO_3$	2.1×10^{-11}	FeS	3.7×10^{-19}
$AgBr$	5.0×10^{-13}	Ag_2CO_3	8.1×10^{-12}	NiS	3×10^{-21}
Hg_2Br_2*	1.3×10^{-22}	$CdCO_3$	5.2×10^{-12}	CoS	5×10^{-22}
		$PbCO_3$	1.5×10^{-15}	ZnS	2.5×10^{-22}
Iodides		$MgCO_3$	1×10^{-15}	SnS	1×10^{-26}
PbI_2	1.4×10^{-8}	Hg_2CO_3*	9.0×10^{-15}	CdS	1.0×10^{-28}
AgI	1.5×10^{-16}			PbS	7×10^{-29}
Hg_2I_2*	4.5×10^{-29}	Hydroxides		CuS	8.5×10^{-45}
		$Ba(OH)_2$	5.0×10^{-3}	Ag_2S	1.6×10^{-49}
Sulfates		$Sr(OH)_2$	3.2×10^{-4}	HgS	1.6×10^{-54}
$CaSO_4$	6.1×10^{-5}	$Ca(OH)_2$	1.3×10^{-6}		
Ag_2SO_4	1.2×10^{-5}	$AgOH$	2.0×10^{-8}	Phosphates	
$SrSO_4$	3.2×10^{-7}	$Mg(OH)_2$	8.9×10^{-12}	Ag_3PO_4	1.8×10^{-18}
$PbSO_4$	1.3×10^{-8}	$Mn(OH)_2$	2×10^{-13}	$Sr_3(PO_4)_2$	1×10^{-31}
$BaSO_4$	1.5×10^{-9}	$Cd(OH)_2$	5.9×10^{-15}	$Ca_3(PO_4)_2$	1.3×10^{-32}
		$Pb(OH)_2$	1.2×10^{-15}	$Ba_3(PO_4)_2$	6×10^{-39}
Chromates		$Fe(OH)_2$	1.8×10^{-15}	$Pb_3(PO_4)_2$	1×10^{-54}
$SrCrO_4$	3.6×10^{-5}				

*Contains Hg_2^{2+} ions. $K_{sp} = [Hg_2^{2+}][X^-]^2$ for Hg_2X_2 salts.

up the attainment of equilibrium, neither procedure changes the amount of solid dissolved at equilibrium. Neither the amount of excess solid nor the size of the particles will shift the *position* of the solubility equilibrium.

K_{sp} is an equilibrium constant; solubility is an equilibrium position.

It is very important to distinguish between the *solubility* of a given solid and its *solubility product*. The solubility product is an *equilibrium constant* and thus has only *one* value for a given solid at a given temperature. Solubility, on the other hand, is an *equilibrium position* and has an *infinite number* of possible values at a given temperature, depending on the other conditions (such as the presence of a common ion). The K_{sp} values at 25°C for many common ionic solids are listed in Table 8.5. The units are customarily omitted.

OWL INTERACTIVE EXAMPLE 8.11

Calculate the K_{sp} value for bismuth sulfide (Bi_2S_3), which has a solubility of 1.0×10^{-15} mol/L at 25°C.

Solution The system initially contains H_2O and solid Bi_2S_3. In the simplest treatment, we assume the solid dissolves as follows:

$$Bi_2S_3(s) \rightleftharpoons 2Bi^{3+}(aq) + 3S^{2-}(aq)$$

Precipitation of bismuth sulfide.

This treatment ignores ion pairs between the Bi^{3+} and S^{2-} ions.

Therefore $$K_{sp} = [Bi^{3+}]^2[S^{2-}]^3$$

Since no Bi^{3+} or S^{2-} ions are present in solution before the Bi_2S_3 dissolves,

$$[Bi^{3+}]_0 = [S^{2-}]_0 = 0$$

Thus the equilibrium concentrations of these ions will be determined by the amount of salt that dissolves to reach equilibrium, which in this case is 1.0×10^{-15} mol/L. Since each Bi_2S_3 unit contains $2Bi^{3+}$ and $3S^{2-}$ ions,

$$1.0 \times 10^{-15} \text{ mol/L } Bi_2S_3(s) \longrightarrow 2(1.0 \times 10^{-15} \text{ mol/L) } Bi^{3+}(aq) + 3(1.0 \times 10^{-15} \text{ mol/L) } S^{2-}(aq)$$

The equilibrium concentrations are

$$[Bi^{3+}] = [Bi^{3+}]_0 + \text{change} = 0 + 2.0 \times 10^{-15} \text{ mol/L}$$

$$[S^{2-}] = [S^{2-}]_0 + \text{change} = 0 + 3.0 \times 10^{-15} \text{ mol/L}$$

Then

$$K_{sp} = [Bi^{3+}]^2[S^{2-}]^3 = (2.0 \times 10^{-15})^2(3.0 \times 10^{-15})^3 = 1.1 \times 10^{-73}$$

In Example 8.11 we used the solubility of an ionic solid to calculate its K_{sp} value. The reverse is also possible: The solubility of an ionic solid can be calculated if its K_{sp} value is known.

OWL INTERACTIVE EXAMPLE 8.12

The K_{sp} value for copper(II) iodate $[Cu(IO_3)_2]$ is 1.4×10^{-7} at 25°C. Calculate its solubility at 25°C.

Solution The system initially contains H_2O and solid $Cu(IO_3)_2$. The solid dissolves according to the following equilibrium:

$$Cu(IO_3)_2(s) \rightleftharpoons Cu^{2+}(aq) + 2IO_3^-(aq)$$

Therefore $$K_{sp} = [Cu^{2+}][IO_3^-]^2$$

A more detailed analysis of this situation would include ion pairs such as $[CuIO_3]^+$, but this is beyond the level of this text.

To find the solubility of $Cu(IO_3)_2$, we must find the equilibrium concentrations of the Cu^{2+} and IO_3^- ions. We do this in the usual way by specifying the initial concentrations (before any solid has dissolved) and then defining the change required to reach equilibrium. Since in this case we do not know the solubility, we will assume that x mol/L of the solid dissolves to reach equilibrium. The 1:2 stoichiometry of the salt means that

$$x \text{ mol/L } Cu(IO_3)_2(s) \longrightarrow x \text{ mol/L } Cu^{2+}(aq) + 2x \text{ mol/L } IO_3^-(aq)$$

The concentrations are as follows:

Initial Concentration (mol/L) [before any $Cu(IO_3)_2$ dissolves]		Equilibrium Concentration (mol/L)
$[Cu^{2+}]_0 = 0$ $[IO_3^-]_0 = 0$	x mol/L dissolves $\longrightarrow$ to reach equilibrium	$[Cu^{2+}] = x$ $[IO_3^-] = 2x$

Substituting the equilibrium concentrations into the expression for K_{sp} gives

$$1.4 \times 10^{-7} = K_{sp} = [Cu^{2+}][IO_3^-]^2 = (x)(2x)^2 = 4x^3$$

Then $$x = \sqrt[3]{3.5 \times 10^{-8}} = 3.3 \times 10^{-3} \text{ mol/L}$$

Thus the solubility of solid $Cu(IO_3)_2$ is 3.3×10^{-3} mol/L.

Relative Solubilities

A salt's K_{sp} value provides information about its solubility. However, we must be careful in using K_{sp} values to predict the *relative* solubilities of a group of salts. There are two possible situations.

1. The salts being compared produce the same number of ions. For example, consider

$$\begin{array}{ll} AgI(s) & K_{sp} = 1.5 \times 10^{-16} \\ CuI(s) & K_{sp} = 5.0 \times 10^{-12} \\ CaSO_4(s) & K_{sp} = 6.1 \times 10^{-5} \end{array}$$

Each of these solids dissolves to produce two ions:

$$\text{Salt} \rightleftharpoons \text{cation} + \text{anion}$$

$$K_{sp} = [\text{cation}][\text{anion}]$$

If x is the solubility in mol/L, then at equilibrium

$$[\text{Cation}] = x$$

$$[\text{Anion}] = x$$

$$K_{sp} = [\text{cation}][\text{anion}] = x^2$$

$$x = \sqrt{K_{sp}} = \text{solubility}$$

Thus in this case we can compare the solubilities of these solids by comparing their K_{sp} values:

$$CaSO_4(s) > CuI(s) > AgI(s)$$

Most soluble; largest K_{sp} — Least soluble; smallest K_{sp}

2. The salts being compared produce different numbers of ions. For example, consider

$$\begin{array}{ll} CuS(s) & K_{sp} = 8.5 \times 10^{-45} \\ Ag_2S(s) & K_{sp} = 1.6 \times 10^{-49} \\ Bi_2S_3(s) & K_{sp} = 1.1 \times 10^{-73} \end{array}$$

Since these salts produce different numbers of ions when they dissolve, the K_{sp} values cannot be compared *directly* to determine the relative solubilities. In fact, if we calculate the solubilities (using the procedure in Example 8.12), we obtain the results summarized in Table 8.6. The order of solubilities is

$$Bi_2S_3(s) > Ag_2S(s) > CuS(s)$$

Most soluble — Least soluble

which is opposite to the order of the K_{sp} values.

Table 8.6

Calculated Solubilities for CuS, Ag_2S, and Bi_2S_3 at 25°C

Salt	K_{sp}	Calculated Solubility (mol/L)
CuS	8.5×10^{-45}	9.2×10^{-23}
Ag_2S	1.6×10^{-49}	3.4×10^{-17}
Bi_2S_3	1.1×10^{-73}	1.0×10^{-15}

Remember that relative solubilities can be predicted by comparing K_{sp} values *only* for salts that produce the same total number of ions.

Common Ion Effect

So far we have considered ionic solids dissolved in pure water. We will now see what happens when the water contains an ion in common with the dissolving salt. For example, consider the solubility of solid silver chromate (Ag_2CrO_4, $K_{sp} = 9.0 \times 10^{-12}$) in a 0.100 M solution of $AgNO_3$. Before any Ag_2CrO_4 dissolves, the solution contains the major species Ag^+, NO_3^-, and H_2O. Since

A potassium chromate solution being added to aqueous silver nitrate, forming silver chromate.

NO_3^- is not found in Ag_2CrO_4, we can ignore it. The relevant initial concentrations (before any Ag_2CrO_4 dissolves) are

$$[Ag^+]_0 = 0.100\ M \qquad \text{(from the dissolved AgNO}_3\text{)}$$
$$[CrO_4^{2-}]_0 = 0$$

The system comes to equilibrium as Ag_2CrO_4 dissolves according to the reaction

$$Ag_2CrO_4(s) \rightleftharpoons 2Ag^+(aq) + CrO_4^{2-}(aq)$$

for which

$$K_{sp} = [Ag^+]^2[CrO_4^{2-}] = 9.0 \times 10^{-12}$$

We assume that x mol/L of Ag_2CrO_4 dissolves to reach equilibrium, which means that

$$x \text{ mol/L } Ag_2CrO_4(s) \longrightarrow 2x \text{ mol/L } Ag^+(aq) + x \text{ mol/L } CrO_4^{2-}(aq)$$

Now we can specify the equilibrium concentrations in terms of x:

$$[Ag^+] = [Ag^+]_0 + \text{change} = 0.100 + 2x$$
$$[CrO_4^{2-}] = [CrO_4^{2-}]_0 + \text{change} = 0 + x = x$$

Substituting these concentrations into the expression for K_{sp} gives

$$9.0 \times 10^{-12} = [Ag^+]^2[CrO_4^{2-}] = (0.100 + 2x)^2(x)$$

The mathematics required here appears to be complicated, since the right-hand side of the equation produces an expression that contains an x^3 term. However, as is usually the case, we can make simplifying assumptions. Since the K_{sp} value for Ag_2CrO_4 is small (the position of the equilibrium lies far to the left), x is expected to be small compared with 0.100 M. Therefore, $0.100 + 2x \approx 0.100$, which allows simplification of the expression:

$$9.0 \times 10^{-12} = (0.100 + 2x)^2(x) \approx (0.100)^2(x)$$

Then
$$x \approx \frac{9.0 \times 10^{-12}}{(0.100)^2} = 9.0 \times 10^{-10} \text{ mol/L}$$

Since x is much less than 0.100 M, the approximation is valid. Thus

$$\text{Solubility of } Ag_2CrO_4 \text{ in } 0.100\ M\ AgNO_3 = x = 9.0 \times 10^{-10} \text{ mol/L}$$

and the equilibrium concentrations are

$$[Ag^+] = 0.100 + 2x = 0.100 + 2(9.0 \times 10^{-10}) = 0.100\ M$$
$$[CrO_4^{2-}] = x = 9.0 \times 10^{-10}\ M$$

Now we compare the solubilities of Ag_2CrO_4 in pure water and in 0.100 M $AgNO_3$:

$$\text{Solubility of } Ag_2CrO_4 \text{ in pure water} = 1.3 \times 10^{-4} \text{ mol/L}$$
$$\text{Solubility of } Ag_2CrO_4 \text{ in } 0.100\ M\ AgNO_3 = 9.0 \times 10^{-10} \text{ mol/L}$$

Note that the solubility of Ag_2CrO_4 is much less in the presence of the Ag^+ ions from $AgNO_3$. This is another example of the common ion effect. The solubility of a solid is lowered if the solution already contains ions common to the solid.

Complications Inherent in Solubility Calculations

So far in this section we have assumed a direct relationship between the observed solubility of a salt and the concentrations of the component ions in the solution. However, this procedure is fraught with difficulties. For example, when we calculated the K_{sp} for Bi_2S_3 earlier, no allowance was made for the fact that S^{2-} is an excellent base, causing a significant amount of the reaction

$$S^{2-}(aq) + H_2O(l) \rightleftharpoons HS^-(aq) + OH^-(aq)$$

to occur in aqueous solution. Thus, although we assumed in the earlier calculation that all of the sulfide from dissolving Bi_2S_3 exists as S^{2-} in solution, this is clearly not the case. The solubility of a salt containing a basic anion can be calculated accurately by simultaneously considering the K_{sp} and K_b equilibria. However, we will not show that calculation here.

Another complication that clouds the relationship between the measured solubility of a salt and its K_{sp} value is ion pairing. For example, when $CaSO_4$ dissolves in water, the solution contains

$$Ca^{2+}(s), \qquad SO_4^{2-}(aq), \qquad \text{and} \qquad CaSO_4(aq)$$

the last representing an ion pair surrounded by water molecules:

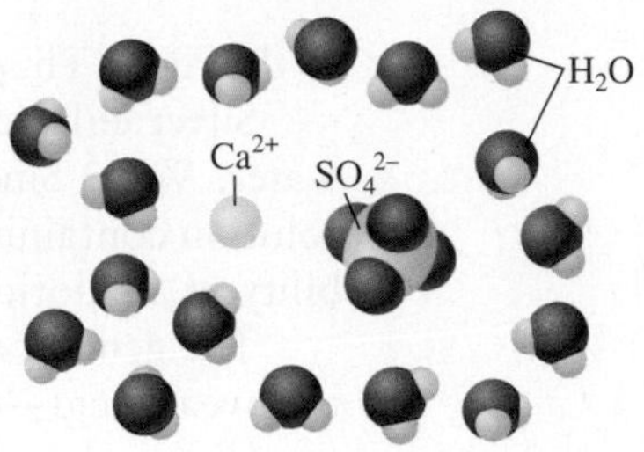

Therefore, from a measured solubility of $CaSO_4$ of $\approx 10^{-3}\ M$, we cannot safely assume that

$$[Ca^{2+}] = [SO_4^{2-}] = 10^{-3}\ M$$

since significant numbers of Ca^{2+} and SO_4^{2-} might be present as ion pairs. In very accurate solubility calculations, the activities of the ions are used instead of the stoichiometric concentrations that we have used in this chapter. In obtaining the ion activities, corrections are made for effects such as ion pairing. However, these calculations are beyond the scope of our treatment of solubility.

Yet another complication in K_{sp} calculations involves the formation of complex ions. For example, when AgCl is dissolved in water, some of the ions combine to form $AgCl_2^-$, a complex ion. Thus a saturated solution of AgCl will contain at least the ions Ag^+, Cl^-, and $AgCl_2^-$. In addition, other complex ions such as $AgCl_3^{2-}$ may exist as well as AgCl ion pairs. Again, the assumption that the concentrations of Ag^+ and Cl^- ions can be obtained directly from the measured solubility of AgCl is suspect. These effects can be corrected for by treating the solubility and complex ion equilibria simultaneously.

The point is this: The assumption that the ion concentrations for a particular solid can be obtained directly from its observed solubility causes our results to be, at best, approximations. We will not deal here with the procedures for correcting solubility calculations for these various effects.*

pH and Solubility

The pH of a solution can affect a salt's solubility quite significantly. For example, magnesium hydroxide dissolves according to the equilibrium

$$Mg(OH)_2(s) \rightleftharpoons Mg^{2+}(aq) + 2OH^-(aq)$$

*For additional information, see J. M. Bonicamp, et al., *J. Chem. Ed.* 75 (1998): 1182.

Addition of OH^- ions (an increase in pH) will, by the common ion effect, force the equilibrium to the left, decreasing the solubility of $Mg(OH)_2$. On the other hand, an addition of H^+ ions (a decrease in pH) increases the solubility because OH^- ions are removed from solution by reacting with the added H^+ ions. In response to the lower concentration of OH^-, the equilibrium position moves to the right. This explains how a suspension of solid $Mg(OH)_2$, known as milk of magnesia, dissolves in the stomach to combat excess acidity.

This concept also applies to salts with other types of anions. For example, the solubility of silver phosphate (Ag_3PO_4) is greater in acid than in pure water because the PO_4^{3-} ion is a strong base that reacts with H^+ to form the HPO_4^{2-} ion. The reaction

$$H^+ + PO_4^{3-} \longrightarrow HPO_4^{2-}$$

occurs in acidic solution, thus lowering the concentration of PO_4^{3-} and shifting the solubility equilibrium

$$Ag_3PO_4(s) \rightleftharpoons 3Ag^+(aq) + PO_4^{3-}(aq)$$

to the right. This in turn increases the solubility of silver phosphate.

Silver chloride (AgCl), however, has the same solubility in acid as in pure water. Why? Since the Cl^- ion is a very weak base, the addition of H^+ to a solution containing Cl^- does not affect $[Cl^-]$ and thus has no effect on the solubility of a chloride salt.

The general rule is that if the anion X^- is an effective base—that is, if HX is a weak acid—the salt MX will show increased solubility in an acidic solution. Examples of common anions that are effective bases are OH^-, S^{2-}, CO_3^{2-}, $C_2O_4^{2-}$, and CrO_4^{2-}. Salts involving these anions are much more soluble in an acidic solution than in pure water.

As mentioned at the beginning of this chapter, one practical result of the increased solubility of carbonates in acid is the formation of huge limestone caves such as Mammoth Cave in Kentucky and Carlsbad Caverns in New Mexico. Carbon dioxide dissolved in groundwater makes it acidic, increasing the solubility of calcium carbonate and eventually producing huge caverns. As the carbon dioxide escapes to the air, the pH of the dripping water goes up and the calcium carbonate precipitates, forming stalactites and stalagmites.

8.9 Precipitation and Qualitative Analysis

So far we have considered solids dissolving in aqueous solutions. Now we will consider the reverse process—the formation of precipitates. When solutions are mixed, various reactions can occur. We have already considered acid–base reactions in some detail. In this section we show how to predict whether a precipitate will form when two solutions are mixed. We will use the **ion product**, which is defined just like the K_{sp} expression for a given solid except that *initial concentrations are used* instead of equilibrium concentrations. For solid CaF_2 the expression for the ion product Q is written

$$Q = [Ca^{2+}]_0[F^-]_0^2$$

If we add a solution containing Ca^{2+} ions to a solution containing F^- ions, a precipitate may or may not form, depending on the concentrations of these ions in the mixed solution. To predict whether precipitation will occur, we consider the relationship between Q and K_{sp}:

If Q *is greater than* K_{sp}, precipitation occurs and will continue until the concentrations of ions remaining in solution satisfy K_{sp}.
If Q *is less than* K_{sp}, no precipitation occurs.

Sometimes we will want to do more than simply predict whether precipitation occurs; we will want to calculate the equilibrium concentrations in the solution after precipitation is complete. For example, we will next calculate the equilibrium concentrations of Pb^{2+} and I^- ions in a solution formed by mixing 100.0 mL of 0.0500 *M* $Pb(NO_3)_2$ and 200.0 mL of 0.100 *M* NaI. First, we must determine whether solid PbI_2 ($K_{sp} = 1.4 \times 10^{-8}$) forms when the solutions are mixed. To do so, we first calculate $[Pb^{2+}]_0$ and $[I^-]_0$ before any reaction occurs:

$$[Pb^{2+}]_0 = \frac{\text{mmol of } Pb^{2+}}{\text{mL of solution}} = \frac{(100.0 \text{ mL})(0.0500 \text{ mmol/mL})}{300.0 \text{ mL}} = 1.67 \times 10^{-2} M$$

$$[I^-]_0 = \frac{\text{mmol of } I^-}{\text{mL of solution}} = \frac{(200.0 \text{ mL})(0.100 \text{ mmol/mL})}{300.0 \text{ mL}} = 6.67 \times 10^{-2} M$$

The ion product for PbI_2 is

$$Q = [Pb^{2+}]_0[I^-]_0^2 = (1.67 \times 10^{-2})(6.67 \times 10^{-2})^2 = 7.43 \times 10^{-5}$$

Since Q is greater than K_{sp}, a precipitate of PbI_2 will form.

Note that since the K_{sp} for PbI_2 is quite small (1.4×10^{-8}), only very small quantities of Pb^{2+} and I^- can coexist in aqueous solution. In other words, when Pb^{2+} and I^- are mixed, most of these ions will precipitate out as PbI_2. That is, the reaction

The equilibrium constant for formation of solid PbI_2 is $1/K_{sp}$, or 7×10^7, so this equilibrium lies far to the right.

$$Pb^{2+}(aq) + 2I^-(aq) \longrightarrow PbI_2(s)$$

which is the reverse of the dissolution reaction, goes essentially to completion.

If, when two solutions are mixed, a reaction that goes virtually to completion occurs, it is essential to do the stoichiometric calculations before considering the equilibrium calculations. In this case we let the system go completely in the direction toward which it tends. Then we let it adjust back to equilibrium. If we let Pb^{2+} and I^- react to completion, we have the following calculations:

	Pb^{2+}	+	$2I^-$	$\longrightarrow$	PbI_2
Before reaction:	(100.0 mL)(0.0500 *M*) = 5.00 mmol		(200.0 mL)(0.100 *M*) = 20.0 mmol		The amount of PbI_2 formed does not influence the equilibrium
After reaction:	0 mmol		20.0 − 2(5.00) = 10.0 mmol		

Next we must allow the system to reach equilibrium. At equilibrium $[Pb^{2+}]$ is not zero, because the reaction really does not quite go to completion. The best way to think about this is that once the PbI_2 is formed, a very small amount redissolves to reach equilibrium. Since I^- is in excess, this PbI_2 is dissolving into a solution that contains 10.0 mmol of I^- per 300.0 mL of solution, or 3.33×10^{-2} *M* I^-.

We can state the resulting problem as follows: What is the solubility of solid PbI_2 in a 3.33×10^{-2} *M* NaI solution? The lead iodide dissolves according to the equation

$$PbI_2(s) \rightleftharpoons Pb^{2+}(aq) + 2I^-(aq)$$

The concentrations are as follows:

Initial Concentration (mol/L)		Equilibrium Concentration (mol/L)
$[Pb^{2+}]_0 = 0$ $[I^-]_0 = 3.33 \times 10^{-2}$	$\xrightarrow[\text{dissolves}]{x \text{ mol/L } PbI_2(s)}$	$[Pb^{2+}] = x$ $[I^-] = 3.33 \times 10^{-2} + 2x$

Substituting into the expression for K_{sp} gives

$$K_{sp} = 1.4 \times 10^{-8} = [Pb^{2+}][I^-]^2 = (x)(3.33 \times 10^{-2} + 2x)^2$$
$$\approx (x)(3.33 \times 10^{-2})^2$$

Then
$$[Pb^{2+}] = x = 1.3 \times 10^{-5}\ M$$
$$[I^-] = 3.33 \times 10^{-2}\ M$$

Note that $3.33 \times 10^{-2} \gg 2x$, so the approximation is valid. These Pb^{2+} and I^- concentrations thus represent the equilibrium concentrations in the solution formed by mixing 100.0 mL of 0.0500 M $Pb(NO_3)_2$ and 200.0 mL of 0.100 M NaI.

Selective Precipitation

Mixtures of metal ions in aqueous solution are often separated by **selective precipitation**—that is, by using a reagent whose anion forms a precipitate with only one of the metal ions in the mixture. For example, suppose we have a solution containing both Ba^{2+} and Ag^+ ions. If NaCl is added to the solution, AgCl precipitates as a white solid, but since $BaCl_2$ is soluble, the Ba^{2+} ions remain in solution.

EXAMPLE 8.13

A solution contains 1.0×10^{-4} M Cu^+ and 2.0×10^{-3} M Pb^{2+}. If a source of I^- is added to this solution gradually, will PbI_2 ($K_{sp} = 1.4 \times 10^{-8}$) or CuI ($K_{sp} = 5.3 \times 10^{-12}$) precipitate first? Specify the concentration of I^- necessary to begin precipitation of each salt.

Solution For PbI_2 the K_{sp} expression is

$$1.4 \times 10^{-8} = K_{sp} = [Pb^{2+}][I^-]^2$$

Since $[Pb^{2+}]$ in this solution is known to be 2.0×10^{-3} M, the greatest concentration of I^- that can be present without causing precipitation of PbI_2 can be calculated from the K_{sp} expression:

$$1.4 \times 10^{-8} = [Pb^{2+}][I^-]^2 = (2.0 \times 10^{-3})[I^-]^2$$
$$[I^-] = 2.6 \times 10^{-3}\ M$$

Any I^- in excess of this concentration will cause solid PbI_2 to form.

Similarly, for CuI the K_{sp} expression is

$$5.3 \times 10^{-12} = K_{sp} = [Cu^+][I^-] = (1.0 \times 10^{-4})[I^-]$$

and
$$[I^-] = 5.3 \times 10^{-8}\ M$$

A concentration of I^- in excess of 5.3×10^{-8} M will cause formation of solid CuI.

When KI(*aq*) is added to a solution containing 1.0×10^{-4} *M* Cu^+ and 2.0×10^{-3} *M* Pb^{2+}, white CuI(*s*) precipitates first.

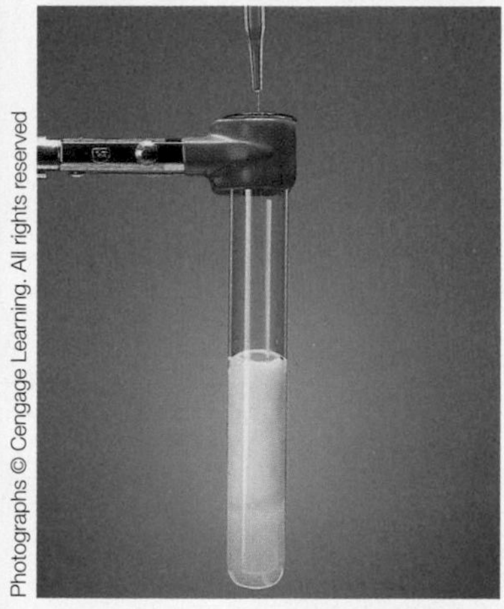
Yellow $PbI_2(s)$ precipitates next.

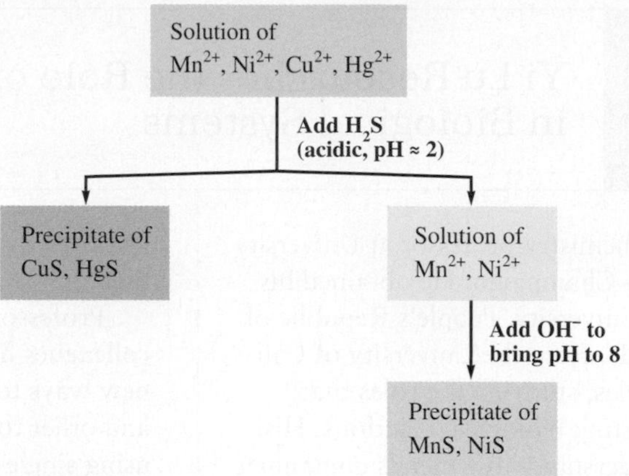

Figure 8.12
The separation of Cu^{2+} and Hg^{2+} from Ni^{2+} and Mn^{2+} using H_2S. At a low pH, $[S^{2-}]$ is relatively low and only the very insoluble HgS and CuS precipitate. When OH^- is added to lower $[H^+]$, the value of $[S^{2-}]$ increases, and MnS and NiS precipitate.

As I^- is added to the mixed solution, CuI will precipitate first, since the $[I^-]$ required is less. Therefore, Cu^+ can be separated from Pb^{2+} by using this reagent.

Since metal sulfide salts differ dramatically in their solubilities, the sulfide ion is often used to separate metal ions by selective precipitation. For example, consider a solution containing a mixture of 10^{-3} *M* Fe^{2+} and 10^{-3} *M* Mn^{2+}. Since FeS ($K_{sp} = 3.7 \times 10^{-19}$) is much less soluble than MnS ($K_{sp} = 2.3 \times 10^{-13}$), careful addition of S^{2-} to the mixture will precipitate Fe^{2+} as FeS, leaving Mn^{2+} in solution.

One real advantage of using the sulfide ion as a precipitating reagent is that because it is basic, its concentration can be controlled by regulating the pH of the solution. H_2S is a diprotic acid that dissociates in two steps, as shown in the following reactions:

$$H_2S(aq) \rightleftharpoons H^+(aq) + HS^-(aq) \qquad K_{a_1} = 1.0 \times 10^{-7}$$

$$HS^-(aq) \rightleftharpoons H^+(aq) + S^{2-}(aq) \qquad K_{a_2} \approx 10^{-19}$$

Note from the small K_{a_2} value that the S^{2-} ion has a high affinity for protons. In an acidic solution (large $[H^+]$), $[S^{2-}]$ will be relatively small, since under these conditions the dissociation equilibria will lie far to the left. On the other hand, in a basic solution, $[S^{2-}]$ will be relatively large, since the very small value of $[H^+]$ will pull both equilibria to the right, producing relatively large amounts of S^{2-}.

Thus the most insoluble sulfide salts, such as CuS ($K_{sp} = 8.5 \times 10^{-45}$) and HgS ($K_{sp} = 1.6 \times 10^{-54}$), can be precipitated from an acidic solution, leaving the more soluble ones, such as MnS ($K_{sp} = 2.3 \times 10^{-13}$) and NiS ($K_{sp} = 3 \times 10^{-21}$), still dissolved. The more soluble sulfides can then be precipitated by making the solution slightly basic. This procedure is diagramed in Fig. 8.12.

We can directly compare K_{sp} values to find relative solubilities because FeS and MnS produce the same number of ions in solution.

Qualitative Analysis

The classic scheme for **qualitative analysis** of a mixture containing all the common cations (listed in Fig. 8.13) involves first separating the cations into five major groups based on solubilities. (These groups are not directly related to the groups of the periodic table.) Each group is then treated further to separate and

Chemistry Explorers

Yi Lu Researches the Role of Metals in Biological Systems

Professor Lu is a chemistry professor at University of Illinois, Urbana–Champaign. He obtained his B.S. from Beijing University, People's Republic of China, and his Ph.D. from the University of California at Los Angeles, studying the roles that metals play in assisting biological reactions. His main goal is to understand how metals containing catalysts work. This knowledge could lead to the design of more efficient catalysts for processes involved in renewable energy, destroying environmental pollutants, fighting diseases such as AIDS, among others.

Based on their knowledge of metal ion chemistry, Professor Lu and his coworkers have designed a quick and accurate method to test for lead in paint and water. Detection of lead is important because lead is very toxic, especially to children. Studies have shown that children exposed to lead can suffer behavioral problems, learning disabilities, and, in severe cases, even death. Lead exposure is a particular problem in old houses where lead-based paint was used.

Courtesy, Yi Lu/University of Illinois at Urbana

Yi Lu

Professor Lu and his colleagues have found new ways to test for lead and other toxic metals using single-strand DNA molecules that change color when they interact with metals such as lead. The colorimetric test for lead involves dipping a treated "indicator" paper into the water to be tested and requires only about 2 minutes to show the result. The test for paint requires extraction of lead from the paint; the whole process takes about 20 minutes. Professor Lu has founded a company (DzymeTech), which is planning to develop a low-cost, easy-to-use kit that can be used to test for possible lead contamination. This should significantly lower the incidence of lead poisoning.

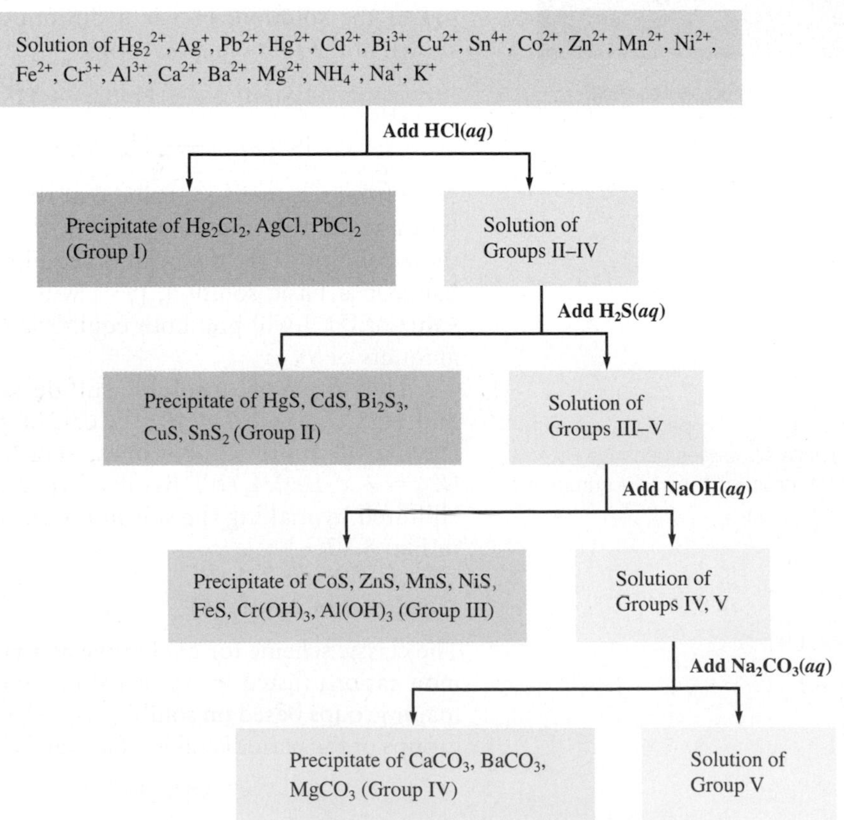

Figure 8.13
A schematic diagram of the classic method for separating the common cations by selective precipitation.

identify the individual ions. We will be concerned here only with separation of the major groups.

- **Group I—insoluble chlorides.**

  When dilute aqueous HCl is added to a solution containing a mixture of the common cations, only Ag^+, Pb^{2+}, and Hg_2^{2+} will precipitate as insoluble chlorides. All other chlorides are soluble and remain in solution. The Group I precipitate is removed, leaving the other ions in solution for treatment with sulfide ion.

- **Group II—sulfides insoluble in acid solution.**

  After the insoluble chlorides are removed, the solution is still acidic, since HCl was added. If H_2S is added to this solution, only the most insoluble sulfides (those of Hg^{2+}, Cd^{2+}, Bi^{3+}, Cu^{2+}, and Sn^{4+}) will precipitate, since $[S^{2-}]$ is relatively low because of the high concentration of H^+. The more soluble sulfides will remain dissolved under these conditions. The precipitate of the insoluble salts is removed.

- **Group III—sulfides insoluble in basic solution.**

  The solution is made basic at this stage and more H_2S is added. As we saw earlier, a basic solution produces a higher $[S^{2-}]$, which leads to precipitation of the more soluble sulfides. The cations precipitated as sulfides at this stage are Co^{2+}, Zn^{2+}, Mn^{2+}, Ni^{2+}, and Fe^{2+}. If any Cr^{3+} and Al^{3+} ions are present, they will also precipitate, but as insoluble hydroxides (remember that the solution is now basic). The precipitate is separated from the solution containing the rest of the ions.

- **Group IV—insoluble carbonates.**

  At this point all the cations have been precipitated except those from Groups 1A and 2A of the periodic table. The Group 2A cations form insoluble carbonates and can be precipitated by the addition of CO_3^{2-}. For example, Ba^{2+}, Ca^{2+}, and Mg^{2+} form solid carbonates and can be removed from the solution.

- **Group V—alkali metal and ammonium ions.**

  The only ions remaining in solution at this point are the Group 1A cations and the NH_4^+ ion, all of which form soluble salts with the common anions.

(top) Flame test for potassium.
(bottom) Flame test for sodium.

From left to right, cadmium sulfide, chromium(III) hydroxide, aluminum hydroxide, and nickel(II) hydroxide.

The Group 1A cations are usually identified by the characteristic colors they produce when heated in a flame. These colors are caused by the emission spectra of these ions.

The qualitative analysis scheme for cations based on the selective precipitation procedure described above is summarized in Fig. 8.13.

8.10 Complex Ion Equilibria

A **complex ion** is a charged species consisting of a metal ion surrounded by *ligands.* A ligand is a molecule or an ion having a lone pair of electrons that can be donated to the metal ion to form a covalent bond. Some common ligands are H_2O, NH_3, Cl^-, and CN^-. The number of ligands attached to a metal ion is called the *coordination number*. The most common coordination numbers are 6, for example, in $Co(H_2O)_6^{2+}$ and $Ni(NH_3)_6^{2+}$; 4, for example, in $CoCl_4^{2-}$ and $Cu(NH_3)_4^{2+}$; and 2, for example, in $Ag(NH_3)_2^+$; but others are known.

The properties of complex ions will be discussed in more detail in Chapter 19. For now we will just look at the equilibria involving these species. Metal ions add ligands one at a time in steps characterized by equilibrium constants called **formation constants,** or **stability constants.** For example, when solutions containing Ag^+ ions and NH_3 molecules are mixed, the following reactions take place:

$$Ag^+(aq) + NH_3(aq) \rightleftharpoons Ag(NH_3)^+(aq) \qquad K_1 = 2.1 \times 10^3$$
$$Ag(NH_3)^+(aq) + NH_3(aq) \rightleftharpoons Ag(NH_3)_2^+(aq) \qquad K_2 = 8.2 \times 10^3$$

where K_1 and K_2 are the formation constants for the two steps. In a solution containing Ag^+ and NH_3, all the species—NH_3, Ag^+, $Ag(NH_3)^+$, and $Ag(NH_3)_2^+$—exist at equilibrium. Calculating the concentrations of all these components can be complicated. However, usually the total concentration of the ligand is much larger than the total concentration of the metal ion, and approximations can greatly simplify the problems.

For example, consider a solution prepared by mixing 100.0 mL of 2.0 *M* NH_3 with 100.0 mL of 1.0×10^{-3} *M* $AgNO_3$. *Before any reaction occurs,* the mixed solution contains the major species Ag^+, NO_3^-, NH_3, and H_2O. What reaction or reactions will occur in this solution? From our discussions of acid–base chemistry, we know that one reaction is

$$NH_3(aq) + H_2O(l) \rightleftharpoons NH_4^+(aq) + OH^-(aq)$$

However, we are interested in the reaction between NH_3 and Ag^+ to form complex ions, and since the position of the preceding equilibrium lies far to the left (K_b for NH_3 is 1.8×10^{-5}), we can neglect the amount of NH_3 consumed in the reaction with water. Thus, before any complex ion formation occurs, the concentrations in the mixed solution are

$$[Ag^+]_0 = \frac{(100.0\text{ mL})(1.0 \times 10^{-3}\ M)}{\underbrace{200.0\text{ mL}}_{\text{Total volume}}} = 5.0 \times 10^{-4}\ M$$

$$[NH_3]_0 = \frac{(100.0\text{ mL})(2.0\ M)}{200.0\text{ mL}} = 1.0\ M$$

As mentioned already, the Ag^+ ion reacts with NH_3 in a stepwise manner to form $AgNH_3^+$ and then $Ag(NH_3)_2^+$:

$$Ag^+(aq) + NH_3(aq) \rightleftharpoons Ag(NH_3)^+(aq) \qquad K_1 = 2.1 \times 10^3$$
$$AgNH_3^+(aq) + NH_3(aq) \rightleftharpoons Ag(NH_3)_2^+(aq) \qquad K_2 = 8.2 \times 10^3$$

Since both K_1 and K_2 are large, and because there is a large excess of NH_3, *both reactions can be assumed to go essentially to completion.* This is equivalent to writing the net reaction in the solution as follows:

$$Ag^+ + 2NH_3 \longrightarrow Ag(NH_3)_2{}^+$$

The stoichiometric calculations are summarized below.

	Ag^+	+	$2NH_3$	$\longrightarrow$	$Ag(NH_3)_2{}^+$
Before reaction:	$5.0 \times 10^{-4}\ M$		$1.0\ M$		0
After reaction:	0		$1.0 - 2(5.0 \times 10^{-4}) \approx 1.0\ M$		$5.0 \times 10^{-4}\ M$
			↗ Twice as much NH_3 as Ag^+ is required		

Note that in this case we have used molarities when performing the calculations and we have assumed this reaction to be complete, using all the original Ag^+ to form $Ag(NH_3)_2{}^+$. In reality, a *very small* amount of the $Ag(NH_3)_2{}^+$ formed will dissociate to produce small amounts of $Ag(NH_3)^+$ and Ag^+. However, since the amount of $Ag(NH_3)_2{}^+$ dissociating will be so small, we can safely assume that $[Ag(NH_3)_2{}^+]$ is $5.0 \times 10^{-4}\ M$ at equilibrium. Also, we know that since so little NH_3 has been consumed, $[NH_3]$ is essentially $1.0\ M$ at equilibrium. We can use these concentrations to calculate $[Ag^+]$ and $[Ag(NH_3)^+]$ using the K_1 and K_2 expressions.

To calculate the equilibrium concentration of $Ag(NH_3)^+$, we use

$$K_2 = 8.2 \times 10^3 = \frac{[Ag(NH_3)_2{}^+]}{[Ag(NH_3)^+][NH_3]}$$

since $[Ag(NH_3)_2{}^+]$ and $[NH_3]$ are known. Rearranging and solving for $[Ag(NH_3)^+]$ gives

$$[Ag(NH_3)^+] = \frac{[Ag(NH_3)_2{}^+]}{K_2[NH_3]} = \frac{5.0 \times 10^{-4}}{(8.2 \times 10^{-3})(1.0)} = 6.1 \times 10^{-8}\ M$$

Now the equilibrium concentration of Ag^+ can be calculated by using K_1:

$$K_1 = 2.1 \times 10^3 = \frac{[Ag(NH_3)^+]}{[Ag^+][NH_3]} = \frac{6.1 \times 10^{-8}}{[Ag^+](1.0)}$$

$$[Ag^+] = \frac{6.1 \times 10^{-8}}{(2.1 \times 10^3)(1.0)} = 2.9 \times 10^{-11}\ M$$

So far we have assumed that $Ag(NH_3)_2{}^+$ is the dominant silver-containing species in solution. Is this a valid assumption? The calculated concentrations are

$$[Ag(NH_3)_2{}^+] = 5.0 \times 10^{-4}\ M$$
$$[AgNH_3{}^+] = 6.1 \times 10^{-8}\ M$$
$$[Ag^+] = 2.9 \times 10^{-11}\ M$$

These values clearly support the conclusion that

$$[Ag(NH_3)_2{}^+] \gg [AgNH_3{}^+] \gg [Ag^+]$$

Essentially all the Ag^+ ions originally present end up in $Ag(NH_3)_2{}^+$ at equilibrium.

Thus the assumption that $[Ag(NH_3)_2{}^+]$ is dominant is valid, and the calculated concentrations are correct.

This analysis shows that although complex ion equilibria have many species present and look complicated, the calculations are actually quite straightforward, especially if the ligand is present in large excess.

EXAMPLE 8.14

Calculate the concentrations of Ag^+, $Ag(S_2O_3)^-$, and $Ag(S_2O_3)_2^{3-}$ in a solution prepared by mixing 150.0 mL of 1.00×10^{-3} *M* $AgNO_3$ with 200.0 mL of 5.00 *M* $Na_2S_2O_3$. The stepwise formation equilibria are

$$Ag^+(aq) + S_2O_3^{2-}(aq) \rightleftharpoons Ag(S_2O_3)^-(aq) \qquad K_1 = 7.4 \times 10^8$$

$$Ag(S_2O_3)^-(aq) + S_2O_3^{2-}(aq) \rightleftharpoons Ag(S_2O_3)_2^{3-}(aq) \qquad K_2 = 3.9 \times 10^4$$

Solution The concentrations of the ligand and metal ion in the mixed solution *before any reaction occurs* are

$$[Ag^+]_0 = \frac{(150.0 \text{ mL})(1.00 \times 10^{-3}\ M)}{150.0 \text{ mL} + 200.0 \text{ mL}} = 4.29 \times 10^{-4}\ M$$

$$[S_2O_3^{2-}]_0 = \frac{(200.0 \text{ mL})(5.00\ M)}{150.0 \text{ mL} + 200.0 \text{ mL}} = 2.86\ M$$

Since $[S_2O_3^{2-}]_0 \gg [Ag^+]_0$, and because K_1 and K_2 are large, both formation reactions can be assumed to go to completion. The net reaction in the solution is as follows:

	Ag^+	+	$2S_2O_3^{2-}$	$\longrightarrow$	$Ag(S_2O_3)_2^{3-}$
Before reaction:	$4.29 \times 10^{-4}\ M$		$2.86\ M$		0
After reaction:	≈ 0		$2.86 - 2(4.29 \times 10^{-4}) \approx 2.86\ M$		$4.29 \times 10^{-4}\ M$

Note that Ag^+ is limiting and that the amount of $S_2O_3^{2-}$ consumed is negligible. Also note that since all these species are in the same solution, the molarities can be used to do the stoichiometry problem.

Of course, the concentrations calculated earlier do not represent the equilibrium concentrations. For example, the concentration of Ag^+ is not zero at equilibrium, and there is some $Ag(S_2O_3)^-$ in the solution. To calculate the equilibrium concentrations of these species, we must use the K_1 and K_2 expressions. We can calculate the concentration of $Ag(S_2O_3)^-$ from K_2:

$$3.9 \times 10^4 = K_2 = \frac{[Ag(S_2O_3)_2^{3-}]}{[Ag(S_2O_3)^-][S_2O_3^{2-}]} = \frac{4.29 \times 10^{-4}}{[Ag(S_2O_3)^-](2.86)}$$

$$[Ag(S_2O_3)^-] = 3.8 \times 10^{-9}\ M$$

We can calculate $[Ag^+]$ from K_1:

$$7.4 \times 10^8 = K_1 = \frac{[Ag(S_2O_3)^-]}{[Ag^+][S_2O_3^{2-}]} = \frac{3.8 \times 10^{-9}}{[Ag^+](2.86)}$$

$$[Ag^+] = 1.8 \times 10^{-18}\ M$$

These results show that

$$[Ag(S_2O_3)_2^{3-}] \gg [Ag(S_2O_3)^-] \gg [Ag^+]$$

Thus the assumption that essentially all the original Ag^+ is converted to $Ag(S_2O_3)_2^{3-}$ at equilibrium is valid.

Complex Ions and Solubility

Often ionic solids that are only slightly soluble in water must be dissolved in aqueous solutions. For example, when the various qualitative analysis groups are precipitated, the precipitates must be redissolved to separate the ions within

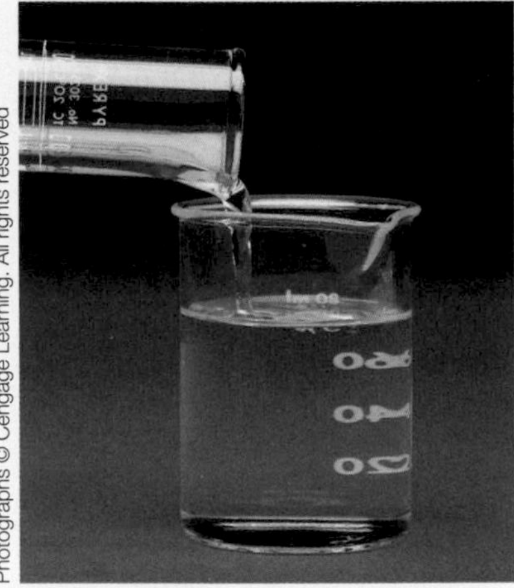

(top) Aqueous ammonia is added to silver chloride (white). (bottom) The silver chloride, insoluble in water, dissolves to form $Ag(NH_3)_2^+(aq)$ and $Cl^-(aq)$.

each group. Consider a solution of cations that contains Ag^+, Pb^{2+}, and Hg_2^{2+}, among others. When dilute aqueous HCl is added to this solution, the Group I ions will form the insoluble chlorides AgCl, $PbCl_2$, and Hg_2Cl_2. Once this mixed precipitate is separated from the solution, it must be redissolved to identify the cations individually. How can this be done? We know that some solids are more soluble in acidic than in neutral solutions. What about chloride salts? For example, can AgCl be dissolved by using a strong acid? The answer is no, because Cl^- ions have virtually no affinity for H^+ ions in aqueous solution. The position of the dissolution equilibrium

$$AgCl(s) \rightleftharpoons Ag^+(aq) + Cl^-(aq)$$

is not affected by the presence of H^+.

How can we pull the dissolution equilibrium to the right, even though Cl^- is an extremely weak base? The key is to lower the concentration of Ag^+ in solution by forming complex ions. For example, Ag^+ reacts with excess NH_3 to form the stable complex ion $Ag(NH_3)_2^+$. As a result, AgCl is quite soluble in concentrated ammonia solutions. The relevant reactions are

$$AgCl(s) \rightleftharpoons Ag^+(aq) + Cl^-(aq) \qquad K_{sp} = 1.6 \times 10^{-10}$$

$$Ag^+(aq) + NH_3(aq) \rightleftharpoons Ag(NH_3)^+(aq) \qquad K_1 = 2.1 \times 10^3$$

$$Ag(NH_3)^+(aq) + NH_3(aq) \rightleftharpoons Ag(NH_3)_2^+(aq) \qquad K_2 = 8.2 \times 10^3$$

The Ag^+ ion produced by dissolving solid AgCl combines with NH_3 to form $Ag(NH_3)_2^+$. This causes more AgCl to dissolve until the point at which

$$[Ag^+][Cl^-] = K_{sp} = 1.6 \times 10^{-10}$$

Here $[Ag^+]$ refers only to the Ag^+ ion that is present as a separate species in solution. It does *not* represent the total silver content of the solution, which is

$$[Ag]_{\text{total dissolved}} = [Ag^+] + [AgNH_3^+] + [Ag(NH_3)_2^+]$$

As we saw in the preceding section, virtually all the Ag^+ from the dissolved AgCl ends up in the complex ion $Ag(NH_3)_2^+$, so we can represent the dissolving of solid AgCl in excess NH_3 by the equation

$$AgCl(s) + 2NH_3(aq) \rightleftharpoons Ag(NH_3)_2^+(aq) + Cl^-(aq)$$

Since this equation is the *sum of the three stepwise reactions* given above, the equilibrium constant for this reaction is the product of the constants for the three reactions. (Demonstrate this result to yourself by multiplying the three expressions for K_{sp}, K_1, and K_2.) The equilibrium expression is

When reactions are added, the equilibrium constant for the overall process is the product of the constants for the individual reactions.

$$K = \frac{[Ag(NH_3)_2^+][Cl^-]}{[NH_3]^2}$$

$$= K_{sp} \times K_1 \times K_2$$

$$= (1.6 \times 10^{-10})(2.1 \times 10^3)(8.2 \times 10^3)$$

$$= 2.8 \times 10^{-3}$$

Using this expression, we will now calculate the solubility of solid AgCl in a 10.0 *M* NH_3 solution. If we let x be the solubility (in mol/L) of AgCl in this solution, we can then write the following expressions for the equilibrium concentrations of the pertinent species:

$$[Cl^-] = x$$

$$[Ag(NH_3)_2^+] = x$$

(x mol/L of AgCl dissolves to produce x mol/L of Cl^- and x mol/L of $Ag(NH_3)_2^+$)

$$[NH_3] = 10.0 - 2x$$

(Formation of x mol/L of $Ag(NH_3)_2^+$ requires $2x$ mol/L of NH_3, since each complex ion contains two NH_3 ligands)

Substituting these concentrations into the equilibrium expression gives

$$K = 2.8 \times 10^{-3} = \frac{[Ag(NH_3)_2^+][Cl^-]}{[NH_3]^2} = \frac{(x)(x)}{(10.0 - 2x)^2} = \frac{x^2}{(10.0 - 2x)^2}$$

No approximations are necessary here. Taking the square root of both sides of the equation gives

$$\sqrt{2.8 \times 10^{-3}} = \frac{x}{10.0 - 2x}$$

$$x = 0.48 \text{ mol/L} = \text{solubility of AgCl}(s) \text{ in } 10.0\ M\ NH_3$$

Thus the solubility of AgCl in 10.0 M NH_3 is much greater than in pure water, which is

$$\sqrt{K_{sp}} = 1.3 \times 10^{-5} \text{ mol/L}$$

In this chapter we have considered two strategies for dissolving a water-insoluble ionic solid. If the *anion* of the solid is a good base, the solubility is greatly increased by acidifying the solution. In cases where the anion is not sufficiently basic, the ionic solid can often be dissolved in a solution containing a ligand that forms stable complex ions with its *cation*.

Sometimes solids are so insoluble that combinations of reactions are needed to dissolve them. For example, to dissolve the extremely insoluble HgS ($K_{sp} - 1.6 \times 10^{-54}$), we must use a mixture of concentrated HCl and concentrated HNO_3, called *aqua regia*. The H^+ ions in the aqua regia react with the S^{2-} ions to form H_2S, and Cl^- reacts with Hg^{2+} to form various complex ions such as $HgCl_4^{2-}$. In addition, NO_3^- oxidizes S^{2-} to elemental sulfur. These processes lower the concentrations of Hg^{2+} and S^{2-} and thus promote the solubility of HgS.

Since the solubility of many salts increases with temperature, simple heating is sometimes enough to make a salt sufficiently soluble. For example, earlier in this section we considered the mixed chloride precipitates of the Group I ions—$PbCl_2$, AgCl, and Hg_2Cl_2. The effect of temperature on the solubility of $PbCl_2$ is such that we can precipitate $PbCl_2$ with cold aqueous HCl and then redissolve it by heating the solution to near boiling. In this way, $PbCl_2$ can be separated from the silver and mercury(I) chlorides, since they are not significantly soluble in hot water. Subsequently, solid AgCl can be dissolved and separated from Hg_2Cl_2 by using aqueous ammonia. The solid Hg_2Cl_2 reacts with NH_3 to form a mixture of elemental mercury and $HgNH_2Cl$:

$$Hg_2Cl_2(s) + 2NH_3(aq) \longrightarrow \underset{\text{White}}{HgNH_2Cl(s)} + \underset{\text{Black}}{Hg(l)} + NH_4^+(aq) + Cl^-(aq)$$

The mixed precipitate appears gray. This is an oxidation–reduction reaction in which one mercury(I) ion in Hg_2Cl_2 is oxidized to Hg^{2+} in $HgNH_2Cl$ and the other mercury(I) ion is reduced to Hg, or elemental mercury.

The treatment of the Group I ions is summarized in Fig. 8.14. Note that the presence of Pb^{2+} is confirmed by adding CrO_4^{2-}, which forms bright yellow lead(II) chromate ($PbCrO_4$). Also note that H^+ added to a solution containing $Ag(NH_3)_2^+$ and Cl^- reacts with the NH_3 to form NH_4^+, thus destroying the $Ag(NH_3)_2^+$ complex. Silver chloride then re-forms:

$$2H^+(aq) + Ag(NH_3)_2^+(aq) + Cl^-(aq) \longrightarrow 2NH_4^+(aq) + AgCl(s)$$

Note that the qualitative analysis of cations by selective precipitation involves all the types of reactions we have discussed and represents an excellent application of the principles of chemical equilibrium.

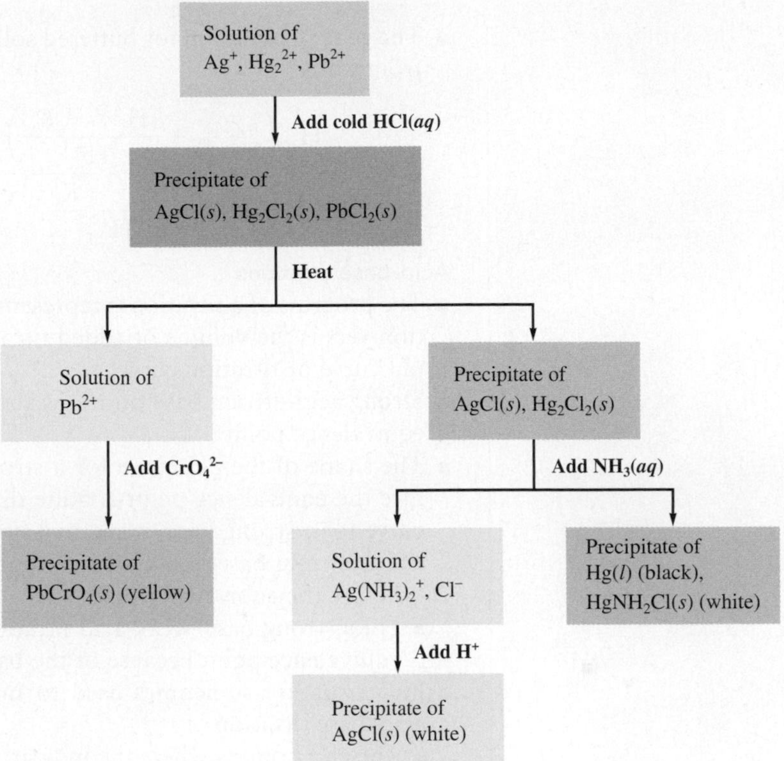

Figure 8.14
The separation of the Group I ions in the classic scheme of qualitative analysis.

Key Terms

Section 8.1
common ion
common ion effect

Section 8.2
buffered solution
Henderson–Hasselbalch equation

Section 8.4
buffer capacity

Section 8.5
pH curve (titration curve)
millimole (mmol)
equivalence point (stoichiometric point)

Section 8.6
acid–base indicator
phenolphthalein

Section 8.8
solubility product constant (solubility product)

Section 8.9
ion product
selective precipitation
qualitative analysis

Section 8.10
complex ion
formation (stability) constant

For Review

Buffered solutions

- Contains a weak acid (HA) and its salt (NaA) or a weak base (B) and its salt (BHCl)
- Resists a change in its pH when H^+ or OH^- is added
- For a buffered solution containing HA and A^-
  - The Henderson–Hasselbalch equation is useful:

$$pH = pK_a + \log\left(\frac{[A^-]}{[HA]}\right)$$

  - The capacity of the buffered solution depends on the amounts of HA and A^- present
- The most efficient buffering occurs when the $\frac{[A^-]}{[HA]}$ ratio is close to 1
- Buffering works because the amounts of HA (which reacts with added OH^-) and A^- (which reacts with added H^+) are large enough that the $\frac{[A^-]}{[HA]}$ ratio does not change significantly when strong acids or bases are added

- The general equation for buffered solutions that includes contributions from water is
- $$K_a = \frac{[H^+]\left([A^-]_0 + \dfrac{[H^+]^2 - K_w}{[H^+]}\right)}{[HA]_0 - \dfrac{[H^+]^2 - K_w}{[H^+]}}$$

Acid–base titrations

- The progress of a titration is represented by plotting the pH of the solution versus the volume of added titrant; the resulting graph is called a pH curve or titration curve
- Strong acid–strong base titrations show a sharp change in pH near the equivalence point
- The shape of the pH curve for a strong base–strong acid titration before the equivalence point is quite different from the shape of the pH curve for a strong base–weak acid titration
  - The strong base–weak acid pH curve shows the effects of buffering before the equivalence point
  - For a strong base–weak acid titration, the pH is greater than 7 at the equivalence point because of the basic properties of A^-
- Indicators are sometimes used to mark the equivalence point of an acid–base titration
  - The end point is where the indicator changes color
  - The goal is to have the end point and the equivalence point be as close as possible

Solids dissolving in water

- For a slightly soluble salt, an equilibrium is set up between the excess solid (MX) and the ions in solution:

$$MX(s) \rightleftharpoons M^+(aq) + X^-(aq)$$

- The corresponding constant is called K_{sp}:

$$K_{sp} \rightleftharpoons [M^+][X^-]$$

  - The solubility of $MX(s)$ is decreased by the presence of another source of either M^+ or X^-; this is called the common ion effect
- Predicting whether precipitation will occur when two solutions are mixed involves calculating Q for the initial concentrations
  - If $Q > K_{sp}$, precipitation occurs
  - If $Q \le K_{sp}$, no precipitation occurs

Qualitative analysis

- A mixture of ions can be separated by selective precipitation
  - The ions are first separated into groups by adding $HCl(aq)$, then $H_2S(aq)$, then $NaOH(aq)$, and finally $Na_2CO_3(aq)$
  - The ions in the groups are separated and identified by further selective dissolution and precipitation

Complex ions

- Complex ions consist of a metal ion surrounded by attached ligands
  - A ligand is a Lewis base
  - The number of ligands is called the *coordination number,* which is commonly 2, 4, or 6
- Complex ion equilibria in solution are described by formation (stability) constants
- The formation of complex ions can be used to selectively dissolve solids in the qualitative analysis scheme

Discussion Questions

These questions are designed to be considered by groups of students in class. Often these questions work well for introducing a particular topic in class.

1. What are the major species in solution after $NaHSO_4$ is dissolved in water? What happens to the pH of the solution as more $NaHSO_4$ is added? Why? Would the results vary if baking soda ($NaHCO_3$) were used instead? Explain.
2. A friend asks the following: "Consider a buffered solution made up of the weak acid HA and its salt NaA. If a strong base such as NaOH is added, the HA reacts with the OH^- to make A^-. Thus the amount of acid (HA) is decreased, and the amount of base (A^-) is increased. Analogously, adding HCl to the buffered solution forms more of the acid (HA) by reacting with the base (A^-). Thus how can we claim that a buffered solution resists changes in the pH of the solution?" How would you explain buffering to your friend?
3. Mixing together solutions of acetic acid and sodium hydroxide can make a buffered solution. Explain. How does the amount of each solution added change the effectiveness of the buffer? Would a buffered solution made by mixing HCl and NaOH be effective? Explain.
4. Sketch two pH curves, one for the titration of a weak acid with a strong base, and one for the titration of a strong acid with a strong base. How are they similar? How are they different? Account for the similarities and the differences.
5. Sketch a pH curve for the titration of a weak acid (HA) with a strong base (NaOH). List the major species, and explain how you would calculate the pH of the solution at various points, including the halfway point and the equivalence point.
6. You have a solution of the weak acid HA and add some HCl to it. What are the major species in the solution? What do you need to know to calculate the pH of the solution, and how would you use this information? How does the pH of the solution of just the HA compare with that of the final mixture? Explain.
7. You have a solution of the weak acid HA and add some of the salt NaA to it. What are the major species in the solution? What do you need to know to calculate the pH of the solution, and how would you use this information? How does the pH of the solution of just the HA compare with that of the final mixture? Explain.
8. Devise as many ways as you can to experimentally determine the K_{sp} value of a solid. Explain why each of these would work.
9. You are browsing through the *Handbook of Hypothetical Chemistry* when you come across a solid that is reported to have a K_{sp} value of zero in water at 25°C. What does this mean?
10. A friend tells you: "The constant K_{sp} of a salt is called the solubility product constant and is calculated from the concentrations of ions in the solution. Thus, if salt A dissolves to a greater extent than salt B, salt A must have a higher K_{sp} than salt B." Do you agree with your friend? Explain.
11. What happens to the K_{sp} value of a solid as the temperature of the solution changes? Consider both increasing and decreasing temperatures, and explain your answer.
12. Which is more likely to dissolve in an acidic solution, silver sulfide or silver chloride? Why?
13. You have two salts AgX and AgY with very similar K_{sp} values. You know that the K_a value for HX is much greater than the K_a value for HY. Which salt is more soluble in an acidic solution? Explain.
14. Under what circumstances can the relative solubilities of two salts be compared by directly comparing values of their solubility products?

Exercises

OWL Interactive versions of these problems may be assigned in OWL.

A blue exercise number indicates that the answer to that exercise appears at the back of this book and a solution appears in the *Solutions Guide*.

Buffers

15. Define a buffered solution. What makes up a buffered solution? Explain how buffers absorb added H^+ or OH^- with little pH change. A certain buffer is made by dissolving $NaHCO_3$ and Na_2CO_3 in some water. Write equations to show how this buffer neutralizes added H^+ and OH^-.
16. A good buffer generally contains relatively equal concentrations of a weak acid and its conjugate base. If you wanted to buffer a solution at pH = 4.00 or pH = 10.00, how would you decide which weak acid–conjugate base or weak base–conjugate acid pair to use? The second characteristic of a good buffer is good buffering capacity. What is the *capacity* of a buffer? How do the following buffers differ in capacity? How do they differ in pH?

    0.01 *M* acetic acid/0.01 *M* sodium acetate

    0.1 *M* acetic acid/0.1 *M* sodium acetate

    1.0 *M* acetic acid/1.0 *M* sodium acetate
17. How many of the following are buffered solutions? Explain your answer. *Note:* Counter-ions and water molecules have been omitted from the illustrations for clarity.

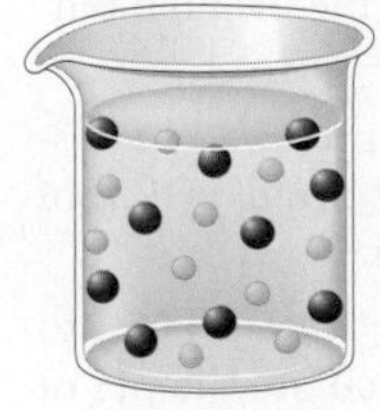

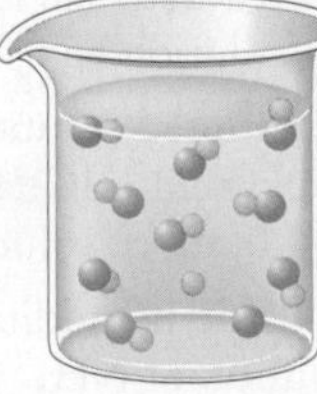

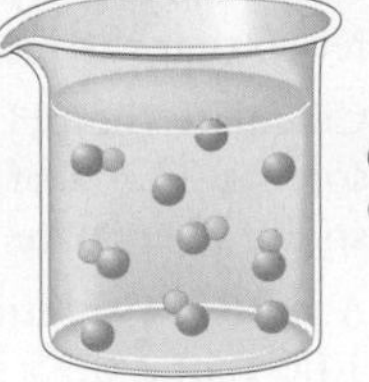

18. Which of the following can be classified as buffer solutions?
    a. 0.25 *M* HBr + 0.25 *M* HOBr
    b. 0.15 *M* $HClO_4$ + 0.20 *M* RbOH
    c. 0.50 *M* HOCl + 0.35 *M* KOCl
    d. 0.70 *M* KOH + 0.70 *M* $HONH_2$
    e. 0.85 *M* H_2NNH_2 + 0.60 *M* $H_2NNH_3NO_3$
19. Consider a buffered solution where [weak acid] > [conjugate base]. How is the pH of the solution related to the pK_a value of the weak acid? If [conjugate base] > [weak acid], how is pH related to pK_a?
20. Derive an equation analogous to the Henderson–Hasselbalch equation that relates pOH and pK_b of a buffered solution composed of a weak base and its conjugate acid, such as NH_3 and NH_4^+.
21. Calculate the pH of each of the following solutions.
    a. 0.100 *M* propanoic acid ($HC_3H_5O_2$, $K_a = 1.3 \times 10^{-5}$)
    b. 0.100 *M* sodium propanoate ($NaC_3H_5O_2$)
    c. pure H_2O
    d. 0.100 *M* $HC_3H_5O_2$ and 0.100 *M* $NaC_3H_5O_2$
22. Calculate the pH after 0.020 mole of HCl is added to 1.00 L of each of the four solutions in Exercise 21.
23. Calculate the pH after 0.020 mole of NaOH is added to 1.00 L of each of the four solutions in Exercise 21.
24. The results of Exercises 21–23 illustrate an important property of buffered solutions. Which solution in Exercise 21 is the buffered solution and what important property is illustrated by the results?
25. Calculate the pH of a solution that is 0.60 *M* HF and 1.00 *M* KF.
26. Calculate the pH of a solution that is 0.100 *M* $HONH_2$ and 0.100 *M* $HONH_3Cl$.
27. Calculate the pH after 0.10 mole of NaOH is added to 1.00 L of the solution in Exercise 25, and calculate the pH after 0.20 mole of HCl is added to 1.00 L of the solution in Exercise 25.
28. Calculate the pH after 0.020 mole of NaOH is added to 1.00 L of the solution in Exercise 26, and calculate the pH after 0.020 mole of HCl is added to 1.00 L of the solution in Exercise 26.
29. Calculate the pH of a solution that is 0.40 *M* H_2NNH_2 and 0.80 *M* $H_2NNH_3NO_3$. In order for this buffer to have pH = pK_a, would you add HCl or NaOH? What quantity (moles) of which reageant would you add to 1.0 L of the original buffer so that the resulting solution has pH = pK_a?
30. Calculate the pH of a solution that is 0.20 *M* HOCl and 0.90 *M* KOCl. In order for this buffer to have pH = pK_a, would you add HCl or NaOH? What quantity (moles) of which reagent would you add to 1.0 L of the original buffer so that the resulting solution has pH = pK_a?
31. Calculate the pH of a buffered solution prepared by dissolving 21.5 g of benzoic acid ($HC_7H_5O_2$) and 37.7 g of sodium benzoate in 200.0 mL of solution.
32. A buffered solution is made by adding 50.0 g NH_4Cl to 1.00 L of a 0.75 *M* solution of NH_3. Calculate the pH of the final solution. (Assume no volume change.)
33. Consider a solution that contains both C_5H_5N and $C_5H_5NHNO_3$. Calculate the ratio $[C_5H_5N]/[C_5H_5NH^+]$ if the solution has the following pH values.
    a. pH = 4.50
    b. pH = 5.00
    c. pH = 5.23
    d. pH = 5.50
34. How many moles of NaOH must be added to 1.0 L of 2.0 *M* $HC_2H_3O_2$ to produce a solution buffered at each pH?
    a. pH = pK_a
    b. pH = 4.00
    c. pH = 5.00
35. Calculate the number of moles of HCl(*g*) that must be added to 1.0 L of 1.0 *M* $NaC_2H_3O_2$ to produce a solution buffered at each pH.
    a. pH = pK_a
    b. pH = 4.20
    c. pH = 5.00
36. You make 1.00 L of a buffered solution (pH = 4.00) by mixing acetic acid and sodium acetate. You have 1.00 *M* solutions of each component of the buffered solution. What volume of each solution do you mix to make such a buffered solution?
37. Calculate the mass of sodium acetate that must be added to 500.0 mL of 0.200 *M* acetic acid to form a pH = 5.00 buffered solution.
38. Calculate the pH after 0.010 mole of gaseous HCl is added to 250.0 mL of each of the following buffered solutions.
    a. 0.050 *M* NH_3 and 0.15 *M* NH_4Cl
    b. 0.50 *M* NH_3 and 1.50 *M* NH_4Cl
39. An aqueous solution contains dissolved $C_6H_5NH_3Cl$ and $C_6H_5NH_2$. The concentration of $C_6H_5NH_2$ is 0.50 *M* and pH is 4.20.
    a. Calculate the concentration of $C_6H_5NH_3^+$ in this buffered solution.
    b. Calculate the pH after 4.0 g of NaOH(*s*) is added to 1.0 L of this solution. (Neglect any volume change.)
40. What volumes of 0.50 *M* HNO_2 and 0.50 *M* $NaNO_2$ must be mixed to prepare 1.00 L of a solution buffered at pH = 3.55?
41. Phosphate buffers are important in regulating the pH of intracellular fluids at pH values generally between 7.1 and 7.2.
    a. What is the concentration ratio of $H_2PO_4^-$ to HPO_4^{2-} in intracellular fluid at pH = 7.15?

    $$H_2PO_4^-(aq) \rightleftharpoons HPO_4^{2-}(aq) + H^+(aq) \quad K_a = 6.2 \times 10^{-8}$$

    b. Why is a buffer composed of H_3PO_4 and $H_2PO_4^-$ ineffective in buffering the pH of intracellular fluid?

    $$H_3PO_4(aq) \rightleftharpoons H_2PO_4^-(aq) + H^+(aq) \quad K_a = 7.5 \times 10^{-3}$$

42. Carbonate buffers are important in regulating the pH of blood at 7.40. If the carbonic acid concentration in a sample of blood is 0.0012 *M*, determine the bicarbonate ion concentration required to buffer the pH of blood at pH = 7.40.

    $$H_2CO_3(aq) \rightleftharpoons HCO_3^-(aq) + H^+(aq) \quad K_a = 4.3 \times 10^{-7}$$

43. When a person exercises, muscle contractions produce lactic acid. Moderate increases in lactic acid can be handled by the blood buffers without decreasing the pH of blood. However, excessive amounts of lactic acid can overload the blood buffer system, resulting in a lowering of the blood pH. A condition called *acidosis* is diagnosed if the blood pH falls to 7.35 or lower. Assume the primary

blood buffer system is the carbonate buffer system described in Exercise 42. Calculate what happens to the $[H_2CO_3]/[HCO_3^-]$ ratio in blood when the pH decreases from 7.40 to 7.35.

44. Which of the following mixtures would result in a buffered solution when 1.0 L of each of the two solutions are mixed?
    a. 0.1 M KOH and 0.1 M CH_3NH_3Cl
    b. 0.1 M KOH and 0.2 M CH_3NH_2
    c. 0.2 M KOH and 0.1 M CH_3NH_3Cl
    d. 0.1 M KOH and 0.2 M CH_3NH_3Cl
45. Which of the following mixtures would result in a buffered solution when 1.0 L of each of the two solutions are mixed?
    a. 0.2 M HNO_3 and 0.4 M $NaNO_3$
    b. 0.2 M HNO_3 and 0.4 M HF
    c. 0.2 M HNO_3 and 0.4 M NaF
    d. 0.2 M HNO_3 and 0.4 M NaOH
46. Calculate the pH of a solution formed by mixing 100.0 mL of 0.100 M NaF and 100.0 mL of 0.025 M HCl.
47. Consider the acids in Table 7.2. Which acid would be the best choice for preparing a pH = 7.00 buffer? Explain how to make 1.0 L of this buffer.
48. Consider the bases in Table 7.3. Which base would be the best choice for preparing a pH = 5.00 buffer? Explain how to make 1.0 L of this buffer.
49. A solution contains 1.0×10^{-6} M HOCl and an unknown concentration of KOCl. If the pH of the solution is 7.20, calculate the KOCl concentration. (*Hint:* The contribution of water to the $[H^+]$ cannot be ignored.)
50. In Section 8.3 an equation was derived for the exact treatment of HA/NaA-type buffers. What would be the expression for B/BHCl-type buffers stated in terms of K_b, $[OH^-]$, [B], and $[BH^+]$? Would it be necessary to use this exact expression to solve for the pH of a solution containing 1.0×10^{-4} M $HONH_2$ and 1.0×10^{-5} M $HONH_3Cl$? Explain.
51. Consider a weak acid HA with a K_a value of 1.6×10^{-7}. Calculate the pH of a solution that is 5.0×10^{-7} M HA and 5.0×10^{-7} M NaA.

Acid–Base Titrations

52. Consider the following pH curves for 100.0 mL of two different acids with the same intital concentration each titrated by 0.10 M NaOH:

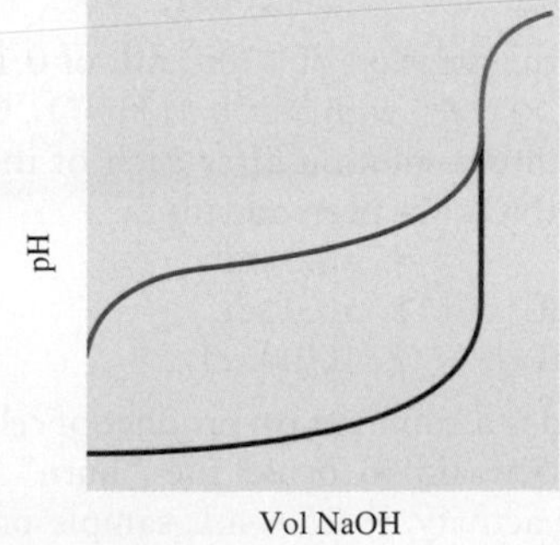

    a. Which plot represents a pH curve of a weak acid, and which plot is for a strong acid? How can you tell? Cite three differences between the plots that help you decide.
    b. In both cases the pH is relatively constant before the pH changes greatly. Does this mean that at some point in each titration each solution was a buffered solution?
    c. True or false? The equivalence point volume for each titration is the same. Explain your answer.
    d. True or false? The pH at the equivalence point for each titration is the same. Explain your answer.
53. An acid is titrated with NaOH. The following beakers are illustrations of the contents of the beaker at various times during the titration. These are presented out of order. *Note:* Counter-ions and water molecules have been omitted from the illustrations for clarity.

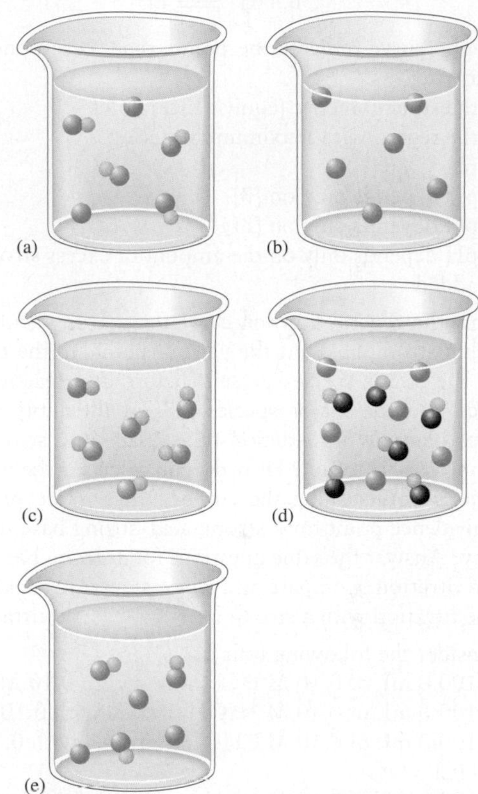

    a. Is the acid a weak or strong acid? How can you tell?
    b. Arrange the beakers in order of what the contents would look like as the titration progresses.
    c. For which beaker would pH = pK_a? Explain your answer.
    d. Which beaker represents the equivalence point of the titration? Explain your answer.
    e. For which beaker would the K_a value for the acid not be necessary to determine the pH? Explain your answer.
54. Consider the titration of a generic weak acid HA with a strong base that gives the following titration curve:

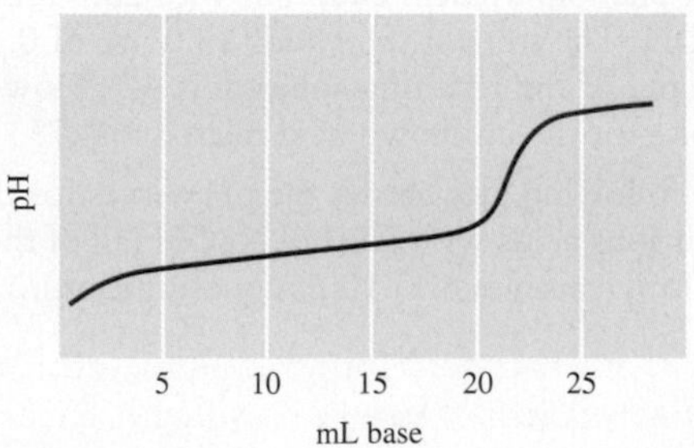

On the curve indicate the points that correspond to the following.
a. the equivalence point
b. the maximum buffering region
c. pH = pK_a
d. pH depends only on [HA]
e. pH depends only on [A^-]
f. pH depends only on the amount of excess strong base added

55. Sketch the titration curve for the titration of a generic weak base B with a strong acid. The titration reaction is

$$B + H^+ \rightleftharpoons BH^+$$

On the curve indicate the points that correspond to the following.
a. the stoichiometric (equivalence) point
b. the region with maximum buffering
c. pH = pK_a
d. pH depends only on [B]
e. pH depends only on [BH^+]
f. pH depends only on the amount of excess strong acid added

56. Draw the general titration curve for a strong acid titrated with a strong base. At the various points in the titration, list the major species present before any reaction takes place and the major species present after any reaction takes place. What reaction takes place in a strong acid–strong base titration? How do you calculate the pH at the various points along the curve? What is the pH at the equivalence point for a strong acid–strong base titration? Why? Answer the same questions for a strong base–strong acid titration. Compare and contrast a strong acid–strong base titration with a strong base–strong acid titration.

57. Consider the following four titrations:
i. 100.0 mL of 0.10 *M* HCl titrated with 0.10 *M* NaOH
ii. 100.0 mL of 0.10 *M* NaOH titrated with 0.10 *M* HCl
iii. 100.0 mL of 0.10 *M* CH_3NH_2 titrated with 0.10 *M* HCl
iv. 100.0 mL of 0.10 *M* HF titrated with 0.10 *M* NaOH

Rank the titrations in order of
a. increasing volume of titrant added to reach the equivalence point.
b. increasing pH initially before any titrant has been added.
c. increasing pH at the halfway point in equivalence.
d. increasing pH at the equivalence point.

How would the rankings change if C_5H_5N replaced CH_3NH_2 and if HOC_6H_5 replaced HF?

58. A student titrates an unknown weak acid HA to a pale-pink phenolphthalein endpoint with 25.0 mL of 0.100 *M* NaOH. The student then adds 13.0 mL of 0.100 *M* HCl. The pH of the resulting solution is 4.7. How is the value of pK_a for the unknown acid related to 4.7?

59. The following plot shows the pH curves for the titrations of various acids with 0.10 *M* NaOH (all of the acids were 50.0-mL samples of 0.10 *M* concentration).

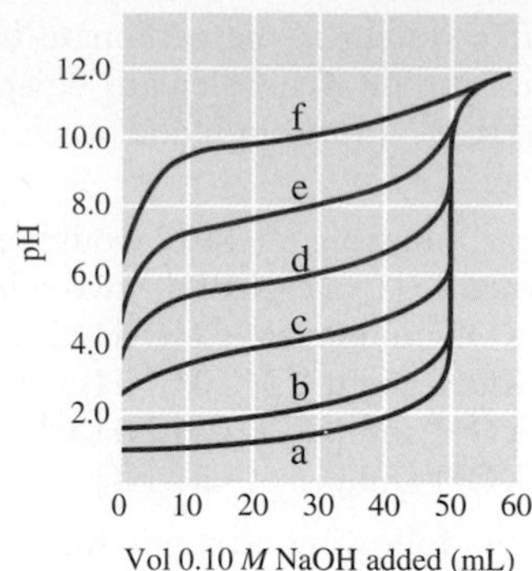

a. Which pH curve corresponds to the weakest acid?
b. Which pH curve corresponds to the strongest acid? Which point on the pH curve would you examine to see if this acid is a strong acid or a weak acid (assuming you did not know the initial concentration of the acid)?
c. Which pH curve corresponds to an acid with $K_a \approx 1 \times 10^{-6}$?

60. The figure in the preceding exercise shows the pH curves for the titrations of six different acids with NaOH. Make a similar plot for the titration of three different bases with 0.10 *M* HCl. Assume 50.0 mL of 0.20 *M* of the bases, and assume the three bases are a strong base (KOH), a weak base with $K_b = 1 \times 10^{-5}$, and another weak base with $K_b = 1 \times 10^{-10}$.

61. Consider the titration of 40.0 mL of 0.200 *M* $HClO_4$ with 0.100 *M* KOH. Calculate the pH of the resulting solution after the following volumes of KOH have been added.
a. 0.0 mL
b. 10.0 mL
c. 40.0 mL
d. 80.0 mL
e. 100.0 mL

62. Consider the titration of 80.0 mL of 0.100 *M* $Ba(OH)_2$ with 0.400 *M* HCl. Calculate the pH of the resulting solution after the following volumes of HCl have been added.
a. 0.0 mL
b. 20.0 mL
c. 30.0 mL
d. 40.0 mL
e. 80.0 mL

63. Consider the titration of 100.0 mL of 0.200 *M* acetic acid ($K_a = 1.8 \times 10^{-5}$) with 0.100 *M* KOH. Calculate the pH of the resulting solution after each of the following volumes of KOH has been added.
a. 0.0 mL
b. 50.0 mL
c. 100.0 mL
d. 150.0 mL
e. 200.0 mL
f. 250.0 mL

64. Consider the titration of 100.0 mL of 0.100 *M* H_2NNH_2 ($K_b = 3.0 \times 10^{-6}$) with 0.200 *M* HNO_3. Calculate the pH of the resulting solution after each of the following volumes of HNO_3 has been added.
a. 0.0 mL
b. 20.0 mL
c. 25.0 mL
d. 40.0 mL
e. 50.0 mL
f. 100.0 mL

65. Lactic acid is a common by-product of cellular respiration and is often said to cause the "burn" associated with strenuous activity. A 25.0-mL sample of 0.100 *M* lactic acid ($HC_3H_5O_3$, pK_a = 3.86) is titrated with 0.100 *M* NaOH solution. Calculate the pH after the addition of 0.0 mL, 4.0 mL, 8.0 mL, 12.5 mL, 20.0 mL, 24.0 mL, 24.5 mL, 24.9 mL, 25.0 mL, 25.1 mL, 26.0 mL, 28.0 mL,

and 30.0 mL of the NaOH. Plot the results of your calculations as pH versus milliliters of NaOH added.

66. Repeat the procedure in Exercise 65 for the titration of 25.0 mL of 0.100 *M* propanoic acid ($HC_3H_5O_2$, $K_a = 1.3 \times 10^{-5}$) with 0.100 *M* KOH.

67. Repeat the procedure in Exercise 65 for the titration of 25.0 mL of 0.100 *M* NH_3 ($K_b = 1.8 \times 10^{-5}$) with 0.100 *M* HCl.

68. Repeat the procedure in Exercise 65 for the titration of 25.0 mL of 0.100 *M* pyridine ($K_b = 1.7 \times 10^{-9}$) with 0.100 *M* hydrochloric acid. Do not do the points at 24.9 mL and 25.1 mL.

69. Calculate the pH at the halfway point and at the equivalence point for each of the following titrations.
   a. 100.0 mL of 0.10 *M* $HC_7H_5O_2$ ($K_a = 6.4 \times 10^{-5}$) titrated with 0.10 *M* NaOH
   b. 100.0 mL of 0.10 *M* $C_2H_5NH_2$ ($K_b = 5.6 \times 10^{-4}$) titrated with 0.20 *M* HNO_3
   c. 100.0 mL of 0.50 *M* HCl titrated with 0.25 *M* NaOH

70. You have 75.0 mL of 0.10 *M* HA. After adding 30.0 mL of 0.10 *M* NaOH, the pH is 5.50. What is the K_a value of HA?

71. A student dissolves 0.0100 mole of an unknown weak base in 100.0 mL water and titrates the solution with 0.100 *M* HNO_3. After 40.0 mL of 0.100 *M* HNO_3 was added, the pH of the resulting solution was 8.00. Calculate the K_b value for the weak base.

Indicators

72. What is an acid–base indicator? Define the equivalence (stoichiometric) point and the endpoint of a titration. Why should you choose an indicator so that the two points coincide? Do the pH values of the two points have to be within ±0.01 pH unit of each other? Explain. Why does an indicator change from its acid color to its base color over a range of pH values? In general, when do color changes start to occur for indicators? Can the indicator thymol blue contain only a single $—CO_2H$ group and no other acidic or basic functional group? Explain.

73. Two drops of indicator HIn ($K_a = 1.0 \times 10^{-9}$), where HIn is yellow and In^- is blue, are placed in 100.0 mL of 0.10 *M* HCl.
   a. What color is the solution initially?
   b. The solution is titrated with 0.10 *M* NaOH. At what pH will the color change (yellow to greenish yellow) occur?
   c. What color will the solution be after 200.0 mL of NaOH has been added?

74. A certain indicator HIn has a pK_a of 3.00 and a color change becomes visible when 7.00% of the indicator has been converted to In^-. At what pH is this color change visible?

75. Estimate the pH of a solution in which bromcresol green is blue and thymol blue is yellow (see Fig. 8.8).

76. A solution has a pH of 7.0. What would be the color of the solution if each of the following indicators were added? (See Fig. 8.8.)
   a. thymol blue
   b. bromthymol blue
   c. methyl red
   d. crystal violet

77. Which of the indicators in Fig. 8.8 could be used for doing the titrations in Exercises 61 and 63?

78. Which of the indicators in Fig. 8.8 could be used for doing the titrations in Exercises 62 and 64?

79. Which of the indicators in Fig. 8.8 could be used for doing the titrations in Exercises 65 and 67?

80. Which of the indicators in Fig. 8.8 could be used for doing the titrations in Exercises 66 and 68?

81. Methyl red ($K_a = 5.0 \times 10^{-6}$) undergoes a color change from red to yellow as the solution gets more basic. Calculate an approximate pH range for which methyl red is useful. What color change occurs and what is the pH at the color change when a weak acid is titrated with a strong base using methyl red as an indicator? What color change occurs and what is the pH at the color change when a weak base is titrated with a strong acid using methyl red as an indicator? For which of these two types of titrations is methyl red a possible indicator?

82. Indicators can be used to estimate the pH values of solutions. To determine the pH of a 0.01 *M* weak acid (HX) solution, a few drops of three different indicators are added to separate portions of 0.01 *M* HX. The resulting colors of the HX solution are summarized in the last column of the accompanying table. What is the approximate pH of the 0.01 *M* HX solution? What is the approximate K_a value for HX?

Indicator (HIn)	Color of HIn	Color of In^-	pK_a of HIn	Color of 0.01 *M* HX
Bromphenol blue	Yellow	Blue	4.0	Blue
Bromcresol purple	Yellow	Purple	6.0	Yellow
Bromcresol green	Yellow	Blue	4.8	Green

Polyprotic Acid Titrations

83. When a diprotic acid, H_2A, is titrated with NaOH, the protons on the diprotic acid are generally removed one at a time, resulting in a pH curve that has the following generic shape:

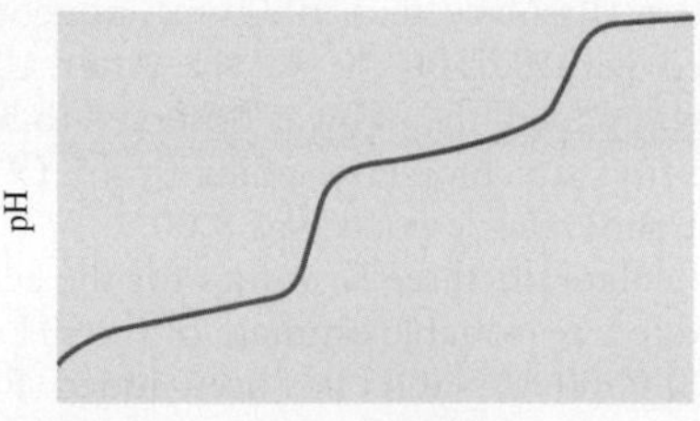

   a. Notice that the plot has essentially two titration curves. If the first equivalence point occurs at 100.0 mL NaOH added, what volume of NaOH added corresponds to the second equivalence point?

b. For the following volumes of NaOH added, list the major species present after the OH^- reacts completely.
   i. 0 mL NaOH added
   ii. beween 0 and 100.0 mL NaOH added
   iii. 100.0 mL NaOH added
   iv. between 100.0 and 200.0 mL NaOH added
   v. 200.0 mL NaOH added
   vi. after 200.0 mL NaOH added

c. If the pH at 50.0 mL NaOH added is 4.0 and the pH at 150.0 mL NaOH added is 8.0, determine the values K_{a_1} and K_{a_2} for the diprotic acid.

84. A student was given a 0.10 *M* solution of an unknown diprotic acid H_2A and asked to determine the K_{a_1} and K_{a_2} values for the diprotic acid. The student titrated 50.0 mL of the 0.10 *M* H_2A with 0.10 *M* NaOH. After 25.0 mL of NaOH was added, the pH of the resulting solution was 6.70. After 50.0 mL of NaOH was added, the pH of the resulting solution was 8.00. What are the values of K_{a_1} and K_{a_2} for the diprotic acid?

85. Consider the titration of 100.0 mL of a 0.0500 *M* solution of the hypothetical weak acid H_3X ($K_{a_1} = 1.0 \times 10^{-3}$, $K_{a_2} = 1.0 \times 10^{-7}$, $K_{a_3} = 1.0 \times 10^{-12}$) with 0.100 *M* KOH. Calculate the pH of the solution under the following conditions.
   a. before any KOH has been added
   b. after 10.0 mL of 0.100 *M* KOH has been added
   c. after 25.0 mL of 0.100 *M* KOH has been added
   d. after 50.0 mL of 0.100 *M* KOH has been added
   e. after 60.0 mL of 0.100 *M* KOH has been added
   f. after 75.0 mL of 0.100 *M* KOH has been added
   g. after 100.0 mL of 0.100 *M* KOH has been added
   h. after 125.0 mL of 0.100 *M* KOH has been added
   i. after 150.0 mL of 0.100 *M* KOH has been added
   j. after 200.0 mL of 0.100 *M* KOH has been added

86. Consider 100.0 mL of a 0.100 *M* solution of H_3A ($K_{a_1} = 1.5 \times 10^{-4}$, $K_{a_2} = 3.0 \times 10^{-8}$, $K_{a_3} = 5.0 \times 10^{-12}$).
   a. Calculate the pH of this solution.
   b. Calculate the pH of the solution after 10.0 mL of 1.00 *M* NaOH has been added to the original solution.
   c. Calculate the pH of the solution after 25.0 mL of 1.00 *M* NaOH has been added to the original solution.

87. A 0.200-g sample of a triprotic acid (molar mass = 165.0 g/mol) is dissolved in a 50.00-mL aqueous solution and titrated with 0.0500 *M* NaOH. After 10.50 mL of the base was added, the pH was observed to be 3.73. The pH at the first stoichiometric point was 5.19 and at the second stoichiometric point was 8.00.
   a. Calculate the three K_a values for the acid.
   b. Make a reasonable estimate of the pH after 59.0 mL of 0.0500 *M* NaOH has been added. Explain your answer.
   c. Calculate the pH after 59.0 mL of 0.0500 *M* NaOH has been added.

88. Consider the titration of 100.0 mL of 0.100 *M* H_3A ($K_{a_1} = 5.0 \times 10^{-4}$, $K_{a_2} = 1.0 \times 10^{-8}$, $K_{a_3} = 1.0 \times 10^{-11}$) with 0.0500 *M* NaOH.
   a. Calculate the pH after 100.0 mL of 0.0500 *M* NaOH has been added.
   b. What total volume of 0.0500 *M* NaOH is required to reach a pH of 8.67?

89. The titration of Na_2CO_3 with HCl has the following qualitative profile:

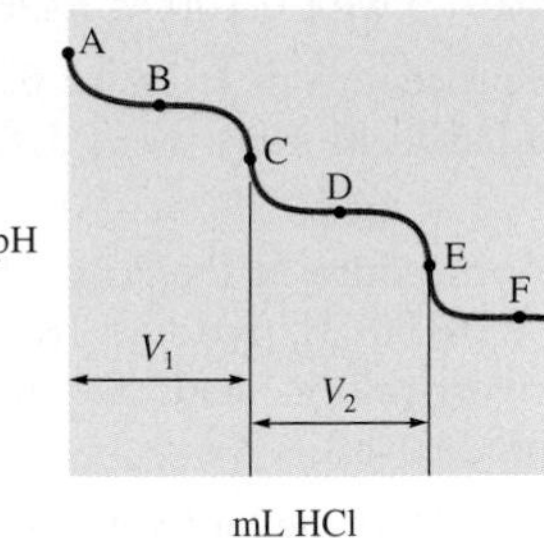

   a. Identify the major species in solution as points A–F.
   b. For the titration of 25.00 mL of 0.100 *M* Na_2CO_3 with 0.100 *M* HCl, calculate the pH at points A–E. (B and D are halfway points to equivalence.)

90. Consider 100.0 mL of a solution of 0.200 *M* Na_2A, where A^{2-} is a base with corresponding acids H_2A ($K_a = 1.0 \times 10^{-3}$) and HA^- ($K_a = 1.0 \times 10^{-8}$).
   a. What volume of 1.00 *M* HCl must be added to this solution to reach pH = 8.00?
   b. Calculate the pH at the second stoichiometric point of the titration of 0.200 *M* Na_2A, with 1.00 *M* HCl.

Solubility Equilibria

91. For which of the following is the K_{sp} value of the ionic compound the largest? The smallest? Explain your answer.

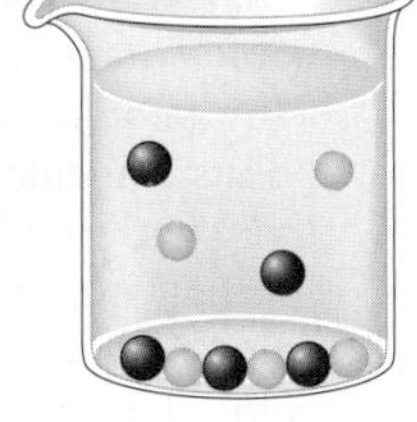

92. $Ag_2S(s)$ has a larger molar solubility than CuS even though Ag_2S has the smaller K_{sp} value. Explain how this is possible.

93. Calculate the solubility of each of the following compounds in moles per liter and grams per liter. (Ignore any acid–base properties.)
   a. Ag_3PO_4, $K_{sp} = 1.8 \times 10^{-18}$
   b. $CaCO_3$, $K_{sp} = 8.7 \times 10^{-9}$
   c. Hg_2Cl_2, $K_{sp} = 1.1 \times 10^{-18}$ (Hg_2^{2+} is the cation in solution.)

94. Calculate the solubility of each of the following compounds in moles per liter. Ignore any acid–base properties.
   a. PbI_2, $K_{sp} = 1.4 \times 10^{-8}$
   b. $CdCO_3$, $K_{sp} = 5.2 \times 10^{-12}$
   c. $Sr_3(PO_4)_2$, $K_{sp} = 1 \times 10^{-31}$

95. Use the following data to calculate the K_{sp} value for each solid.
   a. The solubility of CaC_2O_4 is 6.1×10^{-3} g/L.
   b. The solubility of BiI_3 is 1.32×10^{-5} mol/L.

96. The concentration of Pb^{2+} in a solution saturated with $PbBr_2(s)$ is 2.14×10^{-2} *M*. Calculate K_{sp} for $PbBr_2$.

97. The concentration of Ag^+ in a solution saturated with $Ag_2C_2O_4(s)$ is 2.2×10^{-4} *M*. Calculate K_{sp} for $Ag_2C_2O_4$.

98. The solubility of the ionic compound M_2X_3, having a molar mass of 288 g/mol, is 3.60×10^{-7} g/L. Calculate the K_{sp} of the compound.

99. For each of the following pairs of solids, determine which solid has the smallest molar solubility.
   a. $CaF_2(s)$, $K_{sp} = 4.0 \times 10^{-11}$ or $BaF_2(s)$, $K_{sp} = 2.4 \times 10^{-5}$
   b. $Ca_3(PO_4)_2(s)$, $K_{sp} = 1.3 \times 10^{-32}$ or $FePO_4(s)$, $K_{sp} = 1.0 \times 10^{-22}$

100. The K_{sp} for silver sulfate (Ag_2SO_4) is 1.2×10^{-5}. Calculate the solubility of silver sulfate in each of the following.
   a. water b. 0.10 *M* $AgNO_3$ c. 0.20 *M* K_2SO_4

101. Calculate the solubility (in mol/L) of $Fe(OH)_3$ ($K_{sp} = 4 \times 10^{-38}$) in each of the following.
   a. water (assume pH is 7.0 and constant)
   b. a solution buffered at pH = 5.0
   c. a solution buffered at pH = 11.0

102. The solubility of $Ce(IO_3)_3$ in a 0.20 *M* KIO_3 solution is 4.4×10^{-8} mol/L. Calculate K_{sp} for $Ce(IO_3)_3$.

103. What mass of ZnS ($K_{sp} = 2.5 \times 10^{-22}$) will dissolve in 300.0 mL of 0.050 *M* $Zn(NO_3)_2$? Ignore the basic properties of S^{2-}.

104. The concentration of Mg^{2+} in seawater is 0.052 *M*. At what pH will 99% of the Mg^{2+} be precipitated as the hydroxide salt? [K_{sp} for $Mg(OH)_2 = 8.9 \times 10^{-12}$.]

105. For the substances in Exercises 93 and 94, which will show increased solubility as the pH of the solution becomes more acidic? Write equations for the reactions that occur to increase the solubility.

106. Explain the following phenomenon: You have a test tube with an aqueous solution of silver nitrate as shown in test tube 1 below. A few drops of aqueous sodium chromate solution was added with the end result shown in test tube 2. A few drops of aqueous sodium chloride solution was then added with the end result shown in test tube 3.

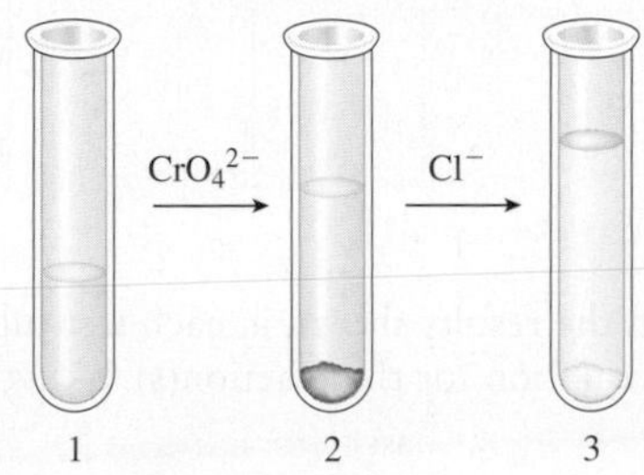

Use the K_{sp} values in the book to support your explanation, and include the balanced equations. Also, list the ions that are present in solution in each test tube.

107. For which salt in each of the following groups will the solubility depend on pH?
   a. AgF, AgCl, AgBr
   b. $Pb(OH)_2$, $PbCl_2$
   c. $Sr(NO_3)_2$, $Sr(NO_2)_2$
   d. $Ni(NO_3)_2$, $Ni(CN)_2$

108. A solution is prepared by mixing 75.0 mL of 0.020 *M* $BaCl_2$ and 125 mL of 0.040 *M* K_2SO_4. What are the concentrations of barium and sulfate ions in this solution? Assume only SO_4^{2-} ions (no HSO_4^-) are present.

109. Calculate the final concentrations of $K^+(aq)$, $C_2O_4^{2-}(aq)$, $Ba^{2+}(aq)$, and $Br^-(aq)$ in a solution prepared by adding 0.100 L of 6.0×10^{-4} *M* $K_2C_2O_4$ to 0.150 L of 1.0×10^{-4} *M* $BaBr_2$. (For BaC_2O_4, $K_{sp} = 2.3 \times 10^{-8}$.)

110. A solution is prepared by mixing 50.0 mL of 0.10 *M* $Pb(NO_3)_2$ with 50.0 mL of 1.0 *M* KCl. Calculate the concentrations of Pb^{2+} and Cl^- at equilibrium. [K_{sp} for $PbCl_2(s) = 1.6 \times 10^{-5}$.]

111. The K_{sp} of $Al(OH)_3$ is 2×10^{-32}. At what pH will a 0.2 *M* Al^{3+} solution begin to show precipitation of $Al(OH)_3$?

112. A solution is 1×10^{-4} *M* in NaF, Na_2S, and Na_3PO_4. What would be the order of precipitation as a source of Pb^{2+} is added gradually to the solution? The relevant K_{sp} values are $K_{sp}(PbF_2) = 4 \times 10^{-8}$, $K_{sp}(PbS) = 7 \times 10^{-29}$, and $K_{sp}[Pb_3(PO_4)_2] = 1 \times 10^{-54}$.

113. A solution contains 1.0×10^{-5} *M* Na_3PO_4. What is the minimum concentration of $AgNO_3$ that would cause precipitation of solid Ag_3PO_4 ($K_{sp} = 1.8 \times 10^{-18}$)?

114. A solution contains 0.25 *M* $Ni(NO_3)_2$ and 0.25 *M* $Cu(NO_3)_2$. Can the metal ions be separated by slowly adding Na_2CO_3? Assume that for successful separation, 99% of the metal ion must be precipitated before the other metal ion begins to precipitate, and assume that no volume change occurs on addition of Na_2CO_3.

115. Describe how you could separate the ions in each of the following groups by selective precipitation.
   a. Ag^+, Mg^{2+}, Cu^{2+}
   b. Pb^{2+}, Ca^{2+}, Fe^{2+}
   c. Cl^-, Br^-, I^-
   d. Pb^{2+}, Bi^{3+}

116. If a solution contains either $Pb^{2+}(aq)$ or $Ag^+(aq)$, how can temperature be manipulated to help identify the ion in solution?

117. Sulfide precipitates are generally grouped as sulfides insoluble in acidic solution and sulfides insoluble in basic solution. Explain why there is a difference between the two groups of sulfide precipitates.

Complex Ion Equilibria

118. Nanotechnology has become an important field, with applications ranging from high-density data storage to the design of "nano machines." One common building block of nanostructured architectures is manganese oxide nanoparticles. The particles can be formed from manganese oxalate nanorods, the formation of which can be described as follows:

$$Mn^{2+}(aq) + C_2O_4^{2-}(aq) \rightleftharpoons MnC_2O_4(aq) \qquad K_1 = 7.9 \times 10^3$$

$$MnC_2O_4(aq) + C_2O_4^{2-}(aq) \rightleftharpoons Mn(C_2O_4)_2^{2-}(aq) \qquad K_2 = 7.9 \times 10^1$$

Calculate the value for the overall formation constant for $Mn(C_2O_4)_2^{2-}$:

$$K = \frac{[Mn(C_2O_4)_2^{2-}]}{[Mn^{2+}][C_2O_4^{2-}]^2}$$

119. When aqueous KI is added gradually to mercury(II) nitrate, an orange precipitate forms. Continued addition of KI causes the precipitate to dissolve. Write balanced

equations to explain these observations. (*Hint:* Hg^{2+} reacts with I^- to form HgI_4^{2-}.)

120. As a sodium chloride solution is added to a solution of silver nitrate, a white precipitate forms. Ammonia is added to the mixture and the precipitate dissolves. When potassium bromide solution is then added, a pale yellow precipitate appears. When a solution of sodium thiosulfate is added, the yellow precipitate dissolves. Finally, potassium iodide is added to the solution and a yellow precipitate forms. Write reactions for all the changes mentioned above. What conclusions can you draw concerning the sizes of the K_{sp} values for AgCl, AgBr, and AgI? What can you say about the relative values of the formation constants of $Ag(NH_3)_2^+$ and $Ag(S_2O_3)_2^{3-}$?

121. The overall formation constant for HgI_4^{2-} is 1.0×10^{30}. That is,

$$1.0 \times 10^{30} = \frac{[HgI_4^{2-}]}{[Hg^{2+}][I^-]^4}$$

What is the concentration of Hg^{2+} in 500.0 mL of a solution that was originally 0.010 *M* Hg^{2+} and had 65 g of KI added to it? The reaction is

$$Hg^{2+}(aq) + 4I^-(aq) \rightleftharpoons HgI_4^{2-}(aq)$$

122. A solution is prepared by adding 0.090 mole of $K_3[Fe(CN)_6]$ to 0.60 L of 2.0 *M* NaCN. Assuming no volume change, calculate the concentrations of $Fe(CN)_6^{3-}$ and Fe^{3+} in this solution. The *K* (overall) for the formation of $Fe(CN)_6^{3-}$ is 1×10^{42}.

123. A solution is prepared by mixing 100.0 mL of 1.0×10^{-4} *M* $Be(NO_3)_2$ and 100.0 mL of 8.0 *M* NaF.

$$Be^{2+}(aq) + F^-(aq) \rightleftharpoons BeF^+(aq) \qquad K_1 = 7.9 \times 10^4$$

$$BeF^+(aq) + F^-(aq) \rightleftharpoons BeF_2(aq) \qquad K_2 = 5.8 \times 10^3$$

$$BeF_2(aq) + F^-(aq) \rightleftharpoons BeF_3^-(aq) \qquad K_3 = 6.1 \times 10^2$$

$$BeF_3^-(aq) + F^-(aq) \rightleftharpoons BeF_4^{2-}(aq) \qquad K_4 = 2.7 \times 10^1$$

Calculate the equilibrum concentrations of F^-, Be^{2+}, BeF^+, BeF_2, BeF_3^-, and BeF_4^{2-} in this solution.

124. K_f for the complex ion $Ag(NH_3)_2^+$ is 1.7×10^7. K_{sp} for AgCl is 1.6×10^{-10}. Calculate the molar solubility of AgCl in 1.0 *M* NH_3.

125. a. Using the K_{sp} for $Cu(OH)_2$ (1.6×10^{-19}) and the overall formation constant for $Cu(NH_3)_4^{2+}$ (1.0×10^{13}), calculate a value for the equilibrium constant for the reaction

$$Cu(OH)_2(s) + 4NH_3(aq) \rightleftharpoons Cu(NH_3)_4^{2+}(aq) + 2OH^-(aq)$$

b. Use the value of the equilibrium constant you calculated in part a to calculate the solubility (in mol/L) of $Cu(OH)_2$ in 5.0 *M* NH_3. In 5.0 *M* NH_3, the concentration of OH^- is 0.0095 *M*.

126. The copper(I) ion forms a chloride salt that has $K_{sp} = 1.2 \times 10^{-6}$. Copper(I) also forms a complex ion with Cl^-:

$$Cu^+(aq) + 2Cl^-(aq) \rightleftharpoons CuCl_2^-(aq) \qquad K = 8.7 \times 10^4$$

a. Calculate the solubility of copper(I) chloride in pure water. (Ignore $CuCl_2^-$ formation for part a.)
b. Calculate the solubility of copper(I) chloride in 0.10 *M* NaCl.

127. Solutions of sodium thiosulfate are used to dissolve unexposed AgBr in the developing process for black-and-white film. What mass of AgBr can dissolve in 1.00 L of 0.500 *M* $Na_2S_2O_3$? Assume the overall formation constant for $Ag(S_2O_3)_2^{3-}$ is 2.9×10^{13} and K_{sp} for AgBr is 5.0×10^{-13}.

128. a. Calculate the molar solubility of AgI in pure water. K_{sp} for AgI is 1.5×10^{-16}.
b. Calculate the molar solubility of AgI in 3.0 *M* NH_3. The overall formation constant for $Ag(NH_3)_2^+$ is 1.7×10^7.
c. Compare the calculated solubilities from parts a and b. Explain any differences.

129. A series of chemicals was added to some $AgNO_3(aq)$. $NaCl(aq)$ was added first to the silver nitrate solution, with the end result shown below in test tube 1; $NH_3(aq)$ was then added, with the end result shown in test tube 2; and $HNO_3(aq)$ was added last, with the end result shown in test tube 3.

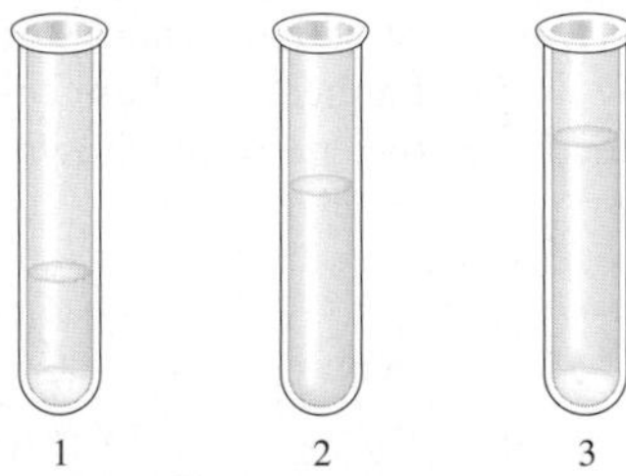

Explain the results shown in each test tube. Include a balanced equation for the reaction(s) taking place.

Additional Exercises

130. Will a precipitate of $Cd(OH)_2$ form if 1.0 mL of 1.0 *M* $Cd(NO_3)_2$ is added to 1.0 L of 5.0 *M* NH_3?

$$Cd^{2+}(aq) + 4NH_3(aq) \rightleftharpoons Cd(NH_3)_4^{2+}(aq) \qquad K = 1.0 \times 10^7$$

$$Cd(OH)_2(s) \rightleftharpoons Cd^{2+}(aq) + 2OH^-(aq) \qquad K_{sp} = 5.9 \times 10^{-15}$$

131. Tris(hydroxymethyl)aminomethane, commonly called TRIS or Trizma, is often used as a buffer in biochemical studies. Its buffering range is from pH 7 to 9, and K_b is 1.19×10^{-6} for the reaction

$$\underset{\text{TRIS}}{(HOCH_2)_3CNH_2(aq)} + H_2O(l) \rightleftharpoons \underset{\text{TRISH}^+}{(HOCH_2)_3CNH_3^+(aq)} + OH^-(aq)$$

a. What is the optimum pH for TRIS buffers?
b. Calculate the ratio [TRIS]/[$TRISH^+$] at pH = 7.00 and at pH = 9.00.
c. A buffer is prepared by diluting 50.0 g of TRIS base and 65.0 g of TRIS hydrochloride (written as TRISHCl) to a total volume of 2.0 L. What is the pH of this buffer? What is the pH after 0.50 mL of 12 *M* HCl is added to a 200.0-mL portion of the buffer?

132. The salts in Table 8.5, with the possible exception of the hydroxide salts, have one of the following mathematical relationships between the K_{sp} value and the molar solubility *s*.
i. $K_{sp} = s^2$　　iii. $K_{sp} = 27s^4$
ii. $K_{sp} = 4s^3$　　iv. $K_{sp} = 108s^5$
For each mathematical relationship, give an example of a salt in Table 8.5 that exhibits that relationship.

133. You have the following reagents on hand:

Solids (pK_a of Acid Form Is Given)	Solutions
Benzoic acid (4.19)	5.0 *M* HCl
Sodium acetate (4.74)	1.0 *M* acetic acid (4.74)
Potassium fluoride (3.14)	2.6 *M* NaOH
Ammonium chloride (9.26)	1.0 *M* HOCl (7.46)

What combinations of reagents would you use to prepare buffers at the following pH values?
a. 3.0　b. 4.0　c. 5.0　d. 7.0　e. 9.0

134. a. Calculate the pH of a buffered solution that is 0.100 *M* in $C_6H_5CO_2H$ (benzoic acid, $K_a = 6.4 \times 10^{-5}$) and 0.100 *M* in $C_6H_5CO_2Na$.
b. Calculate the pH after 20.0% (by moles) of the benzoic acid is converted to benzoate anion by addition of base. Use the dissociation equilibrium:

$$C_6H_5CO_2H(aq) \rightleftharpoons C_6H_5CO_2^-(aq) + H^+(aq)$$

c. Do the same calculation as in part b, but use the following equilibrium to calculate the pH:

$$C_6H_5CO_2^-(aq) + H_2O(l) \rightleftharpoons C_6H_5CO_2H(aq) + OH^-(aq)$$

d. Do your answers in parts b and c agree? Why or why not?

135. One method for determining the purity of aspirin (empirical formula $C_9H_8O_4$) is to hydrolyze it with NaOH solution and then to titrate the remaining NaOH. The reaction of aspirin with NaOH is as follows:

$$\underset{\text{Aspirin}}{C_9H_8O_4(s)} + 2OH^-(aq) \xrightarrow[\text{10 min}]{\text{Boil}} \underset{\text{Salicylate ion}}{C_7H_5O_3^-(aq)} + \underset{\text{Acetate ion}}{C_2H_3O_2^-(aq)} + H_2O(l)$$

A sample of aspirin with a mass of 1.427 g was boiled in 50.00 mL of 0.500 *M* NaOH. After the solution was cooled, it took 31.92 mL of 0.289 *M* HCl to titrate the excess NaOH. Calculate the purity of the aspirin. What indicator should be used for this titration? Why?

136. Another way to treat data from a pH titration is to graph the absolute value of the change in pH per change in milliliters added versus milliliters added (ΔpH/ΔmL versus mL added). Make this graph using your results from Exercise 65. What advantage might this method have over the traditional method for treating titration data?

137. Potassium hydrogen phthalate, known as KHP (molar mass = 204.22 g/mol), can be obtained in high purity and is used to determine the concentration of solutions of strong bases by the reaction

$$HP^-(aq) + OH^-(aq) \longrightarrow H_2O(l) + P^{2-}(aq)$$

If a typical titration experiment begins with approximately 0.5 g of KHP and has a final volume of about 100 mL, what is an appropriate indicator to use? The pK_a for HP^- is 5.51.

138. A 10.00-g sample of the ionic compound NaA, where A^- is the anion of a weak acid, was dissolved in enough water to make 100.0 mL of solution and was then titrated with 0.100 *M* HCl. After 500.0 mL HCl was added, the pH was 5.00. The experimenter found that 1.00 L of 0.100 *M* HCl was required to reach the stoichiometric point of the titration.
a. What is the molar mass of NaA?
b. Calculate the pH of the solution at the stoichiometric point of the titration.

139. What mass of $Ca(NO_3)_2$ must be added to 1.0 L of a 1.0 *M* HF solution to begin precipitation of $CaF_2(s)$? For CaF_2, $K_{sp} = 4.0 \times 10^{-11}$ and K_a for HF $= 7.2 \times 10^{-4}$. Assume no volume change on addition of $Ca(NO_3)_2(s)$.

140. The equilibrium constant for the following reaction is 1.0×10^{23}:

$$Cr^{3+}(aq) + H_2EDTA^{2-}(aq) \rightleftharpoons CrEDTA^-(aq) + 2H^+(aq)$$

$$EDTA^{4-} = \begin{matrix} ^-O_2C-CH_2 & & & & CH_2-CO_2^- \\ & N-CH_2-CH_2-N & \\ ^-O_2C-CH_2 & & & & CH_2-CO_2^- \end{matrix}$$

Ethylenediaminetetraacetate

EDTA is used as a complexing agent in chemical analysis. Solutions of EDTA, usually containing the disodium salt Na_2H_2EDTA, are used to treat heavy metal poisoning. Calculate [Cr^{3+}] at equilibrium in a solution originally 0.0010 *M* in Cr^{3+} and 0.050 *M* in H_2EDTA^{2-} and buffered at pH = 6.00.

141. Calculate the concentration of Pb^{2+} in each of the following.
a. a saturated solution of $Pb(OH)_2$; $K_{sp} = 1.2 \times 10^{-15}$
b. a saturated solution of $Pb(OH)_2$ buffered at pH = 13.00
c. 0.010 mole of $Pb(NO_3)_2$ added to 1.0 L of aqueous solution, buffered at pH = 13.00 and containing 0.050 *M* Na_4EDTA. Does $Pb(OH)_2$ precipitate from this solution? For the reaction,

$$Pb^{2+}(aq) + EDTA^{4-}(aq) \rightleftharpoons PbEDTA^{2-}(aq) \qquad K = 1.1 \times 10^{18}$$

142. The solubility rules outlined in Chapter 4 say that $Ba(OH)_2$, $Sr(OH)_2$, and $Ca(OH)_2$ are marginally soluble hydroxides. Calculate the pH of a saturated solution of each of these marginally soluble hydroxides.

143. A certain acetic acid solution has pH = 2.68. Calculate the volume of 0.0975 *M* KOH required to "neutralize" 25.0 mL of this solution.

144. Calculate the volume of 1.50×10^{-2} *M* NaOH that must be added to 500.0 mL of 0.200 *M* HCl to give a solution that has pH = 2.15.

145. A 0.400 *M* solution of ammonia was titrated with hydrochloric acid to the equivalence point, where the total volume was 1.50 times the original volume. At what pH does the equivalence point occur?

146. A student intends to titrate a solution of a weak monoprotic acid with a sodium hydroxide solution but reverses the two solutions and places the weak acid solution in the buret. After 23.75 mL of the weak acid solution has been added to 50.0 mL of the 0.100 *M* NaOH solution, the pH of the resulting solution is 10.50. Calculate the original concentration of the solution of weak acid.

147. The active ingredient in aspirin is acetylsalicylic acid. A 2.51-g sample of acetylsalicylic acid required 27.36 mL of 0.5106 *M* NaOH for complete reaction. Addition of 15.44 mL of 0.4524 *M* HCl to the flask containing the aspirin and the sodium hydroxide produced a mixture with pH = 3.48. Find the molar mass of acetylsalicylic acid and its *K*a value. Acetylsalicylic acid is a monoprotic acid.

148. A solution is formed by mixing 50.0 mL of 10.0 *M* NaX with 50.0 mL of 2.0×10^{-3} *M* $CuNO_3$. Assume that Cu(I) forms complex ions with X^- as follows:

$$Cu^+(aq) + X^-(aq) \rightleftharpoons CuX(aq) \qquad K_1 = 1.0 \times 10^2$$
$$CuX(aq) + X^-(aq) \rightleftharpoons CuX_2^-(aq) \qquad K_2 = 1.0 \times 10^4$$
$$CuX_2^-(aq) + X^-(aq) \rightleftharpoons CuX_3^{2-}(aq) \qquad K_3 = 1.0 \times 10^3$$

Calculate the following concentrations at equilibrium.
a. CuX_3^{2-} b. CuX_2^- c. Cu^+

149. When phosphoric acid is titrated with a NaOH solution, only two stoichiometric points are seen. Why?

150. Consider the following two acids:

(benzene ring with OH and CO_2H on adjacent carbons) $pK_{a_1} = 2.98$; $pK_{a_2} = 13.40$

Salicylic acid

$HO_2CCH_2CH_2CH_2CH_2CO_2H$
Adipic acid $pK_{a_1} = 4.41$; $pK_{a_2} = 5.28$

In two separate experiments, the pH was measured during the titration of 5.00 mmol of each acid with 0.200 *M* NaOH. Each experiment showed only one stoichiometric point when the data were plotted. In one experiment the stoichiometric point was at 25.00 mL added NaOH, and in the other experiment the stoichiometric point was at 50.00 mL NaOH. Explain these results. (See Exercise 83.)

Challenge Problems

151. A buffer is made using 45.0 mL of 0.750 *M* $HC_3H_5O_2$ ($K_a = 1.3 \times 10^{-5}$) and 55.0 mL of 0.700 *M* $NaC_3H_5O_2$. What volume of 0.10 *M* NaOH must be added to change the pH of the original buffer solution by 2.5%?

152. Consider a solution prepared by mixing the following:
50.0 mL of 0.100 *M* Na_3PO_4
100.0 mL of 0.0500 *M* KOH
200.0 mL of 0.0750 *M* HCl
50.0 mL of 0.150 *M* NaCN

Determine the volume of 0.100 *M* HNO_3 that must be added to this mixture to achieve a final pH value of 7.21.

153. For solutions containing salts of the form NH_4X, the pH is determined by using the equation

$$pH = \frac{pK_a(NH_4^+) + pK_a(HX)}{2}$$

a. Derive this equation. (*Hint:* Review Section 8.7 on the pH of solutions containing amphoteric species.)
b. Use this equation to calculate the pH of the following solutions: ammonium formate, ammonium acetate, and ammonium bicarbonate. See Appendix 5 for K_a values.
c. Solutions of ammonium acetate are commonly used as pH = 7.0 buffers. Write equations to show how an ammonium acetate solution neutralizes added H^+ and OH^-.

154. Consider the titration of 100.0 mL of a solution that contains a mixture of 0.050 *M* H_2SO_4 and 0.20 *M* $H_2C_6H_6O_6$. Calculate the pH
a. before any 0.10 *M* NaOH has been added.
b. after a total of 100.0 mL of 0.10 *M* NaOH has been added.
c. after a total of 300.0 mL of 0.10 *M* NaOH has been added.
d. after a total of 500.0 mL of 0.10 *M* NaOH has been added.

155. The copper(I) ion forms a complex ion with CN^- according to the following equation:

$$Cu^+(aq) + 3CN(aq)^- \rightleftharpoons Cu(CN)_3^{2-}(aq) \qquad K_f = 1.0 \times 10^{11}$$

a. Calculate the solubility of CuBr(*s*) ($K_{sp} = 1.0 \times 10^{-5}$) in 1.0 L of 1.0 *M* NaCN.
b. Calculate the concentration of Br^- at equilibrium.
c. Calculate the concentration of CN^- at equilibrium.

156. Aluminum ions react with the hydroxide ion to form the precipitate $Al(OH)_3(s)$, but can also react to form the soluble complex ion $Al(OH)_4^-$. In terms of solubility, $Al(OH)_3(s)$ will be more soluble in very acidic solutions as well as more soluble in very basic solutions.
a. Write equations for the reactions that occur to increase the solubility of $Al(OH)_3(s)$ in very acidic solutions and in very basic solutions.

b. Show that the solubility of $Al(OH)_3$, as a function of $[H^+]$, obeys the equation

$$S = [H^+]^3 K_{sp}/K_w^3 + KK_w/[H^+]$$

where S = solubility = $[Al^{3+}] + [Al(OH)_4^-]$ and K is the equilibrium constant for

$$Al(OH)_3(s) + OH^-(aq) \rightleftharpoons Al(OH)_4^-(aq)$$

c. The value of K is 40.0, and K_{sp} for $Al(OH)_3$ is 2×10^{-32}. Plot the solubility of $Al(OH)_3$ in the pH range 4–12.

157. a. Calculate the molar solubility of SrF_2 in water, ignoring the basic properties of F^-. (For SrF_2, $K_{sp} = 7.9 \times 10^{-10}$.)
b. Would the measured molar solubility of SrF_2 be greater than or less than the value calculated in part a? Explain.
c. Calculate the molar solubility of SrF_2 in a solution buffered at pH = 2.00. (K_a for HF is 7.2×10^{-4}.)

158. What is the maximum possible concentration of Ni^{2+} ion in water at 25°C that is saturated with 0.10 M H_2S and maintained at pH 3.0 with HCl?

159. A mixture contains 1.0×10^{-3} M Cu^{2+} and 1.0×10^{-3} M Mn^{2+} and is saturated with 0.10 M H_2S. Determine a pH where CuS precipitates but MnS does not precipitate. K_{sp} for CuS = 8.5×10^{-45} and K_{sp} for MnS = 2.3×10^{-13}.

160. Consider 1.0 L of an aqueous solution that contains 0.10 M sulfuric acid to which 0.30 mole barium nitrate is added. Assuming no change in volume of the solution, determine the pH, the concentration of barium ions in the final solution, and the mass of solid formed.

161. Calculate the solubility of AgCN(s) ($K_{sp} = 2.2 \times 10^{-12}$) in a solution containing 1.0 M H^+. (K_a for HCN is 6.2×10^{-10}.)

162. Calcium oxalate (CaC_2O_4) is relatively insoluble in water ($K_{sp} = 2 \times 10^{-9}$). However, calcium oxalate is more soluble in acidic solution. How much more soluble is calcium oxalate in 0.10 M H^+ than in pure water? In pure water, ignore the basic properties of $C_2O_4^{2-}$.

163. What volume of 0.0100 M NaOH must be added to 1.00 L of 0.0500 M HOCl to achieve a pH of 8.00?

164. Consider the titration of 100.0 mL of a 1.00×10^{-4} M solution of an acid HA ($K_a = 5.0 \times 10^{-10}$) with 1.00×10^{-3} M NaOH. Calculate the pH for the following conditions.
a. before any NaOH has been added
b. after 5.00 mL of NaOH has been added
c. at the stoichiometric point

165. Consider a solution formed by mixing 200.0 mL of 0.250 M Na_3PO_4, 135.0 mL of 1.000 M HCl, and 100.0 mL of 0.100 M NaCN.
a. Calculate the pH of this solution.
b. Calculate the concentration of HCN in this solution.

166. Consider a solution formed by mixing 50.0 mL of 0.100 M H_2SO_4, 30.0 mL of 0.100 M HOCl, 25.0 mL of 0.200 M NaOH, 25.0 mL of 0.100 M $Ba(OH)_2$, and 10.0 mL of 0.150 M KOH. Calculate the pH of this solution.

167. Calculate the pH of a solution prepared by mixing 500.0 mL of 0.50 M Na_3PO_4 and 500.0 mL of 0.10 M H_2SO_4.

168. Consider the titration of 100.0 mL of 0.10 M phosphoric acid with 0.10 M NaOH.
a. Determine the pH at the third half-equivalence point by assuming it is a "special point" (see Fig. 8.11).
b. Calculate the pH at the third equivalence point.
c. Why must the answer to part a be incorrect? Why can't we use the "special point" on the graph? (Explain the assumption made in using the special point and why it is not valid in this case.)
d. Calculate the pH at the third half-equivalence point.

169. In the titration of 100.0 mL of a 0.0500 M solution of acid H_3A ($K_{a_1} = 1.0 \times 10^{-3}$, $K_{a_2} = 5.0 \times 10^{-8}$, $K_{a_3} = 2.0 \times 10^{-12}$), calculate the volume of 1.00 M NaOH required to reach pH values of 9.50 and 4.00.

170. Consider the titration curve in Exercise 89 for the titration of Na_2CO_3 with HCl.
a. If a mixture of $NaHCO_3$ and Na_2CO_3 was titrated, what would be the relative sizes of V_1 and V_2?
b. If a mixture of NaOH and Na_2CO_3 was titrated, what would be the relative sizes of V_1 and V_2?
c. A sample contains a mixture of $NaHCO_3$ and Na_2CO_3. When this sample was titrated with 0.100 M HCl, it took 18.9 mL to reach the first stoichiometric point and an additional 36.7 mL to reach the second stoichiometric point. What is the composition in mass percent of the sample?

Marathon Problem

171.* A 225-mg sample of a diprotic acid is dissolved in enough water to make 250. mL of solution. The pH of this solution is 2.06. A saturated solution of calcium hydroxide ($K_{sp} = 1.3 \times 10^{-6}$) is prepared by adding excess calcium hydroxide to pure water and then removing the undissolved solid by filtration. Enough of the calcium hydroxide solution is added to the solution of the acid to reach the second equivalence point. The pH at the second equivalence point (as determined by a pH meter) is 7.96. The first dissociation constant for the acid (K_{a_1}) is 5.90×10^{-2}. Assume that the volumes of the solutions are additive, that all solutions are at 25°C, and that K_{a_1} is at least 1000 times greater than K_{a_2}.
a. Calculate the molar mass of the acid.
b. Calculate the second dissociation constant for the acid (K_{a_2}).

*From James H. Burness, "The Use of "Marathon" Problems as Effective Vehicles for the Presentation of General Chemistry Lectures," Journal of Chemical Education, 68(11).

Appendixes

Appendix One | Mathematical Procedures

A1.1 Exponential Notation

The numbers characteristic of scientific measurements are often very large or very small; thus it is convenient to express them by using powers of 10. For example, the number 1,300,000 can be expressed as 1.3×10^6, which means multiply 1.3 by 10 six times:

$$1.3 \times 10^6 = 1.3 \times \underbrace{10 \times 10 \times 10 \times 10 \times 10 \times 10}_{10^6 = 1 \text{ million}}$$

Note that each multiplication by 10 moves the decimal point one place to the right, and the easiest way to interpret the notation 1.3×10^6 is that it means move the decimal point in 1.3 to the right six times.

In this notation the number 1985 can be expressed as 1.985×10^3. Note that the usual convention is to write the number that appears before the power of 10 as a number between 1 and 10. Some other examples are given below.

Number	Exponential Notation
5.6	5.6×10^0 or 5.6×1
39	3.9×10^1
943	9.43×10^2
1126	1.126×10^3

To represent a number smaller than 1 in exponential notation, start with a number between 1 and 10 and *divide* by the appropriate power of 10:

$$0.0034 = \frac{3.4}{10 \times 10 \times 10} = \frac{3.4}{10^3} = 3.4 \times 10^{-3}$$

Division by 10 moves the decimal point one place to the *left*. Thus the number 0.00000014 can be written as 1.4×10^{-7}.

To summarize, we can write any number in the form

$$N \times 10^{\pm n}$$

where N is between 1 and 10 and the exponent n is an integer. If the sign preceding n is positive, it means the decimal point in N should be moved n places to the right. If a negative sign precedes n, the decimal point in N should be moved n places to the left.

Multiplication and Division

When two numbers expressed in exponential notation are multiplied, the initial numbers are multiplied and the exponents of 10 are added:

$$(M \times 10^m)(N \times 10^n) = (MN) \times 10^{m+n}$$

For example,

$$(3.2 \times 10^4)(2.8 \times 10^3) = 9.0 \times 10^7$$

When the numbers are multiplied, if a result greater than 10 is obtained for the initial number, the number is adjusted to conventional notation:

$$(5.8 \times 10^2)(4.3 \times 10^8) = 24.9 \times 10^{10} = 2.49 \times 10^{11} = 2.5 \times 10^{11}$$

Division of two numbers expressed in exponential notation involves normal division of the initial numbers and *subtraction* of the exponent of the divisor from that of the dividend. For example,

$$\frac{4.8 \times 10^8}{\underbrace{2.1 \times 10^3}_{\text{Divisor}}} = \frac{4.8}{2.1} \times 10^{(8-3)} = 2.3 \times 10^5$$

Addition and Subtraction

When we add or subtract numbers expressed in exponential notation, *the exponents of the numbers must be the same*. For example, to add 1.31×10^5 and 4.2×10^4, rewrite one number so that the exponents of both are the same:

$$\begin{array}{r} 13.1 \times 10^4 \\ +\ \ 4.2 \times 10^4 \\ \hline 17.3 \times 10^4 \end{array}$$

In correct exponential notation, the result is expressed as 1.73×10^5.

Powers and Roots

When a number expressed in exponential notation is taken to some power, the initial number is taken to the appropriate power and the exponent of 10 is multiplied by that power:

$$(N \times 10^n)^m = N^m \times 10^{m \cdot n}$$

For example,*

$$(7.5 \times 10^2)^3 = 7.5^3 \times 10^{3 \cdot 2} = 422 \times 10^6 = 4.22 \times 10^8$$
$$= 4.2 \times 10^8 \text{ (rounded to 2 significant figures)}$$

When a root is taken of a number expressed in exponential notation, the root of the initial number is taken and the exponent of 10 is divided by the number representing the root:

$$\sqrt{N \times 10^n} = (N \times 10^n)^{1/2} = \sqrt{N} \times 10^{n/2}$$

For example, $(2.9 \times 10^6)^{1/2} = \sqrt{2.9} \times 10^{6/2} = 1.7 \times 10^3$

Because the exponent of the result must be an integer, we may sometimes have to change the form of the number so that the power divided by the root equals an integer; for example,

$$\sqrt{1.9 \times 10^3} = (1.9 \times 10^3)^{1/2} = (0.19 \times 10^4)^{1/2}$$
$$= \sqrt{0.19} \times 10^2 = 0.44 \times 10^2$$
$$= 4.4 \times 10^1$$

*Refer to the instruction booklet for your calculator for directions concerning how to take roots and powers of numbers.

The same procedure is followed for roots other than square roots; for example,

$$\sqrt[3]{4.6 \times 10^{10}} = (4.6 \times 10^{10})^{1/3} = (46 \times 10^{9})^{1/3}$$

$$= \sqrt[3]{46} \times 10^{3} = 3.6 \times 10^{3}$$

A1.2 Logarithms

A logarithm is an exponent. Any number N can be expressed as follows:

$$N = 10^{x}$$

For example,

$$1000 = 10^{3}$$

$$100 = 10^{2}$$

$$10 = 10^{1}$$

$$1 = 10^{0}$$

The common, or base 10, logarithm of a number is the power to which 10 must be taken to yield that number. Thus, since $1000 = 10^3$,

$$\log 1000 = 3$$

Similarly,

$$\log 100 = 2$$

$$\log 10 = 1$$

$$\log 1 = 0$$

For a number between 10 and 100, the required exponent of 10 will be between 1 and 2. For example, $65 = 10^{1.8129}$; that is, $\log 65 = 1.8129$. For a number between 100 and 1000, the exponent of 10 will be between 2 and 3. For example, $650 = 10^{2.8129}$ and $\log 650 = 2.8129$.

A number N greater than 0 and less than 1 can be expressed as follows:

$$N = 10^{-x} = \frac{1}{10^{x}}$$

For example,

$$0.001 = \frac{1}{1000} = \frac{1}{10^{3}} = 10^{-3}$$

$$0.01 = \frac{1}{100} = \frac{1}{10^{2}} = 10^{-2}$$

$$0.1 = \frac{1}{10} = \frac{1}{10^{1}} = 10^{-1}$$

Thus

$$\log 0.001 = -3$$

$$\log 0.01 = -2$$

$$\log 0.1 = -1$$

Although common logs are often tabulated, the most convenient method for obtaining such logs is to use a calculator.

Since logs are simply exponents, they are manipulated according to the rules for exponents. For example, if $A = 10^x$ and $B = 10^y$, then their product is

$$A \cdot B = 10^{x} \cdot 10^{y} = 10^{x+y}$$

and

$$\log AB = x + y = \log A + \log B$$

For division we have

$$\frac{A}{B} = \frac{10^{x}}{10^{y}} = 10^{x-y}$$

and $$\log \frac{A}{B} = x - y = \log A - \log B$$

For a number raised to a power, we have

$$A^n = (10^x)^n = 10^{nx}$$

and $$\log A^n = nx = n \log A$$

It follows that $$\log \frac{1}{A^n} = \log A^{-n} = -n \log A$$

or for $n = 1$, $$\log \frac{1}{A} = -\log A$$

When a common log is given, to find the number it represents, we must carry out the process of exponentiation. For example, if the log is 2.673, then $N = 10^{2.673}$. The process of exponentiation is also called taking the antilog, or the inverse logarithm, and is easily carried out by using a calculator.

A second type of logarithm, the natural logarithm, is based on the number 2.7183, which is referred to as e. In this case a number is represented as $N = e^x = 2.7183^x$. For example,

$$N = 7.15 = e^x$$

$$\ln 7.15 = x = 1.967$$

If a natural logarithm is given, to find the number it represents, we must carry out exponentiation to the base e (2.7183) by using a calculator.

A1.3 Graphing Functions

In the interpretation of the results of a scientific experiment, it is often useful to make a graph. It is usually most convenient to graph the function in a form that gives a straight line. The equation for a straight line (a *linear equation*) can be represented by the general form

$$y = mx + b$$

where y is the *dependent variable*, x is the *independent variable*, m is the *slope*, and b is the *intercept* with the y axis.

As an illustration of the characteristics of a linear equation, the function $y = 3x + 4$ is plotted in Fig. A1.1. For this equation, $m = 3$ and $b = 4$. Note that the y intercept occurs when $x = 0$. In this case the intercept is 4, as can be seen from the equation ($b = 4$).

The slope of a straight line is defined as the ratio of the rate of change in y to that in x:

$$m = \text{slope} = \frac{\Delta y}{\Delta x}$$

For the equation $y = 3x + 4$, y changes three times as fast as x (since x has a coefficient of 3). Thus the slope in this case is 3. This can be verified from the graph. For the triangle shown in Fig. A1.1:

$$\text{Slope} = \frac{\Delta y}{\Delta x} = \frac{24}{8} = 3$$

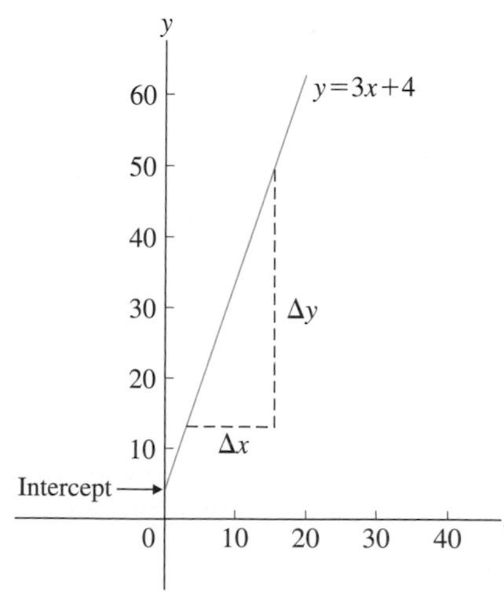

Figure A1.1
Graph of the linear equation $y = 3x + 4$.

Sometimes an equation that is not in standard form can be changed to the form $y = mx + b$ by rearrangement or mathematical manipulation. An example is the equation $k = Ae^{-E_a/RT}$, where A, E_a, and R are constants, k is the

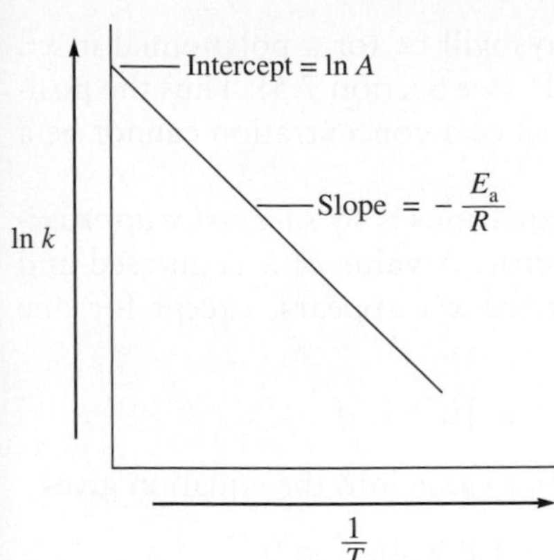

Figure A1.2
Graph of ln *k versus* 1/*T*.

dependent variable, and $1/T$ is the independent variable. This equation can be changed to standard form by taking the natural logarithm of both sides,

$$\ln k = \ln Ae^{-E_a/RT} = \ln A + \ln e^{-Ea/RT} = \ln A - \frac{E_a}{RT}$$

noting that the log of a product is equal to the sum of the logs of the individual terms and that the natural log of $e^{-E_a/RT}$ is simply the exponent $-E_a/RT$. Thus in standard form the equation $k = Ae^{-E_a/RT}$ is written

$$\underbrace{\ln k}_{y} = \underbrace{-\frac{E_a}{R}}_{m}\underbrace{\left(\frac{1}{T}\right)}_{x} + \underbrace{\ln A}_{b}$$

A plot of ln k versus $1/T$ (see Fig. A1.2) gives a straight line with slope $-E_a/R$ and intercept ln A.

Of course, many relationships that arise from the description of natural systems are nonlinear, and the "slope" of a curve is continuously changing. In this case the instantaneous slope is given by the tangent to the curve at that point, which is described by a new function obtained by taking the derivative of the original function. For example, for the function in x, $f = ax^2$, the derivative (df/dx) is $2ax$. Thus the slope at each point on the curve defined by the function ax^2 is given by $2ax$.

A1.4 Solving Quadratic Equations

A *quadratic equation,* a polynomial in which the highest power of x is 2, can be written as

$$ax^2 + bx + c = 0$$

One method for finding the two values of x that satisfy a quadratic equation is to use the *quadratic formula:*

$$x = \frac{-b \pm \sqrt{b^2 - 4ac}}{2a}$$

where a, b, and c represent the coefficients of x^2 and x and the constant, respectively. For example, in the determination of $[H^+]$ in a solution of 1.0×10^{-4} *M* acetic acid, the following expression arises:

$$1.8 \times 10^{-5} = \frac{x^2}{1.0 \times 10^{-4} - x}$$

which yields $\quad x^2 + (1.8 \times 10^{-5})x - 1.8 \times 10^{-9} = 0$

where $a = 1$, $b = 1.8 \times 10^{-5}$, and $c = -1.8 \times 10^{-9}$. Using the quadratic formula, we have

$$x = \frac{-b \pm \sqrt{b^2 - 4ac}}{2a}$$

$$= \frac{-1.8 \times 10^{-5} \pm \sqrt{3.24 \times 10^{-10} - (4)(1)(-1.8 \times 10^{-9})}}{2(1)}$$

and $\quad x = \frac{6.9 \times 10^{-5}}{2} = 3.5 \times 10^{-5}$

or $\quad x = \frac{-10.5 \times 10^{-5}}{2} = -5.2 \times 10^{-5}$

Note that there are two roots, as there always will be for a polynomial in x^2. In this case x represents a concentration of H^+ (see Section 7.5). Thus the positive root is the one that solves the problem, since a concentration cannot be a negative number.

A second method for solving quadratic equations is by *successive approximations*, a systematic method of trial and error. A value of x is guessed and substituted into the equation everywhere x (or x^2) appears, except for one place. For example, for the equation

$$x^2 + (1.8 \times 10^{-5})x - 1.8 \times 10^{-9} = 0$$

we might guess $x = 2 \times 10^{-5}$. Substituting that value into the equation gives

$$x^2 + (1.8 \times 10^{-5})(2 \times 10^{-5}) - 1.8 \times 10^{-9} = 0$$

or $$x^2 = 1.8 \times 10^{-9} - 3.6 \times 10^{-10} = 1.4 \times 10^{-9}$$

Thus $$x = 3.7 \times 10^{-5}$$

Note that the guessed value of x (2×10^{-5}) is not the same as the value of x that is calculated (3.7×10^{-5}) after inserting the estimated value. This means that $x = 2 \times 10^{-5}$ is not the correct solution, and we must try another guess.

We take the calculated value (3.7×10^{-5}) as our next guess:

$$x^2 + (1.8 \times 10^{-5})(3.7 \times 10^{-5}) - 1.8 \times 10^{-9} = 0$$

$$x^2 = 1.8 \times 10^{-9} - 6.7 \times 10^{-10} = 1.1 \times 10^{-9}$$

Thus $$x = 3.3 \times 10^{-5}$$

Now we compare the two values of x again:

Guessed: $x = 3.7 \times 10^{-5}$

Calculated: $x = 3.3 \times 10^{-5}$

These values are closer but still not identical.

Next, we try 3.3×10^{-5} as our guess:

$$x^2 + (1.8 \times 10^{-5})(3.3 \times 10^{-5}) - 1.8 \times 10^{-9} = 0$$

$$x^2 = 1.8 \times 10^{-9} - 5.9 \times 10^{-10} = 1.2 \times 10^{-9}$$

Thus $$x = 3.5 \times 10^{-5}$$

Compare:

Guessed: $x = 3.3 \times 10^{-5}$

Calculated: $x = 3.5 \times 10^{-5}$

Next, we guess $x = 3.5 \times 10^{-5}$, which leads to

$$x^2 + (1.8 \times 10^{-5})(3.5 \times 10^{-5}) - 1.8 \times 10^{-9} = 0$$

$$x^2 = 1.8 \times 10^{-9} - 6.3 \times 10^{-10} = 1.2 \times 10^{-9}$$

Thus $$x = 3.5 \times 10^{-5}$$

Now the guessed value and the calculated value are the same; we have found the correct solution. Note that this agrees with one of the roots found with the quadratic formula in the first method above.

To further illustrate the method of successive approximations, we will solve Example 7.9 by using this procedure. In solving for $[H^+]$ for 0.010 M H_2SO_4, we obtain the following expression:

$$1.2 \times 10^{-2} = \frac{x(0.010 + x)}{0.010 - x}$$

which can be rearranged to give

$$x = (1.2 \times 10^{-2})\left(\frac{0.010 - x}{0.010 + x}\right)$$

We will guess a value for x, substitute it into the right side of the equation, and then calculate a value for x. In guessing a value for x, we know it must be less than 0.010, since a larger value would make the calculated value for x negative and the guessed and calculated values will never match. We start by guessing $x = 0.005$.

The results of the successive approximations are shown in the following table:

Trial	Guessed Value for x	Calculated Value for x
1	0.0050	0.0040
2	0.0040	0.0051
3	0.00450	0.00455
4	0.00452	0.00453

Note that the first guess was close to the actual value and that there was oscillation between 0.004 and 0.005 for the guessed and calculated values. For trial 3, an average of these values was used as the guess, and this led rapidly to the correct value (0.0045 to the correct number of significant figures). Also note that it is useful to carry extra digits until the correct value is obtained, which is then rounded off to the correct number of significant figures.

The method of successive approximations is especially useful for solving polynomials containing x to a power of 3 or higher. The procedure is the same as for quadratic equations: Substitute a guessed value for x into the equation for every x term but one, and then solve for x. Continue this process until the guessed and calculated values agree.

A1.5 Uncertainties in Measurements

The number associated with a measurement is obtained by using some measuring device. For example, consider the measurement of the volume of a liquid in a buret, as shown in Fig. A1.3, where the scale is greatly magnified. The volume is about 22.15 mL. Note that the last number must be estimated by interpolating between the 0.1-mL marks. Since the last number is estimated, its value may vary depending on who makes the measurement. If five different people read the same volume, the results might be as follows:

Person	Result of Measurement
1	22.15 mL
2	22.14 mL
3	22.16 mL
4	22.17 mL
5	22.16 mL

Note from these results that the first three numbers (22.1) remain the same regardless of who makes the measurement; these are called certain digits. However, the digit to the right of the 1 must be estimated and thus varies; it is called an uncertain digit. We customarily report a measurement by recording all the certain digits plus the *first* uncertain digit. In our example it would not make any sense to try to record the volume to thousandths of a milliliter because the value for hundredths of a milliliter must be estimated when using the buret.

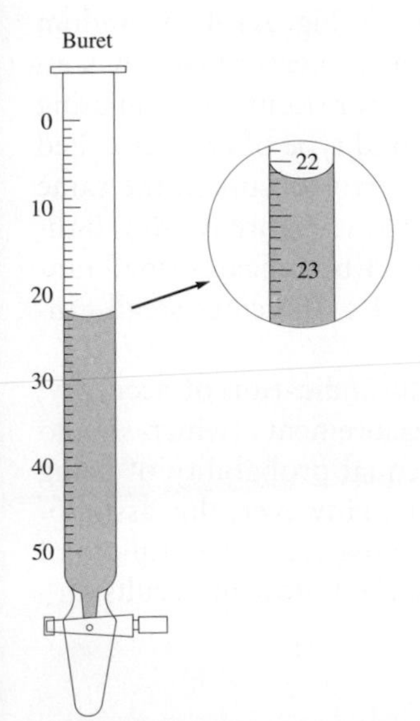

Figure A1.3
Measurement of volume using a buret. The volume is read at the bottom of the liquid curve (called the meniscus).

It is very important to realize that a *measurement always has some degree of uncertainty*. The uncertainty of a measurement depends on the precision of the measuring device. For example, using a bathroom scale, you might estimate that the mass of a grapefruit is about 1.5 pounds. Weighing the same grapefruit on a highly precise balance might produce a result of 1.476 pounds. In the first case the uncertainty occurs in the tenths of a pound place; in the second case the uncertainty occurs in the thousandths of a pound place. Suppose we weigh two similar grapefruit on the two devices and obtain the following results:

	Bathroom Scale	Balance
Grapefruit 1	1.5 lb	1.476 lb
Grapefruit 2	1.5 lb	1.518 lb

Do the two grapefruits have the same mass? The answer depends on which set of results you consider. Thus a conclusion based on a series of measurements depends on the certainty of those measurements. For this reason, it is important to indicate the uncertainty in any measurement. This is done by always recording the certain digits and the first uncertain digit (the estimated number). These numbers are called the **significant figures** of a measurement.

The convention of significant figures automatically gives an indication of the uncertainty in a measurement. The uncertainty in the last number (the estimated number) is usually assumed to be ± 1 unless otherwise indicated. For example, the measurement 1.86 kilograms can be interpreted to mean 1.86 ± 0.01 kilograms.

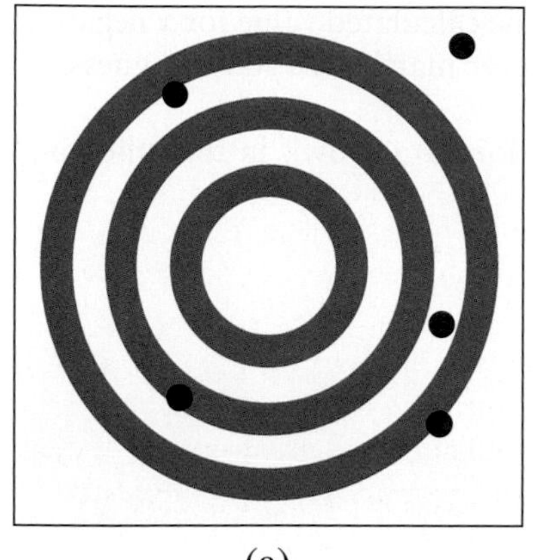

(a)

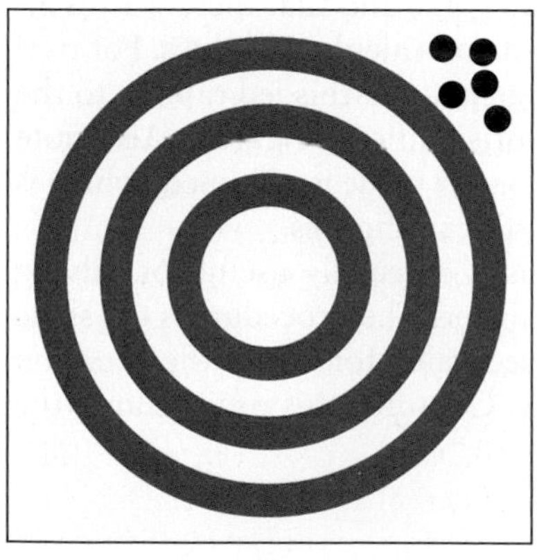

(b)

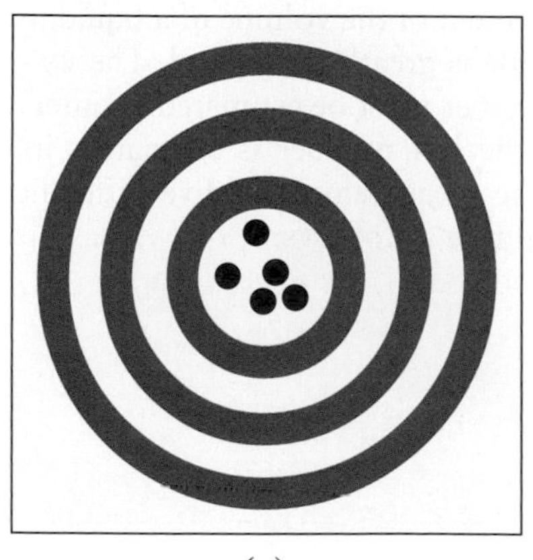

(c)

Figure A1.4
Shooting targets show the difference between *precise* and *accurate*.
(a) Neither accurate nor precise (large random errors). (b) Precise but not accurate (small random errors, large systematic error). (c) Bull's-eye! Both precise and accurate (small random errors, no systematic error).

Precision and Accuracy

Two terms often used to describe uncertainty in measurements are *precision* and *accuracy*. Although these words are frequently used interchangeably in everyday life, they have different meanings in the scientific context. **Accuracy** refers to the agreement of a particular value with the true value. **Precision** refers to the degree of agreement among several measurements of the same quantity. Precision reflects the *reproducibility* of a given type of measurement. The difference between these terms is illustrated by the results of three different target practices shown in Fig. A1.4.

Two different types of errors are also introduced in Fig. A1.4. A **random error** (also called an indeterminate error) means that a measurement has an equal probability of being high or low. This type of error occurs in estimating the value of the last digit of a measurement. The second type of error is called **systematic error** (or determinate error). This type of error occurs in the same direction each time; it is either always high or always low. Figure A1.4(a) indicates large random errors (poor technique). Figure A1.4(b) indicates small random errors but a large systematic error, and Fig. A1.4(c) indicates small random errors and no systematic error.

In quantitative work precision is often used as an indication of accuracy; we assume that the *average* of a series of precise measurements (which should "average out" the random errors because of their equal probability of being high or low) is accurate, or close to the "true" value. However, this assumption is valid only if systematic errors are absent. Suppose we weigh a piece of brass five times on a very precise balance and obtain the following results:

Weighing	Result
1	2.486 g
2	2.487 g
3	2.485 g
4	2.484 g
5	2.488 g

Normally, we would assume that the true mass of the piece of brass is very close to 2.486 grams, which is the average of the five results. However, if the balance has a defect causing it to give a result that is consistently 1.000 gram too high (a systematic error of +1.000 gram), then 2.486 grams would be seriously in error. The point here is that high precision among several measurements is an indication of accuracy *only* if you can be sure that systematic errors are absent.

Expression of Experimental Results

The accuracy of a measurement refers to how close it is to the true value. An inaccurate result occurs as a result of some flaw (systematic error) in the measurement: the presence of an interfering substance, incorrect calibration of an instrument, operator error, and so on. The goal of chemical analysis is to eliminate systematic error, but random errors can only be minimized. In practice, an experiment is almost always done in order to find an unknown value (the true value is not known—someone is trying to obtain that value by doing the experiment). In this case the precision of several replicate determinations is used to assess the accuracy of the result. The results of the replicate experiments are expressed as an average (which we assume is close to the true value) with an error limit that gives some indication of how close the average value may be to the true value. The error limit represents the uncertainty of the experimental result.

To illustrate this procedure, consider a situation that might arise in the pharmaceutical industry. Assume that the specification for a commercial 500-mg acetaminophen (the active painkiller in Tylenol) tablet is that each batch of tablets must contain 450 to 550 mg of acetaminophen per tablet. Suppose that chemical analysis gave the following results for a batch of acetaminophen tablets: 428, 479, 442, and 435 mg. How can these results be used to decide whether the batch of tablets meets the specification? Although the details of how to draw such conclusions from measured data are beyond the scope of this discussion, we will consider some aspects of this process. We will focus here on the types of experimental uncertainty, the expression of experimental results, and a simplified method for estimating experimental uncertainty when several types of measurements contribute to the final result.

There are two common ways of expressing an average: the mean and the median. The mean ($\overline{x}$) is the arithmetic average of the results, or

$$\text{Mean} = \overline{x} = \sum_{i=1}^{n} \frac{x_i}{n} = \frac{x_1 + x_2 + \cdots + x_n}{n}$$

where Σ means take the sum of the values. The mean is equal to the sum of all the measurements divided by the number of measurements. For the acetaminophen results given previously, the mean is

$$\overline{x} = \frac{428 + 479 + 442 + 435}{4} = 446 \text{ mg}$$

The median is the value that lies in the middle among the results. Half of the measurements are above the median and half are below the median. For results of 465, 485, and 492 mg, the median is 485 mg. When there is an even number of results, the median is the average of the two middle results. For the acetaminophen results, the median is

$$\frac{442 + 435}{2} = 439 \text{ mg}$$

There are several advantages to using the median. If a small number of measurements is made, one value can greatly affect the mean. Consider the results for the analysis of acetaminophen: 428, 479, 442, and 435 mg. The mean is 446 mg, which is larger than three of the four results. The median is 439 mg, which lies near the three values that are relatively close to one another.

In addition to expressing an average value for a series of results, we must also express the uncertainty. This usually means expressing either the precision of the measurements or the observed range of the measurements. The range of a series of measurements is defined by the smallest value and the largest value. For the analytical results on the acetaminophen tablets, the range is from 428 to 479 mg. Using this range, we can express the results by saying that the true value lies between 428 and 479 mg. That is, we can express the amount of acetaminophen in a typical tablet as 446 ± 33 mg, where the error limit is chosen to give the observed range (approximately).

The most common way to specify precision is by the standard deviation s, which for a small number of measurements is given by the formula

$$s = \left[\frac{\sum_{i=1}^{n}(x_i - \overline{x})^2}{n - 1}\right]^{1/2}$$

where x_i is an individual result, $\overline{x}$ is the average (either mean or median), and n is the total number of measurements. For the acetaminophen example, we have

$$s = \left[\frac{(428 - 446)^2 + (479 - 446)^2 + (442 - 446)^2 + (435 - 446)^2}{4 - 1}\right]^{1/2} = 23$$

Thus we can say that the amount of acetaminophen in a typical tablet in the batch of tablets is 446 mg with a sample standard deviation of 23 mg. Statistically, this means that any additional measurement has a 68% probability (68 chances out of 100) of being between 423 mg (446 − 23) and 469 mg (446 + 23). Thus the standard deviation is a measure of the precision of a given type of measurement.

In scientific calculations it is also useful to be able to estimate the precision of a procedure that involves several measurements by combining the precisions of the individual steps. That is, we want to answer the following question: How do the uncertainties propagate when we combine the results of several different types of measurements? There are many ways to deal with the propagation of uncertainty. We will discuss one simple method below.

Worst-Case Method for Estimating Experimental Uncertainty

To illustrate this method, we will consider the determination of the density of an irregularly shaped solid. In this determination we make three measurements. First, we measure the mass of the object on a balance. Next, we must obtain the volume of the solid. The easiest method for doing this is to partially fill a graduated cylinder with a liquid and record the volume. Then we add the solid and record the volume again. The difference in the measured volumes is the volume of the solid. We can then calculate the density of the solid from the equation

$$D = \frac{M}{V_2 - V_1}$$

where M is the mass of the solid, V_1 is the initial volume of liquid in the graduated cylinder, and V_2 is the volume of liquid plus solid. Suppose we get the following results:

$$M = 23.06 \text{ g}$$

$$V_1 = 10.4 \text{ mL}$$

$$V_2 = 13.5 \text{ mL}$$

The calculated density is

$$\frac{23.06 \text{ g}}{13.5 \text{ mL} - 10.4 \text{ mL}} = 7.44 \text{ g/mL}$$

Now suppose that the precision of the balance used is ±0.02 g and that the volume measurements are precise to ±0.05 mL. How do we estimate the uncertainty of the density? We can do this by assuming a worst case. That is, we assume the largest uncertainties in all measurements, and we see what combinations of measurements will give the largest and smallest possible results (the greatest range). Since the density is the mass divided by the volume, the largest value of the density will be that obtained by using the largest possible mass and the smallest possible volume:

Largest possible mass = 23.06 + 0.02

$$D_{\text{max}} = \frac{23.08}{13.45 - 10.45} = 7.69 \text{ g/mL}$$

Smallest possible V_2 (13.45); Largest possible V_1 (10.45)

The smallest value of the density is

Smallest possible mass

$$D_{\text{min}} = \frac{23.04}{13.55 - 10.35} = 7.20 \text{ g/mL}$$

Largest possible V_2 (13.55); Smallest possible V_1 (10.35)

Thus the calculated range is from 7.20 to 7.69, and the average of these values is 7.45. The error limit is the number that gives the high and low range values when added and subtracted from the average. Therefore, we can express the density as 7.45 ± 0.25 g/mL, which is the average value plus or minus the quantity that gives the range calculated by assuming the largest uncertainties.

Analysis of the propagation of uncertainties is useful in drawing qualitative conclusions from the analysis of measurements. For example, suppose that we obtained the preceding results for the density of an unknown alloy and we want to know if it is one of the following alloys:

Alloy A: $D = 7.58$ g/mL
Alloy B: $D = 7.42$ g/mL
Alloy C: $D = 8.56$ g/mL

We can safely conclude that the alloy is not C. But the values of the densities for alloys A and B are both within the inherent uncertainty of our method. To distinguish between A and B, we need to improve the precision of our determination. The obvious choice is to improve the precision of the volume measurement.

The worst-case method is useful for estimating the maximum uncertainty expected when the results of several measurements are combined to obtain a result. We assume the maximum uncertainty in each measurement and then calculate the minimum and maximum possible results. These extreme values describe the range and thus the maximum error limit associated with a particular determination.

Table A1.1

Values of t for 90% and 95% Confidence Levels

	Values of t for Confidence Intervals	
n	90%	95%
2	6.31	12.7
3	2.92	4.30
4	2.35	3.18
5	2.13	2.78
6	2.02	2.57
7	1.94	2.45
8	1.90	2.36
9	1.86	2.31
10	1.83	2.26

Confidence Limits

A more sophisticated method for estimating the uncertainty of a particular type of determination involves the use of confidence limits. A confidence limit is defined as

$$\text{Confidence limit} = \pm\frac{ts}{\sqrt{n}}$$

where t = a weighting factor based on statistical analysis

s = the standard deviation

n = the number of experiments carried out

In this context an experiment may refer to a single type of measurement (for example, weighing an object) or to a procedure that requires various types of measurements to obtain a given final result (for example, obtaining the percentage of iron in a particular sample of iron ore). Some representative values of t are listed in Table A1.1.

A 95% confidence level means that the true value (the *average* obtained if the experiment were repeated an *infinite* number of times) will lie within $\pm ts/\sqrt{n}$ of the *observed* average (obtained from n experiments) with a 95% probability (95 of 100 times). Thus the factor $\pm ts/\sqrt{n}$ represents an error limit for a given set of results from a particular type of experiment. Thus we might represent the result of n determinations as

$$\bar{x} \pm \frac{ts}{\sqrt{n}}$$

where $\bar{x}$ is the average of the results from the n experiments. This type of error limit is expected to be considerably smaller than that obtained from a worst-case analysis.

A1.6 Significant Figures

Calculating the final result for an experiment usually involves adding, subtracting, multiplying, or dividing the results of various types of measurements. Thus it is important to be able to estimate the uncertainty in the final result. In the previous section we have considered this process in some detail. A closely related matter concerns the number of digits that should be retained in the result of a given calculation. In other words, how many of the digits in the result are significant (meaningful) relative to the uncertainty expected in the result? From statistical analyses of how uncertainties accumulate when arithmetic operations are carried out, rules have been developed for determining the correct number of significant figures in a final result. First, we must consider how to count the number of significant figures (digits) represented in a particular number.

Rules for Counting Significant Figures (Digits)

1. *Nonzero integers.* Nonzero integers always count as significant figures.
2. *Zeros.* There are three classes of zeros:
   a. *Leading zeros* are zeros that *precede* all the nonzero digits. They do not count as significant figures. In the number 0.0025 the three zeros simply indicate the position of the decimal point. This number has only two significant figures.
   b. *Captive zeros* are zeros *between* nonzero digits. They always count as significant figures. The number 1.008 has four significant figures.

c. *Trailing zeros* are zeros at the *right end* of the number. They are significant only if the number contains a decimal point. The number 100 has only one significant figure, whereas the number 1.00×10^2 has three significant figures. The number one hundred written as 100. also has three significant figures.

3. *Exact numbers.* Many times calculations involve numbers that were not obtained by using measuring devices but were determined by counting: 10 experiments, 3 apples, 8 molecules. Such numbers are called *exact numbers.* They can be assumed to have an infinite number of significant figures. Other examples of exact numbers are the 2 in $2\pi r$ (the circumference of a circle) and the 4 and the 3 in $\frac{4}{3}\pi r^3$ (the volume of a sphere). Exact numbers can also arise from definitions. For example, one inch is defined as exactly 2.54 centimeters. Thus, in the statement 1 in = 2.54 cm, neither the 2.54 nor the 1 limits the number of significant figures when used in a calculation.

The following rules apply for determining the number of significant figures in the result of a calculation.

*Rules for Significant Figures in Mathematical Operations**

1. For *multiplication or division* the number of significant figures in the result is the same as the number in the least precise measurement used in the calculation. For example, consider this calculation:

$$4.56 \times 1.4 = 6.38 \xrightarrow{\text{Corrected}} 6.4$$

↑ Limiting term has two significant figures — Two significant figures

The correct product has only two significant figures, since 1.4 has two significant figures.

2. *For addition or subtraction* the result has the same number of decimal places as the least precise measurement used in the calculation. For example, consider the following sum:

$$\begin{array}{r} 12.11 \\ 18.0 \\ 1.013 \\ \hline 31.123 \end{array} \xrightarrow{\text{Corrected}} 31.1$$

18.0 ← Limiting term has one decimal place

31.1 ↑ One decimal place

The correct result is 31.1, since 18.0 has only one decimal place.

Note that for multiplication and division significant figures are counted. For addition and subtraction the decimal places are counted.

In most calculations you will need to round off numbers to obtain the correct number of significant figures. The following rules should be applied for rounding.

---

*Although these rules work well for most cases, they can give misleading results in certain cases. For a discussion of this, see L. M. Schwartz, "Propagation of Significant Figures," *J. Chem. Ed.* **62** (1985):693.

Rules for Rounding

1. In a series of calculations, carry the extra digits through to the final result, *then* round off.*
2. If the digit to be removed†
   a. is less than 5, the preceding digit stays the same. For example, 1.33 rounds to 1.3.
   b. is equal to or greater than 5, the preceding digit is increased by 1. For example, 1.36 rounds to 1.4.

When rounding, use only the first number to the right of the last significant figure. Do not round off sequentially. For example, the number 4.348 when rounded to two significant figures is 4.3, not 4.4.

Appendix Two Units of Measurement and Conversions Among Units

A2.1 Measurements

Making observations is fundamental to all science. A quantitative observation, or **measurement,** always consists of two parts: a *number* and a scale (a *unit*). Both parts must be present for the measurement to be meaningful.

The two most widely used systems of units are the *English system* used in the United States and the *metric system* used by most of the rest of the industrialized world. This duality obviously causes a good deal of trouble; for example, parts as simple as bolts are not interchangeable between machines built using the different systems. As a result, the United States has begun to adopt the metric system.

For many years, most scientists worldwide have used the metric system. In 1960 an international agreement established a system of units called the *International System* (*le Système International* in French), abbreviated **SI**. This system is based on the metric system and the units derived from the metric system. The fundamental SI units are listed in Table A2.1.

Because the fundamental units are not always convenient (expressing the mass of a pin in kilograms is awkward), the SI system uses prefixes to change the size of the unit. These prefixes are listed in Table A2.2.

Table A2.1

The Fundamental SI Units

Physical Quantity	Name of Unit	Abbreviation
Mass	kilogram	kg
Length	meter	m
Time	second	s
Temperature	Kelvin	K
Electric current	ampere	A
Amount of substance	mole	mol
Luminous intensity	candela	cd

*This practice will not usually be followed in the examples in this text because we want to show the correct number of significant figures in each step. However, in the answers to the end-of-chapter exercises, only the final answer is rounded.

†This procedure is consistent with the operation of calculators.

Table A2.2
The Prefixes Used in the SI System

Prefix	Symbol	Meaning	Exponential Notation*
exa	E	1,000,000,000,000,000,000	10^{18}
peta	P	1,000,000,000,000,000	10^{15}
tera	T	1,000,000,000,000	10^{12}
giga	**G**	**1,000,000,000**	$\mathbf{10^{9}}$
mega	**M**	**1,000,000**	$\mathbf{10^{6}}$
kilo	**k**	**1000**	$\mathbf{10^{3}}$
hecto	h	100	10^{2}
deka	da	10	10^{1}
—	—	1	10^{0}
deci	**d**	**0.1**	$\mathbf{10^{-1}}$
centi	**c**	**0.01**	$\mathbf{10^{-2}}$
milli	**m**	**0.001**	$\mathbf{10^{-3}}$
micro	μ	**0.000001**	$\mathbf{10^{-6}}$
nano	**n**	**0.000000001**	$\mathbf{10^{-9}}$
pico	p	0.000000000001	10^{-12}
femto	f	0.000000000000001	10^{-15}
atto	a	0.000000000000000001	10^{-18}

*The most common notations are shown in bold. See Appendix A1.1 if you need a review of exponential notation.

One physical quantity that is very important in chemistry is *volume,* which is not a fundamental SI unit; it is derived from length. A cube with dimensions of 1 m on each edge has a volume of $(1\text{ m})^3 = 1\text{ m}^3$. Then, recognizing that there are 10 decimeters (dm) in a meter, the volume of the cube is $(10\text{ dm})^3 = 1000\text{ dm}^3$. A cubic decimeter, dm^3, is commonly called a liter (L), which is a unit of volume slightly larger than a quart. Similarly, since 1 dm equals 10 centimeters (cm), the liter $(1\text{ dm})^3$ contains 1000 cm^3, or 1000 milliliters (mL).

A2.2 Unit Conversions

It is often necessary to convert results from one system of units to another. The most common way of converting units is by the *unit factor method,* more commonly called **dimensional analysis.** To illustrate the use of this method, we will look at a simple unit conversion.

Consider a pin measuring 2.85 cm in length. What is its length in inches? To solve this problem, we must use the equivalence statement

$$2.54\text{ cm} = 1\text{ in} \qquad \text{(exactly)}$$

If we divide both sides of this equation by 2.54 cm, we get

$$\frac{2.54\text{ cm}}{2.54\text{ cm}} = 1 = \frac{1\text{ in}}{2.54\text{ cm}}$$

Note that the expression 1 in/2.54 cm equals 1. This expression is called a **unit factor.** Since 1 in and 2.54 cm are exactly equivalent, multiplying any expression by this unit factor will not change its value.

The pin has a length of 2.85 cm. Multiplying this length by the unit factor gives

$$2.85\ \cancel{\text{cm}} \times \frac{1\text{ in}}{1.54\ \cancel{\text{cm}}} = \frac{2.85}{2.54}\text{ in} = 1.12\text{ in}$$

Note that the centimeter units cancel to give inches for the result. This is exactly what we wanted to accomplish. Note also that the result has three significant figures, as required by the number 2.85. Recall that the 1 and 2.54 in the conversion factor are exact numbers by definition.

STEPS

Converting from One Unit to Another

1. To convert from one unit to another, use the equivalence statement that relates the two units.
2. Derive the appropriate unit factor by noting the direction of the required change (to cancel the unwanted units).
3. Multiply the quantity to be converted by the unit factor to give the quantity with the desired units.

In dimensional analysis your verification that everything has been done correctly is that the correct units are obtained in the end. *In doing chemistry problems, you should always include the units for the quantities used.* Always check to see that the units cancel to give the correct units for the final result. This provides a very valuable check, especially for complicated problems.

Appendix Three Spectral Analysis

Although volumetric and gravimetric analyses are still commonly used, spectroscopy is the technique most often used for modern chemical analysis. *Spectroscopy* is the study of electromagnetic radiation emitted or absorbed by a given chemical species. Since the quantity of radiation absorbed or emitted can be related to the quantity of the absorbing or emitting species present, this technique can be used for quantitative analysis. There are many spectroscopic techniques, since electromagnetic radiation spans a wide range of energies to include microwaves, X rays, and ultraviolet, infrared, and visible light, to name a few of its familiar forms. However, we will consider here only one procedure, which is based on the absorption of visible light.

If a liquid is colored, it is because some component of the liquid absorbs visible light. In a solution the greater the concentration of the light-absorbing substance, the more light is absorbed, and the more intense is the color of the solution.

The quantity of light absorbed by a substance can be measured by a *spectrophotometer,* shown schematically in Fig. A3.1. This instrument consists of a source that emits all wavelengths of light in the visible region (wavelengths of $\approx$400–700 nm); a monochromator, which selects a given wavelength of light; a sample holder for the solution being measured; and a detector, which compares the intensity of incident light I_0 with the intensity of light after it has passed through the sample I. The ratio I/I_0, called the *transmittance,* is a measure of the fraction of light that passes through the sample. The amount of light absorbed is given by the *absorbance* A, where

$$A = -\log \frac{I}{I_0}$$

The absorbance can be expressed by the *Beer-Lambert law:*

$$A = \epsilon l c$$

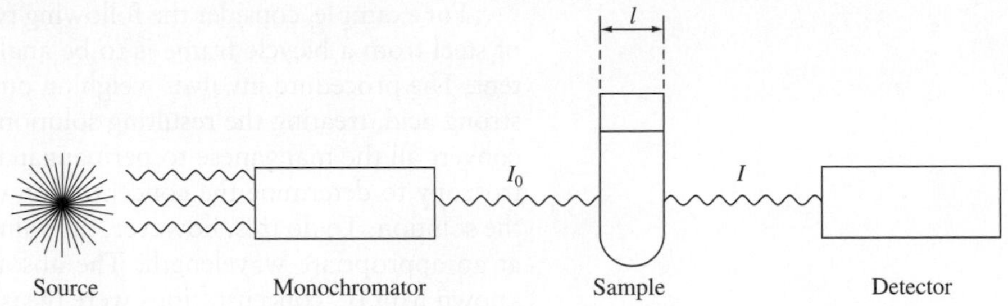

Figure A3.1
A schematic diagram of a simple spectrophotometer. The source emits all wavelengths of visible light, which are dispersed by using a prism or grating and then focused, one wavelength at a time, onto the sample. The detector compares the intensity of the incident light (I_0) with the intensity of the light after it has passed through the sample (I).

where ϵ is the molar absorptivity or the molar extinction coefficient (in L mol^{-1} cm^{-1}), l is the distance the light travels through the solution (in cm), and c is the concentration of the absorbing species (in mol/L). The Beer-Lambert law is the basis for using spectroscopy in quantitative analysis. If ϵ and l are known, determining A for a solution allows us to calculate the concentration of the absorbing species in the solution.

Suppose we have a pink solution containing an unknown concentration of $Co^{2+}(aq)$ ions. A sample of this solution is placed in a spectrophotometer, and the absorbance is measured at a wavelength where ϵ for $Co^{2+}(aq)$ is known to be 12 L mol^{-1} cm^{-1}. The absorbance A is found to be 0.60. The width of the sample tube is 1.0 cm. We want to determine the concentration of $Co^{2+}(aq)$ in the solution. This problem can be solved by a straightforward application of the Beer-Lambert law,

$$A = \epsilon l c$$

where

$$A = 0.60$$

$$\epsilon = \frac{12\text{ L}}{\text{mol cm}}$$

$$l = \text{light path} = 1.0\text{ cm}$$

Solving for the concentration gives

$$c = \frac{A}{\epsilon l} = \frac{0.60}{\left(12\,\frac{\text{L}}{\text{mol cm}}\right)(1.0\text{ cm})} = 5.0 \times 10^{-2}\text{ mol/L}$$

To obtain the unknown concentration of an absorbing species from the measured absorbance, we must know the product ϵl, since

$$c = \frac{A}{\epsilon l}$$

We can obtain the product ϵl by measuring the absorbance of a solution of *known* concentration, since

$$\epsilon l = \frac{A}{c}$$

A: Measured using a spectrophotometer

c: Known from making up the solution

However, a more accurate value of the product ϵl can be obtained by plotting A versus c for a series of solutions. Note that the equation $A = \epsilon l c$ gives a straight line with slope ϵl when A is plotted against c.

For example, consider the following typical spectroscopic analysis. A sample of steel from a bicycle frame is to be analyzed to determine its manganese content. The procedure involves weighing out a sample of the steel, dissolving it in strong acid, treating the resulting solution with a very strong oxidizing agent to convert all the manganese to permanganate ion (MnO_4^-), and then using spectroscopy to determine the concentration of the intensely purple MnO_4^- ions in the solution. To do this, however, the value of ϵl for MnO_4^- must be determined at an appropriate wavelength. The absorbance values for four solutions with known MnO_4^- concentrations were measured to give the following data:

Solution	Concentration of MnO_4^- (mol/L)	Absorbance
1	7.00×10^{-5}	0.175
2	1.00×10^{-4}	0.250
3	2.00×10^{-4}	0.500
4	3.50×10^{-4}	0.875

A plot of absorbance versus concentration for the solutions of known concentration is shown in Fig. A3.2. The slope of this line (change in A/change in c) is 2.48×10^3 L/mol. This quantity represents the product ϵl.

A sample of the steel weighing 0.1523 g was dissolved, and the unknown amount of manganese was converted to MnO_4^- ions. Water was then added to give a solution with a final volume of 100.0 mL. A portion of this solution was placed in a spectrophotometer, and its absorbance was found to be 0.780. We can use these data to calculate the percent manganese in the steel. The MnO_4^- ions from the manganese in the dissolved steel sample show an absorbance of 0.780. Using the Beer-Lambert law, we calculate the concentration of MnO_4^- in this solution:

$$c = \frac{A}{\epsilon l} = \frac{0.780}{2.48 \times 10^3 \text{ L/mol}} = 3.15 \times 10^{-4} \text{ mol/L}$$

However, there is a more direct way for finding c. Using a graph such as that in Fig. A3.2 (often called a Beer's law plot), we can read the concentration that corresponds to $A = 0.780$. This interpolation is shown by dashed lines on

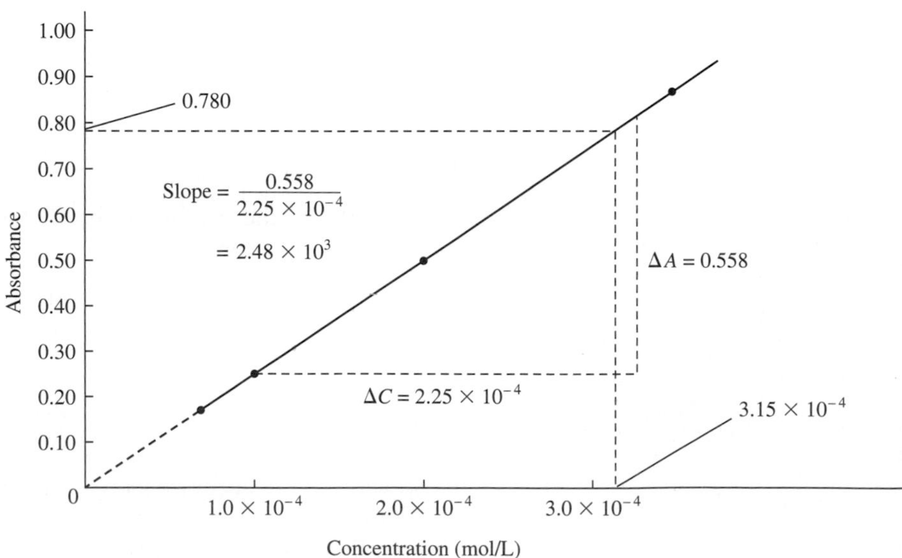

Figure A3.2
A plot of absorbance versus concentration of MnO_4^- in a series of solutions of known concentration.

the graph. By this method, $c = 3.15 \times 10^{-4}$ mol/L, which agrees with the value obtained above.

Recall that the original 0.1523-g steel sample was dissolved, the manganese was converted to permanganate, and the volume was adjusted to 100.0 mL. We now know that the $[MnO_4^-]$ in that solution is 3.15×10^{-4} *M*. Using this concentration, we can calculate the total number of moles of MnO_4^- in that solution:

$$\text{Mol of } MnO_4^- = 100.0 \text{ mL} \times \frac{1 \text{ L}}{1000 \text{ mL}} \times 3.15 \times 10^{-4} \frac{\text{mol}}{\text{L}}$$

$$= 3.15 \times 10^{-5} \text{ mol}$$

Each mole of manganese in the original steel sample yields a mole of MnO_4^-. That is,

$$1 \text{ mol of Mn} \xrightarrow{\text{Oxidation}} 1 \text{ mol of } MnO_4^-$$

so the original steel sample must have contained 3.15×10^{-5} mol of manganese. The mass of manganese present in the sample is

$$3.15 \times 10^{-5} \text{ mol of Mn} \times \frac{54.938 \text{ g of Mn}}{1 \text{ mol of Mn}} = 1.73 \times 10^{-3} \text{ g of Mn}$$

Since the steel sample weighed 0.1523 g, the percent manganese in the steel is

$$\frac{1.73 \times 10^{-3} \text{ g of Mn}}{1.523 \times 10^{-1} \text{ g of sample}} \times 100\% = 1.14\%$$

This example illustrates a typical use of spectroscopy in quantitative analysis. The steps commonly involved are as follows:

1. Preparation of a calibration plot (a Beer's law plot) from the measured absorbance values of a series of solutions with known concentrations.
2. Measurement of the absorbance of the solution of unknown concentration.
3. Use of the calibration plot to determine the unknown concentration.

Appendix Four | Selected Thermodynamic Data*

Substance and State	ΔH_f° (kJ/mol)	ΔG_f° (kJ/mol)	S° (J K^{-1} mol^{-1})
Aluminum			
$Al(s)$	0	0	28
$Al_2O_3(s)$	−1676	−1582	51
$Al(OH)_3(s)$	−1277	—	—
$AlCl_3(s)$	−704	−629	111
Barium			
$Ba(s)$	0	0	67
$BaCO_3(s)$	−1219	−1139	112
$BaO(s)$	−582	−552	70
$Ba(OH)_2(s)$	−946	—	—
$BaSO_4(s)$	−1465	−1353	132
Beryllium			
$Be(s)$	0	0	10
$BeO(s)$	−599	−569	14
$Be(OH)_2(s)$	−904	−815	47
Bromine			
$Br_2(l)$	0	0	152
$Br_2(g)$	31	3	245
$Br_2(aq)$	−3	4	130
$Br^-(aq)$	−121	−104	82
$HBr(g)$	−36	−53	199
Cadmium			
$Cd(s)$	0	0	52
$CdO(s)$	−258	−228	55
$Cd(OH)_2(s)$	−561	−474	96
$CdS(s)$	−162	−156	65
$CdSO_4(s)$	−935	−823	123
Calcium			
$Ca(s)$	0	0	41
$CaC_2(s)$	−63	−68	70

*All values are assumed precise to at least ±1.

(continued)

Appendix Four (continued)

Substance and State	ΔH_f° (kJ/mol)	ΔG_f° (kJ/mol)	S° (J K^{-1} mol^{-1})
$CaCO_3(s)$	−1207	−1129	93
$CaO(s)$	−635	−604	40
$Ca(OH)_2(s)$	−987	−899	83
$Ca_3(PO_4)_2(s)$	−4126	−3890	241
$CaSO_4(s)$	−1433	−1320	107
$CaSiO_3(s)$	−1630	−1550	84
Carbon			
$C(s)$ (graphite)	0	0	6
$C(s)$ (diamond)	2	3	2
$CO(g)$	−110.5	−137	198
$CO_2(g)$	−393.5	−394	214
$CH_4(g)$	−75	−51	186
$CH_3OH(g)$	−201	−163	240
$CH_3OH(l)$	−239	−166	127
$H_2CO(g)$	−116	−110	219
$HCOOH(g)$	−363	−351	249
$HCN(g)$	135.1	125	202
$C_2H_2(g)$	227	209	201
$C_2H_4(g)$	52	68	219
$CH_3CHO(g)$	−166	−129	250
$C_2H_5OH(l)$	−278	−175	161
$C_2H_6(g)$	−84.7	−32.9	229.5
$C_3H_6(g)$	20.9	62.7	266.9
$C_3H_8(g)$	−104	−24	270
$C_2H_4O(g)$ (ethylene oxide)	−53	−13	242
CH_2 P $CHCN(g)$	185.0	195.4	274
$CH_3COOH(l)$	−484	−389	160
$C_6H_{12}O_6(s)$	−1275	−911	212
$CCl_4(l)$	−135	−65	216
Chlorine			
$Cl_2(g)$	0	0	223
$Cl_2(aq)$	−23	7	121
$Cl^-(aq)$	−167	−131	57
$HCl(g)$	−92	−95	187
Chromium			
$Cr(s)$	0	0	24
$Cr_2O_3(s)$	−1128	−1047	81
$CrO_3(s)$	−579	−502	72
Copper			
$Cu(s)$	0	0	33
$CuCO_3(s)$	−595	−518	88
$Cu_2O(s)$	−170	−148	93
$CuO(s)$	−156	−128	43
$Cu(OH)_2(s)$	−450	−372	108
$CuS(s)$	−49	−49	67
Fluorine			
$F_2(g)$	0	0	203
$F^-(aq)$	−333	−279	−14
$HF(g)$	−271	−273	174
Hydrogen			
$H_2(g)$	0	0	131
$H(g)$	217	203	115
$H^+(aq)$	0	0	0
$OH^-(aq)$	−230	−157	−11
$H_2O(l)$	−286	−237	70
$H_2O(g)$	−242	−229	189
Iodine			
$I_2(s)$	0	0	116
$I_2(g)$	62	19	261
$I_2(aq)$	23	16	137
$I^-(aq)$	−55	−52	106
Iron			
$Fe(s)$	0	0	27
$Fe_3C(s)$	21	15	108
$Fe_{0.95}O(s)$ (wustite)	−264	−240	59
$FeO(s)$	−272	−255	61
$Fe_3O_4(s)$ (magnetite)	−1117	−1013	146
$Fe_2O_3(s)$ (hematite)	−826	−740	90
$FeS(s)$	−95	−97	67
$FeS_2(s)$	−178	−166	53
$FeSO_4(s)$	−929	−825	121
Lead			
$Pb(s)$	0	0	65
$PbO_2(s)$	−277	−217	69
$PbS(s)$	−100	−99	91
$PbSO_4(s)$	−920	−813	149
Magnesium			
$Mg(s)$	0	0	33
$MgCO_3(s)$	−1113	−1029	66
$MgO(s)$	−602	−569	27
$Mg(OH)_2(s)$	−925	−834	64
Manganese			
$Mn(s)$	0	0	32
$MnO(s)$	−385	−363	60
$Mn_3O_4(s)$	−1387	−1280	149
$Mn_2O_3(s)$	−971	−893	110
$MnO_2(s)$	−521	−466	53
$MnO_4^-(aq)$	−543	−449	190
Mercury			
$Hg(l)$	0	0	76
$Hg_2Cl_2(s)$	−265	−211	196
$HgCl_2(s)$	−230	−184	144
$HgO(s)$	−90	−59	70
$HgS(s)$	−58	−49	78
Nickel			
$Ni(s)$	0	0	30
$NiCl_2(s)$	−316	−272	107
$NiO(s)$	−241	−213	38
$Ni(OH)_2(s)$	−538	−453	79
$NiS(s)$	−93	−90	53
Nitrogen			
$N_2(g)$	0	0	192
$NH_3(g)$	−46	−17	193
$NH_3(aq)$	−80	−27	111
$NH_4^+(aq)$	−132	−79	113
$NO(g)$	90	87	211

Appendix Four (continued)

Substance and State	ΔH_f° (kJ/mol)	ΔG_f° (kJ/mol)	S° (J K^{-1} mol^{-1})
$NO_2(g)$	34	52	240
$N_2O(g)$	82	104	220
$N_2O_4(g)$	10	98	304
$N_2O_4(l)$	−20	97	209
$N_2O_5(s)$	−42	134	178
$N_2H_4(l)$	51	149	121
$N_2H_3CH_3(l)$	54	180	166
$HNO_3(aq)$	−207	−111	146
$HNO_3(l)$	−174	−81	156
$NH_4ClO_4(s)$	−295	−89	186
$NH_4Cl(s)$	−314	−203	96
Oxygen			
$O_2(g)$	0	0	205
$O(g)$	249	232	161
$O_3(g)$	143	163	239
Phosphorus			
$P(s)$ (white)	0	0	41
$P(s)$ (red)	−18	−12	23
$P(s)$ (black)	−39	−33	23
$P_4(g)$	59	24	280
$PF_5(g)$	−1578	−1509	296
$PH_3(g)$	5	13	210
$H_3PO_4(s)$	−1279	−1119	110
$H_3PO_4(l)$	−1267	—	—
$H_3PO_4(aq)$	−1288	−1143	158
$P_4O_{10}(s)$	−2984	−2698	229
Potassium			
$K(s)$	0	0	64
$KCl(s)$	−436	−408	83
$KClO_3(s)$	−391	−290	143
$KClO_4(s)$	−433	−304	151
$K_2O(s)$	−361	−322	98
$K_2O_2(s)$	−496	−430	113
$KO_2(s)$	−283	−238	117
$KOH(s)$	−425	−379	79
$KOH(aq)$	−481	−440	9.20
Silicon			
$SiO_2(s)$ (quartz)	−911	−856	42
$SiCl_4(l)$	−687	−620	240
Silver			
$Ag(s)$	0	0	43
$Ag^+(aq)$	105	77	73
$AgBr(s)$	−100	−97	107
$AgCN(s)$	146	164	84
$AgCl(s)$	−127	−110	96
$Ag_2CrO_4(s)$	−712	−622	217
$AgI(s)$	−62	−66	115
$Ag_2O(s)$	−31	−11	122
$Ag_2S(s)$	−32	−40	146
Sodium			
$Na(s)$	0	0	51
$Na^+(aq)$	−240	−262	59
$NaBr(s)$	−360	−347	84
$Na_2CO_3(s)$	−1131	−1048	136
$NaHCO_3(s)$	−948	−852	102
$NaCl(s)$	−411	−384	72
$NaH(s)$	−56	−33	40
$NaI(s)$	−288	−282	91
$NaNO_2(s)$	−359	—	—
$NaNO_3(s)$	−467	−366	116
$Na_2O(s)$	−416	−377	73
$Na_2O_2(s)$	−515	−451	95
$NaOH(s)$	−427	−381	64
$NaOH(aq)$	−470	−419	50
Sulfur			
$S(s)$ (rhombic)	0	0	32
$S(s)$ (monoclinic)	0.3	0.1	33
$S^{2-}(aq)$	33	86	−15
$S_8(g)$	102	50	431
$SF_6(g)$	−1209	−1105	292
$H_2S(g)$	−21	−34	206
$SO_2(g)$	−297	−300	248
$SO_3(g)$	−396	−371	257
$SO_4^{2-}(aq)$	−909	−745	20
$H_2SO_4(l)$	−814	−690	157
$H_2SO_4(aq)$	−909	−745	20
Tin			
$Sn(s)$ (white)	0	0	52
$Sn(s)$ (gray)	−2	0.1	44
$SnO(s)$	−285	−257	56
$SnO_2(s)$	−581	−520	52
$Sn(OH)_2(s)$	−561	−492	155
Titanium			
$TiCl_4(g)$	−763	−727	355
$TiO_2(s)$	−945	−890	50
Uranium			
$U(s)$	0	0	50
$UF_6(s)$	−2137	−2008	228
$UF_6(g)$	−2113	−2029	380
$UO_2(s)$	−1084	−1029	78
$U_3O_8(s)$	−3575	−3393	282
$UO_3(s)$	−1230	−1150	99
Xenon			
$Xe(g)$	0	0	170
$XeF_2(g)$	−108	−48	254
$XeF_4(s)$	−251	−121	146
$XeF_6(g)$	−294	—	—
$XeO_3(s)$	402	—	—
Zinc			
$Zn(s)$	0	0	42
$ZnO(s)$	−348	−318	44
$Zn(OH)_2(s)$	−642	—	—
$ZnS(s)$ (wurtzite)	−193	—	—
$ZnS(s)$ (zinc blende)	−206	−201	58
$ZnSO_4(s)$	−983	−874	120

Appendix Five Equilibrium Constants and Reduction Potentials

Table A5.1

K_a for Some Common Monoprotic Acids

Name	Formula	Value of K_a
Hydrogen sulfate ion	HSO_4^-	1.2×10^{-2}
Chlorous acid	$HClO_2$	1.2×10^{-2}
Monochloracetic acid	$HC_2H_2ClO_2$	1.35×10^{-3}
Hydrofluoric acid	HF	7.2×10^{-4}
Nitrous acid	HNO_2	4.0×10^{-4}
Formic acid	HCO_2H	1.8×10^{-4}
Lactic acid	$HC_3H_5O_3$	1.38×10^{-4}
Benzoic acid	$HC_7H_5O_2$	6.4×10^{-5}
Acetic acid	$HC_2H_3O_2$	1.8×10^{-5}
Hydrated aluminum(III) ion	$[Al(H_2O)_6]^{3+}$	1.4×10^{-5}
Propanoic acid	$HC_3H_5O_2$	1.3×10^{-5}
Hypochlorous acid	$HOCl$	3.5×10^{-8}
Hypobromous acid	$HOBr$	2×10^{-9}
Hydrocyanic acid	HCN	6.2×10^{-10}
Boric acid	H_3BO_3	5.8×10^{-10}
Ammonium ion	NH_4^+	5.6×10^{-10}
Phenol	HOC_6H_5	1.6×10^{-10}
Hypoiodous acid	HOI	2×10^{-11}

Table A5.2

Stepwise Dissociation Constants for Several Common Polyprotic Acids

Name	Formula	K_{a_1}	K_{a_2}	K_{a_3}
Phosphoric acid	H_3PO_4	7.5×10^{-3}	6.2×10^{-8}	4.8×10^{-13}
Arsenic acid	H_3AsO_4	5×10^{-3}	8×10^{-8}	6×10^{-10}
Carbonic acid	H_2CO_3	4.3×10^{-7}	4.8×10^{-11}	
Sulfuric acid	H_2SO_4	Large	1.2×10^{-2}	
Sulfurous acid	H_2SO_3	1.5×10^{-2}	1.0×10^{-7}	
Hydrosulfuric acid	H_2S	1.0×10^{-7}	$\sim 10^{-19}$	
Oxalic acid	$H_2C_2O_4$	6.5×10^{-2}	6.1×10^{-5}	
Ascorbic acid (vitamin C)	$H_2C_6H_6O_6$	7.9×10^{-5}	1.6×10^{-12}	
Citric acid	$H_3C_6H_5O_7$	8.4×10^{-4}	1.8×10^{-5}	4.0×10^{-6}

Table A5.3

K_b for Some Common Weak Bases

Name	Formula	Conjugate Acid	K_b
Ammonia	NH_3	NH_4^+	1.8×10^{-5}
Methylamine	CH_3NH_2	$CH_3NH_3^+$	4.38×10^{-4}
Ethylamine	$C_2H_5NH_2$	$C_2H_5NH_3^+$	5.6×10^{-4}
Diethylamine	$(C_2H_5)_2NH$	$(C_2H_5)_2NH_2^+$	1.3×10^{-3}
Triethylamine	$(C_2H_5)_3N$	$(C_2H_5)_3NH^+$	4.0×10^{-4}
Hydroxylamine	$HONH_2$	$HONH_3^+$	1.1×10^{-8}
Hydrazine	H_2NNH_2	$H_2NNH_3^+$	3.0×10^{-6}
Aniline	$C_6H_5NH_2$	$C_6H_5NH_3^+$	3.8×10^{-10}
Pyridine	C_5H_5N	$C_5H_5NH^+$	1.7×10^{-9}

Table A5.4

Values of K_{sp} at 25°C for Common Ionic Solids

Ionic Solid	K_{sp} (at 25°C)	Ionic Solid	K_{sp} (at 25°C)	Ionic Solid	K_{sp} (at 25°C)
Fluorides		Chromates (*continued*)		Hydroxides (*continued*)	
BaF_2	2.4×10^{-5}	Hg_2CrO_4*	2×10^{-9}	$Co(OH)_3$	2.5×10^{-16}
MgF_2	6.4×10^{-9}	$BaCrO_4$	8.5×10^{-11}	$Ni(OH)_2$	1.6×10^{-16}
PbF_2	4×10^{-8}	Ag_2CrO_4	9.0×10^{-12}	$Zn(OH)_2$	4.5×10^{-17}
SrF_2	7.9×10^{-10}	$PbCrO_4$	2×10^{-16}	$Cu(OH)_2$	1.6×10^{-19}
CaF_2	4.0×10^{-11}			$Hg(OH)_2$	3×10^{-26}
		Carbonates		$Sn(OH)_2$	3×10^{-27}
Chlorides		$NiCO_3$	1.4×10^{-7}	$Cr(OH)_3$	6.7×10^{-31}
$PbCl_2$	1.6×10^{-5}	$CaCO_3$	8.7×10^{-9}	$Al(OH)_3$	2×10^{-32}
$AgCl$	1.6×10^{-10}	$BaCO_3$	1.6×10^{-9}	$Fe(OH)_3$	4×10^{-38}
Hg_2Cl_2*	1.1×10^{-18}	$SrCO_3$	7×10^{-10}	$Co(OH)_3$	2.5×10^{-43}
		$CuCO_3$	2.5×10^{-10}		
Bromides		$ZnCO_3$	2×10^{-10}	Sulfides	
$PbBr_2$	4.6×10^{-6}	$MnCO_3$	8.8×10^{-11}	MnS	2.3×10^{-13}
$AgBr$	5.0×10^{-13}	$FeCO_3$	2.1×10^{-11}	FeS	3.7×10^{-19}
Hg_2Br_2*	1.3×10^{-22}	Ag_2CO_3	8.1×10^{-12}	NiS	3×10^{-21}
		$CdCO_3$	5.2×10^{-12}	CoS	5×10^{-22}
Iodides		$PbCO_3$	1.5×10^{-15}	ZnS	2.5×10^{-22}
PbI_2	1.4×10^{-8}	$MgCO_3$	1×10^{-15}	SnS	1×10^{-26}
AgI	1.5×10^{-16}	Hg_2CO_3*	9.0×10^{-15}	CdS	1.0×10^{-28}
Hg_2I_2*	4.5×10^{-29}			PbS	7×10^{-29}
		Hydroxides		CuS	8.5×10^{-45}
Sulfates		$Ba(OH)_2$	5.0×10^{-3}	Ag_2S	1.6×10^{-49}
$CaSO_4$	6.1×10^{-5}	$Sr(OH)_2$	3.2×10^{-4}	HgS	1.6×10^{-54}
Ag_2SO_4	1.2×10^{-5}	$Ca(OH)_2$	1.3×10^{-6}		
$SrSO_4$	3.2×10^{-7}	$AgOH$	2.0×10^{-8}	Phosphates	
$PbSO_4$	1.3×10^{-8}	$Mg(OH)_2$	8.9×10^{-12}	Ag_3PO_4	1.8×10^{-18}
$BaSO_4$	1.5×10^{-9}	$Mn(OH)_2$	2×10^{-13}	$Sr_3(PO_4)_2$	1×10^{-31}
		$Cd(OH)_2$	5.9×10^{-15}	$Ca_3(PO_4)_2$	1.3×10^{-32}
Chromates		$Pb(OH)_2$	1.2×10^{-15}	$Ba_3(PO_4)_2$	6×10^{-39}
$SrCrO_4$	3.6×10^{-5}	$Fe(OH)_2$	1.8×10^{-15}	$Pb_3(PO_4)_2$	1×10^{-54}

*Contains Hg_2^{2+} ions. $K_{sp} = [Hg_2^{2+}][X^-]^2$ for Hg_2X_2 salts.

Table A5.5

Standard Reduction Potentials at 25°C (298 K) for Many Common Half-Reactions

Half-Reaction	$\mathcal{E}^\circ$ (V)	Half-Reaction	$\mathcal{E}^\circ$ (V)
$F_2 + 2e^- \longrightarrow 2F^-$	2.87	$O_2 + 2H_2O + 4e^- \longrightarrow 4OH^-$	0.40
$Ag^{2+} + e^- \longrightarrow Ag^+$	1.99	$Cu^{2+} + 2e^- \longrightarrow Cu$	0.34
$Co^{3+} + e^- \longrightarrow Co^{2+}$	1.82	$Hg_2Cl_2 + 2e^- \longrightarrow 2Hg + 2Cl^-$	0.27
$H_2O_2 + 2H^+ + 2e^- \longrightarrow 2H_2O$	1.78	$AgCl + e^- \longrightarrow Ag + Cl^-$	0.22
$Ce^{4+} + e^- \longrightarrow Ce^{3+}$	1.70	$SO_4^{2-} + 4H^+ + 2e^- \longrightarrow H_2SO_3 + H_2O$	0.20
$PbO_2 + 4H^+ + SO_4^{2-} + 2e^- \longrightarrow PbSO_4 + 2H_2O$	1.69	$Cu^{2+} + e^- \longrightarrow Cu^+$	0.16
$MnO_4^+ + 4H^+ + 3e^- \longrightarrow MnO_2 + 2H_2O$	1.68	$2H^+ + 2e^- \longrightarrow H_2$	0.00
$IO_4^- + 2H^+ + 2e^- \longrightarrow IO_3^- + H_2O$	1.60	$Fe^{3+} + 3e^- \longrightarrow Fe$	−0.036
$MnO_4^+ + 8H^+ + 5e^- \longrightarrow Mn^{2+} + 4H_2O$	1.51	$Pb^{2+} + 2e^- \longrightarrow Pb$	−0.13
$Au^{3+} + 3e^- \longrightarrow Au$	1.50	$Sn^{2+} + 2e^- \longrightarrow Sn$	−0.14
$PbO_2 + 4H^+ + 2e^- \longrightarrow Pb^{2+} + 2H_2O$	1.46	$Ni^{2+} + 2e^- \longrightarrow Ni$	−0.23
$Cl_2 + 2e^- \longrightarrow 2Cl^-$	1.36	$PbSO_4 + 2e^- \longrightarrow Pb + SO_4^{2-}$	−0.35
$Cr_2O_7^{2-} + 14H^+ + 6e^- \longrightarrow 2Cr^{3+} + 7H_2O$	1.33	$Cd^{2+} + 2e^- \longrightarrow Cd$	−0.40
$O_2 + 4H^+ + 4e^- \longrightarrow 2H_2O$	1.23	$Fe^{2+} + 2e^- \longrightarrow Fe$	−0.44
$MnO_2 + 4H^+ + 2e^- \longrightarrow Mn^{2+} + 2H_2O$	1.21	$Cr^{3+} + e^- \longrightarrow Cr^{2+}$	−0.50
$IO_3^- + 6H^+ + 5e^- \longrightarrow \frac{1}{2}I_2 + 3H_2O$	1.20	$Cr^{3+} + 3e^- \longrightarrow Cr$	−0.73
$Br_2 + 2e^- \longrightarrow 2Br^-$	1.09	$Zn^{2+} + 2e^- \longrightarrow Zn$	−0.76
$VO_2^+ + 2H^+ + e^- \longrightarrow VO^{2+} + H_2O$	1.00	$2H_2O + 2e^- \longrightarrow H_2 + 2OH^-$	−0.83
$AuCl_4^- + 3e^- \longrightarrow Au + 4Cl^-$	0.99	$Mn^{2+} + 2e^- \longrightarrow Mn$	−1.18
$NO_3^- + 4H^+ + 3e^- \longrightarrow NO + 2H_2O$	0.96	$Al^{3+} + 3e^- \longrightarrow Al$	−1.66
$ClO_2 + e^- \longrightarrow ClO_2^-$	0.954	$H_2 + 2e^- \longrightarrow 2H^-$	−2.23
$2Hg^{2+} + 2e^- \longrightarrow Hg_2^{2+}$	0.91	$Mg^{2+} + 2e^- \longrightarrow Mg$	−2.37
$Ag^+ + e^- \longrightarrow Ag$	0.80	$La^{3+} + 3e^- \longrightarrow La$	−2.37
$Hg_2^{2+} + 2e^- \longrightarrow 2Hg$	0.80	$Na^+ + e^- \longrightarrow Na$	−2.71
$Fe^{3+} + e^- \longrightarrow Fe^{2+}$	0.77	$Ca^{2+} + 2e^- \longrightarrow Ca$	−2.76
$O_2 + 2H^+ + 2e^- \longrightarrow H_2O_2$	0.68	$Ba^{2+} + 2e^- \longrightarrow Ba$	−2.90
$MnO_4^- + e^- \longrightarrow MnO_4^{2-}$	0.56	$K^+ + e^- \longrightarrow K$	−2.92
$I_2 + 2e^- \longrightarrow 2I^-$	0.54	$Li^+ + e^- \longrightarrow Li$	−3.05
$Cu^+ + e^- \longrightarrow Cu$	0.52		

Glossary

Note to the Student: The Glossary includes brief definitions of some of the fundamental terms used in chemistry. It does not include complex concepts that require detailed explanation for understanding. Please refer to the appropriate sections of the text for complete discussion of particular topics or concepts.

Accuracy: the agreement of a particular value with the true value. (A1.5)

Acid: a substance that produces hydrogen ions in solution; a proton donor. (4.2)

Acid–base indicator: a substance that marks the endpoint of an acid–base titration by changing color. (8.6)

Acid dissociation constant (K_a): the equilibrium constant for a reaction in which a proton is removed from an acid by H_2O to form the conjugate base and H_3O^+. (7.1)

Acid rain: a result of air pollution by sulfur dioxide. (5.11)

Actinide series: a group of 14 elements following actinium in the periodic table, in which the $5f$ orbitals are being filled. (12.13; 18.1)

Activated complex (transition state): the arrangement of atoms found at the top of the potential energy barrier as a reaction proceeds from reactants to products. (15.8)

Activation energy: the threshold energy that must be overcome to produce a chemical reaction. (15.8)

Addition polymerization: a type of polymerization in which the monomers simply add together to form the polymer, with no other products. (21.5)

Addition reaction: a reaction in which atoms add to a carbon–carbon multiple bond. (21.2)

Adiabatic process: a process that occurs without the transfer of energy as heat. (10.14)

Adsorption: the collection of one substance on the surface of another. (15.9)

Air pollution: contamination of the atmosphere, mainly by the gaseous products of transportation and production of electricity. (5.11)

Alcohol: an organic compound in which the hydroxyl group is a substituent on a hydrocarbon. (21.4)

Aldehyde: an organic compound containing the carbonyl group bonded to at least one hydrogen atom. (21.4)

Alkali metal: a Group 1A metal. (2.8; 18.2)

Alkaline earth metal: a Group 2A metal. (2.8; 18.4)

Alkane: a saturated hydrocarbon with the general formula C_nH_{2n+2}. (21.1)

Alkene: an unsaturated hydrocarbon containing a carbon–carbon double bond. The general formula is C_nH_{2n}. (21.2)

Alkyne: an unsaturated hydrocarbon containing a triple carbon–carbon bond. The general formula is C_nH_{2n-2}. (21.2)

Alloy: a substance that contains a mixture of elements and has metallic properties. (16.4)

Alloy steel: a form of steel containing carbon plus other metals such as chromium, cobalt, manganese, and molybdenum. (19.2)

Alpha (α) particle: a helium nucleus. (20.1)

Alpha-particle production: a common mode of decay for radioactive nuclides in which the mass number changes. (20.1)

Amine: an organic base derived from ammonia in which one or more of the hydrogen atoms are replaced by organic groups. (7.6; 21.4)

α-Amino acid: an organic acid in which an amino group and an R group are attached to the carbon atom next to the carboxyl group. (21.6)

Amorphous solid: a solid with considerable disorder in its structure. (16.3)

Ampere: the unit of electric current equal to one coulomb of charge per second. (11.7)

Amphoteric substance: a substance that can behave either as an acid or as a base. (7.2)

Angular momentum quantum number (ℓ): the quantum number relating to the shape of an atomic orbital, which can assume any integral value from 0 to $n - 1$ for each value of n. (12.9)

Anion: a negative ion. (2.7)

Anode: the electrode in a galvanic cell at which oxidation occurs. (11.1)

Antibonding molecular orbital: an orbital higher in energy than the atomic orbitals of which it is composed. (14.2)

Aqueous solution: a solution in which water is the dissolving medium or solvent. (4)

Aromatic hydrocarbon: one of a special class of cyclic unsaturated hydrocarbons, the simplest of which is benzene. (21.3)

Arrhenius concept: a concept postulating that acids produce hydrogen ions in aqueous solution, whereas bases produce hydroxide ions. (7.1)

Arrhenius equation: the equation representing the rate constant as $k = Ae^{-E_a/RT}$ where A represents the product of the collision frequency and the steric factor, and $e^{-E_a/RT}$ is the fraction of collisions with sufficient energy to produce a reaction. (15.8)

Atmosphere: the mixture of gases that surrounds the earth's surface. (5.11)

Atomic mass (average): the weighted average mass of the atoms in a naturally occurring element. (2.3)

Atomic number: the number of protons in the nucleus of an atom. (2.6)

Atomic radius: half the distance between the nuclei in a molecule consisting of identical atoms. (12.15)

Atomic solid: a solid that contains atoms at the lattice points. (16.3)

Aufbau principle: the principle stating that as protons are added one by one to the nucleus to build up the elements, electrons are similarly added to hydrogenlike orbitals. (12.13)

Autoionization: the transfer of a proton from one molecule to another of the same substance. (7.2)

Avogadro's law: equal volumes of gases at the same temperature and pressure contain the same number of particles. (5.2)

Avogadro's number: the number of atoms in exactly 12 grams of pure ^{12}C, equal to 6.022×10^{23}. (3.2)

Ball-and-stick model: a molecular model that distorts the sizes of atoms, but shows bond relationships clearly. (2.7)

Band model: a molecular model for metals in which the electrons are assumed to travel around the metal crystal in molecular orbitals formed from the valence atomic orbitals of the metal atoms. (16.4)

Barometer: a device for measuring atmospheric pressure. (5.1)

Base: a substance that produces hydroxide ions in aqueous solution, a proton acceptor. (7.2)

Base dissociation constant (K_b): the equilibrium constant for the reaction of a base with water to produce the conjugate acid and hydroxide ion. (7.6)

Basic oxide: an ionic oxide that dissolves in water to produce a basic solution. (18.4)

Battery: a group of galvanic cells connected in series. (11.5)

Beta (β) particle: an electron produced in radioactive decay. (20.1)

Beta-particle production: a decay process for radioactive nuclides in which the mass number remains constant and the atomic number changes. The net effect is to change a neutron to a proton. (20.1)

Bidentate ligand: a ligand that can form two bonds to a metal ion. (19.3)

Bimolecular step: a reaction involving the collision of two molecules. (15.6)

Binary compound: a two-element compound. (2.9)

Binding energy (nuclear): the energy required to decompose a nucleus into its component nucleons. (20.5)

Biomolecule: a molecule responsible for maintaining and/or reproducing life. (22)

Bond energy: the energy required to break a given chemical bond. (13.1)

Bond length: the distance between the nuclei of the two atoms connected by a bond; the distance where the total energy of a diatomic molecule is minimal. (13.1)

Bond order: the difference between the number of bonding electrons and the number of antibonding electrons, divided by two. It is an index of bond strength. (14.2)

Bonding molecular orbital: an orbital lower in energy than the atomic orbitals of which it is composed. (14.2)

Bonding pair: an electron pair found in the space between two atoms. (13.9)

Borane: a covalent hydride of boron. (18.5)

Boyle's law: the volume of a given sample of gas at constant temperature varies inversely with the pressure. (5.2)

Breeder reactor: a nuclear reactor in which fissionable fuel is produced while the reactor runs. (20.6)

Brønsted–Lowry definition (model): a model proposing that an acid is a proton donor, and a base is a proton acceptor. (7.1)

Buffer capacity: the ability of a buffered solution to absorb protons or hydroxide ions without a significant change in pH; determined by the magnitudes of [HA] and $[A^-]$ in the solution. (8.4)

Buffered solution: a solution that resists a change in its pH when either hydroxide ions or protons are added. (8.2)

Calorimetry: the science of measuring heat flow. (9.4)

Capillary action: the spontaneous rising of a liquid in a narrow tube. (16.2)

Carbohydrate: a polyhydroxyl ketone or polyhydroxyl aldehyde or a polymer composed of these. (21.6)

Carboxyhemoglobin: a stable complex of hemoglobin and carbon monoxide that prevents normal oxygen uptake in the blood. (19.8)

Carboxyl group: the —COOH group in an organic acid. (7.2; 21.4)

Carboxylic acid: an organic compound containing the carboxyl group; an acid with the general formula RCOOH. (21.4)

Catalyst: a substance that speeds up a reaction without being consumed. (15.9)

Cathode: the electrode in a galvanic cell at which reduction occurs. (11.1)

Cathode rays: the "rays" emanating from the negative electrode (cathode) in a partially evacuated tube; a stream of electrons. (2.5)

Cathodic protection: a method in which an active metal, such as magnesium, is connected to steel to protect it from corrosion. (11.6)

Cation: a positive ion. (2.7)

Cell potential (electromotive force): the driving force in a galvanic cell that pulls electrons from the reducing agent in one compartment to the oxidizing agent in the other. (11.1)

Ceramic: a nonmetallic material made from clay and hardened by firing at high temperature; it contains minute silicate crystals suspended in a glassy cement. (16.5)

Chain reaction (nuclear): a self-sustaining fission process caused by the production of neutrons that proceed to split other nuclei. (20.6)

Charge balance: the positive and negative charges carried by the ions in an aqueous solution must balance. (7.9)

Charles's law: the volume of a given sample of gas at constant pressure is directly proportional to the temperature in kelvins. (5.2)

Chelating ligand (chelate): a ligand having more than one atom with a lone pair that can be used to bond to a metal ion. (19.3)

Chemical bond: the energy that holds two atoms together in a compound. (2.7)

Chemical equation: a representation of a chemical reaction showing the relative numbers of reactant and product molecules. (3.6)

Chemical equilibrium: a dynamic reaction system in which the concentrations of all reactants and products remain constant as a function of time. (6)

Chemical formula: the representation of a molecule in which the symbols for the elements are used to indicate the types of atoms present and subscripts are used to show the relative numbers of atoms. (2.7)

Chemical kinetics: the area of chemistry that concerns reaction rates. (15)

Chemical stoichiometry: the calculation of the quantities of material consumed and produced in chemical reactions. (3)

Chirality: the quality of having nonsuperimposable mirror images. (19.4)

Chlor-alkali process: the process for producing chlorine and sodium hydroxide by electrolyzing brine in a mercury cell. (11.8)

Coagulation: the destruction of a colloid by causing particles to aggregate and settle out. (17.8)

Codons: organic bases in sets of three that form the genetic code. (21.6)

Colligative properties: properties of a solution that depend on the number, and not on the identity, of the solute particles. (17.5)

Collision model: a model based on the idea that molecules must collide to react; used to account for the observed characteristics of reaction rates. (15.8)

Colloid: a suspension of particles in a dispersing medium. (17.8)

Combustion reaction: the vigorous and exothermic reaction that takes place between certain substances, particularly organic compounds, and oxygen. (21.1)

Common ion effect: the shift in an equilibrium position caused by the addition or presence of an ion involved in the equilibrium reaction. (8.1)

Complete ionic equation: an equation that shows all substances that are strong electrolytes as ions. (4.6)

Complex ion: a charged species consisting of a metal ion surrounded by ligands. (8.9; 19.1)

Compound: a substance with constant composition that can be broken down into elements by chemical processes. (2.7)

Concentration cell: a galvanic cell in which both compartments contain the same components, but at different concentrations. (11.4)

Condensation: the process by which vapor molecules re-form a liquid. (16.10)

Condensation polymerization: a type of polymerization in which the formation of a small molecule, such as water, accompanies the extension of the polymer chain. (21.5)

Condensed states of matter: liquids and solids. (16.1)

Conduction bands: the molecular orbitals that can be occupied by mobile electrons, which are free to travel throughout a metal crystal to conduct electricity or heat. (16.4)

Conjugate acid: the species formed when a proton is added to a base. (7.1)

Conjugate acid–base pair: two species related to each other by the donating and accepting of a single proton. (7.1)

Conjugate base: what remains of an acid molecule after a proton is lost. (7.1)

Continuous spectrum: a spectrum that exhibits all the wavelengths of visible light. (12.3)

Control rods: rods in a nuclear reactor composed of substances that absorb neutrons. These rods regulate the power level of the reactor. (20.6)

Coordinate covalent bond: a metal–ligand bond resulting from the interaction of a Lewis base (the ligand) and a Lewis acid (the metal ion). (19.3)

Coordination compound: a compound composed of a complex ion and counter ions sufficient to give no net charge. (19.3)

Coordination isomerism: isomerism in a coordination compound in which the composition of the coordination sphere of the metal ion varies. (19.4)

Coordination number: the number of bonds formed between the metal ion and the ligands in a complex ion. (19.3)

Copolymer: a polymer formed from the polymerization of more than one type of monomer. (21.5)

Core electron: an inner electron in an atom; one not in the outermost (valence) principal quantum level. (12.13)

Corrosion: the process by which metals are oxidized in the atmosphere. (11.6)

Coulomb's law: $E = 2.31 \times 10^{-19}\ (Q_1Q_2/r)$, where E is the energy of interaction between a pair of ions, expressed in joules; r is the distance between the ion centers in nm; and Q_1 and Q_2 are the numerical ion charges. (13.1)

Counter ions: anions or cations that balance the charge on the complex ion in a coordination compound. (19.3)

Covalent bonding: a type of bonding in which electrons are shared by atoms. (2.7; 13.1)

Critical mass: the mass of fissionable material required to produce a self-sustaining chain reaction. (20.6)

Critical point: the point on a phase diagram at which the temperature and pressure have their critical values; the endpoint of the liquid–vapor line. (16.11)

Critical pressure: the minimum pressure required to produce liquefaction of a substance at the critical temperature. (16.11)

Critical reaction (nuclear): a reaction in which exactly one neutron from each fission event causes another fission event, thus sustaining the chain reaction. (20.6)

Critical temperature: the temperature above which vapor cannot be liquefied, no matter what pressure is applied. (16.11)

Crosslinking: the existence of bonds between adjacent chains in a polymer, thus adding strength to the material. (21.5)

Crystal field model: a model used to explain the magnetism and colors of coordination complexes through the splitting of the *d* orbital energies. (19.6)

Crystalline solid: a solid with a regular arrangement of its components. (16.3)

Cubic closest packed (ccp) structure: a solid modeled by the closest packing of spheres with an *abcabc* arrangement of layers; the unit cell is face-centered cubic. (16.4)

Cyclotron: a type of particle accelerator in which an ion introduced at the center is accelerated in an expanding spiral path by use of alternating electric fields in the presence of a magnetic field. (20.3)

Cytochromes: a series of iron-containing species composed of heme and a protein. Cytochromes are the principal electron-transfer molecules in the respiratory chain. (19.8)

Dalton's law of partial pressures: for a mixture of gases in a container, the total pressure exerted is the sum of the pressures that each gas would exert if it were alone. (5.5)

Degenerate orbitals: a group of orbitals with the same energy. (12.9)

Dehydrogenation reaction: a reaction in which two hydrogen atoms are removed from adjacent carbons of a saturated hydrocarbon, giving an unsaturated hydrocarbon. (21.1)

Delocalization: the condition where the electrons in a molecule are not localized between a pair of atoms but can move throughout the molecule. (13.9)

Denaturation: the breaking down of the three-dimensional structure of a protein resulting in the loss of its function. (21.6)

Denitrification: the return of nitrogen from decomposed matter to the atmosphere by bacteria that change nitrates to nitrogen gas. (18.8)

Deoxyribonucleic acid (DNA): a huge nucleotide polymer having a double-helical structure with complementary bases on the two strands. Its major functions are protein synthesis and the storage and transport of genetic information. (21.6)

Desalination: the removal of dissolved salts from an aqueous solution. (17.6)

Dialysis: a phenomenon in which a semipermeable membrane allows transfer of both solvent molecules and small solute molecules and ions. (17.6)

Diamagnetism: a type of magnetism, associated with paired electrons, that causes a substance to be repelled from the inducing magnetic field. (14.3)

Differential rate law: an expression that gives the rate of a reaction as a function of concentrations; often called the rate law. (15.2)

Diffraction: the scattering of light from a regular array of points or lines, producing constructive and destructive interference. (12.2)

Diffusion: the mixture of gases. (5.7)

Dilution: the process of adding solvent to lower the concentration of solute in a solution. (4.3)

Dimer: a molecule formed by the joining of two identical monomers. (21.5)

Dipole–dipole attraction: the attractive force resulting when polar molecules line up so that the positive and negative ends are close to each other. (16.1)

Dipole moment: a property of a molecule whose charge distribution can be represented by a center of positive charge and a center of negative charge. (13.3)

Disaccharide: a sugar formed from two monosaccharides joined by a glycoside linkage. (21.6)

Disproportionation reaction: a reaction in which a given element is both oxidized and reduced. (18.13)

Disulfide linkage: a S—S bond that stabilizes the tertiary structure of many proteins. (21.6)

Double bond: a bond in which two pairs of electrons are shared by two atoms. (13.8)

Downs cell: a cell used for electrolyzing molten sodium chloride. (11.8)

Dry cell battery: a common battery used in calculators, watches, radios, and portable audio players. (11.5)

Dual nature of light: the statement that light exhibits both wave and particulate properties. (12.2)

$E = mc^2$: Einstein's equation proposing that energy has mass; E is energy, m is mass, and c is the speed of light. (12.2)

Effective nuclear charge: the apparent nuclear charge exerted on a particular electron, equal to the actual nuclear charge minus the effect of electron repulsions. (12.11)

Effusion: the passage of a gas through a tiny orifice into an evacuated chamber. (5.7)

Electrical conductivity: the ability to conduct an electric current. (4.2)

Electrochemistry: the study of the interchange of chemical and electrical energy. (11)

Electrolysis: a process that involves forcing a current through a cell to cause a nonspontaneous chemical reaction to occur. (11.7)

Electrolyte: a material that dissolves in water to give a solution that conducts an electric current. (4.2)

Electrolytic cell: a cell that uses electrical energy to produce a chemical change that would otherwise not occur spontaneously. (11.7)

Electromagnetic radiation: radiant energy that exhibits wavelike behavior and travels through space at the speed of light in a vacuum. (12.1)

Electron: a negatively charged particle that moves around the nucleus of an atom. (2.5)

Electron affinity: the energy change associated with the addition of an electron to a gaseous atom. (12.15)

Electron capture: a process in which one of the inner-orbital electrons in an atom is captured by the nucleus. (20.1)

Electron sea model: a model for metals postulating a regular array of cations in a "sea" of electrons. (16.4)

Electron spin quantum number: a quantum number representing one of the two possible values for the electron spin; either $+\frac{1}{2}$ or $-\frac{1}{2}$. (12.10)

Electronegativity: the tendency of an atom in a molecule to attract shared electrons to itself. (13.2)

Element: a substance that cannot be decomposed into simpler substances by chemical or physical means. (2.1)

Elementary step: a reaction whose rate law can be written from its molecularity. (15.6)

Empirical formula: the simplest whole number ratio of atoms in a compound. (3.5)

Enantiomers: isomers that are nonsuperimposable mirror images of each other. (19.4)

Endpoint: the point in a titration at which the indicator changes color. (4.9)

Endothermic: refers to a reaction where energy (as heat) flows into the system. (9.1)

Energy: the capacity to do work or to cause heat flow. (9.1)

Enthalpy: a property of a system equal to $E + PV$, where E is the internal energy of the system, P is the pressure of the system, and V is the volume of the system. At constant pressure, where only PV work is allowed, the change in enthalpy equals the energy flow as heat. (9.2)

Enthalpy of fusion: the enthalpy change that occurs to melt a solid at its melting point. (16.10)

Entropy: a thermodynamic function that measures randomness or disorder. (10.1)

Enzyme: a large molecule, usually a protein, that catalyzes biological reactions. (15.9)

Equilibrium (thermodynamic definition): the position where the free energy of a reaction system has its lowest possible value. (10.11)

Equilibrium constant: the value obtained when equilibrium concentrations of the chemical species are substituted in the equilibrium expression. (6.2)

Equilibrium expression: the expression (from the law of mass action) obtained by multiplying the product concentrations and dividing by the multiplied reactant concentrations, with each concentration raised to a power represented by the coefficient in the balanced equation. (6.2)

Equilibrium position: a particular set of equilibrium concentrations. (6.2)

Equivalence point (stoichiometric point): the point in a titration when enough titrant has been added to react exactly with the substance in solution being titrated. (4.9; 8.4)

Exothermic: refers to a reaction where energy (as heat) flows out of the system. (9.1)

Exponential notation: expresses a number as $N \times 10^M$, a convenient method for representing a very large or very small number and for easily indicating the number of significant figures. (A1.1)

Faraday: a constant representing the charge on one mole of electrons; 96,485 coulombs. (11.3)

First law of thermodynamics: the energy of the universe is constant; same as the law of conservation of energy. (9.1)

Fission: the process of using a neutron to split a heavy nucleus into two nuclei with smaller mass numbers. (20.6)

Formal charge: the charge assigned to an atom in a molecule or polyatomic ion derived from a specific set of rules. (13.12)

Formation constant (stability constant): the equilibrium constant for each step of the formation of a complex ion by the addition of an individual ligand to a metal ion or complex ion in aqueous solution. (8.9)

Fossil fuel: coal, petroleum, or natural gas; consists of carbon-based molecules derived from decomposition of once-living organisms. (9.7)

Frasch process: the recovery of sulfur from underground deposits by melting it with hot water and forcing it to the surface by air pressure. (18.12)

Free energy: a thermodynamic function equal to the enthalpy (H) minus the product of the entropy (S) and the kelvin temperature (T); $G = H - TS$. Under certain conditions the change in free energy for a process is equal to the maximum useful work. (10.7)

Free radical: a species with an unpaired electron. (21.5)

Frequency: the number of waves (cycles) per second that pass a given point in space. (12.1)

Fuel cell: a galvanic cell for which the reactants are continuously supplied. (11.5)

Functional group: an atom or group of atoms in hydrocarbon derivatives that contains elements in addition to carbon and hydrogen. (21.4)

Fusion: the process of combining two light nuclei to form a heavier, more stable nucleus. (20.6)

Galvanic cell: a device in which chemical energy from a spontaneous redox reaction is changed to electrical energy that can be used to do work. (11.1)

Galvanizing: a process in which steel is coated with zinc to prevent corrosion. (11.6)

Gamma (γ) ray: a high-energy photon. (20.1)

Geiger-Müller counter (Geiger counter): an instrument that measures the rate of radioactive decay based on the ions and electrons produced as a radioactive particle passes through a gas-filled chamber. (20.4)

Gene: a given segment of the DNA molecule that contains the code for a specific protein. (21.6)

Geometrical (*cis-trans*) isomerism: isomerism in which atoms or groups of atoms can assume different positions around a rigid ring or bond. (19.4; 21.2)

Glass: an amorphous solid obtained when silica is mixed with other compounds, heated above its melting point, and then cooled rapidly. (16.5)

Glass electrode: an electrode for measuring pH from the potential difference that develops when it is dipped into an aqueous solution containing H^+ ions. (11.4)

Glycosidic linkage: a C—O—C bond formed between the rings of two cyclic monosaccharides by the elimination of water. (21.6)

Graham's law of effusion: the rate of effusion of a gas is inversely proportional to the square root of the mass of its particles. (5.7)

Gravimetric analysis: a method for determining the amount of a given substance in a solution by precipitation, filtration, drying, and weighing. (4.8)

Greenhouse effect: a warming effect exerted by the earth's atmosphere (particularly CO_2 and H_2O) due to thermal energy retained by absorption of infrared radiation. (9.7)

Ground state: the lowest possible energy state of an atom or molecule. (12.4)

Group (of the periodic table): a vertical column of elements having the same valence electron configuration and showing similar properties. (2.8)

Haber process: the manufacture of ammonia from nitrogen and hydrogen, carried out at high pressure and high temperature with the aid of a catalyst. (3.9; 6.1; 18.8)

Half-life (of a radioactive sample): the time required for the number of nuclides in a radioactive sample to reach half of the original value. (20.2)

Half-life (of a reaction): the time required for a reactant to reach half of its original concentration. (15.4)

Half-reactions: the two parts of an oxidation–reduction reaction, one representing oxidation, the other reduction. (4.11; 11.1)

Halogen: a Group 7A element. (2.8; 18.13)

Halogenation: the addition of halogen atoms to unsaturated hydrocarbons. (21.2)

Hard water: water from natural sources that contains relatively large concentrations of calcium and magnesium ions. (18.4)

Heat: energy transferred between two objects caused by a temperature difference between them. (9.1)

Heat capacity: the amount of energy required to raise the temperature of an object by one degree Celsius. (9.4)

Heat of fusion: the enthalpy change that occurs to melt a solid at its melting point. (16.10)

Heat of hydration: the enthalpy change associated with placing gaseous molecules or ions in water; the sum of the energy needed to expand the solvent and the energy released from the solvent–solute interactions. (17.2)

Heat of solution: the enthalpy change associated with dissolving a solute in a solvent; the sum of the energies needed to expand both solvent and solute in a solution and the energy released from the solvent–solute interactions. (17.2)

Heat of vaporization: the energy required to vaporize one mole of a liquid at a pressure of one atmosphere. (16.10)

Heating curve: a plot of temperature versus time for a substance where energy is added at a constant rate. (16.10)

Heisenberg uncertainty principle: a principle stating that there is a fundamental limitation to how precisely both the position and momentum of a particle can be known at a given time. (12.5)

Heme: an iron complex. (19.8)

Hemoglobin: a biomolecule composed of four myoglobin-like units (proteins plus heme) that can bind and transport four oxygen molecules in the blood. (19.8)

Henderson–Hasselbalch equation: an equation giving the relationship between the pH of an acid–base system and the concentrations of base and acid

$$pH = pK_a + \log\left(\frac{[\text{base}]}{[\text{acid}]}\right). \quad (8.2)$$

Henry's law: the amount of a gas dissolved in a solution is directly proportional to the pressure of the gas above the solution. (17.3)

Hess's law: in going from a particular set of reactants to a particular set of products, the enthalpy change is the same whether the reaction takes place in one step or in a series of steps; in summary, enthalpy is a state function. (9.5)

Heterogeneous equilibrium: an equilibrium involving reactants and/or products in more than one phase. (6.5)

Hexagonal closest packed (hcp) structure: a structure composed of closest packed spheres with an *ababab* arrangement of layers; the unit cell is hexagonal. (16.4)

Homogeneous equilibrium: an equilibrium system where all reactants and products are in the same phase. (6.5)

Homopolymer: a polymer formed from the polymerization of only one type of monomer. (21.5)

Hund's rule: the lowest-energy configuration for an atom is the one having the maximum number of unpaired electrons allowed by the Pauli exclusion principle in a particular set of degenerate orbitals, with all unpaired electrons having parallel spins. (12.13)

Hybrid orbitals: a set of atomic orbitals adopted by an atom in a molecule different from those of the atom in the free state. (14.1)

Hybridization: a mixing of the native orbitals on a given atom to form special atomic orbitals for bonding. (14.1)

Hydration: the interaction between solute particles and water molecules. (4.1)

Hydride: a binary compound containing hydrogen. The hydride ion, H^-, exists in ionic hydrides. The three classes of hydrides are covalent, interstitial, and ionic. (18.3)

Hydrocarbon: a compound composed of carbon and hydrogen. (23.1)

Hydrocarbon derivative: an organic molecule that contains one or more elements in addition to carbon and hydrogen. (21.4)

Hydrogen bonding: unusually strong dipole–dipole attractions that occur among molecules in which hydrogen is bonded to a highly electronegative atom. (16.1)

Hydrogenation reaction: a reaction in which hydrogen is added, with a catalyst present, to a carbon–carbon multiple bond. (21.2)

Hydrohalic acid: an aqueous solution of a hydrogen halide. (18.13)

Hydronium ion: the H_3O^+ ion; a hydrated proton. (7.1)

Hypothesis: one or more assumptions put forth to explain the observed behavior of nature. (1.3)

Ideal gas: a gas that obeys the equation, $PV = nRT$. (5.2)

Ideal gas law: an equation of state for a gas, where the state of the gas is its condition at a given time; expressed by $PV = nRT$, where P = pressure, V = volume, n = moles of the gas, R = the universal gas constant, and T = absolute temperature. This equation expresses behavior approached by real gases at high T and low P. (5.3)

Ideal solution: a solution whose vapor pressure is directly proportional to the mole fraction of solvent present. (17.4)

Indicator: a chemical that changes color and is used to mark the endpoint of a titration. (4.9; 8.5)

Inert pair effect: the tendency for the heavier Group 3A elements to exhibit the +1 as well as the expected +3 oxidation states, and Group 4A elements to exhibit the +2 as well as the +4 oxidation states. (18.5)

Integrated rate law: an expression that shows the concentration of a reactant as a function of time. (15.2)

Intermediate: a species that is neither a reactant nor a product but that is formed and consumed in the reaction sequence. (15.6)

Intermolecular forces: relatively weak interactions that occur between molecules. (16.1)

Internal energy: a property of a system that can be changed by a flow of work, heat, or both; $\Delta E = q + w$, where ΔE is the change in the internal energy of the system, q is heat, and w is work. (9.1)

Ion: an atom or a group of atoms that has a net positive or negative charge. (2.7)

Ion exchange (water softening): the process in which an ion-exchange resin removes unwanted ions (for example, Ca^{2+} and Mg^{2+}) and replaces them with Na^+ ions, which do not interfere with soap and detergent action. (18.4)

Ion pairing: a phenomenon occurring in solution when oppositely charged ions aggregate and behave as a single particle. (17.7)

Ion-product constant (K_w): the equilibrium constant for the autoionization of water; $K_w = [H^+][OH^-]$. At 25°C, K_w equals 1.0×10^{-14}. (7.2)

Ion-selective electrode: an electrode sensitive to the concentration of a particular ion in solution. (11.4)

Ionic bonding: the electrostatic attraction between oppositely charged ions. (2.7; 13.1)

Ionic compound (binary): a compound that results when a metal reacts with a nonmetal to form a cation and an anion. (13.1)

Ionic solid: a solid containing cations and anions that dissolves in water to give a solution containing the separated ions, which are mobile and thus free to conduct electric current. (16.3)

Ionization energy: the quantity of energy required to remove an electron from a gaseous atom or ion. (12.15)

Irreversible process: any real process. When a system undergoes the changes State 1 → State 2 → State 1 by any real pathway, the universe is different than before the cyclic process took place in the system. (10.2)

Isoelectronic ions: ions containing the same number of electrons. (13.4)

Isomers: species with the same formula but different properties. (19.4)

Isothermal process: a process in which the temperature remains constant. (10.2)

Isotonic solutions: solutions having identical osmotic pressures. (17.6)

Isotopes: atoms of the same element (the same number of protons) with different numbers of neutrons. They have identical atomic numbers but different mass numbers. (2.6)

Ketone: an organic compound containing the carbonyl group

bonded to two carbon atoms. (21.4)

Kinetic energy ($\frac{1}{2}mv^2$): energy resulting from the motion of an object; dependent on the mass of the object and the square of its velocity. (9.1)

Kinetic molecular theory: a model that assumes that an ideal gas is composed of tiny particles (molecules) in constant motion. (5.6)

Lanthanide contraction: the decrease in the atomic radii of the lanthanide series elements, going from left to right in the periodic table. (19.1)

Lanthanide series: a group of 14 elements following lanthanum in the periodic table, in which the 4*f* orbitals are being filled. (12.13; 18.1; 19.1)

Lattice: a three-dimensional system of points designating the positions of the centers of the components of a solid (atoms, ions, or molecules). (16.3)

Lattice energy: the energy change occurring when separated gaseous ions are packed together to form an ionic solid. (13.5)

Law of conservation of energy: energy can be converted from one form to another but can be neither created nor destroyed. (9.1)

Law of conservation of mass: mass is neither created nor destroyed. (2.2)

Law of definite proportion: a given compound always contains exactly the same proportion of elements by mass. (2.2)

Law of mass action: a general description of the equilibrium condition; it defines the equilibrium constant expression. (6.2)

Law of multiple proportions: when two elements form a series of compounds, the ratios of the masses of the second element that combine with one gram of the first element can always be reduced to small whole numbers. (2.2)

Lead storage battery: a battery (used in cars) in which the anode is lead, the cathode is lead coated with lead dioxide, and the electrolyte is a sulfuric acid solution. (11.5)

Le Châtelier's principle: if a change is imposed on a system at equilibrium, the position of the equilibrium will shift in a direction that tends to reduce the effect of that change. (6.8)

Lewis acid: an electron-pair acceptor. (19.3)

Lewis base: an electron-pair donor. (19.3)

Lewis structure: a diagram of a molecule showing how the valence electrons are arranged among the atoms in the molecule. (13.10)

Ligand: a neutral molecule or ion having a lone pair of electrons that can be used to form a bond to a metal ion; a Lewis base. (19.3)

Lime-soda process: a water-softening method in which lime and soda ash are added to water to remove calcium and magnesium ions by precipitation. (7.6)

Limiting reactant (limiting reagent): the reactant that is completely consumed when a reaction is run to completion. (3.9)

Line spectrum: a spectrum showing only certain discrete wavelengths. (12.3)

Linear accelerator: a type of particle accelerator in which a changing electric field is used to accelerate a positive ion along a linear path. (20.3)

Linkage isomerism: isomerism involving a complex ion where the ligands are all the same but the point of attachment of at least one of the ligands differs. (19.4)

Liquefaction: the transformation of a gas into a liquid. (18.1)

Localized electron (LE) model: a model that assumes that a molecule is composed of atoms that are bound together by sharing pairs of electrons using the atomic orbitals of the bound atoms. (13.9)

London dispersion forces: the forces, existing among noble gas atoms and nonpolar molecules, that involve an accidental dipole that induces a momentary dipole in a neighbor. (16.1)

Lone pair: an electron pair that is localized on a given atom; an electron pair not involved in bonding. (13.9)

Magnetic quantum number (m_ℓ): the quantum number relating to the orientation of an orbital in space relative to the other orbitals with the same ℓ quantum number. It can have integral values between ℓ and $-\ell$, including zero. (12.9)

Main-group (representative) elements: elements in the groups labeled 1A, 2A, 3A, 4A, 5A, 6A, 7A, and 8A in the periodic table. The group number gives the sum of valence *s* and *p* electrons. (12.13; 18.1)

Major species: the components present in relatively large amounts in a solution. (7.4)

Manometer: a device for measuring the pressure of a gas in a container. (5.1)

Mass defect: the change in mass occurring when a nucleus is formed from its component nucleons. (20.5)

Mass number: the total number of protons and neutrons in the atomic nucleus of an atom. (2.6)

Mass percent: the percent by mass of a component of a mixture (17.1) or of a given element in a compound. (3.4)

Mass spectrometer: an instrument used to determine the relative masses of atoms by the deflection of their ions in a magnetic field. (3.1)

Matter: the material of the universe.

Mean free path: the average distance a molecule in a given gas sample travels between collisions with other molecules. (5.6; 5.9)

Measurement: a quantitative observation. (A1.5)

Messenger RNA (mRNA): a special RNA molecule built in the cell nucleus that migrates into the cytoplasm and participates in protein synthesis. (21.6)

Metal: an element that gives up electrons relatively easily and is lustrous, malleable, and a good conductor of heat and electricity. (2.8)

Metalloids (semimetals): elements along the division line in the periodic table between metals and nonmetals. These elements exhibit both metallic and nonmetallic properties. (12.16; 18.1)

Metallurgy: the process of separating a metal from its ore and preparing it for use. (18.1)

Millimeters of mercury (mm Hg): a unit of pressure, also called a torr; 760 mm Hg = 760 torr = 101,325 Pa = 1 standard atmosphere. (5.1)

Mixture: a material of variable composition that contains two or more substances.

Model (theory): a set of assumptions put forth to explain the observed behavior of matter. The models of chemistry usually involve assumptions about the behavior of individual atoms or molecules. (1.3)

Moderator: a substance used in a nuclear reactor to slow down the neutrons. (20.6)

Molal boiling-point elevation constant: a constant characteristic of a particular solvent that gives the change in boiling point as a function of solution molality; used in molecular weight determinations. (17.5)

Molal freezing-point depression constant: a constant characteristic of a particular solvent that gives the change in freezing point as a function of the solution molality; used in molecular weight determinations. (17.5)

Molality: the number of moles of solute per kilogram of solvent in a solution. (17.1)

Molar heat capacity: the energy required to raise the temperature of one mole of a substance by one degree Celsius. (9.3; 9.4)

Molar mass: the mass in grams of one mole of molecules or formula units of a substance; also called molecular weight. (3.3)

Molar volume: the volume of one mole of an ideal gas; equal to 22.42 liters at STP. (5.4)

Molarity: moles of solute per volume of solution in liters. (4.3; 17.1)

Mole (mol): the number equal to the number of carbon atoms in exactly 12 grams of pure ^{12}C; Avogadro's number. One mole represents 6.022×10^{23} units. (3.2)

Mole fraction: the ratio of the number of moles of a given component in a mixture to the total number of moles in the mixture. (5.5; 17.1)

Mole ratio (stoichiometry): the ratio of moles of one substance to moles of another substance in a balanced chemical equation. (3.8)

Molecular equation: an equation representing a reaction in solution showing the reactants and products in undissociated form, whether they are strong or weak electrolytes. (4.6)

Molecular formula: the exact formula of a molecule, giving the types of atoms and the number of each type. (3.5)

Molecular orbital (MO) model: a model that regards a molecule as a collection of nuclei and electrons, where the electrons are assumed to occupy orbitals much as they do in atoms, but having the orbitals extend over the entire molecule. In this model the electrons are assumed to be delocalized rather than always located between a given pair of atoms. (14.2)

Molecular orientations (kinetics): orientations of molecules during collisions, some of which can lead to a reaction and some of which cannot. (15.8)

Molecular solid: a solid composed of neutral molecules at the lattice points. (16.3)

Molecular structure: the three-dimensional arrangement of atoms in a molecule. (13.13)

Molecular weight: the mass in grams of one mole of molecules or formula units of a substance; also called molar mass. (3.3)

Molecularity: the number of species that must collide to produce the reaction represented by an elementary step in a reaction mechanism. (15.6)

Molecule: a bonded collection of two or more atoms of the same or different elements. (2.7)

Monodentate (unidentate) ligand: a ligand that can form one bond to a metal ion. (19.3)

Monoprotic acid: an acid with one acidic proton. (7.2)

Monosaccharide (simple sugar): a polyhydroxy ketone or aldehyde containing from three to nine carbon atoms. (21.6)

Myoglobin: an oxygen-storing biomolecule consisting of a heme complex and a protein. (19.8)

Natural law: a statement that expresses generally observed behavior. (1.3)

Nernst equation: an equation relating the potential of an electrochemical cell to the concentrations of the cell components

$$\mathscr{E} = \mathscr{E}^\circ - \frac{0.0591}{n}\log(Q) \text{ at } 25^\circ\text{C. (11.4)}$$

Net ionic equation: an equation for a reaction in solution, where strong electrolytes are written as ions, showing only those components that are directly involved in the chemical change. (4.6)

Network solid: an atomic solid containing strong directional covalent bonds. (16.5)

Neutralization reaction: an acid–base reaction. (4.9)

Neutron: a particle in the atomic nucleus with mass virtually equal to the proton's but with no charge. (2.6)

Nitrogen cycle: the conversion of N_2 to nitrogen-containing compounds, followed by the return of nitrogen gas to the atmosphere by natural decay processes. (18.8)

Nitrogen fixation: the process of transforming N_2 to nitrogen-containing compounds useful to plants. (18.8)

Nitrogen-fixing bacteria: bacteria in the root nodules of plants that can convert atmospheric nitrogen to ammonia and other nitrogen-containing compounds useful to plants. (18.8)

Noble gas: a Group 8A element. (2.8; 18.14)

Node: an area of an orbital having zero electron probability. (12.9)

Nonelectrolyte: a substance that, when dissolved in water, gives a nonconducting solution. (4.2)

Nonmetal: an element not exhibiting metallic characteristics. Chemically, a typical nonmetal accepts electrons from a metal. (2.8)

Normal boiling point: the temperature at which the vapor pressure of a liquid is exactly one atmosphere. (16.10)

Normal melting point: the temperature at which the solid and liquid states have the same vapor pressure under conditions where the total pressure on the system is one atmosphere. (16.10)

Normality: the number of equivalents of a substance dissolved in a liter of solution. (17.1)

Nuclear atom: an atom having a dense center of positive charge (the nucleus) with electrons moving around the outside. (2.5)

Nuclear transformation: the change of one element into another. (20.3)

Nucleon: a particle in an atomic nucleus, either a neutron or a proton. (2.6)

Nucleotide: a monomer of the nucleic acids composed of a five-carbon sugar, a nitrogen-containing base, and phosphoric acid. (21.6)

Nucleus: the small, dense center of positive charge in an atom. (2.5)

Nuclide: the general term applied to each unique atom; represented by ${}^{A}_{Z}X$, where X is the symbol for a particular element. (20.2)

Octet rule: the observation that atoms of nonmetals tend to form the most stable molecules when they are surrounded by eight electrons (to fill their valence orbitals). (13.10)

Optical isomerism: isomerism in which the isomers have opposite effects on plane-polarized light. (19.4)

Orbital: a specific wave function for an electron in an atom. The square of this function gives the probability distribution for the electron. (12.5)

***d*-Orbital splitting:** a splitting of the *d* orbitals of the metal ion in a complex such that the orbitals pointing at the ligands have higher energies than those pointing between the ligands. (19.6)

Order (of reactant): the positive or negative exponent, determined by experiment, of the reactant concentration in a rate law. (15.2)

Organic acid: an acid with a carbon-atom backbone; often contains the carboxyl group. (7.2)

Organic chemistry: the study of carbon-containing compounds (typically chains of carbon atoms) and their properties. (21)

Osmosis: the flow of solvent into a solution through a semipermeable membrane. (17.6)

Osmotic pressure (π): the pressure that must be applied to a solution to stop osmosis; $= MRT$. (17.6)

Ostwald process: a commercial process for producing nitric acid by the oxidation of ammonia. (18.8)

Oxidation: an increase in oxidation state (a loss of electrons). (4.10; 11.1)

Oxidation–reduction (redox) reaction: a reaction in which one or more electrons are transferred. (4.4; 4.10; 11.1)

Oxidation states: a concept that provides a way to keep track of electrons in oxidation–reduction reactions according to certain rules. (4.10)

Oxidizing agent (electron acceptor): a reactant that accepts electrons from another reactant. (4.10; 11.1)

Oxyacid: an acid in which the acidic proton is attached to an oxygen atom. (7.2)

Ozone: O_3, the form of elemental oxygen in addition to the much more common O_2. (18.11)

Paramagnetism: a type of induced magnetism, associated with unpaired electrons, that causes a substance to be attracted into the inducing magnetic field. (14.3)

Partial pressures: the independent pressures exerted by different gases in a mixture. (5.5)

Particle accelerator: a device used to accelerate nuclear particles to very high speeds. (20.3)

Pascal: the SI unit of pressure; equal to newtons per meter squared. (5.1)

Pauli exclusion principle: in a given atom no two electrons can have the same set of four quantum numbers. (12.10)

Penetration effect: the effect whereby a valence electron penetrates the core electrons, thus reducing the shielding effect and increasing the effective nuclear charge. (12.14)

Peptide linkage: the bond resulting from the condensation reaction between amino acids; represented by

$$\overset{\displaystyle O}{\overset{\|}{-C}}-\overset{\displaystyle H}{\overset{|}{N}}- \qquad (22.6)$$

Percent dissociation: the ratio of the amount of a substance that is dissociated at equilibrium to the initial concentration of the substance in a solution, multiplied by 100. (7.5)

Percent yield: the actual yield of a product as a percentage of the theoretical yield. (3.9)

Periodic table: a chart showing all the elements arranged in columns with similar chemical properties. (2.8)

pH curve (titration curve): a plot showing the pH of a solution being analyzed as a function of the amount of titrant added. (8.5)

pH scale: a log scale based on 10 and equal to $-\log[H^+]$; a convenient way to represent solution acidity. (7.3)

Phase diagram: a convenient way of representing the phases of a substance in a closed system as a function of temperature and pressure. (16.11)

Phenyl group: the benzene molecule minus one hydrogen atom. (21.3)

Photochemical smog: air pollution produced by the action of light on oxygen, nitrogen oxides, and unburned fuel from auto exhaust to form ozone and other pollutants. (5.11)

Photon: a quantum of electromagnetic radiation. (12.2)

Physical change: a change in the form of a substance, but not in its chemical composition; chemical bonds are not broken in a physical change.

Pi (π) bond: a covalent bond in which parallel p orbitals share an electron pair occupying the space above and below the line joining the atoms. (14.1)

Planck's constant: the constant relating the change in energy for a system to the frequency of the electromagnetic radiation absorbed or emitted; equal to 6.626×10^{-34} J s. (12.2)

Polar covalent bond: a covalent bond in which the electrons are not shared equally because one atom attracts them more strongly than the other. (13.1)

Polar molecule: a molecule that has a permanent dipole moment. (4.1)

Polyatomic ion: an ion containing a number of atoms. (2.7)

Polyelectronic atom: an atom with more than one electron. (12.11)

Polymer: a large, usually chainlike molecule built from many small molecules (monomers). (21.5)

Polymerization: a process in which many small molecules (monomers) are joined together to form a large molecule. (21.2)

Polypeptide: a polymer formed from amino acids joined together by peptide linkages. (21.6)

Polyprotic acid: an acid with more than one acidic proton. It dissociates in a stepwise manner, one proton at a time. (7.7)

Porous disk: a disk in a tube connecting two different solutions in a galvanic cell that allows ion flow without extensive mixing of the solutions. (11.1)

Porphyrin: a planar ligand with a central ring structure and various substituent groups at the edges of the ring. (19.8)

Positional probability: a type of probability that depends on the number of arrangements in space that yield a particular state. (10.1)

Positron production: a mode of nuclear decay in which a particle is formed having the same mass as an electron but opposite charge. The net effect is to change a proton to a neutron. (20.1)

Potential energy: energy resulting from position or composition. (9.1)

Precipitation reaction: a reaction in which an insoluble substance forms and separates from the solution. (4.5)

Precision: the degree of agreement among several measurements of the same quantity; the reproducibility of a measurement. (A1.5)

Primary structure (of a protein): the order (sequence) of amino acids in the protein chain. (21.6)

Principal quantum number: the quantum number relating to the size and energy of an orbital; it can have any positive integer value. (12.9)

Probability distribution: the square of the wave function indicating the probability of finding an electron at a particular point in space. (12.8)

Product: a substance resulting from a chemical reaction. It is shown to the right of the arrow in a chemical equation. (3.6)

Protein: a natural high-molecular-weight polymer formed by condensation reactions between amino acids. (21.6)

Proton: a positively charged particle in an atomic nucleus. (2.6; 20)

Qualitative analysis: the separation and identification of individual ions from a mixture. (4.7; 8.9)

Quantization: the concept that energy can occur only in discrete units called quanta. (12.2)

Rad: a unit of radiation dosage corresponding to 10^{-2} J of energy deposited per kilogram of tissue (from *r*adiation *a*bsorbed *d*ose). (20.7)

Radioactive decay (radioactivity): the spontaneous decomposition of a nucleus to form a different nucleus. (20.1)

Radiocarbon dating (carbon-14 dating): a method for dating ancient wood or cloth based on the rate of radioactive decay of the nuclide $^{14}_{6}C$. (20.4)

Radiotracer: a radioactive nuclide, introduced into an organism for diagnostic purposes, whose pathway can be traced by monitoring its radioactivity. (20.4)

Random error: an error that has an equal probability of being high or low. (A1.5)

Raoult's law: the vapor pressure of a solution is directly proportional to the mole fraction of solvent present. (17.4)

Rate constant: the proportionality constant in the relationship between reaction rate and reactant concentrations. (15.2)

Rate of decay: the change in the number of radioactive nuclides in a sample per unit time. (20.2)

Rate-determining step: the slowest step in a reaction mechanism, the one determining the overall rate. (15.6)

Rate law (differential rate law): an expression that shows how the rate of reaction depends on the concentration of reactants. (15.2)

Reactant: a starting substance in a chemical reaction. It appears to the left of the arrow in a chemical equation. (3.6)

Reaction mechanism: the series of elementary steps involved in a chemical reaction. (15.6)

Reaction quotient: a quotient obtained by applying the law of mass action to initial concentrations rather than to equilibrium concentrations. (6.6)

Reaction rate: the change in concentration of a reactant or product per unit time. (15.1)

Reactor core: the part of a nuclear reactor where the fission reaction takes place. (20.6)

Reducing agent (electron donor): a reactant that donates electrons to another substance to reduce the oxidation state of one of its atoms. (4.10; 11.1)

Reduction: a decrease in oxidation state (a gain of electrons). (4.10; 11.1)

Rem: a unit of radiation dosage that accounts for both the energy of the dose and its effectiveness in causing biological damage (from *r*oentgen *e*quivalent for *m*an). (20.7)

Resonance: a condition occurring when more than one valid Lewis structure can be written for a particular molecule. The actual electronic structure is not represented by any one of the Lewis structures but by the average of all of them. (13.11)

Reverse osmosis: the process occurring when the external pressure on a solution causes a net flow of solvent through a semipermeable membrane from the solution to the solvent. (17.6)

Reversible process: a cyclic process carried out by a hypothetical pathway, which leaves the universe exactly the same as it was before the process. No real process is reversible. (10.2)

Ribonucleic acid (RNA): a nucleotide polymer that transmits the genetic information stored in DNA to the ribosomes for protein synthesis. (21.6)

Root mean square velocity: the square root of the average of the squares of the individual velocities of gas particles. (5.6)

Salt: an ionic compound. (7.8)

Salt bridge: a U-tube containing an electrolyte that connects the two compartments of a galvanic cell, allowing ion flow without extensive mixing of the different solutions. (11.1)

Scientific method: the process of studying natural phenomena, involving observations, forming laws and theories, and testing of theories by experimentation. (1.3)

Scintillation counter: an instrument that measures radioactive decay by sensing the flashes of light produced in a substance by the radiation. (20.4)

Second law of thermodynamics: in any spontaneous process, there is always an increase in the entropy of the universe. (10.5)

Secondary structure (of a protein): the three-dimensional structure of the protein chain (for example, α-helix, random coil, or pleated sheet). (21.6)

Selective precipitation: a method of separating metal ions from an aqueous mixture by using a reagent whose anion forms a precipitate with only one or a few of the ions in the mixture. (4.7; 8.8)

Semiconductor: a substance conducting only a slight electric current at room temperature, but showing increased conductivity at higher temperatures. (16.5)

Semipermeable membrane: a membrane that allows solvent but not solute molecules to pass through. (17.6)

Shielding: the effect by which the other electrons screen, or shield, a given electron from some of the nuclear charge. (12.14)

SI units: International System of units based on the metric system and units derived from the metric system. (A2.1)

Side chain (of amino acid): the hydrocarbon group on an amino acid represented by H, CH_3, or a more complex substituent. (21.6)

Sigma (σ) bond: a covalent bond in which the electron pair is shared in an area centered on a line running between the atoms. (14.1)

Significant figures: the certain digits and the first uncertain digit of a measurement. (A1.5)

Silica: the fundamental silicon–oxygen compound, which has the empirical formula SiO_2, and forms the basis of quartz and certain types of sand. (16.5)

Silicates: salts that contain metal cations and polyatomic silicon–oxygen anions that are usually polymeric. (16.5)

Single bond: a bond in which one pair of electrons is shared by two atoms. (13.8)

Solubility: the amount of a substance that dissolves in a given volume of solvent at a given temperature. (4.2)

Solubility product constant: the constant for the equilibrium expression representing the dissolving of an ionic solid in water. (8.8)

Solute: a substance dissolved in a liquid to form a solution. (4.2; 17.1)

Solution: a homogeneous mixture. (17)

Solvent: the dissolving medium in a solution. (4.2)

Somatic damage: radioactive damage to an organism resulting in its sickness or death. (20.7)

Space-filling model: a model of a molecule showing the relative sizes of the atoms and their relative orientations. (2.7)

Specific heat capacity: the energy required to raise the temperature of one gram of a substance by one degree Celsius. (9.4)

Spectator ions: ions present in solution that do not participate directly in a reaction. (4.6)

Spectrochemical series: a listing of ligands in order based on their ability to produce *d*-orbital splitting. (19.6)

Spectroscopy: the study of the interaction of electromagnetic radiation within matter. (14.7)

Spontaneous fission: the spontaneous splitting of a heavy nuclide into two lighter nuclides. (20.1)

Spontaneous process: a process that occurs without outside intervention. (10.1)

Standard atmosphere: a unit of pressure equal to 760 mm Hg. (5.1)

Standard enthalpy of formation: the enthalpy change that accompanies the formation of one mole of a compound at 25°C from its elements, with all substances in their standard states at that temperature. (9.6)

Standard free energy change: the change in free energy that will occur for one unit of reaction if the reactants in their standard states are converted to products in their standard states. (10.9)

Standard free energy of formation: the change in free energy that accompanies the formation of one mole of a substance from its constituent elements with all reactants and products in their standard states. (10.9)

Standard hydrogen electrode: a platinum conductor in contact with 1 M H^+ ions and bathed by hydrogen gas at one atmosphere. (11.2)

Standard reduction potential: the potential of a half-reaction under standard state conditions, as measured against the potential of the standard hydrogen electrode. (11.2)

Standard solution: a solution whose concentration is accurately known. (4.3)

Standard state: a reference state for a specific substance defined according to a set of conventional definitions. (9.6)

Standard temperature and pressure (STP): the condition 0°C and 1 atm of pressure. (5.4)

Standing wave: a stationary wave as on a string of a musical instrument; in the wave mechanical model, the electron in the hydrogen atom is considered to be a standing wave. (12.5)

State function: a property that is independent of the pathway. (9.1)

States of matter: the three different forms in which matter can exist: solid, liquid, and gas. (5)

Stereoisomerism: isomerism in which all the bonds in the isomers are the same but the spatial arrangements of the atoms are different. (19.4)

Steric factor: the factor (always less than one) that reflects the fraction of collisions with orientations that can produce a chemical reaction. (15.8)

Stoichiometric quantities: quantities of reactants mixed in exactly the correct amounts so that all are used up at the same time. (3.9)

Strong acid: an acid that completely dissociates to produce a H^+ ion and the conjugate base. (4.2; 7.2)

Strong base: a metal hydroxide salt that completely dissociates into its ions in water. (4.2; 7.6)

Strong electrolyte: a material that, when dissolved in water, gives a solution that conducts an electric current very efficiently. (4.2)

Structural formula: the representation of a molecule in which the relative positions of the atoms are shown and the bonds are indicated by lines. (2.7)

Structural isomerism: isomerism in which the isomers contain the same atoms but one or more bonds differ. (19.4; 21.1)

Subcritical reaction (nuclear): a reaction in which less than one neutron causes another fission event and the process dies out. (20.6)

Sublimation: the process by which a substance goes directly from the solid to the gaseous state without passing through the liquid state. (16.10)

Subshell: a set of orbitals with a given angular momentum quantum number. (12.9)

Substitution reaction (hydrocarbons): a reaction in which an atom, usually a halogen, replaces a hydrogen atom in a hydrocarbon. (21.1)

Supercooling: the process of cooling a liquid below its freezing point without its changing to a solid. (16.10)

Supercritical reaction (nuclear): a reaction in which more than one neutron from each fission event causes another fission event. The process rapidly escalates to a violent explosion. (20.6)

Superheating: the process of heating a liquid above its boiling point without its boiling. (16.10)

Superoxide: a compound containing the O_2^- anion. (18.2)

Surface tension: the resistance of a liquid to an increase in its surface area. (16.2)

Surroundings: everything in the universe surrounding a thermodynamic system. (9.1)

Syngas: synthetic gas, a mixture of carbon monoxide and hydrogen, obtained by coal gasification. (9.8)

System (thermodynamic): that part of the universe on which attention is to be focused. (9.1)

Systematic error: an error that always occurs in the same direction. (A1.5)

Termolecular step: a reaction involving the simultaneous collision of three molecules. (15.6)

Tertiary structure (of a protein): the overall shape of a protein, long and narrow or globular, maintained by different types of intramolecular interactions. (21.6)

Theoretical yield: the maximum amount of a given product that can be formed when the limiting reactant is completely consumed. (3.9)

Theory: a set of assumptions put forth to explain some aspect of the observed behavior of matter. (1.3)

Thermal pollution: the oxygen-depleting effect on lakes and rivers of using water for industrial cooling and returning it to its natural source at a higher temperature. (17.3)

Thermodynamic stability (nuclear): the potential energy of a particular nucleus as compared with the sum of the potential energies of its component protons and neutrons. (20.1)

Thermodynamics: the study of energy and its interconversions. (9.1)

Third law of thermodynamics: the entropy of a perfect crystal at 0 K is zero. (10.8)

Titration: a technique in which one solution is used to analyze another. (4.9)

Torr: another name for millimeter of mercury (mm Hg). (5.1)

Transfer RNA (tRNA): a small RNA fragment that finds specific amino acids and attaches them to the protein chain as dictated by the codons in mRNA. (21.6)

Transition metals: several series of elements in which inner orbitals (*d* or *f* orbitals) are being filled. (12.13; 18.1)

Transuranium elements: the elements beyond uranium that are made artificially by particle bombardment. (20.3)

Triple bond: a bond in which three pairs of electrons are shared by two atoms. (13.8)

Triple point: the point on a phase diagram at which all three states of a substance are present. (16.11)

Tyndall effect: the scattering of light by particles in a suspension. (17.8)

Uncertainty (in measurement): the characteristics that any measurement involves estimates and cannot be exactly reproduced. (A1.5)

Unimolecular step: a reaction step involving only one molecule. (15.6)

Unit cell: the smallest repeating unit of a lattice. (16.3)

Unit factor: an equivalence statement between units used for converting from one unit to another. (A2.2)

Universal gas constant: the combined proportionality constant in the ideal gas law; 0.08206 L atm/K mol or 8.3145 J/K mol. (5.3)

Valence electrons: the electrons in the outermost principal quantum level of an atom. (12.13)

Valence shell electron-pair repulsion (VSEPR) model: a model whose main postulate is that the structure around a given atom in a molecule is determined principally by minimizing electron-pair repulsions. (13.13)

van der Waals's equation: a mathematical expression for describing the behavior of real gases. (5.10)

van't Hoff factor: the ratio of moles of particles in solution to moles of solute dissolved. (17.7)

Vapor pressure: the pressure of the vapor over a liquid at equilibrium. (16.10)

Vaporization: the change in state that occurs when a liquid evaporates to form a gas. (16.10)

Viscosity: the resistance of a liquid to flow. (16.2)

Volt: the unit of electrical potential defined as one joule of work per coulomb of charge transferred. (11.1)

Voltmeter: an instrument that measures cell potential by drawing electric current through a known resistance. (11.1)

Volumetric analysis: a process involving titration of one solution with another. (4.9)

Wave function: a function of the coordinates of an electron's position in three-dimensional space that describes the properties of the electron. (12.5)

Wave mechanical model: a model for the hydrogen atom in which the electron is assumed to behave as a standing wave. (12.7)

Wavelength: the distance between two consecutive peaks or troughs in a wave. (12.1)

Weak acid: an acid that dissociates only slightly in aqueous solution. (4.2; 7.2)

Weak base: a base that reacts with water to produce hydroxide ions to only a slight extent in aqueous solution. (4.2; 7.6)

Weak electrolyte: a material that, when dissolved in water, gives a solution that conducts only a small electric current. (4.2)

Weight: the force exerted on an object by gravity. (2.3)

Work: force acting over a distance. (9.1)

X-ray diffraction: a technique for establishing the structures of crystalline solids by directing X rays of a single wavelength at a crystal and obtaining a diffraction pattern from which interatomic spaces can be determined. (16.3)

Zone of nuclear stability: the area encompassing the stable nuclides on a plot of their positions as a function of the number of protons and the number of neutrons in the nucleus. (20.1)

Index

Atom(s)
ancient Greek ideas on, 16, 524
Dalton's theory of, 18, 19–21, 524, 958
early experiments on, 24–28
modern view of, 29–30, 524
See also Hydrogen atom; Quantum mechanics

Ion(s), 31–33
  electrolysis of mixtures of, 504, 506
  in electrolytes, 97–100
  energy of interaction of, 597
  independence in solution, 96, 106
  naming of, 36–39
  oxidation states of, 126
  polyatomic, 32, 39, 614
  separating mixtures of, 112–114, 338–342, 346–347
  sizes of, 608–609
  spectator, 111–112
  See also Complex ions; Hydration

Student Solutions Manual To Accompany

General Chemistry 142

TO THE STUDENT: HOW TO USE THIS GUIDE

Solutions to odd-numbered chapter exercises are in this manual. This "Solutions Guide" can be a valuable resource if you use it properly. The way NOT to use it is to look at an exercise in the book and then immediately check the solution, often saying to yourself, "That's easy, I can do it." Developing problem solving skills takes practice. Don't look up a solution to a problem until you have tried to work it on your own. If you are completely stuck, see if you can find a similar problem in the Sample Exercises in the chapter. Only look up the solution as a last resort. If you do this for a problem, look for a similar problem in the end of chapter exercises and try working it. The more problems you do, the easier chemistry becomes. It is also in your self interest to try to work as many problems as possible. Most exams that you will take in chemistry will involve a lot of problem solving. If you have worked several problems similar to the ones on an exam, you will do much better than if the exam is the first time you try to solve a particular type of problem. No matter how much you read and study the text, or how well you think you understand the material, you don't really understand it until you have taken the information in the text and applied the principles to problem solving. You will make mistakes, but the good students learn from their mistakes.

In this manual we have worked problems as in the textbook. We have shown intermediate answers to the correct number of significant figures and used the rounded answer in later calculations. Thus, some of your answers may differ slightly from ours. When we have not followed this convention, we have usually noted this in the solution. The most common exception is when working with the natural logarithm (ln) function, where we usually carried extra significant figures in order to reduce round-off error. In addition, we tried to use constants and conversion factors reported to at least one more significant figure as compared to numbers given in the problem. For some problems, this required the use of more precise atomic masses for H, C, N, and O as given in Chapter 3. This practice of carrying one extra significant figure in constants helps minimize round-off error.

TJH
SSZ

CHAPTER 2

ATOMS, MOLECULES, AND IONS

Development of the Atomic Theory

19. From Avogadro's hypothesis (law), volume ratios are equal to molecule ratios at constant temperature and pressure. Therefore, we can write a balanced equation using the volume data, $Cl_2 + 5\ F_2 \rightarrow 2\ X$. Two molecules of X contain 10 atoms of F and two atoms of Cl. The formula of X is ClF_5 for a balanced equation.

21. Avogadro's hypothesis (law) implies that volume ratios are equal to molecule ratios at constant temperature and pressure. Here, 1 volume of N_2 reacts with 3 volumes of H_2 to produce 2 volumes of the gaseous product or in terms of molecule ratios:

$$1\ N_2 + 3\ H_2 \rightarrow 2\ \text{product}$$

In order for the equation to be balanced, the product must be NH_3.

23. Hydrazine: 1.44×10^{-1} g H/g N; ammonia: 2.16×10^{-1} g H/g N; hydrogen azide: 2.40×10^{-2} g H/g N. Let's try all of the ratios:

$$\frac{0.144}{0.0240} = 6.00; \quad \frac{0.216}{0.0240} = 9.00; \quad \frac{0.0240}{0.0240} = 1.00; \quad \frac{0.216}{0.144} = 1.50 = \frac{3}{2}$$

All the masses of hydrogen in these three compounds can be expressed as simple whole-number ratios. The g H/g N in hydrazine, ammonia, and hydrogen azide are in the ratios 6 : 9 : 1.

25. To get the atomic mass of H to be 1.00, we divide the mass that reacts with 1.00 g of oxygen by 0.126, that is, 0.126/0.126 = 1.00. To get Na, Mg, and O on the same scale, we do the same division.

$$\text{Na: } \frac{2.875}{0.126} = 22.8; \quad \text{Mg: } \frac{1.500}{0.126} = 11.9; \quad \text{O: } \frac{1.00}{0.126} = 7.94$$

	H	O	Na	Mg
Relative value	1.00	7.94	22.8	11.9
Accepted value	1.0079	15.999	22.99	24.31

The atomic masses of O and Mg are incorrect. The atomic masses of H and Na are close. Something must be wrong about the assumed formulas of the compounds. It turns out that the correct formulas are H_2O, Na_2O, and MgO. The smaller discrepancies result from the error in the assumed atomic mass of H.

The Nature of the Atom

27. From section 2.6, the nucleus has "a diameter of about 10^{-13} cm" and the electrons "move about the nucleus at an average distance of about 10^{-8} cm from it." We will use these statements to help determine the densities. Density of hydrogen nucleus (contains one proton only):

$$V_{nucleus} = \frac{4}{3}\pi r^3 = \frac{4}{3}(3.14)(5 \times 10^{-14}\text{ cm})^3 = 5 \times 10^{-40}\text{ cm}^3$$

$$d = \text{density} = \frac{1.67 \times 10^{-24}\text{ g}}{5 \times 10^{-40}\text{ cm}^3} = 3 \times 10^{15}\text{ g/cm}^3$$

Density of H atom (contains one proton and one electron):

$$V_{atom} = \frac{4}{3}(3.14)(1 \times 10^{-8}\text{ cm})^3 = 4 \times 10^{-24}\text{ cm}^3$$

$$d = \frac{1.67 \times 10^{-24}\text{ g} + 9 \times 10^{-28}\text{ g}}{4 \times 10^{-24}\text{ cm}^3} = 0.4\text{ g/cm}^3$$

29. First, divide all charges by the smallest quantity, 6.40×10^{-13}.

$$\frac{2.56 \times 10^{-12}}{6.40 \times 10^{-13}} = 4.00; \quad \frac{7.68}{0.640} = 12.00; \quad \frac{3.84}{0.640} = 6.00$$

Because all charges are whole-number multiples of 6.40×10^{-13} zirkombs, the charge on one electron could be 6.40×10^{-13} zirkombs. However, 6.40×10^{-13} zirkombs could be the charge of two electrons (or three electrons, etc.). All one can conclude is that the charge of an electron is 6.40×10^{-13} zirkombs or an integer fraction of 6.40×10^{-13}.

31. If the plum pudding model were correct (a diffuse positive charge with electrons scattered throughout), then α particles should have traveled through the thin foil with very minor deflections in their path. This was not the case because a few of the α particles were deflected at very large angles. Rutherford reasoned that the large deflections of these α particles could be caused only by a center of concentrated positive charge that contains most of the atom's mass (the nuclear model of the atom).

Elements, Ions, and the Periodic Table

33. The atomic number of an element is equal to the number of protons in the nucleus of an atom of that element. The mass number is the sum of the number of protons plus neutrons in the nucleus. The atomic mass is the actual mass of a particular isotope (including electrons). As is discussed in Chapter 3, the average mass of an atom is taken from a measurement made on a large number of atoms. The average atomic mass value is listed in the periodic table.

35. a. The noble gases are He, Ne, Ar, Kr, Xe, and Rn (helium, neon, argon, krypton, xenon, and radon). Radon has only radioactive isotopes. In the periodic table, the whole number enclosed in parentheses is the mass number of the longest-lived isotope of the element.

    b. promethium (Pm) and technetium (Tc)

37. Use the periodic table to identify the elements.

    a. Cl; halogen
    b. Be; alkaline earth metal
    c. Eu; lanthanide metal
    d. Hf; transition metal
    e. He; noble gas
    f. U; actinide metal
    g. Cs; alkali metal

39. For lighter, stable isotopes, the number of protons in the nucleus is about equal to the number of neutrons. When the number of protons and neutrons is equal to each other, the mass number (protons + neutrons) will be twice the atomic number (protons). Therefore, for lighter isotopes, the ratio of the mass number to the atomic number is close to 2. For example, consider ^{28}Si, which has 14 protons and (28 – 14 =) 14 neutrons. Here, the mass number to atomic number ratio is 28/14 = 2.0. For heavier isotopes, there are more neutrons than protons in the nucleus. Therefore, the ratio of the mass number to the atomic number increases steadily upward from 2 as the isotopes get heavier and heavier. For example, ^{238}U has 92 protons and (238 – 92 =) 146 neutrons. The ratio of the mass number to the atomic number for ^{238}U is 238/92 = 2.6.

41. a. $^{24}_{12}Mg$: 12 protons, 12 neutrons, 12 electrons

    b. $^{24}_{12}Mg^{2+}$: 12 p, 12 n, 10 e
    c. $^{59}_{27}Co^{2+}$: 27 p, 32 n, 25 e
    d. $^{59}_{27}Co^{3+}$: 27 p, 32 n, 24 e
    e. $^{59}_{27}Co$: 27 p, 32 n, 27 e
    f. $^{79}_{34}Se$: 34 p, 45 n, 34 e
    g. $^{79}_{34}Se^{2-}$: 34 p, 45 n, 36 e
    h. $^{63}_{28}Ni$: 28 p, 35 n, 28 e
    i. $^{59}_{28}Ni^{2+}$: 28 p, 31 n, 26 e

43. Atomic number = 63 (Eu); net charge = +63 – 60 = 3+; mass number = 63 + 88 = 151; symbol: $^{151}_{63}Eu^{3+}$

Atomic number = 50 (Sn); mass number = 50 + 68 = 118; net charge = +50 − 48 = 2+; symbol: $^{118}_{50}Sn^{2+}$.

45. In ionic compounds, metals lose electrons to form cations, and nonmetals gain electrons to form anions. Group 1A, 2A, and 3A metals form stable 1+, 2+, and 3+ charged cations, respectively. Group 5A, 6A, and 7A nonmetals form 3−, 2−, and 1− charged anions, respectively.

a. Lose 2 e^- to form Ra^{2+}. b. Lose 3 e^- to form In^{3+}. c. Gain 3 e^- to form P^{3-}.

d. Gain 2 e^- to form Te^{2-}. e. Gain 1 e^- to form Br^-. f. Lose 1 e^- to form Rb^+.

Nomenclature

47. $AlCl_3$, aluminum chloride; $CrCl_3$, chromium(III) chloride; ICl_3, iodine trichloride; $AlCl_3$ and $CrCl_3$ are ionic compounds following the rules for naming ionic compounds. The major difference is that $CrCl_3$ contains a transition metal (Cr) that generally exhibits two or more stable charges when in ionic compounds. We need to indicate which charged ion we have in the compound. This is generally true whenever the metal in the ionic compound is a transition metal. ICl_3 is made from only nonmetals and is a covalent compound. Predicting formulas for covalent compounds is extremely difficult. Because of this, we need to indicate the number of each nonmetal in the binary covalent compound. The exception is when there is only one of the first species present in the formula; when this is the case, mono- is not used (it is assumed).

49. a. sulfur difluoride b. dinitrogen tetroxide

c. iodine trichloride d. tetraphosphorus hexoxide

51. a. copper(I) iodide b. copper(II) iodide c. cobalt(II) iodide

d. sodium carbonate e. sodium hydrogen carbonate or sodium bicarbonate

f. tetrasulfur tetranitride g. selenium tetrabromide h. sodium hypochlorite

i. barium chromate j. ammonium nitrate

53. a. SO_2 b. SO_3 c. Na_2SO_3 d. $KHSO_3$

e. Li_3N f. $Cr_2(CO_3)_3$ g. $Cr(C_2H_3O_2)_2$ h. SnF_4

i. NH_4HSO_4: composed of NH_4^+ and HSO_4^- ions

j. $(NH_4)_2HPO_4$ k. $KClO_4$ l. NaH

m. HBrO n. HBr

55. a. $Pb(C_2H_3O_2)_2$; lead(II) acetate b. $CuSO_4$; copper(II) sulfate

c. CaO; calcium oxide d. $MgSO_4$; magnesium sulfate

e. $Mg(OH)_2$; magnesium hydroxide f. $CaSO_4$; calcium sulfate

g. N_2O; dinitrogen monoxide or nitrous oxide (common name)

57. a. nitric acid, HNO_3 b. perchloric acid, $HClO_4$ c. acetic acid, $HC_2H_3O_2$

d. sulfuric acid, H_2SO_4 e. phosphoric acid, H_3PO_4

Additional Exercises

59. The equation for the reaction between the elements of sodium and chlorine is 2 Na(s) + Cl_2(g) → 2 NaCl(s). The sodium reactant exists as singular sodium atoms packed together very tightly and in a very organized fashion. This type of packing of atoms represents the solid phase. The chlorine reactant exists as Cl_2 molecules. In the picture of chlorine, there is a lot of empty space present. This only occurs in the gaseous phase. When sodium and chlorine react, the ionic compound NaCl is the product. NaCl exists as separate Na^+ and Cl^- ions. Because the ions are packed very closely together and are packed in a very organized fashion, NaCl is depicted in the solid phase.

61. From the law of definite proportions, a given compound always contains exactly the same proportion of elements by mass. The first sample of chloroform has a total mass of 12.0 g C + 106.4 g Cl + 1.01 g H = 119.41 g (carrying extra significant figures). The mass percent of carbon in this sample of chloroform is:

$$\frac{12.0\text{ g C}}{119.41\text{ g total}} \times 100 = 10.05\% \text{ C by mass}$$

From the law of definite proportions, the second sample of chloroform must also contain 10.05% C by mass. Let x = mass of chloroform in the second sample:

$$\frac{30.0\text{ g C}}{x} \times 100 = 10.05, \quad x = 299 \text{ g chloroform}$$

63. From the Na_2X formula, X has a 2− charge. Because 36 electrons are present, X has 34 protons, 79 − 34 = 45 neutrons, and is selenium.

a. True. Nonmetals bond together using covalent bonds and are called covalent compounds.

b. False. The isotope has 34 protons.

c. False. The isotope has 45 neutrons.

d. False. The identity is selenium, Se.

65. From the XBr_2 formula, the charge on element X is 2+. Therefore, the element has 88 protons, which identifies it as radium, Ra. 230 − 88 = 142 neutrons.

67. In the case of sulfur, SO_4^{2-} is sulfate, and SO_3^{2-} is sulfite. By analogy:

SeO_4^{2-}: selenate; SeO_3^{2-}: selenite; TeO_4^{2-}: tellurate; TeO_3^{2-}: tellurite

69. If the formula is InO, then one atomic mass of In would combine with one atomic mass of O, or:

$$\frac{A}{16.00} = \frac{4.784 \text{ g In}}{1.000 \text{ g O}}, \quad A = \text{atomic mass of In} = 76.54$$

If the formula is In_2O_3, then two times the atomic mass of In will combine with three times the atomic mass of O, or:

$$\frac{2A}{(3)16.00} = \frac{4.784 \text{ g In}}{1.000 \text{ g O}}, \quad A = \text{atomic mass of In} = 114.8$$

The latter number is the atomic mass of In used in the modern periodic table.

71. The cation has 51 protons and 48 electrons. The number of protons corresponds to the atomic number. Thus this is element 51, antimony. There are 3 fewer electrons than protons. Therefore, the charge on the cation is 3+. The anion has one-third the number of protons of the cation which corresponds to 17 protons; this is element 17, chlorine. The number of electrons in this anion of chlorine is 17 + 1 = 18 electrons. The anion must have a charge of 1−.

The formula of the compound formed between Sb^{3+} and Cl^- is $SbCl_3$. The name of the compound is antimony(III) chloride. The Roman numeral is used to indicate the charge of Sb because the predicted charge is not obvious from the periodic table.

73. Because this is a relatively small number of neutrons, the number of protons will be very close to the number of neutrons present. The heavier elements have significantly more neutrons than protons in their nuclei. Because this element forms anions, it is a nonmetal and will be a halogen because halogens form stable 1− charged ions in ionic compounds. From the halogens listed, chlorine, with an average atomic mass of 35.45, fits the data. The two isotopes are ^{35}Cl and ^{37}Cl, and the number of electrons in the 1− ion is 18. Note that because the atomic mass of chlorine listed in the periodic table is closer to 35 than 37, we can assume that ^{35}Cl is the more abundant isotope. This is discussed in Chapter 3.

Challenge Problems

75. a. Both compounds have C_2H_6O as the formula. Because they have the same formula, their mass percent composition will be identical. However, these are different compounds with different properties because the atoms are bonded together differently. These compounds are called isomers of each other.

b. When wood burns, most of the solid material in wood is converted to gases, which escape. The gases produced are most likely CO_2 and H_2O.

c. The atom is not an indivisible particle but is instead composed of other smaller particles, for example, electrons, neutrons, and protons.

d. The two hydride samples contain different isotopes of either hydrogen and/or lithium. Although the compounds are composed of different isotopes, their properties are similar because different isotopes of the same element have similar properties (except, of course, their mass).

77. Compound I: $\frac{14.0 \text{ g R}}{3.00 \text{ g Q}} = \frac{4.67 \text{ g R}}{1.00 \text{ g Q}}$; Compound II: $\frac{7.00 \text{ g R}}{4.50 \text{ g Q}} = \frac{1.56 \text{ g R}}{1.00 \text{ g Q}}$

The ratio of the masses of R that combines with 1.00 g Q is $\frac{4.67}{1.56} = 2.99 \approx 3$.
As expected from the law of multiple proportions, this ratio is a small whole number.

Because compound I contains three times the mass of R per gram of Q as compared with compound II (RQ), the formula of compound I should be R_3Q.

79. Avogadro proposed that equal volumes of gases (at constant temperature and pressure) contain equal numbers of molecules. In terms of balanced equations, Avogadro's hypothesis (law) implies that volume ratios will be identical to molecule ratios. Assuming one molecule of octane reacts, then 1 molecule of C_xH_y produces 8 molecules of CO_2 and 9 molecules of H_2O. $C_xH_y + n\ O_2 \rightarrow 8\ CO_2 + 9\ H_2O$. Because all the carbon in octane ends up as carbon in CO_2, octane must contain 8 atoms of C. Similarly, all hydrogen in octane ends up as hydrogen in H_2O, so one molecule of octane must contain $9 \times 2 = 18$ atoms of H. Octane formula = C_8H_{18} and the ratio of C:H = 8:18 or 4:9.

CHAPTER 3

STOICHIOMETRY

Atomic Masses and the Mass Spectrometer

23. Average atomic mass = A = 0.0800(45.95269) + 0.0730(46.951764) + 0.7380(47.947947) + 0.0550(48.947841) + 0.0540(49.944792) = 47.88 amu

    This is element Ti (titanium).

25. If silver is 51.82% ^{107}Ag, then the remainder is ^{109}Ag (48.18%). Determining the atomic mass (A) of ^{109}Ag:

$$107.868 = \frac{51.82(106.905) + 48.18(A)}{100}$$

$$10786.8 = 5540. + (48.18)A,\ \ A = 108.9 \text{ amu} = \text{atomic mass of } ^{109}\text{Ag}$$

27. 186.207 = 0.6260(186.956) + 0.3740(A), 186.207 − 117.0 = 0.3740(A)

$$A = \frac{69.2}{0.3740} = 185 \text{ amu } (A = 184.95 \text{ amu without rounding to proper significant figures})$$

29. There are three peaks in the mass spectrum, each 2 mass units apart. This is consistent with two isotopes, differing in mass by two mass units. The peak at 157.84 corresponds to a Br_2 molecule composed of two atoms of the lighter isotope. This isotope has mass equal to 157.84/2, or 78.92. This corresponds to ^{79}Br. The second isotope is ^{81}Br with mass equal to 161.84/2 = 80.92. The peaks in the mass spectrum correspond to $^{79}Br_2$, $^{79}Br^{81}Br$, and $^{81}Br_2$ in order of increasing mass. The intensities of the highest and lowest masses tell us the two isotopes are present at about equal abundance. The actual abundance is 50.68% ^{79}Br and 49.32% ^{81}Br.

31. GaAs can be either ^{69}GaAs or ^{71}GaAs. The mass spectrum for GaAs will have two peaks at 144 (= 69 + 75) and 146 (= 71 + 75) with intensities in the ratio of 60 : 40 or 3 : 2.

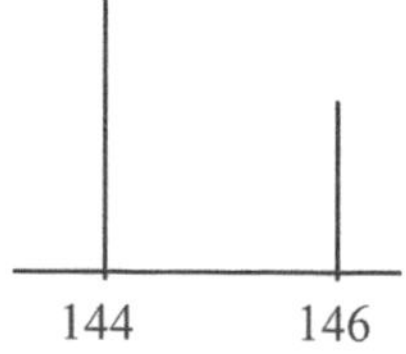

Ga_2As_2 can be $^{69}Ga_2As_2$, $^{69}Ga^{71}GaAs_2$, or $^{71}Ga_2As_2$. The mass spectrum will have three peaks at 288, 290, and 292 with intensities in the ratio of 36 : 48 : 16 or 9 : 12 : 4. We get this ratio from the following probability table:

	^{69}Ga (0.60)	^{71}Ga (0.40)
^{69}Ga (0.60)	0.36	0.24
^{71}Ga (0.40)	0.24	0.16

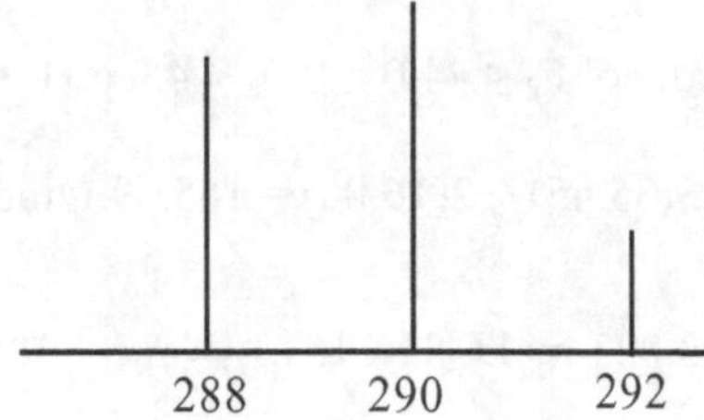

Moles and Molar Masses

33. a. $9(12.011) + 8(1.0079) + 4(15.999) = 180.158$ g/mol

b. $500.\text{ mg} \times \dfrac{1\text{ g}}{1000\text{ mg}} \times \dfrac{1\text{ mol}}{180.16\text{ g}} = 2.78 \times 10^{-3}\text{ mol}$

$$2.78 \times 10^{-3}\text{ mol} \times \frac{6.022 \times 10^{23}\text{ molecules}}{\text{mol}} = 1.67 \times 10^{21}\text{ molecules}$$

35. a. $20.0\text{ mg } C_8H_{10}N_4O_2 \times \dfrac{1\text{ g}}{1000\text{ mg}} \times \dfrac{1\text{ mol}}{194.20\text{ g}} = 1.03 \times 10^{-4}\text{ mol } C_8H_{10}N_4O_2$

b. $2.72 \times 10^{21}\text{ molecules } C_2H_5OH \times \dfrac{1\text{ mol}}{6.022 \times 10^{23}\text{ molecules}} = 4.52 \times 10^{-3}\text{ mol } C_2H_5OH$

c. $1.50\text{ g } CO_2 \times \dfrac{1\text{ mol}}{44.01\text{ g}} = 3.41 \times 10^{-2}\text{ mol } CO_2$

37. $4.0\text{ g } H_2 \times \dfrac{1\text{ mol } H_2}{2.016\text{ g } H_2} \times \dfrac{2\text{ mol H}}{1\text{ mol } H_2} \times \dfrac{6.022 \times 10^{23}\text{ atoms H}}{1\text{ mol H}} = 2.4 \times 10^{24}\text{ atoms}$

$$4.0\text{ g He} \times \frac{1\text{ mol He}}{4.003\text{ g He}} \times \frac{6.022 \times 10^{23}\text{ atoms He}}{1\text{ mol He}} = 6.0 \times 10^{23}\text{ atoms}$$

$$1.0 \text{ mol } F_2 \times \frac{2 \text{ mol F}}{1 \text{ mol } F_2} \times \frac{6.022 \times 10^{23} \text{ atoms F}}{1 \text{ mol F}} = 1.2 \times 10^{24} \text{ atoms}$$

$$44.0 \text{ g } CO_2 \times \frac{1 \text{ mol } CO_2}{44.01 \text{ g } CO_2} \times \frac{3 \text{ mol atoms} (1\text{ C} + 2\text{ O})}{1 \text{ mol } CO_2} \times \frac{6.022 \times 10^{23} \text{ atoms}}{1 \text{ mol atoms}}$$
$$= 1.81 \times 10^{24} \text{ atoms}$$

$$146 \text{ g } SF_6 \times \frac{1 \text{ mol } SF_6}{146.07 \text{ g } SF_6} \times \frac{7 \text{ mol atoms} (1\text{ S} + 6\text{ F})}{1 \text{ mol } SF_6} \times \frac{6.022 \times 10^{23} \text{ atoms}}{1 \text{ mol atoms}} = 4.21 \times 10^{24} \text{ atoms}$$

The order is: 4.0 g He < 1.0 mol F_2 < 44.0 g CO_2 < 4.0 g H_2 < 146 g SF_6

39. a. 2(12.01) + 3(1.008) + 3(35.45) + 2(16.00) = 165.39 g/mol

b. $500.0 \text{ g} \times \frac{1 \text{ mol}}{165.39 \text{ g}} = 3.023 \text{ mol } C_2H_3Cl_3O_2$

c. $2.0 \times 10^{-2} \text{ mol} \times \frac{165.39 \text{ g}}{\text{mol}} = 3.3 \text{ g } C_2H_3Cl_3O_2$

d. $5.0 \text{ g } C_2H_3Cl_3O_2 \times \frac{1 \text{ mol}}{165.39 \text{ g}} \times \frac{6.02 \times 10^{23} \text{ molecules}}{\text{mol}} \times \frac{3 \text{ atoms Cl}}{\text{molecule}}$

$= 5.5 \times 10^{22}$ atoms of chlorine

e. $1.0 \text{ g Cl} \times \frac{1 \text{ mol Cl}}{35.45 \text{ g}} \times \frac{1 \text{ mol } C_2H_3Cl_3O_2}{3 \text{ mol Cl}} \times \frac{165.39 \text{ g } C_2H_3Cl_3O_2}{\text{mol } C_2H_3Cl_3O_2} = 1.6 \text{ g chloral hydrate}$

f. $500 \text{ molecules} \times \frac{1 \text{ mol}}{6.022 \times 10^{23} \text{ molecules}} \times \frac{165.39 \text{ g}}{\text{mol}} = 1.373 \times 10^{-19} \text{ g}$

Percent Composition

41. Molar mass = 20(12.01) + 29(1.008) + 19.00 + 3(16.00) = 336.43 g/mol

$$\text{Mass \% C} = \frac{20(12.01) \text{ g C}}{336.43 \text{ g compound}} \times 100 = 71.40\% \text{ C}$$

$$\text{Mass \% H} = \frac{29(1.008) \text{ g H}}{336.43 \text{ g compound}} \times 100 = 8.689\% \text{ H}$$

$$\text{Mass \% F} = \frac{19.00\text{ g F}}{336.43\text{ g compound}} \times 100 = 5.648\%\text{ F}$$

Mass % O = 100.00 – (71.40 + 8.689 + 5.648) = 14.26% O or:

$$\text{Mass \% O} = \frac{3(16.00)\text{ g O}}{336.43\text{ g compound}} \times 100 = 14.27\%\text{ O}$$

43. In 1 mole of $YBa_2Cu_3O_7$, there are 1 mole of Y, 2 moles of Ba, 3 moles of Cu, and 7 moles of O.

$$\text{Molar mass} = 1\text{ mol Y}\left(\frac{88.91\text{ g Y}}{\text{mol Y}}\right) + 2\text{ mol Ba}\left(\frac{137.3\text{ g Ba}}{\text{mol Ba}}\right)$$

$$+ 3\text{ mol Cu}\left(\frac{63.55\text{ g Cu}}{\text{mol Cu}}\right) + 7\text{ mol O}\left(\frac{16.00\text{ g O}}{\text{mol O}}\right)$$

Molar mass = 88.91 + 274.6 + 190.65 + 112.00 = 666.2 g/mol

$$\text{Mass \% Y} = \frac{88.91\text{ g}}{666.2\text{ g}} \times 100 = 13.35\%\text{ Y};\quad \text{mass \% Ba} = \frac{274.6\text{ g}}{666.2\text{ g}} \times 100 = 41.22\%\text{ Ba}$$

$$\text{Mass \% Cu} = \frac{190.65\text{ g}}{666.2\text{ g}} \times 100 = 28.62\%\text{ Cu};\quad \text{mass \% O} = \frac{112.0\text{ g}}{666.2\text{ g}} \times 100 = 16.81\%\text{ O}$$

45. NO: $\text{Mass \% N} = \frac{14.01\text{ g N}}{30.01\text{ g NO}} \times 100 = 46.68\%\text{ N}$

NO_2: $\text{Mass \% N} = \frac{14.01\text{ g N}}{46.01\text{ g NO}_2} \times 100 = 30.45\%\text{ N}$

N_2O: $\text{Mass \% N} = \frac{2(14.01)\text{ g N}}{44.02\text{ g N}_2\text{O}} \times 100 = 63.65\%\text{ N}$

From the calculated mass percents, only NO is 46.7% N by mass, so NO could be this species. Any other compound having NO as an empirical formula could also be the compound.

47. There are 0.390 g Cu for every 100.000 g of fungal laccase. Let's assume 100.000 g fungal laccase.

$$\text{Mol fungal laccase} = 0.390\text{ g Cu} \times \frac{1\text{ mol Cu}}{63.55\text{ g Cu}} \times \frac{1\text{ mol fungal laccase}}{4\text{ mol Cu}} = 1.53 \times 10^{-3}\text{ mol}$$

$$\frac{x\text{ g fungal laccase}}{1\text{ mol fungal laccase}} = \frac{100.000\text{ g}}{1.53 \times 10^{-3}\text{ mol}},\quad x = \text{molar mass} = 6.54 \times 10^4\text{ g/mol}$$

Empirical and Molecular Formulas

49. a. Molar mass of CH_2O = $1 \text{ mol C}\left(\frac{12.011 \text{ g}}{\text{mol C}}\right) + 2 \text{ mol H}\left(\frac{1.0079 \text{ g}}{\text{mol H}}\right)$

$$+ 1 \text{ mol O}\left(\frac{15.999 \text{ g}}{\text{mol O}}\right) = 30.026 \text{ g/mol}$$

$$\% \text{C} = \frac{12.011 \text{ g C}}{30.026 \text{ g CH}_2\text{O}} \times 100 = 40.002\% \text{ C}; \ \% \text{H} = \frac{2.0158 \text{ g H}}{30.026 \text{ g CH}_2\text{O}} \times 100 = 6.7135\% \text{ H}$$

$$\% \text{O} = \frac{15.999 \text{ g O}}{30.026 \text{ g CH}_2\text{O}} \times 100 = 53.284\% \text{ O or } \% \text{O} = 100.000 - (40.002 + 6.7135)$$

$$= 53.285\%$$

b. Molar mass of $C_6H_{12}O_6$ = 6(12.011) + 12(1.0079) + 6(15.999) = 180.155 g/mol

$$\% \text{C} = \frac{72.066 \text{ g C}}{180.155 \text{ g C}_6\text{H}_{12}\text{O}_6} \times 100 = 40.002\%; \quad \% \text{H} = \frac{12(1.0079) \text{ g}}{180.155 \text{ g}} \times 100 = 6.7136\%$$

% O = 100.00 – (40.002 + 6.7136) = 53.284%

c. Molar Mass of $HC_2H_3O_2$ = 2(12.011) + 4(1.0079) + 2(15.999) = 60.052 g/mol

$$\% \text{C} = \frac{24.022 \text{ g}}{60.052 \text{ g}} \times 100 = 40.002\%; \quad \% \text{H} = \frac{4.0316 \text{ g}}{60.052 \text{ g}} \times 100 = 6.7135\%$$

% O = 100.000 – (40.002 + 6.7135) = 53.285%

All three compounds have the same empirical formula, CH_2O, and different molecular formulas. The composition of all three in mass percent is also the same (within rounding differences). Therefore, elemental analysis will give us only the empirical formula.

51. a. SNH: Empirical formula mass = 32.07 + 14.01 + 1.008 = 47.09 g/mol

$$\frac{188.35 \text{ g}}{47.09 \text{ g}} = 4.000;$$ so the molecular formula is $(SNH)_4$ or $S_4N_4H_4$.

b. $NPCl_2$: Empirical formula mass = 14.01 + 30.97 + 2(35.45) = 115.88 g/mol

$$\frac{347.64 \text{ g}}{115.88 \text{ g}} = 3.0000;$$ molecular formula is $(NPCl_2)_3$ or $N_3P_3Cl_6$.

c. CoC_4O_4: 58.93 + 4(12.01) + 4(16.00) = 170.97 g/mol

$\frac{341.94\text{ g}}{170.97\text{ g}} = 2.0000$; molecular formula: $Co_2C_8O_8$

d. SN: 32.07 + 14.01 = 46.08 g/mol; $\frac{184.32\text{ g}}{46.08\text{ g}} = 4.000$; molecular formula: S_4N_4

53. Compound I: mass O = 0.6498 g Hg_xO_y − 0.6018 g Hg = 0.0480 g O

$$0.6018\text{ g Hg} \times \frac{1\text{ mol Hg}}{200.6\text{ g Hg}} = 3.000 \times 10^{-3}\text{ mol Hg}$$

$$0.0480\text{ g O} \times \frac{1\text{ mol O}}{16.00\text{ g O}} = 3.00 \times 10^{-3}\text{ mol O}$$

The mole ratio between Hg and O is 1 : 1, so the empirical formula of compound I is HgO.

Compound II: mass Hg = 0.4172 g Hg_xO_y − 0.016 g O = 0.401 g Hg

$$0.401\text{ g Hg} \times \frac{1\text{ mol Hg}}{200.6\text{ g Hg}} = 2.00 \times 10^{-3}\text{ mol Hg};\ 0.016\text{ g O} \times \frac{1\text{ mol O}}{16.00\text{ g O}} = 1.0 \times 10^{-3}\text{ mol O}$$

The mole ratio between Hg and O is 2 : 1, so the empirical formula is Hg_2O.

55. First, we will determine composition in mass percent. We assume that all the carbon in the 0.213 g CO_2 came from the 0.157 g of the compound and that all the hydrogen in the 0.0310 g H_2O came from the 0.157 g of the compound.

$$0.213\text{ g CO}_2 \times \frac{12.01\text{ g C}}{44.01\text{ g CO}_2} = 0.0581\text{ g C};\ \%\text{ C} = \frac{0.0581\text{ g C}}{0.157\text{ g compound}} \times 100 = 37.0\%\text{ C}$$

$$0.0310\text{ g H}_2\text{O} \times \frac{2.016\text{ g H}}{18.02\text{ g H}_2\text{O}} = 3.47 \times 10^{-3}\text{ g H};\ \%\text{ H} = \frac{3.47 \times 10^{-3}\text{ g}}{0.157\text{ g}} \times 100 = 2.21\%\text{ H}$$

We get the mass percent of N from the second experiment:

$$0.0230\text{ g NH}_3 \times \frac{14.01\text{ g N}}{17.03\text{ g NH}_3} = 1.89 \times 10^{-2}\text{ g N}$$

$$\%\text{ N} = \frac{1.89 \times 10^{-2}\text{ g}}{0.103\text{ g}} \times 100 = 18.3\%\text{ N}$$

The mass percent of oxygen is obtained by difference:

$$\% \text{ O} = 100.00 - (37.0 + 2.21 + 18.3) = 42.5\% \text{ O}$$

So, out of 100.00 g of compound, there are:

$$37.0 \text{ g C} \times \frac{1 \text{ mol C}}{12.01 \text{ g C}} = 3.08 \text{ mol C}; \quad 2.21 \text{ g H} \times \frac{1 \text{ mol H}}{1.008 \text{ g H}} = 2.19 \text{ mol H}$$

$$18.3 \text{ g N} \times \frac{1 \text{ mol N}}{14.01 \text{ g N}} = 1.31 \text{ mol N}; \quad 42.5 \text{ g O} \times \frac{1 \text{ mol O}}{16.00 \text{ g O}} = 2.66 \text{ mol O}$$

Lastly, and often the hardest part, we need to find simple whole number ratios. Divide all mole values by the smallest number:

$$\frac{3.08}{1.31} = 2.35; \quad \frac{2.19}{1.31} = 1.67; \quad \frac{1.31}{1.31} = 1.00; \quad \frac{2.66}{1.31} = 2.03$$

Multiplying all these ratios by 3 gives an empirical formula of $C_7H_5N_3O_6$.

57. Assuming 100.0 g of compound:

$$26.7 \text{ g P} \times \frac{1 \text{ mol P}}{30.97 \text{ g P}} = 0.862 \text{ mol P}; \quad 12.1 \text{ g N} \times \frac{1 \text{ mol N}}{14.01 \text{ g N}} = 0.864 \text{ mol N}$$

$$61.2 \text{ g Cl} \times \frac{1 \text{ mol Cl}}{35.45 \text{ g Cl}} = 1.73 \text{ mol Cl}$$

$\frac{1.73}{0.862} = 2.01$; the empirical formula is $PNCl_2$.

The empirical formula mass is ≈ 31.0 + 14.0 + 2(35.5) = 116 g/mol.

$\frac{\text{Molar mass}}{\text{Empirical formula mass}} = \frac{580}{116} = 5.0$; the molecular formula is $(PNCl_2)_5 = P_5N_5Cl_{10}$.

59. First, we will determine composition by mass percent:

$$16.01 \text{ mg } CO_2 \times \frac{1 \text{ g}}{1000 \text{ mg}} \times \frac{12.011 \text{ g C}}{44.009 \text{ g } CO_2} \times \frac{1000 \text{ mg}}{\text{g}} = 4.369 \text{ mg C}$$

$$\% \text{ C} = \frac{4.369 \text{ mg C}}{10.68 \text{ mg compound}} \times 100 = 40.91\% \text{ C}$$

$$4.37 \text{ mg } H_2O \times \frac{1 \text{ g}}{1000 \text{ mg}} \times \frac{2.016 \text{ g H}}{18.02 \text{ g } H_2O} \times \frac{1000 \text{ mg}}{\text{g}} = 0.489 \text{ mg H}$$

$$\% \text{ H} = \frac{0.489 \text{ mg}}{10.68 \text{ mg}} \times 100 = 4.58\% \text{ H}; \ \% \text{ O} = 100.00 - (40.91 + 4.58) = 54.51\% \text{ O}$$

So, in 100.00 g of the compound, we have:

$$40.91 \text{ g C} \times \frac{1 \text{ mol C}}{12.011 \text{ g C}} = 3.406 \text{ mol C}; \ 4.58 \text{ g H} \times \frac{1 \text{ mol H}}{1.008 \text{ g H}} = 4.54 \text{ mol H}$$

$$54.51 \text{ g O} \times \frac{1 \text{ mol O}}{15.999 \text{ g O}} = 3.407 \text{ mol O}$$

Dividing by the smallest number: $\frac{4.54}{3.406} = 1.33 \approx \frac{4}{3}$; the empirical formula is $C_3H_4O_3$.

The empirical formula mass of $C_3H_4O_3$ is $\approx 3(12) + 4(1) + 3(16) = 88$ g.

Because $\frac{176.1}{88} = 2.0$, the molecular formula is $C_6H_8O_6$.

Balancing Chemical Equations

61. Only one product is formed in this representation. This product has two Ys bonded to an X. The other substance present in the product mixture is just the excess of one of the reactants (Y). The best equation has smallest whole numbers. Here, answer c would be this smallest whole number equation ($X + 2\ Y \rightarrow XY_2$). Answers a and b have incorrect products listed, and for answer d, an equation only includes the reactants that go to produce the product; excess reactants are not shown in an equation.

63. When balancing reactions, start with elements that appear in only one of the reactants and one of the products, and then go on to balance the remaining elements.

a. $C_6H_{12}O_6(s) + O_2(g) \rightarrow CO_2(g) + H_2O(g)$

Balance C atoms: $C_6H_{12}O_6 + O_2 \rightarrow 6\ CO_2 + H_2O$

Balance H atoms: $C_6H_{12}O_6 + O_2 \rightarrow 6\ CO_2 + 6\ H_2O$

Lastly, balance O atoms: $C_6H_{12}O_6(s) + 6\ O_2(g) \rightarrow 6\ CO_2(g) + 6\ H_2O(g)$

b. $Fe_2S_3(s) + HCl(g) \rightarrow FeCl_3(s) + H_2S(g)$

Balance Fe atoms: $Fe_2S_3 + HCl \rightarrow 2\ FeCl_3 + H_2S$

Balance S atoms: $Fe_2S_3 + HCl \rightarrow 2\ FeCl_3 + 3\ H_2S$

There are 6 H and 6 Cl on right, so balance with 6 HCl on left:

$Fe_2S_3(s) + 6\ HCl(g) \rightarrow 2\ FeCl_3(s) + 3\ H_2S(g)$

c. $CS_2(l) + NH_3(g) \rightarrow H_2S(g) + NH_4SCN(s)$

C and S are balanced; balance N:

$$CS_2 + 2\ NH_3 \rightarrow H_2S + NH_4SCN$$

H is also balanced. $CS_2(l) + 2\ NH_3(g) \rightarrow H_2S(g) + NH_4SCN(s)$.

65. a. $16\ Cr(s) + 3\ S_8(s) \rightarrow 8\ Cr_2S_3(s)$

b. $2\ NaHCO_3(s) \rightarrow Na_2CO_3(s) + CO_2(g) + H_2O(g)$

c. $2\ KClO_3(s) \rightarrow 2\ KCl(s) + 3\ O_2(g)$

d. $2\ Eu(s) + 6\ HF(g) \rightarrow 2\ EuF_3(s) + 3\ H_2(g)$

e. $2\ C_6H_6(l) + 15\ O_2(g) \rightarrow 12\ CO_2(g) + 6\ H_2O(g)$

Reaction Stoichiometry

67. $$1.000\text{ kg Al} \times \frac{1000\text{ g Al}}{\text{kg Al}} \times \frac{1\text{ mol Al}}{26.98\text{ g Al}} \times \frac{3\text{ mol NH}_4\text{ClO}_4}{3\text{ mol Al}} \times \frac{117.49\text{ g NH}_4\text{ClO}_4}{\text{mol NH}_4\text{ClO}_4} = 4355\text{ g NH}_4\text{ClO}_4$$

69. $Fe_2O_3(s) + 2\ Al(s) \rightarrow 2\ Fe(l) + Al_2O_3(s)$

$$15.0\text{ g Fe} \times \frac{1\text{ mol Fe}}{55.85\text{ g Fe}} = 0.269\text{ mol Fe};\ 0.269\text{ mol Fe} \times \frac{2\text{ mol Al}}{2\text{ mol Fe}} \times \frac{26.98\text{ g Al}}{\text{mol Al}} = 7.26\text{ g Al}$$

$$0.269\text{ mol Fe} \times \frac{1\text{ mol Fe}_2\text{O}_3}{2\text{ mol Fe}} \times \frac{159.70\text{ g Fe}_2\text{O}_3}{\text{mol Fe}_2\text{O}_3} = 21.5\text{ g Fe}_2\text{O}_3$$

$$0.269\text{ mol Fe} \times \frac{1\text{ mol Al}_2\text{O}_3}{2\text{ mol Fe}} \times \frac{101.96\text{ g Al}_2\text{O}_3}{\text{mol Al}_2\text{O}_3} = 13.7\text{ g Al}_2\text{O}_3$$

71. $2\ LiOH(s) + CO_2(g) \rightarrow Li_2CO_3(aq) + H_2O(l)$

The total volume of air exhaled each minute for the 7 astronauts is $7 \times 20. = 140$ L/min.

$$25{,}000\text{ g LiOH} \times \frac{1\text{ mol LiOH}}{23.95\text{ g LiOH}} \times \frac{1\text{ mol CO}_2}{2\text{ mol LiOH}} \times \frac{44.01\text{ g CO}_2}{\text{mol CO}_2} \times \frac{100\text{ g air}}{4.0\text{ g CO}_2} \times$$

$$\frac{1\text{ mL air}}{0.0010\text{ g air}} \times \frac{1\text{ L}}{1000\text{ mL}} \times \frac{1\text{ min}}{140\text{ L air}} \times \frac{1\text{ h}}{60\text{ min}} = 68\text{ h} = 2.8\text{ days}$$

73. $1.0 \times 10^3 \text{ g phosphorite} \times \dfrac{75 \text{ g Ca}_3(\text{PO}_4)_2}{100 \text{ g phosphorite}} \times \dfrac{1 \text{ mol Ca}_3(\text{PO}_4)_2}{310.18 \text{ g Ca}_3(\text{PO}_4)_2} \times$

$$\frac{1 \text{ mol P}_4}{2 \text{ mol Ca}_3(\text{PO}_4)_2} \times \frac{123.88 \text{ g P}_4}{\text{mol P}_4} = 150 \text{ g P}_4$$

Limiting Reactants and Percent Yield

75. The product formed in the reaction is NO_2; the other species present in the product picture is excess O_2. Therefore, NO is the limiting reactant. In the pictures, 6 NO molecules react with 3 O_2 molecules to form 6 NO_2 molecules.

$$6 \text{ NO(g)} + 3 \text{ O}_2\text{(g)} \rightarrow 6 \text{ NO}_2\text{(g)}$$

For smallest whole numbers, the balanced reaction is:

$$2 \text{ NO(g)} + \text{O}_2\text{(g)} \rightarrow 2 \text{ NO}_2\text{(g)}$$

77. $1.50 \text{ g BaO}_2 \times \dfrac{1 \text{ mol BaO}_2}{169.3 \text{ g BaO}_2} = 8.86 \times 10^{-3} \text{ mol BaO}_2$

$$25.0 \text{ mL} \times \frac{0.0272 \text{ g HCl}}{\text{mL}} \times \frac{1 \text{ mol HCl}}{36.46 \text{ g HCl}} = 1.87 \times 10^{-2} \text{ mol HCl}$$

The required mole ratio from the balanced reaction is 2 mol HCl to 1 mol BaO_2. The actual mole ratio is:

$$\frac{1.87 \times 10^{-2} \text{ mol HCl}}{8.86 \times 10^{-3} \text{ mol BaO}_2} = 2.11$$

Because the actual mole ratio is larger than the required mole ratio, the denominator (BaO_2) is the limiting reagent.

$$8.86 \times 10^{-3} \text{ mol BaO}_2 \times \frac{1 \text{ mol H}_2\text{O}_2}{\text{mol BaO}_2} \times \frac{34.02 \text{ g H}_2\text{O}_2}{\text{mol H}_2\text{O}_2} = 0.301 \text{ g H}_2\text{O}_2$$

The amount of HCl reacted is:

$$8.86 \times 10^{-3} \text{ mol BaO}_2 \times \frac{2 \text{ mol HCl}}{\text{mol BaO}_2} = 1.77 \times 10^{-2} \text{ mol HCl}$$

Excess mol HCl = 1.87×10^{-2} mol – 1.77×10^{-2} mol = 1.0×10^{-3} mol HCl

Mass of excess HCl = $1.0 \times 10^{-3} \text{ mol HCl} \times \dfrac{36.46 \text{ g HCl}}{\text{mol HCl}} = 3.6 \times 10^{-2} \text{ g HCl}$

79. $2.50 \text{ metric tons } Cu_3FeS_3 \times \frac{1000 \text{ kg}}{\text{metric ton}} \times \frac{1000 \text{ g}}{\text{kg}} \times \frac{1 \text{ mol } Cu_3FeS_3}{342.71 \text{ g}} \times \frac{3 \text{ mol Cu}}{1 \text{ mol } Cu_3FeS_3} \times$

$$\frac{63.55 \text{ g}}{\text{mol Cu}} = 1.39 \times 10^6 \text{ g Cu (theoretical)}$$

$$1.39 \times 10^6 \text{ g Cu (theoretical)} \times \frac{86.3 \text{ g Cu (actual)}}{100. \text{ g Cu (theoretical)}} = 1.20 \times 10^6 \text{ g Cu} = 1.20 \times 10^3 \text{ kg Cu}$$

$$= 1.20 \text{ metric tons Cu (actual)}$$

81. An alternative method to solve limiting-reagent problems is to assume that each reactant is limiting and then calculate how much product could be produced from each reactant. The reactant that produces the smallest amount of product will run out first and is the limiting reagent.

$$5.00 \times 10^6 \text{ g } NH_3 \times \frac{1 \text{ mol } NH_3}{17.03 \text{ g } NH_3} \times \frac{2 \text{ mol HCN}}{2 \text{ mol } NH_3} = 2.94 \times 10^5 \text{ mol HCN}$$

$$5.00 \times 10^6 \text{ g } O_2 \times \frac{1 \text{ mol } O_2}{32.00 \text{ g } O_2} \times \frac{2 \text{ mol HCN}}{3 \text{ mol } O_2} = 1.04 \times 10^5 \text{ mol HCN}$$

$$5.00 \times 10^6 \text{ g } CH_4 \times \frac{1 \text{ mol } CH_4}{16.04 \text{ g } CH_4} \times \frac{2 \text{ mol HCN}}{2 \text{ mol } CH_4} = 3.12 \times 10^5 \text{ mol HCN}$$

O_2 is limiting because it produces the smallest amount of HCN. Although more product could be produced from NH_3 and CH_4, only enough O_2 is present to produce 1.04×10^5 mol HCN. The mass of HCN that can be produced is:

$$1.04 \times 10^5 \text{ mol HCN} \times \frac{27.03 \text{ g HCN}}{\text{mol HCN}} = 2.81 \times 10^6 \text{ g HCN}$$

$$5.00 \times 10^6 \text{ g } O_2 \times \frac{1 \text{ mol } O_2}{32.00 \text{ g } O_2} \times \frac{6 \text{ mol } H_2O}{3 \text{ mol } O_2} \times \frac{18.02 \text{ g } H_2O}{1 \text{ mol } H_2O} = 5.63 \times 10^6 \text{ g } H_2O$$

83. $P_4(s) + 6\ F_2(g) \rightarrow 4\ PF_3(g)$; the theoretical yield of PF_3 is:

$$120. \text{ g } PF_3 \text{ (actual)} \times \frac{100.0 \text{ g } PF_3 \text{ (theoretical)}}{78.1 \text{ g } PF_3 \text{ (actual)}} = 154 \text{ g } PF_3 \text{ (theoretical)}$$

$$154 \text{ g } PF_3 \times \frac{1 \text{ mol } PF_3}{87.97 \text{ g } PF_3} \times \frac{6 \text{ mol } F_2}{4 \text{ mol } PF_3} \times \frac{38.00 \text{ g } F_2}{\text{mol } F_2} = 99.8 \text{ g } F_2$$

99.8 g F_2 are needed to actually produce 120. g of PF_3 if the percent yield is 78.1%.

Additional Exercises

85. $17.3 \text{ g H} \times \dfrac{1 \text{ mol H}}{1.008 \text{ g H}} = 17.2 \text{ mol H}$; $82.7 \text{ g C} \times \dfrac{1 \text{ mol C}}{12.01 \text{ g C}} = 6.89 \text{ mol C}$

$\dfrac{17.2}{6.89} = 2.50$; the empirical formula is C_2H_5.

The empirical formula mass is ~29 g, so two times the empirical formula would put the compound in the correct range of the molar mass. Molecular formula = $(C_2H_5)_2 = C_4H_{10}$

$$2.59 \times 10^{23} \text{ atoms H} \times \frac{1 \text{ molecule } C_4H_{10}}{10 \text{ atoms H}} \times \frac{1 \text{ mol } C_4H_{10}}{6.022 \times 10^{23} \text{ molecules}} = 4.30 \times 10^{-2} \text{ mol } C_4H_{10}$$

$$4.30 \times 10^{-2} \text{ mol } C_4H_{10} \times \frac{58.12 \text{ g}}{\text{mol } C_4H_{10}} = 2.50 \text{ g } C_4H_{10}$$

87. $\text{Molar mass } X_2 = \dfrac{0.105 \text{ g}}{8.92 \times 10^{20} \text{ molecules} \times \dfrac{1 \text{ mol}}{6.022 \times 10^{23} \text{ molecules}}} = 70.9 \text{ g/mol}$

The mass of X = 1/2(70.9 g/mol) = 35.5 g/mol. This is the element chlorine.

Assuming 100.00 g of MX_3 compound:

$$54.47 \text{ g Cl} \times \frac{1 \text{ mol}}{35.45 \text{ g}} = 1.537 \text{ mol Cl}$$

$$1.537 \text{ mol Cl} \times \frac{1 \text{ mol M}}{3 \text{ mol Cl}} = 0.5123 \text{ mol M}$$

$$\text{Molar mass of M} = \frac{45.53 \text{ g M}}{0.5123 \text{ mol M}} = 88.87 \text{ g/mol M}$$

M is the element yttrium (Y), and the name of YCl_3 is yttrium(III) chloride.

The balanced equation is $2\ Y + 3\ Cl_2 \rightarrow 2\ YCl_3$.

Assuming Cl_2 is limiting:

$$1.00 \text{ g } Cl_2 \times \frac{1 \text{ mol } Cl_2}{70.90 \text{ g } Cl_2} \times \frac{2 \text{ mol } YCl_3}{3 \text{ mol } Cl_2} \times \frac{195.26 \text{ g } YCl_3}{1 \text{ mol } YCl_3} = 1.84 \text{ g } YCl_3$$

Assuming Y is limiting:

$$1.00 \text{ g Y} \times \frac{1 \text{ mol Y}}{88.91 \text{ g Y}} \times \frac{2 \text{ mol YCl}_3}{2 \text{ mol Y}} \times \frac{195.26 \text{ g YCl}_3}{1 \text{ mol YCl}_3} = 2.20 \text{ g YCl}_3$$

Because Cl_2, when it all reacts, produces the smaller amount of product, Cl_2 is the limiting reagent, and the theoretical yield is 1.84 g YCl_3.

89. Mass of H_2O = 0.755 g $CuSO_4{\bullet}xH_2O$ – 0.483 g $CuSO_4$ = 0.272 g H_2O

$$0.483 \text{ g CuSO}_4 \times \frac{1 \text{ mol CuSO}_4}{159.62 \text{ g CuSO}_4} = 0.00303 \text{ mol CuSO}_4$$

$$0.272 \text{ g H}_2\text{O} \times \frac{1 \text{ mol H}_2\text{O}}{18.02 \text{ g H}_2\text{O}} = 0.0151 \text{ mol H}_2\text{O}$$

$$\frac{0.0151 \text{ mol H}_2\text{O}}{0.00303 \text{ mol CuSO}_4} = \frac{4.98 \text{ mol H}_2\text{O}}{1 \text{ mol CuSO}_4}$$; compound formula = $CuSO_4{\bullet}5H_2O$, $x = 5$

91. Consider the case of aluminum plus oxygen. Aluminum forms Al^{3+} ions; oxygen forms O^{2-} anions. The simplest compound of the two elements is Al_2O_3. Similarly, we would expect the formula of a Group 6A element with Al to be Al_2X_3. Assuming this, out of 100.00 g of compound, there are 18.56 g Al and 81.44 g of the unknown element, X. Let's use this information to determine the molar mass of X, which will allow us to identify X from the periodic table.

$$18.56 \text{ g Al} \times \frac{1 \text{ mol Al}}{26.98 \text{ g Al}} \times \frac{3 \text{ mol X}}{2 \text{ mol Al}} = 1.032 \text{ mol X}$$

81.44 g of X must contain 1.032 mol of X.

$$\text{Molar mass of X} = \frac{81.44 \text{ g X}}{1.032 \text{ mol X}} = 78.91 \text{ g/mol}$$

From the periodic table, the unknown element is selenium, and the formula is Al_2Se_3.

93. $$1.20 \text{ g CO}_2 \times \frac{1 \text{ mol CO}_2}{44.01 \text{ g}} \times \frac{1 \text{ mol C}}{\text{mol CO}_2} \times \frac{1 \text{ mol C}_{24}\text{H}_{30}\text{N}_3\text{O}}{24 \text{ mol C}} \times \frac{376.51 \text{ g}}{\text{mol C}_{24}\text{H}_{30}\text{N}_3\text{O}} = 0.428 \text{ g C}_{24}\text{H}_{30}\text{N}_3\text{O}$$

$$\frac{0.428 \text{ g C}_{24}\text{H}_{30}\text{N}_3\text{O}}{1.00 \text{ g sample}} \times 100 = 42.8\% \text{ C}_{24}\text{H}_{30}\text{N}_3\text{O (LSD)}$$

95. $2 \text{ NaNO}_3(s) \rightarrow 2 \text{ NaNO}_2(s) + \text{O}_2(g)$; the amount of $NaNO_3$ in the impure sample is:

$$0.2864 \text{ g NaNO}_2 \times \frac{1 \text{ mol NaNO}_2}{69.00 \text{ g NaNO}_2} \times \frac{2 \text{ mol NaNO}_3}{2 \text{ mol NaNO}_2} \times \frac{85.00 \text{ g NaNO}_3}{\text{mol NaNO}_3} = 0.3528 \text{ g NaNO}_3$$

$$\text{Mass percent NaNO}_3 = \frac{0.3528\text{ g NaNO}_3}{0.4230\text{ g sample}} \times 100 = 83.40\%$$

97. $$453\text{ g Fe} \times \frac{1\text{ mol Fe}}{55.85\text{ g Fe}} \times \frac{1\text{ mol Fe}_2\text{O}_3}{2\text{ mol Fe}} \times \frac{159.70\text{ g Fe}_2\text{O}_3}{\text{mol Fe}_2\text{O}_3} = 648\text{ g Fe}_2\text{O}_3$$

$$\text{Mass \% Fe}_2\text{O}_3 = \frac{648\text{ g Fe}_2\text{O}_3}{752\text{ g ore}} \times 100 = 86.2\%$$

99. $\frac{^{85}\text{Rb atoms}}{^{87}\text{Rb atoms}} = 2.591$; If we had exactly 100 atoms, x = number of ^{85}Rb atoms and $100 - x$ = number of ^{87}Rb atoms.

$$\frac{x}{100 - x} = 2.591,\ x = 259.1 - (2.591)x,\ x = \frac{259.1}{3.591} = 72.15;\ 72.15\%\ ^{85}\text{Rb}$$

$$0.7215(84.9117) + 0.2785(\text{A}) = 85.4678,\ \text{A} = \frac{85.4678 - 61.26}{0.2785} = 86.92\text{ amu}$$

101. The volume of a gas is proportional to the number of molecules of gas. Thus the formulas are:

I: NH_3 II: N_2H_4 III: HN_3

The mass ratios are:

I: $\frac{4.634\text{ g N}}{\text{g H}}$ II: $\frac{6.949\text{ g N}}{\text{g H}}$ III: $\frac{41.7\text{ g N}}{\text{g H}}$

If we set the atomic mass of H equal to 1.008, then the atomic mass, A, for nitrogen is:

I: 14.01 II: 14.01 III. 14.0

For example, for compound I: $\frac{\text{A}}{3(1.008)} = \frac{4.634}{1}$, A = 14.01

103. $$1.375\text{ g AgI} \times \frac{1\text{ mol AgI}}{234.8\text{ g AgI}} = 5.856 \times 10^{-3}\text{ mol AgI} = 5.856 \times 10^{-3}\text{ mol I}$$

$$1.375\text{ g AgI} \times \frac{126.9\text{ g I}}{234.8\text{ g AgI}} = 0.7431\text{ g I};$$ XI_2 contains 0.7431 g I and 0.257 g X.

$$5.856 \times 10^{-3}\text{ mol I} \times \frac{1\text{ mol X}}{2\text{ mol I}} = 2.928 \times 10^{-3}\text{ mol X}$$

$$\text{Molar mass} = \frac{0.257\text{ g X}}{2.928 \times 10^{-3}\text{ mol X}} = \frac{87.8\text{ g}}{\text{mol}};$$ atomic mass = 87.8 amu (X is Sr.)

105. Assuming 1 mole of vitamin A (286.4 g vitamin A):

$$\text{mol C} = 286.4\text{ g vitamin A} \times \frac{0.8396\text{ g C}}{\text{g vitamin A}} \times \frac{1\text{ mol C}}{12.011\text{ g C}} = 20.00\text{ mol C}$$

$$\text{mol H} = 286.4\text{ g vitamin A} \times \frac{0.1056\text{ g H}}{\text{g vitamin A}} \times \frac{1\text{ mol H}}{1.0079\text{ g H}} = 30.01\text{ mol H}$$

Because 1 mole of vitamin A contains 20 mol C and 30 mol H, the molecular formula of vitamin A is $C_{20}H_{30}E$. To determine E, lets calculate the molar mass of E:

$$286.4\text{ g} = 20(12.01) + 30(1.008) + \text{molar mass E},\ \ \text{molar mass E} = 16.0\text{ g/mol}$$

From the periodic table, E = oxygen, and the molecular formula of vitamin A is $C_{20}H_{30}O$.

Challenge Problems

107. When the discharge voltage is low, the ions present are in the form of molecules. When the discharge voltage is increased, the bonds in the molecules are broken, and the ions present are in the form of individual atoms. Therefore, the high discharge data indicate that the ions $^{16}O^+$, $^{18}O^+$, and $^{40}Ar^+$ are present. The only combination of these individual ions that can explain the mass data at low discharge is $^{16}O^{16}O^+$ (mass = 32), $^{16}O^{18}O^+$ (mass = 34), and $^{40}Ar^+$ (mass = 40). Therefore, the gas mixture contains $^{16}O^{16}O$, $^{16}O^{18}O$, and ^{40}Ar. To determine the percent composition of each isotope, we use the relative intensity data from the high discharge data to determine the percentage that each isotope contributes to the total relative intensity. For ^{40}Ar:

$$\frac{1.0000}{0.7500 + 0.0015 + 1.0000} \times 100 = \frac{1.0000}{1.7515} \times 100 = 57.094\%\ ^{40}Ar$$

For ^{16}O: $\frac{0.7500}{1.7515} \times 100 = 42.82\%\ ^{16}O$; for ^{18}O: $\frac{0.0015}{1.7515} \times 100 = 8.6 \times 10^{-2}\%\ ^{18}O$

Note: ^{18}F instead of ^{18}O could also explain the data. However, OF(g) is not a stable compound. This is why ^{18}O is the best choice because $O_2(g)$ does form.

109. 10.00 g XCl_2 + excess $Cl_2 \rightarrow$ 12.55 g XCl_4; 2.55 g Cl reacted with XCl_2 to form XCl_4. XCl_4 contains 2.55 g Cl and 10.00 g XCl_2. From mole ratios, 10.00 g XCl_2 must also contain 2.55 g Cl; mass X in XCl_2 = 10.00 – 2.55 = 7.45 g X.

$$2.55\text{ g Cl} \times \frac{1\text{ mol Cl}}{35.45\text{ g Cl}} \times \frac{1\text{ mol XCl}_2}{2\text{ mol Cl}} \times \frac{1\text{ mol X}}{\text{mol XCl}_2} = 3.60 \times 10^{-2}\text{ mol X}$$

So, 3.60×10^{-2} mol X has a mass equal to 7.45 g X. The molar mass of X is:

$$\frac{7.45 \text{ g X}}{3.60 \times 10^{-2} \text{ mol X}} = 207 \text{ g/mol X; atomic mass} = 207 \text{ amu, so X is Pb.}$$

111. For a gas, density and molar mass are directly proportional to each other.

$$\text{Molar mass } XH_n = 2.393(32.00) = \frac{76.58 \text{ g}}{\text{mol}}$$

$$0.803 \text{ g } H_2O \times \frac{2 \text{ mol H}}{18.02 \text{ g } H_2O} = 8.91 \times 10^{-2} \text{ mol H}$$

$$\frac{8.91 \times 10^{-2} \text{ mol H}}{2.23 \times 10^{-2} \text{ mol } XH_n} = \frac{4 \text{ mol H}}{\text{mol } XH_n}$$

Molar mass X = 76.58 – 4(1.008 g) = 72.55 g/mol; the element is Ge.

113. 4.000 g $M_2S_3 \rightarrow$ 3.723 g MO_2

There must be twice as many moles of MO_2 as moles of M_2S_3 in order to balance M in the reaction. Setting up an equation for 2(mol M_2S_3) = mol MO_2 where A = molar mass M:

$$2\left(\frac{4.000 \text{ g}}{2A + 3(32.07)}\right) = \frac{3.723 \text{ g}}{A + 2(16.00)}, \quad \frac{8.000}{2A + 96.21} = \frac{3.723}{A + 32.00}$$

(8.000)A + 256.0 = (7.446)A + 358.2, (0.554)A = 102.2, A = 184 g/mol; atomic mass = 184 amu

115. The balanced equations are:

$C(s) + 1/2\ O_2(g) \rightarrow CO(g)$ and $C(s) + O_2(g) \rightarrow CO_2(g)$

If we have 100.0 mol of products, then we have 72.0 mol CO_2, 16.0 mol CO, and 12.0 mol O_2. The initial moles of C equals 72.0 (from CO_2) + 16.00 (from CO) = 88.0 mol C and the initial moles of O_2 equals 72.0 (from CO_2) + 16.0/2 (from CO) + 12.0 (unreacted O_2) = 92.0 mol O_2. The initial reaction mixture contained:

$$\frac{92.0 \text{ mol } O_2}{88.0 \text{ mol C}} = 1.05 \text{ mol } O_2\text{/mol C}$$

117. $LaH_{2.90}$ is the formula. If only La^{3+} is present, LaH_3 would be the formula. If only La^{2+} is present, LaH_2 would be the formula. Let x = mol La^{2+} and y = mol La^{3+}:

$(La^{2+})_x(La^{3+})_yH_{(2x+3y)}$ where $x + y = 1.00$ and $2x + 3y = 2.90$

Solving by simultaneous equations:

$$\begin{array}{r} 2x + 3y = 2.90 \\ \underline{-2x - 2y = -2.00} \\ y = 0.90 \end{array} \text{ and } x = 0.10$$

$LaH_{2.90}$ contains $\frac{1}{10}$ La^{2+}, or 10.% La^{2+}, and $\frac{9}{10}$ La^{3+}, or 90.% La^{3+}.

119. Let x = mass KCl and y = mass KNO_3. Assuming 100.0 g of mixture, $x + y = 100.0$ g.

Molar mass KCl = 74.55 g/mol; molar mass KNO_3 = 101.11 g/mol

Mol KCl = $\frac{x}{74.55}$; mol KNO_3 = $\frac{y}{101.11}$

Knowing that the mixture is 43.2% K, then in the 100.0 g mixture:

$$39.10\left(\frac{x}{74.55} + \frac{y}{101.11}\right) = 43.2$$

We have two equations and two unknowns:

$$\begin{aligned} (0.5245)x + (0.3867)y &= 43.2 \\ x + y &= 100.0 \end{aligned}$$

Solving, $x = 32.9$ g KCl; $\frac{32.9 \text{ g}}{100.0 \text{ g}} \times 100 = 32.9\%$ KCl

121. The balanced equations are:

$4\,NH_3(g) + 5\,O_2(g) \rightarrow 4\,NO(g) + 6\,H_2O(g)$ and $4\,NH_3(g) + 7\,O_2(g) \rightarrow 4\,NO_2(g) + 6\,H_2O(g)$

Let $4x$ = number of moles of NO formed, and let $4y$ = number of moles of NO_2 formed. Then:

$4x\,NH_3 + 5x\,O_2 \rightarrow 4x\,NO + 6x\,H_2O$ and $4y\,NH_3 + 7y\,O_2 \rightarrow 4y\,NO_2 + 6y\,H_2O$

All the NH_3 reacted, so $4x + 4y = 2.00$.

$10.00 - 6.75 = 3.25$ mol O_2 reacted, so $5x + 7y = 3.25$.

Solving by the method of simultaneous equations:

$$\begin{array}{r} 20x + 28y = 13.0 \\ \underline{-20x - 20y = -10.0} \\ 8y = 3.0 \end{array}, \quad y = 0.38; \quad 4x + 4 \times 0.38 = 2.00, \quad x = 0.12$$

Mol NO = $4x = 4 \times 0.12 = 0.48$ mol NO formed

CHAPTER 4

TYPES OF CHEMICAL REACTIONS AND SOLUTION STOICHIOMETRY

Aqueous Solutions: Strong and Weak Electrolytes

11. Solution A: $\frac{4 \text{ molecules}}{1.0 \text{ L}}$; solution B: $\frac{6 \text{ molecules}}{4.0 \text{ L}} = \frac{1.5 \text{ molecules}}{1.0 \text{ L}}$

Solution C: $\frac{4 \text{ molecules}}{2.0 \text{ L}} = \frac{2 \text{ molecules}}{1.0 \text{ L}}$; solution D: $\frac{6 \text{ molecules}}{2.0 \text{ L}} = \frac{3 \text{ molecules}}{1.0 \text{ L}}$

Solution A has the most molecules per unit volume so solution A is most concentrated. This is followed by solution D, then solution C. Solution B has the fewest molecules per unit volume, so solution B is least concentrated.

13. a. Polarity is a term applied to covalent compounds. Polar covalent compounds have an unequal sharing of electrons in bonds that results in unequal charge distribution in the overall molecule. Polar molecules have a partial negative end and a partial positive end. These are not full charges as in ionic compounds but are charges much smaller in magnitude. Water is a polar molecule and dissolves other polar solutes readily. The oxygen end of water (the partial negative end of the polar water molecule) aligns with the partial positive end of the polar solute, whereas the hydrogens of water (the partial positive end of the polar water molecule) align with the partial negative end of the solute. These opposite charge attractions stabilize polar solutes in water. This process is called hydration. Nonpolar solutes do not have permanent partial negative and partial positive ends; nonpolar solutes are not stabilized in water and do not dissolve.

b. KF is a soluble ionic compound, so it is a strong electrolyte. KF(aq) actually exists as separate hydrated K^+ ions and hydrated F^- ions in solution. $C_6H_{12}O_6$ is a polar covalent molecule that is a nonelectrolyte. $C_6H_{12}O_6$ is hydrated as described in part a.

c. RbCl is a soluble ionic compound, so it exists as separate hydrated Rb^+ ions and hydrated Cl^- ions in solution. AgCl is an insoluble ionic compound so the ions stay together in solution and fall to the bottom of the container as a precipitate.

d. HNO_3 is a strong acid and exists as separate hydrated H^+ ions and hydrated NO_3^- ions in solution. CO is a polar covalent molecule and is hydrated as explained in part a.

15. a. $Ba(NO_3)_2(aq) \rightarrow Ba^{2+}(aq) + 2\ NO_3^-(aq)$; picture iv represents the Ba^{2+} and NO_3^- ions present in $Ba(NO_3)_2(aq)$.

b. $NaCl(aq) \rightarrow Na^+(aq) + Cl^-(aq)$; picture ii represents NaCl(aq).

c. $K_2CO_3(aq) \rightarrow 2\ K^+(aq) + CO_3^{2-}(aq)$; picture iii represents $K_2CO_3(aq)$.

d. $MgSO_4(aq) \rightarrow Mg^{2+}(aq) + SO_4^{2-}(aq)$; picture i represents $MgSO_4(aq)$.

Solution Concentration: Molarity

17. a. $2.00\text{ L} \times \dfrac{0.250\text{ mol NaOH}}{\text{L}} \times \dfrac{40.00\text{ g NaOH}}{\text{mol}} = 20.0\text{ g NaOH}$

Place 20.0 g NaOH in a 2-L volumetric flask; add water to dissolve the NaOH, and fill to the mark with water, mixing several times along the way.

b. $2.00\text{ L} \times \dfrac{0.250\text{ mol NaOH}}{\text{L}} \times \dfrac{1\text{ L stock}}{1.00\text{ mol NaOH}} = 0.500\text{ L}$

Add 500. mL of 1.00 *M* NaOH stock solution to a 2-L volumetric flask; fill to the mark with water, mixing several times along the way.

c. $2.00\text{ L} \times \dfrac{0.100\text{ mol }K_2CrO_4}{\text{L}} \times \dfrac{194.20\text{ g }K_2CrO_4}{\text{mol }K_2CrO_4} = 38.8\text{ g }K_2CrO_4$

Similar to the solution made in part a, instead using 38.8 g K_2CrO_4.

d. $2.00\text{ L} \times \dfrac{0.100\text{ mol }K_2CrO_4}{\text{L}} \times \dfrac{1\text{ L stock}}{1.75\text{ mol }K_2CrO_4} = 0.114\text{ L}$

Similar to the solution made in part b, instead using 114 mL of the 1.75 *M* K_2CrO_4 stock solution.

19. Molar mass of NaOH = 22.99 + 16.00 + 1.008 = 40.00 g/mol

Mass NaOH = $0.2500\text{ L} \times \dfrac{0.400\text{ mol NaOH}}{\text{L}} \times \dfrac{40.00\text{ g NaOH}}{\text{mol NaOH}} = 4.00\text{ g NaOH}$

21. Mol solute = volume (L) × molarity $\left(\dfrac{\text{mol}}{\text{L}}\right)$; $AlCl_3(s) \rightarrow Al^{3+}(aq) + 3\ Cl^-(aq)$

Mol Cl^- = $0.1000\text{ L} \times \dfrac{0.30\text{ mol }AlCl_3}{\text{L}} \times \dfrac{3\text{ mol }Cl^-}{\text{mol }AlCl_3} = 9.0 \times 10^{-2}\text{ mol }Cl^-$

$MgCl_2(s) \rightarrow Mg^{2+}(aq) + 2\ Cl^-(aq)$

Mol Cl^- = $0.0500\text{ L} \times \dfrac{0.60\text{ mol }MgCl_2}{\text{L}} \times \dfrac{2\text{ mol }Cl^-}{\text{mol }MgCl_2} = 6.0 \times 10^{-2}\text{ mol }Cl^-$

$NaCl(s) \rightarrow Na^+(aq) + Cl^-(aq)$

$$\text{Mol } Cl^- = 0.2000 \text{ L} \times \frac{0.40 \text{ mol NaCl}}{\text{L}} \times \frac{1 \text{ mol } Cl^-}{\text{mol NaCl}} = 8.0 \times 10^{-2} \text{ mol } Cl^-$$

100.0 mL of 0.30 *M* $AlCl_3$ contains the most moles of Cl^- ions.

23. $\text{Mol } Na_2CO_3 = 0.0700 \text{ L} \times \dfrac{3.0 \text{ mol } Na_2CO_3}{\text{L}} = 0.21 \text{ mol } Na_2CO_3$

$Na_2CO_3(s) \rightarrow 2\ Na^+(aq) + CO_3^{2-}(aq)$; mol Na^+ = 2(0.21 mol) = 0.42 mol

$\text{Mol } NaHCO_3 = 0.0300 \text{ L} \times \dfrac{1.0 \text{ mol } NaHCO_3}{\text{L}} = 0.030 \text{ mol } NaHCO_3$

$NaHCO_3(s) \rightarrow Na^+(aq) + HCO_3^-(aq)$; mol Na^+ = 0.030 mol

$$M_{Na^+} = \frac{\text{total mol } Na^+}{\text{total volume}} = \frac{0.42 \text{ mol} + 0.030 \text{ mol}}{0.0700 \text{ L} + 0.0300 \text{ L}} = \frac{0.45 \text{ mol}}{0.1000 \text{ L}} = 4.5\ M\ Na^+$$

25. $\text{Stock solution} = \dfrac{10.0 \text{ mg}}{500.0 \text{ mL}} = \dfrac{10.0 \times 10^{-3} \text{ g}}{500.0 \text{ mL}} = \dfrac{2.00 \times 10^{-5} \text{ g steroid}}{\text{mL}}$

$$100.0 \times 10^{-6} \text{ L stock} \times \frac{1000 \text{ mL}}{\text{L}} \times \frac{2.00 \times 10^{-5} \text{ g steroid}}{\text{mL}} = 2.00 \times 10^{-6} \text{ g steroid}$$

This is diluted to a final volume of 100.0 mL.

$$\frac{2.00 \times 10^{-6} \text{ g steroid}}{100.0 \text{ mL}} \times \frac{1000 \text{ mL}}{\text{L}} \times \frac{1 \text{ mol steroid}}{336.4 \text{ g steroid}} = 5.95 \times 10^{-8}\ M \text{ steroid}$$

27. a. $5.0 \text{ ppb Hg in water} = \dfrac{5.0 \text{ ng Hg}}{\text{mL } H_2O} = \dfrac{5.0 \times 10^{-9} \text{ g Hg}}{\text{mL } H_2O}$

$$\frac{5.0 \times 10^{-9} \text{ g Hg}}{\text{mL}} \times \frac{1 \text{ mol Hg}}{200.6 \text{ g Hg}} \times \frac{1000 \text{ mL}}{\text{L}} = 2.5 \times 10^{-8}\ M \text{ Hg}$$

b. $\dfrac{1.0 \times 10^{-9} \text{ g } CHCl_3}{\text{mL}} \times \dfrac{1 \text{ mol } CHCl_3}{119.4 \text{ g } CHCl_3} \times \dfrac{1000 \text{ mL}}{\text{L}} = 8.4 \times 10^{-9}\ M\ CHCl_3$

c. $10.0 \text{ ppm As} = \dfrac{10.0\ \mu\text{g As}}{\text{mL}} = \dfrac{10.0 \times 10^{-6} \text{ g As}}{\text{mL}}$

$$\frac{10.0 \times 10^{-6} \text{ g As}}{\text{mL}} \times \frac{1 \text{ mol As}}{74.92 \text{ g As}} \times \frac{1000 \text{ mL}}{\text{L}} = 1.33 \times 10^{-4}\ M \text{ As}$$

d. $\frac{0.10 \times 10^{-6}\text{ g DDT}}{\text{mL}} \times \frac{1\text{ mol DDT}}{354.5\text{ g DDT}} \times \frac{1000\text{ mL}}{\text{L}} = 2.8 \times 10^{-7}\ M\text{ DDT}$

Precipitation Reactions

29. Use the solubility rules in Table 4.1. Some soluble bromides by Rule 2 would be NaBr, KBr, and NH_4Br (there are others). The insoluble bromides by Rule 3 would be AgBr, $PbBr_2$, and Hg_2Br_2. Similar reasoning is used for the other parts to this problem.

Sulfates: Na_2SO_4, K_2SO_4, and $(NH_4)_2SO_4$ (and others) would be soluble, and $BaSO_4$, $CaSO_4$, and $PbSO_4$ (or Hg_2SO_4) would be insoluble.

Hydroxides: NaOH, KOH, $Ca(OH)_2$ (and others) would be soluble, and $Al(OH)_3$, $Fe(OH)_3$, and $Cu(OH)_2$ (and others) would be insoluble.

Phosphates: Na_3PO_4, K_3PO_4, $(NH_4)_3PO_4$ (and others) would be soluble, and Ag_3PO_4, $Ca_3(PO_4)_2$, and $FePO_4$ (and others) would be insoluble.

Lead: $PbCl_2$, $PbBr_2$, PbI_2, $Pb(OH)_2$, $PbSO_4$, and PbS (and others) would be insoluble. $Pb(NO_3)_2$ would be a soluble Pb^{2+} salt.

31. Use Table 4.1 to predict the solubility of the possible products.

a. Possible products = Hg_2SO_4 and $Cu(NO_3)_2$; precipitate = Hg_2SO_4

b. Possible products = $NiCl_2$ and $Ca(NO_3)_2$; both salts are soluble so no precipitate forms.

c. Possible products = KI and $MgCO_3$; precipitate = $MgCO_3$

d. Possible products = NaBr and $Al_2(CrO_4)_3$; precipitate = $Al_2(CrO_4)_3$

33. For the following answers, the balanced molecular equation is first, followed by the complete ionic equation, and then the net ionic equation.

a. $(NH_4)_2SO_4(aq) + Ba(NO_3)_2(aq) \rightarrow 2\ NH_4NO_3(aq) + BaSO_4(s)$

$2\ NH_4^+(aq) + SO_4^{2-}(aq) + Ba^{2+}(aq) + 2\ NO_3^-(aq) \rightarrow 2\ NH_4^+(aq) + 2\ NO_3^-(aq) + BaSO_4(s)$

$Ba^{2+}(aq) + SO_4^{2-}(aq) \rightarrow BaSO_4(s)$ is the net ionic equation (spectator ions omitted).

b. $Pb(NO_3)_2(aq) + 2\ NaCl(aq) \rightarrow PbCl_2(s) + 2\ NaNO_3(aq)$

$Pb^{2+}(aq) + 2\ NO_3^-(aq) + 2\ Na^+(aq) + 2\ Cl^-(aq) \rightarrow PbCl_2(s) + 2\ Na^+(aq) + 2\ NO_3^-(aq)$

$Pb^{2+}(aq) + 2\ Cl^-(aq) \rightarrow PbCl_2(s)$

c. The possible products, potassium phosphate and sodium nitrate, are both soluble in water. Therefore, no reaction occurs.

d. No reaction occurs because all possible products are soluble.

e. $CuCl_2(aq) + 2\ NaOH(aq) \rightarrow Cu(OH)_2(s) + 2\ NaCl(aq)$

$Cu^{2+}(aq) + 2\ Cl^-(aq) + 2\ Na^+(aq) + 2\ OH^-(aq) \rightarrow Cu(OH)_2(s) + 2\ Na^+(aq) + 2\ Cl^-(aq)$

$Cu^{2+}(aq) + 2\ OH^-(aq) \rightarrow Cu(OH)_2(s)$

35. a. When $CuSO_4(aq)$ is added to $Na_2S(aq)$, the precipitate that forms is CuS(s). Therefore, Na^+ (the gray spheres) and SO_4^{2-} (the bluish green spheres) are the spectator ions.

$CuSO_4(aq) + Na_2S(aq) \rightarrow CuS(s) + Na_2SO_4(aq)$; $Cu^{2+}(aq) + S^{2-}(aq) \rightarrow CuS(s)$

b. When $CoCl_2(aq)$ is added to NaOH(aq), the precipitate that forms is $Co(OH)_2(s)$. Therefore, Na^+ (the gray spheres) and Cl^- (the green spheres) are the spectator ions.

$CoCl_2(aq) + 2\ NaOH(aq) \rightarrow Co(OH)_2(s) + 2\ NaCl(aq)$

$Co^{2+}(aq) + 2\ OH^-(aq) \rightarrow Co(OH)_2(s)$

c. When $AgNO_3(aq)$ is added to KI(aq), the precipitate that forms is AgI(s). Therefore, K^+ (the red spheres) and NO_3^- (the blue spheres) are the spectator ions.

$AgNO_3(aq) + KI(aq) \rightarrow AgI(s) + KNO_3(aq)$; $Ag^+(aq) + I^-(aq) \rightarrow AgI(s)$

37. Because a precipitate formed with Na_2SO_4, the possible cations are Ba^{2+}, Pb^{2+}, Hg_2^{2+}, and Ca^{2+} (from the solubility rules). Because no precipitate formed with KCl, Pb^{2+}, and Hg_2^{2+} cannot be present. Because both Ba^{2+} and Ca^{2+} form soluble chlorides and soluble hydroxides, both these cations could be present. Therefore, the cations could be Ba^{2+} and Ca^{2+} (by the solubility rules in Table 4.1). For students who do a more rigorous study of solubility, Sr^{2+} could also be a possible cation (it forms an insoluble sulfate salt, whereas the chloride and hydroxide salts of strontium are soluble).

39. $2\ AgNO_3(aq) + CaCl_2(aq) \rightarrow 2\ AgCl(s) + Ca(NO_3)_2(aq)$

$$\text{Mol } AgNO_3 = 0.1000\ L \times \frac{0.20\ \text{mol } AgNO_3}{L} = 0.020\ \text{mol } AgNO_3$$

$$\text{Mol } CaCl_2 = 0.1000\ L \times \frac{0.15\ \text{mol } CaCl_2}{L} = 0.015\ \text{mol } CaCl_2$$

The required mol $AgNO_3$ to mol $CaCl_2$ ratio is 2 : 1 (from the balanced equation). The actual mole ratio present is 0.020/0.015 = 1.3 (1.3 : 1). Therefore, $AgNO_3$ is the limiting reagent.

$$\text{Mass AgCl} = 0.020\ \text{mol } AgNO_3 \times \frac{1\ \text{mol AgCl}}{1\ \text{mol } AgNO_3} \times \frac{143.4\ \text{g AgCl}}{\text{mol AgCl}} = 2.9\ \text{g AgCl}$$

The net ionic equation is $Ag^+(aq) + Cl^-(aq) \rightarrow AgCl(s)$. The ions remaining in solution are the unreacted Cl^- ions and the spectator ions, NO_3^- and Ca^{2+} (all Ag^+ is used up in forming AgCl). The moles of each ion present initially (before reaction) can be easily determined from the moles of each reactant. 0.020 mol $AgNO_3$ dissolves to form 0.020 mol Ag^+ and 0.020 mol NO_3^-. 0.015 mol $CaCl_2$ dissolves to form 0.015 mol Ca^{2+} and 2(0.015) = 0.030 mol Cl^-.

Mol unreacted Cl^- = 0.030 mol Cl^- initially – 0.020 mol Cl^- reacted

Mol unreacted Cl^- = 0.010 mol Cl^-

$$M_{Cl^-} = \frac{0.010 \text{ mol Cl}^-}{\text{total volume}} = \frac{0.010 \text{ mol Cl}^-}{0.1000 \text{ L} + 0.1000 \text{ L}} = 0.050\ M \text{ Cl}^-$$

The molarity of the spectator ions are:

$$M_{NO_3^-} = \frac{0.020 \text{ mol NO}_3^-}{0.2000 \text{ L}} = 0.10\ M \text{ NO}_3^-;\quad M_{Ca_2^+} = \frac{0.015 \text{ mol Ca}^{2+}}{0.2000 \text{ L}} = 0.075\ M \text{ Ca}^{2+}$$

41. $2\ AgNO_3(aq) + Na_2CrO_4(aq) \rightarrow Ag_2CrO_4(s) + 2\ NaNO_3(aq)$

$$0.0750 \text{ L} \times \frac{0.100 \text{ mol AgNO}_3}{\text{L}} \times \frac{1 \text{ mol Na}_2\text{CrO}_4}{2 \text{ mol AgNO}_3} \times \frac{161.98 \text{ g Na}_2\text{CrO}_4}{\text{mol Na}_2\text{CrO}_4} = 0.607 \text{ g Na}_2\text{CrO}_4$$

43. Use aluminum in the formulas to convert from mass of $Al(OH)_3$ to mass of $Al_2(SO_4)_3$ in the mixture.

$$0.107 \text{ g Al(OH)}_3 \times \frac{1 \text{ mol Al(OH)}_3}{78.00 \text{ g}} \times \frac{1 \text{ mol Al}^{3+}}{\text{mol Al(OH)}_3} \times \frac{1 \text{ mol Al}_2(\text{SO}_4)_3}{2 \text{ mol Al}^{3+}} \times$$

$$\frac{342.17 \text{ g Al}_2(\text{SO}_4)_3}{\text{mol Al}_2(\text{SO}_4)_3} = 0.235 \text{ g Al}_2(\text{SO}_4)_3$$

$$\text{Mass \% Al}_2(\text{SO}_4)_3 = \frac{0.235 \text{ g}}{1.45 \text{ g}} \times 100 = 16.2\%$$

45. All the sulfur in $BaSO_4$ came from the saccharin. The conversion from $BaSO_4$ to saccharin uses the molar masses and formulas of each compound.

$$0.5032 \text{ g BaSO}_4 \times \frac{32.07 \text{ g S}}{233.4 \text{ g BaSO}_4} \times \frac{183.9 \text{ g saccharin}}{32.07 \text{ g S}} = 0.3949 \text{ g saccharin}$$

$$\frac{\text{Average mass}}{\text{Tablet}} = \frac{0.3949 \text{ g}}{10 \text{ tablets}} = \frac{3.949 \times 10^{-2} \text{ g}}{\text{tablet}} = \frac{39.49 \text{ mg}}{\text{tablet}}$$

$$\text{Average mass \%} = \frac{0.3949 \text{ g saccharin}}{0.5894 \text{ g}} \times 100 = 67.00\% \text{ saccharin by mass}$$

47. $M_2SO_4(aq) + CaCl_2(aq) \rightarrow CaSO_4(s) + 2\ MCl(aq)$

$$1.36 \text{ g CaSO}_4 \times \frac{1 \text{ mol CaSO}_4}{136.15 \text{ g CaSO}_4} \times \frac{1 \text{ mol M}_2\text{SO}_4}{\text{mol CaSO}_4} = 9.99 \times 10^{-3} \text{ mol M}_2\text{SO}_4$$

From the problem, 1.42 g M_2SO_4 was reacted, so:

$$\text{molar mass} = \frac{1.42\text{ g } M_2SO_4}{9.99 \times 10^{-3}\text{ mol } M_2SO_4} = 142\text{ g/mol}$$

142 amu = 2(atomic mass M) + 32.07 + 4(16.00), atomic mass M = 23 amu

From periodic table, M is Na (sodium).

Acid-Base Reactions

49. a. Perchloric acid reacted with potassium hydroxide is a possibility.

$HClO_4(aq) + KOH(aq) \rightarrow H_2O(l) + KClO_4(aq)$

b. Nitric acid reacted with cesium hydroxide is a possibility.

$HNO_3(aq) + CsOH(aq) \rightarrow H_2O(l) + CsNO_3(aq)$

c. Hydroiodic acid reacted with calcium hydroxide is a possibility.

$2\ HI(aq) + Ca(OH)_2(aq) \rightarrow 2\ H_2O(l) + CaI_2(aq)$

51. If we begin with 50.00 mL of 0.100 *M* NaOH, then:

$$50.00 \times 10^{-3}\text{ L} \times \frac{0.100\text{ mol}}{\text{L}} = 5.00 \times 10^{-3}\text{ mol NaOH to be neutralized.}$$

a. $NaOH(aq) + HCl(aq) \rightarrow NaCl(aq) + H_2O(l)$

$$5.00 \times 10^{-3}\text{ mol NaOH} \times \frac{1\text{ mol HCl}}{\text{mol NaOH}} \times \frac{1\text{ L soln}}{0.100\text{ mol}} = 5.00 \times 10^{-2}\text{ L or 50.0 mL}$$

b. $2\ NaOH(aq) + H_2SO_3(aq) \rightarrow 2\ H_2O(l) + Na_2SO_3(aq)$

$$5.00 \times 10^{-3}\text{ mol NaOH} \times \frac{1\text{ mol } H_2SO_3}{2\text{ mol NaOH}} \times \frac{1\text{ L soln}}{0.100\text{ mol } H_2SO_3} = 2.50 \times 10^{-2}\text{ L or 25.0 mL}$$

c. $3\ NaOH(aq) + H_3PO_4(aq) \rightarrow Na_3PO_4(aq) + 3\ H_2O(l)$

$$5.00 \times 10^{-3}\text{ mol NaOH} \times \frac{1\text{ mol } H_3PO_4}{3\text{ mol NaOH}} \times \frac{1\text{ L soln}}{0.200\text{ mol } H_3PO_4} = 8.33 \times 10^{-3}\text{ L or 8.33 mL}$$

d. $HNO_3(aq) + NaOH(aq) \rightarrow H_2O(l) + NaNO_3(aq)$

$$5.00 \times 10^{-3}\text{ mol NaOH} \times \frac{1\text{ mol } HNO_3}{\text{mol NaOH}} \times \frac{1\text{ L soln}}{0.150\text{ mol } HNO_3} = 3.33 \times 10^{-2}\text{ L or 33.3 mL}$$

e. $HC_2H_3O_2(aq) + NaOH(aq) \rightarrow H_2O(l) + NaC_2H_3O_2(aq)$

$$5.00 \times 10^{-3} \text{ mol NaOH} \times \frac{1 \text{ mol } HC_2H_3O_2}{\text{mol NaOH}} \times \frac{1 \text{ L soln}}{0.200 \text{ mol } HC_2H_3O_2} = 2.50 \times 10^{-2} \text{ L}$$

or 25.0 mL

f. $H_2SO_4(aq) + 2\ NaOH(aq) \rightarrow 2\ H_2O(l) + Na_2SO_4(aq)$

$$5.00 \times 10^{-3} \text{ mol NaOH} \times \frac{1 \text{ mol } H_2SO_4}{2 \text{ mol NaOH}} \times \frac{1 \text{ L soln}}{0.300 \text{ mol } H_2SO_4} = 8.33 \times 10^{-3} \text{ L or } 8.33 \text{ mL}$$

53. The acid is a diprotic acid (H_2A) meaning that it has two H^+ ions in the formula to donate to a base. The reaction is $H_2A(aq) + 2\ NaOH(aq) \rightarrow 2\ H_2O(l) + Na_2A(aq)$, where A^{2-} is what is left over from the acid formula when the two protons (H^+ ions) are reacted.

For the HCl reaction, the base has the ability to accept two protons. The most common examples are $Ca(OH)_2$, $Sr(OH)_2$, and $Ba(OH)_2$. A possible reaction would be $2\ HCl(aq) + Ca(OH)_2(aq) \rightarrow 2\ H_2O(l) + CaCl_2(aq)$.

55. The pertinent reactions are:

$$2\ NaOH(aq) + H_2SO_4(aq) \rightarrow Na_2SO_4(aq) + 2\ H_2O(l)$$

$$HCl(aq) + NaOH(aq) \rightarrow NaCl(aq) + H_2O(l)$$

Amount of NaOH added $= 0.0500 \text{ L} \times \frac{0.213 \text{ mol}}{\text{L}} = 1.07 \times 10^{-2}$ mol NaOH

Amount of NaOH neutralized by HCl:

$$0.01321 \text{ L HCl H } \frac{0.103 \text{ mol HCl}}{\text{L HCl}} \times \frac{1 \text{ mol NaOH}}{\text{mol HCl}} = 1.36 \times 10^{-3} \text{ mol NaOH}$$

The difference, 9.3×10^{-3} mol, is the amount of NaOH neutralized by the sulfuric acid.

$$9.3 \times 10^{-3} \text{ mol NaOH} \times \frac{1 \text{ mol } H_2SO_4}{2 \text{ mol NaOH}} = 4.7 \times 10^{-3} \text{ mol } H_2SO_4$$

Concentration of H_2SO_4 $= \frac{4.7 \times 10^{-3} \text{ mol}}{0.1000 \text{ L}} = 4.7 \times 10^{-2}\ M\ H_2SO_4$

57. $HC_2H_3O_2(aq) + NaOH(aq) \rightarrow H_2O(l) + NaC_2H_3O_2(aq)$

a. $16.58 \times 10^{-3} \text{ L soln H } \frac{0.5062 \text{ mol NaOH}}{\text{L soln}} \times \frac{1 \text{ mol acetic acid}}{\text{mol NaOH}}$

$= 8.393 \times 10^{-3}$ mol acetic acid

Concentration of acetic acid $= \frac{8.393 \times 10^{-3} \text{ mol}}{0.01000 \text{ L}} = 0.8393\ M\ HC_2H_3O_2$

b. If we have 1.000 L of solution: total mass = 1000. mL × $\frac{1.006\text{ g}}{\text{mL}}$ = 1006 g solution

Mass of $HC_2H_3O_2$ = 0.8393 mol × $\frac{60.052\text{ g}}{\text{mol}}$ = 50.40 g $HC_2H_3O_2$

Mass % acetic acid = $\frac{50.40\text{ g}}{1006\text{ g}}$ × 100 = 5.010%

59. HCl and HNO_3 are strong acids; $Ca(OH)_2$ and RbOH are strong bases. The net ionic equation that occurs is $H^+(aq) + OH^-(aq) \rightarrow H_2O(l)$.

$$\text{Mol H}^+ = 0.0500\text{ L} \times \frac{0.100\text{ mol HCl}}{\text{L}} \times \frac{1\text{ mol H}^+}{\text{mol HCl}} +$$

$$0.1000\text{ L} \times \frac{0.200\text{ mol HNO}_3}{\text{L}} \times \frac{1\text{ mol H}^+}{\text{mol HNO}_3} = 0.00500 + 0.0200 = 0.0250\text{ mol H}^+$$

$$\text{Mol OH}^- = 0.5000\text{ L} \times \frac{0.0100\text{ mol Ca(OH)}_2}{\text{L}} \times \frac{2\text{ mol OH}^-}{\text{mol Ca(OH)}_2} +$$

$$0.2000\text{ L} \times \frac{0.100\text{ mol RbOH}}{\text{L}} \times \frac{1\text{ mol OH}^-}{\text{mol RbOH}} = 0.0100 + 0.0200 = 0.0300\text{ mol OH}^-$$

We have an excess of OH^-, so the solution is basic (not neutral). The moles of excess OH^- = 0.0300 mol OH^- initially – 0.0250 mol OH^- reacted (with H^+) = 0.0050 mol OH^- excess.

$$M_{\text{OH}^-} = \frac{0.0050\text{ mol OH}^-}{(0.05000 + 0.1000 + 0.5000 + 0.2000)\text{ L}} = \frac{0.0050\text{ mol}}{0.8500\text{ L}} = 5.9 \times 10^{-3}\ M$$

61. $Ba(OH)_2(aq) + 2\ HCl(aq) \rightarrow BaCl_2(aq) + 2\ H_2O(l)$; $H^+(aq) + OH^-(aq) \rightarrow H_2O(l)$

$$75.0 \times 10^{-3}\text{ L} \times \frac{0.250\text{ mol HCl}}{\text{L}} = 1.88 \times 10^{-2}\text{ mol HCl} = 1.88 \times 10^{-2}\text{ mol H}^+ + 1.88 \times 10^{-2}\text{ mol Cl}^-$$

$$225.0 \times 10^{-3}\text{ L} \times \frac{0.0550\text{ mol Ba(OH)}_2}{\text{L}} = 1.24 \times 10^{-2}\text{ mol Ba(OH)}_2 = 1.24 \times 10^{-2}\text{ mol Ba}^{2+} + 2.48 \times 10^{-2}\text{ mol OH}^-$$

The net ionic equation requires a 1 : 1 mol ratio between OH^- and H^+. The actual mol OH^- to mol H^+ ratio is greater than 1 : 1, so OH^- is in excess. Because 1.88×10^{-2} mol OH^- will be neutralized by the H^+, we have $(2.48 - 1.88) \times 10^{-2} = 0.60 \times 10^{-2}$ mol OH^- in excess.

$$M_{\text{OH}^-} = \frac{\text{mol OH}^-\text{ excess}}{\text{total volume}} = \frac{6.0 \times 10^{-3}\text{ mol OH}^-}{0.0750\text{ L} + 0.2250\text{ L}} = 2.0 \times 10^{-2}\ M\text{ OH}^-$$

Oxidation-Reduction Reactions

63. a. The species reduced is the element that gains electrons. The reducing agent causes reduction to occur by itself being oxidized. The reducing agent generally refers to the entire formula of the compound/ion that contains the element oxidized.

b. The species oxidized is the element that loses electrons. The oxidizing agent causes oxidation to occur by itself being reduced. The oxidizing agent generally refers to the entire formula of the compound/ion that contains the element reduced.

c. For simple binary ionic compounds, the actual charge on the ions are the same as the oxidation states. For covalent compounds and ions, nonzero oxidation states are imaginary charges the elements would have if they were held together by ionic bonds (assuming the bond is between two different nonmetals). Nonzero oxidation states for elements in covalent compounds are not actual charges. Oxidation states for covalent compounds are a bookkeeping method to keep track of electrons in a reaction.

65. Apply rules in Table 4.3.

a. $KMnO_4$ is composed of K^+ and MnO_4^- ions. Assign oxygen an oxidation state value of −2, which gives manganese a +7 oxidation state because the sum of oxidation states for all atoms in MnO_4^- must equal the 1− charge on MnO_4^-. K, +1; O, −2; Mn, +7.

b. Assign O a −2 oxidation state, which gives nickel a +4 oxidation state. Ni, +4; O, −2.

c. $K_4Fe(CN)_6$ is composed of K^+ cations and $Fe(CN)_6^{4-}$ anions. $Fe(CN)_6^{4-}$ is composed of iron and CN^- anions. For an overall anion charge of 4−, iron must have a +2 oxidation state.

d. $(NH_4)_2HPO_4$ is made of NH_4^+ cations and HPO_4^{2-} anions. Assign +1 as oxidation state of H and −2 as the oxidation state of O. For N in NH_4^+: $x + 4(+1) = +1$, $x = -3$ = oxidation state of N. For P in HPO_4^{2-}: $+1 + y + 4(-2) = -2$, $y = +5$ = oxidation state of P.

e. O, −2; P, +3

f. O, −2; Fe, + 8/3

g. O, −2; F, −1; Xe, +6

h. F, −1; S, +4

i. O, −2; C, +2

j. H, +1; O, −2; C, 0

67. a. $SrCr_2O_7$: Composed of Sr^{2+} and $Cr_2O_7^{2-}$ ions. Sr, +2; O, −2; Cr, $2x + 7(-2) = -2$, $x = +6$

b. Cu, +2; Cl, −1;

c. O, 0;

d. H, +1; O, −1

e. Mg^{2+} and CO_3^{2-} ions present. Mg, +2; O, −2; C, +4;

f. Ag, 0

g. Pb^{2+} and SO_3^{2-} ions present. Pb, +2; O, −2; S, +4;

h. O, −2; Pb, +4

i. Na^+ and $C_2O_4^{2-}$ ions present. Na, +1; O, −2; C, $2x + 4(-2) = -2$, $x = +3$

j. O, −2; C, +4

k. Ammonium ion has a 1+ charge (NH_4^+), and sulfate ion has a 2− charge (SO_4^{2-}). Therefore, the oxidation state of cerium must be +4 (Ce^{4+}). H, +1; N, −3; O, −2; S, +6

l. O, −2; Cr, +3

69. a. $Al(s) + 3\ HCl(aq) \rightarrow AlCl_3(aq) + 3/2\ H_2(g)$ or $2\ Al(s) + 6\ HCl(aq) \rightarrow 2\ AlCl_3(aq) + 3\ H_2(g)$

Hydrogen is reduced (goes from the +1 oxidation state to the 0 oxidation state), and aluminum Al is oxidized ($0 \rightarrow +3$).

b. Balancing S is most complicated because sulfur is in both products. Balance C and H first; then worry about S.

$CH_4(g) + 4\ S(s) \rightarrow CS_2(l) + 2\ H_2S(g)$

Sulfur is reduced ($0 \rightarrow -2$), and carbon is oxidized ($-4 \rightarrow +4$).

c. Balance C and H first; then balance O.

$C_3H_8(g) + 5\ O_2(g) \rightarrow 3\ CO_2(g) + 4\ H_2O(l)$

Oxygen is reduced ($0 \rightarrow -2$), and carbon is oxidized ($-8/3 \rightarrow +4$).

d. Although this reaction is mass balanced, it is not charge balanced. We need 2 mol of silver on each side to balance the charge.

$Cu(s) + 2\ Ag^+(aq) \rightarrow 2\ Ag(s) + Cu^{2+}(aq)$

Silver is reduced ($+1 \rightarrow 0$), and copper is oxidized ($0 \rightarrow +2$).

71. a. Review Section 4.11 of the text for rules on balancing by the half-reaction method. The first step is to separate the reaction into two half-reactions, and then balance each half-reaction separately.

$(Cu \rightarrow Cu^{2+} + 2\ e^-) \times 3$

$NO_3^- \rightarrow NO + 2\ H_2O$

$(3\ e^- + 4\ H^+ + NO_3^- \rightarrow NO + 2\ H_2O) \times 2$

Adding the two balanced half-reactions so electrons cancel:

$$3\ Cu \rightarrow 3\ Cu^{2+} + 6\ e^-$$
$$6\ e^- + 8\ H^+ + 2\ NO_3^- \rightarrow 2\ NO + 4\ H_2O$$

$$3\ Cu(s) + 8\ H^+(aq) + 2\ NO_3^-(aq) \rightarrow 3\ Cu^{2+}(aq) + 2\ NO(g) + 4\ H_2O(l)$$

The final step is to simplify the equation by cancelling identical species on both sides of the equations. Other than the electrons, this equation has no identical species to cancel, so this is the balanced equation. Typically, H^+ and H_2O are the species which can be cancelled in this final step (other than the electrons).

b. $(2\ Cl^- \rightarrow Cl_2 + 2\ e^-) \times 3$

$$Cr_2O_7^{2-} \rightarrow 2\ Cr^{3+} + 7\ H_2O$$
$$6\ e^- + 14\ H^+ + Cr_2O_7^{2-} \rightarrow 2\ Cr^{3+} + 7\ H_2O$$

Add the two balanced half-reactions with six electrons transferred:

$$6\ Cl^- \rightarrow 3\ Cl_2 + 6\ e^-$$
$$6\ e^- + 14\ H^+ + Cr_2O_7^{2-} \rightarrow 2\ Cr^{3+} + 7\ H_2O$$

$$14\ H^+(aq) + Cr_2O_7^{2-}(aq) + 6\ Cl^-(aq) \rightarrow 3\ Cl_2(g) + 2\ Cr^{3+}(aq) + 7\ H_2O(l)$$

c. $Pb \rightarrow PbSO_4$

$$Pb + H_2SO_4 \rightarrow PbSO_4 + 2\ H^+$$
$$Pb + H_2SO_4 \rightarrow PbSO_4 + 2\ H^+ + 2\ e^-$$

$$PbO_2 \rightarrow PbSO_4$$
$$PbO_2 + H_2SO_4 \rightarrow PbSO_4 + 2\ H_2O$$
$$2\ e^- + 2\ H^+ + PbO_2 + H_2SO_4 \rightarrow PbSO_4 + 2\ H_2O$$

Add the two half-reactions with two electrons transferred:

$$2\ e^- + 2\ H^+ + PbO_2 + H_2SO_4 \rightarrow PbSO_4 + 2\ H_2O$$
$$Pb + H_2SO_4 \rightarrow PbSO_4 + 2\ H^+ + 2\ e^-$$

$$Pb(s) + 2\ H_2SO_4(aq) + PbO_2(s) \rightarrow 2\ PbSO_4(s) + 2\ H_2O(l)$$

This is the reaction that occurs in an automobile lead storage battery.

d. $Mn^{2+} \rightarrow MnO_4^-$

$$(4\ H_2O + Mn^{2+} \rightarrow MnO_4^- + 8\ H^+ + 5\ e^-) \times 2$$

$$NaBiO_3 \rightarrow Bi^{3+} + Na^+$$
$$6\ H^+ + NaBiO_3 \rightarrow Bi^{3+} + Na^+ + 3\ H_2O$$
$$(2\ e^- + 6\ H^+ + NaBiO_3 \rightarrow Bi^{3+} + Na^+ + 3\ H_2O) \times 5$$

$$8\ H_2O + 2\ Mn^{2+} \rightarrow 2\ MnO_4^- + 16\ H^+ + 10\ e^-$$
$$10\ e^- + 30\ H^+ + 5\ NaBiO_3 \rightarrow 5\ Bi^{3+} + 5\ Na^+ + 15\ H_2O$$

$$8\ H_2O + 30\ H^+ + 2\ Mn^{2+} + 5\ NaBiO_3 \rightarrow 2\ MnO_4^- + 5\ Bi^{3+} + 5\ Na^+ + 15\ H_2O + 16\ H^+$$

Simplifying:

$$14\ H^+(aq) + 2\ Mn^{2+}(aq) + 5\ NaBiO_3(s) \rightarrow 2\ MnO_4^-(aq) + 5\ Bi^{3+}(aq) + 5\ Na^+(aq) + 7\ H_2O(l)$$

e. $H_3AsO_4 \rightarrow AsH_3$

$$H_3AsO_4 \rightarrow AsH_3 + 4\ H_2O$$
$$8\ e^- + 8\ H^+ + H_3AsO_4 \rightarrow AsH_3 + 4\ H_2O$$

$$(Zn \rightarrow Zn^{2+} + 2\ e^-) \times 4$$

$$8\ e^- + 8\ H^+ + H_3AsO_4 \rightarrow AsH_3 + 4\ H_2O$$
$$4\ Zn \rightarrow 4\ Zn^{2+} + 8\ e^-$$

$$8\ H^+(aq) + H_3AsO_4(aq) + 4\ Zn(s) \rightarrow 4\ Zn^{2+}(aq) + AsH_3(g) + 4\ H_2O(l)$$

f.
$$As_2O_3 \rightarrow H_3AsO_4$$
$$As_2O_3 \rightarrow 2\ H_3AsO_4$$
$$(5\ H_2O + As_2O_3 \rightarrow 2\ H_3AsO_4 + 4\ H^+ + 4\ e^-) \times 3$$

$$NO_3^- \rightarrow NO + 2\ H_2O$$
$$4\ H^+ + NO_3^- \rightarrow NO + 2\ H_2O$$
$$(3\ e^- + 4\ H^+ + NO_3^- \rightarrow NO + 2\ H_2O) \times 4$$

$$12\ e^- + 16\ H^+ + 4\ NO_3^- \rightarrow 4\ NO + 8\ H_2O$$
$$15\ H_2O + 3\ As_2O_3 \rightarrow 6\ H_3AsO_4 + 12\ H^+ + 12\ e^-$$

$$7\ H_2O(l) + 4\ H^+(aq) + 3\ As_2O_3(s) + 4\ NO_3^-(aq) \rightarrow 4\ NO(g) + 6\ H_3AsO_4(aq)$$

g.
$$(2\ Br^- \rightarrow Br_2 + 2\ e^-) \times 5$$
$$MnO_4^- \rightarrow Mn^{2+} + 4\ H_2O$$
$$(5\ e^- + 8\ H^+ + MnO_4^- \rightarrow Mn^{2+} + 4\ H_2O) \times 2$$

$$10\ Br^- \rightarrow 5\ Br_2 + 10\ e^-$$
$$10\ e^- + 16\ H^+ + 2\ MnO_4^- \rightarrow 2\ Mn^{2+} + 8\ H_2O$$

$$16\ H^+(aq) + 2\ MnO_4^-(aq) + 10\ Br^-(aq) \rightarrow 5\ Br_2(l) + 2\ Mn^{2+}(aq) + 8\ H_2O(l)$$

h.
$$CH_3OH \rightarrow CH_2O$$
$$(CH_3OH \rightarrow CH_2O + 2\ H^+ + 2\ e^-) \times 3$$
$$Cr_2O_7^{2-} \rightarrow Cr^{3+}$$
$$14\ H^+ + Cr_2O_7^{2-} \rightarrow 2\ Cr^{3+} + 7\ H_2O$$
$$6\ e^- + 14\ H^+ + Cr_2O_7^{2-} \rightarrow 2\ Cr^{3+} + 7\ H_2O$$

$$3\ CH_3OH \rightarrow 3\ CH_2O + 6\ H^+ + 6\ e^-$$
$$6\ e^- + 14\ H^+ + Cr_2O_7^{2-} \rightarrow 2\ Cr^{3+} + 7\ H_2O$$

$$8\ H^+(aq) + 3\ CH_3OH(aq) + Cr_2O_7^{2-}(aq) \rightarrow 2\ Cr^{3+}(aq) + 3\ CH_2O(aq) + 7\ H_2O(l)$$

73. a. HCl(aq) dissociates to $H^+(aq) + Cl^-(aq)$. For simplicity, let's use H^+ and Cl^- separately.

$$H^+ \rightarrow H_2$$
$$(2\ H^+ + 2\ e^- \rightarrow H_2) \times 3$$
$$Fe \rightarrow HFeCl_4$$
$$(H^+ + 4\ Cl^- + Fe \rightarrow HFeCl_4 + 3\ e^-) \times 2$$

$$6\ H^+ + 6\ e^- \rightarrow 3\ H_2$$
$$2\ H^+ + 8\ Cl^- + 2\ Fe \rightarrow 2\ HFeCl_4 + 6\ e^-$$

$$8\ H^+ + 8\ Cl^- + 2\ Fe \rightarrow 2\ HFeCl_4 + 3\ H_2$$

or $8\ HCl(aq) + 2\ Fe(s) \rightarrow 2\ HFeCl_4(aq) + 3\ H_2(g)$

b. $IO_3^- \rightarrow I_3^-$ $\quad$ $I^- \rightarrow I_3^-$

$3\ IO_3^- \rightarrow I_3^-$ $\quad$ $(3\ I^- \rightarrow I_3^- + 2\ e^-) \times 8$

$3\ IO_3^- \rightarrow I_3^- + 9\ H_2O$

$16\ e^- + 18\ H^+ + 3\ IO_3^- \rightarrow I_3^- + 9\ H_2O$

$$16\ e^- + 18\ H^+ + 3\ IO_3^- \rightarrow I_3^- + 9\ H_2O$$
$$24\ I^- \rightarrow 8\ I_3^- + 16\ e^-$$

$$18\ H^+ + 24\ I^- + 3\ IO_3^- \rightarrow 9\ I_3^- + 9\ H_2O$$

Reducing: $6\ H^+(aq) + 8\ I^-(aq) + IO_3^-(aq) \rightarrow 3\ I_3^-(aq) + 3\ H_2O(l)$

c. $(Ce^{4+} + e^- \rightarrow Ce^{3+}) \times 97$

$$Cr(NCS)_6^{4-} \rightarrow Cr^{3+} + NO_3^- + CO_2 + SO_4^{2-}$$
$$54\ H_2O + Cr(NCS)_6^{4-} \rightarrow Cr^{3+} + 6\ NO_3^- + 6\ CO_2 + 6\ SO_4^{2-} + 108\ H^+$$

Charge on left $= -4$. Charge on right $= +3 + 6(-1) + 6(-2) + 108(+1) = +93$. Add 97 e^- to the product side, and then add the two balanced half-reactions with a common factor of 97 e^- transferred.

$$54\ H_2O + Cr(NCS)_6^{4-} \rightarrow Cr^{3+} + 6\ NO_3^- + 6\ CO_2 + 6\ SO_4^{2-} + 108\ H^+ + 97\ e^-$$
$$97\ e^- + 97\ Ce^{4+} \rightarrow 97\ Ce^{3+}$$

$$97\ Ce^{4+}(aq) + 54\ H_2O(l) + Cr(NCS)_6^{4-}(aq) \rightarrow 97\ Ce^{3+}(aq) + Cr^{3+}(aq) + 6\ NO_3^-(aq) + 6\ CO_2(g) + 6\ SO_4^{2-}(aq) + 108\ H^+(aq)$$

This is very complicated. A check of the net charge is a good check to see if the equation is balanced. Left: charge $= 97(+4) - 4 = +384$. Right: charge $= 97(+3) + 3 + 6(-1) + 6(-2) + 108(+1) = +384$.

d. $CrI_3 \rightarrow CrO_4^{2-} + IO_4^-$ $\quad$ $Cl_2 \rightarrow Cl^-$

$(16\ H_2O + CrI_3 \rightarrow CrO_4^{2-} + 3\ IO_4^- + 32\ H^+ + 27\ e^-) \times 2$ $\quad$ $(2\ e^- + Cl_2 \rightarrow 2\ Cl^-) \times 27$

Common factor is a transfer of 54 e^-.

$$54\ e^- + 27\ Cl_2 \rightarrow 54\ Cl^-$$
$$32\ H_2O + 2\ CrI_3 \rightarrow 2\ CrO_4^{2-} + 6\ IO_4^- + 64\ H^+ + 54\ e^-$$

$$32\ H_2O + 2\ CrI_3 + 27\ Cl_2 \rightarrow 54\ Cl^- + 2\ CrO_4^{2-} + 6\ IO_4^- + 64\ H^+$$

Add 64 OH^- to both sides and convert 64 H^+ into 64 H_2O.

$64\ OH^- + 32\ H_2O + 2\ CrI_3 + 27\ Cl_2 \rightarrow 54\ Cl^- + 2\ CrO_4^{2-} + 6\ IO_4^- + 64\ H_2O$

Reducing gives:

$$64\ OH^-(aq) + 2\ CrI_3(s) + 27\ Cl_2(g) \rightarrow 54\ Cl^-(aq) + 2\ CrO_4^{2-}(aq) + 6\ IO_4^-(aq) + 32\ H_2O(l)$$

e. $Ce^{4+} \rightarrow Ce(OH)_3$

$(e^- + 3\ H_2O + Ce^{4+} \rightarrow Ce(OH)_3 + 3\ H^+) \times 61$

$Fe(CN)_6^{4-} \rightarrow Fe(OH)_3 + CO_3^{2-} + NO_3^-$

$Fe(CN)_6^{4-} \rightarrow Fe(OH)_3 + 6\ CO_3^{2-} + 6\ NO_3^-$

There are 39 extra O atoms on right. Add 39 H_2O to left, then add 75 H^+ to right to balance H^+.

$39\ H_2O + Fe(CN)_6^{4-} \rightarrow Fe(OH)_3 + 6\ CO_3^{2-} + 6\ NO_3^- + 75\ H^+$

net charge = 4– net charge = 57+

Add 61 e^- to the product side, and then add the two balanced half-reactions with a common factor of 61 e^- transferred.

$$39\ H_2O + Fe(CN)_6^{4-} \rightarrow Fe(OH)_3 + 6\ CO_3^- + 6\ NO_3^- + 75\ H^+ + 61\ e^-$$
$$61\ e^- + 183\ H_2O + 61\ Ce^{4+} \rightarrow 61\ Ce(OH)_3 + 183\ H^+$$

$$222\ H_2O + Fe(CN)_6^{4-} + 61\ Ce^{4+} \rightarrow 61\ Ce(OH)_3 + Fe(OH)_3 + 6\ CO_3^{2-} + 6\ NO_3^- + 258\ H^+$$

Adding 258 OH^- to each side, and then reducing gives:

$$258\ OH^-(aq) + Fe(CN)_6^{4-}(aq) + 61\ Ce^{4+}(aq) \rightarrow 61\ Ce(OH)_3(s) + Fe(OH)_3(s) + 6\ CO_3^{2-}(aq) + 6\ NO_3^-(aq) + 36\ H_2O(l)$$

75. $(H_2C_2O_4 \rightarrow 2\ CO_2 + 2\ H^+ + 2\ e^-) \times 5$ $(5\ e^- + 8\ H^+ + MnO_4^- \rightarrow Mn^{2+} + 4\ H_2O) \times 2$

$$5\ H_2C_2O_4 \rightarrow 10\ CO_2 + 10\ H^+ + 10\ e^-$$
$$10\ e^- + 16\ H^+ + 2\ MnO_4^- \rightarrow 2\ Mn^{2+} + 8\ H_2O$$

$$6\ H^+(aq) + 5\ H_2C_2O_4(aq) + 2\ MnO_4^-(aq) \rightarrow 10\ CO_2(g) + 2\ Mn^{2+}(aq) + 8\ H_2O(l)$$

$$0.1058\ g\ H_2C_2O_4 \times \frac{1\ mol\ H_2C_2O_4}{90.034\ g} \times \frac{2\ mol\ MnO_4^-}{5\ mol\ H_2C_2O_4} = 4.700 \times 10^{-4}\ mol\ MnO_4^-$$

$$\text{Molarity} = \frac{4.700 \times 10^{-4}\ mol\ MnO_4^-}{28.97\ mL} \times \frac{1000\ mL}{L} = 1.622 \times 10^{-2}\ M\ MnO_4^-$$

77. $(Fe^{2+} \rightarrow Fe^{3+} + e^-) \times 5$

$5\ e^- + 8\ H^+ + MnO_4^- \rightarrow Mn^{2+} + 4\ H_2O$

$$8\ H^+(aq) + MnO_4^-(aq) + 5\ Fe^{2+}(aq) \rightarrow 5\ Fe^{3+}(aq) + Mn^{2+}(aq) + 4\ H_2O(l)$$

From the titration data we can get the number of moles of Fe^{2+}. We then convert this to a mass of iron and calculate the mass percent of iron in the sample.

$$38.37 \times 10^{-3}\ \text{L}\ MnO_4^- \times \frac{0.0198\ \text{mol}\ MnO_4^-}{\text{L}} \times \frac{5\ \text{mol}\ Fe^{2+}}{\text{mol}\ MnO_4^-} = 3.80 \times 10^{-3}\ \text{mol}\ Fe^{2+}$$

$$= 3.80 \times 10^{-3}\ \text{mol Fe present}$$

$$3.80 \times 10^{-3}\ \text{mol Fe} \times \frac{55.85\ \text{g Fe}}{\text{mol Fe}} = 0.212\ \text{g Fe}$$

$$\text{Mass \% Fe} = \frac{0.212\ \text{g}}{0.6128\ \text{g}} \times 100 = 34.6\%\ \text{Fe}$$

79. $Mg(s) + 2\ HCl(aq) \rightarrow MgCl_2(aq) + H_2(g)$

$$3.00\ \text{g Mg} \times \frac{1\ \text{mol Mg}}{24.31\ \text{g Mg}} \times \frac{2\ \text{mol HCl}}{\text{mol Mg}} \times \frac{1\ \text{L HCl}}{5.0\ \text{mol HCl}} = 0.0494\ \text{L} = 49.4\ \text{mL HCl}$$

Additional Exercises

81. Mol $CaCl_2$ present = $0.230\ \text{L}\ CaCl_2 \times \frac{0.275\ \text{mol}\ CaCl_2}{\text{L}\ CaCl_2} = 6.33 \times 10^{-2}\ \text{mol}\ CaCl_2$

The volume of $CaCl_2$ solution after evaporation is:

$$6.33 \times 10^{-2}\ \text{mol}\ CaCl_2 \times \frac{1\ \text{L}\ CaCl_2}{1.10\ \text{mol}\ CaCl_2} = 5.75 \times 10^{-2}\ \text{L} = 57.5\ \text{mL}\ CaCl_2$$

Volume H_2O evaporated = 230. mL – 57.5 mL = 173 mL H_2O evaporated

83. a. $MgCl_2(aq) + 2\ AgNO_3(aq) \rightarrow 2\ AgCl(s) + Mg(NO_3)_2(aq)$

$$0.641\ \text{g AgCl} \times \frac{1\ \text{mol AgCl}}{143.4\ \text{g AgCl}} \times \frac{1\ \text{mol}\ MgCl_2}{2\ \text{mol AgCl}} \times \frac{95.21\ \text{g}}{\text{mol}\ MgCl_2} = 0.213\ \text{g}\ MgCl_2$$

$$\frac{0.213\ \text{g}\ MgCl_2}{1.50\ \text{g mixture}} \times 100 = 14.2\%\ MgCl_2$$

b. $0.213\ \text{g}\ MgCl_2 \times \frac{1\ \text{mol}\ MgCl_2}{95.21\ \text{g}} \times \frac{2\ \text{mol}\ AgNO_3}{\text{mol}\ MgCl_2} \times \frac{1\ \text{L}}{0.500\ \text{mol}\ AgNO_3} \times \frac{1000\ \text{mL}}{1\ \text{L}}$

$$= 8.95\ \text{mL}\ AgNO_3$$

85. a. $0.308\ \text{g AgCl} \times \frac{35.45\ \text{g Cl}}{143.4\ \text{g AgCl}} = 0.0761\ \text{g Cl}$; $\%\ \text{Cl} = \frac{0.0761\ \text{g}}{0.256\ \text{g}} \times 100 = 29.7\%\ \text{Cl}$

Cobalt(III) oxide, Co_2O_3: 2(58.93) + 3(16.00) = 165.86 g/mol

$$0.145 \text{ g } Co_2O_3 \times \frac{117.86 \text{ g Co}}{165.86 \text{ g } Co_2O_3} = 0.103 \text{ g Co}; \ \% \text{ Co} = \frac{0.103 \text{ g}}{0.416 \text{ g}} \times 100 = 24.8\% \text{ Co}$$

The remainder, 100.0 – (29.7 + 24.8) = 45.5%, is water.

Assuming 100.0 g of compound:

$$45.5 \text{ g } H_2O \times \frac{2.016 \text{ g H}}{18.02 \text{ g } H_2O} = 5.09 \text{ g H}; \ \% \text{ H} = \frac{5.09 \text{ g H}}{100.0 \text{ g compound}} \times 100 = 5.09\% \text{ H}$$

$$45.5 \text{ g } H_2O \times \frac{16.00 \text{ g O}}{18.02 \text{ g } H_2O} = 40.4 \text{ g O}; \ \% \text{ O} = \frac{40.4 \text{ g O}}{100.0 \text{ g compound}} \times 100 = 40.4\% \text{ O}$$

The mass percent composition is 24.8% Co, 29.7% Cl, 5.09% H, and 40.4% O.

b. Out of 100.0 g of compound, there are:

$$24.8 \text{ g Co} \times \frac{1 \text{ mol}}{58.93 \text{ g Co}} = 0.421 \text{ mol Co}; \ 29.7 \text{ g Cl} \times \frac{1 \text{ mol}}{35.45 \text{ g Cl}} = 0.838 \text{ mol Cl}$$

$$5.09 \text{ g H} \times \frac{1 \text{ mol}}{1.008 \text{ g H}} = 5.05 \text{ mol H}; \ 40.4 \text{ g O} \times \frac{1 \text{ mol}}{16.00 \text{ g O}} = 2.53 \text{ mol O}$$

Dividing all results by 0.421, we get $CoCl_2 \bullet 6H_2O$ for the empirical formula, which is also the molecular formula.

c. $CoCl_2 \bullet 6H_2O(aq) + 2\ AgNO_3(aq) \rightarrow 2\ AgCl(s) + Co(NO_3)_2(aq) + 6\ H_2O(l)$

$CoCl_2 \bullet 6H_2O(aq) + 2\ NaOH(aq) \rightarrow Co(OH)_2(s) + 2\ NaCl(aq) + 6\ H_2O(l)$

$Co(OH)_2 \rightarrow Co_2O_3$ This is an oxidation-reduction reaction. Thus we also need to include an oxidizing agent. The obvious choice is O_2.

$4\ Co(OH)_2(s) + O_2(g) \rightarrow 2\ Co_2O_3(s) + 4\ H_2O(l)$

87. $Ag^+(aq) + Cl^-(aq) \rightarrow AgCl(s)$; let x = mol NaCl and y = mol KCl.

$(22.90 \times 10^{-3} \text{ L}) \times 0.1000 \text{ mol/L} = 2.290 \times 10^{-3} \text{ mol } Ag^+ = 2.290 \times 10^{-3} \text{ mol } Cl^- \text{ total}$

$x + y = 2.290 \times 10^{-3} \text{ mol } Cl^-, \ x = 2.290 \times 10^{-3} - y$

Because the molar mass of NaCl is 58.44 g/mol and the molar mass of KCl is 74.55 g/mol:

$(58.44)x + (74.55)y = 0.1586 \text{ g}$

$58.44(2.290 \times 10^{-3} - y) + (74.55)y = 0.1586,\ (16.11)y = 0.0248,\ y = 1.54 \times 10^{-3}$ mol KCl

$$\text{Mass \% KCl} = \frac{1.54 \times 10^{-3}\ \text{mol} \times 74.55\ \text{g/mol}}{0.1586\ \text{g}} \times 100 = 72.4\%\ \text{KCl}$$

% NaCl = 100.0 − 72.4 = 27.6% NaCl

89. $Cr(NO_3)_3(aq) + 3\ NaOH(aq) \rightarrow Cr(OH)_3(s) + 3\ NaNO_3(aq)$

$$\text{Mol NaOH used} = 2.06\ \text{g Cr(OH)}_3 \times \frac{1\ \text{mol Cr(OH)}_3}{103.02\ \text{g}} \times \frac{3\ \text{mol NaOH}}{\text{mol Cr(OH)}_3} = 6.00 \times 10^{-2}\ \text{mol}$$

to form precipitate

$NaOH(aq) + HCl(aq) \rightarrow NaCl(aq) + H_2O(l)$

$$\text{Mol NaOH used} = 0.1000\ \text{L} \times \frac{0.400\ \text{mol HCl}}{\text{L}} \times \frac{1\ \text{mol NaOH}}{\text{mol HCl}} = 4.00 \times 10^{-2}\ \text{mol}$$

to react with HCl

$$M_{\text{NaOH}} = \frac{\text{total mol NaOH}}{\text{volume}} = \frac{6.00 \times 10^{-2}\ \text{mol} + 4.00 \times 10^{-2}\ \text{mol}}{0.0500\ \text{L}} = 2.00\ M\ \text{NaOH}$$

91. Mol KHP used = 0.4016 g × 1 mol/204.22 g = 1.967×10^{-3} mol KHP

Because 1 mole of NaOH reacts completely with 1 mole of KHP, the NaOH solution contains 1.967×10^{-3} mol NaOH.

$$\text{Molarity of NaOH} = \frac{1.967 \times 10^{-3}\ \text{mol}}{25.06 \times 10^{-3}\ \text{L}} = \frac{7.849 \times 10^{-2}\ \text{mol NaOH}}{\text{L}}$$

$$\text{Maximum molarity} = \frac{1.967 \times 10^{-3}\ \text{mol}}{25.01 \times 10^{-3}\ \text{L}} = \frac{7.865 \times 10^{-2}\ \text{mol NaOH}}{\text{L}}$$

$$\text{Minimum molarity} = \frac{1.967 \times 10^{-3}\ \text{mol}}{25.11 \times 10^{-3}\ \text{L}} = \frac{7.834 \times 10^{-2}\ \text{mol NaOH}}{\text{L}}$$

We can express this as 0.07849 ±0.00016 *M*. An alternate way is to express the molarity as 0.0785 ±0.0002 *M*. This second way shows the actual number of significant figures in the molarity. The advantage of the first method is that it shows that we made all our individual measurements to four significant figures.

93. $$\text{Mol } C_6H_8O_7 = 0.250\ \text{g } C_6H_8O_7 \times \frac{1\ \text{mol } C_6H_8O_7}{192.1\ \text{g } C_6H_8O_7} = 1.30 \times 10^{-3}\ \text{mol } C_6H_8O_7$$

Let H_xA represent citric acid, where x is the number of acidic hydrogens. The balanced neutralization reaction is:

$H_xA(aq) + x\ OH^-(aq) \rightarrow x\ H_2O(l) + A^{x-}(aq)$

$$\text{Mol OH}^- \text{ reacted} = 0.0372 \text{ L} \times \frac{0.105 \text{ mol OH}^-}{\text{L}} = 3.91 \times 10^{-3} \text{ mol OH}^-$$

$$x = \frac{\text{mol OH}^-}{\text{mol citric acid}} = \frac{3.91 \times 10^{-3} \text{ mol}}{1.30 \times 10^{-3} \text{ mol}} = 3.01$$

Therefore, the general acid formula for citric acid is H_3A, meaning that citric acid has three acidic hydrogens per citric acid molecule (citric acid is a triprotic acid).

95. $H_2SO_4(aq) + 2\ NaOH(aq) \rightarrow Na_2SO_4(aq) + 2\ H_2O(l)$

$$0.02844 \text{ L} \times \frac{0.1000 \text{ mol NaOH}}{\text{L}} \times \frac{1 \text{ mol } H_2SO_4}{2 \text{ mol NaOH}} \times \frac{1 \text{ mol } SO_2}{\text{mol } H_2SO_4} \times \frac{32.07 \text{ g S}}{\text{mol } SO_2} = 4.560 \times 10^{-2} \text{ g S}$$

$$\text{Mass \% S} = \frac{0.04560 \text{ g}}{1.325 \text{ g}} \times 100 = 3.442\%$$

Challenge Problems

97. a. Let x = mass of Mg, so $10.00 - x$ = mass of Zn. $Ag^+(aq) + Cl^-(aq) \rightarrow AgCl(s)$.

From the given balanced equations, there is a 2 : 1 mole ratio between mol Mg and mol Cl^-. The same is true for Zn. Because mol Ag^+ = mol Cl^- present, one can setup an equation relating mol Cl^- present to mol Ag^+ added.

$$x \text{ g Mg} \times \frac{1 \text{ mol Mg}}{24.31 \text{ g Mg}} \times \frac{2 \text{ mol Cl}^-}{\text{mol Mg}} + (10.00 - x) \text{ g Zn} \times \frac{1 \text{ mol Zn}}{65.38 \text{ g Zn}} \times \frac{2 \text{ mol Cl}^-}{\text{mol Zn}}$$
$$= 0.156 \text{ L} \times \frac{3.00 \text{ mol Ag}^+}{\text{L}} \times \frac{1 \text{ mol Cl}^-}{\text{mol Ag}^+} = 0.468 \text{ mol Cl}^-$$

$$\frac{2x}{24.31} + \frac{2(10.00 - x)}{65.38} = 0.468, \quad 24.31 \times 65.38 \left(\frac{2x}{24.31} + \frac{20.00 - 2x}{65.38} = 0.468 \right)$$

$(130.8)x + 486.2 - (48.62)x = 743.8$ (carrying 1 extra significant figure)

$$(82.2)x = 257.6, \quad x = 3.13 \text{ g Mg}; \quad \% \text{ Mg} = \frac{3.13 \text{ g Mg}}{10.00 \text{ g mixture}} \times 100 = 31.3\% \text{ Mg}$$

b. $0.156 \text{ L} \times \frac{3.00 \text{ mol Ag}^+}{\text{L}} \times \frac{1 \text{ mol Cl}^-}{\text{mol Ag}^+} = 0.468 \text{ mol Cl}^- = 0.468 \text{ mol HCl added}$

$$M_{HCl} = \frac{0.468 \text{ mol}}{0.0780 \text{ L}} = 6.00\ M \text{ HCl}$$

99. $Zn(s) + 2\ AgNO_2(aq) \rightarrow 2\ Ag(s) + Zn(NO_2)_2(aq)$

Let x = mass of Ag and y = mass of Zn after the reaction has stopped. Then $x + y = 29.0$ g. Because the moles of Ag produced will equal two times the moles of Zn reacted:

$$(19.0 - y)\text{ g Zn} \times \frac{1\text{ mol Zn}}{65.38\text{ g Zn}} \times \frac{2\text{ mol Ag}}{1\text{ mol Zn}} = x\text{ g Ag} \times \frac{1\text{ mol Ag}}{107.9\text{ g Ag}}$$

Simplifying:

$$3.059 \times 10^{-2}(19.0 - y) = (9.268 \times 10^{-3})x$$

Substituting $x = 29.0 - y$ into the equation gives:

$$3.059 \times 10^{-2}(19.0 - y) = 9.268 \times 10^{-3}(29.0 - y)$$

Solving:

$$0.581 - (3.059 \times 10^{-2})y = 0.269 - (9.268 \times 10^{-3})y,\ (2.132 \times 10^{-2})y = 0.312,\ \ y = 14.6\text{ g Zn}$$

14.6 g Zn are present, and 29.0 – 14.6 = 14.4 g Ag are also present after the reaction is stopped.

101. Molar masses: KCl, 39.10 + 35.45 = 74.55 g/mol; KBr, 39.10 + 79.90 = 119.00 g/mol, AgCl, 107.9 + 35.45 = 143.4 g/mol; AgBr, 107.9 + 79.90 = 187.8 g/mol

Let x = number of moles of KCl in mixture and y = number of moles of KBr in mixture. $Ag^+ + Cl^- \rightarrow AgCl$ and $Ag^+ + Br^- \rightarrow AgBr$; so, x = moles AgCl and y = moles AgBr.

Setting up two equations from the given information:

$$0.1024\text{ g} = (74.55)x + (119.0)y \text{ and } 0.1889\text{ g} = (143.4)x + (187.8)y$$

Multiply the first equation by $\frac{187.8}{119.0}$, and then subtract from the second.

$$\begin{array}{rl} 0.1889 = & (143.4)x + (187.8)y \\ \underline{-0.1616 = } & \underline{-(117.7)x - (187.8)y} \\ 0.0273 = & (25.7)x, \end{array} \qquad x = 1.06 \times 10^{-3}\text{ mol KCl}$$

$$1.06 \times 10^{-3}\text{ mol KCl} \times \frac{74.55\text{ g KCl}}{\text{mol KCl}} = 0.0790\text{ g KCl}$$

$$\text{Mass \% KCl} = \frac{0.0790\text{ g}}{0.1024\text{ g}} \times 100 = 77.1\%,\ \ \%\text{ KBr} = 100.0 - 77.1 = 22.9\%$$

103. a. $C_{12}H_{10-n}Cl_n + n\ Ag^+ \rightarrow n\ AgCl$; molar mass of AgCl = 143.4 g/mol

Molar mass of PCB = 12(12.01) + (10 – n)(1.008) + n(35.45) = 154.20 + (34.44)n

Because n mol AgCl are produced for every 1 mol PCB reacted, n(143.4) g of AgCl will be produced for every [154.20 + (34.44)n] g of PCB reacted.

$$\frac{\text{Mass of AgCl}}{\text{Mass of PCB}} = \frac{(143.4)n}{154.20 + (34.44)n} \text{ or } \text{mass}_{AgCl}[154.20 + (34.44)n] = \text{mass}_{PCB}(143.4)n$$

b. 0.4971[154.20 + (34.44)n] = 0.1947(143.4)n, 76.65 + (17.12)n = (27.92)n

76.65 = (10.80)n, n = 7.097

105. a. Flow rate = 5.00×10^4 L/s + 3.50×10^3 L/s = 5.35×10^4 L/s

b. $$C_{HCl} = \frac{3.50 \times 10^3(65.0)}{5.35 \times 10^4} = 4.25 \text{ ppm HCl}$$

c. 1 ppm = 1 mg/kg H_2O = 1 mg/L (assuming density = 1.00 g/mL)

$$8.00 \text{ h} \times \frac{60 \text{ min}}{\text{h}} \times \frac{60 \text{ s}}{\text{min}} \times \frac{1.80 \times 10^4 \text{ L}}{\text{s}} \times \frac{4.25 \text{ mg HCl}}{\text{L}} \times \frac{1 \text{ g}}{1000 \text{ mg}} = 2.20 \times 10^6 \text{ g HCl}$$

$$2.20 \times 10^6 \text{ g HCl} \times \frac{1 \text{ mol HCl}}{36.46 \text{ g HCl}} \times \frac{1 \text{ mol CaO}}{2 \text{ mol HCl}} \times \frac{56.08 \text{ g Ca}}{\text{mol CaO}} = 1.69 \times 10^6 \text{ g CaO}$$

d. The concentration of Ca^{2+} going into the second plant was:

$$\frac{5.00 \times 10^4(10.2)}{5.35 \times 10^4} = 9.53 \text{ ppm}$$

The second plant used: 1.80×10^4 L/s × (8.00 × 60 × 60) s = 5.18×10^8 L of water.

$$1.69 \times 10^6 \text{ g CaO} \times \frac{40.08 \text{ g } Ca^{2+}}{56.08 \text{ g CaO}} = 1.21 \times 10^6 \text{ g } Ca^{2+} \text{ was added to this water.}$$

$$C_{Ca^{2+}} \text{ (plant water)} = 9.53 + \frac{1.21 \times 10^9 \text{ mg}}{5.18 \times 10^8 \text{ L}} = 9.53 + 2.34 = 11.87 \text{ ppm}$$

Because 90.0% of this water is returned, $(1.80 \times 10^4) \times 0.900 = 1.62 \times 10^4$ L/s of water with 11.87 ppm Ca^{2+} is mixed with $(5.35 - 1.80) \times 10^4 = 3.55 \times 10^4$ L/s of water containing 9.53 ppm Ca^{2+}.

$$C_{Ca^{2+}} \text{ (final)} = \frac{(1.62 \times 10^4 \text{ L/s})(11.87 \text{ ppm}) + (3.55 \times 10^4 \text{ L/s})(9.53 \text{ ppm})}{1.62 \times 10^4 \text{ L/s} + 3.55 \times 10^4 \text{ L/s}} = 10.3 \text{ ppm}$$

107. a. $YBa_2Cu_3O_{6.5}$:

$+3 + 2(+2) + 3x + 6.5(-2) = 0$

$7 + 3x - 13 = 0,\ 3x = 6,\ x = +2$ Only Cu^{2+} present.

$YBa_2Cu_3O_7$:

$+3 + 2(+2) + 3x + 7(-2) = 0,\ x = +2\ 1/3$ or 2.33

This corresponds to two Cu^{2+} and one Cu^{3+} present.

$YBa_2Cu_3O_8$:

$+3 + 2(+2) + 3x + 8(-2) = 0,\ x = +3;$ Only Cu^{3+} present.

b.

$$(e^- + Cu^{2+} + I^- \rightarrow CuI) \times 2$$
$$3I^- \rightarrow I_3^- + 2\ e^-$$
$$\overline{2\ Cu^{2+}(aq) + 5\ I^-(aq) \rightarrow 2\ CuI(s) + I_3^-(aq)}$$

$$2\ e^- + Cu^{3+} + I^- \rightarrow CuI$$
$$3I^- \rightarrow I_3^- + 2\ e^-$$
$$\overline{Cu^{3+}(aq) + 4\ I^-(aq) \rightarrow CuI(s) + I_3^-(aq)}$$

$$2\ S_2O_3^{2-} \rightarrow S_4O_6^{2-} + 2\ e^-$$
$$2\ e^- + I_3^- \rightarrow 3\ I^-$$
$$\overline{2\ S_2O_3^{2-}(aq) + I_3^-(aq) \rightarrow 3\ I^-(aq) + S_4O_6^{2-}(aq)}$$

c. Step II data: All Cu is converted to Cu^{2+}. *Note*: Superconductor abbreviated as "123."

$$22.57 \times 10^{-3}\ L \times \frac{0.1000\ mol\ S_2O_3^{2-}}{L} \times \frac{1\ mol\ I_3^-}{2\ mol\ S_2O_3^{2-}} \times \frac{2\ mol\ Cu^{2+}}{mol\ I_3^-}$$
$$= 2.257 \times 10^{-3}\ mol\ Cu^{2+}$$

$$2.257 \times 10^{-3}\ mol\ Cu \times \frac{1\ mol\ "123"}{3\ mol\ Cu} = 7.523 \times 10^{-4}\ mol\ "123"$$

$$\text{Molar mass of } YBa_2Cu_3O_x = \frac{0.5402\ g}{7.523 \times 10^{-4}\ mol} = 670.2\ g/mol$$

$670.2 = 88.91 + 2(137.3) + 3(63.55) + x(16.00),\ 670.2 = 554.2 + x(16.00)$

$x = 7.250$; formula is $YBa_2Cu_3O_{7.25}$.

Check with Step I data: Both Cu^{2+} and Cu^{3+} present.

$$37.77 \times 10^{-3}\ L \times \frac{0.1000\ mol\ S_2O_3^{2-}}{L} \times \frac{1\ mol\ I_3^-}{2\ mol\ S_2O_3^{2-}} = 1.889 \times 10^{-3}\ mol\ I_3^-$$

We get 1 mol I_3^- per mol Cu^{3+} and 1 mol I_3^- per 2 mol Cu^{2+}. Let $n_{Cu^{3+}}$ = mol Cu^{3+} and $n_{Cu^{2+}}$ = mol Cu^{2+}, then:

$$n_{Cu^{3+}} + \frac{n_{Cu^{2+}}}{2} = 1.889 \times 10^{-3} \text{ mol}$$

In addition: $\frac{0.5625 \text{ g}}{670.2 \text{ g/mol}} = 8.393 \times 10^{-4}$ mol "123"; this amount of "123" contains:

$3(8.393 \times 10^{-4}) = 2.518 \times 10^{-3}$ mol Cu total $= n_{Cu^{3+}} + n_{Cu^{2+}}$

Solving by simultaneous equations:

$$n_{Cu^{3+}} + n_{Cu^{2+}} = 2.518 \times 10^{-3}$$

$$-n_{Cu^{3+}} - \frac{n_{Cu^{2+}}}{2} = -1.889 \times 10^{-3}$$

$$\frac{n_{Cu^{2+}}}{2} = 6.29 \times 10^{-4}$$

$n_{Cu^{2+}} = 1.26 \times 10^{-3}$ mol Cu^{2+}; $n_{Cu^{3+}} = 2.518 \times 10^{-3} - 1.26 \times 10^{-3} = 1.26 \times 10^{-3}$ mol Cu^{3+}

This sample of superconductor contains equal moles of Cu^{2+} and Cu^{3+}. Therefore, 1 mole of $YBa_2Cu_3O_x$ contains 1.50 mol Cu^{2+} and 1.50 mol Cu^{3+}. Solving for x using oxidation states:

$$+3 + 2(+2) + 1.50(+2) + 1.50(+3) + x(-2) = 0, \quad 14.50 = 2x, \quad x = 7.25$$

The two experiments give the same result, $x = 7.25$ with formula $YBa_2Cu_3O_{7.25}$.

Average oxidation state of Cu:

$$+3 + 2(+2) + 3(x) + 7.25(-2) = 0, \quad 3x = 7.50, \quad x = +2.50$$

As determined from Step I data, this superconductor sample contains equal moles of Cu^{2+} and Cu^{3+}, giving an average oxidation state of +2.50.

109. There are three unknowns so we need three equations to solve for the unknowns. Let x = mass $AgNO_3$, y = mass $CuCl_2$, and z = mass $FeCl_3$. Then $x + y + z = 1.0000$ g. The Cl^- in $CuCl_2$ and $FeCl_3$ will react with the excess $AgNO_3$ to form the precipitate AgCl(s). Assuming silver has an atomic mass of 107.90:

$$\text{Mass of Cl in mixture} = 1.7809 \text{ g AgCl} \times \frac{35.45 \text{ g Cl}}{143.35 \text{ g AgCl}} = 0.4404 \text{ g Cl}$$

$$\text{Mass of Cl from } CuCl_2 = y \text{ g } CuCl_2 \times \frac{2(35.45) \text{ g Cl}}{134.45 \text{ g } CuCl_2} = (0.5273)y$$

$$\text{Mass of Cl from } FeCl_3 = z \text{ g } FeCl_3 \times \frac{3(35.45) \text{ g Cl}}{162.20 \text{ g } FeCl_3} = (0.6557)z$$

The second equation is: 0.4404 g Cl = (0.5273)y + (0.6557)z

Similarly, let's calculate the mass of metals in each salt.

Mass of Ag in $AgNO_3$ = x g $AgNO_3$ × $\frac{107.9 \text{ g Ag}}{169.91 \text{ g } AgNO_3}$ = (0.6350)x

For $CuCl_2$ and $FeCl_3$, we already calculated the amount of Cl in each initial amount of salt; the remainder must be the mass of metal in each salt.

Mass of Cu in $CuCl_2$ = $y - (0.5273)y = (0.4727)y$

Mass of Fe in $FeCl_3$ = $z - (0.6557)z = (0.3443)z$

The third equation is: 0.4684 g metals = $(0.6350)x + (0.4727)y + (0.3443)z$

We now have three equations with three unknowns. Solving:

$$-0.6350\,(1.0000 = x + y + z)$$
$$0.4684 = (0.6350)x + (0.4727)y + (0.3443)z$$
$$\overline{-0.1666 = -(0.1623)y - (0.2907)z}$$

$$\frac{0.5273}{0.1623}[-0.1666 = -(0.1623)y - (0.2907)z]$$
$$0.4404 = (0.5273)y + (0.6557)z$$
$$\overline{-0.1009 = -(0.2888)z,} \quad z = \frac{0.1009}{0.2888} = 0.3494 \text{ g } FeCl_3$$

$0.4404 = (0.5273)y + 0.6557(0.3494)$, $y = 0.4007$ g $CuCl_2$

$x = 1.0000 - y - z = 1.0000 - 0.4007 - 0.3494 = 0.2499$ g $AgNO_3$

Mass % $AgNO_3$ = $\frac{0.2499 \text{ g}}{1.0000 \text{ g}} \times 100 = 24.99\%$ $AgNO_3$

Mass % $CuCl_2$ = $\frac{0.4007 \text{ g}}{1.0000 \text{ g}} \times 100 = 40.07\%$ $CuCl_2$; mass % $FeCl_3$ = 34.94%

CHAPTER 5

GASES

Pressure

21. $4.75 \text{ cm} \times \frac{10 \text{ mm}}{\text{cm}} = 47.5 \text{ mm Hg}$ or 47.5 torr; $47.5 \text{ torr} \times \frac{1 \text{ atm}}{760 \text{ torr}} = 6.25 \times 10^{-2} \text{ atm}$

$$6.25 \times 10^{-2} \text{ atm} \times \frac{1.013 \times 10^5 \text{ Pa}}{\text{atm}} = 6.33 \times 10^3 \text{ Pa}$$

23. Suppose we have a column of mercury $1.00 \text{ cm} \times 1.00 \text{ cm} \times 76.0 \text{ cm} = V = 76.0 \text{ cm}^3$:

$$\text{mass} = 76.0 \text{ cm}^3 \times 13.59 \text{ g/cm}^3 = 1.03 \times 10^3 \text{ g} \times \frac{1 \text{ kg}}{1000 \text{ g}} = 1.03 \text{ kg}$$

$$F = mg = 1.03 \text{ kg} \times 9.81 \text{ m/s}^2 = 10.1 \text{ kg m/s}^2 = 10.1 \text{ N}$$

$$\frac{\text{Force}}{\text{Area}} = \frac{10.1 \text{ N}}{\text{cm}^2} \times \left(\frac{100 \text{ cm}}{\text{m}}\right)^2 = 1.01 \times 10^5 \frac{\text{N}}{\text{m}^2} \text{ or } 1.01 \times 10^5 \text{ Pa}$$

(*Note*: 76.0 cm Hg = 1 atm = 1.01×10^5 Pa.)

To exert the same pressure, a column of water will have to contain the same mass as the 76.0-cm column of mercury. Thus the column of water will have to be 13.59 times taller or 76.0 cm × 13.59 = 1.03×10^3 cm = 10.3 m.

25. a. $4.8 \text{ atm} \times \frac{760 \text{ mm Hg}}{\text{atm}} = 3.6 \times 10^3 \text{ mm Hg}$; b. $3.6 \times 10^3 \text{ mm Hg} \times \frac{1 \text{ torr}}{\text{mm Hg}} = 3.6 \times 10^3 \text{ torr}$

c. $4.8 \text{ atm} \times \frac{1.013 \times 10^5 \text{ Pa}}{\text{atm}} = 4.9 \times 10^5 \text{ Pa}$; d. $4.8 \text{ atm} \times \frac{14.7 \text{ psi}}{\text{atm}} = 71 \text{ psi}$

Gas Laws

27. The decrease in temperature causes the balloon to contract (V and T are directly related). Because weather balloons do expand, the effect of the decrease in pressure must be dominant.

29. Treat each gas separately, and use the relationship $P_1V_1 = P_2V_2$ (n and T are constant).

$$\text{For } H_2\text{: } P_2 = \frac{P_1V_1}{V_2} = 475 \text{ torr} \times \frac{2.00 \text{ L}}{3.00 \text{ L}} = 317 \text{ torr}$$

$$\text{For } N_2\text{: } P_2 = 0.200 \text{ atm} \times \frac{1.00 \text{ L}}{3.00 \text{ L}} = 0.0667 \text{ atm; } 0.0667 \text{ atm} \times \frac{760 \text{ torr}}{\text{atm}} = 50.7 \text{ torr}$$

$$P_{total} = P_{H_2} + P_{N_2} = 317 + 50.7 = 368 \text{ torr}$$

31. $PV = nRT,\ \frac{nT}{P} = \frac{V}{R} = \text{constant},\ \frac{n_1T_1}{P_1} = \frac{n_2T_2}{P_2}$; moles × molar mass = mass

$$\frac{n_1(\text{molar mass})T_1}{P_1} = \frac{n_2(\text{molar mass})T_2}{P_2},\quad \frac{\text{mass}_1 \times T_1}{P_1} = \frac{\text{mass}_2 \times T_2}{P_2}$$

$$\text{mass}_2 = \frac{\text{mass}_1 \times T_1P_2}{T_2P_1} = \frac{1.00 \times 10^3 \text{ g} \times 291 \text{ K} \times 650. \text{ psi}}{299 \text{ K} \times 2050. \text{ psi}} = 309 \text{ g}$$

33. $$P = P_{CO_2} = \frac{n_{CO_2}RT}{V} = \frac{\left(22.0 \text{ g} \times \frac{1 \text{ mol}}{44.01 \text{ g}}\right) \times \frac{0.08206 \text{ L atm}}{\text{K mol}} \times 300. \text{ K}}{4.00 \text{ L}} = 3.08 \text{ atm}$$

With air present, the partial pressure of CO_2 will still be 3.08 atm. The total pressure will be the sum of the partial pressures.

$$P_{total} = P_{CO_2} + P_{air} = 3.08 \text{ atm} + \left(740. \text{ torr} \times \frac{1 \text{ atm}}{760 \text{ torr}}\right) = 3.08 + 0.974 = 4.05 \text{ atm}$$

35. $$n = \frac{PV}{RT} = \frac{135 \text{ atm} \times 200.0 \text{ L}}{\frac{0.08206 \text{ L atm}}{\text{K mol}} \times (273 + 24) \text{ K}} = 1.11 \times 10^3 \text{ mol}$$

$$\text{For He: } 1.11 \times 10^3 \text{ mol} \times \frac{4.003 \text{ g He}}{\text{mol}} = 4.44 \times 10^3 \text{ g He}$$

$$\text{For } H_2\text{: } 1.11 \times 10^3 \text{ mol} \times \frac{2.016 \text{ g } H_2}{\text{mol}} = 2.24 \times 10^3 \text{ g } H_2$$

37. $\frac{PV}{nT} = R$; for a gas at two conditions:

$$\frac{P_1V_1}{n_1T_1} = \frac{P_2V_2}{n_2T_2}; \text{ because n and V are constant: } \frac{P_1}{T_1} = \frac{P_2}{T_2}$$

$$T_2 = \frac{P_2T_1}{P_1} = \frac{2500 \text{ torr} \times 294.2 \text{ K}}{758 \text{ torr}} = 970 \text{ K} = 7.0 \times 10^2 \text{ °C}$$

For two-condition problems, units for P and V just need to be the same units for both conditions, not necessarily atm and L. The unit conversions from other P or V units would cancel when applied to both conditions. However, temperature always must be converted to the Kelvin scale. The temperature conversions between other units and Kelvin will not cancel each other.

39. As NO_2 is converted completely into N_2O_4, the moles of gas present will decrease by a factor of one-half (from the 2 : 1 mol ratio in the balanced equation). Using Avogadro's law:

$$\frac{V_1}{n_1} = \frac{V_2}{n_2}, \quad V_2 = V_1 \times \frac{n_2}{n_1} = 25.0 \text{ mL} \times \frac{1}{2} = 12.5 \text{ mL}$$

$N_2O_4(g)$ will occupy one-half the original volume of $NO_2(g)$.

41. PV = nRT, P is constant. $\frac{nT}{V} = \frac{P}{R} = \text{constant}, \quad \frac{n_1T_1}{V_1} = \frac{n_2T_2}{V_2}$

$$\frac{n_2}{n_1} = \frac{T_1V_2}{T_2V_1} = \frac{294 \text{ K}}{335 \text{ K}} \times \frac{4.20 \times 10^3 \text{ m}^3}{4.00 \times 10^3 \text{ m}^3} = 0.921$$

43. a. There are 6 He atoms and 4 Ne atoms, and each flask has the same volume. The He flask has 1.5 times as many atoms of gas present as the Ne flask, so the pressure in the He flask will be 1.5 times greater (assuming a constant temperature).

b. Because the flask volumes are the same, your drawing should have the various atoms equally distributed between the two flasks. So each flask should have 3 He atoms and 2 Ne atoms.

c. After the stopcock is opened, each flask will have 5 total atoms and the pressures will be equal. If six atoms of He gave an initial pressure of $P_{He, initial}$, then 5 total atoms will have a pressure of $5/6 \times P_{He, initial}$.

Using similar reasoning, 4 atoms of Ne gave an initial pressure of $P_{Ne, initial}$, so 5 total atoms will have a pressure of $5/4 \times P_{Ne, initial}$. Summarizing:

$$P_{final} = \frac{5}{6}P_{He, initial} = \frac{5}{4}P_{Ne, initial}$$

d. For the partial pressures, treat each gas separately. For helium, when the stopcock is opened, the six atoms of gas are now distributed over a larger volume. To solve for the final partial pressures, use Boyle's law for each gas.

For He: $P_2 = \dfrac{P_1V_1}{V_2} = P_{He,\ initial} \times \dfrac{X}{2X} = \dfrac{P_{He,\ initial}}{2}$

The partial pressure of helium is exactly halved. The same result occurs with neon so that when the volume is doubled, the partial pressure is halved. Summarizing:

$$P_{He,\ final} = \frac{P_{He,\ initial}}{2};\ P_{Ne,\ final} = \frac{P_{Ne,\ initial}}{2}$$

45. $P_{He} + P_{H_2O} = 1.00\ \text{atm} = 760.\ \text{torr} = P_{He} + 23.8\ \text{torr},\ P_{He} = 736\ \text{torr}$

$n_{He} = 0.586\ \text{g} \times \dfrac{1\ \text{mol}}{4.003\ \text{g}} = 0.146\ \text{mol He}$

$$V = \frac{n_{He}RT}{P_{He}} = \frac{0.146\ \text{mol} \times \dfrac{0.08206\ \text{L atm}}{\text{K mol}} \times 298\ \text{K}}{736\ \text{torr} \times \dfrac{1\ \text{atm}}{760\ \text{torr}}} = 3.69\ \text{L}$$

47. a. Mole fraction $CH_4 = \chi_{CH_4} = \dfrac{P_{CH_4}}{P_{total}} = \dfrac{0.175\ \text{atm}}{0.175\ \text{atm} + 0.250\ \text{atm}} = 0.412$

$\chi_{O_2} = 1.000 - 0.412 = 0.588$

b. $PV = nRT,\ n_{total} = \dfrac{P_{total} \times V}{RT} = \dfrac{0.425\ \text{atm} \times 10.5\ \text{L}}{\dfrac{0.08206\ \text{L atm}}{\text{K mol}} \times 338\ \text{K}} = 0.161\ \text{mol}$

c. $\chi_{CH_4} = \dfrac{n_{CH_4}}{n_{total}},\ n_{CH_4} = \chi_{CH_4} \times n_{total} = 0.412 \times 0.161\ \text{mol} = 6.63 \times 10^{-2}\ \text{mol } CH_4$

$6.63 \times 10^{-2}\ \text{mol } CH_4 \times \dfrac{16.04\ \text{g } CH_4}{\text{mol } CH_4} = 1.06\ \text{g } CH_4$

$n_{O_2} = 0.588 \times 0.161\ \text{mol} = 9.47 \times 10^{-2}\ \text{mol } O_2;\ 9.47 \times 10^{-2}\ \text{mol } O_2 \times \dfrac{32.00\ \text{g } O_2}{\text{mol } O_2}$

$= 3.03\ \text{g } O_2$

49. We can use the ideal gas law to calculate the partial pressure of each gas or to calculate the total pressure. There will be less math if we calculate the total pressure from the ideal gas law.

$$n_{O_2} = 1.5 \times 10^2 \text{ mg } O_2 \times \frac{1 \text{ g}}{1000 \text{ mg}} \times \frac{1 \text{ mol } O_2}{32.00 \text{ g } O_2} = 4.7 \times 10^{-3} \text{ mol } O_2$$

$$n_{NH_3} = 5.0 \times 10^{21} \text{ molecules } NH_3 \times \frac{1 \text{ mol } NH_3}{6.022 \times 10^{23} \text{ molecules } NH_3} = 8.3 \times 10^{-3} \text{ mol } NH_3$$

$$n_{total} = n_{N_2} + n_{O_3} + n_{NH_3} = 5.0 \times 10^{-2} + 4.7 \times 10^{-3} + 8.3 \times 10^{-3} = 6.3 \times 10^{-2} \text{ mol total}$$

$$P_{total} = \frac{n_{total} \times RT}{V} = \frac{6.3 \times 10^{-2} \text{ mol} \times \frac{0.08206 \text{ L atm}}{\text{K mol}} \times 273 \text{ K}}{1.0 \text{ L}} = 1.4 \text{ atm}$$

$$P_{N_2} = \chi_{N_2} \times P_{total}, \ \chi_{N_2} = \frac{n_{N_2}}{n_{total}}; \ P_{N_2} = \frac{5.0 \times 10^{-2} \text{ mol}}{6.3 \times 10^{-2} \text{ mol}} \times 1.4 \text{ atm} = 1.1 \text{ atm}$$

$$P_{O_2} = \frac{4.7 \times 10^{-3}}{6.3 \times 10^{-2}} \times 1.4 \text{ atm} = 0.10 \text{ atm}; \ P_{NH_3} = \frac{8.3 \times 10^{-3}}{6.3 \times 10^{-2}} \times 1.4 \text{ atm} = 0.18 \text{ atm}$$

Gas Density, Molar Mass, and Reaction Stoichiometry

51. Rigid container: As temperature is increased, the gas molecules move with a faster average velocity. This results in more frequent and more forceful collisions, resulting in an increase in pressure. Density = mass/volume; the moles of gas are constant, and the volume of the container is constant, so density in this case must be temperature-independent (density is constant).

Flexible container: The flexible container is a constant-pressure container. Therefore, the final internal pressure will be unaffected by an increase in temperature. The density of the gas, however, will be affected because the container volume is affected. As T increases, there is an immediate increase in P inside the container. The container expands its volume to reduce the internal pressure back to the external pressure. We have the same mass of gas in a larger volume. Gas density will decrease in the flexible container as T increases.

53. Out of 100.0 g of compound, there are:

$$87.4 \text{ g N} \times \frac{1 \text{ mol N}}{14.01 \text{ g N}} = 6.24 \text{ mol N}; \ \frac{6.24}{6.24} = 1.00$$

$$12.6 \text{ g H} \times \frac{1 \text{ mol H}}{1.008 \text{ g H}} = 12.5 \text{ mol H}; \ \frac{12.5}{6.24} = 2.00$$

Empirical formula is NH_2. P × (molar mass) = dRT, where d = density.

$$\text{Molar mass} = \frac{dRT}{P} = \frac{\frac{0.977 \text{ g}}{\text{L}} \times \frac{0.08206 \text{ L atm}}{\text{K mol}} \times 373 \text{ K}}{710. \text{ torr} \times \frac{1 \text{ atm}}{760 \text{ torr}}} = 32.0 \text{ g/mol}$$

Empirical formula mass of NH_2 = 16.0 g. Therefore, the molecular formula is N_2H_4.

55. If Be^{3+}, the formula is $Be(C_5H_7O_2)_3$ and molar mass ≈ 13.5 + 15(12) + 21(1) + 6(16) = 311 g/mol. If Be^{2+}, the formula is $Be(C_5H_7O_2)_2$ and molar mass ≈ 9.0 + 10(12) + 14(1) + 4(16) = 207 g/mol.

Data set I (molar mass = dRT/P and d = mass/V):

$$\text{molar mass} = \frac{\text{mass} \times RT}{PV} = \frac{0.2022 \text{ g} \times \frac{0.08206 \text{ L atm}}{\text{K mol}} \times 286 \text{ K}}{(765.2 \text{ torr} \times \frac{1 \text{ atm}}{760 \text{ torr}}) \times (22.6 \times 10^{-3} \text{ L})} = 209 \text{ g/mol}$$

Data set II:

$$\text{molar mass} = \frac{\text{mass} \times RT}{PV} = \frac{0.2224 \text{ g} \times \frac{0.08206 \text{ L atm}}{\text{K mol}} \times 290. \text{ K}}{(764.6 \text{ torr} \times \frac{1 \text{ atm}}{760 \text{ torr}}) \times (26.0 \times 10^{-3} \text{ L})} = 202 \text{ g/mol}$$

These results are close to the expected value of 207 g/mol for $Be(C_5H_7O_2)_2$. Thus we conclude from these data that beryllium is a divalent element with an atomic weight (mass) of 9.0 g/mol.

57. $$\text{Molar mass} = \frac{dRT}{P} = \frac{\frac{0.70902 \text{ g}}{\text{L}} \times \frac{0.08206 \text{ L atm}}{\text{K mol}} \times 273.2 \text{ K}}{1.000 \text{ atm}} = 15.90 \text{ g/mol}$$

15.90 g/mol is the average molar mass of the mixture of methane and helium. Assume 100.00 mol of total gas present, and let x = mol of CH_4 in the 100.00 mol mixture. This value of x is also equal to the volume percentage of CH_4 in 100.00 L of mixture because T and P are constant.

$$15.90 = \frac{x(16.04) + (100.00 - x)(4.003)}{100.00}, \quad 1590. = (16.04)x + 400.3 - (4.003)x$$

1190. = $(12.04)x$, x = 98.84% CH_4 by volume; % He = 100.00 − x = 1.16% He by volume

59. $$n_{H_2} = \frac{PV}{RT} = \frac{1.0\text{ atm} \times \left[4800\text{ m}^3 \times \left(\frac{100\text{ cm}}{\text{m}}\right)^3 \times \frac{1\text{ L}}{1000\text{ cm}^3}\right]}{\frac{0.08206\text{ L atm}}{\text{K mol}} \times 273\text{ K}} = 2.1 \times 10^5\text{ mol}$$

2.1×10^5 mol H_2 are in the balloon. This is 80.% of the total amount of H_2 that had to be generated:

$$0.80(\text{total mol } H_2) = 2.1 \times 10^5,\quad \text{total mol } H_2 = 2.6 \times 10^5\text{ mol } H_2$$

$$2.6 \times 10^5\text{ mol } H_2 \times \frac{1\text{ mol Fe}}{\text{mol } H_2} \times \frac{55.85\text{ g Fe}}{\text{mol Fe}} = 1.5 \times 10^7\text{ g Fe}$$

$$2.6 \times 10^5\text{ mol } H_2 \times \frac{1\text{ mol } H_2SO_4}{\text{mol } H_2} \times \frac{98.09\text{ g } H_2SO_4}{\text{mol } H_2SO_4} \times \frac{100\text{ g reagent}}{98\text{ g } H_2SO_4} = 2.6 \times 10^7\text{ g of 98\% sulfuric acid}$$

61. Because P and T are constant, V and n are directly proportional. The balanced equation requires 2 L of H_2 to react with 1 L of CO (2 : 1 volume ratio due to 2 : 1 mole ratio in the balanced equation). The actual volume ratio present in 1 minute is 16.0 L/25.0 L = 0.640 (0.640 : 1). Because the actual volume ratio present is smaller than the required volume ratio, H_2 is the limiting reactant. The volume of CH_3OH produced at STP will be one-half the volume of H_2 reacted due to the 1 : 2 mole ratio in the balanced equation. In 1 minute, 16.0 L/2 = 8.00 L CH_3OH are produced (theoretical yield).

$$n_{CH_3OH} = \frac{PV}{RT} = \frac{1.00\text{ atm} \times 8.00\text{ L}}{\frac{0.08206\text{ L atm}}{\text{K mol}} \times 273\text{ K}} = 0.357\text{ mol } CH_3OH\text{ in 1 minute}$$

$$0.357\text{ mol } CH_3OH \times \frac{32.04\text{ g } CH_3OH}{\text{mol } CH_3OH} = 11.4\text{ g } CH_3OH\text{ (theoretical yield per minute)}$$

$$\text{Percent yield} = \frac{\text{actual yield}}{\text{theoretical yield}} \times 100 = \frac{5.30\text{ g}}{11.4\text{ g}} \times 100 = 46.5\%\text{ yield}$$

63. $$150\text{ g } (CH_3)_2N_2H_2 \times \frac{1\text{ mol } (CH_3)_2N_2H_2}{60.10\text{ g}} \times \frac{3\text{ mol } N_2}{\text{mol } (CH_3)_2N_2H_2} = 7.5\text{ mol } N_2\text{ produced}$$

$$P_{N_2} = \frac{nRT}{V} = \frac{7.5\text{ mol} \times \frac{0.08206\text{ L atm}}{\text{K mol}} \times 300.\text{ K}}{250\text{ L}} = 0.74\text{ atm}$$

We could do a similar calculation for P_{H_2O} and P_{CO_2} and then calculate P_{total} (= $P_{N_2} + P_{H_2O} + P_{CO_2}$). Or we can recognize that 9 total moles of gaseous products form for every mole of $(CH_3)_2N_2H_2$ reacted. This is three times the moles of N_2 produced. Therefore, P_{total} will be three times larger than P_{N_2}. $P_{total} = 3 \times P_{N_2} = 3 \times 0.74\text{ atm} = 2.2\text{ atm}$.

65. $2\ NaClO_3(s) \rightarrow 2\ NaCl(s) + 3\ O_2(g)$

$P_{total} = P_{O_2} + P_{H_2O}$, $P_{O_2} = P_{total} - P_{H_2O} = 734\text{ torr} - 19.8\text{ torr} = 714\text{ torr}$

$$n_{O_2} = \frac{P_{O_2} \times V}{RT} = \frac{\left(714\text{ torr} \times \frac{1\text{ atm}}{760\text{ torr}}\right) \times 0.0572\text{ L}}{\frac{0.08206\text{ L atm}}{\text{K mol}} \times (273 + 22)\text{ K}} = 2.22 \times 10^{-3}\text{ mol } O_2$$

$$\text{Mass } NaClO_3 \text{ decomposed} = 2.22 \times 10^{-3}\text{ mol } O_2 \times \frac{2\text{ mol } NaClO_3}{3\text{ mol } O_2} \times \frac{106.44\text{ g } NaClO_3}{\text{mol } NaClO_3}$$

$$= 0.158\text{ g } NaClO_3$$

$$\text{Mass \% } NaClO_3 = \frac{0.158\text{ g}}{0.8765\text{ g}} \times 100 = 18.0\%$$

67. $P_{total} = P_{N_2} + P_{H_2O}$, $P_{N_2} = 726\text{ torr} - 23.8\text{ torr} = 702\text{ torr H } \frac{1\text{ atm}}{760\text{ torr}} = 0.924\text{ atm}$

$$n_{N_2} = \frac{P_{N_2} \times V}{RT} = \frac{0.924\text{ atm} \times 31.8 \times 10^{-3}\text{ L}}{\frac{0.08206\text{ L atm}}{\text{K mol}} \times 298\text{ K}} = 1.20 \times 10^{-3}\text{ mol } N_2$$

$$\text{Mass of N in compound} = 1.20 \times 10^{-3}\text{ mol } N_2 \times \frac{28.02\text{ g } N_2}{\text{mol}} = 3.36 \times 10^{-2}\text{ g nitrogen}$$

$$\text{Mass \% N} = \frac{3.36 \times 10^{-2}\text{ g}}{0.253\text{ g}} \times 100 = 13.3\%\text{ N}$$

69. For NH_3: $P_2 = \frac{P_1V_1}{V_2} = 0.500\text{ atm} \times \frac{2.00\text{ L}}{3.00\text{ L}} = 0.333\text{ atm}$

For O_2: $P_2 = \frac{P_1V_1}{V_2} = 1.50\text{ atm} \times \frac{1.00\text{ L}}{3.00\text{ L}} = 0.500\text{ atm}$

After the stopcock is opened, V and T will be constant, so $P \propto n$. The balanced equation requires:

$$\frac{n_{O_2}}{n_{NH_3}} = \frac{P_{O_2}}{P_{NH_3}} = \frac{5}{4} = 1.25$$

The actual ratio present is: $\frac{P_{O_2}}{P_{NH_3}} = \frac{0.500\text{ atm}}{0.333\text{ atm}} = 1.50$

The actual ratio is larger than the required ratio, so NH_3 in the denominator is limiting. Because equal moles of NO will be produced as NH_3 reacted, the partial pressure of NO produced is 0.333 atm (the same as P_{NH_3} reacted).

71. $2\ NH_3(g) \rightarrow N_2(g) + 3\ H_2(g)$; as reactants are converted into products, we go from 2 moles of gaseous reactants to 4 moles of gaseous products (1 mol N_2 + 3 mol H_2). Because the moles of gas doubles as reactants are converted into products, the volume of the gases will double (at constant P and T).

$PV = nRT,\ P = \left(\frac{RT}{V}\right)n = (\text{constant})n$; pressure is directly related to n at constant T and V.

As the reaction occurs, the moles of gas will double, so the pressure will double. Because 1 mol of N_2 is produced for every 2 mol of NH_3 reacted, $P_{N_2} = 1/2\ P^{o}_{NH_3}$. Owing to the 3 to 2 mole ratio in the balanced equation, $P_{H_2} = 3/2\ P^{o}_{NH_3}$.

Note: $P_{total} = P_{H_2} + P_{N_2} = 3/2\ P^{o}_{NH_3} + 1/2\ P^{o}_{NH_3} = 2\ P^{o}_{NH_3}$. As we said earlier, the total pressure doubles as reactants are completely converted into products for this reaction.

Kinetic Molecular Theory and Real Gases

73. The number of gas particles is constant, so at constant moles of gas, either a temperature change or a pressure change results in the smaller volume. If the temperature is constant, an increase in the external pressure would cause the volume to decrease. Gases are mostly empty space so gases are easily compressible.

If the pressure is constant, a decrease in temperature would cause the volume to decrease. As the temperature is lowered, the gas particles move with a slower average velocity and don't collide with the container walls as frequently and as forcefully. As a result, the internal pressure decreases. In order to keep the pressure constant, the volume of the container must decrease in order to increase the gas particle collisions per unit area.

75. V, T, and P are all constant, so n must be constant. Because we have equal moles of gas in each container, gas B molecules must be heavier than gas A molecules.

a. Both gas samples have the same number of molecules present (n is constant).

b. Because T is constant, KE_{ave} must be the same for both gases ($KE_{ave} = 3/2\ RT$).

c. The lighter gas A molecules will have the faster average velocity.

d. The heavier gas B molecules do collide more forcefully, but gas A molecules, with the faster average velocity, collide more frequently. The end result is that P is constant between the two containers.

77. $(KE)_{avg}$ = 3/2 RT; KE depends only on temperature. At each temperature CH_4 and N_2 will have the same average KE. For energy units of joules (J), use R = 8.3145 J K^{-1} mol^{-1}. To determine average KE per molecule, divide by Avogadro's number, 6.022 × 10^{23} molecules/mol.

At 273 K: $(KE)_{avg} = \frac{3}{2} \times \frac{8.3145 \text{ J}}{\text{K mol}} \times 273 \text{ K} = 3.40 \times 10^3 \text{ J/mol} = 5.65 \times 10^{-21} \text{ J/molecule}$

At 546 K: $(KE)_{avg} = \frac{3}{2} \times \frac{8.3145 \text{ J}}{\text{K mol}} \times 546 \text{ K} = 6.81 \times 10^3 \text{ J/mol} = 1.13 \times 10^{-20} \text{ J/molecule}$

79. No; the numbers calculated in Exercise 77 are the average kinetic energies at the various temperatures. At each temperature, there is a distribution of energies. Similarly, the numbers calculated in Exercise 78 are a special kind of average velocity. There is a distribution of velocities as shown in Figs. 5.15 to 5.17 of the text. Note that the major reason there is a distribution of kinetic energies is because there is a distribution of velocities for any gas sample at some temperature.

81. a. They will all have the same average kinetic energy because they are all at the same temperature. Average kinetic energy depends only on temperature.

b. Flask C; at constant T, $u_{rms} \propto (1/M)^{1/2}$. In general, the lighter the gas molecules, the greater is the root mean square velocity (at constant T).

c. Flask A: collision frequency is proportional to average velocity × n/V (as the average velocity doubles, the number of collisions will double, and as the number of molecules in the container doubles, the number of collisions again doubles). At constant T and V, n is proportional to P, and average velocity is proportional to $(1/M)^{1/2}$. We use these relationships and the data in the exercise to determine the following relative values.

	n (relative)	u_{avg} (relative)	Coll. Freq. (relative) = n × u_{avg}
A	1.0	1.0	1.0
B	0.33	1.0	0.33
C	0.13	3.7	0.48

83. Graham's law of effusion: $\frac{\text{Rate}_1}{\text{Rate}_2} = \left(\frac{M_2}{M_1}\right)^{1/2}$

Let Freon-12 = gas 1 and Freon-11 = gas 2:

$$\frac{1.07}{1.00} = \left(\frac{137.4}{M_1}\right)^{1/2}, \quad 1.14 = \frac{137.4}{M_1}, \quad M_1 = 121 \text{ g/mol}$$

The molar mass of CF_2Cl_2 is equal to 121 g/mol, so Freon-12 is CF_2Cl_2.

85. $\frac{\text{Rate}_1}{\text{Rate}_2} = \left(\frac{M_2}{M_1}\right)^{1/2}$; $\text{rate}_1 = \frac{24.0 \text{ mL}}{\text{min}}$; $\text{rate}_2 = \frac{47.8 \text{ mL}}{\text{min}}$; $M_2 = \frac{16.04 \text{ g}}{\text{mol}}$; $M_1 = ?$

$$\frac{24.0}{47.8} = \left(\frac{16.04}{M_1}\right)^{1/2} = 0.502,\ 16.04 = (0.502)^2 \times M_1,\ M_1 = \frac{16.04}{0.252} = \frac{63.7 \text{ g}}{\text{mol}}$$

87. a. $PV = nRT$

$$P = \frac{nRT}{V} = \frac{0.5000 \text{ mol} \times \frac{0.08206 \text{ L atm}}{\text{K mol}} \times (25.0 + 273.2) \text{ K}}{1.0000 \text{ L}} = 12.24 \text{ atm}$$

b. $\left[P + a\left(\frac{n}{V}\right)^2\right](V - nb) = nRT$; for N_2: $a = 1.39 \text{ atm L}^2/\text{mol}^2$ and $b = 0.0391 \text{ L/mol}$

$$\left[P + 1.39\left(\frac{0.5000}{1.0000}\right)^2 \text{ atm}\right](1.0000 \text{ L} - 0.5000 \times 0.0391 \text{ L}) = 12.24 \text{ L atm}$$

$$(P + 0.348 \text{ atm})(0.9805 \text{ L}) = 12.24 \text{ L atm}$$

$$P = \frac{12.24 \text{ L atm}}{0.9805 \text{ L}} - 0.348 \text{ atm} = 12.48 - 0.348 = 12.13 \text{ atm}$$

c. The ideal gas law is high by 0.11 atm, or $\frac{0.11}{12.13} \times 100 = 0.91\%$.

89. The kinetic molecular theory assumes that gas particles do not exert forces on each other and that gas particles are volumeless. Real gas particles do exert attractive forces for each other, and real gas particles do have volumes. A gas behaves most ideally at low pressures and high temperatures. The effect of attractive forces is minimized at high temperatures because the gas particles are moving very rapidly. At low pressure, the container volume is relatively large (P and V are inversely related), so the volume of the container taken up by the gas particles is negligible.

91. The pressure measured for real gases is too low compared to ideal gases. This is due to the attractions gas particles do have for each other; these attractions "hold" them back from hitting the container walls as forcefully. To make up for this slight decrease in pressure for real gases, a factor is added to the measured pressure. The measured volume is too large. A fraction of the space of the container volume is taken up by the volume of the molecules themselves. Therefore, the actual volume available to real gas molecules is slightly less than the container volume. A term is subtracted from the container volume to correct for the volume taken up by real gas molecules.

93. The values of a are: H_2, $\frac{0.244 \text{ atm L}^2}{\text{mol}^2}$; CO_2, 3.59; N_2, 1.39; CH_4, 2.25

Because a is a measure of intermolecular attractions, the attractions are greatest for CO_2.

95. $$u_{rms} = \left(\frac{3RT}{M}\right)^{1/2} = \left[\frac{3\left(\frac{8.3145 \text{ kg m}^2}{\text{s}^2 \text{ K mol}}\right)(227 + 273) \text{ K}}{28.02 \times 10^{-3} \text{ kg/mol}}\right]^{1/2} = 667 \text{ m/s}$$

$$u_{mp} = \left(\frac{2RT}{M}\right)^{1/2} = \left[\frac{2\left(\frac{8.3145 \text{ kg m}^2}{\text{s}^2 \text{ K mol}}\right)(500. \text{ K})}{28.02 \times 10^{-3} \text{ kg/mol}}\right]^{1/2} = 545 \text{ m/s}$$

$$u_{avg} = \left(\frac{8RT}{\pi M}\right)^{1/2} = \left[\frac{8\left(\frac{8.3145 \text{ kg m}^2}{\text{s}^2 \text{ K mol}}\right)(500. \text{ K})}{\pi(28.02 \times 10^{-3} \text{ kg/mol})}\right]^{1/2} = 615 \text{ m/s}$$

97. The force per impact is proportional to $\Delta(mu) = 2mu$. Because $m \propto M$, the molar mass, and $u \propto (1/M)^{1/2}$ at constant T, the force per impact at constant T is proportional to $M \times (1/M)^{1/2} = \sqrt{M}$.

$$\frac{\text{Impact force } (H_2)}{\text{Impact force (He)}} = \sqrt{\frac{M_{H_2}}{M_{He}}} = \sqrt{\frac{2.016}{4.003}} = 0.7097$$

99. $\Delta(mu) = 2mu$ = change in momentum per impact. Because m is proportional to M, the molar mass, and u is proportional to $(T/M)^{1/2}$:

$$\Delta(mu)_{O_2} \propto 2M_{O_2}\left(\frac{T}{M_{O_2}}\right)^{1/2} \text{ and } \Delta(mu)_{He} \propto 2M_{He}\left(\frac{T}{M_{He}}\right)^{1/2}$$

$$\frac{\Delta(mu)_{O_2}}{\Delta(mu)_{He}} = \frac{2M_{O_2}\left(\frac{T}{M_{O_2}}\right)^{1/2}}{2M_{He}\left(\frac{T}{M_{He}}\right)^{1/2}} = \frac{M_{O_2}}{M_{He}}\left(\frac{M_{He}}{M_{O_2}}\right)^{1/2} = \frac{31.998}{4.003}\left(\frac{4.003}{31.998}\right)^{1/2} = 2.827$$

The change in momentum per impact is 2.827 times larger for O_2 molecules than for He atoms.

$$Z_A = A\frac{N}{V}\left(\frac{RT}{2\pi M}\right)^{1/2} = \text{collision rate}$$

$$\frac{Z_{O_2}}{Z_{He}} = \frac{A\left(\frac{N}{V}\right)\left(\frac{RT}{2\pi M_{O_2}}\right)^{1/2}}{A\left(\frac{N}{V}\right)\left(\frac{RT}{2\pi M_{He}}\right)^{1/2}} = \frac{\left(\frac{1}{M_{O_2}}\right)^{1/2}}{\left(\frac{1}{M_{He}}\right)^{1/2}} = 0.3537;\ \frac{Z_{He}}{Z_{O_2}} = 2.827$$

There are 2.827 times as many impacts per second for He as for O_2.

101. Intermolecular collision frequency = Z = $4\frac{N}{V}d^2\left(\frac{\pi RT}{M}\right)^{1/2}$, where d = diameter of He atom

$$\frac{n}{V} = \frac{P}{RT} = \frac{3.0\text{ atm}}{\frac{0.08206\text{ L atm}}{\text{K mol}} \times 300.\text{ K}} = 0.12\text{ mol/L}$$

$$\frac{N}{V} = \frac{0.12\text{ mol}}{\text{L}} \times \frac{6.022 \times 10^{23}\text{ molecules}}{\text{mol}} \times \frac{1000\text{ L}}{\text{m}^3} = \frac{7.2 \times 10^{25}\text{ molecules}}{\text{m}^3}$$

$$Z = 4 \times \frac{7.2 \times 10^{25}\text{ molecules}}{\text{m}^3} \times (50. \times 10^{-12}\text{ m})^2 \times \left(\frac{\pi(8.3145)(300.)}{4.00 \times 10^{-3}}\right)^{1/2}$$

$$= 1.0 \times 10^9\text{ collisions/s}$$

$$\text{Mean free path} = \lambda = \frac{u_{avg}}{Z};\ u_{avg} = \left(\frac{8\,RT}{\pi M}\right)^{1/2} = 1260\text{ m/s};\ \lambda = \frac{1260\text{ m/s}}{1.0 \times 10^9\text{ s}^{-1}} = 1.3 \times 10^{-6}\text{ m}$$

Atmospheric Chemistry

103. a. If we have 1.0×10^6 L of air, then there are 3.0×10^2 L of CO.

$$P_{CO} = \chi_{CO}P_{total};\ \chi_{CO} = \frac{V_{CO}}{V_{total}}\text{ because V \% n};\ P_{CO} = \frac{3.0 \times 10^2}{1.0 \times 10^6} \times 628\text{ torr} = 0.19\text{ torr}$$

b. $n_{CO} = \frac{P_{CO}V}{RT}$; Assuming 1.0 m^3 air, 1 m^3 = 1000 L:

$$n_{CO} = \frac{\frac{0.19}{760}\text{ atm} \times (1.0 \times 10^3\text{ L})}{\frac{0.08206\text{ L atm}}{\text{K mol}} \times 273\text{ K}} = 1.1 \times 10^{-2}\text{ mol CO}$$

$$1.1 \times 10^{-2}\text{ mol} \times \frac{6.02 \times 10^{23}\text{ molecules}}{\text{mol}} = 6.6 \times 10^{21}\text{ CO molecules in 1.0 m}^3\text{ of air}$$

c. $$\frac{6.6 \times 10^{21}\text{ molecules}}{\text{m}^3} \times \left(\frac{1\text{ m}}{100\text{ cm}}\right)^3 = \frac{6.6 \times 10^{15}\text{ molecules CO}}{\text{cm}^3}$$

105. For benzene:

$$89.6 \times 10^{-9}\text{ g} \times \frac{1\text{ mol}}{78.11\text{ g}} = 1.15 \times 10^{-9}\text{ mol benzene}$$

$$V_{\text{benzene}} = \frac{n_{\text{benzene}}RT}{P} = \frac{1.15 \times 10^{-9}\text{ mol} \times \frac{0.08206\text{ L atm}}{\text{K mol}} \times 296\text{ K}}{748\text{ torr} \times \frac{1\text{ atm}}{760\text{ torr}}} = 2.84 \times 10^{-8}\text{ L}$$

$$\text{Mixing ratio} = \frac{2.84 \times 10^{-8}\text{ L}}{3.00\text{ L}} \times 10^6 = 9.47 \times 10^{-3}\text{ ppmv}$$

$$\text{or ppbv} = \frac{\text{vol. of X} \times 10^9}{\text{total vol.}} = \frac{2.84 \times 10^{-8}\text{ L}}{3.00\text{ L}} \times 10^9 = 9.47\text{ ppbv}$$

$$\frac{1.15 \times 10^{-9}\text{ mol benzene}}{3.00\text{ L}} \times \frac{1\text{ L}}{1000\text{ cm}^3} \times \frac{6.022 \times 10^{23}\text{ molecules}}{\text{mol}}$$

$$= 2.31 \times 10^{11}\text{ molecules benzene/cm}^3$$

For toluene:

$$153 \times 10^{-9}\text{ g } C_7H_8 \times \frac{1\text{ mol}}{92.13\text{ g}} = 1.66 \times 10^{-9}\text{ mol toluene}$$

$$V_{\text{toluene}} = \frac{n_{\text{toluene}}RT}{P} = \frac{1.66 \times 10^{-9}\text{ mol} \times \frac{0.08206\text{ L atm}}{\text{K mol}} \times 296\text{ K}}{748\text{ torr} \times \frac{1\text{ atm}}{760\text{ torr}}} = 4.10 \times 10^{-8}\text{ L}$$

$$\text{Mixing ratio} = \frac{4.10 \times 10^{-8}\text{ L}}{3.00\text{ L}} \times 10^6 = 1.37 \times 10^{-2}\text{ ppmv (or 13.7 ppbv)}$$

$$\frac{1.66 \times 10^{-9}\text{ mol toluene}}{3.00\text{ L}} \times \frac{1\text{ L}}{1000\text{ cm}^3} \times \frac{6.022 \times 10^{23}\text{ molecules}}{\text{mol}}$$

$$= 3.33 \times 10^{11}\text{ molecules toluene/cm}^3$$

Additional Exercises

107. Processes a, c, and d will all result in a doubling of the pressure. Process a has the effect of halving the volume, which would double the pressure (Boyle's law). Process c doubles the pressure because the absolute temperature is doubled (from 200. K to 400. K). Process d doubles the pressure because the moles of gas are doubled (28 g N_2 is 1 mol of N_2). Process b won't double the pressure since the absolute temperature is not doubled (303 K to 333 K).

109. $0.050 \text{ mL} \times \frac{1.149 \text{ g}}{\text{mL}} \times \frac{1 \text{ mol } O_2}{32.0 \text{ g}} = 1.8 \times 10^{-3} \text{ mol } O_2$

$$V = \frac{nRT}{P} = \frac{1.8 \times 10^{-3} \text{ mol} \times \frac{0.08206 \text{ L atm}}{\text{K mol}} \times 310. \text{ K}}{1.0 \text{ atm}} = 4.6 \times 10^{-2} \text{ L} = 46 \text{ mL}$$

111. PV = nRT, V and T are constant. $\frac{P_1}{n_1} = \frac{P_2}{n_2}$ or $\frac{P_1}{P_2} = \frac{n_1}{n_2}$

When V and T are constant, then pressure is directly proportional to moles of gas present, and pressure ratios are identical to mole ratios.

At 25°C: $2\ H_2(g) + O_2(g) \rightarrow 2\ H_2O(l)$, $H_2O(l)$ is produced at 25°C.

The balanced equation requires 2 mol H_2 for every mol O_2 reacted. The same ratio (2 : 1) holds true for pressure units. The actual pressure ratio present is 2 atm H_2 to 3 atm O_2, well below the required 2 : 1 ratio. Therefore, H_2 is the limiting reagent. The only gas present at 25°C after the reaction goes to completion will be the excess O_2.

$$P_{O_2} \text{ (reacted)} = 2.00 \text{ atm } H_2 \times \frac{1 \text{ atm } O_2}{2 \text{ atm } H_2} = 1.00 \text{ atm } O_2$$

$$P_{O_2} \text{ (excess)} = P_{O_2} \text{ (initial)} - P_{O_2} \text{ (reacted)} = 3.00 \text{ atm} - 1.00 \text{ atm} = 2.00 \text{ atm } O_2 = P_{total}$$

At 125°C: $2\ H_2(g) + O_2(g) \rightarrow 2\ H_2O(g)$, $H_2O(g)$ is produced at 125°C.

The major difference in the problem is that gaseous H_2O is now a product (instead of liquid H_2O), which will increase the total pressure because an additional gas is present.

$$P_{H_2O} \text{ (produced)} = 2.00 \text{ atm } H_2 \times \frac{2 \text{ atm } H_2O}{2 \text{ atm } H_2} = 2.00 \text{ atm } H_2O$$

$$P_{total} = P_{O_2} \text{ (excess)} + P_{H_2O} \text{ (produced)} = 2.00 \text{ atm } O_2 + 2.00 \text{ atm } H_2O = 4.00 \text{ atm}$$

113. $Mn(s) + x\,HCl(g) \rightarrow MnCl_x(s) + \frac{x}{2}H_2(g)$

$$n_{H_2} = \frac{PV}{RT} = \frac{0.951\text{ atm} \times 3.22\text{ L}}{\frac{0.08206\text{ L atm}}{\text{K mol}} \times 373\text{ K}} = 0.100\text{ mol }H_2$$

$$\text{Mol Cl in compound} = \text{mol HCl} = 0.100\text{ mol }H_2 \times \frac{x\text{ mol Cl}}{\frac{x}{2}\text{ mol }H_2} = 0.200\text{ mol Cl}$$

$$\frac{\text{Mol Cl}}{\text{Mol Mn}} = \frac{0.200\text{ mol Cl}}{2.747\text{ g Mn} \times \frac{1\text{ mol Mn}}{54.94\text{ g Mn}}} = \frac{0.200\text{ mol Cl}}{0.05000\text{ mol Mn}} = 4.00$$

The formula of compound is $MnCl_4$.

115. At constant T and P, Avogadro's law applies; that is, equal volumes contain equal moles of molecules. In terms of balanced equations, we can say that mole ratios and volume ratios between the various reactants and products will be equal to each other. $Br_2 + 3\,F_2 \rightarrow 2\,X$; 2 moles of X must contain 2 moles of Br and 6 moles of F; X must have the formula BrF_3 for a balanced equation.

117. PV = nRT, V and T are constant. $\frac{P_1}{n_1} = \frac{P_2}{n_2}, \frac{P_2}{P_1} = \frac{n_2}{n_1}$

We will do this limiting-reagent problem using an alternative method than described in Chapter 3. Let's calculate the partial pressure of C_3H_3N that can be produced from each of the starting materials assuming each reactant is limiting. The reactant that produces the smallest amount of product will run out first and is the limiting reagent.

$$P_{C_3H_3N} = 0.500\text{ MPa} \times \frac{2\text{ MPa }C_3H_3N}{2\text{ MPa }C_3H_6} = 0.500\text{ MPa if }C_3H_6\text{ is limiting}$$

$$P_{C_3H_3N} = 0.800\text{ MPa} \times \frac{2\text{ MPa }C_3H_3N}{2\text{ MPa }NH_3} = 0.800\text{ MPa if }NH_3\text{ is limiting}$$

$$P_{C_3H_3N} = 1.500\text{ MPa} \times \frac{2\text{ MPa }C_3H_3N}{3\text{ MPa }O_2} = 1.000\text{ MPa if }O_2\text{ is limiting}$$

C_3H_6 is limiting. Although more product could be produced from NH_3 and O_2, there is only enough C_3H_6 to produce 0.500 MPa of C_3H_3N. The partial pressure of C_3H_3N in atmospheres after the reaction is:

$$0.500 \times 10^6 \text{ Pa} \times \frac{1 \text{ atm}}{1.013 \times 10^5 \text{ Pa}} = 4.94 \text{ atm}$$

$$n = \frac{PV}{RT} = \frac{4.94 \text{ atm} \times 150. \text{ L}}{\frac{0.08206 \text{ L atm}}{\text{K mol}} \times 298 \text{ K}} = 30.3 \text{ mol } C_3H_3N$$

$$30.3 \text{ mol} \times \frac{53.06 \text{ g}}{\text{mol}} = 1.61 \times 10^3 \text{ g } C_3H_3N \text{ can be produced.}$$

119. $P_{total} = P_{H_2} + P_{H_2O}$, $1.032 \text{ atm} = P_{H_2} + 32 \text{ torr} \times \frac{1 \text{ atm}}{760 \text{ torr}}$, $1.032 - 0.042 = 0.990 \text{ atm} = P_{H_2}$

$$n_{H_2} = \frac{P_{H_2}V}{RT} = \frac{0.990 \text{ atm} \times 0.240 \text{ L}}{\frac{0.08206 \text{ L atm}}{\text{K mol}} \times 303 \text{ K}} = 9.56 \times 10^{-3} \text{ mol } H_2$$

$$9.56 \times 10^{-3} \text{ mol } H_2 \times \frac{1 \text{ mol Zn}}{\text{mol } H_2} \times \frac{65.38 \text{ g Zn}}{\text{mol Zn}} = 0.625 \text{ g Zn}$$

121. $P_1V_1 = P_2V_2$; the total volume is 1.00 L + 1.00 L + 2.00 L = 4.00 L.

For He: $P_2 = \frac{P_1V_1}{V_2} = 200. \text{ torr} \times \frac{1.00 \text{ L}}{4.00 \text{ L}} = 50.0 \text{ torr He}$

For Ne: $P_2 = 0.400 \text{ atm} \times \frac{1.00 \text{ L}}{4.00 \text{ L}} = 0.100 \text{ atm}$; $0.100 \text{ atm} \times \frac{760 \text{ torr}}{\text{atm}} = 76.0 \text{ torr Ne}$

For Ar: $P_2 = 24.0 \text{ kPa} \times \frac{2.00 \text{ L}}{4.00 \text{ L}} = 12.0 \text{ kPa}$; $12.0 \text{ kPa} \times \frac{1 \text{ atm}}{101.3 \text{ kPa}} \times \frac{760 \text{ torr}}{\text{atm}}$

$= 90.0 \text{ torr Ar}$

$P_{total} = 50.0 + 76.0 + 90.0 = 216.0 \text{ torr}$

123. a. $156 \text{ mL} \times 1.34 \text{ g/mL} = 209 \text{ g } HSiCl_3$ = actual yield of $HSiCl_3$

$$n_{HCl} = \frac{PV}{RT} = \frac{10.0 \text{ atm} \times 15.0 \text{ L}}{\frac{0.08206 \text{ L atm}}{\text{K mol}} \times 308 \text{ K}} = 5.93 \text{ mol HCl}$$

$$5.93 \text{ mol HCl} \times \frac{1 \text{ mol } HSiCl_3}{3 \text{ mol HCl}} \times \frac{135.45 \text{ g } HSiCl_3}{\text{mol } HSiCl_3} = 268 \text{ g } HSiCl_3$$

$$\text{Percent yield} = \frac{\text{actual yield}}{\text{theoretical yield}} \times 100 = \frac{209 \text{ g}}{268 \text{ g}} \times 100 = 78.0\%$$

b. $209 \text{ g HiSCl}_3 \times \dfrac{1 \text{ mol HSiCl}_3}{135.45 \text{ g HSiCl}_3} \times \dfrac{1 \text{ mol SiH}_4}{4 \text{ mol HSiCl}_3} = 0.386 \text{ mol SiH}_4$

This is the theoretical yield. If the percent yield is 93.1%, then the actual yield is:

$0.386 \text{ mol SiH}_4 \times 0.931 = 0.359 \text{ mol SiH}_4$

$$V_{SiH_4} = \frac{nRT}{P} = \frac{0.359 \text{ mol} \times \dfrac{0.08206 \text{ L atm}}{\text{K mol}} \times 308 \text{ K}}{10.0 \text{ atm}} = 0.907 \text{ L} = 907 \text{ mL SiH}_4$$

125. We will apply Boyle's law to solve. $PV = nRT = \text{constant}$, $P_1V_1 = P_2V_2$

Let condition (1) correspond to He from the tank that can be used to fill balloons. We must leave 1.0 atm of He in the tank, so $P_1 = 200. - 1.00 = 199$ atm and $V_1 = 15.0$ L. Condition (2) will correspond to the filled balloons with $P_2 = 1.00$ atm and $V_2 = N(2.00 \text{ L})$, where N is the number of filled balloons, each at a volume of 2.00 L.

199 atm × 15.0 L = 1.00 atm × N(2.00 L), N = 1492.5; we can't fill 0.5 of a balloon, so N = 1492 balloons, or to 3 significant figures, 1490 balloons.

127. $n_{Ar} = \dfrac{228 \text{ g}}{39.95 \text{ g/mol}} = 5.71 \text{ mol Ar}$; $\chi_{CH_4} = \dfrac{n_{CH_4}}{n_{CH_4} + n_{Ar}}$, $0.650 = \dfrac{n_{CH_4}}{n_{CH_4} + 5.71}$

$0.650(n_{CH_4} + 5.71) = n_{CH_4}$, $3.71 = (0.350)n_{CH_4}$, $n_{CH_4} = 10.6 \text{ mol CH}_4$

$KE_{avg} = \dfrac{3}{2}RT$ for 1 mol

Thus $KE_{total} = (10.6 + 5.71 \text{ mol}) \times 3/2 \times 8.3145 \text{ J K}^{-1} \text{ mol}^{-1} \times 298 \text{ K} = 6.06 \times 10^4 \text{ J} = 60.6 \text{ kJ}$

129. Mol of He removed $= \dfrac{PV}{RT} = \dfrac{1.00 \text{ atm} \times (1.75 \times 10^{-3} \text{ L})}{\dfrac{0.08206 \text{ L atm}}{\text{K mol}} \times 298 \text{ K}} = 7.16 \times 10^{-5} \text{ mol He}$

In the original flask, 7.16×10^{-5} mol of He exerted a partial pressure of 1.960 – 1.710 = 0.250 atm.

$$V = \frac{nRT}{V} = \frac{(7.16 \times 10^{-5} \text{ mol}) \times 0.08206 \text{ L atm K}^{-1} \text{ mol}^{-1} \times 298 \text{ K}}{0.250 \text{ atm}} = 7.00 \times 10^{-3} \text{ L} = 7.00 \text{ mL}$$

131. a. $2\ CH_4(g) + 2\ NH_3(g) + 3\ O_2(g) \rightarrow 2\ HCN(g) + 6\ H_2O(g)$

b. Volumes of gases are proportional to moles at constant T and P. Using the balanced equation, methane and ammonia are in stoichiometric amounts and oxygen is in excess. In 1 second:

$$n_{CH_4} = \frac{PV}{RT} = \frac{1.00\text{ atm} \times 20.0\text{ L}}{0.08206\text{ L atm K}^{-1}\text{ mol}^{-1} \times 423\text{ K}} = 0.576\text{ mol CH}_4$$

$$\frac{0.576\text{ mol CH}_4}{\text{s}} \times \frac{2\text{ mol HCN}}{2\text{ mol CH}_4} \times \frac{27.03\text{ g HCN}}{\text{mol HCN}} = 15.6\text{ g HCN/s}$$

Challenge Problems

133. Initially we have 1.00 mol CH_4 (16.0 g/mol = molar mass) and 2.00 mol O_2 (32.0 g/mol = molar mass).

$CH_4(g) + a\ O_2(g) \rightarrow b\ CO(g) + c\ CO_2(g) + d\ H_2O(g)$

$b + c = 1.00$ (C balance); $2a = b + 2c + d$ (O balance)

$2d = 4$ (H balance), $d = 2 = 2.00$ mol H_2O

$$V_{initial} = \frac{nRT}{P} = \frac{3.00\text{ mol} \times 0.08206\text{ L atm K}^{-1}\text{ mol}^{-1} \times 425\text{ K}}{1.00\text{ atm}} = 104.6\text{ L (1 extra sig .fig.)}$$

$$\text{Density}_{initial} = \frac{80.0\text{ g}}{104.6\text{ L}} = 0.7648\text{ g/L (1 extra significant figure)}$$

Because mass is constant:

$$\text{mass} = V_{initial} \times d_{initial} = V_{final} \times d_{final},\ V_{final} = V_{initial} \times \frac{d_{initial}}{d_{final}} = 104.6\text{ L} \times \frac{0.7648\text{ g/L}}{0.7282\text{ g/L}}$$

$V_{final} = 109.9$ L (1 extra significant figure)

$$n_{final} = \frac{PV}{RT} = \frac{1.00\text{ atm} \times 109.9\text{ L}}{\frac{0.08206\text{ L atm}}{\text{K mol}} \times 425\text{ K}} = 3.15\text{ total moles of gas}$$

Assuming an excess of O_2 is present after reaction, an expression for the total moles of gas present at completion is:

$b + c + 2.00 + (2.00 - a) = 3.15$; *Note*: $d = 2.00$ mol H_2O was determined previously.

Because $b + c = 1.00$, solving gives $a = 1.85$ mol O_2 reacted. Indeed, O_2 is in excess.

From the O balance equation:

$2a = 3.70 = b + 2c + 2.00,\ b + 2c = 1.70$

Because $b + c = 1.00$, solving gives $b = 0.30$ mol CO and $c = 0.70$ mol CO_2.

The fraction of methane that reacts to form CO is 0.30 mol CO/1.00 mol CH_4 = 0.30 (or 30.% by moles of the reacted methane forms CO).

135. $Cr(s) + 3\ HCl(aq) \rightarrow CrCl_3(aq) + 3/2\ H_2(g);\ Zn(s) + 2\ HCl(aq) \rightarrow ZnCl_2(aq) + H_2(g)$

$$\text{Mol } H_2 \text{ produced} = n = \frac{PV}{RT} = \frac{\left(750.\text{ torr} \times \frac{1\text{ atm}}{760\text{ torr}}\right) \times 0.225\text{ L}}{\frac{0.08206\text{ L atm}}{\text{K mol}} \times (273 + 27)\text{ K}} = 9.02 \times 10^{-3}\text{ mol } H_2$$

9.02×10^{-3} mol H_2 = mol H_2 from Cr reaction + mol H_2 from Zn reaction

From the balanced equation: 9.02×10^{-3} mol H_2 = mol Cr × (3/2) + mol Zn × 1

Let x = mass of Cr and y = mass of Zn, then:

$$x + y = 0.362\text{ g and } 9.02 \times 10^{-3} = \frac{(1.5)x}{52.00} + \frac{y}{65.38}$$

We have two equations and two unknowns. Solving by simultaneous equations:

$$\begin{aligned} 9.02 \times 10^{-3} &= (0.02885)x + (0.01530)y \\ -0.01530 \times 0.362 &= -(0.01530)x - (0.01530)y \\ \hline 3.48 \times 10^{-3} &= (0.01355)x, \end{aligned} \qquad x = \text{mass of Cr} = \frac{3.48 \times 10^{-3}}{0.01355} = 0.257\text{ g}$$

$$y = \text{mass of Zn} = 0.362\text{ g} - 0.257\text{ g} = 0.105\text{ g Zn};\ \text{mass \% Zn} = \frac{0.105\text{ g}}{0.362\text{ g}} \times 100 = 29.0\%\text{ Zn}$$

137. Molar mass = $\frac{dRT}{P}$, P and molar mass are constant; $dT = \frac{P \times \text{molar mass}}{R}$ = constant

d = constant(1/T) or $d_1T_1 = d_2T_2$, where T is in kelvin (K).

$T = x + °C;\ 1.2930(x + 0.0) = 0.9460(x + 100.0)$

$(1.2930)x = (0.9460)x + 94.60,\ (0.3470)x = 94.60,\ x = 272.6$

From these data, absolute zero would be −272.6°C. The actual value is −273.15°C.

139. $\frac{PV}{nRT} = 1 + \beta P;\quad \frac{n}{V} \times \text{molar mass} = d$

$$\frac{\text{molar mass}}{RT} \times \frac{P}{d} = 1 + \beta P,\quad \frac{P}{d} = \frac{RT}{\text{molar mass}} + \frac{\beta RTP}{\text{molar mass}}$$

This is in the equation for a straight line: $y = b + mx$. If we plot P/d versus P and extrapolate to P = 0, we get a y intercept = b = 1.398 = RT/molar mass.

At 0.00°C, molar mass = $\frac{0.08206 \times 273.15}{1.398} = 16.03$ g/mol.

141. Figure 5.16 shows the effect of temperature on the Maxwell-Boltzmann distribution of velocities of molecules. Note that as temperature increases, the probability that a gas particle has the most probable velocity decreases. Thus, since the probability of the gas particle with the most probable velocity decreased by one-half, then the temperature must be higher than 300. K.

The equation that determines the probability that a gas molecule has a certain velocity is:

$$f(u) = 4\pi\left(\frac{m}{2\pi k_B T}\right)^{3/2} u^2 e^{-mu^2/2k_BT}$$

Let T_x = the unknown temperature, then:

$$\frac{f(u_{mp,x})}{f(u_{mp,300})} = \frac{1}{2} = \frac{4\pi\left(\frac{m}{2\pi k_B T_x}\right)^{3/2} u_{mp,x}^2\, e^{-mu_{mp,x}^2/2k_BT_x}}{4\pi\left(\frac{m}{2\pi k_B T_{300}}\right)^{3/2} u_{mp,300}^2\, e^{-mu_{mp,300}^2/2k_BT_{300}}}$$

Because $u_{mp} = \sqrt{\frac{2k_BT}{m}}$, the equation reduces to:

$$\frac{1}{2} = \frac{\left(\frac{1}{T_x}\right)^{3/2}(T_x)}{\left(\frac{1}{T_{300}}\right)^{3/2}(T_{300})} = \left(\frac{T_{300}}{T_x}\right)^{1/2}$$

Note that the overall exponent term cancels from the expression when $2k_BT/m$ is substituted for u_{mp}^2 in the exponent term; the temperatures cancel. Solving for T_x:

$\frac{1}{2} = \left(\frac{300.\text{ K}}{T_x}\right)$, $T_x = 1.20 \times 10^3$ K; as expected, T_x is higher than 300. K.

143. From the problem, we want $Z_A/Z = 1.00 \times 10^{18}$ where Z_A is the collision frequency of the gas particles with the walls of the container and Z is the intermolecular collision frequency.

From the text: $$\frac{Z_A}{Z} = \frac{A\frac{N}{V}\sqrt{\frac{RT}{2\pi M}}}{4\frac{N}{V}d^2\sqrt{\frac{\pi RT}{M}}} = 1.00 \times 10^{18}, \quad 1.00 \times 10^{18} = \frac{A}{4\,d^2\,\pi\sqrt{2}}$$

If l = length of the cube edge container, then the area A of one cube face is l^2 and the total area in the cube is $6l^2$ (6 faces/cube). He diameter = d = $2(3.2 \times 10^{-11}\text{ m}) = 6.4 \times 10^{-11}$ m.

Solving the above expression for A, and then for l gives l = 0.11 m = 1.1 dm.

Volume = $l^3 = (1.1\text{ dm})^3 = 1.3\text{ dm}^3 = 1.3$ L

145. The reactions are:

$$C(s) + 1/2\ O_2(g) \rightarrow CO(g) \text{ and } C(s) + O_2(g) \rightarrow CO_2(g)$$

$$PV = nRT, \quad P = n\left(\frac{RT}{V}\right) = n(\text{constant})$$

Because the pressure has increased by 17.0%, the number of moles of gas has also increased by 17.0%.

$$n_{final} = (1.170)n_{initial} = 1.170(5.00) = 5.85 \text{ mol gas} = n_{O_2} + n_{CO} + n_{CO_2}$$

$n_{CO} + n_{CO_2} = 5.00$ (balancing moles of C). Solving by simultaneous equations:

$$\begin{array}{rl} n_{O_2} + n_{CO} + n_{CO_2} & = 5.85 \\ -(n_{CO} + n_{CO_2} & = 5.00) \\ \hline n_{O_2} \qquad\qquad & = 0.85 \end{array}$$

If all C were converted to CO_2, no O_2 would be left. If all C were converted to CO, we would get 5 mol CO and 2.5 mol excess O_2 in the reaction mixture. In the final mixture, moles of CO equals twice the moles of O_2 present ($n_{CO} = 2n_{O_2}$).

$$n_{CO} = 2n_{O_2} = 1.70 \text{ mol CO}; \ 1.70 + n_{CO_2} = 5.00, \ n_{CO_2} = 3.30 \text{ mol } CO_2$$

$$\chi_{CO} = \frac{1.70}{5.85} = 0.291; \quad \chi_{CO_2} = \frac{3.30}{5.85} = 0.564; \quad \chi_{O_2} = 1.000 - 0.291 - 0.564 = 0.145$$

147. a. The reaction is: $CH_4(g) + 2\ O_2(g) \rightarrow CO_2(g) + 2\ H_2O(g)$

$$PV = nRT,\quad \frac{PV}{n} = RT = \text{constant},\quad \frac{P_{CH_4}V_{CH_4}}{n_{CH_4}} = \frac{P_{air}V_{air}}{n_{air}}$$

The balanced equation requires 2 mol O_2 for every mol of CH_4 that reacts. For three times as much oxygen, we would need 6 mol O_2 per mol of CH_4 reacted ($n_{O_2} = 6n_{CH_4}$). Air is 21% mole percent O_2, so $n_{O_2} = (0.21)n_{air}$. Therefore, the moles of air we would need to deliver the excess O_2 are:

$$n_{O_2} = (0.21)n_{air} = 6n_{CH_4},\quad n_{air} = 29n_{CH_4},\quad \frac{n_{air}}{n_{CH_4}} = 29$$

In 1 minute:

$$V_{air} = V_{CH_4} \times \frac{n_{air}}{n_{CH_4}} \times \frac{P_{CH_4}}{P_{air}} = 200.\ \text{L} \times 29 \times \frac{1.50\ \text{atm}}{1.00\ \text{atm}} = 8.7 \times 10^3\ \text{L air/min}$$

b. If x mol of CH_4 were reacted, then $6x$ mol O_2 were added, producing $(0.950)x$ mol CO_2 and $(0.050)x$ mol of CO. In addition, $2x$ mol H_2O must be produced to balance the hydrogens.

$CH_4(g) + 2\ O_2(g) \rightarrow CO_2(g) + 2\ H_2O(g)$; $CH_4(g) + 3/2\ O_2(g) \rightarrow CO(g) + 2\ H_2O(g)$

Amount O_2 reacted:

$$(0.950)x\ \text{mol}\ CO_2 \times \frac{2\ \text{mol}\ O_2}{\text{mol}\ CO_2} = (1.90)x\ \text{mol}\ O_2$$

$$(0.050)x\ \text{mol CO} \times \frac{1.5\ \text{mol}\ O_2}{\text{mol CO}} = (0.075)x\ \text{mol}\ O_2$$

Amount of O_2 left in reaction mixture $= (6.00)x - (1.90)x - (0.075)x = (4.03)x$ mol O_2

$$\text{Amount of}\ N_2 = (6.00)x\ \text{mol}\ O_2 \times \frac{79\ \text{mol}\ N_2}{21\ \text{mol}\ O_2} = (22.6)x \approx 23x\ \text{mol}\ N_2$$

The reaction mixture contains:

$(0.950)x$ mol CO_2 + $(0.050)x$ mol CO + $(4.03)x$ mol O_2 + $(2.00)x$ mol H_2O + $23x$ mol N_2 = $(30.)x$ mol of gas total

$$\chi_{CO} = \frac{(0.050)x}{(30.)x} = 0.0017;\quad \chi_{CO_2} = \frac{(0.950)x}{(30.)x} = 0.032;\quad \chi_{O_2} = \frac{(4.03)x}{(30.)x} = 0.13$$

$$\chi_{H_2O} = \frac{(2.00)x}{(30.)x} = 0.067;\quad \chi_{N_2} = \frac{23x}{(30.)x} = 0.77$$

c. The partial pressures are determined by $P = \chi P_{total}$. Because P_{total} = 1.00 atm, P_{CO} = 0.0017 atm, P_{CO_2} = 0.032 atm, P_{O_2} = 0.13 atm, P_{H_2O} = 0.067 atm, and P_{N_2} = 0.77 atm.

149. Each stage will give an enrichment of:

$$\frac{\text{Diffusion rate } ^{12}CO_2}{\text{Diffusion rate } ^{13}CO_2} = \left(\frac{M_{^{13}CO_2}}{M_{^{12}CO_2}}\right)^{1/2} = \left(\frac{45.001}{43.998}\right) = 1.0113$$

Because $^{12}CO_2$ moves slightly faster, each successive stage will have less $^{13}CO_2$.

$$\frac{99.90\ ^{12}CO_2}{0.10\ ^{13}CO_2} \times 1.0113^N = \frac{99.990\ ^{12}CO_2}{0.010\ ^{13}CO_2}$$

$$1.0113^N = \frac{9{,}999.0}{999.00} = 10.009 \quad \text{(carrying extra significant figures)}$$

$$N \log(1.0113) = \log(10.009),\ N = \frac{1.000391}{4.88 \times 10^{-3}} = 2.05 \times 10^2 \approx 2.1 \times 10^2 \text{ stages are needed.}$$

151. a. Average molar mass of air = 0.790 × 28.02 g/mol + 0.210 × 32.00 g/mol = 28.9 g/mol; molar mass of helium = 4.003 g/mol

A given volume of air at a given set of conditions has a larger density than helium at those conditions. We need to heat the air to a temperature greater than 25°C in order to lower the air density (by driving air out of the hot air balloon) until the density is the same as that for helium (at 25°C and 1.00 atm).

b. To provide the same lift as the helium balloon (assume V = 1.00 L), the mass of air in the hot-air balloon (V = 1.00 L) must be the same as that in the helium balloon. Let MM = molar mass:

$$P \bullet MM = dRT,\ \text{mass} = \frac{MM \bullet PV}{RT};\ \text{solving: mass He} = 0.164\text{ g}$$

$$\text{Mass air} = 0.164\text{ g} = \frac{28.9\text{ g/mol} \times 1.00\text{ atm} \times 1.00\text{ L}}{\frac{0.08206\text{ L atm}}{\text{K mol}} \times T},\ T = 2150\text{ K (a very high temperature)}$$

153. d = molar mass(P/RT); at constant P and T, the density of gas is directly proportional to the molar mass of the gas. Thus the molar mass of the gas has a value which is 1.38 times that of the molar mass of O_2.

Molar mass = 1.38(32.00 g/mol) = 44.2 g/mol

Because H_2O is produced when the unknown binary compound is combusted, the unknown must contain hydrogen. Let A_xH_y be the formula for unknown compound.

$$\text{Mol } A_xH_y = 10.0 \text{ g } A_xH_y \times \frac{1 \text{ mol } A_xH_y}{44.2 \text{ g}} = 0.226 \text{ mol } A_xH_y$$

$$\text{Mol H} = 16.3 \text{ g } H_2O \times \frac{1 \text{ mol } H_2O}{18.02 \text{ g}} \times \frac{2 \text{ mol H}}{\text{mol } H_2O} = 1.81 \text{ mol H}$$

$$\frac{1.81 \text{ mol H}}{0.226 \text{ mol } A_xH_y} = 8 \text{ mol H/mol } A_xH_y\text{ ; } A_xH_y = A_xH_8$$

The mass of the x moles of A in the A_xH_8 formula is:

$$44.2 \text{ g} - 8(1.008 \text{ g}) = 36.1 \text{ g}$$

From the periodic table and by trial and error, some possibilities for A_xH_8 are ClH_8, F_2H_8, C_3H_8, and Be_4H_8. C_3H_8 and Be_4H_8 fit the data best and because C_3H_8 (propane) is a known substance, C_3H_8 is the best possible identity from the data in this problem.

CHAPTER 6

CHEMICAL EQUILIBRIUM

Characteristics of Chemical Equilibrium

11. $2\ NOCl(g) \rightleftharpoons 2\ NO(g) + Cl_2(g)$ $K = 1.6 \times 10^{-5}$

    The expression for K is the product concentrations divided by the reactant concentrations. When K has a value much less than one, the product concentrations are relatively small, and the reactant concentrations are relatively large.

    $2\ NO(g) \rightleftharpoons N_2(g) + O_2(g)$ $K = 1 \times 10^{31}$

    When K has a value much greater than one, the product concentrations are relatively large, and the reactant concentrations are relatively small. In both cases, however, the rate of the forward reaction equals the rate of the reverse reaction at equilibrium (this is a definition of equilibrium).

13. No, it doesn't matter which direction the equilibrium position is reached. Both experiments will give the same equilibrium position because both experiments started with stoichiometric amounts of reactants or products.

15. When equilibrium is reached, there is no net change in the amount of reactants and products present because the rates of the forward and reverse reactions are equal to each other. The first diagram has 4 A_2B molecules, 2 A_2 molecules, and 1 B_2 molecule present. The second diagram has 2 A_2B molecules, 4 A_2 molecules, and 2 B_2 molecules. Therefore, the first diagram cannot represent equilibrium because there was a net change in reactants and products. Is the second diagram the equilibrium mixture? That depends on whether there is a net change between reactants and products when going from the second diagram to the third diagram. The third diagram contains the same number and type of molecules as the second diagram, so the second diagram is the first illustration that represents equilibrium.

    The reaction container initially contained only A_2B. From the first diagram, 2 A_2 molecules and 1 B_2 molecule are present (along with 4 A_2B molecules). From the balanced reaction, these 2 A_2 molecules and 1 B_2 molecule were formed when 2 A_2B molecules decomposed. Therefore, the initial number of A_2B molecules present equals 4 + 2 = 6 molecules A_2B.

The Equilibrium Constant

17. K and K_p are equilibrium constants as determined by the law of mass action. For K, concentration units of mol/L are used, and for K_p, partial pressures in units of atm are used (generally). Q is called the reaction quotient. Q has the exact same form as K or K_p, but instead of equilibrium concentrations, initial concentrations are used to calculate the Q value. We use Q to determine if a reaction is at equilibrium. When Q = K (or when $Q_p = K_p$), the reaction is at equilibrium. When Q ≠ K, the reaction is not at equilibrium, and one can deduce the net change that must occur for the system to get to equilibrium.

19. Solids and liquids do not appear in equilibrium expressions. Only gases and dissolved solutes appear in equilibrium expressions.

a. $K = \dfrac{[H_2O]}{[NH_3]^2[CO_2]}$; $K_p = \dfrac{P_{H_2O}}{P_{NH_3}^2 \times P_{CO_2}}$

b. $K = [N_2][Br_2]^3$; $K_p = P_{N_2} \times P_{Br_2}^3$

c. $K = [O_2]^3$; $K_p = P_{O_2}^3$

d. $K = \dfrac{[H_2O]}{[H_2]}$; $K_p = \dfrac{P_{H_2O}}{P_{H_2}}$

21. $[NO] = \dfrac{4.5 \times 10^{-3}\ \text{mol}}{3.0\ \text{L}} = 1.5 \times 10^{-3}\ M$; $[Cl_2] = \dfrac{2.4\ \text{mol}}{3.0\ \text{L}} = 0.80\ M$

$[NOCl] = \dfrac{1.0\ \text{mol}}{3.0\ \text{L}} = 0.33\ M$; $K = \dfrac{[NO]^2[Cl_2]}{[NOCl]^2} = \dfrac{(1.5 \times 10^{-3})^2(0.80)}{(0.33)^2} = 1.7 \times 10^{-5}$

23. $K_p = K(RT)^{\Delta n}$, where Δn = sum of gaseous product coefficients – sum of gaseous reactant coefficients. For this reaction, Δn = 3 – 1 = 2.

$$K = \frac{[CO][H_2]^2}{[CH_3OH]} = \frac{(0.24)(1.1)^2}{(0.15)} = 1.9$$

$$K_p = K(RT)^2 = 1.9(0.08206\ \text{L atm K}^{-1}\ \text{mol}^{-1} \times 600.\ \text{K})^2 = 4.6 \times 10^3$$

25. $[N_2O] = \dfrac{2.00 \times 10^{-2}\ \text{mol}}{2.00\ \text{L}}$; $[N_2] = \dfrac{2.80 \times 10^{-4}\ \text{mol}}{2.00\ \text{L}}$; $[O_2] = \dfrac{2.50 \times 10^{-5}\ \text{mol}}{2.00\ \text{L}}$

$$K = \frac{[N_2O]^2}{[N_2]^2[O_2]} = \frac{\left(\dfrac{2.00 \times 10^{-2}}{2.00}\right)^2}{\left(\dfrac{2.80 \times 10^{-4}}{2.00}\right)^2\left(\dfrac{2.50 \times 10^{-5}}{2.00}\right)} = \frac{(1.00 \times 10^{-2})^2}{(1.40 \times 10^{-4})^2(1.25 \times 10^{-5})}$$

$$= 4.08 \times 10^8$$

If the given concentrations represent equilibrium concentrations, then they should give a value of $K = 4.08 \times 10^8$.

$$\frac{(0.200)^2}{(2.00 \times 10^{-4})^2(0.00245)} = 4.08 \times 10^8$$

Because the given concentrations when plugged into the equilibrium constant expression give a value equal to K (4.08×10^8), this set of concentrations is a system at equilibrium

27. $K = \frac{[H_2]^2[O_2]}{[H_2O]^2}$, $2.4 \times 10^{-3} = \frac{(1.9 \times 10^{-2})^2[O_2]}{(0.11)^2}$, $[O_2] = 0.080\ M$

$$\text{Mol } O_2 = 2.0 \text{ L} \times \frac{0.080 \text{ mol } O_2}{\text{L}} = 0.16 \text{ mol } O_2$$

29. $K_p = \frac{P_{H_2}^4}{P_{H_2O}^4}$; $P_{total} = P_{H_2O} + P_{H_2}$, 36.3 torr = 15.0 torr + P_{H_2}, $P_{H_2} = 21.3$ torr

$$\text{Because 1 atm = 760 torr: } K_p = \frac{\left(21.3 \text{ torr} \times \frac{1 \text{ atm}}{760 \text{ torr}}\right)^4}{\left(15.0 \text{ torr} \times \frac{1 \text{ atm}}{760 \text{ torr}}\right)^4} = 4.07$$

Note: Solids and pure liquids are not included in K expressions.

31. $PCl_5(g) \rightleftharpoons PCl_3(g) + Cl_2(g) \quad K_p = \frac{P_{PCl_3} \times P_{Cl_2}}{P_{PCl_5}}$

To determine K_p, we must determine the equilibrium partial pressures of each gas. Initially, $P_{PCl_5} = 0.50$ atm and $P_{PCl_3} = P_{Cl_2} = 0$ atm. To reach equilibrium, some of the PCl_5 reacts to produce some PCl_3 and Cl_2, all in a 1 : 1 mole ratio. We must determine the change in partial pressures necessary to reach equilibrium. Because moles ∝ P at constant V and T, if we let x = atm of PCl_5 that reacts to reach equilibrium, this will produce x atm of PCl_3 and x atm of Cl_2 at equilibrium. The equilibrium partial pressures of each gas will be the initial partial pressure of each gas plus the change necessary to reach equilibrium. The equilibrium partial pressures are:

$$P_{PCl_5} = 0.50 \text{ atm} - x, \quad P_{PCl_3} = P_{Cl_2} = x$$

Now we solve for x using the information in the problem:

$$P_{total} = P_{PCl_5} + P_{PCl_3} + P_{Cl_2}, \ 0.84 \text{ atm} = 0.50 - x + x + x, \ 0.84 \text{ atm} = 0.50 + x,$$

$$x = 0.34 \text{ atm}$$

The equilibrium partial pressures are:

$$P_{PCl_5} = 0.50 - 0.34 = 0.16 \text{ atm}, \; P_{PCl_3} = P_{Cl_2} = 0.34 \text{ atm}$$

$$K_p = \frac{P_{PCl_3} \times P_{Cl_2}}{P_{PCl_5}} = \frac{(0.34)(0.34)}{(0.16)} = 0.72$$

$$K = \frac{K_p}{(RT)^{\Delta n}}, \; \Delta n = 2 - 1 = 1; \; K_p = \frac{0.72}{(0.08206)(523)} = 0.017$$

33. When solving equilibrium problems, a common method to summarize all the information in the problem is to set up a table. We commonly call this table an ICE table because it summarizes *i*nitial concentrations, *c*hanges that must occur to reach equilibrium, and *e*quilibrium concentrations (the sum of the initial and change columns). For the change column, we will generally use the variable *x*, which will be defined as the amount of reactant (or product) that must react to reach equilibrium. In this problem, the reaction must shift right to reach equilibrium because there are no products present initially. Therefore, *x* is defined as the amount of reactant SO_3 that reacts to reach equilibrium, and we use the coefficients in the balanced equation to relate the net change in SO_3 to the net change in SO_2 and O_2. The general ICE table for this problem is:

	$2\ SO_3(g)$	$\rightleftharpoons$	$2\ SO_2(g)$	+	$O_2(g)$	$K = \frac{[SO_2]^2[O_2]}{[SO_3]^2}$
Initial	12.0 mol/3.0 L		0		0	
	Let x mol/L of SO_3 react to reach equilibrium.					
Change	$-x$	$\rightarrow$	$+x$		$+x/2$	
Equil.	$4.0 - x$		x		$x/2$	

From the problem, we are told that the equilibrium SO_2 concentration is 3.0 mol/3.0 L = 1.0 *M* ($[SO_2]_e = 1.0\ M$). From the ICE table setup, $[SO_2]_e = x$, so $x = 1.0$. Solving for the other equilibrium concentrations: $[SO_3]_e = 4.0 - x = 4.0 - 1.0 = 3.0\ M$; $[O_2] = x/2 = 1.0/2 = 0.50\ M$.

$$K = \frac{[SO_2]^2[O_2]}{[SO_3]^2} = \frac{(1.0\ M)^2\,(0.50\ M)}{(3.0\ M)^2} = 0.056$$

Alternate method: Fractions in the change column can be avoided (if you want) be defining *x* differently. If we were to let 2*x* mol/L of SO_3 react to reach equilibrium, then the ICE table setup is:

	$2\ SO_3(g)$	$\rightleftharpoons$	$2\ SO_2(g)$	+	$O_2(g)$	$K = \frac{[SO_2]^2[O_2]}{[SO_3]^2}$
Initial	4.0 *M*		0		0	
	Let $2x$ mol/L of SO_3 react to reach equilibrium.					
Change	$-2x$	$\rightarrow$	$+2x$		$+x$	
Equil.	$4.0 - 2x$		$2x$		x	

Solving: $2x = [SO_2]_e = 1.0\ M$, $x = 0.50\ M$; $[SO_3]_e = 4.0 - 2(0.50) = 3.0\ M$; $[O_2]_e = x = 0.50\ M$

These are exactly the same equilibrium concentrations as solved for previously, thus K will be the same (as it must be). The moral of the story is to define x in a manner that is most comfortable for you. Your final answer is independent of how you define x initially.

Equilibrium Calculations

35. $H_2O(g) + Cl_2O(g) \rightarrow 2\ HOCl(g) \qquad K = \dfrac{[HOCl]^2}{[H_2O][Cl_2O]} = 0.0900$

Use the reaction quotient Q to determine which way the reaction shifts to reach equilibrium. For the reaction quotient, initial concentrations given in a problem are used to calculate the value for Q. If Q < K, then the reaction shifts right to reach equilibrium. If Q > K, then the reaction shifts left to reach equilibrium. If Q = K, then the reaction does not shift in either direction because the reaction is already at equilibrium.

a. $$Q = \frac{[HOCl]_0^2}{[H_2O]_0[Cl_2O]_0} = \frac{\left(\frac{1.0\ mol}{1.0\ L}\right)^2}{\left(\frac{0.10\ mol}{1.0\ L}\right)\left(\frac{0.10\ mol}{1.0\ L}\right)} = 1.0 \times 10^2$$

Q > K, so the reaction shifts left to produce more reactants in order to reach equilibrium.

b. $$Q = \frac{\left(\frac{0.084\ mol}{2.0\ L}\right)^2}{\left(\frac{0.98\ mol}{2.0\ L}\right)\left(\frac{0.080\ mol}{2.0\ L}\right)} = 0.090 = K;\quad \text{at equilibrium}$$

c. $$Q = \frac{\left(\frac{0.25\ mol}{3.0\ L}\right)^2}{\left(\frac{0.56\ mol}{3.0\ L}\right)\left(\frac{0.0010\ mol}{3.0\ L}\right)} = 110$$

Q > K, so the reaction shifts to the left to reach equilibrium.

37. $CaCO_3(s) \rightleftharpoons CaO(s) + CO_2(g) \qquad K_p = P_{CO_2} = 1.04\ atm$

We only need to calculate the initial partial pressure of CO_2 and compare this value to 1.04 atm. At this temperature, all CO_2 will be in the gas phase.

a. $PV = nRT,\ Q = P_{CO_2} = \dfrac{n_{CO_2}RT}{V} = \dfrac{\dfrac{58.4\text{ g }CO_2}{44.01\text{ g/mol}} \times \dfrac{0.08206\text{ L atm}}{\text{K mol}} \times 1173\text{ K}}{50.0\text{ L}} =$

$2.55\text{ atm} > K_p$

Reaction will shift to the left because $Q > K_p$; the mass of CaO will decrease.

b. $Q = P_{CO_2} = \dfrac{(23.76)(0.08206)(1173)}{(44.01)(50.0)} = 1.04\text{ atm} = K_p$

At equilibrium because $Q = K_p$; mass of CaO will not change.

c. Mass of CO_2 is the same as in part b. $P = 1.04\text{ atm} = K_p$. At equilibrium; mass of CaO will not change.

d. $Q = P_{CO_2} = \dfrac{(4.82)(0.08206)(1173)}{(44.01)(50.0)} = 0.211\text{ atm} < K_p$

Reaction will shift to the right because $Q < K_p$; the mass of CaO will increase.

39. $H_2O(g) + Cl_2O(g) \rightleftharpoons 2\ HOCl(g)$ $\qquad K = 0.090 = \dfrac{[HOCl]^2}{[H_2O][Cl_2O]}$

a. The initial concentrations of H_2O and Cl_2O are:

$$\frac{1.0\text{ g }H_2O}{1.0\text{ L}} \times \frac{1\text{ mol}}{18.0\text{ g}} = 5.6 \times 10^{-2}\text{ mol/L};\quad \frac{2.0\text{ g }Cl_2O}{1.0\text{ L}} \times \frac{1\text{ mol}}{86.9\text{ g}} = 2.3 \times 10^{-2}\text{ mol/L}$$

Because only reactants are present initially, the reaction must proceed to the right to reach equilibrium. Summarizing the problem in a table:

	$H_2O(g)$ +	$Cl_2O(g)$	$\rightleftharpoons 2\ HOCl(g)$
Initial	$5.6 \times 10^{-2}\ M$	$2.3 \times 10^{-2}\ M$	0
	x mol/L of H_2O reacts to reach equilibrium		
Change	$-x$	$-x$	$\rightarrow +2x$
Equil.	$5.6 \times 10^{-2} - x$	$2.3 \times 10^{-2} - x$	$2x$

$$K = 0.090 = \frac{(2x)^2}{(5.6 \times 10^{-2} - x)(2.3 \times 10^{-2} - x)}$$

$1.16 \times 10^{-4} - (7.11 \times 10^{-3})x + (0.090)x^2 = 4x^2$

$(3.91)x^2 + (7.11 \times 10^{-3})x - 1.16 \times 10^{-4} = 0$ (We carried extra significant figures.)

Solving using the quadratic formula (see Appendix 1 of the text):

$$x = \frac{-7.11 \times 10^{-3} \pm (5.06 \times 10^{-5} + 1.81 \times 10^{-3})^{1/2}}{7.82} = 4.6 \times 10^{-3}\ M \text{ or } -6.4 \times 10^{-3}\ M$$

A negative answer makes no physical sense; we can't have less than nothing. Thus $x = 4.6 \times 10^{-3}$ *M*.

[HOCl] = $2x = 9.2 \times 10^{-3}$ *M*; [Cl_2O] = $2.3 \times 10^{-2} - x = 0.023 - 0.0046 = 1.8 \times 10^{-2}$ *M*

[H_2O] = $5.6 \times 10^{-2} - x = 0.056 - 0.0046 = 5.1 \times 10^{-2}$ *M*

b. $H_2O(g)$ + $Cl_2O(g)$ ⇌ 2 HOCl(g)

	$H_2O(g)$	$Cl_2O(g)$		2 HOCl(g)
Initial	0	0		1.0 mol/2.0 L = 0.50 *M*
	2*x* mol/L of HOCl reacts to reach equilibrium			
Change	$+x$	$+x$	←	$-2x$
Equil.	x	x		$0.50 - 2x$

$$K = 0.090 = \frac{[HOCl]^2}{[H_2O][Cl_2O]} = \frac{(0.50 - 2x)^2}{x^2}$$

The expression is a perfect square, so we can take the square root of each side:

$$0.30 = \frac{0.50 - 2x}{x},\quad (0.30)x = 0.50 - 2x,\ (2.30)x = 0.50$$

$x = 0.217$ *M* (We carried extra significant figures.)

x = [H_2O] = [Cl_2O] = 0.217 = 0.22 *M*; [HOCl] = $0.50 - 2x = 0.50 - 0.434 = 0.07$ *M*

41. $2\ SO_2(g)$ + $O_2(g)$ ⇌ $2\ SO_3(g)$ $K_p = 0.25$

	$2\ SO_2(g)$	$O_2(g)$		$2\ SO_3(g)$
Initial	0.50 atm	0.50 atm		0
	2*x* atm of SO_2 reacts to reach equilibrium			
Change	$-2x$	$-x$	→	$+2x$
Equil.	$0.50 - 2x$	$0.50 - x$		$2x$

$$K_p = 0.25 = \frac{P_{SO_3}^2}{P_{SO_2}^2 \times P_{O_2}} = \frac{(2x)^2}{(0.50 - 2x)^2(0.50 - x)}$$

This will give a cubic equation. Graphing calculators can be used to solve this expression. If you don't have a graphing calculator, an alternative method for solving a cubic equation is to use the method of successive approximations (see Appendix 1 of the text). The first step is to guess a value for x. Because the value of K is small (K < 1), not much of the forward reaction will occur to reach equilibrium. This tells us that x is small. Let's guess that x =

0.050 atm. Now we take this estimated value for x and substitute it into the equation everywhere that x appears except for one. For equilibrium problems, we will substitute the estimated value for x into the denominator, and then solve for the numerator value of x. We continue this process until the estimated value of x and the calculated value of x converge on the same number. This is the same answer we would get if we were to solve the cubic equation exactly. Applying the method of successive approximations and carrying extra significant figures:

$$\frac{4x^2}{[0.50-2(0.050)]^2-[0.50-(0.050)]} = \frac{4x^2}{(0.40)^2(0.45)} = 0.25\,,\ x = 0.067$$

$$\frac{4x^2}{[0.50-2(0.067)]^2\,[0.50-(0.067)]} = \frac{4x^2}{(0.366)^2(0.433)} = 0.25\,,\ x = 0.060$$

$$\frac{4x^2}{(0.38)^2(0.44)} = 0.25,\ x = 0.063;\quad \frac{4x^2}{(0.374)^2(0.437)} = 0.25,\quad x = 0.062$$

The next trial gives the same value for x = 0.062 atm. We are done except for determining the equilibrium concentrations. They are:

$$P_{SO_2} = 0.50 - 2x = 0.50 - 2(0.062) = 0.376 = 0.38 \text{ atm}$$

$$P_{O_2} = 0.50 - x = 0.438 = 0.44 \text{ atm};\ P_{SO_3} = 2x = 0.124 = 0.12 \text{ atm}$$

43. The assumption comes from the value of K being much less than 1. For these reactions, the equilibrium mixture will not have a lot of products present; mostly reactants are present at equilibrium. If we define the change that must occur in terms of x as the amount (molarity or partial pressure) of a reactant that must react to reach equilibrium, then x must be a small number because K is a very small number. We want to know the value of x in order to solve the problem, so we don't assume $x = 0$. Instead, we concentrate on the equilibrium row in the ICE table. Those reactants (or products) that have equilibrium concentrations in the form of $0.10 - x$ or $0.25 + x$ or $3.5 - 3x$, etc., is where an important assumption can be made. The assumption is that because $K \ll 1$, x will be small ($x \ll 1$), and when we add x or subtract x from some initial concentration, it will make little or no difference. That is, we assume that $0.10 - x \approx 0.10$ or $0.25 + x \approx 0.25$ or $3.5 - 3x \approx 3.5$, etc.; we assume that the initial concentration of a substance is equal to the final concentration. This assumption makes the math much easier and usually gives a value of x that is well within 5% of the true value of x (we get about the same answer with a lot less work).

We check the assumptions for validity using the 5% rule. From doing a lot of these calculations, it is found that when an assumption such as $0.20 - x \approx 0.20$ is made, if x is less than 5% of the number the assumption was made against, then our final answer is within acceptable error limits of the true value of x (as determined when the equation is solved exactly). For our example above ($0.20 - x \approx 0.20$), if $(x/0.20) \times 100 \le 5\%$, then our assumption is valid by the 5% rule. If the error is greater than 5%, then we must solve the equation exactly or use a math trick called the method of successive approximations. See Appendix 1 for details regarding the method of successive approximations, as well as for a review in solving quadratic equations exactly.

45. $2\ CO_2(g) \rightleftharpoons 2\ CO(g) + O_2(g) \qquad K = \frac{[CO]^2[O_2]}{[CO_2]^2} = 2.0 \times 10^{-6}$

	$2\ CO_2(g)$	$\rightleftharpoons$	$2\ CO(g)$	+	$O_2(g)$
Initial	2.0 mol/5.0 L		0		0
	$2x$ mol/L of CO_2 reacts to reach equilibrium				
Change	$-2x$	$\rightarrow$	$+2x$		$+x$
Equil.	$0.40 - 2x$		$2x$		x

$K = 2.0 \times 10^{-6} = \frac{[CO]^2[O_2]}{[CO_2]^2} = \frac{(2x)^2(x)}{(0.40 - 2x)^2}$; assuming $2x << 0.40$ (K is small, so x is small.):

$2.0 \times 10^{-6} \approx \frac{4x^3}{(0.40)^2}$, $2.0 \times 10^{-6} = \frac{4x^3}{0.16}$, $x = 4.3 \times 10^{-3}\ M$

Checking assumption: $\frac{2(4.3 \times 10^{-3})}{0.40} \times 100 = 2.2\%$; assumption is valid by the 5% rule.

$[CO_2] = 0.40 - 2x = 0.40 - 2(4.3 \times 10^{-3}) = 0.39\ M$

$[CO] = 2x = 2(4.3 \times 10^{-3}) = 8.6 \times 10^{-3}\ M$; $[O_2] = x = 4.3 \times 10^{-3}\ M$

47. $CaCO_3(s) \rightleftharpoons CaO(s) + CO_2(g) \qquad K_p = 1.16 = P_{CO_2}$

Some of the 20.0 g of $CaCO_3$ will react to reach equilibrium. The amount that reacts is the quantity of $CaCO_3$ required to produce a CO_2 pressure of 1.16 atm (from the K_p expression).

$$n_{CO_2} = \frac{P_{CO_2}V}{RT} = \frac{1.16\text{ atm} \times 10.0\text{ L}}{\frac{0.08206\text{ L atm}}{\text{K mol}} \times 1073\text{ K}} = 0.132\text{ mol } CO_2$$

$$\text{Mass } CaCO_3 \text{ reacted} = 0.132\text{ mol } CO_2 \times \frac{1\text{ mol } CaCO_3}{\text{mol } CO_2} \times \frac{100.09\text{ g}}{\text{mol } CaCO_3} = 13.2\text{ g } CaCO_3$$

$$\text{Mass \% } CaCO_3 \text{ reacted} = \frac{13.2\text{ g}}{20.0\text{ g}} \times 100 = 66.0\%$$

49. a. $K_p = K(RT)^{\Delta n} = 4.5 \times 10^9 \left(\frac{0.08206\text{ L atm}}{\text{K mol}} \times 373\text{ K}\right)^{-1}$, where $\Delta n = 1 - 2 = -1$

$K_p = 1.5 \times 10^8$

b. K_p is so large that at equilibrium we will have almost all $COCl_2$. Assume $P_{total} \approx P_{COCl_2} \approx 5.0$ atm.

	$CO(g)$ +	$Cl_2(g)$	$\rightleftharpoons$	$COCl_2(g)$	$K_p = 1.5 \times 10^8$
Initial	0	0		5.0 atm	
	x atm $COCl_2$ reacts to reach equilibrium				
Change	$+x$	$+x$	$\leftarrow$	$-x$	
Equil.	x	x		$5.0 - x$	

$$K_p = 1.5 \times 10^8 = \frac{5.0 - x}{x^2} \approx \frac{5.0}{x^2} \quad \text{(Assuming } 5.0 - x \approx 5.0.\text{)}$$

Solving: $x = 1.8 \times 10^{-4}$ atm. Check assumptions: $5.0 - x = 5.0 - 1.8 \times 10^{-4} = 5.0$ atm. Assumptions are good (well within the 5% rule).

$P_{CO} = P_{Cl_2} = 1.8 \times 10^{-4}$ atm and $P_{COCl_2} = 5.0$ atm

Le Châtelier's Principle

51. Only statement d is correct. Addition of a catalyst has no effect on the equilibrium position; the reaction just reaches equilibrium more quickly. Statement a is false for reactants that are either solids or liquids (adding more of these has no effect on the equilibrium). Statement b is false always. If temperature remains constant, then the value of K is constant. Statement c is false for exothermic reactions where an increase in temperature decreases the value of K.

53. a. No effect; adding more of a pure solid or pure liquid has no effect on the equilibrium position.

    b. Shifts left; HF(g) will be removed by reaction with the glass. As HF(g) is removed, the reaction will shift left to produce more HF(g).

    c. Shifts right; as $H_2O(g)$ is removed, the reaction will shift right to produce more $H_2O(g)$.

55. $H^+ + OH^- \rightarrow H_2O$; sodium hydroxide (NaOH) will react with the H^+ on the product side of the reaction. This effectively removes H^+ from the equilibrium, which will shift the reaction to the right to produce more H^+ and CrO_4^{2-}. Because more CrO_4^{2-} is produced, the solution turns yellow.

57. a. Right b. Right c. No effect; He(g) is neither a reactant nor a product.

    d. Left; because the reaction is exothermic, heat is a product:

    $CO(g) + H_2O(g) \rightarrow H_2(g) + CO_2(g) + \text{heat}$

    Increasing T will add heat. The equilibrium shifts to the left to use up the added heat.

    e. No effect; because the moles of gaseous reactants equals the moles of gaseous products (2 mol versus 2 mol), a change in volume will have no effect on the equilibrium.

59. a. Left b. Right c. Left

d. No effect; the reactant and product concentrations/partial pressures are unchanged.

e. No effect; because there are equal numbers of product and reactant gas molecules, a change in volume has no effect on this equilibrium position.

f. Right; a decrease in temperature will shift the equilibrium to the right because heat is a product in this reaction (as is true in all exothermic reactions).

61. An endothermic reaction, where heat is a reactant, will shift right to products with an increase in temperature. The amount of $NH_3(g)$ will increase as the reaction shifts right, so the smell of ammonia will increase.

Additional Exercises

63. a. $N_2(g) + O_2(g) \rightleftharpoons 2\ NO(g) \quad K_p = 1 \times 10^{-31} = \dfrac{P_{NO}^2}{P_{N_2} \times P_{O_2}} = \dfrac{P_{NO}^2}{(0.8)(0.2)}$

$P_{NO} = 1 \times 10^{-16}$ atm

In 1.0 cm³ of air: $n_{NO} = \dfrac{PV}{RT} = \dfrac{(1 \times 10^{-16}\ \text{atm})(1.0 \times 10^{-3}\ \text{L})}{\left(\dfrac{0.08206\ \text{L atm}}{\text{K mol}}\right)(298\ \text{K})} = 4 \times 10^{-21}$ mol NO

$$\frac{4 \times 10^{-21}\ \text{mol NO}}{\text{cm}^3} \times \frac{6.02 \times 10^{23}\ \text{molecules}}{\text{mol NO}} = \frac{2 \times 10^3\ \text{molecules NO}}{\text{cm}^3}$$

b. There is more NO in the atmosphere than we would expect from the value of K. The answer must lie in the rates of the reaction. At 25°C, the rates of both reactions:

$$N_2 + O_2 \rightarrow 2\ NO \quad \text{and} \quad 2\ NO \rightarrow N_2 + O_2$$

are so slow that they are essentially zero. Very strong bonds must be broken; the activation energy is very high. Therefore, the reaction essentially doesn't occur at low temperatures. Nitric oxide, however, can be produced in high-energy or high-temperature environments because the production of NO is endothermic. In nature, some NO is produced by lightning and the primary manmade source is automobiles. At these high temperatures, K will increase, and the rates of the reaction will also increase, resulting in a higher production of NO. Once the NO gets into a more normal temperature environment, it doesn't go back to N_2 and O_2 because of the slow rate.

65.

$O(g) + NO(g) \rightleftharpoons NO_2(g)$	$K = 1/6.8 \times 10^{-49} = 1.5 \times 10^{48}$
$NO_2(g) + O_2(g) \rightleftharpoons NO(g) + O_3(g)$	$K = 1/5.8 \times 10^{-34} = 1.7 \times 10^{33}$
$O_2(g) + O(g) \rightleftharpoons O_3(g)$	$K = (1.5 \times 10^{48})(1.7 \times 10^{33}) = 2.6 \times 10^{81}$

67. $3\,H_2(g) + N_2(g) \rightleftharpoons 2\,NH_3(g)$

	$3\,H_2(g)$	$N_2(g)$		$2\,NH_3(g)$
Initial	$[H_2]_0$	$[N_2]_0$		0
	x mol/L of N_2 reacts to reach equilibrium			
Change	$-3x$	$-x$	$\rightarrow$	$+2x$
Equil.	$[H_2]_0 - 3x$	$[N_2]_0 - x$		$2x$

From the problem:

$$[NH_3]_e = 4.0\,M = 2x,\; x = 2.0\,M;\; [H_2]_e = 5.0\,M = [H_2]_0 - 3x;\; [N_2]_e = 8.0\,M = [N_2]_0 - x$$

$5.0\,M = [H_2]_0 - 3(2.0\,M)$, $[H_2]_0 = 11.0\,M$; $8.0\,M = [N_2]_0 - 2.0\,M$, $[N_2]_0 = 10.0\,M$

69. a. $PCl_5(g) \rightleftharpoons PCl_3(g) + Cl_2(g) \qquad K_p = (P_{PCl_3} \times P_{Cl_2})/P_{PCl_5}$

	$PCl_5(g)$		$PCl_3(g)$	$Cl_2(g)$	
Initial	P_0		0	0	P_0 = initial PCl_5 pressure
Change	$-x$	$\rightarrow$	$+x$	$+x$	
Equil.	$P_0 - x$		x	x	

$P_{total} = P_0 - x + x + x = P_0 + x = 358.7$ torr

$$P_0 = \frac{n_{PCl_5}RT}{V} = \frac{\dfrac{2.4156\text{ g}}{208.22\text{ g/mol}} \times \dfrac{0.08206\text{ L atm}}{\text{K mol}} \times 523.2\text{ K}}{2.000\text{ L}} = 0.2490\text{ atm (or 189.2 torr)}$$

$x = P_{total} - P_0 = 358.7 - 189.2 = 169.5$ torr

$P_{PCl_3} = P_{Cl_2} = 169.5\text{ torr} \times 1\text{ atm}/760\text{ torr} = 0.2230\text{ atm}$

$P_{PCl_5} = 189.2 - 169.5 = 19.7\text{ torr} \times 1\text{ atm}/760\text{ torr} = 0.0259\text{ atm}$

$$K_p = \frac{(0.2230)^2}{0.0259} = 1.92$$

b. $$P_{Cl_2} = \frac{n_{Cl_2}RT}{V} = \frac{0.250 \times 0.08206 \times 523.2}{2.000} = 5.37\text{ atm } Cl_2\text{ added}$$

	$PCl_5(g)$	$\rightleftharpoons$	$PCl_3(g)$	$+\;Cl_2(g)$	
Initial	0.0259 atm		0.2230 atm	0.2230 atm	(from a)
	Adding 0.250 mol Cl_2 increases P_{Cl_2} by 5.37 atm.				
Initial'	0.0259		0.2230	5.59	
Change	+0.2230	$\leftarrow$	−0.2230	−0.2230	React completely
After	0.2489		0	5.37	New initial
Change	$-x$	$\rightarrow$	$+x$	$+x$	
Equil.	$0.2489 - x$		x	$5.37 + x$	

$$\frac{(5.37 + x)(x)}{(0.2489 - x)} = 1.92,\ x^2 + (7.29)x - 0.478 = 0$$

Solving using the quadratic formula: $x = 0.0650$ atm

$P_{PCl_3} = 0.0650$ atm; $P_{PCl_5} = 0.2489 - 0.0650 = 0.1839$ atm; $P_{Cl_2} = 5.37 + 0.0650 = 5.44$ atm

71. $N_2O_4(g) \rightleftharpoons 2\ NO_2(g)$ $\qquad K_p = \frac{P^2_{NO_2}}{P_{N_2O_4}} = \frac{(1.20)^2}{0.34} = 4.2$

Doubling the volume decreases each partial pressure by a factor of 2 (P = nRT/V). $P_{NO_2} = 0.600$ atm and $P_{N_2O_4} = 0.17$ atm are the new partial pressures.

$$Q = \frac{(0.600)^2}{0.17} = 2.1,\ Q < K;$$ equilibrium will shift to the right.

	$N_2O_4(g)$	$\rightleftharpoons$	$2\ NO_2(g)$
Initial	0.17 atm		0.600 atm
Equil.	$0.17 - x$		$0.600 + 2x$

$$K_p = 4.2 = \frac{(0.600 + 2x)^2}{(0.17 - x)},\ 4x^2 + (6.6)x - 0.354 = 0$$ (carrying extra sig. figs.)

Solving using the quadratic formula: $x = 0.052$ atm

$P_{NO_2} = 0.600 + 2(0.052) = 0.704$ atm; $P_{N_2O_4} = 0.17 - 0.052 = 0.12$ atm

73. a. $2\ NaHCO_3(s) \rightleftharpoons Na_2CO_3(s) + CO_2(g) + H_2O(g)$ $\qquad K_p = 0.25$

	$2\ NaHCO_3(s)$		$Na_2CO_3(s)$	$CO_2(g)$	$H_2O(g)$
Initial	–		–	0	0

$NaHCO_3(s)$ decomposes to form x atm each of $CO_2(g)$ and $H_2O(g)$ at equilibrium.

	$2\ NaHCO_3(s)$		$Na_2CO_3(s)$	$CO_2(g)$	$H_2O(g)$
Change	–	→	–	$+x$	$+x$
Equil.	–		–	x	x

$K_p = 0.25 = P_{CO_2} \times P_{H_2O}$, $0.25 = x^2$, $x = P_{CO_2} = P_{H_2O} = 0.50$ atm

b. $$n_{CO_2} = \frac{P_{CO_2}V}{RT} = \frac{(0.50\ \text{atm})(1.00\ \text{L})}{(0.08206\ \text{L atm K}^{-1}\ \text{mol}^{-1})(398\ \text{K})} = 1.5 \times 10^{-2}\ \text{mol } CO_2$$

Mass of Na_2CO_3 produced:

$$1.5 \times 10^{-2} \text{ mol } CO_2 \times \frac{1 \text{ mol } Na_2CO_3}{\text{mol } CO_2} \times \frac{106.0 \text{ g } Na_2CO_3}{\text{mol } Na_2CO_3} = 1.6 \text{ g } Na_2CO_3$$

Mass of $NaHCO_3$ reacted:

$$1.5 \times 10^{-2} \text{ mol } CO_2 \times \frac{2 \text{ mol } NaHCO_3}{\text{mol } CO_2} \times \frac{84.01 \text{ g } NaHCO_3}{\text{mol}} = 2.5 \text{ g } NaHCO_3$$

Mass of $NaHCO_3$ remaining = 10.0 – 2.5 = 7.5 g

c. $$10.0 \text{ g } NaHCO_3 \times \frac{1 \text{ mol } NaHCO_3}{84.01 \text{ g } NaHCO_3} \times \frac{1 \text{ mol } CO_2}{2 \text{ mol } NaHCO_3} = 5.95 \times 10^{-2} \text{ mol } CO_2$$

When all the $NaHCO_3$ has just been consumed, we will have 5.95×10^{-2} mol CO_2 gas at a pressure of 0.50 atm (from a).

$$V = \frac{nRT}{P} = \frac{(5.95 \times 10^{-2} \text{ mol})(0.08206 \text{ L atm K}^{-1} \text{ mol}^{-1})(398 \text{ K})}{0.50 \text{ atm}} = 3.9 \text{ L}$$

75. $$NH_3(g) + H_2S(g) \rightleftharpoons NH_4HS(s) \quad K = 400. = \frac{1}{[NH_3][H_2S]}$$

	$NH_3(g)$	$H_2S(g)$	$NH_4HS(s)$
Initial	$\frac{2.00 \text{ mol}}{5.00 \text{ L}}$	$\frac{2.00 \text{ mol}}{5.00 \text{ L}}$	–
	x mol/L of NH_3 reacts to reach equilibrium		
Change	$-x$	$-x$	–
Equil.	$0.400 - x$	$0.400 - x$	–

$$K = 400. = \frac{1}{(0.400 - x)(0.400 - x)}, \quad 0.400 - x = \left(\frac{1}{400.}\right)^{1/2} = 0.0500, \quad x = 0.350\ M$$

$$\text{Mol } NH_4HS(s) \text{ produced} = 5.00 \text{ L} \times \frac{0.350 \text{ mol } NH_3}{\text{L}} \times \frac{1 \text{ mol } NH_4HS}{\text{mol } NH_3} = 1.75 \text{ mol}$$

Total mol $NH_4HS(s)$ = 2.00 mol initially + 1.75 mol produced = 3.75 mol total

$$3.75 \text{ mol } NH_4HS \times \frac{51.12 \text{ g } NH_4HS}{\text{mol } NH_4HS} = 192 \text{ g } NH_4HS$$

$[H_2S]_e = 0.400\ M - x = 0.400\ M - 0.350\ M = 0.050\ M\ H_2S$

$$P_{H_2S} = \frac{n_{H_2S}RT}{V} = \frac{n_{H_2S}}{V} \times RT = \frac{0.050 \text{ mol}}{\text{L}} \times \frac{0.08206 \text{ L atm}}{\text{K mol}} \times 308.2 \text{ K} = 1.3 \text{ atm}$$

77. $5.63 \text{ g } C_5H_6O_3 \times \dfrac{1 \text{ mol } C_5H_6O_3}{114.10 \text{ g}} = 0.0493 \text{ mol } C_5H_6O_3$ initially

Total moles of gas at equilibrium $= n_{total} = \dfrac{P_{total}V}{RT} = \dfrac{1.63 \text{ atm} \times 2.50 \text{ L}}{\dfrac{0.08206 \text{ L atm}}{\text{K mol}} \times 473 \text{ K}} = 0.105 \text{ mol}$

$$C_5H_6O_3(g) \rightleftharpoons C_2H_6(g) + 3\,CO(g)$$

	$C_5H_6O_3(g)$		$C_2H_6(g)$	$3\,CO(g)$
Initial	0.0493 mol		0	0
	Let x mol $C_5H_6O_3$ react to reach equilibrium.			
Change	$-x$	$\rightarrow$	$-x$	$-3x$
Equil.	$0.0493 - x$		x	$3x$

$0.105 \text{ mol total} = 0.0493 - x + x + 3x = 0.0493 + 3x, \; x = 0.0186 \text{ mol}$

$$K = \frac{[C_2H_6][CO]^3}{[C_5H_6O_3]} = \frac{\left[\dfrac{0.0186 \text{ mol } C_2H_6}{2.50 \text{ L}}\right]\left[\dfrac{3(0.0186) \text{ mol CO}}{2.50 \text{ L}}\right]^3}{\left[\dfrac{(0.0493 - 0.0186) \text{ mol } C_5H_6O_3}{2.50 \text{ L}}\right]} = 6.74 \times 10^{-6}$$

Challenge Problems

79. a.

$$2\,NO(g) + Br_2(g) \rightleftharpoons 2\,NOBr(g)$$

	$2\,NO(g)$	$Br_2(g)$		$2\,NOBr(g)$
Initial	98.4 torr	41.3 torr		0
	$2x$ torr of NO reacts to reach equilibrium			
Change	$-2x$	$-x$	$\rightarrow$	$+2x$
Equil.	$98.4 - 2x$	$41.3 - x$		$2x$

$P_{total} = P_{NO} + P_{Br_2} + P_{NOBr} = (98.4 - 2x) + (41.3 - x) + 2x = 139.7 - x$

$P_{total} = 110.5 = 139.7 - x, \; x = 29.2 \text{ torr}; \; P_{NO} = 98.4 - 2(29.2) = 40.0 \text{ torr} = 0.0526 \text{ atm}$

$P_{Br_2} = 41.3 - 29.2 = 12.1 \text{ torr} = 0.0159 \text{ atm}; \; P_{NOBr} = 2(29.2) = 58.4 \text{ torr} = 0.0768 \text{ atm}$

$$K_p = \frac{P_{NOBr}^2}{P_{NO}^2 \times P_{Br_2}} = \frac{(0.0768 \text{ atm})^2}{(0.0526 \text{ atm})^2(0.0159 \text{ atm})} = 134$$

b.

$$2\,NO(g) + Br_2(g) \rightleftharpoons 2\,NOBr(g)$$

	$2\,NO(g)$	$Br_2(g)$		$2\,NOBr(g)$
Initial	0.30 atm	0.30 atm		0
	$2x$ atm of NO reacts to reach equilibrium			
Change	$-2x$	$-x$	$\rightarrow$	$+2x$
Equil.	$0.30 - 2x$	$0.30 - x$		$2x$

This would yield a cubic equation, which can be difficult to solve unless you have a graphing calculator. Because K_p is pretty large, let's approach equilibrium in two steps: Assume the reaction goes to completion, and then solve the back equilibrium problem.

	2 NO	+	Br_2	⇌	2 NOBr	
Before	0.30 atm		0.30 atm		0	
	Let 0.30 atm NO react completely.					
Change	−0.30		−0.15	→	+0.30	React completely
After	0		0.15		0.30	New initial
	$2y$ atm of NOBr reacts to reach equilibrium					
Change	$+2y$		$+y$	←	$-2y$	
Equil.	$2y$		$0.15 + y$		$0.30 - 2y$	

$$K_p = 134 = \frac{(0.30 - 2y)^2}{(2y)^2(0.15 + y)}, \quad \frac{(0.30 - 2y)^2}{(0.15 + y)} = 134 \times 4y^2 = 536y^2$$

If $y << 0.15$: $\dfrac{(0.30)^2}{0.15} \approx 536y^2$ and $y = 0.034$; assumptions are poor (y is 23% of 0.15).

Use 0.034 as an approximation for y, and solve by successive approximations (see Appendix 1):

$$\frac{(0.30 - 0.068)^2}{0.15 + 0.034} = 536y^2,\ y = 0.023; \qquad \frac{(0.30 - 0.046)^2}{0.15 + 0.023} = 536y^2,\ y = 0.026$$

$$\frac{(0.30 - 0.052)^2}{0.15 + 0.026} = 536y^2,\ y = 0.026 \text{ atm}$$ (We have converged on the correct answer.)

So: $P_{NO} = 2y = 0.052$ atm; $P_{Br_2} = 0.15 + y = 0.18$ atm; $P_{NOBr} = 0.30 - 2y = 0.25$ atm

81. $P_4(g) \rightleftharpoons 2\ P_2(g)$ $K_p = 0.100 = \dfrac{P_{P_2}^2}{P_{P_4}}$; $P_{P_4} + P_{P_2} = P_{total} = 1.00$ atm, $P_{P_4} = 1.00 - P_{P_2}$

Let $y = P_{P_2}$ at equilibrium, then $K_p = \dfrac{y^2}{1.00 - y} = 0.100$

Solving: $y = 0.270$ atm $= P_{P_2}$; $P_{P_4} = 1.00 - 0.270 = 0.73$ atm

To solve for the fraction dissociated, we need the initial pressure of P_4.

	$P_4(g)$	⇌	$2\ P_2(g)$	
Initial	P_0		0	P_0 = initial pressure of P_4
	x atm of P_4 reacts to reach equilibrium			
Change	$-x$	→	$+2x$	
Equil.	$P_0 - x$		$2x$	

$P_{total} = P_0 - x + 2x = 1.00 \text{ atm} = P_0 + x$

Solving: $0.270 \text{ atm} = P_{P_2} = 2x,\ x = 0.135 \text{ atm};\ P_0 = 1.00 - 0.135 = 0.87 \text{ atm}$

Fraction dissociated $= \dfrac{x}{P_0} = \dfrac{0.135}{0.87} = 0.16$, or 16% of P_4 is dissociated to reach equilibrium.

83. $$d = \text{density} = \frac{P \times (\text{molar mass})}{RT} = \frac{P_{O_2}(\text{molar mass}_{O_2}) + P_{O_3}(\text{molar mass}_{O_3})}{RT}$$

$$0.168 \text{ g/L} = \frac{P_{O_2}(32.00 \text{ g/mol}) + P_{O_3}(48.00 \text{ g/mol})}{\frac{0.08206 \text{ L atm}}{\text{K mol}} \times 448 \text{ K}},\quad (32.00)P_{O_2} + (48.00)P_{O_3} = 6.18$$

$$P_{total} = P_{O_2} + P_{O_3} = 128 \text{ torr} \times \frac{1 \text{ atm}}{760 \text{ torr}} = 0.168 \text{ atm}$$

We have two equations in two unknowns. Solving using simultaneous equations:

$$\begin{array}{rcl} (32.00)P_{O_2} + (48.00)P_{O_3} & = & 6.18 \\ -(32.00)P_{O_2} - (32.00)P_{O_3} & = & -5.38 \\ \hline (16.00)P_{O_3} & = & 0.80 \end{array}$$

$$P_{O_3} = \frac{0.80}{16.00} = 0.050 \text{ atm and } P_{O_2} = 0.118 \text{ atm};\ K_p = \frac{P_{O_3}^2}{P_{O_2}^3} = \frac{(0.050)^2}{(0.118)^3} = 1.5$$

85. $$4.72 \text{ g } CH_3OH \times \frac{1 \text{ mol}}{32.04 \text{ g}} = 0.147 \text{ mol } CH_3OH \text{ initially}$$

Graham's law of effusion: $\dfrac{\text{Rate}_1}{\text{Rate}_2} = \sqrt{\dfrac{M_2}{M_1}}$

$$\frac{\text{Rate}_{H_2}}{\text{Rate}_{CH_3OH}} = \sqrt{\frac{M_{CH_3OH}}{M_{H_2}}} = \sqrt{\frac{32.04}{2.016}} = 3.987$$

The effused mixture has 33.0 times as much H_2 as CH_3OH. When the effusion rate ratio is multiplied by the equilibrium mole ratio of H_2 to CH_3OH, the effused mixture will have 33.0 times as much H_2 as CH_3OH. Let n_{H_2} and n_{CH_3OH} equal the equilibrium moles of H_2 and CH_3OH, respectively.

$$33.0 = 3.987 \times \frac{n_{H_2}}{n_{CH_3OH}},\quad \frac{n_{H_2}}{n_{CH_3OH}} = 8.28$$

	$CH_3OH(g)$	$\rightleftharpoons$	$CO(g)$	$+ 2\ H_2(g)$
Initial	0.147 mol		0	0
Change	$-x$	$\rightarrow$	$+x$	$+2x$
Equil.	$0.147 - x$		x	$2x$

From the ICE table, $8.28 = \dfrac{n_{H_2}}{n_{CH_3OH}} = \dfrac{2x}{0.147 - x}$

Solving: $x = 0.118$ mol

$$K = \frac{[CO][H_2]^2}{[CH_3OH]} = \frac{\left(\dfrac{0.118\ \text{mol}}{1.00\ \text{L}}\right)\left(\dfrac{2(0.118\ \text{mol})}{1.00\ \text{L}}\right)^2}{\dfrac{(0.147 - 0.118)\ \text{mol}}{1.00\ \text{L}}} = 0.23$$

87. a. $P_{PCl_5} = \dfrac{n_{PCl_5}RT}{V} = \dfrac{0.100\ \text{mol} \times \dfrac{0.08206\ \text{L atm}}{\text{K mol}} \times 480.\ \text{K}}{12.0\ \text{L}} = 0.328$ atm

	$PCl_5(g)$	$\rightleftharpoons$	$PCl_3(g)$	+	$Cl_2(g)$	$K_p = 0.267$
Initial	0.328 atm		0		0	
Change	$-x$	$\rightarrow$	$+x$		$+x$	
Equil.	$0.328 - x$		x		x	

$K_p = \dfrac{x^2}{0.328 - x} = 0.267$, $x^2 + (0.267)x - 0.08758 = 0$ (carrying extra sig. figs.)

Solving using the quadratic formula: $x = 0.191$ atm

$P_{PCl_3} = P_{Cl_2} = 0.191$ atm; $P_{PCl_5} = 0.328 - 0.191 = 0.137$ atm

b.

	$PCl_5(g)$	$\rightleftharpoons$	$PCl_3(g)$	+	$Cl_2(g)$	
Initial	P_0		0		0	P_0 = initial pressure of PCl_5
Change	$-x$	$\rightarrow$	$+x$		$+x$	
Equil.	$P_0 - x$		x		x	

$P_{total} = 2.00\ \text{atm} = (P_0 - x) + x + x = P_0 + x$, $P_0 = 2.00 - x$

$K_p = \dfrac{x^2}{P_0 - x} = 0.267$; $\dfrac{x^2}{2.00 - 2x} = 0.267$, $x^2 = 0.534 - (0.534)x$

$x^2 + (0.534)x - 0.534 = 0$; solving using the quadratic formula:

$$x = \frac{-0.534 \pm \sqrt{(0.534)^2 + 4(0.534)}}{2} = 0.511\ \text{atm}$$

$P_0 = 2.00 - x = 2.00 - 0.511 = 1.49$ atm; the initial pressure of PCl_5 was 1.49 atm.

$$n_{PCl_5} = \frac{P_{PCl_5}V}{RT} = \frac{(1.49\text{ atm})(5.00\text{ L})}{(0.08206\text{ L atm K}^{-1}\text{ mol}^{-1})(480.\text{ K})} = 0.189\text{ mol }PCl_5$$

0.189 mol PCl_5 × 208.22 g PCl_5/mol = 39.4 g PCl_5 was initially introduced.

89. $N_2(g) + O_2(g) \rightleftharpoons 2\,NO(g)$ Let:

equilibrium $P_{O_2} = p$

Equil. $(3.7)p$ p x

equilibrium $P_{N_2} = (78/21)P_{O_2} = (3.7)p$

equilibrium $P_{NO} = x$

equilibrium $P_{NO_2} = y$

$$K_p = 1.5 \times 10^{-4} = \frac{P_{NO}^2}{P_{O_2} \times P_{N_2}}$$

$N_2 + 2\,O_2 \rightleftharpoons 2\,NO_2$

Equil. $(3.7)p$ p y

$$K_p = 1.0 \times 10^{-5} = \frac{P_{NO_2}^2}{P_{O_2}^2 \times P_{N_2}}$$

We want $P_{NO_2} = P_{NO}$ at equilibrium, so $x = y$.

Taking the ratio of the two K_p expressions:

$$\frac{\dfrac{P_{NO}^2}{P_{O_2} \times P_{N_2}}}{\dfrac{P_{NO_2}^2}{P_{O_2}^2 \times P_{N_2}}} = \frac{1.5 \times 10^{-4}}{1.0 \times 10^{-5}};\ \text{because } P_{NO} = P_{NO_2}:\ P_{O_2} = \frac{1.5 \times 10^{-4}}{1.0 \times 10^{-5}} = 15\text{ atm}$$

Air is 21 mol % O_2, so: $P_{O_2} = (0.21)P_{total}$, $P_{total} = \dfrac{15\text{ atm}}{0.21} = 71$ atm

To solve for the equilibrium concentrations of all gases (not required to answer the question), solve one of the K_p expressions where $p = P_{O_2} = 15$ atm.

$$1.5 \times 10^{-4} = \frac{x^2}{15[3.7(15)]},\ x = P_{NO} = P_{NO_2} = 0.35\text{ atm}$$

Equilibrium pressures:

$P_{O_2} = 15$ atm; $P_{N_2} = 3.7(15) = 55.5 = 56$ atm; $P_{NO} = P_{NO_2} = 0.35$ atm

91. $SO_3(g) \rightleftharpoons SO_2(g) + 1/2\ O_2(g)$

	$SO_3(g)$		$SO_2(g)$	$1/2\ O_2(g)$	
Initial	P_0		0	0	P_0 = initial pressure of SO_3
Change	$-x$	$\rightarrow$	$+x$	$+x/2$	
Equil.	$P_0 - x$		x	$x/2$	

Average molar mass of the mixture is:

$$\text{average molar mass} = \frac{dRT}{P} = \frac{(1.60\ \text{g/L})(0.08206\ \text{L atm K}^{-1}\ \text{mol}^{-1})(873\ \text{K})}{1.80\ \text{atm}} = 63.7\ \text{g/mol}$$

The average molar mass is determined by:

$$\text{average molar mass} = \frac{n_{SO_3}(80.07\ \text{g/mol}) + n_{SO_2}(64.07\ \text{g/mol}) + n_{O_2}(32.00\ \text{g/mol})}{n_{total}}$$

Because χ_A = mol fraction of component A = $n_A/n_{total} = P_A/P_{total}$:

$$63.7\ \text{g/mol} = = \frac{P_{SO_3}(80.07) + P_{SO_2}(64.07) + P_{O_2}(32.00)}{P_{total}}$$

$P_{total} = P_0 - x + x + x/2 = P_0 + x/2 = 1.80$ atm, $P_0 = 1.80 - x/2$

$$63.7 = \frac{(P_0 - x)(80.07) + x(64.07) + \frac{x}{2}(32.00)}{1.80}$$

$$63.7 = \frac{(1.80 - 3/2\ x)(80.07) + x(64.07) + \frac{x}{2}(32.00)}{1.80}$$

$115 = 144 - (120.1)x + (64.07)x + (16.00)x$, $(40.0)x = 29$, $x = 0.73$ atm

$P_{SO_3} = P_0 - x = 1.80 - (3/2)x = 0.71$ atm; $P_{SO_2} = 0.73$ atm; $P_{O_2} = x/2 = 0.37$ atm

$$K_p = \frac{P_{SO_2} \times P_{O_2}^{1/2}}{P_{SO_3}} = \frac{(0.73)(0.37)^{1/2}}{(0.71)} = 0.63$$

93. $N_2(g) + 3\ H_2(g) \rightleftharpoons 2\ NH_3(g)$ $\quad K_p = \frac{P_{NH_3}^2}{P_{N_2} \times P_{H_2}^3} = 6.5 \times 10^{-3}$

<u>1.0 atm</u>	$N_2(g)$	+	$3\ H_2(g)$	$\rightleftharpoons$	$2\ NH_3(g)$
Initial	0.25 atm		0.75 atm		0
Equil.	$0.25 - x$		$0.75 - 3x$		$2x$

$$\frac{(2x)^2}{(0.75-3x)^3(0.25-x)} = 6.5 \times 10^{-3}; \text{ using successive approximations:}$$

$x = 1.2 \times 10^{-2}$ atm; $P_{NH_3} = 2x = 0.024$ atm

10 atm	$N_2(g)$	+	$3\ H_2(g)$	$\rightleftharpoons$	$2\ NH_3(g)$
Initial	2.5 atm		7.5 atm		0
Equil.	$2.5 - x$		$7.5 - 3x$		$2x$

$$\frac{(2x)^2}{(7.5-3x)^3(2.5-x)} = 6.5 \times 10^{-3}; \text{ using successive approximations:}$$

$x = 0.69$ atm; $P_{NH_3} = 1.4$ atm

100 atm Using the same setup as above: $\dfrac{4x^2}{(75-3x)^3(25-x)} = 6.5 \times 10^{-3}$

Solving by successive approximations: $x = 16$ atm; $P_{NH_3} = 32$ atm

1000 atm

	$N_2(g)$	+	$3\ H_2(g)$	$\rightleftharpoons$	$2\ NH_3(g)$
Initial	250 atm		750 atm		0
	Let 250 atm N_2 react completely.				
New initial	0		0		5.0×10^2
Equil.	x		$3x$		$5.0 \times 10^2 - 2x$

$$\frac{(5.0 \times 10^2 - 2x)^2}{(3x)^3 x} = 6.5 \times 10^{-3}; \text{ using successive approximations:}$$

$x = 32$ atm; $P_{NH_3} = 5.0 \times 10^2 - 2x = 440$ atm

The results are plotted as $\log P_{NH_3}$ versus $\log P_{total}$. Notice that as P_{total} increases, a larger fraction of N_2 and H_2 is converted to NH_3, that is, as P_{total} increases (V decreases), the reaction shifts further to the right, as predicted by LeChatelier's principle.

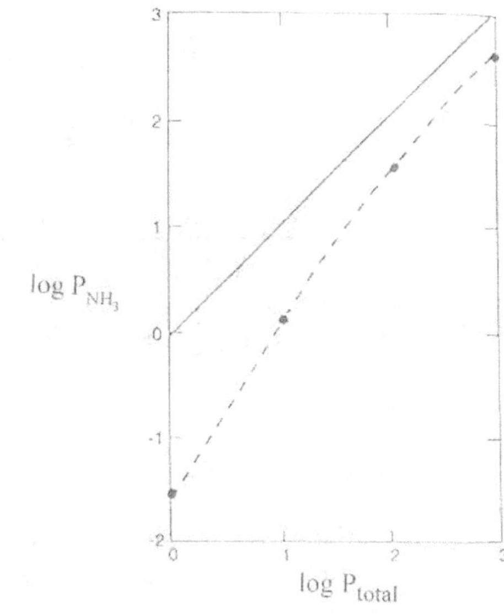

95. $\dfrac{2.00\text{ g}}{165\text{ g/mol}} = 0.0121$ mol XY (initially)

$(0.350)(0.0121\text{ mol}) = 4.24 \times 10^{-3}$ mol XY dissociated

	XY	→	X	+	Y
Initial	0.0121 mol		0		0
Change	−0.00424	→	+0.00424		+0.00424
Equil.	0.0079 mol		0.00424 mol		0.00424 mol

Total moles of gas = 0.0079 + 0.00424 + 0.00424 = 0.0164 mol

$$V \propto n\text{, so: } \frac{V_{final}}{V_{initial}} = \frac{n_{final}}{n_{initial}} = \frac{0.0164\text{ mol}}{0.0121\text{ mol}} = 1.36$$

$$V_{initial} = \frac{nRT}{P} = \frac{(0.0121\text{ mol})(0.008206\text{ L atm K}^{-1}\text{ mol}^{-1})(298\text{ K})}{0.967\text{ atm}} = 0.306\text{ L}$$

$V_{final} = 0.306\text{ L}(1.36) = 0.416\text{ L}$

Because mass is conserved in a chemical reaction:

$$\text{density (final)} = \frac{\text{mass}}{\text{volume}} = \frac{2.00\text{ g}}{0.416\text{ L}} = 4.81\text{ g/L}$$

$$K = \frac{[X][Y]}{[XY]} = \frac{\left(\dfrac{0.00424\text{ mol}}{0.416\text{ L}}\right)^2}{\left(\dfrac{0.0079\text{ mol}}{0.416\text{ L}}\right)} = 5.5 \times 10^{-3}$$

CHAPTER 7

ACIDS AND BASES

Nature of Acids and Bases

17. a. The first equation is for the reaction of some generic acid, HA, with H_2O.

HA + H_2O	$\rightleftharpoons$	H_3O^+	+	A^-
Acid Base		Conjugate Acid of H_2O		Conjugate Base of HA

HA is the proton donor (the acid) and H_2O is the proton acceptor (the base). In the reverse reaction, H_3O^+ is the proton donor (the acid) and A^- is the proton acceptor (the base).

The second equation is for some generic base, B, with some generic acid, HX. Note that B has three hydrogens bonded to it.

B + HX	$\rightleftharpoons$	BH^+	+	X^-
Base Acid		Conjugate Acid of B		Conjugate Base of HX

B is the proton acceptor (the base) and HX is the proton donor (the acid). When B accepts a proton, the central atom goes from having 3 bonded hydrogens to 4 bonded hydrogens. In the reverse reaction, BH^+ is the proton donor (the acid) and X^- is the proton acceptor (the base).

b. Arrhenius acids produce H^+ in solution. So HA in the first equation is an Arrhenius acid. However, in the second equation, H^+ is not a product, so HX is not an Arrhenius acid. Both HA in the first equation and HX in the second equation are proton donors, so both are considered Brønsted-Lowry acids.

For the bases in the two equations, H_2O and B, neither of them produce OH^- in their equations, so neither of them are Arrhenius bases. Both H_2O and B accept protons, so both are Brønsted-Lowry bases.

19. An acid is a proton (H^+) donor, and a base is a proton acceptor. A conjugate acid-base pair differs by only a proton (H^+) in the formulas.

	Acid	Base	Conjugate Base of Acid	Conjugate Acid of Base
a.	H_2CO_3	H_2O	HCO_3^-	H_3O^+
b.	$C_5H_5NH^+$	H_2O	C_5H_5N	H_3O^+
c.	$C_5H_5NH^+$	HCO_3^-	C_5H_5N	H_2CO_3

21. The dissociation reaction (the K_a reaction) of an acid in water commonly omits water as a reactant. We will follow this practice. All dissociation reactions produce H^+ and the conjugate base of the acid that is dissociated.

a. $HC_2H_3O_2(aq) \rightleftharpoons H^+(aq) + C_2H_3O_2^-(aq)$ $\quad K_a = \dfrac{[H^+][C_2H_3O_2^-]}{[HC_2H_3O_2]}$

b. $Co(H_2O)_6^{3+}(aq) \rightleftharpoons H^+(aq) + Co(H_2O)_5(OH)^{2+}(aq)$ $\quad K_a = \dfrac{[H^+][Co(H_2O)_5(OH)^{2+}]}{[Co(H_2O)_6^{3+}]}$

c. $CH_3NH_3^+(aq) \rightleftharpoons H^+(aq) + CH_3NH_2(aq)$ $\quad K_a = \dfrac{[H^+][CH_3NH_2]}{[CH_3NH_3^+]}$

23. The beaker on the left represents a strong acid in solution; the acid HA is 100% dissociated into the H^+ and A^- ions. The beaker on the right represents a weak acid in solution; only a little bit of the acid HB dissociates into ions, so the acid exists mostly as undissociated HB molecules in water.

a. HNO_2: weak acid beaker
b. HNO_3: strong acid beaker
c. HCl: strong acid beaker
d. HF: weak acid beaker
e. $HC_2H_3O_2$: weak acid beaker

25. The K_a value is directly related to acid strength. As K_a increases, acid strength increases. For water, use K_w when comparing the acid strength of water to other species. The K_a values are:

$HClO_4$: strong acid ($K_a >> 1$); $HClO_2$: $K_a = 1.2 \times 10^{-2}$

NH_4^+: $K_a = 5.6 \times 10^{-10}$; H_2O: $K_a = K_w = 1.0 \times 10^{-14}$

From the K_a values, the ordering is: $HClO_4 > HClO_2 > NH_4^+ > H_2O$

27. a. HCl is a strong acid, and water is a very weak acid with $K_a = K_w = 1.0 \times 10^{-14}$. HCl is a much stronger acid than H_2O.

b. H_2O, $K_a = K_w = 1.0 \times 10^{-14}$; HNO_2, $K_a = 4.0 \times 10^{-4}$; HNO_2 is a stronger acid than H_2O because K_a for $HNO_2 > K_w$ for H_2O.

c. HOC_6H_5, $K_a = 1.6 \times 10^{-10}$; HCN, $K_a = 6.2 \times 10^{-10}$; HCN is a slightly stronger acid than HOC_6H_5 because K_a for HCN > K_a for HOC_6H_5.

29. a. H_2O and $CH_3CO_2^-$

b. An acid-base reaction can be thought of as a competition between two opposing bases. Because this equilibrium lies far to the left ($K_a < 1$), $CH_3CO_2^-$ is a stronger base than H_2O.

c. The acetate ion is a better base than water and produces basic solutions in water. When we put acetate ion into solution as the only major basic species, the reaction is:

$$CH_3CO_2^- + H_2O \rightleftharpoons CH_3CO_2H + OH^-$$

Now the competition is between $CH_3CO_2^-$ and OH^- for the proton. Hydroxide ion is the strongest base possible in water. The preceding equilibrium lies far to the left resulting in a K_b value of less than 1. Those species we specifically call weak bases ($10^{-14} < K_b < 1$) lie between H_2O and OH^- in base strength. Weak bases are stronger bases than water but are weaker bases than OH^-.

31. In deciding whether a substance is an acid or a base, strong or weak, you should keep in mind a couple ideas:

1. There are only a few common strong acids and strong bases all of which should be memorized. Common strong acids = HCl, HBr, HI, HNO_3, $HClO_4$, and H_2SO_4. Common strong bases = LiOH, NaOH, KOH, RbOH, CsOH, $Ca(OH)_2$, $Sr(OH)_2$, and $Ba(OH)_2$.

2. All other acids and bases are weak and will have K_a and K_b values of less than 1 but greater than K_w (10^{-14}). Reference Table 7.2 for K_a values for some weak acids and Table 7.3 for K_b values for some weak bases. There are too many weak acids and weak bases to memorize them all. Therefore, use the tables of K_a and K_b values to help you identify weak acids and weak bases. Appendix 5 contains more complete tables of K_a and K_b values.

a. weak acid ($K_a = 4.0 \times 10^{-4}$)
b. strong acid
c. weak base ($K_b = 4.38 \times 10^{-4}$)
d. strong base
e. weak base ($K_b = 1.8 \times 10^{-5}$)
f. weak acid ($K_a = 7.2 \times 10^{-4}$)
g. weak acid ($K_a = 1.8 \times 10^{-4}$)
h. strong base
i. strong acid

Autoionization of Water and pH Scale

33. a. $H_2O(l) \rightleftharpoons H^+(aq) + OH^-(aq)$ $K_w = 2.92 \times 10^{-14} = [H^+][OH^-]$

In pure water: $[H^+] = [OH^-]$, $2.92 \times 10^{-14} = [H^+]^2$, $[H^+] = 1.71 \times 10^{-7}\ M = [OH^-]$

b. $pH = -\log[H^+] = -\log(1.71 \times 10^{-7}) = 6.767$

c. $[H^+] = K_w/[OH^-] = (2.92 \times 10^{-14})/0.10 = 2.9 \times 10^{-13}\ M$; $pH = -\log(2.9 \times 10^{-13}) = 12.54$

35. At 25°C, the relationship $[H^+][OH^-] = K_w = 1.0 \times 10^{-14}$ always holds for aqueous solutions. When $[H^+]$ is greater than $1.0 \times 10^{-7}\ M$, the solution is acidic; when $[H^+]$ is less than $1.0 \times 10^{-7}\ M$, the solution is basic; when $[H^+] = 1.0 \times 10^{-7}\ M$, the solution is neutral. In terms of $[OH^-]$, an acidic solution has $[OH^-] < 1.0 \times 10^{-7}\ M$, a basic solution has $[OH^-] > 1.0 \times 10^{-7}\ M$, and a neutral solution has $[OH^-] = 1.0 \times 10^{-7}\ M$. At 25°C, pH + pOH = 14.00.

a. $[H^+] = \frac{K_W}{[OH^-]} = \frac{1.0 \times 10^{-14}}{1.5} = 6.7 \times 10^{-15}\ M$; basic

$pOH = -\log[OH^-] = -\log(1.5) = -0.18$; $pH = 14.00 - pOH = 14.00 - (-0.18) = 14.18$

b. $[H^+] = \frac{1.0 \times 10^{-14}}{3.6 \times 10^{-15}} = 2.8\ M$; acidic

$pOH = -\log(3.6 \times 10^{-15}) = 14.44$; $pH = 14.00 - 14.44 = -0.44$

c. $[H^+] = \frac{1.0 \times 10^{-14}}{1.0 \times 10^{-7}} = 1.0 \times 10^{-7}\ M$; neutral

$pOH = -\log(1.0 \times 10^{-7}) = 7.00$; $pH = 14.00 - 7.00 = 7.00$

d. $[H^+] = \frac{1.0 \times 10^{-14}}{7.3 \times 10^{-4}} = 1.4 \times 10^{-11}\ M$; basic

$pOH = -\log(7.3 \times 10^{-4}) = 3.14$; $pH = 14.00 - 3.14 = 10.86$

Note that pH is greater than 14.00 when $[OH^-]$ is greater than 1.0 *M* (an extremely basic solution). Also note the the pH is negative when $[H^+]$ is greater than 1.0 *M* (an extremely acidic solution).

37. a. $[H^+] = 10^{-pH}$, $[H^+] = 10^{-7.40} = 4.0 \times 10^{-8}\ M$

$pOH = 14.00 - pH = 14.00 - 7.40 = 6.60$; $[OH^-] = 10^{-pOH} = 10^{-6.60} = 2.5 \times 10^{-7}\ M$

or $[OH^-] = \frac{K_W}{[H^+]} = \frac{1.0 \times 10^{-14}}{4.0 \times 10^{-8}} = 2.5 \times 10^{-7}\ M$; this solution is basic since pH > 7.00.

b. $[H^+] = 10^{-15.3} = 5 \times 10^{-16}\ M$; $pOH = 14.00 - 15.3 = -1.3$; $[OH^-] = 10^{-(-1.3)} = 20\ M$; basic

c. $[H^+] = 10^{-(-1.0)} = 10\ M$; $pOH = 14.0 - (-1.0) = 15.0$; $[OH^-] = 10^{-15.0} =$
$1 \times 10^{-15}\ M$; acidic

d. $[H^+] = 10^{-3.20} = 6.3 \times 10^{-4}$ *M*; pOH = 14.00 – 3.20 = 10.80; $[OH^-] = 10^{-10.80} = 1.6 \times 10^{-11}$ *M*; acidic

e. $[OH^-] = 10^{-5.0} = 1 \times 10^{-5}$ *M*; pH = 14.0 – pOH = 14.0 – 5.0 = 9.0; $[H^+] = 10^{-9.0} = 1 \times 10^{-9}$ *M*; basic

f. $[OH^-] = 10^{-9.60} = 2.5 \times 10^{-10}$ *M*; pH = 14.00 – 9.60 = 4.40; $[H^+] = 10^{-4.40} = 4.0 \times 10^{-5}$ *M*; acidic

Solutions of Acids

39. Strong acids are assumed to completely dissociate in water, for example, $HCl(aq) + H_2O(l) \rightarrow H_3O^+(aq) + Cl^-(aq)$ or $HCl(aq) \rightarrow H^+(aq) + Cl^-(aq)$.

a. A 0.10 *M* HCl solution gives 0.10 *M* H^+ and 0.10 *M* Cl^- because HCl completely dissociates. The amount of H^+ from H_2O will be insignificant.

$pH = -\log[H^+] = -\log(0.10) = 1.00$

b. 5.0 *M* H^+ is produced when 5.0 *M* $HClO_4$ completely dissociates. The amount of H^+ from H_2O will be insignificant. pH = –log(5.0) = –0.70 (Negative pH values just indicate very concentrated acid solutions.)

c. 1.0×10^{-11} *M* H^+ is produced when 1.0×10^{-11} *M* HI completely dissociates. If you take the negative log of 1.0×10^{-11}, this gives pH = 11.00. This is impossible! We dissolved an acid in water and got a basic pH. What we must consider in this problem is that water by itself donates 1.0×10^{-7} *M* H^+. We can normally ignore the small amount of H^+ from H_2O except when we have a very dilute solution of an acid (as in the case here). Therefore, the pH is that of neutral water (pH = 7.00) because the amount of HI present is insignificant.

41. HCl is a strong acid. $[H^+] = 10^{-1.50} = 3.16 \times 10^{-2}$ *M* (carrying one extra sig. fig.)

$$M_1V_1 = M_2V_2, \quad V_1 = \frac{M_2V_2}{M_1} = \frac{3.16 \times 10^{-2}\ \text{mol/L} \times 1.6\ \text{L}}{12\ \text{mol/L}} = 4.2 \times 10^{-3}\ \text{L}$$

4.2 mL of 12 *M* HCl with enough water added to make 1600 mL of solution will result in a solution having $[H^+] = 3.2 \times 10^{-2}$ *M* and pH = 1.50.

43. a. HNO_2 ($K_a = 4.0 \times 10^{-4}$) and H_2O ($K_a = K_w = 1.0 \times 10^{-14}$) are the major species. HNO_2 is a much stronger acid than H_2O, so it is the major source of H^+. However, HNO_2 is a weak acid ($K_a < 1$), so it only partially dissociates in water. We must solve an equilibrium problem to determine $[H^+]$. In the Solutions Guide, we will summarize the *i*nitial, *c*hange, and *e*quilibrium concentrations into one table called the ICE table. Solving the weak acid problem:

	HNO_2	$\rightleftharpoons$	H^+	+	NO_2^-
Initial	0.250 *M*		~0		0
	x mol/L HNO_2 dissociates to reach equilibrium				
Change	$-x$	$\rightarrow$	$+x$		$+x$
Equil.	$0.250 - x$		x		x

$$K_a = \frac{[H^+][NO_2^-]}{[HNO_2]} = 4.0 \times 10^{-4} = \frac{x^2}{0.250 - x};\ \text{if we assume } x << 0.250, \text{ then:}$$

$$4.0 \times 10^{-4} \approx \frac{x^2}{0.250}, \quad x = \sqrt{4.0 \times 10^{-4}(0.250)} = 0.010\ M$$

We must check the assumption: $\frac{x}{0.250} \times 100 = \frac{0.010}{0.250} \times 100 = 4.0\%$

All the assumptions are good. The H^+ contribution from water (1×10^{-7} *M*) is negligible, and *x* is small compared to 0.250 (percent error = 4.0%). If the percent error is less than 5% for an assumption, we will consider it a valid assumption (called the 5% rule). Finishing the problem: $x = 0.010\ M = [H^+]$; pH = −log(0.010) = 2.00

b. CH_3CO_2H ($K_a = 1.8 \times 10^{-5}$) and H_2O ($K_a = K_w = 1.0 \times 10^{-14}$) are the major species. CH_3CO_2H is the major source of H^+. Solving the weak acid problem:

	CH_3CO_2H	$\rightleftharpoons$	H^+	+	$CH_3CO_2^-$
Initial	0.250 *M*		~0		0
	x mol/L CH_3CO_2H dissociates to reach equilibrium				
Change	$-x$	$\rightarrow$	$+x$		$+x$
Equil.	$0.250 - x$		x		x

$$K_a = \frac{[H^+][CH_3CO_2^-]}{[CH_3CO_2H]},\ 1.8 \times 10^{-5} = \frac{x^2}{0.250 - x} \approx \frac{x^2}{0.250} \quad (\text{assuming } x << 0.250)$$

$x = 2.1 \times 10^{-3}$ *M*; checking assumption: $\frac{2.1 \times 10^{-3}}{0.250} \times 100 = 0.84\%$. Assumptions good.

$[H^+] = x = 2.1 \times 10^{-3}$ *M*; pH = $-\log(2.1 \times 10^{-3}) = 2.68$

45. This is a weak acid in water. Solving the weak acid problem:

	HF	$\rightleftharpoons$	H^+	+	F^-	$K_a = 7.2 \times 10^{-4}$
Initial	0.020 *M*		~0		0	
	x mol/L HF dissociates to reach equilibrium					
Change	$-x$	$\rightarrow$	$+x$		$+x$	
Equil.	$0.020 - x$		x		x	

$$K_a = 7.2 \times 10^{-4} = \frac{[H^+][F^-]}{[HF]} = \frac{x^2}{0.020 - x} \approx \frac{x^2}{0.020} \quad \text{(assuming } x << 0.020\text{)}$$

$x = [H^+] = 3.8 \times 10^{-3}$ *M*; check assumptions:

$$\frac{x}{0.020} \times 100 = \frac{3.8 \times 10^{-3}}{0.020} \times 100 = 19\%$$

The assumption $x << 0.020$ is not good (x is more than 5% of 0.020). We must solve $x^2/(0.020 - x) = 7.2 \times 10^{-4}$ exactly by using either the quadratic formula or the method of successive approximations (see Appendix 1 of the text). Using successive approximations, we let 0.016 *M* be a new approximation for [HF]. That is, in the denominator try $x = 0.0038$ (the value of x we calculated making the normal assumption) so that $0.020 - 0.0038 = 0.016$; then solve for a new value of x in the numerator.

$$\frac{x^2}{0.020 - x} \approx \frac{x^2}{0.016} = 7.2 \times 10^{-4}, \ x = 3.4 \times 10^{-3}$$

We use this new value of x to further refine our estimate of [HF], that is, $0.020 - x = 0.020 - 0.0034 = 0.0166$ (carrying an extra sig. fig.).

$$\frac{x^2}{0.020 - x} \approx \frac{x^2}{0.0166} = 7.2 \times 10^{-4}, \ x = 3.5 \times 10^{-3}$$

We repeat until we get a self-consistent answer. This would be the same answer we would get solving exactly using the quadratic equation. In this case it is, $x = 3.5 \times 10^{-3}$. Thus:

$[H^+] = [F^-] = x = 3.5 \times 10^{-3}$ *M*; $[OH^-] = K_w/[H^+] = 2.9 \times 10^{-12}$ *M*

$[HF] = 0.020 - x = 0.020 - 0.0035 = 0.017$ *M*; pH = 2.46

Note: When the 5% assumption fails, use whichever method you are most comfortable with to solve exactly. The method of successive approximations is probably fastest when the percent error is less than ~25% (unless you have a graphing calculator).

47. a. HA is a weak acid. Most of the acid is present as HA molecules; only one set of H^+ and A^- ions is present. In a strong acid, all of the acid would be dissociated into H^+ and A^- ions.

b. This picture is the result of 1 out of 10 HA molecules dissociating.

$$\text{Percent dissociation} = \frac{1}{10} \times 100 = 10\% \text{ (an exact number)}$$

	HA	⇌	H^+	+	A^-	$K_a = \frac{[H^+][A^-]}{[HA]}$
Initial	0.20 *M*		~0		0	
	x mol/L HA dissociates to reach equilibrium					
Change	$-x$	→	$+x$		$+x$	
Equil.	$0.20 - x$		x		x	

$[H^+] = [A^-] = x = 0.10 \times 0.20\ M = 0.020\ M$; $[HA] = 0.20 - 0.020 = 0.18\ M$

$$K_a = \frac{(0.020)^2}{0.18} = 2.2 \times 10^{-3}$$

49. Major species: HIO_3, H_2O; major source of H^+: HIO_3 (a weak acid, $K_a = 0.17$)

	HIO_3	⇌	H^+	+	IO_3^-
Initial	0.010 *M*		~0		0
	x mol/L HIO_3 dissociates to reach equilibrium				
Change	$-x$	→	$+x$		$+x$
Equil.	$0.010 - x$		x		x

$$K_a = 0.17 = \frac{[H^+][IO_3^-]}{[HIO_3]} = \frac{x^2}{0.010 - x} \approx \frac{x^2}{0.010},\ x = 0.041;\ \text{check assumption.}$$

Assumption is horrible (*x* is more than 400% of 0.010). When the assumption is this poor, it is generally quickest to solve exactly using the quadratic formula (see Appendix 1 in text). Using the quadratic formula and carrying extra significant figures:

$$0.17 = \frac{x^2}{0.010 - x},\ x^2 = 0.17(0.010 - x),\ x^2 + (0.17)x - 1.7 \times 10^{-3} = 0$$

$$x = \frac{-0.17 \pm [(0.17)^2 - 4(1)(-1.7 \times 10^{-3})]^{1/2}}{2(1)} = \frac{-0.17 \pm 0.189}{2},\ x = 9.5 \times 10^{-3}\ M$$

(*x* must be positive)

$x = 9.5 \times 10^{-3}\ M = [H^+]$; $pH = -\log(9.5 \times 10^{-3}) = 2.02$

51. This is a weak acid in water. We must solve a weak acid problem. Let HBz = $C_6H_5CO_2H$.

$$0.56\ \text{g HBz} \times \frac{1\ \text{mol HBz}}{122.1\ \text{g}} = 4.6 \times 10^{-3}\ \text{mol};\ [HBz]_0 = 4.6 \times 10^{-3}\ M$$

	HBz	⇌	H^+	+	Bz^-
Initial	$4.6 \times 10^{-3}\ M$		~0		0
	x mol/L HBz dissociates to reach equilibrium				
Change	$-x$	→	$+x$		$+x$
Equil.	$4.6 \times 10^{-3} - x$		x		x

$$K_a = 6.4 \times 10^{-5} = \frac{[H^+][Bz^-]}{[HBz]} = \frac{x^2}{(4.6 \times 10^{-3} - x)} \approx \frac{x^2}{4.6 \times 10^{-3}}$$

$x = [H^+] = 5.4 \times 10^{-4}$; check assumptions: $\frac{x}{4.6 \times 10^{-3}} \times 100 = \frac{5.4 \times 10^{-4}}{4.6 \times 10^{-3}} \times 100 = 12\%$

Assumption is not good (x is 12% of 4.6×10^{-3}). When assumption(s) fail, we must solve exactly using the quadratic formula or the method of successive approximations (see Appendix 1 of text). Using successive approximations:

$$\frac{x^2}{(4.6 \times 10^{-3}) - (5.4 \times 10^{-4})} = 6.4 \times 10^{-5},\ x = 5.1 \times 10^{-4}$$

$$\frac{x^2}{(4.6 \times 10^{-3}) - (5.1 \times 10^{-4})} = 6.4 \times 10^{-5},\ x = 5.1 \times 10^{-4}\ M \quad \text{(consistent answer)}$$

Thus: $x = [H^+] = [Bz^-] = [C_6H_5CO_2^-] = 5.1 \times 10^{-4}\ M$

$[HBz] = [C_6H_5CO_2H] = 4.6 \times 10^{-3} - x = 4.1 \times 10^{-3}\ M$

$pH = -\log(5.1 \times 10^{-4}) = 3.29$; $pOH = 14.00 - pH = 10.71$; $[OH^-] = 10^{-10.71} = 1.9 \times 10^{-11}\ M$

53. $$[HC_9H_7O_4] = \frac{2\ \text{tablets} \times \frac{0.325\ \text{g}\ HC_9H_7O_4}{\text{tablet}} \times \frac{1\ \text{mol}\ HC_9H_7O_4}{180.15\ \text{g}}}{0.237\ \text{L}} = 0.0152\ M$$

	$HC_9H_7O_4$	$\rightleftharpoons$	H^+	+	$C_9H_7O_4^-$
Initial	0.0152 M		~0		0
	x mol/L $HC_9H_7O_4$ dissociates to reach equilibrium				
Change	$-x$	→	$-x$		$-x$
Equil.	$0.0152 - x$		x		x

$$K_a = 3.3 \times 10^{-4} = \frac{[H^+][C_9H_7O_4^-]}{[HC_9H_7O_4]} = \frac{x^2}{0.0152 - x} \approx \frac{x^2}{0.0152},\ x = 2.2 \times 10^{-3}\ M$$

Assumption that $0.0152 - x \approx 0.0152$ fails the 5% rule: $\frac{2.2 \times 10^{-3}}{0.0152} \times 100 = 14\%$

Using successive approximations or the quadratic equation gives an exact answer of $x = 2.1 \times 10^{-3}\ M$.

$[H^+] = x = 2.1 \times 10^{-3}\ M$; $pH = -\log(2.1 \times 10^{-3}) = 2.68$

55. a. HCl is a strong acid. It will produce 0.10 *M* H^+. HOCl is a weak acid. Let's consider the equilibrium:

	HOCl	⇌	H^+	+	OCl^-	$K_a = 3.5 \times 10^{-8}$
Initial	0.10 *M*		0.10 *M*		0	
	x mol/L HOCl dissociates to reach equilibrium					
Change	$-x$	→	$+x$		$+x$	
Equil.	$0.10 - x$		$0.10 + x$		x	

$$K_a = 3.5 \times 10^{-8} = \frac{[H^+][OCl^-]}{[HOCl]} = \frac{(0.10 + x)(x)}{0.10 - x} \approx x, \; x = 3.5 \times 10^{-8}\ M$$

Assumptions are great (x is 0.000035% of 0.10). We are really assuming that HCl is the only important source of H^+, which it is. The $[H^+]$ contribution from HOCl, x, is negligible. Therefore, $[H^+] = 0.10\ M$; pH = 1.00.

b. HNO_3 is a strong acid, giving an initial concentration of H^+ equal to 0.050 *M*. Consider the equilibrium:

	$HC_2H_3O_2$	⇌	H^+	+	$C_2H_3O_2^-$	$K_a = 1.8 \times 10^{-5}$
Initial	0.50 *M*		0.050 *M*		0	
	x mol/L $HC_2H_3O_2$ dissociates to reach equilibrium					
Change	$-x$	→	$+x$		$+x$	
Equil.	$0.50 - x$		$0.050 + x$		x	

$$K_a = 1.8 \times 10^{-5} = \frac{[H^+][C_2H_3O_2^-]}{[HC_2H_3O_2]} = \frac{(0.050 + x)x}{(0.50 - x)} \approx \frac{(0.050)x}{0.50}$$

$x = 1.8 \times 10^{-4}$; assumptions are good (well within the 5% rule).

$[H^+] = 0.050 + x = 0.050\ M$ and pH = 1.30

57.

	HX	⇌	H^+	+	X^-	
Initial	I		~0		0	where $I = [HX]_0$
	x mol/L HX dissociates to reach equilibrium					
Change	$-x$	→	$+x$		$+x$	
Equil.	$I - x$		x		x	

From the problem, $x = 0.25(I)$ and $I - x = 0.30\ M$.

$I - 0.25(I) = 0.30\ M$, $I = 0.40\ M$ and $x = 0.25(0.40\ M) = 0.10\ M$

$$K_a = \frac{[H^+][X^-]}{[HX]} = \frac{x^2}{I - x} = \frac{(0.10)^2}{0.30} = 0.033$$

59. pH = 2.77, $[H^+] = 10^{-2.77} = 1.7 \times 10^{-3}$ *M*

	HOCN	⇌	H^+	+	OCN^-
Initial	0.0100		~0		0
Equil.	$0.0100 - x$		x		x

$x = [H^+] = [OCN^-] = 1.7 \times 10^{-3}$ *M*; [HOCN] = $0.0100 - x = 0.0100 - 0.0017 = 0.0083$ *M*

$$K_a = \frac{[H^+][OCN^-]}{[HOCN]} = \frac{(1.7 \times 10^{-3})^2}{8.3 \times 10^{-3}} = 3.5 \times 10^{-4}$$

61. Major species: $HC_2H_3O_2$ (acetic acid) and H_2O; major source of H^+: $HC_2H_3O_2$

	$HC_2H_3O_2$	⇌	H^+	+	$C_2H_3O_2^-$	
Initial	C		~0		0	where C = $[HC_2H_3O_2]_0$
	x mol/L $HC_2H_3O_2$ dissociates to reach equilibrium					
Change	$-x$	→	$+x$		$+x$	
Equil.	$C - x$		x		x	

$$K_a = 1.8 \times 10^{-5} = \frac{[H^+][C_2H_3O_2^-]}{[HC_2H_3O_2]} = \frac{x^2}{C - x}, \text{ where } x = [H^+]$$

$$1.8 \times 10^{-5} = \frac{[H^+]^2}{C - [H^+]}; \text{ from pH = 3.0: } [H^+] = 10^{-3.0} = 1 \times 10^{-3}\ M$$

$$1.8 \times 10^{-5} = \frac{(1 \times 10^{-3})^2}{C - (1 \times 10^{-3})}, \ C - (1 \times 10^{-3}) = \frac{1 \times 10^{-6}}{1.8 \times 10^{-5}}, \ C = 5.7 \times 10^{-2} \approx 6 \times 10^{-2}\ M$$

A 6×10^{-2} *M* acetic acid solution will have pH = 3.0.

Solutions of Bases

63. NO_3^-: $K_b << K_w$ because HNO_3 is a strong acid. All conjugate bases of strong acids have no base strength in water. H_2O: $K_b = K_w = 1.0 \times 10^{-14}$; NH_3: $K_b = 1.8 \times 10^{-5}$; C_5H_5N: $K_b = 1.7 \times 10^{-9}$

Base strength = $NH_3 > C_5H_5N > H_2O > NO_3^-$ (As K_b increases, base strength increases.)

65. a. $C_6H_5NH_2$ b. $C_6H_5NH_2$ c. OH^- d. CH_3NH_2

The base with the largest K_b value is the strongest base ($K_{b,\,C_6H_5NH_2} = 3.8 \times 10^{-10}$, $K_{b,\,CH_3NH_2} = 4.4 \times 10^{-4}$). OH^- is the strongest base possible in water.

67. NaOH(aq) → Na^+(aq) + OH^-(aq); NaOH is a strong base that completely dissociates into Na^+ and OH^-. The initial concentration of NaOH will equal the concentration of OH^- donated by NaOH.

a. $[OH^-] = 0.10\ M$; pOH = −log[OH^-] = −log(0.10) = 1.00

pH = 14.00 − pOH = 14.00 − 1.00 = 13.00

Note that H_2O is also present, but the amount of OH^- produced by H_2O will be insignificant compared to the 0.10 *M* OH^- produced from the NaOH.

b. The [OH^-] concentration donated by the NaOH is $1.0 \times 10^{-10}\ M$. Water by itself donates $1.0 \times 10^{-7}\ M$. In this exercise, water is the major OH^- contributor, and $[OH^-] = 1.0 \times 10^{-7}\ M$.

pOH = $-\log(1.0 \times 10^{-7}) = 7.00$; pH = 14.00 − 7.00 = 7.00

c. $[OH^-] = 2.0\ M$; pOH = −log(2.0) = −0.30; pH = 14.00 − (−0.30) = 14.30

69. pH = 10.50; pOH = 14.00 − 10.50 = 3.50; $[OH^-] = 10^{-3.50} = 3.2 \times 10^{-4}\ M$

$Ba(OH)_2$(aq) → Ba^{2+}(aq) + 2 OH^-(aq); $Ba(OH)_2$ donates 2 mol OH^- per mol $Ba(OH)_2$.

$$[Ba(OH)_2] = 3.2 \times 10^{-4}\ M\ OH^- \times \frac{1\ M\ Ba(OH)_2}{2\ M\ OH^-} = 1.6 \times 10^{-4}\ M\ Ba(OH)_2$$

A $1.6 \times 10^{-4}\ M$ $Ba(OH)_2$ solution will produce a pH = 10.50 solution.

71. Major species: H_2NNH_2 ($K_b = 3.0 \times 10^{-6}$) and H_2O ($K_b = K_w = 1.0 \times 10^{-14}$); the weak base H_2NNH_2 will dominate OH^- production. We must perform a weak base equilibrium calculation.

	H_2NNH_2 + H_2O	⇌	$H_2NNH_3^+$	+	OH^-	$K_b = 3.0 \times 10^{-6}$
Initial	2.0 *M*		0		~0	
	x mol/L H_2NNH_2 reacts with H_2O to reach equilibrium					
Change	$-x$	→	$+x$		$+x$	
Equil.	$2.0 - x$		x		x	

$$K_b = 3.0 \times 10^{-6} = \frac{[H_2NNH_3^+][OH^-]}{[H_2NNH_2]} = \frac{x^2}{2.0 - x} \approx \frac{x^2}{2.0} \quad \text{(assuming } x \ll 2.0)$$

$x = [OH^-] = 2.4 \times 10^{-3}\ M$; pOH = 2.62; pH = 11.38; assumptions good (*x* is 0.12% of 2.0).

$[H_2NNH_3^+] = 2.4 \times 10^{-3}\ M$; $[H_2NNH_2] = 2.0\ M$; $[H^+] = 10^{-11.38} = 4.2 \times 10^{-12}\ M$

73. Neutrally charged organic compounds containing at least one nitrogen atom generally behave as weak bases. The nitrogen atom has an unshared pair of electrons around it. This lone pair of electrons is used to form a bond to H^+.

75. This is a solution of a weak base in water. We must solve a weak base equilibrium problem.

	$C_2H_5NH_2$ + H_2O	$\rightleftharpoons$	$C_2H_5NH_3^+$	+ OH^-	$K_b = 5.6 \times 10^{-4}$
Initial	0.20 M		0	~0	
	x mol/L $C_2H_5NH_2$ reacts with H_2O to reach equilibrium				
Change	$-x$	$\rightarrow$	$+x$	$+x$	
Equil.	$0.20 - x$		x	x	

$$K_b = \frac{[C_2H_5NH_3^+][OH^-]}{[C_2H_5NH_2]} = \frac{x^2}{0.20 - x} \approx \frac{x^2}{0.20} \text{ (assuming } x << 0.20)$$

$x = 1.1 \times 10^{-2}$; checking assumption: $(1.1 \times 10^{-2}/0.20) \times 100 = 5.5\%$

The assumption fails the 5% rule. We must solve exactly using either the quadratic equation or the method of successive approximations (see Appendix 1 of the text). Using successive approximations and carrying extra significant figures:

$$\frac{x^2}{0.20 - 0.011} = \frac{x^2}{0.189} = 5.6 \times 10^{-4}, \quad x = 1.0 \times 10^{-2}\ M \text{ (consistent answer)}$$

$$x = [OH^-] = 1.0 \times 10^{-2}\ M;\ [H^+] = \frac{K_w}{[OH^-]} = \frac{1.0 \times 10^{-14}}{1.0 \times 10^{-2}} = 1.0 \times 10^{-12}\ M;\ pH = 12.00$$

77. $\frac{5.0 \times 10^{-3}\ g}{0.0100\ L} \times \frac{1\ mol}{299.4\ g} = 1.7 \times 10^{-3}\ M = [codeine]_0$; let cod = codeine ($C_{18}H_{21}NO_3$).

Solving the weak base equilibrium problem:

	cod + H_2O	$\rightleftharpoons$	$codH^+$	+ OH^-	$K_b = 10^{-6.05} = 8.9 \times 10^{-7}$
Initial	$1.7 \times 10^{-3}\ M$		0	~0	
	x mol/L codeine reacts with H_2O to reach equilibrium				
Change	$-x$	$\rightarrow$	$+x$	$+x$	
Equil.	$1.7 \times 10^{-3} - x$		x	x	

$$K_b = 8.9 \times 10^{-7} = \frac{x^2}{(1.7 \times 10^{-3} - x)} \approx \frac{x^2}{1.7 \times 10^{-3}},\ x = 3.9 \times 10^{-5};\ \text{assumptions good.}$$

$[OH^-] = 3.9 \times 10^{-5}\ M$; $[H^+] = K_w/[OH^-] = 2.6 \times 10^{-10}\ M$; $pH = -\log[H^+] = 9.59$

79. To solve for percent ionization, just solve the weak base equilibrium problem.

a.

	NH_3 + H_2O	$\rightleftharpoons$	NH_4^+	+ OH^-	$K_b = 1.8 \times 10^{-5}$
Initial	0.10 M		0	~0	
Equil.	$0.10 - x$		x	x	

$$K_b = 1.8 \times 10^{-5} = \frac{x^2}{0.10 - x} \approx \frac{x^2}{0.10}, \; x = [OH^-] = 1.3 \times 10^{-3}\ M; \text{ assumptions good.}$$

$$\text{Percent ionization} = \frac{[OH^-]}{[NH_3]_0} \times 100 = \frac{1.3 \times 10^{-3}\ M}{0.10\ M} \times 100 = 1.3\%$$

b. $NH_3 + H_2O \rightleftharpoons NH_4^+ + OH^-$

	NH_3	NH_4^+	OH^-
Initial	0.010 *M*	0	~0
Equil.	$0.010 - x$	x	x

$$1.8 \times 10^{-5} = \frac{x^2}{0.010 - x} \approx \frac{x^2}{0.010}, \; x = [OH^-] = 4.2 \times 10^{-4}\ M; \text{ assumptions good.}$$

$$\text{Percent ionization} = \frac{4.2 \times 10^{-4}}{0.010} \times 100 = 4.2\%$$

Note: For the same base, the percent ionization increases as the initial concentration of base decreases.

c. $CH_3NH_2 + H_2O \rightleftharpoons CH_3NH_3^+ + OH^-$ $K_b = 4.38 \times 10^{-4}$

	CH_3NH_2	$CH_3NH_3^+$	OH^-
Initial	0.10 *M*	0	~0
Equil.	$0.10 - x$	x	x

$$4.38 \times 10^{-4} = \frac{x^2}{0.10 - x} \approx \frac{x^2}{0.10}, \; x = 6.6 \times 10^{-3};$$ assumption fails the 5% rule (x is 6.6% of 0.10). Using successive approximations and carrying extra significant figures:

$$\frac{x^2}{0.10 - 0.0066} = \frac{x^2}{0.093} = 4.38 \times 10^{-4}, \; x = 6.4 \times 10^{-3} \quad \text{(consistent answer)}$$

$$\text{Percent ionization} = \frac{6.4 \times 10^{-3}}{0.10} \times 100 = 6.4\%$$

81. Using the K_b reaction to solve where PT = p-toluidine ($CH_3C_6H_4NH_2$):

$PT + H_2O \rightleftharpoons PTH^+ + OH^-$

	PT		PTH^+	OH^-
Initial	0.016 *M*		0	~0
	x mol/L of PT reacts with H_2O to reach equilibrium			
Change	$-x$	→	$+x$	$+x$
Equil.	$0.016 - x$		x	x

$$K_b = \frac{[PTH^+][OH^-]}{[PT]} = \frac{x^2}{0.016 - x}$$

Since pH = 8.60: pOH = 14.00 – 8.60 = 5.40 and $[OH^-] = x = 10^{-5.40} = 4.0 \times 10^{-6}$ *M*

$$K_b = \frac{(4.0 \times 10^{-6})^2}{0.016 - (4.0 \times 10^{-6})} = 1.0 \times 10^{-9}$$

Polyprotic Acids

83. $H_3C_6H_5O_7(aq) \rightleftharpoons H_2C_6H_5O_7^-(aq) + H^+(aq)$ $\quad K_{a_1} = \frac{[H_2C_6H_5O_7^-][H^+]}{[H_3C_6H_5O_7]}$

$H_2C_6H_5O_7^-(aq) \rightleftharpoons HC_6H_5O_7^{2-}(aq) + H^+(aq)$ $\quad K_{a_2} = \frac{[HC_6H_5O_7^{2-}][H^+]}{[H_2C_6H_5O_7^-]}$

$HC_6H_5O_7^{2-}(aq) \rightleftharpoons C_6H_5O_7^{3-}(aq) + H^+(aq)$ $\quad K_{a_3} = \frac{[C_6H_5O_7^{3-}][H^+]}{[HC_6H_5O_7^{2-}]}$

85. The reactions are:

$H_3AsO_4 \rightleftharpoons H^+ + H_2AsO_4^-$ $\quad K_{a_1} = 5 \times 10^{-3}$

$H_2AsO_4^- \rightleftharpoons H^+ + HAsO_4^{2-}$ $\quad K_{a_2} = 8 \times 10^{-8}$

$HAsO_4^{2-} \rightleftharpoons H^+ + AsO_4^{3-}$ $\quad K_{a_3} = 6 \times 10^{-10}$

We will deal with the reactions in order of importance, beginning with the largest K_a, K_{a_1}.

	H_3AsO_4	$\rightleftharpoons$	H^+	+	$H_2AsO_4^-$
Initial	0.20 *M*		~0		0
Equil.	0.20 - *x*		*x*		*x*

$$K_{a_1} = 5 \times 10^{-3} = \frac{[H^+][H_2AsO_4^-]}{[H_3AsO_4]}$$

$5 \times 10^{-3} = \frac{x^2}{0.20 - x} \approx \frac{x^2}{0.20}$, $x = 3 \times 10^{-2}$ *M*; assumption fails the 5% rule.

Solving by the method of successive approximations:

$5 \times 10^{-3} = x^2/(0.20 - 0.03)$, $x = 3 \times 10^{-2}$ (consistent answer)

$[H^+] = [H_2AsO_4^-] = 3 \times 10^{-2}$ *M*; $[H_3AsO_4] = 0.20 - 0.03 = 0.17$ *M*

Because $K_{a_2} = \frac{[H^+][HAsO_4^{2-}]}{[H_2AsO_4^-]} = 8 \times 10^{-8}$ is much smaller than the K_{a_1} value, very little of $H_2AsO_4^-$ (and $HAsO_4^{2-}$) dissociates compared to H_3AsO_4. Therefore, $[H^+]$ and $[H_2AsO_4^-]$ will not change significantly by the K_{a_2} reaction. Using the previously calculated concentrations of H^+ and $H_2AsO_4^-$ to calculate the concentration of $HAsO_4^{2-}$:

$$8 \times 10^{-8} = \frac{(3 \times 10^{-2})[HAsO_4^{2-}]}{3 \times 10^{-2}}, \quad [HAsO_4^{2-}] = 8 \times 10^{-8}\ M$$

The assumption that the K_{a_2} reaction does not change $[H^+]$ and $[H_2AsO_4^-]$ is good. We repeat the process using K_{a_3} to get $[AsO_4^{3-}]$.

$$K_{a_3} = 6 \times 10^{-10} = \frac{[H^+][AsO_4^{3-}]}{[HAsO_4^{2-}]} = \frac{(3 \times 10^{-2})[AsO_4^{3-}]}{8 \times 10^{-8}}$$

$[AsO_4^{3-}] = 1.6 \times 10^{-15} \approx 2 \times 10^{-15}\ M$; assumption good.

So in 0.20 M analytical concentration of H_3AsO_4:

$[H_3AsO_4] = 0.17\ M$; $[H^+] = [H_2AsO_4^-] = 3 \times 10^{-2}\ M$;

$[HAsO_4^{2-}] = 8 \times 10^{-8}\ M$; $[AsO_4^{3-}] = 2 \times 10^{-15}\ M$; $[OH^-] = K_w/[H^+] = 3 \times 10^{-13}\ M$

87. For $H_2C_6H_6O_6$. $K_{a_1} = 7.9 \times 10^{-5}$ and $K_{a_2} = 1.6 \times 10^{-12}$. Because $K_{a_1} >> K_{a_2}$, the amount of H^+ produced by the K_{a_2} reaction will be negligible.

$$[H_2C_6H_6O_6]_0 = \frac{0.500\ g \times \frac{1\ mol\ H_2C_6H_6O_6}{176.12\ g}}{0.2000\ L} = 0.0142\ M$$

	$H_2C_6H_6O_6(aq)$	$\rightleftharpoons$	$HC_6H_6O_6^-(aq)$	+	$H^+(aq)$	$K_{a_1} = 7.9 \times 10^{-5}$
Initial	0.0142 M		0		~0	
Equil.	$0.0142 - x$		x		x	

$$K_{a_1} = 7.9 \times 10^{-5} = \frac{x^2}{0.0142 - x} \approx \frac{x^2}{0.0142}, \quad x = 1.1 \times 10^{-3};$$ assumption fails the 5% rule.

Solving by the method of successive approximations:

$$7.9 \times 10^{-5} = \frac{x^2}{0.0142 - 1.1 \times 10^{-3}}, \quad x = 1.0 \times 10^{-3}\ M \text{ (consistent answer)}$$

Because H^+ produced by the K_{a_2} reaction will be negligible, $[H^+] = 1.0 \times 10^{-3}$ and pH = 3.00.

89. The dominant H^+ producer is the strong acid H_2SO_4. A 2.0 M H_2SO_4 solution produces 2.0 M HSO_4^- and 2.0 M H^+. However, HSO_4^- is a weak acid that could also add H^+ to the solution.

	HSO_4^-	$\rightleftharpoons$	H^+	+	SO_4^{2-}
Initial	2.0 *M*		2.0 *M*		0
	x mol/L HSO_4^- dissociates to reach equilibrium				
Change	$-x$	$\rightarrow$	$+x$		$+x$
Equil.	$2.0 - x$		$2.0 + x$		x

$$K_{a_2} = 1.2 \times 10^{-2} = \frac{[H^+][SO_4^{2-}]}{[HSO_4^-]} = \frac{(2.0+x)x}{2.0-x} \approx \frac{2.0(x)}{2.0}, \quad x = 1.2 \times 10^{-2}\ M$$

Because *x* is 0.60% of 2.0, the assumption is valid by the 5% rule. The amount of additional H^+ from HSO_4^- is 1.2×10^{-2} *M*. The total amount of H^+ present is:

$$[H^+] = 2.0 + (1.2 \times 10^{-2}) = 2.0\ M;\ \ pH = -\log(2.0) = -0.30$$

Note: In this problem H^+ from HSO_4^- could have been ignored. However, this is not usually the case in more dilute solutions of H_2SO_4.

Acid-Base Properties of Salts

91. a. These are strong acids like HCl, HBr, HI, HNO_3, H_2SO_4, or $HClO_4$.

b. These are salts of the conjugate acids of the bases in Table 7.3. These conjugate acids are all weak acids. NH_4Cl, $CH_3NH_3NO_3$, and $C_2H_5NH_3Br$ are three examples. Note that the anions used to form these salts are conjugate bases of strong acids; this is so because they have no acidic or basic properties in water (with the exception of HSO_4^-, which has weak acid properties).

c. These are strong ases like LiOH, NaOH, KOH, RbOH, CsOH, $Ca(OH)_2$, $Sr(OH)_2$, and $Ba(OH)_2$.

d. These are salts of the conjugate bases of the neutrally charged weak acids in Table 7.2. The conjugate bases of weak acids are weak bases themselves. Three examples are $NaClO_2$, $KC_2H_3O_2$, and CaF_2. The cations used to form these salts are Li^+, Na^+, K^+, Rb^+, Cs^+, Ca^{2+}, Sr^{2+}, or Ba^{2+} because these cations have no acidic or basic properties in water. Notice that these are the cations of the strong bases you should memorize.

e. There are two ways to make a neutral salt. The easiest way is to combine a conjugate base of a strong acid (except for HSO_4^-) with one of the cations from a strong base. These ions have no acidic/basic properties in water, so salts of these ions are neutral. Three examples are NaCl, KNO_3, and SrI_2. Another type of strong electrolyte that can produce neutral solutions are salts that contain an ion with weak acid properties combined with an ion of opposite charge having weak base properties. If the K_a for the weak acid ion is equal to the K_b for the weak base ion, then the salt will produce a neutral solution. The most common example of this type of salt is ammonium acetate ($NH_4C_2H_3O_2$). For this salt, K_a for NH_4^+ = K_b for $C_2H_3O_2^-$ = 5.6×10^{-10}. This salt at any concentration produces a neutral solution.

93. One difficult aspect of acid-base chemistry is recognizing what types of species are present in solution, that is, whether a species is a strong acid, strong base, weak acid, weak base, or a neutral species. Below are some ideas and generalizations to keep in mind that will help in recognizing types of species present.

a. Memorize the following strong acids: HCl, HBr, HI, HNO_3, $HClO_4$, and H_2SO_4

b. Memorize the following strong bases: LiOH, NaOH, KOH, RbOH, $Ca(OH)_2$, $Sr(OH)_2$, and $Ba(OH)_2$

c. Weak acids have a K_a value of less than 1 but greater than K_w. Some weak acids are listed in Table 7.2 of the text. Weak bases have a K_b value of less than 1 but greater than K_w. Some weak bases are listed in Table 7.3 of the text.

d. Conjugate bases of weak acids are weak bases, that is, all have a K_b value of less than 1 but greater than K_w. Some examples of these are the conjugate bases of the weak acids listed in Table 7.2 of the text.

e. Conjugate acids of weak bases are weak acids, that is, all have a K_a value of less than 1 but greater than K_w. Some examples of these are the conjugate acids of the weak bases listed in Table 7.3 of the text.

f. Alkali metal ions (Li^+, Na^+, K^+, Rb^+, Cs^+) and some alkaline earth metal ions (Ca^{2+}, Sr^{2+}, Ba^{2+}) have no acidic or basic properties in water.

g. Conjugate bases of strong acids (Cl^-, Br^-, I^-, NO_3^-, ClO_4^-, HSO_4^-) have no basic properties in water ($K_b << K_w$), and only HSO_4^- has any acidic properties in water.

Let's apply these ideas to this problem to see what types of species are present.

a. HI: Strong acid; HF: weak acid ($K_a = 7.2 \times 10^{-4}$)

NaF: F^- is the conjugate base of the weak acid HF, so F^- is a weak base. The K_b value for $F^- = K_w/K_{a,\,HF} = 1.4 \times 10^{-11}$. Na^+ has no acidic or basic properties.

NaI: Neutral (pH = 7.0); Na^+ and I^- have no acidic/basic properties.

In order of increasing pH, we place the compounds from most acidic (lowest pH) to most basic (highest pH). Increasing pH: HI < HF < NaI < NaF.

b. NH_4Br: NH_4^+ is a weak acid ($K_a = 5.6 \times 10^{-10}$), and Br^- is a neutral species.

HBr: Strong acid

KBr: Neutral; K^+ and Br^- have no acidic/basic properties.

NH_3: Weak base, $K_b = 1.8 \times 10^{-5}$

Increasing pH: HBr < NH_4Br < KBr < NH_3

HBr	NH_4Br	KBr	NH_3
Most acidic			Most basic

c. $C_6H_5NH_3NO_3$: $C_6H_5NH_3^+$ is a weak acid ($K_a = K_w/K_{b,\,C_6H_5NH_2} = 1.0 \times 10^{-14}/3.8 \times 10^{-10} = 2.6 \times 10^{-5}$), and NO_3^- is a neutral species.

$NaNO_3$: Neutral; Na^+ and NO_3^- have no acidic/basic properties.

$NaOH$: Strong base

HOC_6H_5: Weak acid ($K_a = 1.6 \times 10^{-10}$)

KOC_6H_5: $OC_6H_5^-$ is a weak base ($K_b = K_w/K_{a,\,HOC_6H_5} = 6.3 \times 10^{-5}$), and K^+ is a neutral species.

$C_6H_5NH_2$: Weak base ($K_b = 3.8 \times 10^{-10}$)

HNO_3: Strong acid

This is a little more difficult than the previous parts of this problem because two weak acids and two weak bases are present. Between the weak acids, $C_6H_5NH_3^+$ is a stronger weak acid than HOC_6H_5 since the K_a value for $C_6H_5NH_3^+$ is larger than the K_a value for HOC_6H_5. Between the two weak bases, because the K_b value for $OC_6H_5^-$ is larger than the K_b value for $C_6H_5NH_2$, $OC_6H_5^-$ is a stronger weak base than $C_6H_5NH_2$.

Increasing pH: $HNO_3 < C_6H_5NH_3NO_3 < HOC_6H_5 < NaNO_3 < C_6H_5NH_2 < KOC_6H_5 < NaOH$
Most acidic Most basic

95. Reference Table 7.6 of the text and the solution to Exercise 93 for some generalizations on acid-base properties of salts.

a. $Sr(NO_3)_2 \rightarrow Sr^{2+} + 2\ NO_3^-$ neutral; Sr^{2+} and NO_3^- have no effect on pH.

b. $C_2H_5NH_3CN \rightarrow C_2H_5NH_3^+ + CN^-$ basic; $C_2H_5NH_3^+$ is a weak acid ($K_a = K_w/K_{b,C_2H_5NH_2} = 1.0 \times 10^{-14}/5.6 \times 10^{-4} = 1.8 \times 10^{-11}$), and CN^- is a weak base ($K_b = K_w/K_{a,\,HCN} = 1.0 \times 10^{-14}/6.2 \times 10^{-10} = 1.6 \times 10^{-5}$). Because $K_{b,\,CN^-} > K_{a,\,C_2H_5NH_3^+}$, the solution of $C_2H_5NH_3CN$ will be basic.

c. $C_5H_5NHF \rightarrow C_5H_5NH^+ + F^-$ acidic; $C_5H_5NH^+$ is a weak acid ($K_a = K_w/K_{b,C_5H_5N} = 5.9 \times 10^{-6}$), and F^- is a weak base ($K_b = K_w/K_{a,\,HF} = 1.4 \times 10^{-11}$). Because $K_{a,\,C_5H_5NH^+} > K_{b,\,F^-}$, the solution of C_5H_5NHF will be acidic.

d. $NH_4C_2H_3O_2 \rightarrow NH_4^+ + C_2H_3O_2^-$ neutral; NH_4^+ is a weak acid ($K_a = 5.6 \times 10^{-10}$), and $C_2H_3O_2^-$ is a weak base ($K_b = K_w/K_{a,\,HC_2H_3O_2} = 5.6 \times 10^{-10}$). Because $K_{a,\,NH_4^+} = K_{b,\,C_2H_3O_2^-}$, the solution of $NH_4C_2H_3O_2$ will have pH = 7.00.

e. $NaHCO_3 \rightarrow Na^+ + HCO_3^-$ basic; ignore Na^+; HCO_3^- is a weak acid ($K_{a_2} = 4.8 \times 10^{-11}$), and HCO_3^- is a weak base ($K_b = K_w/K_{a_1,\,H_2CO_3} = 2.3 \times 10^{-8}$). HCO_3^- is a stronger base than an acid because $K_b > K_a$. Therefore, the solution is basic.

97. a. KCl is a soluble ionic compound that dissolves in water to produce $K^+(aq)$ and $Cl^-(aq)$. K^+ (like the other alkali metal cations) has no acidic or basic properties. Cl^- is the conjugate base of the strong acid HCl. Cl^- has no basic (or acidic) properties. Therefore, a solution of KCl will be neutral because neither of the ions has any acidic or basic properties. The 1.0 *M* KCl solution has $[H^+] = [OH^-] = 1.0 \times 10^{-7}$ *M* and pH = pOH = 7.00.

b. KF is also a soluble ionic compound that dissolves in water to produce $K^+(aq)$ and $F^-(aq)$. The difference between the KCl solution and the KF solution is that F^- does have basic properties in water, unlike Cl^-. F^- is the conjugate base of the weak acid HF, and as is true for all conjugate bases of weak acids, F^- is a weak base in water. We must solve an equilibrium problem in order to determine the amount of OH^- this weak base produces in water.

	F^- + H_2O	⇌	HF	+	OH^-	$K_b = \dfrac{K_w}{K_{a,\,HF}} = \dfrac{1.0 \times 10^{-14}}{7.2 \times 10^{-4}}$
Initial	1.0 *M*		0		~0	$K_b = 1.4 \times 10^{-11}$
	x mol/L of F^- reacts with H_2O to reach equilibrium					
Change	$-x$	→	$+x$		$+x$	
Equil.	$1.0 - x$		x		x	

$$K_b = 1.4 \times 10^{-11} = \frac{[HF][OH^-]}{[F^-]},\quad 1.4 \times 10^{-11} = \frac{x^2}{1.0 - x} \approx \frac{x^2}{1.0}$$

$x = [OH^-] = 3.7 \times 10^{-6}$ *M*; assumptions good

pOH = 5.43; pH = 14.00 – 5.43 = 8.57; $[H^+] = 10^{-8.57} = 2.7 \times 10^{-9}$ *M*

99. B^- is a weak base. Use the weak base data to determine K_b for B^-.

	B^- + H_2O	⇌	HB	+	OH^-
Initial	0.050 *M*		0		~0
Equil.	$0.050 - x$		x		x

From pH = 9.00: pOH = 5.00, $[OH^-] = 10^{-5.00} = 1.0 \times 10^{-5}$ *M* = *x*.

$$K_b = \frac{[HB][OH^-]}{[B^-]} = \frac{x^2}{0.050 - x} = \frac{(1.0 \times 10^{-5})^2}{0.050 - (1.0 \times 10^{-5})} = 2.0 \times 10^{-9}$$

Because B^- is a weak base, HB will be a weak acid. Solve the weak acid problem.

	HB	⇌	H^+	+	B^-
Initial	0.010 *M*		~ 0		0
Equil.	$0.010 - x$		x		x

$$K_a = \frac{K_w}{K_b} = \frac{1.0 \times 10^{-14}}{2.0 \times 10^{-9}},\quad 5.0 \times 10^{-6} = \frac{x^2}{0.010 - x} \approx \frac{x^2}{0.010}$$

$x = [H^+] = 2.2 \times 10^{-4}\ M$; pH = 3.66; assumptions good.

101. a. $KNO_2 \rightarrow K^+ + NO_2^-$: NO_2^- is a weak base. Ignore K^+.

$$NO_2^- + H_2O \rightleftharpoons HNO_2 + OH^- \qquad K_b = \frac{K_w}{K_a} = \frac{1.0 \times 10^{-14}}{4.0 \times 10^{-4}} = 2.5 \times 10^{-11}$$

	NO_2^-	HNO_2	OH^-
Initial	0.12 *M*	0	~0
Equil.	$0.12 - x$	x	x

$$K_b = 2.5 \times 10^{-11} = \frac{[OH^-][HNO_2]}{[NO_2^-]} = \frac{x^2}{0.12 - x} \approx \frac{x^2}{0.12}$$

$x = [OH^-] = 1.7 \times 10^{-6}\ M$; pOH = 5.77; pH = 8.23; assumptions good.

b. $NaOCl \rightarrow Na^+ + OCl^-$: OCl^- is a weak base. Ignore Na^+.

$$OCl^- + H_2O \rightleftharpoons HOCl + OH^- \qquad K_b = \frac{K_w}{K_a} = \frac{1.0 \times 10^{-14}}{3.5 \times 10^{-8}} = 2.9 \times 10^{-7}$$

	OCl^-	$HOCl$	OH^-
Initial	0.45 *M*	0	~0
Equil.	$0.45 - x$	x	x

$$K_b = 2.9 \times 10^{-7} = \frac{[HOCl][OH^-]}{[OCl^-]} = \frac{x^2}{0.45 - x} \approx \frac{x^2}{0.45}$$

$x = [OH^-] = 3.6 \times 10^{-4}\ M$; pOH = 3.44; pH = 10.56; assumptions good.

c. $NH_4ClO_4 \rightarrow NH_4^+ + ClO_4^-$: NH_4^+ is a weak acid. ClO_4^- is the conjugate base of a strong acid. ClO_4^- has no basic (or acidic) properties.

$$NH_4^+ \rightleftharpoons NH_3 + H^+ \qquad K_a = \frac{K_w}{K_b} = \frac{1.0 \times 10^{-14}}{1.8 \times 10^{-5}} = 5.6 \times 10^{-10}$$

	NH_4^+	NH_3	H^+
Initial	0.40 *M*	0	~0
Equil.	$0.40 - x$	x	x

$$K_a = 5.6 \times 10^{-10} = \frac{[NH_3][H^+]}{[NH_4^+]} = \frac{x^2}{0.40 - x} \approx \frac{x^2}{0.40}$$

$x = [H^+] = 1.5 \times 10^{-5} M$; pH = 4.82; assumptions good.

103. All these salts contain Na^+, which has no acidic/basic properties and a conjugate base of a weak acid (except for NaCl, where Cl^- is a neutral species). All conjugate bases of weak acids are weak bases since K_b values for these species are between K_w and 1. To identify the species, we will use the data given to determine the K_b value for the weak conjugate base. From the K_b value and data in Table 7.2 of the text, we can identify the conjugate base present by calculating the K_a value for the weak acid. We will use A^- as an abbreviation for the weak conjugate base.

$$A^- + H_2O \rightleftharpoons HA + OH^-$$

	A^-		HA	OH^-
Initial	0.100 mol/1.00 L		0	~0
	x mol/L A^- reacts with H_2O to reach equilibrium			
Change	$-x$	→	$+x$	$+x$
Equil.	$0.100 - x$		x	x

$$K_b = \frac{[HA][OH^-]}{[A^-]} = \frac{x^2}{0.100 - x}$$; from the problem, pH = 8.07:

$$pOH = 14.00 - 8.07 = 5.93;\ [OH^-] = x = 10^{-5.93} = 1.2 \times 10^{-6}\ M$$

$$K_b = \frac{(1.2 \times 10^{-6})^2}{0.100 - (1.2 \times 10^{-6})} = 1.4 \times 10^{-11}$$ = K_b value for the conjugate base of a weak acid.

The K_a value for the weak acid equals K_w/K_b: $K_a = \frac{1.0 \times 10^{-14}}{1.4 \times 10^{-11}} = 7.1 \times 10^{-4}$

From Table 7.2 of the text, this K_a value is closest to HF. Therefore, the unknown salt is NaF.

105. Major species: $Co(H_2O)_6^{3+}$ ($K_a = 1.0 \times 10^{-5}$), Cl^- (neutral), and H_2O ($K_w = 1.0 \times 10^{-14}$); $Co(H_2O)_6^{3+}$ will determine the pH since it is a stronger acid than water. Solving the weak acid problem in the usual manner:

$$Co(H_2O)_6^{3+} \rightleftharpoons Co(H_2O)_5(OH)^{2+} + H^+ \quad K_a = 1.0 \times 10^{-5}$$

	$Co(H_2O)_6^{3+}$	$Co(H_2O)_5(OH)^{2+}$	H^+
Initial	0.10 M	0	~0
Equil.	0.10 - x	x	x

$$K_a = 1.0 \times 10^{-5} = \frac{x^2}{0.10 - x} \approx \frac{x^2}{0.10},\ x = [H^+] = 1.0 \times 10^{-3}\ M$$

$pH = -\log(1.0 \times 10^{-3}) = 3.00$; assumptions good.

107. Major species: NH_4^+, OCl^-, and H_2O; K_a for $NH_4^+ = (1.0 \times 10^{-14})/(1.8 \times 10^{-5}) = 5.6 \times 10^{-10}$ and K_b for $OCl^- = (1.0 \times 10^{-14})/(3.5 \times 10^{-8}) = 2.9 \times 10^{-7}$.

Because OCl^- is a better base than NH_4^+ is an acid, the solution will be basic. The dominant equilibrium is the best acid (NH_4^+) reacting with the best base (OCl^-) present.

	NH_4^+	+	OCl^-	$\rightleftharpoons$	NH_3	+	HOCl
Initial	0.50 *M*		0.50 *M*		0		0
Change	$-x$		$-x$	$\rightarrow$	$+x$		$+x$
Equil.	$0.50 - x$		$0.50 - x$		x		x

$$K = K_{a, NH_4^+} \times \frac{1}{K_{a, HOCl}} = (5.6 \times 10^{-10})/(3.5 \times 10^{-8}) = 0.016$$

$$K = 0.016 = \frac{[NH_3][HOCl]}{[NH_4^+][OCl^-]} = \frac{x(x)}{(0.50 - x)(0.50 - x)}$$

$$\frac{x^2}{(0.50 - x)^2} = 0.016, \quad \frac{x}{0.50 - x} = (0.016)^{1/2} = 0.13, \quad x = 0.058\ M$$

To solve for the H^+, use any pertinent K_a or K_b value. Using K_a for NH_4^+:

$$K_{a, NH_4^+} = 5.6 \times 10^{-10} = \frac{[NH_3][H^+]}{[NH_4^+]} = \frac{(0.058)[H^+]}{0.50 - 0.058}, \quad [H^+] = 4.3 \times 10^{-9}\ M, \quad pH = 8.37$$

Solutions of Dilute Acids and Bases

109.

	HBrO	$\rightleftharpoons$	H^+	+	BrO^-	$K_a = 2 \times 10^{-9}$
Initial	$1.0 \times 10^{-6}\ M$		~0		0	
	x mol/L HBrO dissociates to reach equilibrium					
Change	$-x$	$\rightarrow$	$+x$		$+x$	
Equil.	$1.0 \times 10^{-6} - x$		x		x	

$$K_a = 2 \times 10^{-9} = \frac{x^2}{(1.0 \times 10^{-6} - x)} \approx \frac{x^2}{1.0 \times 10^{-6}}, \quad x = [H^+] = 4 \times 10^{-8}\ M; \quad pH = 7.4$$

Let's check the assumptions. This answer is impossible! We can't add a small amount of an acid to a neutral solution and get a basic solution. The highest pH possible for an acid in water is 7.0. In the correct solution we would have to take into account the autoionization of water.

111.

	HCN	$\rightleftharpoons$	H^+	+	CN^-	$K_a = 6.2 \times 10^{-10}$
Initial	$5.0 \times 10^{-4}\ M$		~0		0	
Equil.	$5.0 \times 10^{-4} - x$		x		x	

$$K_a = \frac{x^2}{(5.0 \times 10^{-4} - x)} \approx \frac{x^2}{5.0 \times 10^{-4}} = 6.2 \times 10^{-10}, \quad x = 5.6 \times 10^{-7}; \text{ check assumptions.}$$

The assumption that the H^+ contribution from water is negligible is poor. Whenever the calculated pH is greater than 6.0 for a weak acid, the water contribution to $[H^+]$ must be considered. From Section 7.9 in text:

$$\text{if } \frac{[H^+]^2 - K_w}{[H^+]} << [HCN]_0 = 5.0 \times 10^{-4}, \text{ then we can use } [H^+] = (K_a[HCN]_o + K_w)^{1/2}.$$

Using this formula: $[H^+] = [(6.2 \times 10^{-10})(5.0 \times 10^{-4}) + (1.0 \times 10^{-14})]^{1/2}$, $[H^+] = 5.7 \times 10^{-7}\ M$

Checking assumptions: $\frac{[H^+]^2 - K_w}{[H^+]} = 5.5 \times 10^{-7} << 5.0 \times 10^{-4}$

Assumptions good. $pH = -\log(5.7 \times 10^{-7}) = 6.24$

113. We can't neglect the $[H^+]$ contribution from H_2O since this is a very dilute solution of the strong acid. Following the strategy developed in Section 7.10 of the text, we first determine the charge balance equation and then manipulate this equation to get into one unknown.

[Positive charge] = [negative charge]

$$[H^+] = [Cl^-] + [OH^-] = 7.0 \times 10^{-7} + \frac{K_w}{[H^+]} \text{ (because } [Cl^-] = 7.0 \times 10^{-7} \text{ and } [OH^-] = \frac{K_w}{[H^+]})$$

$$\frac{[H^+]^2 - K_w}{[H^+]} = 7.0 \times 10^{-7},\ [H^+]^2 - (7.0 \times 10^{-7})[H^+] - 1.0 \times 10^{-14} = 0$$

Using the quadratic formula to solve:

$$[H^+] = \frac{-(-7.0 \times 10^{-7}) \pm [(-7.0 \times 10^{-7})^2 - 4(1)(-1.0 \times 10^{-14})]^{1/2}}{2(1)}$$

$[H^+] = 7.1 \times 10^{-7}\ M$; $pH = -\log(7.1 \times 10^{-7}) = 6.15$

Additional Exercises

115. a. $NH_3 + H_3O^+ \rightleftharpoons NH_4^+ + H_2O$

$$K_{eq} = \frac{[NH_4^+]}{[NH_3][H^+]} = \frac{1}{K_a \text{ for } NH_4^+} = \frac{K_b}{K_w} = \frac{1.8 \times 10^{-5}}{1.0 \times 10^{-14}} = 1.8 \times 10^9$$

b. $NO_2^- + H_3O^+ \rightleftharpoons H_2O + HNO_2$ $\quad K_{eq} = \frac{[HNO_2]}{[NO_2^-][H^+]} = \frac{1}{K_a} = \frac{1}{4.0 \times 10^{-4}} = 2.5 \times 10^3$

c. $NH_4^+ + CH_3CO_2^- \rightleftharpoons NH_3 + CH_3CO_2H$ $\quad K_{eq} = \dfrac{[NH_3][CH_3CO_2H]}{[NH_4^+][CH_3CO_2^-]} \times \dfrac{[H^+]}{[H^+]}$

$$K_{eq} = \frac{K_a \text{ for } NH_4^+}{K_a \text{ for } CH_3CO_2H} = \frac{K_w}{(K_b \text{ for } NH_3)(K_a \text{ for } CH_3CO_2H)}$$

$$K_{eq} = \frac{1.0 \times 10^{-14}}{(1.8 \times 10^{-5})(1.8 \times 10^{-5})} = 3.1 \times 10^{-5}$$

d. $H_3O^+ + OH^- \rightleftharpoons 2\ H_2O \quad K_{eq} = \dfrac{1}{K_w} = 1.0 \times 10^{14}$

e. $NH_4^+ + OH^- \rightleftharpoons NH_3 + H_2O \quad K_{eq} = \dfrac{1}{K_b \text{ for } NH_3} = 5.6 \times 10^4$

f. $HNO_2 + OH^- \rightleftharpoons H_2O + NO_2^-$

$$K_{eq} = \frac{[NO_2^-]}{[HNO_2][OH^-]} \times \frac{[H^+]}{[H^+]} = \frac{K_a \text{ for } HNO_2}{K_w} = \frac{4.0 \times 10^{-4}}{1.0 \times 10^{-14}} = 4.0 \times 10^{10}$$

117. At pH = 2.000, $[H^+] = 10^{-2.000} = 1.00 \times 10^{-2}\ M$

At pH = 4.000, $[H^+] = 10^{-4.000} = 1.00 \times 10^{-4}\ M$

Mol H^+ present $= 0.0100\text{ L} \times \dfrac{0.0100\text{ mol } H^+}{\text{L}} = 1.00 \times 10^{-4}\text{ mol } H^+$

Let V = total volume of solution at pH = 4.000:

$$1.00 \times 10^{-4}\text{ mol/L} = \frac{1.00 \times 10^{-4}\text{ mol } H^+}{V},\quad V = 1.00\text{ L}$$

Volume of water added = 1.00 L – 0.0100 L = 0.99 L = 990 mL

119. a. In the lungs there is a lot of O_2, and the equilibrium favors $Hb(O_2)_4$. In the cells there is a lower concentration of O_2, and the equilibrium favors HbH_4^{4+}.

b. CO_2 is a weak acid, $CO_2 + H_2O \rightleftharpoons HCO_3^- + H^+$. Removing CO_2 essentially decreases H^+, which causes the hemoglobin reaction to shift right. $Hb(O_2)_4$ is then favored, and O_2 is not released by hemoglobin in the cells. Breathing into a paper bag increases CO_2 in the blood, thus increasing $[H^+]$, which shifts the hemoglobin reaction left.

c. CO_2 builds up in the blood, and it becomes too acidic, driving the hemoglobin equilibrium to the left. Hemoglobin can't bind O_2 as strongly in the lungs. Bicarbonate ion acts as a base in water and neutralizes the excess acidity.

121. The light bulb is bright because a strong electrolyte is present; that is, a solute is present that dissolves to produce a lot of ions in solution. The pH meter value of 4.6 indicates that a weak acid is present. (If a strong acid were present, the pH would be close to zero.) Of the possible substances, only HCl (strong acid), NaOH (strong base), and NH_4Cl are strong electrolytes. Of these three substances, only NH_4Cl contains a weak acid (the HCl solution would have a pH close to zero, and the NaOH solution would have a pH close to 14.0). NH_4Cl dissociates into NH_4^+ and Cl^- ions when dissolved in water. Cl^- is the conjugate base of a strong acid, so it has no basic (or acidic properties) in water. NH_4^+, however, is the conjugate acid of the weak base NH_3, so NH_4^+ is a weak acid and would produce a solution with a pH = 4.6 when the concentration is ~1.0 *M*. NH_4Cl is the solute.

123. $CaO(s) + H_2O(l) \rightarrow Ca(OH)_2(aq)$; $Ca(OH)_2(aq) \rightarrow Ca^{2+}(aq) + 2\ OH^-(aq)$

$$[OH^-] = \frac{0.25\text{ g CaO} \times \frac{1\text{ mol CaO}}{56.08\text{ g}} \times \frac{1\text{ mol Ca(OH)}_2}{1\text{ mol CaO}} \times \frac{2\text{ mol OH}^-}{\text{mol Ca(OH)}_2}}{1.5\text{ L}} = 5.9 \times 10^{-3}\ M$$

$$pOH = -\log(5.9 \times 10^{-3}) = 2.23,\ \ pH = 14.00 - 2.23 = 11.77$$

125. $$\frac{30.0\text{ mg papH}^+\text{Cl}^-}{\text{mL soln}} \times \frac{1000\text{ mL}}{\text{L}} \times \frac{1\text{ g}}{1000\text{ mg}} \times \frac{1\text{ mol papH}^+\text{Cl}^-}{378.85\text{ g}} \times \frac{1\text{ mol papH}^+}{\text{mol papH}^+\text{Cl}^-} = 0.0792\ M$$

$$\text{papH}^+ \rightleftharpoons \text{pap} + \text{H}^+ \quad K_a = \frac{K_w}{K_{b,\ pap}} = \frac{2.1 \times 10^{-14}}{8.33 \times 10^{-9}} = 2.5 \times 10^{-6}$$

	papH$^+$	pap	H$^+$
Initial	0.0792 *M*	0	~0
Equil.	$0.0792 - x$	x	x

$$K_a = 2.5 \times 10^{-6} = \frac{x^2}{0.0792 - x} \approx \frac{x^2}{0.0792},\ \ x = [H^+] = 4.4 \times 10^{-4}\ M$$

$pH = -\log(4.4 \times 10^{-4}) = 3.36$; assumptions good.

127. a. $$Fe(H_2O)_6^{3+} + H_2O \rightleftharpoons Fe(H_2O)_5(OH)^{2+} + H_3O^+$$

	$Fe(H_2O)_6^{3+}$	$Fe(H_2O)_5(OH)^{2+}$	H_3O^+
Initial	0.10 *M*	0	~0
Equil.	$0.10 - x$	x	x

$$K_a = \frac{[H_3O^+][Fe(H_2O)_5(OH)^{2+}]}{[Fe(H_2O)_6^{3+}]},\ \ 6.0 \times 10^{-3} = \frac{x^2}{0.10 - x} \approx \frac{x^2}{0.10}$$

$x = 2.4 \times 10^{-2}\ M$; assumption is poor (24% error).

Using successive approximations:

$$\frac{x^2}{0.10 - 0.024} = 6.0 \times 10^{-3},\ x = 0.021$$

$$\frac{x^2}{0.10 - 0.021} = 6.0 \times 10^{-3},\ x = 0.022;\quad \frac{x^2}{0.10 - 0.022} = 6.0 \times 10^{-3},\ x = 0.022$$

$x = [H^+] = 0.022\ M$; pH = 1.66

b. $\frac{[Fe(H_2O)_5(OH)^{2+}]}{[Fe(H_2O)_6{}^{3+}]} = \frac{0.0010}{0.9990}$; $K_a = 6.0 \times 10^{-3} = \frac{[H^+](0.0010)}{0.9990}$

Solving: $[H^+] = 6.0\ M$; pH = –log(6.0) = –0.78

c. Because of the lower charge, Fe^{2+}(aq) will not be as strong an acid as Fe^{3+}(aq). A solution of iron(II) nitrate will be less acidic (have a higher pH) than a solution with the same concentration of iron(III) nitrate.

129. 0.50 M HA, $K_a = 1.0 \times 10^{-3}$; 0.20 M HB, $K_a = 1.0 \times 10^{-10}$; 0.10 M HC, $K_a = 1.0 \times 10^{-12}$

Major source of H^+ is HA because its K_a value is significantly larger than other K_a values.

	HA	$\rightleftharpoons$	H^+	+	A^-
Initial	0.50 M		~0		0
Equil.	$0.50 - x$		x		x

$K_a = \frac{x^2}{0.50 - x}$, $1.0 \times 10^{-3} \approx \frac{x^2}{0.50}$, $x = 0.022\ M = [H^+]$, $\frac{0.022}{0.50} \times 100 = 4.4\%$ error

Assumption good. Let's check out the assumption that only HA is an important source of H^+.

For HB: $1.0 \times 10^{-10} = \frac{(0.022)[B^-]}{(0.20)}$, $[B^-] = 9.1 \times 10^{-10}\ M$

At most, HB will produce an additional $9.1 \times 10^{-10}\ M\ H^+$. Even less will be produced by HC. Thus our original assumption was good. $[H^+] = 0.022\ M$.

131. Since NH_3 is so concentrated, we need to calculate the OH^- contribution from the weak base NH_3.

	NH_3 + H_2O	$\rightleftharpoons$	$NH_4{}^+$	+	OH^-	$K_b = 1.8 \times 10^{-5}$
Initial	15.0 M		0		0.0100 M	(Assume no volume change.)
Equil.	$15.0 - x$		x		$0.0100 + x$	

$K_b = 1.8 \times 10^{-5} = \frac{x(0.0100 + x)}{15.0 - x} \approx \frac{x(0.0100)}{15.0}$, $x = 0.027$; assumption is horrible (x is 270% of 0.0100).

Using the quadratic formula:

$(1.8 \times 10^{-5})(15.0 - x) = (0.0100)x + x^2, \ x^2 + (0.0100)x - 2.7 \times 10^{-4} = 0$

$x = 1.2 \times 10^{-2}\ M, \ \ [OH^-] = (1.2 \times 10^{-2}) + 0.0100 = 0.022\ M$

133. a. The initial concentrations are halved since equal volumes of the two solutions are mixed.

	$HC_2H_3O_2$	$\rightleftharpoons$	H^+	+	$C_2H_3O_2^-$
Initial	$0.100\ M$		$5.00 \times 10^{-4}\ M$		0
Equil.	$0.100 - x$		$5.00 \times 10^{-4} + x$		x

$$K_a = 1.8 \times 10^{-5} = \frac{x(5.00 \times 10^{-4} + x)}{0.100 - x} \approx \frac{x(5.00 \times 10^{-4})}{0.100}$$

$x = 3.6 \times 10^{-3}$; assumption is horrible. Using the quadratic formula:

$x^2 + (5.18 \times 10^{-4})x - 1.8 \times 10^{-6} = 0$

$x = 1.1 \times 10^{-3}\ M; \ [H^+] = 5.00 \times 10^{-4} + x = 1.6 \times 10^{-3}\ M; \ pH = 2.80$

b. $x = [C_2H_3O_2^-] = 1.1 \times 10^{-3}\ M$

135. Because the values of K_{a_1} and K_{a_2} are fairly close to each other, we should consider the amount of H^+ produced by the K_{a_1} and K_{a_2} reactions.

	$H_3C_6H_5O_7$	$\rightleftharpoons$	$H_2C_6H_5O_7^-$	+	H^+	$K_{a_1} = 8.4 \times 10^{-4}$
Initial	$0.15\ M$		0		~0	
Equil.	$0.15 - x$		x		x	

$$8.4 \times 10^{-4} = \frac{x^2}{0.15 - x} \approx \frac{x^2}{0.15}, \ x = 1.1 \times 10^{-2}; \ \text{assumption fails the 5\% rule.}$$

Solving more exactly using the method of successive approximations:

$$8.4 \times 10^{-4} = \frac{x^2}{(0.15 - 1.1 \times 10^{-2})}, \ x = 1.1 \times 10^{-2}\ M \ \text{(consistent answer)}$$

Now let's solve for the H^+ contribution from the K_{a_2} reaction.

	$H_2C_6H_5O_7^-$	$\rightleftharpoons$	$HC_6H_5O_7^{2-}$	+	H^+	$K_{a_2} = 1.8 \times 10^{-5}$
Initial	$1.1 \times 10^{-2}\ M$		0		$1.1 \times 10^{-2}\ M$	
Equil.	$1.1 \times 10^{-2} - x$		x		$1.1 \times 10^{-2} + x$	

$$1.8 \times 10^{-5} = \frac{x(1.1 \times 10^{-2} + x)}{(1.1 \times 10^{-2} - x)} \approx \frac{x(1.1 \times 10^{-2})}{1.1 \times 10^{-2}}, \ x = 1.8 \times 10^{-5}\ M; \ \text{assumption good (0.2\% error).}$$

At most, 1.8×10^{-5} *M* H^+ will be added from the K_{a_2} reaction.

$[H^+]_{total} = (1.1 \times 10^{-2}) + (1.8 \times 10^{-5}) = 1.1 \times 10^{-2}$ *M*

Note that the H^+ contribution from the K_{a_2} reaction was negligible compared to the H^+ contribution from the K_{a_1} reaction even though the two K_a values only differed by a factor of 50. Therefore, the H^+ contribution from the K_{a_3} reaction will also be negligible since $K_{a_3} < K_{a_2}$.

Solving: pH = $-\log(1.1 \times 10^{-2}) = 1.96$

Challenge Problems

137. a. $HCO_3^- + HCO_3^- \rightleftharpoons H_2CO_3 + CO_3^{2-}$

$$K_{eq} = \frac{[H_2CO_3][CO_3^{2-}]}{[HCO_3^-][HCO_3^-]} \times \frac{[H^+]}{[H^+]} = \frac{K_{a_2}}{K_{a_1}} = \frac{4.8 \times 10^{-11}}{4.3 \times 10^{-7}} = 1.1 \times 10^{-4}$$

b. $[H_2CO_3] = [CO_3^{2-}]$ since the reaction in part a is the principal equilibrium reaction.

c. $H_2CO_3 \rightleftharpoons 2\ H^+ + CO_3^{2-}$ $\quad K_{eq} = \frac{[H^+]^2[CO_3^{2-}]}{[H_2CO_3]} = K_{a_1} \times K_{a_2}$

Because $[H_2CO_3] = [CO_3^{2-}]$ from part b, $[H^+]^2 = K_{a_1} \times K_{a_2}$.

$[H^+] = (K_{a_1} \times K_{a_2})^{1/2}$, or taking the –log of both sides: $pH = \frac{pK_{a_1} + pK_{a_2}}{2}$

d. $[H^+] = [(4.3 \times 10^{-7}) \times (4.8 \times 10^{-11})]^{1/2}$, $[H^+] = 4.5 \times 10^{-9}$ *M*; pH = 8.35

139. $HC_2H_3O_2 \rightleftharpoons H^+ + C_2H_3O_2^-$ $\quad K_a = 1.8 \times 10^{-5}$

	$HC_2H_3O_2$	H^+	$C_2H_3O_2^-$
Initial	1.00 *M*	~0	0
Equil.	$1.00 - x$	x	x

$$1.8 \times 10^{-5} = \frac{x^2}{1.00 - x} \approx \frac{x^2}{1.00},\quad x = [H^+] = 4.24 \times 10^{-3}\ M \text{ (using one extra sig. fig.)}$$

pH = $-\log(4.24 \times 10^{-3}) = 2.37$; assumptions good.

We want to double the pH to 2(2.37) = 4.74 by addition of the strong base NaOH. As is true with all strong bases, they are great at accepting protons. In fact, they are so good that we can assume they accept protons 100% of the time. The best acid present will react the strong base. This is $HC_2H_3O_2$. The initial reaction that occurs when the strong base is added is:

$$HC_2H_3O_2 + OH^- \rightarrow C_2H_3O_2^- + H_2O$$

Note that this reaction has the net effect of converting $HC_2H_3O_2$ into its conjugate base, $C_2H_3O_2^-$.

For a pH = 4.74, let's calculate the ratio of $[C_2H_3O_2^-]/[HC_2H_3O_2]$ necessary to achieve this pH.

$$HC_2H_3O_2 \rightleftharpoons H^+ + C_2H_3O_2^- \quad K_a = \frac{[H^+][C_2H_3O_2^-]}{[HC_2H_3O_2]}$$

When pH = 4.74, $[H^+] = 10^{-4.74} = 1.8 \times 10^{-5}$.

$$K_a = 1.8 \times 10^{-5} = \frac{(1.8 \times 10^{-5})[C_2H_3O_2^-]}{[HC_2H_3O_2]}, \quad \frac{[C_2H_3O_2^-]}{[HC_2H_3O_2]} = 1.0$$

For a solution having pH = 4.74, we need to have equal concentrations (equal moles) of $C_2H_3O_2^-$ and $HC_2H_3O_2$. Therefore, we need to add an amount of NaOH that will convert one-half of the $HC_2H_3O_2$ into $C_2H_3O_2^-$. This amount is 0.50 *M* NaOH.

	$HC_2H_3O_2$	+ OH^-	$\rightarrow$	$C_2H_3O_2^-$ + H_2O
Before	1.00 *M*	0.50 *M*		0
Change	– 0.50	– 0.50	$\rightarrow$	+0.50
After completion	0.50 *M*	0		0.50 *M*

From the preceding stoichiometry problem, adding enough NaOH(s) to produce a 0.50 *M* OH^- solution will convert one-half the $HC_2H_3O_2$ into $C_2H_3O_2^-$; this results in a solution with pH = 4.74.

$$\text{Mass NaOH} = 1.00\ \text{L} \times \frac{0.50\ \text{mol NaOH}}{\text{L}} \times \frac{40.00\ \text{g NaOH}}{\text{mol}} = 20.\ \text{g NaOH}$$

141. Major species: BH^+, X^-, and H_2O; because BH^+ is the best acid and X^- is the best base in solution, the principal equilibrium is:

	BH^+	+ X^-	$\rightleftharpoons$ B	+ HX
Initial	0.100 *M*	0.100 *M*	0	0
Equil.	$0.100 - x$	$0.100 - x$	x	x

$$K = \frac{K_{a,BH^+}}{K_{a,HX}} = \frac{[B][HX]}{[BH^+][X^-]}, \text{ where } [B] = [HX] \text{ and } [BH^+] = [X^-]$$

To solve for the K_a of HX, let's use the equilibrium expression to derive a general expression that relates pH to the pK_a for BH^+ and to the pK_a for HX.

$$\frac{K_{a,BH^+}}{K_{a,HX}} = \frac{[HX]^2}{[X^-]^2};\quad K_{a,HX} = \frac{[H^+][X^-]}{[HX]},\quad \frac{[HX]}{[X^-]} = \frac{[H^+]}{K_{a,HX}}$$

$$\frac{K_{a,BH^+}}{K_{a,HX}} = \frac{[HX]^2}{[X^-]^2} = \left(\frac{[H^+]}{K_{a,HX}}\right)^2,\quad [H^+]^2 = K_{a,BH^+} \times K_{a,HX}$$

Taking the –log of both sides: $pH = \dfrac{pK_{a,BH^+} + pK_{a,HX}}{2}$

This is a general equation that applies to all BHX type salts. Solving the problem:

K_b for B = 1.0×10^{-3}; K_a for $BH^+ = \dfrac{K_w}{K_b} = 1.0 \times 10^{-11}$

$pH = 8.00 = \dfrac{11.00 + pK_{a,HX}}{2}$, $pK_{a,HX} = 5.00$ and K_a for HX = $10^{-5.00} = 1.0 \times 10^{-5}$

143. 0.0500 *M* HCO_2H (HA), $K_a = 1.77 \times 10^{-4}$; 0.150 *M* $CH_3CH_2CO_2H$ (HB), $K_a = 1.34 \times 10^{-5}$

Because two comparable weak acids are present, each contributes to the total pH.

Charge balance: $[H^+] = [A^-] + [B^-] + [OH^-] = [A^-] + [B^-] + K_w/[H^+]$

Mass balance for HA and HB: $0.0500 = [HA] + [A^-]$ and $0.150 = [HB] + [B^-]$

$$\frac{[H^+][A^-]}{[HA]} = 1.77 \times 10^{-4};\quad \frac{[H^+][B^-]}{[HB]} = 1.34 \times 10^{-5}$$

We have five equations and five unknowns. Manipulate the equations to solve.

$[H^+] = [A^-] + [B^-] + K_w/[H^+]$; $[H^+]^2 = [H^+][A^-] + [H^+][B^-] + K_w$

$[H^+][A^-] = (1.77 \times 10^{-4})[HA] = (1.77 \times 10^{-4})(0.0500 - [A^-])$

If $[A^-] << 0.0500$, then $[H^+][A^-] \approx (1.77 \times 10^{-4})(0.0500) = 8.85 \times 10^{-6}$.

Similarly, assume $[H^+][B^-] \approx (1.34 \times 10^{-5})(0.150) = 2.01 \times 10^{-6}$.

$[H^+]^2 = 8.85 \times 10^{-6} + 2.01 \times 10^{-6} + 1.00 \times 10^{-14}$, $[H^+] = 3.30 \times 10^{-3}$ mol/L

Check assumptions: $[H^+][A^-] \approx 8.85 \times 10^{-6}$, $[A^-] \approx \dfrac{8.85 \times 10^{-6}}{3.30 \times 10^{-3}} \approx 2.68 \times 10^{-3}$

Assumed $0.0500 - [A^-] \approx 0.0500$. This assumption is borderline (2.68×10^{-3} is 5.4% of 0.0500). The HB assumption is good (0.4% error).

Using successive approximations to refine the $[H^+][A^-]$ value:

$$[H^+] = 3.22 \times 10^{-3}\ M,\ \ pH = -\log(3.22 \times 10^{-3}) = 2.492$$

Note: If we treat each acid separately:

H^+ from HA = 2.9×10^{-3}
H^+ from HB = 1.4×10^{-3}

$4.3 \times 10^{-3}\ M = [H^+]_{total}$

This assumes the acids did not suppress each other's ionization. They do, and we expect the $[H^+]$ to be less than $4.3 \times 10^{-3}\ M$. We get such an answer.

145. $HA \rightleftharpoons H^+ + A^-$ $K_a = 5.00 \times 10^{-10}$

	HA	⇌	H^+	A^-
Initial	$[HA]_0$		~0	0
Change	$-x$	→	$+x$	$+x$
Equil.	$[HA]_0 - x$		x	x

From the problem: pH = 5.650, so $[H^+] = x = 10^{-5.650} = 2.24 \times 10^{-6}\ M$

$$5.00 \times 10^{-10} = \frac{x^2}{[HA]_0 - x} = \frac{(2.24 \times 10^{-6})^2}{([HA]_0 - 2.24 \times 10^{-6})},\ \ [HA]_0 = 1.00 \times 10^{-2}\ M$$

After the water is added, the pH of the solution is between 6 and 7, so the water contribution to the $[H^+]$ must be considered. The general expression for a very dilute weak acid solution is:

$$K_a = \frac{[H^+]^2 - K_w}{[HA]_0 - \dfrac{[H^+]^2 - K_w}{[H^+]}}$$

pH = 6.650; $[H^+] = 10^{-6.650} = 2.24 \times 10^{-7}\ M$; let V = volume of water added:

$$5.00 \times 10^{-10} = \frac{(2.24 \times 10^{-7})^2 - (1.00 \times 10^{-14})}{(1.00 \times 10^{-2})\left(\dfrac{0.0500}{0.0500 + V}\right) - \dfrac{(2.24 \times 10^{-7})^2 - (1.00 \times 10^{-14})}{2.24 \times 10^{-7}}}$$

Solving, V = 6.16 L of water were added.

147. $\dfrac{0.135\ \text{mol}\ CO_2}{2.50\ \text{L}} = 5.40 \times 10^{-2}\ \text{mol}\ CO_2/\text{L} = 5.40 \times 10^{-2}\ M\ H_2CO_3$; $0.105\ M\ CO_3^{2-}$

The best acid (H_2CO_3) reacts with the best base present (CO_3^{2-}) for the principal equilibrium.

$$H_2CO_3 + CO_3^{2-} \rightarrow 2\ HCO_3^- \quad K = \frac{K_{a_1,\ H_2CO_3}}{K_{a_2,\ H_2CO_3}} = \frac{4.3 \times 10^{-7}}{4.8 \times 10^{-11}} = 9.0 \times 10^3$$

Because K >> 1, assume all CO_2 (H_2CO_3) is converted into HCO_3^-; that is, 5.40×10^{-2} mol/L CO_3^{2-} is converted into HCO_3^-.

$[HCO_3^-] = 2(5.40 \times 10^{-2}) = 0.108\ M$; $[CO_3^{2-}] = 0.105 - 0.0540 = 0.051\ M$

Note: If we solve for the $[H_2CO_3]$ using these concentrations, we get $[H_2CO_3] = 2.5 \times 10^{-5}\ M$; our assumption that the reaction goes to completion is good (2.5×10^{-5} is 0.05% of 0.051). Whenever K >> 1, always assume the reaction goes to completion.

To solve for the $[H^+]$ in equilibrium with HCO_3^- and CO_3^{2-}, use the K_a expression for HCO_3^-.

$HCO_3^- \rightleftharpoons H^+ + CO_3^{2-} \quad K_{a2} = 4.8 \times 10^{-11}$

$$4.8 \times 10^{-11} = \frac{[H^+][CO_3^{2-}]}{[HCO_3^-]} = \frac{[H^+](0.051)}{0.108}$$

$[H^+] = 1.0 \times 10^{-10}$; pH = 10.00; assumptions good.

149. Major species: H_2O, Na^+, and NO_2^-; NO_2^- is a weak base. $NO_2^- + H_2O \rightleftharpoons HNO_2 + OH^-$

Because this is a very dilute solution of a weak base, the OH^- contribution from H_2O must be considered. The weak base equations for dilute solutions are analogous to the weak acid equations derived in Section 7.9 of the text.

For A^- type bases ($A^- + H_2O \rightleftharpoons HA + OH^-$), the general equation is:

$$K_b = \frac{[OH^-]^2 - K_w}{[A^-]_0 - \dfrac{[OH^-]^2 - K_w}{[OH^-]}}$$

When $[A^-]_0 >> \dfrac{[OH^-]^2 - K_w}{[OH^-]}$, then $K_b = \dfrac{[OH^-]^2 - K_w}{[A^-]_0}$ and:

$$[OH^-] = (K_b[A^-]_0 + K_w)^{1/2}$$

Try: $$[OH^-] = \left(\frac{1.0 \times 10^{-14}}{4.0 \times 10^{-4}} \times (6.0 \times 10^{-4}) + (1.0 \times 10^{-14})\right)^{1/2} = 1.6 \times 10^{-7}\ M$$

Checking assumption: $$6.0 \times 10^{-4} >> \frac{(1.6 \times 10^{-7})^2 - (1.0 \times 10^{-14})}{1.6 \times 10^{-7}} = 9.8 \times 10^{-8}$$

Assumption good. $[OH^-] = 1.6 \times 10^{-7}\ M$; pOH = 6.80; pH = 7.20

151. Major species: H_2O, NH_3, H^+, and Cl^-; the H^+ from the strong acid will react with the best base present (NH_3). Because strong acids are great at donating protons, the reaction between H^+ and NH_3 essentially goes to completion, that is, until one or both of the reactants runs out. The reaction is:

$$NH_3 + H^+ \rightarrow NH_4^+$$

Because equal volumes of 1.0×10^{-4} *M* NH_3 and 1.0×10^{-4} *M* H^+ are mixed, both reactants are in stoichiometric amounts, and both reactants will run out at the same time. After reaction, only NH_4^+ and Cl^- remain. Cl^- has no basic properties since it is the conjugate base of a strong acid. Therefore, the only species with acid-base properties is NH_4^+, a weak acid. The initial concentration of NH_4^+ will be exactly one-half of 1.0×10^{-4} *M* since equal volumes of NH_3 and HCl were mixed. Now we must solve the weak acid problem involving 5.0×10^{-5} *M* NH_4^+.

	NH_4^+	$\rightleftharpoons$	H^+	+	NH_3	$K_a = \frac{K_w}{K_b} = 5.6 \times 10^{-10}$
Initial	5.0×10^{-5} *M*		~0		0	
Equil.	$5.0 \times 10^{-5} - x$		x		x	

$$K_a = \frac{x^2}{(5.0 \times 10^{-5} - x)} \approx \frac{x^2}{5.0 \times 10^{-5}} = 5.6 \times 10^{-10},\ x = 1.7 \times 10^{-7}\ M;\ \text{check assumptions.}$$

We cannot neglect $[H^+]$ that comes from H_2O. As discussed in Section 7.9 of the text, assume $5.0 \times 10^{-5} >> ([H^+]^2 - K_w)/[H^+]$. If this is the case, then:

$$[H^+] = (K_a[HA]_0 + K_w)^{1/2} = 1.9 \times 10^{-7}\ M;\ \text{checking assumption:}$$

$$\frac{[H^+]^2 - K_w}{[H^+]} = 1.4 \times 10^{-7} << 5.0 \times 10^{-5}\ \text{(assumption good)}$$

So: $[H^+] = 1.9 \times 10^{-7}$ *M*; pH = 6.72

CHAPTER 8

APPLICATIONS OF AQUEOUS EQUILIBRIA

Buffers

15. A buffer solution is one that resists a change in its pH when either hydroxide ions or protons (H^+) are added. Any solution that contains a weak acid and its conjugate base or a weak base and its conjugate acid is classified as a buffer. The pH of a buffer depends on the [base]/[acid] ratio. When H^+ is added to a buffer, the weak base component of the buffer reacts with the H^+ and forms the acid component of the buffer. Even though the concentrations of the acid and base components of the buffer change some, the ratio of [base]/[acid] does not change that much. This translates into a pH that doesn't change much. When OH^- is added to a buffer, the weak acid component is converted into the base component of the buffer. Again, the [base]/[acid] ratio does not change a lot (unless a large quantity of OH^- is added), so the pH does not change much.

$$H^+(aq) + CO_3^{2-}(aq) \rightarrow HCO_3^-(aq);\ OH^-(aq) + HCO_3^-(aq) \rightarrow H_2O(l) + CO_3^{2-}(aq)$$

17. Only the third beaker represents a buffer solution. A weak acid and its conjugate base must both be present in large quantities in order to have a buffer solution. This is only the case in the third beaker. The first beaker respresents a beaker full of strong acid which is 100°% dissociated. The second beaker represents a weak acid solution. In a weak acid solution, only a small fraction of the acid is dissociated. In this representation, 1/10 of the weak acid has dissociated. The only B^- present in this beaker is from the dissociation of the weak acid. A buffer solution has B^- added from another source.

19. $pH = pK_a + \log\frac{[base]}{[acid]}$; when [acid] > [base], then $\frac{[base]}{[acid]} < 1$ and $\log\left(\frac{[base]}{[acid]}\right) < 0$.

From the Henderson-Hasselbalch equation, if the log term is negative, then $pH < pK_a$. When one has more acid than base in a buffer, the pH will be on the acidic side of the pK_a value; that is, the pH is at a value lower than the pK_a value. When one has more base than acid in a buffer ([conjugate base] > [weak acid]), then the log term in the Henderson-Hasselbalch equation is positive, resulting in $pH > pK_a$. When one has more base than acid in a buffer, the pH is on the basic side of the pK_a value; that is, the pH is at a value greater than the pK_a value. The other scenario you can run across in a buffer is when [acid] = [base]. Here, the log term is equal to zero, and $pH = pK_a$.

21. a. This is a weak acid problem. Let $HC_3H_5O_2$ = HOPr and $C_3H_5O_2^-$ = OPr^-.

	HOPr(aq)	⇌	H^+(aq)	+	OPr^-(aq)	$K_a = 1.3 \times 10^{-5}$
Initial	0.100 *M*		~0		0	
	x mol/L HOPr dissociates to reach equilibrium					
Change	$-x$	→	$+x$		$+x$	
Equil.	$0.100 - x$		x		x	

$$K_a = 1.3 \times 10^{-5} = \frac{[H^+][OPr^-]}{[HOPr]} = \frac{x^2}{0.100 - x} \approx \frac{x^2}{0.100}$$

$x = [H^+] = 1.1 \times 10^{-3}$ *M*; pH = 2.96; assumptions good by the 5% rule.

b. This is a weak base problem.

	OPr^-(aq) + H_2O(l)	⇌	HOPr(aq)	+	OH^-(aq)	$K_b = \frac{K_w}{K_a} = 7.7 \times 10^{-10}$
Initial	0.100 *M*		0		~0	
	x mol/L OPr^- reacts with H_2O to reach equilibrium					
Change	$-x$	→	$+x$		$+x$	
Equil.	$0.100 - x$		x		x	

$$K_b = 7.7 \times 10^{-10} = \frac{[HOPr][OH^-]}{[OPr^-]} = \frac{x^2}{0.100 - x} \approx \frac{x^2}{0.100}$$

$x = [OH^-] = 8.8 \times 10^{-6}$ *M*; pOH = 5.06; pH = 8.94; assumptions good.

c. Pure H_2O, $[H^+] = [OH^-] = 1.0 \times 10^{-7}$ *M*; pH = 7.00

d. This solution contains a weak acid and its conjugate base. This is a buffer solution. We will solve for the pH through the weak acid equilibrium reaction.

	HOPr(aq)	⇌	H^+(aq)	+	OPr^-(aq)	$K_a = 1.3 \times 10^{-5}$
Initial	0.100 *M*		~0		0.100 *M*	
	x mol/L HOPr dissociates to reach equilibrium					
Change	$-x$	→	$+x$		$+x$	
Equil.	$0.100 - x$		x		$0.100 + x$	

$$1.3 \times 10^{-5} = \frac{(0.100 + x)(x)}{0.100 - x} \approx \frac{(0.100)(x)}{0.100} = x = [H^+]$$

$[H^+] = 1.3 \times 10^{-5}$ *M*; pH = 4.89; assumptions good.

Alternately, we can use the Henderson-Hasselbalch equation to calculate the pH of buffer solutions.

$$pH = pK_a + \log\frac{[\text{base}]}{[\text{acid}]} = pK_a + \log\left(\frac{0.100}{0.100}\right) = pK_a = -\log(1.3 \times 10^{-5}) = 4.89$$

The Henderson-Hasselbalch equation will be valid when an assumption of the type $0.1 + x \approx 0.1$ that we just made in this problem is valid. From a practical standpoint, this will almost always be true for useful buffer solutions. If the assumption is not valid, the solution will have such a low buffering capacity it will not be of any use to control the pH. *Note*: The Henderson-Hasselbalch equation can only be used to solve for the pH of buffer solutions.

23. a. OH^- will react completely with the best acid present, HOPr.

	HOPr	+	OH^-	→	OPr^-	+	H_2O	
Before	0.100 *M*		0.020 *M*		0			
Change	−0.020		−0.020	→	+0.020			Reacts completely
After	0.080		0		0.020			

A buffer solution results after the reaction. Using the Henderson-Hasselbalch equation:

$$pH = pK_a + \log\frac{[\text{base}]}{[\text{acid}]} = 4.89 + \log\frac{(0.020)}{(0.080)} = 4.29; \text{ assumptions good.}$$

b. We have a weak base and a strong base present at the same time. The amount of OH^- added by the weak base will be negligible. To prove it, let's consider the weak base equilibrium:

$$OPr^- + H_2O \rightleftharpoons HOPr + OH^- \qquad K_b = 7.7 \times 10^{-10}$$

	OPr^-		HOPr	OH^-
Initial	0.100 *M*		0	0.020 *M*
	x mol/L OPr^- reacts with H_2O to reach equilibrium			
Change	$-x$	→	$+x$	$+x$
Equil.	$0.100 - x$		x	$0.020 + x$

$[OH^-] = 0.020 + x \approx 0.020$ *M*; pOH = 1.70; pH = 12.30; assumption good.

Note: The OH^- contribution from the weak base OPr^- was negligible ($x = 3.9 \times 10^{-9}$ *M* as compared to 0.020 *M* OH^- from the strong base). The pH can be determined by only considering the amount of strong base present.

c. This is a strong base in water. $[OH^-] = 0.020$ *M*; pOH = 1.70; pH = 12.30

d. OH^- will react completely with HOPr, the best acid present.

	HOPr	+	OH^-	→	OPr^-	+	H_2O	
Before	0.100 *M*		0.020 *M*		0.100 *M*			
Change	–0.020		–0.020	→	+0.020			Reacts completely
After	0.080		0		0.120			

Using the Henderson-Hasselbalch equation to solve for the pH of the resulting buffer solution:

$$pH = pK_a + \log\frac{[base]}{[acid]} = 4.89 + \log\frac{(0.120)}{(0.080)} = 5.07;\ \text{assumptions good.}$$

25. Major species: HF, F^-, K^+, and H_2O. K^+ has no acidic or basic properties. This is a solution containing a weak acid and its conjugate base. This is a buffer solution. One appropriate equilibrium reaction you can use is the K_a reaction of HF, which contains both HF and F^-. However, you could also use the K_b reaction for F^- and come up with the same answer. Alternately, you could use the Henderson-Hasselblach equation to solve for the pH. For this problem, we will use the K_a reaction and set up an ICE table to solve for the pH.

	HF	⇌	F^-	+	H^+
Initial	0.60 *M*		1.00 *M*		~0
	x mol/L HF dissociates to reach equilibrium				
Change	$-x$	→	$+x$		$+x$
Equil.	$0.60 - x$		$1.00 + x$		x

$$K_a = 7.2 \times 10^{-4} = \frac{[F^-][H^+]}{[HF]} = \frac{(1.00 + x)(x)}{0.60 - x} \approx \frac{(1.00)(x)}{0.60}\quad (\text{assuming } x << 0.60)$$

$x = [H^+] = 0.60 \times (7.2 \times 10^{-4}) = 4.3 \times 10^{-4}\ M$; assumptions good.

$pH = -\log(4.3 \times 10^{-4}) = 3.37$

27. Major species after NaOH added: HF, F^-, K^+, Na^+, OH^-, and H_2O. The OH^- from the strong base will react with the best acid present (HF). Any reaction involving a strong base is assumed to go to completion. Because all species present are in the same volume of solution, we can use molarity units to do the stoichiometry part of the problem (instead of moles). The stoichiometry problem is:

	OH^-	+	HF	→	F^-	+ H_2O	
Before	0.10 mol/1.00 L		0.60 *M*		1.00 *M*		
Change	–0.10 *M*		–0.10 *M*	→	+0.10 *M*		Reacts completely
After	0		0.50		1.10		

After all the OH^- reacts, we are left with a solution containing a weak acid (HF) and its conjugate base (F^-). This is what we call a buffer problem. We will solve this buffer problem using the K_a equilibrium reaction. One could also use the K_b equilibrium reaction or use the Henderson-Hasselbalch equation to solve for the pH.

	HF	$\rightleftharpoons$	F^-	+	H^+
Initial	0.50 *M*		1.10 *M*		~0
	x mol/L HF dissociates to reach equilibrium				
Change	$-x$	$\rightarrow$	$+x$		$+x$
Equil.	$0.50 - x$		$1.10 + x$		x

$$K_a = 7.2 \times 10^{-4} = \frac{(1.10 + x)(x)}{0.50 - x} \approx \frac{(1.10)(x)}{0.50},\ x = [H^+] = 3.3 \times 10^{-4}\ M;\ pH = 3.48;$$ assumptions good.

Note: The added NaOH to this buffer solution changes the pH only from 3.37 to 3.48. If the NaOH were added to 1.0 L of pure water, the pH would change from 7.00 to 13.00.

Major species after HCl added: HF, F^-, H^+, K^+, Cl^-, and H_2O; the added H^+ from the strong acid will react completely with the best base present (F^-).

	H^+	+	F^-	$\rightarrow$	HF	
Before	$\frac{0.20\text{ mol}}{1.00\text{ L}}$		1.00 *M*		0.60 *M*	
Change	−0.20 *M*		−0.20 *M*	$\rightarrow$	+0.20 *M*	Reacts completely
After	0		0.80		0.80	

After all the H^+ has reacted, we have a buffer solution (a solution containing a weak acid and its conjugate base). Solving the buffer problem:

	HF	$\rightleftharpoons$	F^-	+	H^+
Initial	0.80 *M*		0.80 *M*		0
Equil.	$0.80 - x$		$0.80 + x$		x

$$K_a = 7.2 \times 10^{-4} = \frac{(0.80 + x)(x)}{0.80 - x} \approx \frac{(0.80)(x)}{0.80},\ x = [H^+] = 7.2 \times 10^{-4}\ M;\ pH = 3.14;$$ assumptions good.

Note: The added HCl to this buffer solution changes the pH only from 3.37 to 3.14. If the HCl were added to 1.0 L of pure water, the pH would change from 7.00 to 0.70.

29. K_a for $H_2NNH_3^+ = K_w/K_{b,\,H_2NNH_2} = 1.0 \times 10^{-14}/3.0 \times 10^{-6} = 3.3 \times 10^{-9}$

$$pH = pK_a + \log\frac{[H_2NNH_2]}{[H_2NNH_3^+]} = -\log(3.3 \times 10^{-9}) + \log\left(\frac{0.40}{0.80}\right) = 8.48 + (-0.30) = 8.18$$

pH = pK_a for a buffer when [acid] = [base]. Here, the acid ($H_2NNH_3^+$) concentration needs to decrease, while the base (H_2NNH_2) concentration needs to increase in order for $[H_2NNH_3^+] = [H_2NNH_2]$. Both of these changes are accomplished by adding a strong base (like NaOH) to the original buffer. The added OH^- from the strong base converts the acid component of the buffer into the conjugate base. Here, the reaction is $H_2NNH_3^+ + OH^- \rightarrow H_2NNH_2 + H_2O$.

Because a strong base is reacting, the reaction is assumed to go to completion. The following set-up determines the number of moles of OH^- (x) that must be added so that mol $H_2NNH_3^+$ = mol H_2NNH_2 . When mol acid = mol base in a buffer, then [acid] = [base] and pH = pK_a.

$$H_2NNH_3^+ \quad + \quad OH^- \quad \rightarrow \quad H_2NNH_2 \quad + \quad H_2O$$

	$H_2NNH_3^+$	OH^-		H_2NNH_2	
Before	1.0 L × 0.80 mol/L	x		1.0 L × 0.40 mol/L	
Change	$-x$	$-x$	→	$+x$	Reacts completely
After	$0.80 - x$	0		$0.40 + x$	

We want mol $H_2NNH_3^+$ = mol H_2NNH_2. So:

$$0.80 - x = 0.40 + x, \; 2x = 0.40, \; x = 0.20 \text{ mol OH}^-$$

When 0.20 mol OH^- is added to the initial buffer, mol $H_2NNH_3^+$ is decreased to 0.60 mol, while mol H_2NNH_2 is increased to 0.60 mol. Therefore, 0.20 mol of NaOH must be added to the initial buffer solution in order to produce a solution where pH = pK_a.

31. $$[HC_7H_5O_2] = \frac{21.5 \text{ g } HC_7H_5O_2 \times \dfrac{1 \text{ mol } HC_7H_5O_2}{122.12 \text{ g}}}{0.2000 \text{ L}} = 0.880\ M$$

$$[C_7H_5O_2^-] = \frac{37.7 \text{ g } NaC_7H_5O_2 \times \dfrac{1 \text{ mol } NaC_7H_5O_2}{144.10 \text{ g}} \times \dfrac{1 \text{ mol } C_7H_5O_2^-}{\text{mol } NaC_7H_5O_2}}{0.2000 \text{ L}} = 1.31\ M$$

We have a buffer solution since we have both a weak acid and its conjugate base present at the same time. One can use the K_a reaction or the K_b reaction to solve. We will use the K_a reaction for the acid component of the buffer.

$$HC_7H_5O_2 \rightleftharpoons H^+ + C_7H_5O_2^-$$

	$HC_7H_5O_2$	H^+	$C_7H_5O_2^-$
Initial	0.880 M	~0	1.31 M
	x mol/L of $HC_7H_5O_2$ dissociates to reach equilibrium		
Change	$-x$	→ $+x$	$+x$
Equil.	$0.880 - x$	x	$1.31 + x$

$$K_a = 6.4 \times 10^{-5} = \frac{x(1.31 + x)}{0.880 - x} \approx \frac{x(1.31)}{0.880}, \; x = [H^+] = 4.3 \times 10^{-5}\ M$$

pH = $-\log(4.3 \times 10^{-5}) = 4.37$; assumptions good.

Alternatively, we can use the Henderson-Hasselbalch equation to calculate the pH of buffer solutions.

$$pH = pK_a + \log\frac{[\text{base}]}{[\text{acid}]} = pK_a + \log\frac{[C_7H_5O_2^-]}{[HC_7H_5O_2]}$$

$$pH = -\log(6.4 \times 10^{-5}) + \log\left(\frac{1.31}{0.880}\right) = 4.19 + 0.173 = 4.36$$

Within round-off error, this is the same answer we calculated solving the equilibrium problem using the K_a reaction.

The Henderson-Hasselbalch equation will be valid when an assumption of the type $1.31 + x \approx 1.31$ that we just made in this problem is valid. From a practical standpoint, this will almost always be true for useful buffer solutions. If the assumption is not valid, the solution will have such a low buffering capacity that it will be of no use to control the pH. *Note*: The Henderson-Hasselbalch equation can only be used to solve for the pH of buffer solutions.

33. $C_5H_5NH^+ \rightleftharpoons H^+ + C_5H_5N \quad K_a = \frac{K_w}{K_b} = \frac{1.0 \times 10^{-14}}{1.7 \times 10^{-9}} = 5.9 \times 10^{-6}$

$pK_a = -\log(5.9 \times 10^{-6}) = 5.23$

We will use the Henderson-Hasselbalch equation to calculate the concentration ratio necessary for each buffer.

$$pH = pK_a + \log\frac{[\text{base}]}{[\text{acid}]}, \quad pH = 5.23 + \log\frac{[C_5H_5N]}{[C_5H_5NH^+]}$$

a. $4.50 = 5.23 + \log\frac{[C_5H_5N]}{[C_5H_5NH^+]}$

$$\log\frac{[C_5H_5N]}{[C_5H_5NH^+]} = -0.73$$

$$\frac{[C_5H_5N]}{[C_5H_5NH^+]} = 10^{-0.73} = 0.19$$

b. $5.00 = 5.23 + \log\frac{[C_5H_5N]}{[C_5H_5NH^+]}$

$$\log\frac{[C_5H_5N]}{[C_5H_5NH^+]} = -0.23$$

$$\frac{[C_5H_5N]}{[C_5H_5NH^+]} = 10^{-0.23} = 0.59$$

c. $5.23 = 5.23 + \log\frac{[C_5H_5N]}{[C_5H_5NH^+]}$

$$\frac{[C_5H_5N]}{[C_5H_5NH^+]} = 10^{0.0} = 1.0$$

d. $5.50 = 5.23 + \log\frac{[C_5H_5N]}{[C_5H_5NH^+]}$

$$\frac{[C_5H_5N]}{[C_5H_5NH^+]} = 10^{0.27} = 1.9$$

35. When H^+ is added, it converts $C_2H_3O_2^-$ into $HC_2H_3O_2$: $C_2H_3O_2^- + H^+ \rightarrow HC_2H_3O_2$. From this reaction, the moles of $HC_2H_3O_2$ produced must equal the moles of H^+ added and the total concentration of acetate ion + acetic acid must equal 1.0 *M* (assuming no volume change). Summarizing for each solution:

$[C_2H_3O_2^-] + [HC_2H_3O_2] = 1.0\ M$ and $[HC_2H_3O_2] = [H^+]$ added

a. $pH = pK_a + \log\frac{[C_2H_3O_2^-]}{[HC_2H_3O_2]}$; for $pH = pK_a$, $[C_2H_3O_2^-] = [HC_2H_3O_2]$.

For this to be true, $[C_2H_3O_2^-] = [HC_2H_3O_2] = 0.50\ M = [H^+]$ added, which means that 0.50 mol of HCl must be added to 1.0 L of the initial solution to produce a solution with $pH = pK_a$.

b. $4.20 = 4.74 + \log\frac{[C_2H_3O_2^-]}{[HC_2H_3O_2]}$, $\frac{[C_2H_3O_2^-]}{[HC_2H_3O_2]} = 10^{-0.54} = 0.29$

$[C_2H_3O_2^-] = 0.29[HC_2H_3O_2]$; $0.29[HC_2H_3O_2] + [HC_2H_3O_2] = 1.0\ M$

$[HC_2H_3O_2] = 0.78\ M = [H^+]$ added

0.78 mol of HCl must be added to produce a solution with pH = 4.20.

c. $5.00 = 4.74 + \log\frac{[C_2H_3O_2^-]}{[HC_2H_3O_2]}$, $\frac{[C_2H_3O_2^-]}{[HC_2H_3O_2]} = 10^{0.26} = 1.8$

$[C_2H_3O_2^-] = 1.8[HC_2H_3O_2]$; $1.8[HC_2H_3O_2] + [HC_2H_3O_2] = 1.0\ M$

$[HC_2H_3O_2] = 0.36\ M = [H^+]$ added

0.36 mol of HCl must be added to produce a solution with pH = 5.00.

37. $pH = pK_a + \log\frac{[C_2H_3O_2^-]}{[HC_2H_3O_2]}$; $pK_a = -\log(1.8 \times 10^{-5}) = 4.74$

Because the buffer components, $C_2H_3O_2^-$ and $HC_2H_3O_2$, are both in the same volume of water, the concentration ratio of $[C_2H_3O_2^-]/[HC_2H_3O_2]$ will equal the mole ratio of mol $C_2H_3O_2^-$/mol $HC_2H_3O_2$.

$5.00 = 4.74 + \log\frac{\text{mol } C_2H_3O_2^-}{\text{mol } HC_2H_3O_2}$; mol $HC_2H_3O_2 = 0.5000\ L \times \frac{0.200\ \text{mol}}{L} = 0.100$ mol

$0.26 = \log\frac{\text{mol } C_2H_3O_2^-}{0.100\ \text{mol}}$, $\frac{\text{mol } C_2H_3O_2^-}{0.100\ \text{mol}} = 10^{0.26} = 1.8$, mol $C_2H_3O_2^- = 0.18$ mol

Mass $NaC_2H_3O_2 = 0.18$ mol $NaC_2H_3O_2 \times \frac{82.03\ g}{\text{mol}} = 15$ g $NaC_2H_3O_2$

39. a. pK_b for $C_6H_5NH_2 = -\log(3.8 \times 10^{-10}) = 9.42$; pK_a for $C_6H_5NH_3^+ = 14.00 - 9.42 = 4.58$

$pH = pK_a + \log\frac{[C_6H_5NH_2]}{[C_6H_5NH_3^+]}$, $4.20 = 4.58 + \log\frac{0.50\ M}{[C_6H_5NH_3^+]}$

$-0.38 = \log\frac{0.50\ M}{[C_6H_5NH_3^+]}$, $[C_6H_5NH_3^+] = [C_6H_5NH_3Cl] = 1.2\ M$

b. $4.0 \text{ g NaOH} \times \frac{1 \text{ mol NaOH}}{40.00 \text{ g}} \times \frac{1 \text{ mol OH}^-}{\text{mol NaOH}} = 0.10 \text{ mol OH}^-$; $[OH^-] = \frac{0.10 \text{ mol}}{1.0 \text{ L}} = 0.10\ M$

	$C_6H_5NH_3^+$	+	OH^-	$\rightarrow$	$C_6H_5NH_2$	+	H_2O
Before	1.2 *M*		0.10 *M*		0.50 *M*		
Change	−0.10		−0.10	$\rightarrow$	+0.10		
After	1.1		0		0.60		

A buffer solution exists. $\text{pH} = 4.58 + \log\left(\frac{0.60}{1.1}\right) = 4.32$

41. a. $\text{pH} = \text{p}K_a + \log\frac{[\text{base}]}{[\text{acid}]}$, $7.15 = -\log(6.2 \times 10^{-8}) + \log\frac{[HPO_4^{2-}]}{[H_2PO_4^-]}$

$7.15 = 7.21 + \log\frac{[HPO_4^{2-}]}{[H_2PO_4^-]}$, $\frac{[HPO_4^{2-}]}{[H_2PO_4^-]} = 10^{-0.06} = 0.9$, $\frac{[H_2PO_4^-]}{[HPO_4^{2-}]} = \frac{1}{0.9} = 1.1 \approx 1$

b. A best buffer has approximately equal concentrations of weak acid and conjugate base, so $\text{pH} \approx \text{p}K_a$ for a best buffer. The $\text{p}K_a$ value for a $H_3PO_4/H_2PO_4^-$ buffer is $-\log(7.5 \times 10^{-3}) = 2.12$. A pH of 7.15 is too high for a $H_3PO_4/H_2PO_4^-$ buffer to be effective. At this high of pH, there would be so little H_3PO_4 present that we could hardly consider it a buffer; this solution would not be effective in resisting pH changes, especially when a strong base is added.

43. At pH = 7.40: $7.40 = -\log(4.3 \times 10^{-7}) + \log\frac{[HCO_3^-]}{[H_2CO_3]}$

$\log\frac{[HCO_3^-]}{[H_2CO_3]} = 7.40 - 6.37 = 1.03$, $\frac{[HCO_3^-]}{[H_2CO_3]} = 10^{1.03}$, $\frac{[H_2CO_3]}{[HCO_3^-]} = 10^{-1.03} = 0.093$

At pH = 7.35: $\log\frac{[HCO_3^-]}{[H_2CO_3]} = 7.35 - 6.37 = 0.98$, $\frac{[HCO_3^-]}{[H_2CO_3]} = 10^{0.98}$

$\frac{[H_2CO_3]}{[HCO_3^-]} = 10^{-0.98} = 0.10$

The $[H_2CO_3]$: $[HCO_3^-]$ concentration ratio must increase from 0.093 to 0.10 in order for the onset of acidosis to occur.

45. a. No; a solution of a strong acid (HNO_3) and its conjugate base (NO_3^-) is not generally considered a buffer solution.

b. No; two acids are present (HNO_3 and HF), so it is not a buffer solution.

c. H^+ reacts completely with F^-. Since equal volumes are mixed, the initial concentrations in the mixture are 0.10 *M* HNO_3 and 0.20 *M* NaF.

	H^+	+	F^-	→	HF	
Before	0.10 *M*		0.20 *M*		0	
Change	−0.10		−0.10	→	+0.10	Reacts completely
After	0		0.10		0.10	

After H^+ reacts completely, a buffer solution results; that is, a weak acid (HF) and its conjugate base (F^-) are both present in solution in large quantities.

d. No; a strong acid (HNO_3) and a strong base (NaOH) do not form buffer solutions. They will neutralize each other to form H_2O.

47. A best buffer has large and equal quantities of weak acid and conjugate base. Because [acid] = [base] for a best buffer, $pH = pK_a + \log\frac{[\text{base}]}{[\text{acid}]} = pK_a + 0 = pK_a$ ($pH \approx pK_a$ for a best buffer).

The best acid choice for a pH = 7.00 buffer would be the weak acid with a pK_a close to 7.0 or $K_a \approx 1 \times 10^{-7}$. HOCl is the best choice in Table 7.2 ($K_a = 3.5 \times 10^{-8}$; $pK_a = 7.46$). To make this buffer, we need to calculate the [base]/[acid] ratio.

$$7.00 = 7.46 + \log\frac{[\text{base}]}{[\text{acid}]},\quad \frac{[\text{OCl}^-]}{[\text{HOCl}]} = 10^{-0.46} = 0.35$$

Any OCl^-/HOCl buffer in a concentration ratio of 0.35 : 1 will have a pH = 7.00. One possibility is [NaOCl] = 0.35 *M* and [HOCl] = 1.0 *M*.

49. To solve for [KOCl], we need to use the equation derived in Section 8.3 of the text on the exact treatment of buffered solutions. The equation is:

$$K_a = \frac{[H^+]\left([A^-]_0 + \dfrac{[H^+]^2 - K_w}{[H^+]}\right)}{[HA]_0 - \dfrac{[H^+]^2 - K_w}{[H^+]}}$$

Because pH = 7.20, $[H^+] = 10^{-7.20} = 6.3 \times 10^{-8}$ *M*.

$$K_a = 3.5 \times 10^{-8} = \frac{6.3 \times 10^{-8}\left([\text{OCl}^-] + \dfrac{(6.3 \times 10^{-8})^2 - (1.0 \times 10^{-14})}{6.3 \times 10^{-8}}\right)}{1.0 \times 10^{-6} - \dfrac{(6.3 \times 10^{-8})^2 - (1.0 \times 10^{-14})}{6.3 \times 10^{-8}}}$$

$$3.5 \times 10^{-8} = \frac{6.3 \times 10^{-8}([\text{OCl}^-] - 9.57 \times 10^{-8})}{(1.0 \times 10^{-6}) + (9.57 \times 10^{-8})} \quad \text{(Carrying extra significant figures.)}$$

$3.83 \times 10^{-14} = 6.3 \times 10^{-8}([\text{OCl}^-] - 9.57 \times 10^{-8})$, $[\text{OCl}^-] = [\text{KOCl}] = 7.0 \times 10^{-7}\ M$

51. Using regular procedures, pH = $pK_a = -\log(1.6 \times 10^{-7}) = 6.80$ since $[A^-]_0 = [HA]_0$ in this buffer solution. However, the pH is very close to that of neutral water, so maybe we need to consider the H^+ contribution from water. Another problem with this answer is that x (= $[H^+]$) is not small as compared with $[HA]_0$ and $[A^-]_0$, which was assumed when solving using the regular procedures. Because the concentrations of the buffer components are less than 10^{-6} M, let us use the expression for the exact treatment of buffers to solve.

$$K_a = 1.6 \times 10^{-7} = \frac{[H^+]\left([A^-]_0 + \dfrac{[H^+]^2 - K_w}{[H^+]}\right)}{[HA]_0 - \dfrac{[H^+]^2 - K_w}{[H^+]}} = \frac{[H^+]\left(5.0 \times 10^{-7} + \dfrac{[H^+]^2 - (1.0 \times 10^{-14})}{[H^+]}\right)}{5.0 \times 10^{-7} - \dfrac{[H^+]^2 - (1.0 \times 10^{-14})}{[H^+]}}$$

Solving exactly requires solving a cubic equation. Instead, we will use the method of successive approximations where our initial guess for $[H^+] = 1.6 \times 10^{-7}\ M$ (the value obtained using the regular procedures).

$$1.6 \times 10^{-7} = \frac{[H^+]\left(5.0 \times 10^{-7} + \dfrac{(1.6 \times 10^{-7})^2 - (1.0 \times 10^{-14})}{1.6 \times 10^{-7}}\right)}{5.0 \times 10^{-7} - \dfrac{(1.6 \times 10^{-7})^2 - (1.0 \times 10^{-14})}{1.6 \times 10^{-7}}}, \quad [H^+] = 1.1 \times 10^{-7}$$

We continue the process using 1.1×10^{-7} as our estimate for $[H^+]$. This gives $[H^+] = 1.5 \times 10^{-7}$. We continue the process until we get a self consistent answer. After three more iterations, we converge on $[H^+] = 1.3 \times 10^{-7}\ M$. Solving for the pH:

$$\text{pH} = -\log(1.3 \times 10^{-7}) = 6.89$$

Note that if we were to solve this problem exactly (using the quadratic formula) while ignoring the H^+ contribution from water, the answer comes out to $[H^+] = 1.0 \times 10^{-7}\ M$. We get a significantly different answer when we consider the H^+ contribution from H_2O.

Acid-Base Titrations

53. a. Let's call the acid HB, which is a weak acid. When HB is present in the beakers, it exists in the undissociated form, making it a weak acid. A strong acid would exist as separate H^+ and B^- ions.

b. Beaker a contains 4 HB molecules and 2 B^- ions, beaker b contains 6 B^- ions, beaker c contains 6 HB molecules, beaker d contains 6 B^- and 6 OH^- ions, and beaker e contains 3 HB molecules and 3 B^- ions. $HB + OH^- \rightarrow B^- + H_2O$; this is the neutralization reaction that occurs when OH^- is added. We start off the titration with a beaker full of weak acid (beaker c). When some OH^- is added, we convert some weak acid HB into its conjugate base B^- (beaker a). At the halfway point to equivalence, we have converted exactly one-half of the initial amount of acid present into its conjugate base (beaker e). We finally reach the equivalence point when we have added just enough OH^- to convert all of the acid present initially into its conjugate base (beaker b). Past the equivalence point, we have added an excess of OH^-, so we have excess OH^- present as well as the conjugate base of the acid produced from the neutralization reaction (beaker d). The order of the beakers from start to finish is:

beaker c $\rightarrow$ beaker a $\rightarrow$ beaker e $\rightarrow$ beaker b $\rightarrow$ beaker d

c. $pH = pK_a$ when a buffer solution is present that has equal concentrations of the weak acid and conjugate base. This is beaker e.

d. The equivalence point is when just enough OH^- has been added to exactly react with all of the acid present initially. This is beaker b.

e. Past the equivalence, the pH is dictated by the concentration of excess OH^- added from the strong base. We can ignore the amount of hydroxide added by the weak conjugate base that is also present. This is beaker d.

55.

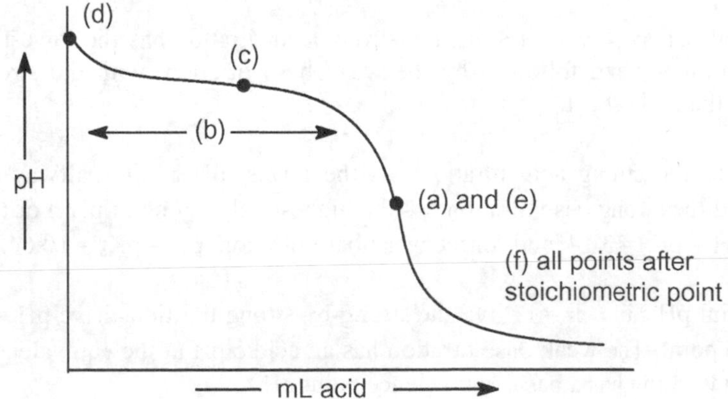

$B + H^+ \rightarrow BH^+$; added H^+ from the strong acid converts the weak base B into its conjugate acid BH^+. Initially, before any H^+ is added (point d), B is the dominant species present. After H^+ is added, both B and BH^+ are present, and a buffered solution results (region b). At the equivalence point (points a and e), exactly enough H^+ has been added to convert all the weak base present initially into its conjugate acid BH^+. Past the equivalence point (region f), excess H^+ is present. For the answer to b, we included almost the entire buffer region. The maximum buffer region is around the halfway point to equivalence (point c), where [B] = $[BH^+]$. Here, pH = pK_a, which is a characteristic of a best buffer.

57. Titration i is a strong acid titrated by a strong base. The pH is very acidic until just before the equivalence point; at the equivalence point, pH = 7.00; and past the equivalence the pH is very basic. Titration ii is a strong base titrated by a strong acid. Here the pH is very basic until just before the equivalence point; at the equivalence point, pH = 7.00; and past the equivalence point, the pH is very acidic. Titration iii is a weak base titrated by a strong acid. The pH starts out basic because a weak base is present. However, the pH will not be as basic as in titration ii, where a strong base is titrated. The pH drops as HCl is added; then at the halfway point to equivalence, pH = pK_a. Because $K_b = 4.4 \times 10^{-4}$ for CH_3NH_2, $CH_3NH_3^+$ has $K_a = K_w/K_b = 2.3 \times 10^{-11}$ and $pK_a = 10.64$. So, at the halfway point to equivalence for this weak base-strong acid titration, pH = 10.64. The pH continues to drop as HCl is added; then at the equivalence point the pH is acidic (pH < 7.00) because the only important major species present is a weak acid (the conjugate acid of the weak base). Past the equivalence point the pH becomes more acidic as excess HCl is added. Titration iv is a weak acid titrated by a strong base. The pH starts off acidic, but not nearly as acidic as the strong acid titration (i). The pH increases as NaOH is added; then, at the halfway point to equivalence, pH = pK_a for HF = $-\log(7.2 \times 10^{-4}) = 3.14$. The pH continues to increase past the halfway point; then at the equivalence point, the pH is basic (pH > 7.0) because the only important major species present is a weak base (the conjugate base of the weak acid). Past the equivalence point, the pH becomes more basic as excess NaOH is added.

a. All require the same volume of titrant to reach the equivalence point. At the equivalence point for all these titrations, moles acid = moles base ($M_AV_A = M_BV_B$). Because all the molarities and volumes are the same in the titrations, the volume of titrant will be the same (50.0 mL titrant added to reach equivalence point).

b. Increasing initial pH: i < iv < iii < ii; the strong acid titration has the lowest pH, the weak acid titration is next, followed by the weak base titration, with the strong base titration having the highest pH.

c. i < iv < iii < ii; the strong acid titration has the lowest pH at the halfway point to equivalence, and the strong base titration has the highest halfway point pH. For the weak acid titration, pH = pK_a = 3.14, and for the weak base titration, pH = pK_a = 10.64.

d. Equivalence point pH: iii < ii = i < iv; the strong-by-strong titrations have pH = 7.00 at the equivalence point. The weak base titration has an acidic pH at the equivalence point, and a weak acid titration has a basic equivalence point pH.

The only different answer when the weak acid and weak base are changed would be for part c. This is for the halfway point to equivalence, where pH = pK_a.

$$HOC_6H_5;\ K_a = 1.6 \times 10^{-10},\ pK_a = -\log(1.6 \times 10^{-10}) = 9.80$$

$$C_5H_5NH^+,\ K_a = \frac{K_w}{K_{b,\,C_5H_5N}} = \frac{1.0 \times 10^{-14}}{1.7 \times 10^{-9}} = 5.9 \times 10^{-6},\ pK_a = 5.23$$

From the pK_a values, the correct ordering at the halfway point to equivalence would be i < iii < iv < ii. Note that for the weak base-strong acid titration using C_5H_5N, the pH is acidic at the halfway point to equivalence, whereas the weak acid-strong base titration using HOC_6H_5 is basic at the halfway point to equivalence. This is fine; this will always happen when the weak base titrated has a $K_b < 1 \times 10^{-7}$ (so K_a of the conjugate acid is greater than 1×10^{-7}) and when the weak acid titrated has a $K_a < 1 \times 10^{-7}$ (so K_b of the conjugate base is greater than 1×10^{-7}).

59. a. Because all acids are the same initial concentration, the pH curve with the highest pH at 0 mL of NaOH added will correspond to the titration of the weakest acid. This is curve f.

b. The pH curve with the lowest pH at 0 mL of NaOH added will correspond to the titration of the strongest acid. This is pH curve a.

The best point to look at to differentiate a strong acid from a weak acid titration (if initial concentrations are not known) is the equivalence point pH. If the pH = 7.00, the acid titrated is a strong acid; if the pH is greater than 7.00, the acid titrated is a weak acid.

c. For a weak acid-strong base titration, the pH at the halfway point to equivalence is equal to the pK_a value. The pH curve, which represents the titration of an acid with $K_a = 1.0 \times 10^{-6}$, will have a $pH = -\log(1 \times 10^{-6}) = 6.0$ at the halfway point. The equivalence point, from the plots, occurs at 50 mL NaOH added, so the halfway point is 25 mL. Plot d has a $pH \approx 6.0$ at 25 mL of NaOH added, so the acid titrated in this pH curve (plot d) has $K_a \approx 1 \times 10^{-6}$.

61. This is a strong acid ($HClO_4$) titrated by a strong base (KOH). Added OH^- from the strong base will react completely with the H^+ present from the strong acid to produce H_2O.

a. Only strong acid present. $[H^+] = 0.200\ M$; pH = 0.699

b. $\text{mmol OH}^- \text{ added} = 10.0\text{ mL} \times \dfrac{0.100\text{ mmol OH}^-}{\text{mL}} = 1.00\text{ mmol OH}^-$

$\text{mmol H}^+ \text{ present} = 40.0\text{ mL} \times \dfrac{0.200\text{ mmol H}^+}{\text{mL}} = 8.0\text{ mmol H}^+$

Note: The units millimoles are usually easier numbers to work with. The units for molarity are moles per liter but are also equal to millimoles per milliliter.

	H^+	+	OH^-	$\rightarrow$ H_2O	
Before	8.00 mmol		1.00 mmol		
Change	−1.00 mmol		−1.00 mmol		Reacts completely
After	7.00 mmol		0		

The excess H^+ determines the pH. $[H^+]_{excess} = \dfrac{7.00 \text{ mmol } H^+}{40.0 \text{ mL} + 10.0 \text{ mL}} = 0.140\ M$

pH = –log(0.140) = 0.854

c. mmol OH^- added = 40.0 mL × 0.100 M = 4.00 mmol OH^-

	H^+	+	OH^-	→	H_2O
Before	8.00 mmol		4.00 mmol		
After	4.00 mmol		0		

$[H^+]_{excess} = \dfrac{4.00 \text{ mmol}}{(40.0 + 40.0) \text{ mL}} = 0.0500\ M$; pH = 1.301

d. mmol OH^- added = 80.0 mL × 0.100 M = 8.00 mmol OH^-; this is the equivalence point because we have added just enough OH^- to react with all the acid present. For a strong acid-strong base titration, pH = 7.00 at the equivalence point because only neutral species are present (K^+, ClO_4^-, H_2O).

e. mmol OH^- added = 100.0 mL × 0.100 M = 10.0 mmol OH^-

	H^+	+	OH^-	→	H_2O
Before	8.00 mmol		10.0 mmol		
After	0		2.0 mmol		

Past the equivalence point, the pH is determined by the excess OH^- present.

$[OH^-]_{excess} = \dfrac{2.0 \text{ mmol}}{(40.0 + 100.0) \text{ mL}} = 0.014\ M$; pOH = 1.85; pH = 12.15

63. This is a weak acid ($HC_2H_3O_2$) titrated by a strong base (KOH).

a. Only weak acid is present. Solving the weak acid problem:

	$HC_2H_3O_2$	⇌	H^+	+	$C_2H_3O_2^-$
Initial	0.200 M		~0		0
	x mol/L $HC_2H_3O_2$ dissociates to reach equilibrium				
Change	$-x$	→	$+x$		$+x$
Equil.	$0.200 - x$		x		x

$$K_a = 1.8 \times 10^{-5} = \frac{x^2}{0.200 - x} \approx \frac{x^2}{0.200},\quad x = [H^+] = 1.9 \times 10^{-3}\ M$$

pH = 2.72; assumptions good.

b. The added OH^- will react completely with the best acid present, $HC_2H_3O_2$.

$$\text{mmol } HC_2H_3O_2 \text{ present} = 100.0 \text{ mL} \times \frac{0.200 \text{ mmol } HC_2H_3O_2}{\text{mL}} = 20.0 \text{ mmol } HC_2H_3O_2$$

$$\text{mmol } OH^- \text{ added} = 50.0 \text{ mL} \times \frac{0.100 \text{ mmol } OH^-}{\text{mL}} = 5.00 \text{ mmol } OH^-$$

	$HC_2H_3O_2$	+	OH^-	→	$C_2H_3O_2^-$ + H_2O	
Before	20.0 mmol		5.00 mmol		0	
Change	–5.00 mmol		–5.00 mmol	→	+5.00 mmol	Reacts completely
After	15.0 mmol		0		5.00 mmol	

After reaction of all the strong base, we have a buffer solution containing a weak acid ($HC_2H_3O_2$) and its conjugate base ($C_2H_3O_2^-$). We will use the Henderson-Hasselbalch equation to solve for the pH.

$$pH = pK_a + \log\frac{[C_2H_3O_2^-]}{[HC_2H_3O_2]} = -\log(1.8 \times 10^{-5}) + \log\left(\frac{5.00 \text{ mmol}/V_T}{15.0 \text{ mmol}/V_T}\right), \text{ where } V_T = \text{total volume}$$

$$pH = 4.74 + \log\left(\frac{5.00}{15.0}\right) = 4.74 + (-0.477) = 4.26$$

Note that the total volume cancels in the Henderson-Hasselbalch equation. For the [base]/[acid] term, the mole ratio equals the concentration ratio because the components of the buffer are always in the same volume of solution.

c. mmol OH^- added = 100.0 mL × (0.100 mmol OH^-/mL) = 10.0 mmol OH^-; the same amount (20.0 mmol) of $HC_2H_3O_2$ is present as before (it doesn't change). As before, let the OH^- react to completion, then see what is remaining in solution after this reaction.

	$HC_2H_3O_2$	+	OH^-	→	$C_2H_3O_2^-$ + H_2O
Before	20.0 mmol		10.0 mmol		0
After	10.0 mmol		0		10.0 mmol

A buffer solution results after reaction. Because $[C_2H_3O_2^-] = [HC_2H_3O_2] = 10.0$ mmol/total volume, $pH = pK_a$. This is always true at the halfway point to equivalence for a weak acid-strong base titration, $pH = pK_a$.

$$pH = -\log(1.8 \times 10^{-5}) = 4.74$$

d. mmol OH^- added = 150.0 mL × 0.100 M = 15.0 mmol OH^-. Added OH^- reacts completely with the weak acid.

	$HC_2H_3O_2$	+	OH^-	→	$C_2H_3O_2^-$ + H_2O
Before	20.0 mmol		15.0 mmol		0
After	5.0 mmol		0		15.0 mmol

We have a buffer solution after all the OH^- reacts to completion. Using the Henderson-Hasselbalch equation:

$$pH = 4.74 + \log\frac{[C_2H_3O_2^-]}{[HC_2H_3O_2]} = 4.74 + \log\left(\frac{15.0\text{ mmol}}{5.0\text{ mmol}}\right)$$

$$pH = 4.74 + 0.48 = 5.22$$

e. mmol OH^- added = 200.00 mL × 0.100 M = 20.0 mmol OH^-; as before, let the added OH^- react to completion with the weak acid; then see what is in solution after this reaction.

	$HC_2H_3O_2$	+	OH^-	→	$C_2H_3O_2^-$	+	H_2O
Before	20.0 mmol		20.0 mmol		0		
After	0		0		20.0 mmol		

This is the equivalence point. Enough OH^- has been added to exactly neutralize all the weak acid present initially. All that remains that affects the pH at the equivalence point is the conjugate base of the weak acid ($C_2H_3O_2^-$). This is a weak base equilibrium problem.

	$C_2H_3O_2^-$ + H_2O ⇌	$HC_2H_3O_2$	+ OH^-	$K_b = \frac{K_w}{K_b} = \frac{1.0 \times 10^{-14}}{1.8 \times 10^{-5}}$
Initial	20.0 mmol/300.0 mL	0	0	$K_b = 5.6 \times 10^{-9}$
	x mol/L $C_2H_3O_2^-$ reacts with H_2O to reach equilibrium			
Change	$-x$ →	$+x$	$+x$	
Equil.	$0.0667 - x$	x	x	

$$K_b = 5.6 \times 10^{-10} = \frac{x^2}{0.0667 - x} \approx \frac{x^2}{0.0667},\ x = [OH^-] = 6.1 \times 10^{-6}\ M$$

pOH = 5.21; pH = 8.79; assumptions good.

f. mmol OH^- added = 250.0 mL × 0.100 M = 25.0 mmol OH^-

	$HC_2H_3O_2$	+	OH^-	→	$C_2H_3O_2^-$	+	H_2O
Before	20.0 mmol		25.0 mmol		0		
After	0		5.0 mmol		20.0 mmol		

After the titration reaction, we have a solution containing excess OH^- and a weak base $C_2H_3O_2^-$. When a strong base and a weak base are both present, assume that the amount of OH^- added from the weak base will be minimal; that is, the pH past the equivalence point is determined by the amount of excess strong base.

$$[OH^-]_{excess} = \frac{5.0\text{ mmol}}{100.0\text{ mL} + 250.0\text{ mL}} = 0.014\ M;\ pOH = 1.85;\ pH = 12.15$$

65. We will do sample calculations for the various parts of the titration. All results are summarized in Table 8.1 at the end of Exercise 67.

At the beginning of the titration, only the weak acid $HC_3H_5O_3$ is present. Let HLac = $HC_3H_5O_3$ and $Lac^- = C_3H_5O_3^-$.

	HLac	$\rightleftharpoons$	H^+	+	Lac^-	$K_a = 10^{-3.86} = 1.4 \times 10^{-4}$
Initial	0.100 *M*		~0		0	
	x mol/L HLac dissociates to reach equilibrium					
Change	$-x$	→	$+x$		$+x$	
Equil.	$0.100 - x$		x		x	

$$1.4 \times 10^{-4} = \frac{x^2}{0.100 - x} \approx \frac{x^2}{0.100},\ x = [H^+] = 3.7 \times 10^{-3}\ M;\ \text{pH} = 2.43;\ \text{assumptions good.}$$

Up to the stoichiometric point, we calculate the pH using the Henderson-Hasselbalch equation. This is the buffer region. For example, at 4.0 mL of NaOH added:

$$\text{initial mmol HLac present} = 25.0\ \text{mL} \times \frac{0.100\ \text{mmol}}{\text{mL}} = 2.50\ \text{mmol HLac}$$

$$\text{mmol OH}^-\ \text{added} = 4.0\ \text{mL} \times \frac{0.100\ \text{mmol}}{\text{mL}} = 0.40\ \text{mmol OH}^-$$

Note: The units millimoles are usually easier numbers to work with. The units for molarity are moles per liter but are also equal to millimoles per milliliter.

The 0.40 mmol of added OH^- converts 0.40 mmol HLac to 0.40 mmol Lac^- according to the equation:

$HLac + OH^- \rightarrow Lac^- + H_2O$ Reacts completely since a strong base is added.

mmol HLac remaining = 2.50 – 0.40 = 2.10 mmol; mmol Lac^- produced = 0.40 mmol

We have a buffer solution. Using the Henderson-Hasselbalch equation where $pK_a = 3.86$:

$$\text{pH} = pK_a + \log\frac{[Lac^-]}{[HLac]} = 3.86 + \log\frac{(0.40)}{(2.10)}$$ (Total volume cancels, so we can use use the ratio of moles or millimoles.)

$$\text{pH} = 3.86 - 0.72 = 3.14$$

Other points in the buffer region are calculated in a similar fashion. Perform a stoichiometry problem first, followed by a buffer problem. The buffer region includes all points up to and including 24.9 mL OH^- added.

At the stoichiometric point (25.0 mL OH^- added), we have added enough OH^- to convert all of the HLac (2.50 mmol) into its conjugate base (Lac^-). All that is present is a weak base. To determine the pH, we perform a weak base calculation.

$$[Lac^-]_0 = \frac{2.50 \text{ mmol}}{25.0 \text{ mL} + 25.0 \text{ mL}} = 0.0500\ M$$

	Lac^- + H_2O	$\rightleftharpoons$	HLac	+	OH^-	$K_b = \dfrac{1.0 \times 10^{-14}}{1.4 \times 10^{-4}} = 7.1 \times 10^{-11}$
Initial	0.0500 M		0		0	
	x mol/L Lac^- reacts with H_2O to reach equilibrium					
Change	$-x$	$\rightarrow$	$+x$		$+x$	
Equil.	$0.0500 - x$		x		x	

$$K_b = \frac{x^2}{0.0500 - x} \approx \frac{x^2}{0.0500} = 7.1 \times 10^{-11}$$

$x = [OH^-] = 1.9 \times 10^{-6}\ M$; pOH = 5.72; pH = 8.28; assumptions good.

Past the stoichiometric point, we have added more than 2.50 mmol of NaOH. The pH will be determined by the excess OH^- ion present. An example of this calculation follows.

At 25.1 mL: OH^- added $= 25.1 \text{ mL} \times \dfrac{0.100 \text{ mmol}}{\text{mL}} = 2.51 \text{ mmol } OH^-$

2.50 mmol OH^- neutralizes all the weak acid present. The remainder is excess OH^-.

Excess $OH^- = 2.51 - 2.50 = 0.01 \text{ mmol } OH^-$

$$[OH^-]_{excess} = \frac{0.01 \text{ mmol}}{(25.0 + 25.1) \text{ mL}} = 2 \times 10^{-4}\ M;\ \text{pOH} = 3.7;\ \text{pH} = 10.3$$

All results are listed in Table 8.1 at the end of the solution to Exercise 67.

67. At beginning of the titration, only the weak base NH_3 is present. As always, solve for the pH using the K_b reaction for NH_3.

	NH_3 + H_2O	$\rightleftharpoons$	NH_4^+	+	OH^-	$K_b = 1.8 \times 10^{-5}$
Initial	0.100 M		0		~0	
Equil.	$0.100 - x$		x		x	

$$K_b = \frac{x^2}{0.100 - x} \approx \frac{x^2}{0.100} = 1.8 \times 10^{-5}$$

$x = [OH^-] = 1.3 \times 10^{-3}\ M$; pOH = 2.89; pH = 11.11; assumptions good.

In the buffer region (4.0 – 24.9 mL), we can use the Henderson-Hasselbalch equation:

$$K_a = \frac{1.0 \times 10^{-14}}{1.8 \times 10^{-5}} = 5.6 \times 10^{-10};\ pK_a = 9.25;\ pH = 9.25 + \log\frac{[NH_3]}{[NH_4^+]}$$

We must determine the amounts of NH_3 and NH_4^+ present after the added H^+ reacts completely with the NH_3. For example, after 8.0 mL HCl added:

$$\text{initial mmol } NH_3 \text{ present} = 25.0 \text{ mL} \times \frac{0.100 \text{ mmol}}{\text{mL}} = 2.50 \text{ mmol } NH_3$$

$$\text{mmol } H^+ \text{ added} = 8.0 \text{ mL} \times \frac{0.100 \text{ mmol}}{\text{mL}} = 0.80 \text{ mmol } H^+$$

Added H^+ reacts with NH_3 to completion: $NH_3 + H^+ \rightarrow NH_4^+$

mmol NH_3 remaining = 2.50 – 0.80 = 1.70 mmol; mmol NH_4^+ produced = 0.80 mmol

$$pH = 9.25 + \log\frac{1.70}{0.80} = 9.58$$(Mole ratios can be used since the total volume cancels.)

Other points in the buffer region are calculated in similar fashion. Results are summarized in Table 8.1 on the next page.

At the stoichiometric point (25.0 mL H^+ added), just enough HCl has been added to convert all the weak base (NH_3) into its conjugate acid (NH_4^+). Perform a weak acid calculation.

$[NH_4^+]_0$ = 2.50 mmol/50.0 mL = 0.0500 M

	NH_4^+	$\rightleftharpoons$	H^+	+	NH_3	$K_a = 5.6 \times 10^{-10}$
Initial	0.0500 M		0		0	
Equil.	0.0500 - x		x		x	

$$5.6 \times 10^{-10} = \frac{x^2}{0.0500 - x} \approx \frac{x^2}{0.0500},\quad x = [H^+] = 5.3 \times 10^{-6}\ M;\ pH = 5.28;$$ assumptions good.

Beyond the stoichiometric point, the pH is determined by the excess H^+. For example, at 28.0 mL of H^+ added:

$$H^+ \text{ added} = 28.0 \text{ mL} \times \frac{0.100 \text{ mmol}}{\text{mL}} = 2.80 \text{ mmol } H^+$$

Excess H^+ = 2.80 mmol – 2.50 mmol = 0.30 mmol excess H^+

$$[H^+]_{excess} = \frac{0.30 \text{ mmol}}{(25.0 + 28.0) \text{ mL}} = 5.7 \times 10^{-3}\ M;\ pH = 2.24$$

Table 8.1 Summary of pH Results for Exercises 65 and 67 (Graph follows)

Titrant mL	Exercise 65	Exercise 67
0.0	2.43	11.11
4.0	3.14	9.97
8.0	3.53	9.58
12.5	3.86	9.25
20.0	4.46	8.65
24.0	5.24	7.87
24.5	5.6	7.6
24.9	6.3	6.9
25.0	8.28	5.28
25.1	10.3	3.7
26.0	11.30	2.71
28.0	11.75	2.24
30.0	11.96	2.04

Note: The following figure includes the pH curves for Exercises 66 and 68 in addition to the pH curves for Exercises 65 and 67. The solid circles are the data points for Exercises 65 and 67, and the open circles are the data points for Exercises 66 and 68.

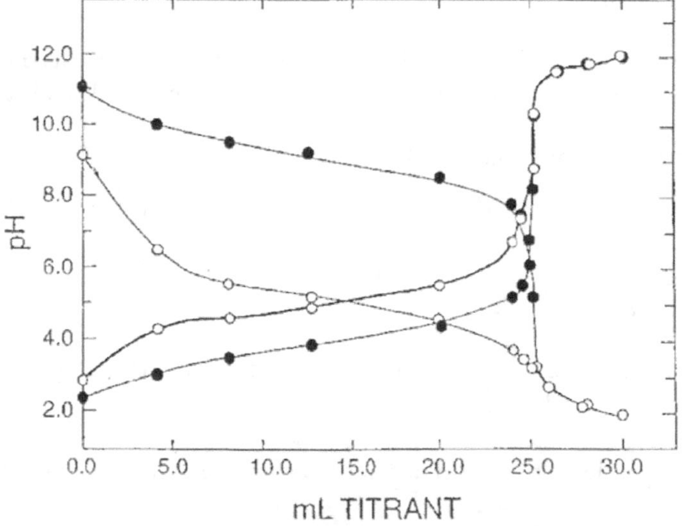

69. a. This is a weak acid-strong base titration. At the halfway point to equivalence, [weak acid] = [conjugate base], so pH = pK_a (always for a weak acid-strong base titration).

$pH = -\log(6.4 \times 10^{-5}) = 4.19$

mmol $HC_7H_5O_2$ present = 100.0 mL × 0.10 *M* = 10. mmol $HC_7H_5O_2$. For the equivalence point, 10. mmol of OH^- must be added. The volume of OH^- added to reach the equivalence point is:

$$10.\ \text{mmol OH}^- \times \frac{1\ \text{mL}}{0.10\ \text{mmol OH}^-} = 1.0 \times 10^2\ \text{mL OH}^-$$

At the equivalence point, 10. mmol of $HC_7H_5O_2$ is neutralized by 10. mmol of OH^- to produce 10. mmol of $C_7H_5O_2^-$. This is a weak base. The total volume of the solution is 100.0 mL + 1.0 × 10^2 mL = 2.0 × 10^2 mL. Solving the weak base equilibrium problem:

$$C_7H_5O_2^- + H_2O \rightleftharpoons HC_7H_5O_2 + OH^- \quad K_b = \frac{1.0 \times 10^{-14}}{6.4 \times 10^{-5}} = 1.6 \times 10^{-10}$$

	$C_7H_5O_2^-$	$HC_7H_5O_2$	OH^-
Initial	10. mmol/2.0 × 10^2 mL	0	0
Equil.	$0.050 - x$	x	x

$$K_b = 1.6 \times 10^{-10} = \frac{x^2}{0.050 - x} \approx \frac{x^2}{0.050},\ x = [OH^-] = 2.8 \times 10^{-6}\ M$$

pOH = 5.55; pH = 8.45; assumptions good.

b. At the halfway point to equivalence for a weak base-strong acid titration, pH = pK_a because [weak base] = [conjugate acid].

$$K_a = \frac{K_w}{K_b} = \frac{1.0 \times 10^{-14}}{5.6 \times 10^{-4}} = 1.8 \times 10^{-11};\ pH = pK_a = -\log(1.8 \times 10^{-11}) = 10.74$$

For the equivalence point (mmol acid added = mmol base present):

mmol $C_2H_5NH_2$ present = 100.0 mL × 0.10 M = 10. mmol $C_2H_5NH_2$

$$\text{mL H}^+\ \text{added} = 10.\ \text{mmol H}^+ \times \frac{1\ \text{mL}}{0.20\ \text{mmol H}^+} = 50.\ \text{mL H}^+$$

The strong acid added completely converts the weak base into its conjugate acid. Therefore, at the equivalence point, $[C_2H_5NH_3^+]_0$ = 10. mmol/(100.0 + 50.) mL = 0.067 M. Solving the weak acid equilibrium problem:

$$C_2H_5NH_3^+ \rightleftharpoons H^+ + C_2H_5NH_2$$

	$C_2H_5NH_3^+$	H^+	$C_2H_5NH_2$
Initial	0.067 M	0	0
Equil.	$0.067 - x$	x	x

$$K_a = 1.8 \times 10^{-11} = \frac{x^2}{0.067 - x} \approx \frac{x^2}{0.067},\ x = [H^+] = 1.1 \times 10^{-6}\ M$$

pH = 5.96; assumptions good.

c. In a strong acid-strong base titration, the halfway point has no special significance other than that exactly one-half of the original amount of acid present has been neutralized.

mmol H^+ present = 100.0 mL × 0.50 M = 50. mmol H^+

$$\text{mL OH}^- \text{ added} = 25 \text{ mmol OH}^- \times \frac{1 \text{ mL}}{0.25 \text{ mmol}} = 1.0 \times 10^2 \text{ mL OH}^-$$

	H^+	+	OH^-	→	H_2O
Before	50. mmol		25 mmol		
After	25 mmol		0		

$$[H^+]_{excess} = \frac{25 \text{ mmol}}{(100.0 + 1.0 \times 10^2) \text{ mL}} = 0.13\ M; \ \text{pH} = 0.89$$

At the equivalence point of a strong acid-strong base titration, only neutral species are present (Na^+, Cl^-, and H_2O), so the pH = 7.00.

71. Mol H^+ added = 0.0400 L × 0.100 mol/L = 0.00400 mol H^+

The added strong acid reacts to completion with the weak base to form the conjugate acid of the weak base and H_2O. Let B = weak base:

	B	+	H^+	→	BH^+
Before	0.0100 mol		0.00400 mol		0
After	0.0060		0		0.0400 mol

After the H^+ reacts to completion, we have a buffer solution. Using the Henderson-Hasselbalch equation:

$$\text{pH} = \text{pK}_a + \log\frac{[\text{base}]}{[\text{acid}]}, \ 8.00 = \text{pK}_a + \log\frac{(0.0060/V_T)}{(0.00400/V_T)}, \text{ where } V_T = \text{total volume of solution}$$

$$\text{pK}_a = 8.00 - \log\frac{(0.0060)}{(0.00400)} = 8.00 - 0.18, \ \text{pK}_a = 7.82$$

For a conjugate acid-base pair, $pK_a + pK_b$ = 14,00, so:

$$\text{pK}_b = 14.00 - 7.82 = 6.18; \ K_b = 10^{-6.18} = 6.6 \times 10^{-7}$$

Indicators

73. $$\text{HIn} \rightleftharpoons \text{In}^- + \text{H}^+ \quad K_a = \frac{[\text{In}^-][\text{H}^+]}{[\text{HIn}]} = 1.0 \times 10^{-9}$$

a. In a very acid solution, the HIn form dominates, so the solution will be yellow.

b. The color change occurs when the concentration of the more dominant form is approximately ten times as great as the less dominant form of the indicator.

$$\frac{[\text{HIn}]}{[\text{In}^-]} = \frac{10}{1}; \ K_a = 1.0 \times 10^{-9} = \left(\frac{1}{10}\right)[\text{H}^+], \ [\text{H}^+] = 1 \times 10^{-8} M; \ \text{pH} = 8.0 \text{ at color change}$$

c. This is way past the equivalence point (100.0 mL OH^- added), so the solution is very basic and the In^- form of the indicator dominates. The solution will be blue.

75. pH > 5 for bromcresol green to be blue. pH < 8 for thymol blue to be yellow. The pH is between 5 and 8.

77. When choosing an indicator, we want the color change of the indicator to occur approximately at the pH of the equivalence point. Since the pH generally changes very rapidly at the equivalence point, we don't have to be exact. This is especially true for strong acid-strong base titrations. The following are some indicators where the color change occurs at about the pH of the equivalence point.

Exercise	pH at Eq. Pt.	Indicator
61	7.00	bromthymol blue or phenol red
63	8.79	o-cresolphthalein or phenolphthalein

79.

Exercise	pH at Eq. Pt.	Indicator
65	8.28	o-cresolphthalein or phenolphthalein
67	5.28	bromcresol green

81. The color of the indicator will change over the approximate range of pH = $pK_a \pm 1 = 5.3 \pm 1$. Therefore, the useful pH range of methyl red where it changes color would be about 4.3 (red) to 6.3 (yellow). Note that at pH < 4.3, the HIn form of the indicator dominates, and the color of the solution is the color of HIn (red). At pH > 6.3, the In^- form of the indicator dominates, and the color of the solution is the color of In^- (yellow). In titrating a weak acid with base, we start off with an acidic solution with pH < 4.3, so the color would change from red to reddish orange at pH ≈ 4.3. In titrating a weak base with acid, the color change would be from yellow to yellowish orange at pH ≈ 6.3. Only a weak base-strong acid titration would have an acidic pH at the equivalence point, so only in this type of titration would the color change of methyl red indicate the approximate endpoint.

Polyprotic Acid Titrations

83. The first titration plot (from 0 – 100.0 mL) corresponds to the titration of H_2A by OH^-. The reaction is $H_2A + OH^- \rightarrow HA^- + H_2O$. After all the H_2A has been reacted, the second titration (from 100.0 – 200.0 mL) corresponds to the titration of HA^- by OH^-. The reaction is $HA^- + OH^- \rightarrow A^{2-} + H_2O$.

a. At 100.0 mL of NaOH, just enough OH^- has been added to react completely with all of the H_2A present (mol OH^- added = mol H_2A present initially). From the balanced equation, the mol of HA^- produced will equal the mol of H_2A present initially. Because mol of HA^- present at 100.0 mL OH^- added equals the mol of H_2A present initially, exactly 100.0 mL more of NaOH must be added to react with all of the HA^-. The volume of NaOH added to reach the second equivalence point equals 100.0 mL + 100.0 mL = 200.0 mL.

b. $H_2A + OH^- \rightarrow HA^- + H_2O$ is the reaction occurring from 0 – 100.0 mL NaOH added.

i. No reaction has taken place, so H_2A and H_2O are the major species.

ii. Adding OH^- converts H_2A into HA^-. The major species between 0 mL and 100.0 mL NaOH added are H_2A, HA^-, H_2O, and Na^+.

iii. At 100.0 mL NaOH added, mol of OH^- = mol H_2A, so all of the H_2A present initially has been converted into HA^-. The major species are HA^-, H_2O, and Na^+.

iv. Between 100.0 and 200.0 mL NaOH added, the OH^- converts HA^- into A^{2-}. The major species are HA^-, A^{2-}, H_2O, and Na^+.

v. At the second equivalence point (200.0 mL), just enough OH^- has been added to convert all of the HA^- into A^{2-}. The major species are A^{2-}, H_2O, and Na^+.

vi. Past 200.0 mL NaOH added, excess OH^- is present. The major species are OH^-, A^{2-}, H_2O, and Na^+.

c. 50.0 mL of NaOH added corresponds to the first halfway point to equivalence. Exactly one-half of the H_2A present initially has been converted into its conjugate base HA^-, so $[H_2A] = [HA^-]$ in this buffer solution.

$$H_2A \rightleftharpoons HA^- + H^+ \qquad K_{a_1} = \frac{[HA^-][H^+]}{[H_2A]}$$

When $[HA^-] = [H_2A]$, then $K_{a_1} = [H^+]$ or pK_{a_1} = pH.

Here, pH = 4.0, so $pK_{a_1} = 4.0$ and $K_{a_1} = 10^{-4.0} = 1 \times 10^{-4}$.

150.0 mL of NaOH added correspond to the second halfway point to equivalence, where $[HA^-] = [A^{2-}]$ in this buffer solution.

$$HA^- \rightleftharpoons A^{2-} + H^+ \qquad K_{a_2} = \frac{[A^{2-}][H^+]}{[HA^-]}$$

When $[A^{2-}] = [HA^-]$, then $K_{a_2} = [H^+]$ or pK_{a_2} = pH.

Here, pH = 8.0, so $pK_{a_2} = 8.0$ and $K_{a_2} = 10^{-8.0} = 1 \times 10^{-8}$.

85. 100.0 mL × 0.0500 M = 5.00 mmol H_3X initially

a. Because $K_{a_1} >> K_{a_2} >> K_{a_3}$, pH initially is determined by H_3X equilibrium reaction.

	H_3X	$\rightleftharpoons$	H^+	+	H_2X^-
Initial	0.0500 M		~0		0
Equil.	$0.0500 - x$		x		x

$$K_{a_1} = 1.0 \times 10^{-3} = \frac{x^2}{0.0500 - x} \approx \frac{x^2}{0.0500}, \quad x = 7.1 \times 10^{-3}; \text{ assumption poor.}$$

Using the quadratic formula:

$$x^2 + (1.0 \times 10^{-3})x - 5.0 \times 10^{-5} = 0, \quad x = 6.6 \times 10^{-3}\ M = [H^+];\ pH = 2.18$$

b. 1.00 mmol OH^- added converts H_3X into H_2X^-. After this reaction goes to completion, 4.00 mmol H_3X and 1.00 mmol H_2X^- are in a total volume of 110.0 mL. Solving the buffer problem:

	H_3X	$\rightleftharpoons$	H^+	+	H_2X^-
Initial	0.0364 *M*		~0		0.00909 *M*
Equil.	$0.0364 - x$		x		$0.00909 + x$

$$K_{a_1} = 1.0 \times 10^{-3} = \frac{x(0.00909 + x)}{0.0364 - x};$$ assumption that x is small does not work here.

Using the quadratic formula and carrying extra significant figures:

$$x^2 + (1.01 \times 10^{-2})x - 3.64 \times 10^{-5} = 0,\ x = 2.8 \times 10^{-3}\ M = [H^+];\ pH = 2.55$$

c. 2.50 mmol OH^- added results in 2.50 mmol H_3X and 2.50 mmol H_2X^- after OH^- reacts completely with H_3X. This is the first halfway point to equivalence. $pH = pK_{a_1} = 3.00$; assumptions good (5% error).

d. 5.00 mmol OH^- added results in 5.00 mmol H_2X^- after OH^- reacts completely with H_3X. This is the first stoichiometric point.

$$pH = \frac{pK_{a_1} + pK_{a_2}}{2} = \frac{3.00 + 7.00}{2} = 5.00$$

e. 6.00 mmol OH^- added results in 4.00 mmol H_2X^- and 1.00 mmol HX^{2-} after OH^- reacts completely with H_3X and then reacts completely with H_2X^-.

Using the $H_2X^- \rightleftharpoons H^+ + HX^{2-}$ reaction:

$$pH = pK_{a_2} + \log\frac{[HX^{2-}]}{[H_2X^-]} = 7.00 - \log(1.00/4.00) = 6.40;$$ assumptions good.

f. 7.50 mmol KOH added results in 2.50 mmol H_2X^- and 2.50 mmol HX^{2-} after OH^- reacts completely. This is the second halfway point to equivalence.

$pH = pK_{a_2} = 7.00$; assumptions good.

g. 10.0 mmol OH^- added results in 5.0 mmol HX^{2-} after OH^- reacts completely. This is the second stoichiometric point.

$$pH = \frac{pK_{a_2} + pK_{a_3}}{2} = \frac{7.00 + 12.00}{2} = 9.50$$

h. 12.5 mmol OH^- added results in 2.5 mmol HX^{2-} and 2.5 mmol X^{3-} after OH^- reacts completely with H_3X first, then H_2X^-, and finally HX^{2-}. This is the third halfway point to equivalence. Usually $pH = pK_{a_3}$ but normal assumptions don't hold. We must solve for the pH exactly.

$[X^{3-}] = [HX^{2-}] = 2.5 \text{ mmol}/225.0 \text{ mL} = 1.1 \times 10^{-2}\ M$

	X^{3-} + H_2O	$\rightleftharpoons$	HX^{2-}	+ OH^-	$K_b = \frac{K_w}{K_{a_3}} = 1.0 \times 10^{-2}$
Initial	$0.011\ M$		$0.011\ M$	0	
Equil.	$0.011 - x$		$0.011 + x$	x	

$K_b = 1.0 \times 10^{-2} = \frac{x(0.011 + x)}{0.011 - x}$; using the quadratic formula:

$x^2 + (2.1 \times 10^{-2})x - 1.1 \times 10^{-4} = 0,\ x = 4.3 \times 10^{-3}\ M = OH^-;\ pH = 11.63$

i. 15.0 mmol OH^- added results in 5.0 mmol X^{3-} after OH^- reacts completely. This is the third stoichiometric point.

	X^{3-} + H_2O	$\rightleftharpoons$	HX^{2-}	+ OH^-	$K_b = \frac{K_w}{K_{a_3}} = 1.0 \times 10^{-2}$
Initial	$\frac{5.0 \text{ mmol}}{250.0 \text{ mL}} = 0.020\ M$		0	0	
Equil.	$0.020 - x$		x	x	

$K_b = \frac{x^2}{0.020 - x},\quad 1.0 \times 10^{-2} \approx \frac{x^2}{0.020},\ x = 1.4 \times 10^{-2}$; assumption poor.

Using the quadratic formula: $x^2 + (1.0 \times 10^{-2})x - 2.0 \times 10^{-4} = 0$

$x = [OH^-] = 1.0 \times 10^{-2}\ M;\ pH = 12.00$

j. 20.0 mmol OH^- added results in 5.0 mmol X^{3-} and 5.0 mmol OH^- excess after OH^- reacts completely. Because K_b for X^{3-} is fairly large for a weak base, we have to worry about the OH^- contribution from X^{3-}.

$[X^{3-}] = [OH^-] = 5.0 \text{ mmol}/300.0 \text{ mL} = 1.7 \times 10^{-2}\ M$

	X^{3-} + H_2O	$\rightleftharpoons$	OH^-	+ HX^{2-}
Initial	$1.7 \times 10^{-2}\ M$		$1.7 \times 10^{-2}\ M$	0
Equil.	$1.7 \times 10^{-2} - x$		$1.7 \times 10^{-2} + x$	x

$K_b = 1.0 \times 10^{-2} = \frac{(1.7 \times 10^{-2} + x)x}{(1.7 \times 10^{-2} - x)}$

Using the quadratic formula: $x^2 + (2.7 \times 10^{-2})x - 1.7 \times 10^{-4} = 0,\ x = 5.3 \times 10^{-3}\ M$

$[OH^-] = (1.7 \times 10^{-2}) + x = (1.7 \times 10^{-2}) + (5.3 \times 10^{-3}) = 2.2 \times 10^{-2}\ M$; pH = 12.34

87. $\dfrac{0.200\text{ g}}{165.0\text{ g/mol}} = 1.212 \times 10^{-3}$ mol = 1.212 mmol H_3A (carrying extra sig. figs.)

a. 10.50 mL × 0.0500 *M* = 0.525 mmol OH^- added; $H_3A + OH^- \rightarrow H_2A^- + H_2O$; 1.212 − 0.525 = 0.687 mmol H_3A remains after OH^- reacts completely and 0.525 mmol H_2A^- formed. Solving the buffer problem using the K_{a_1} reaction gives:

$$K_{a_1} = \frac{(10^{-3.73})\left(\dfrac{0.525}{60.50} + 10^{-3.73}\right)}{\dfrac{0.687}{60.50} - 10^{-3.73}} = 1.5 \times 10^{-4};\ pK_{a_1} = -\log(1.5 \times 10^{-4}) = 3.82$$

First stoichiometric point: $pH = \dfrac{pK_{a_1} + pK_{a_2}}{2} = 5.19 = \dfrac{3.82 + pK_{a_2}}{2}$

$pK_{a_2} = 6.56;\ K_{a_2} = 10^{-6.56} = 2.8 \times 10^{-7}$

Second stoichiometric point: $pH = \dfrac{pK_{a_2} + pK_{a_3}}{2},\ 8.00 = \dfrac{6.56 + pK_{a_3}}{2}$

$pK_{a_3} = 9.44;\ K_{a_3} = 10^{-9.44} = 3.6 \times 10^{-10}$

b. 1.212 mmol H_3A = $0.0500\ M\ OH^- \times V_{OH^-}$, V_{OH^-} = 24.2 mL; 24.2 mL of OH^- are necessary to reach the first stoichiometric point. It will require 60.5 mL to reach the third halfway point to equivalence, where pH = pK_{a_3} = 9.44. The pH at 59.0 mL of NaOH added should be a little lower than 9.44.

c. 59.0 mL of 0.0500 *M* OH^- = 2.95 mmol OH^- added

	H_3A	+ OH^-	→ H_2A^-	+ H_2O
Before	1.212 mmol	2.95 mmol	0	
After	0	1.74	1.212	

	H_2A^-	+ OH^-	→ HA^{2-}	+ H_2O
Before	1.212	1.74	0	
After	0	0.53	1.212	

	HA^{2-}	+ OH^-	→ A^{3-}	+ H_2O
Before	1.212	0.53	0	
After	0.68 mmol	0	0.53 mmol	

Use the K_{a_3} reaction to solve for the $[H^+]$ in this buffer solution and make the normal assumptions.

$$K_{a_3} = 3.6 \times 10^{-10} = \frac{\left(\frac{0.53 \text{ mmol}}{109 \text{ mL}}\right)[H^+]}{\left(\frac{0.68 \text{ mmol}}{109 \text{ mL}}\right)}, \quad [H^+] = 4.6 \times 10^{-10}\ M; \ \text{pH} = 9.34$$

Assumptions good.

89. a. Na^+ is present in all solutions. The added H^+ from HCl reacts completely with CO_3^{2-} to convert it into HCO_3^-. After all CO_3^{2-} is reacted (after point C, the first equivalence point), H^+ then reacts completely with the next best base present, HCO_3^-. Point E represents the second equivalence point. The major species present at the various points after H^+ reacts completely follow.

A. CO_3^{2-}, H_2O, Na^+

B. CO_3^{2-}, HCO_3^-, H_2O, Cl^-, Na^+

C. HCO_3^-, H_2O, Cl^-, Na^+

D. HCO_3^-, CO_2 (H_2CO_3), H_2O, Cl^-, Na^+

E. CO_2 (H_2CO_3), H_2O, Cl^-, Na^+

F. H^+ (excess), CO_2 (H_2CO_3), H_2O, Cl^-, Na^+

b. Point A (initially):

$$CO_3^{2-} + H_2O \rightleftharpoons HCO_3^- + OH^- \qquad K_{b,CO_3^{2-}} = \frac{K_w}{K_{a_2}} = \frac{1.0 \times 10^{-14}}{4.8 \times 10^{-11}}$$

	CO_3^{2-}	HCO_3^-	OH^-	
Initial	$0.100\ M$	0	~0	$K_b = 2.1 \times 10^{-4}$
Equil.	$0.100 - x$	x	x	

$$K_b = 2.1 \times 10^{-4} = \frac{[HCO_3^-][OH^-]}{[CO_3^{2-}]} = \frac{x^2}{0.100 - x} \approx \frac{x^2}{0.100}$$

$x = 4.6 \times 10^{-3}\ M = [OH^-]$; pH = 11.66; assumptions good.

Point B: The first halfway point where $[CO_3^{2-}] = [HCO_3^-]$.

$\text{pH} = \text{p}K_{a_2} = -\log(4.8 \times 10^{-11}) = 10.32$; assumptions good.

Point C: First equivalence point (25.00 mL of 0.100 M HCl added). The amphoteric HCO_3^- is the major acid-base species present.

$$\text{pH} = \frac{\text{p}K_{a_1} + \text{p}K_{a_2}}{2}; \quad \text{p}K_{a_1} = -\log(4.3 \times 10^{-7}) = 6.37$$

$$\text{pH} = \frac{6.37 + 10.32}{2} = 8.35$$

Point D: The second halfway point where $[HCO_3^-] = [H_2CO_3]$.

$pH = pK_{a_1} = 6.37$; assumptions good.

Point E: This is the second equivalence point, where all of the CO_3^{2-} present initially has been converted into H_2CO_3 by the added strong acid. 50.0 mL HCl added.

$[H_2CO_3] = 2.50$ mmol/75.0 mL = 0.0333 M

$$H_2CO_3 \rightleftharpoons H^+ + HCO_3^- \qquad K_{a_1} = 4.3 \times 10^{-7}$$

	H_2CO_3	H^+	HCO_3^-
Initial	0.0333 M	0	0
Equil.	$0.0333 - x$	x	x

$$K_{a_1} = 4.3 \times 10^{-7} = \frac{x^2}{0.0333 - x} \approx \frac{x^2}{0.0333}$$

$x = [H^+] = 1.2 \times 10^{-4}$ M; pH = 3.92; assumptions good.

Solubility Equilibria

91. $MX(s) \rightleftharpoons M^{n+}(aq) + X^{n-}(aq)$ $K_{sp} = [M^{n+}][X^{n-}]$; the K_{sp} reaction always refers to a solid breaking up into its ions. The representations all show 1 : 1 salts, i.e., the formula of the solid contains 1 cation for every 1 anion (either +1 and −1, or +2 and −2, or +3 and −3). The solution with the largest number of ions (largest $[M^{n+}]$ and $[X^{n-}]$) will have the largest K_{sp} value. From the representations, the second beaker has the largest number of ions present, so this salt has the largest K_{sp} value. Conversely, the third beaker, with the fewest number of hydrated ions, will have the smallest K_{sp} value.

93. In our setups, s = solubility in mol/L. Because solids do not appear in the K_{sp} expression, we do not need to worry about their initial or equilibrium amounts.

a. $$Ag_3PO_4(s) \rightleftharpoons 3\,Ag^+(aq) + PO_4^{3-}(aq)$$

	$Ag_3PO_4(s)$		$3\,Ag^+(aq)$	$PO_4^{3-}(aq)$
Initial			0	0
	s mol/L of $Ag_3PO_4(s)$ dissolves to reach equilibrium			
Change	$-s$	→	$+3s$	$+s$
Equil.			$3s$	s

$$K_{sp} = 1.8 \times 10^{-18} = [Ag^+]^3[PO_4^{3-}] = (3s)^3(s) = 27s^4$$

$27s^4 = 1.8 \times 10^{-18}$, $s = (6.7 \times 10^{-20})^{1/4} = 1.6 \times 10^{-5}$ mol/L = molar solubility

$$\frac{1.6 \times 10^{-5} \text{ mol } Ag_3PO_4}{\text{L}} \times \frac{418.7 \text{ g } Ag_3PO_4}{\text{mol } Ag_3PO_4} = 6.7 \times 10^{-3} \text{ g/L}$$

b. $CaCO_3(s) \rightleftharpoons Ca^{2+}(aq) + CO_3^{2-}(aq)$

Initial	s = solubility (mol/L)	0	0
Equil.		s	s

$K_{sp} = 8.7 \times 10^{-9} = [Ca^{2+}][CO_3^{2-}] = s^2$, $s = 9.3 \times 10^{-5}$ mol/L

$$\frac{9.3 \times 10^{-5}\ \text{mol}}{\text{L}} \times \frac{100.1\ \text{g}}{\text{mol}} = 9.3 \times 10^{-3}\ \text{g/L}$$

c. $Hg_2Cl_2(s) \rightleftharpoons Hg_2^{2+}(aq) + 2\ Cl^-(aq)$

Initial	s = solubility (mol/L)	0	0
Equil.		s	$2s$

$K_{sp} = 1.1 \times 10^{-18} = [Hg_2^{2+}][Cl^-]^2 = (s)(2s)^2 = 4s^3$, $s = 6.5 \times 10^{-7}$ mol/L

$$\frac{6.5 \times 10^{-7}\ \text{mol}}{\text{L}} \times \frac{472.1\ \text{g}}{\text{mol}} = 3.1 \times 10^{-4}\ \text{g/L}$$

95. In our setup, s = solubility of the ionic solid in mol/L. This is defined as the maximum amount of a salt that can dissolve. Because solids do not appear in the K_{sp} expression, we do not need to worry about their initial and equilibrium amounts.

a. $CaC_2O_4(s) \rightleftharpoons Ca^{2+}(aq) + C_2O_4^{2-}(aq)$

Initial			0	0
	s mol/L of $CaC_2O_4(s)$ dissolves to reach equilibrium			
Change	$-s$	→	$+s$	$+s$
Equil.			s	s

From the problem, $s = \dfrac{6.1 \times 10^{-3}\ \text{g}}{\text{L}} \times \dfrac{1\ \text{mol}\ CaC_2O_4}{128.10\ \text{g}} = 4.8 \times 10^{-5}$ mol/L.

$K_{sp} = [Ca^{2+}][C_2O_4^{2-}] = (s)(s) = s^2$, $K_{sp} = (4.8 \times 10^{-5})^2 = 2.3 \times 10^{-9}$

b. $BiI_3(s) \rightleftharpoons Bi^{3+}(aq) + 3\ I^-(aq)$

Initial			0	0
	s mol/L of $BiI_3(s)$ dissolves to reach equilibrium			
Change	$-s$	→	$+s$	$+3s$
Equil.			s	$3s$

$K_{sp} = [Bi^{3+}][I^-]^3 = (s)(3s)^3 = 27s^4$, $K_{sp} = 27(1.32 \times 10^{-5})^4 = 8.20 \times 10^{-19}$

97. $Ag_2C_2O_4(s) \rightleftharpoons 2\ Ag^+(aq) + C_2O_4^{2-}(aq)$

Initial	s = solubility (mol/L)	0	0
Equil.		$2s$	s

From problem, $[Ag^+] = 2s = 2.2 \times 10^{-4}\ M$, $s = 1.1 \times 10^{-4}\ M$

$K_{sp} = [Ag^+]^2[C_2O_4^{2-}] = (2s)^2(s) = 4s^3 = 4(1.1 \times 10^{-4})^3 = 5.3 \times 10^{-12}$

99. a. Because both solids dissolve to produce three ions in solution, we can compare values of K_{sp} to determine relative solubility. Because the K_{sp} for CaF_2 is the smallest, $CaF_2(s)$ has the smallest molar solubility.

b. We must calculate molar solubilities because each salt yields a different number of ions when it dissolves.

$Ca_3(PO_4)_2(s) \rightleftharpoons 3\ Ca^{2+}(aq) + 2\ PO_4^{3-}(aq) \quad K_{sp} = 1.3 \times 10^{-32}$

Initial	s = solubility (mol/L)	0	0
Equil.		$3s$	$2s$

$K_{sp} = [Ca^{2+}]^3[PO_4^{3-}]^2 = (3s)^3(2s)^2 = 108s^5$, $s = (1.3 \times 10^{-32}/108)^{1/5} = 1.6 \times 10^{-7}$ mol/L

$FePO_4(s) \rightleftharpoons Fe^{3+}(aq) + PO_4^{3-}(aq) \quad K_{sp} = 1.0 \times 10^{-22}$

Initial	s = solubility (mol/L)	0	0
Equil.		s	s

$K_{sp} = [Fe^{3+}][PO_4^{3-}] = s^2$, $s = \sqrt{1.0 \times 10^{-22}} = 1.0 \times 10^{-11}$ mol/L

$FePO_4$ has the smallest molar solubility.

101. a. $Fe(OH)_3(s) \rightleftharpoons Fe^{3+}(aq) + 3\ OH^-(aq)$

Initial			0	$1 \times 10^{-7}\ M$ (from water)
	s mol/L of $Fe(OH)_3(s)$ dissolves to reach equilibrium = molar solubility			
Change	$-s$	→	$+s$	$+3s$
Equil.			s	$1 \times 10^{-7} + 3s$

$K_{sp} = 4 \times 10^{-38} = [Fe^{3+}][OH^-]^3 = (s)(1 \times 10^{-7} + 3s)^3 \approx s(1 \times 10^{-7})^3$

$s = 4 \times 10^{-17}$ mol/L; assumption good ($3s << 1 \times 10^{-7}$)

b. $Fe(OH)_3(s) \rightleftharpoons Fe^{3+}(aq) + 3\ OH^-(aq) \quad pH = 5.0,\ [OH^-] = 1 \times 10^{-9}\ M$

Initial			0	$1 \times 10^{-9}\ M$ (buffered)
	s mol/L dissolves to reach equilibrium			
Change	$-s$	→	$+s$	(assume no pH change in buffer)
Equil.			s	1×10^{-9}

$K_{sp} = 4 \times 10^{-38} = [Fe^{3+}][OH^-]^3 = (s)(1 \times 10^{-9})^3$, $s = 4 \times 10^{-11}$ mol/L = molar solubility

c. $Fe(OH)_3(s) \rightleftharpoons Fe^{3+}(aq) + 3\ OH^-(aq)$ pH = 11.0, $[OH^-] = 1 \times 10^{-3}\ M$

Initial			0	0.001 *M*	(buffered)
	s mol/L dissolves to reach equilibrium				
Change	−*s*	→	+*s*		(assume no pH change)
Equil.			*s*	0.001	

$K_{sp} = 4 \times 10^{-38} = [Fe^{3+}][OH^-]^3 = (s)(0.001)^3$, $s = 4 \times 10^{-29}$ mol/L = molar solubility

Note: As $[OH^-]$ increases, solubility decreases. This is the common ion effect.

103. $ZnS(s) \rightleftharpoons Zn^{2+}(aq) + S^{2-}(aq)$ $K_{sp} = [Zn^{2+}][S^{2-}]$

Initial	*s* = solubility (mol/L)	0.050 *M*	0
Equil.		0.050 + *s*	*s*

$K_{sp} = 2.5 \times 10^{-22} = (0.050 + s)(s) \approx (0.050)s$, $s = 5.0 \times 10^{-21}$ mol/L; assumption good.

Mass ZnS that dissolves $= 0.3000\ L \times \dfrac{5.0 \times 10^{-21}\ \text{mol ZnS}}{L} \times \dfrac{97.45\ \text{g ZnS}}{\text{mol}} = 1.5 \times 10^{-19}$ g

105. If the anion in the salt can act as a base in water, then the solubility of the salt will increase as the solution becomes more acidic. Added H^+ will react with the base, forming the conjugate acid. As the basic anion is removed, more of the salt will dissolve to replenish the basic anion. The salts with basic anions are Ag_3PO_4, $CaCO_3$, $CdCO_3$ and $Sr_3(PO_4)_2$. Hg_2Cl_2 and PbI_2 do not have any pH dependence because Cl^- and I^- are terrible bases (the conjugate bases of a strong acids).

$$Ag_3PO_4(s) + H^+(aq) \rightarrow 3\ Ag^+(aq) + HPO_4^{2-}(aq) \xrightarrow{\text{excess } H^+} 3\ Ag^+(aq) + H_3PO_4(aq)$$

$$CaCO_3(s) + H^+ \rightarrow Ca^{2+} + HCO_3^- \xrightarrow{\text{excess } H^+} Ca^{2+} + H_2CO_3\ [H_2O(l) + CO_2(g)]$$

$$CdCO_3(s) + H^+ \rightarrow Cd^{2+} + HCO_3^- \xrightarrow{\text{excess } H^+} Cd^{2+} + H_2CO_3\ [H_2O(l) + CO_2(g)]$$

$$Sr_3(PO_4)_2(s) + 2\ H^+ \rightarrow 3\ Sr^{2+} + 2\ HPO_4^{2-} \xrightarrow{\text{excess } H^+} 3\ Sr^{2+} + 2\ H_3PO_4$$

107. a. AgF b. $Pb(OH)_2$ c. $Sr(NO_2)_2$ d. $Ni(CN)_2$

All these salts have anions that are bases. The anions of the other choices are conjugate bases of strong acids. They have no basic properties in water and, therefore, do not have solubilities that depend on pH.

109. $[BaBr_2]_0 = \dfrac{0.150\text{ L}(1.0 \times 10^{-4}\text{ mol/L})}{0.250\text{ L}} = 6.0 \times 10^{-5}\ M$

$[K_2C_2O_4]_0 = \dfrac{0.100\text{ L}(6.0 \times 10^{-4}\text{ mol/L})}{0.250\text{ L}} = 2.4 \times 10^{-4}\ M$

$Q = [Ba^{2+}]_0[C_2O_4^{2-}]_0 = (6.0 \times 10^{-5})(2.4 \times 10^{-4}) = 1.5 \times 10^{-8}\ M$

Because $Q < K_{sp}$, $BaC_2O_4(s)$ will not precipitate. The final concentration of ions will be:

$[Ba^{2+}] = 6.0 \times 10^{-5}\ M,\ [Br^-] = 1.2 \times 10^{-4}\ M$

$[K^+] = 4.8 \times 10^{-4}\ M,\ [C_2O_4^{2-}] = 2.4 \times 10^{-4}\ M$

111. $Al(OH)_3(s) \rightleftharpoons Al^{3+}(aq) + 3\ OH^-(aq) \qquad K_{sp} = 2 \times 10^{-32}$

$Q = 2 \times 10^{-32} = [Al^{3+}]_0[OH^-]_0^3 = (0.2)[OH^-]_0^3$, $[OH^-]_0 = 4.6 \times 10^{-11}$ (carrying extra sig. fig.)

$pOH = -\log(4.6 \times 10^{-11}) = 10.3$; when the pOH of the solution equals 10.3, $K_{sp} = Q$. For precipitation, we want $Q > K_{sp}$. This will occur when $[OH^-]_0 > 4.6 \times 10^{-11}$ or when pOH < 10.3. Because pH + pOH = 14.00, precipitation of $Al(OH)_3(s)$ will begin when pH > 3.7 because this corresponds to a solution with pOH < 10.3.

113. $Ag_3PO_4(s) \rightleftharpoons 3\ Ag^+(aq) + PO_4^{3-}(aq)$; when Q is greater than K_{sp}, precipitation will occur. We will calculate the $[Ag^+]_0$ necessary for $Q = K_{sp}$. Any $[Ag^+]_0$ greater than this calculated number will cause precipitation of $Ag_3PO_4(s)$. In this problem, $[PO_4^{3-}]_0 = [Na_3PO_4]_0 = 1.0 \times 10^{-5}\ M$.

$K_{sp} = 1.8 \times 10^{-18}$; $Q = 1.8 \times 10^{-18} = [Ag^+]_0^3[PO_4^{3-}]_0 = [Ag^+]_0^3(1.0 \times 10^{-5}\ M)$

$[Ag^+]_0 = \left(\dfrac{1.8 \times 10^{-18}}{1.0 \times 10^{-5}}\right)^{1/3}$, $[Ag^+]_0 = 5.6 \times 10^{-5}\ M$

When $[Ag^+]_0 = [AgNO_3]_0$ is greater than $5.6 \times 10^{-5}\ M$, $Ag_3PO_4(s)$ will precipitate.

115. a.

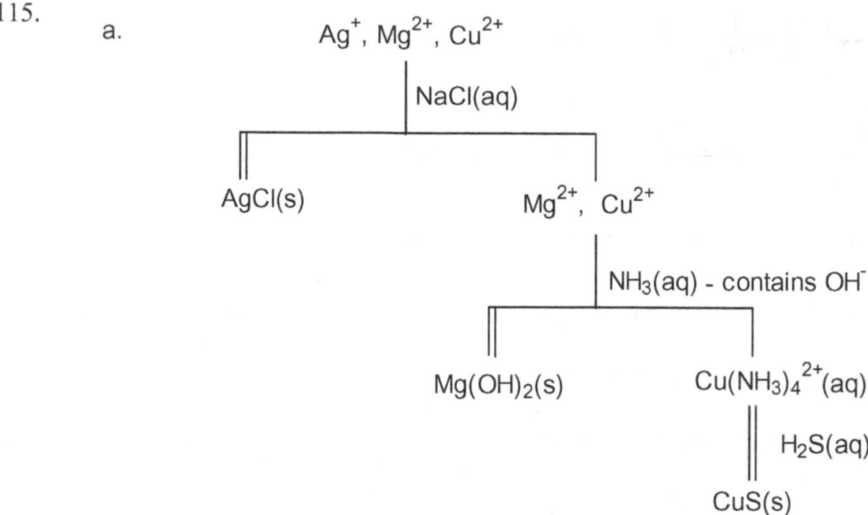
Ag^+, Mg^{2+}, Cu^{2+}
NaCl(aq)
AgCl(s)
Mg^{2+}, Cu^{2+}
NH_3(aq) - contains OH^-
$Mg(OH)_2$(s)
$Cu(NH_3)_4^{2+}$(aq)
H_2S(aq)
CuS(s)

b.

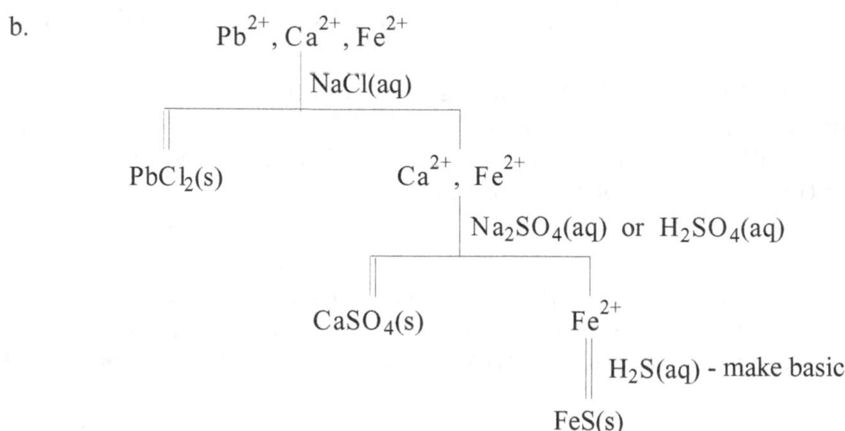
Pb^{2+}, Ca^{2+}, Fe^{2+}
NaCl(aq)
$PbCl_2$(s)
Ca^{2+}, Fe^{2+}
Na_2SO_4(aq) or H_2SO_4(aq)
$CaSO_4$(s)
Fe^{2+}
H_2S(aq) - make basic
FeS(s)

c.

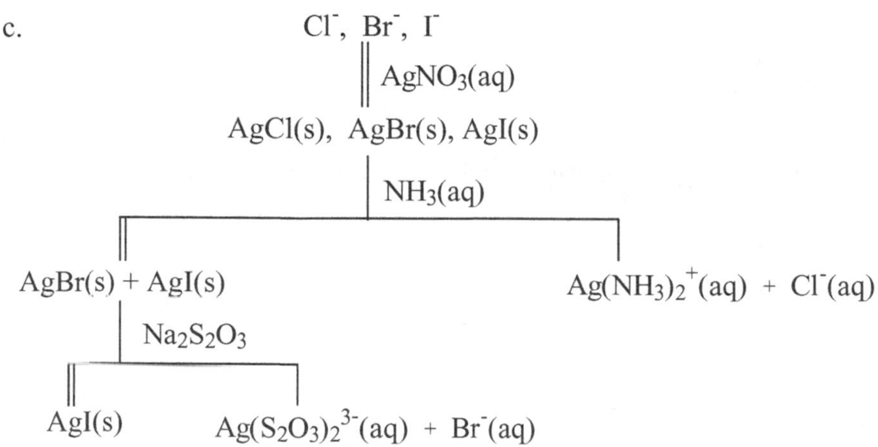
Cl^-, Br^-, I^-
$AgNO_3$(aq)
AgCl(s), AgBr(s), AgI(s)
NH_3(aq)
AgBr(s) + AgI(s)
$Ag(NH_3)_2^+$(aq) + Cl^-(aq)
$Na_2S_2O_3$
AgI(s)
$Ag(S_2O_3)_2^{3-}$(aq) + Br^-(aq)

d.

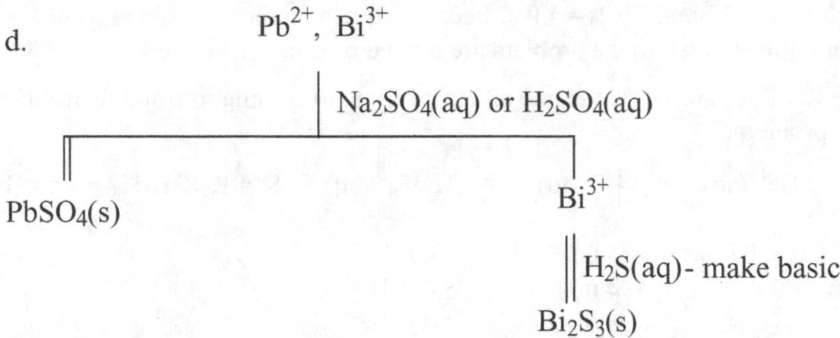

117. S^{2-} is a very basic anion and reacts significantly with H^+ to form HS^- ($S^{2-} + H^+ \rightleftharpoons HS^-$). Thus, the actual concentration of S^{2-} in solution depends on the amount of H^+ present. In basic solutions, little H^+ is present, which shifts the above equilibrium to the left. In basic solutions, the S^{2-} concentration is relatively high. So, in basic solutions, a wider range of sulfide salts will precipitate. However, in acidic solutions, added H^+ shifts the equilibrium to the right resulting in a lower S^{2-} concentration. In acidic solutions, only the least soluble sulfide salts will precipitate out of solution.

Complex Ion Equilibria

119. $Hg^{2+}(aq) + 2\,I^-(aq) \rightarrow HgI_2(s)$, orange ppt; $HgI_2(s) + 2\,I^-(aq) \rightarrow HgI_4^{2-}(aq)$
Soluble complex ion

121. $\frac{65\text{ g KI}}{0.500\text{ L}} \times \frac{1\text{ mol KI}}{166.0\text{ g KI}} = 0.78\ M\text{ KI}$

The formation constant for HgI_4^{2-} is an extremely large number. Because of this, we will let the Hg^{2+} and I^- ions present initially react to completion and then solve an equilibrium problem to determine the Hg^{2+} concentration.

	$Hg^{2+}(aq)$ +	$4\,I^-(aq)$	$\rightleftharpoons$	$HgI_4^{2-}(aq)$	$K = 1.0 \times 10^{30}$
Before	0.010 *M*	0.78 *M*		0	
Change	−0.010	−0.040	→	+0.010	Reacts completely (K large)
After	0	0.74		0.010	New initial
	x mol/L HgI_4^{2-} dissociates to reach equilibrium				
Change	$+x$	$+4x$	←	$-x$	
Equil.	x	$0.74 + 4x$		$0.010 - x$	

$$K = 1.0 \times 10^{30} = \frac{[HgI_4^{\ 2-}]}{[Hg^{2+}][I^-]^4} = \frac{(0.010 - x)}{(x)(0.74 + 4x)^4};\ \text{making usual assumptions:}$$

$$1.0 \times 10^{30} \approx \frac{(0.010)}{(x)(0.74)^4},\ x = [Hg^{2+}] = 3.3 \times 10^{-32}\ M;\ \text{assumptions good.}$$

Note: 3.3×10^{-32} mol/L corresponds to one Hg^{2+} ion per 5×10^7 L. It is very reasonable to approach the equilibrium in two steps. The reaction does essentially go to completion.

123. $[Be^{2+}]_0 = 5.0 \times 10^{-5}\ M$ and $[F^-]_0 = 4.0\ M$ because equal volumes of each reagent are mixed, so all concentrations given in the problem are diluted by a factor of one-half.

Because the K values are large, assume all reactions go to completion, and then solve an equilibrium problem.

$$Be^{2+}(aq) \ + \ 4\,F^-(aq) \ \rightleftharpoons \ BeF_4^{2-}(aq) \qquad K = K_1K_2K_3K_4 = 7.5 \times 10^{12}$$

	Be^{2+}	F^-	BeF_4^{2-}
Before	$5.0 \times 10^{-5}\ M$	$4.0\ M$	0
After	0	$4.0\ M$	$5.0 \times 10^{-5}\ M$
Equil.	x	$4.0 + 4x$	$5.0 \times 10^{-5} - x$

$$K = 7.5 \times 10^{12} = \frac{[BeF_4^{2-}]}{[Be^{2+}][F^-]^4} = \frac{5.0 \times 10^{-5} - x}{x(4.0 + 4x)^4} \approx \frac{5.0 \times 10^{-5}}{x(4.0)^4}$$

$x = [Be^{2+}] = 2.6 \times 10^{-20}\ M$; assumptions good. $[F^-] = 4.0\ M$; $[BeF_4^{2-}] = 5.0 \times 10^{-5}\ M$

Now use the stepwise K values to determine the other concentrtations.

$$K_1 = 7.9 \times 10^4 = \frac{[BeF^+]}{[Be^{2+}][F^-]} = \frac{[BeF^+]}{(2.6 \times 10^{-20})(4.0)}, \quad [BeF^+] = 8.2 \times 10^{-15}\ M$$

$$K_2 = 5.8 \times 10^3 = \frac{[BeF_2]}{[BeF^+][F^-]} = \frac{[BeF_2]}{(8.2 \times 10^{-15})(4.0)}, \quad [BeF_2] = 1.9 \times 10^{-10}\ M$$

$$K_3 = 6.1 \times 10^2 = \frac{[BeF_3^-]}{[BeF_2][F^-]} = \frac{[BeF_3^-]}{(1.9 \times 10^{-10})(4.0)}, \quad [BeF_3^-] = 4.6 \times 10^{-7}\ M$$

125. a.

$$Cu(OH)_2 \rightleftharpoons Cu^{2+} + 2\,OH^- \qquad K_{sp} = 1.6 \times 10^{-19}$$
$$Cu^{2+} + 4\,NH_3 \rightleftharpoons Cu(NH_3)_4^{2+} \qquad K_f = 1.0 \times 10^{13}$$

$$Cu(OH)_2(s) + 4\,NH_3(aq) \rightleftharpoons Cu(NH_3)_4^{2+}(aq) + 2\,OH^-(aq) \qquad K = K_{sp}K_f = 1.6 \times 10^{-6}$$

b.

$$Cu(OH)_2(s) \ + \ 4\,NH_3 \ \rightleftharpoons \ Cu(NH_3)_4^{2+} \ + \ 2\,OH^- \qquad K = 1.6 \times 10^{-6}$$

	NH_3	$Cu(NH_3)_4^{2+}$	OH^-
Initial	$5.0\ M$	0	$0.0095\ M$
	s mol/L $Cu(OH)_2$ dissolves to reach equilibrium		
Equil.	$5.0 - 4s$	s	$0.0095 + 2s$

$$K = 1.6 \times 10^{-6} = \frac{[Cu(NH_3)_4^{2+}][OH^-]^2}{[NH_3]^4} = \frac{s(0.0095 + 2s)^2}{(5.0 - 4s)^4}$$

If s is small: $1.6 \times 10^{-6} = \dfrac{s(0.0095)^2}{(5.0)^4}$, $s = 11.$ mol/L

Assumptions are not good. We will solve the problem by successive approximations.

$$s_{calc} = \frac{1.6 \times 10^{-6}(5.0 - 4s_{guess})^4}{(0.0095 + 2s_{guess})^2};$$ the results from six trials are:

s_{guess}: 0.10, 0.050, 0.060, 0.055, 0.056

s_{calc}: 1.6×10^{-2}, 0.071, 0.049, 0.058, 0.056

Thus the solubility of $Cu(OH)_2$ is 0.056 mol/L in 5.0 M NH_3.

127. $AgBr(s) \rightleftharpoons Ag^+ + Br^-$ $K_{sp} = 5.0 \times 10^{-13}$

$Ag^+ + 2\ S_2O_3^{2-} \rightleftharpoons Ag(S_2O_3)_2^{3-}$ $K_f = 2.9 \times 10^{13}$

$AgBr(s) + 2\ S_2O_3^{2-} \rightleftharpoons Ag(S_2O_3)_2^{3-} + Br^-$ $K = K_{sp} \times K_f = 14.5$ (Carry extra sig. figs.)

	$AgBr(s)$ +	$2\ S_2O_3^{2-}(aq)$	$\rightleftharpoons$	$Ag(S_2O_3)_2^{3-}(aq)$ +	$Br^-aq)$
Initial		0.500 M		0	0
	s mol/L $AgBr(s)$ dissolves to reach equilibrium				
Change	$-s$	$-2s$	$\rightarrow$	$+s$	$+s$
Equil.		$0.500 - 2s$		s	s

$$K = \frac{s^2}{(0.500 - 2s)^2} = 14.5;$$ taking the square root of both sides:

$$\frac{s}{0.500 - 2s} = 3.81,\ s = 1.91 - (7.62)s,\ s = 0.222 \text{ mol/L}$$

$$1.00 \text{ L} \times \frac{0.222 \text{ mol AgBr}}{\text{L}} \times \frac{187.8 \text{ g AgBr}}{\text{mol AgBr}} = 41.7 \text{ g AgBr} = 42 \text{ g AgBr}$$

129. Test tube 1: Added Cl^- reacts with Ag^+ to form a silver chloride precipitate. The net ionic equation is $Ag^+(aq) + Cl^-(aq) \rightarrow AgCl(s)$. Test tube 2: Added NH_3 reacts with Ag^+ ions to form a soluble complex ion, $Ag(NH_3)_2^+$. As this complex ion forms, Ag^+ is removed from the solution, which causes the $AgCl(s)$ to dissolve. When enough NH_3 is added, all the silver chloride precipitate will dissolve. The equation is $AgCl(s) + 2\ NH_3(aq) \rightarrow Ag(NH_3)_2^+(aq) + Cl^-(aq)$. Test tube 3: Added H^+ reacts with the weak base, NH_3, to form NH_4^+. As NH_3 is removed from the $Ag(NH_3)_2^+$ complex ion, Ag^+ ions are released to solution and can then react with Cl^- to re-form $AgCl(s)$. The equations are $Ag(NH_3)_2^+(aq) + 2\ H^+(aq) \rightarrow Ag^+(aq) + 2\ NH_4^+(aq)$, and $Ag^+(aq) + Cl^-(aq) \rightarrow AgCl(s)$.

Additional Exercises

131. a. The optimum pH for a buffer is when pH = pK_a. At this pH a buffer will have equal neutralization capacity for both added acid and base. As shown next, because the pK_a for $TRISH^+$ is 8.1, the optimal buffer pH is about 8.1.

$K_b = 1.19 \times 10^{-6}$; $K_a = K_w/K_b = 8.40 \times 10^{-9}$; $pK_a = -\log(8.40 \times 10^{-9}) = 8.076$

b. $pH = pK_a + \log\frac{[TRIS]}{[TRISH^+]}$, $7.00 = 8.076 + \log\frac{[TRIS]}{[TRISH^+]}$

$$\frac{[TRIS]}{[TRISH^+]} = 10^{-1.08} = 0.083 \quad \text{(at pH = 7.00)}$$

$$9.00 = 8.076 + \log\frac{[TRIS]}{[TRISH^+]}, \quad \frac{[TRIS]}{[TRISH^+]} = 10^{0.92} = 8.3 \quad \text{(at pH = 9.00)}$$

c. $\frac{50.0 \text{ g TRIS}}{2.0 \text{ L}} \times \frac{1 \text{ mol}}{121.14 \text{ g}} = 0.206\ M = 0.21\ M = [TRIS]$

$$\frac{65.0 \text{ g TRISHCl}}{2.0 \text{ L}} \times \frac{1 \text{ mol}}{157.60 \text{ g}} = 0.206\ M = 0.21\ M = [TRISHCl] = [TRISH^+]$$

$$pH = pK_a + \log\frac{[TRIS]}{[TRISH^+]} = 8.076 + \log\frac{(0.21)}{(0.21)} = 8.08$$

The amount of H^+ added from HCl is: $(0.50 \times 10^{-3}\text{ L}) \times 12\text{ mol/L} = 6.0 \times 10^{-3}$ mol H^+

The H^+ from HCl will convert TRIS into $TRISH^+$. The reaction is:

	TRIS	+	H^+	→	$TRISH^+$	
Before	0.21 M		$\frac{6.0 \times 10^{-3}}{0.2005} = 0.030\ M$		0.21 M	
Change	−0.030		−0.030	→	+0.030	Reacts completely
After	0.18		0		0.24	

Now use the Henderson-Hasselbalch equation to solve this buffer problem.

$$pH = 8.076 + \log\left(\frac{0.18}{0.24}\right) = 7.95$$

133. A best buffer is when pH ≈ pK_a; these solutions have about equal concentrations of weak acid and conjugate base. Therefore, choose combinations that yield a buffer where pH ≈ pK_a; that is, look for acids whose pK_a is closest to the pH.

a. Potassium fluoride + HCl will yield a buffer consisting of HF (pK_a = 3.14) and F^-.

b. Benzoic acid + NaOH will yield a buffer consisting of benzoic acid (pK_a = 4.19) and benzoate anion.

c. Sodium acetate + acetic acid (pK_a = 4.74) is the best choice for pH = 5.0 buffer since acetic acid has a pK_a value closest to 5.0.

d. HOCl and NaOH: This is the best choice to produce a conjugate acid-base pair with pH = 7.0. This mixture would yield a buffer consisting of HOCl (pK_a = 7.46) and OCl^-. Actually, the best choice for a pH = 7.0 buffer is an equimolar mixture of ammonium chloride and sodium acetate. NH_4^+ is a weak acid ($K_a = 5.6 \times 10^{-10}$), and $C_2H_3O_2^-$ is a weak base ($K_b = 5.6 \times 10^{-10}$). A mixture of the two will give a buffer at pH = 7.0 because the weak acid and weak base are the same strengths (K_a for NH_4^+ = K_b for $C_2H_3O_2^-$). $NH_4C_2H_3O_2$ is commercially available, and its solutions are used for pH = 7.0 buffers.

e. Ammonium chloride + NaOH will yield a buffer consisting of NH_4^+ (pK_a = 9.26) and NH_3.

135. $$\text{NaOH added} = 50.0\ \text{mL} \times \frac{0.500\ \text{mmol}}{\text{mL}} = 25.0\ \text{mmol NaOH}$$

$$\text{NaOH left unreacted} = 31.92\ \text{mL HCl} \times \frac{0.289\ \text{mmol}}{\text{mL}} \times \frac{1\ \text{mmol NaOH}}{\text{mmol HCl}} = 9.22\ \text{mmol NaOH}$$

NaOH reacted with aspirin = 25.0 – 9.22 = 15.8 mmol NaOH

$$15.8\ \text{mmol NaOH} \times \frac{1\ \text{mmol aspirin}}{2\ \text{mmol NaOH}} \times \frac{180.2\ \text{mg}}{\text{mmol}} = 1420\ \text{mg} = 1.42\ \text{g aspirin}$$

$$\text{Purity} = \frac{1.42\ \text{g}}{1.427\ \text{g}} \times 100 = 99.5\%$$

Here, a strong base is titrated by a strong acid. The equivalence point will be at pH = 7.0. Bromthymol blue would be the best indicator since it changes color at pH ≈ 7 (from base color to acid color). See Fig. 8.8 of the text.

137. At the equivalence point, P^{2-} is the major species. P^{2-} is a weak base in water because it is the conjugate base of a weak acid.

	P^{2-} + H_2O	⇌	HP^-	+	OH^-	
Initial	$\frac{0.5\ \text{g}}{0.1\ \text{L}} \times \frac{1\ \text{mol}}{204.2\ \text{g}} = 0.024\ M$		0		~0	(carry extra sig. fig.)
Equil.	$0.024 - x$		x		x	

$$K_b = \frac{[HP^-][OH^-]}{P^{2-}} = \frac{K_w}{K_a} = \frac{1.0 \times 10^{-14}}{10^{-5.51}},\ 3.2 \times 10^{-9} = \frac{x^2}{0.024 - x} \approx \frac{x^2}{0.024}$$

$x = [OH^-] = 8.8 \times 10^{-6}$ *M*; pOH = 5.1; pH = 8.9; assumptions good.

Phenolphthalein would be the best indicator for this titration because it changes color at pH ≈ 9 (from acid color to base color).

139. $CaF_2(s) \rightleftharpoons Ca^{2+}(aq) + 2\ F^-(aq) \quad K_{sp} = [Ca^{2+}][F^-]^2$

We need to determine the F^- concentration present in a 1.0 *M* HF solution. Solving the weak acid equilibrium problem:

$$HF(aq) \rightleftharpoons H^+(aq) + F^-(aq) \quad K_a = \frac{[H^+][F^-]}{[HF]}$$

	HF(aq)	H^+(aq)	F^-(aq)
Initial	1.0 *M*	~0	0
Equil.	$1.0 - x$	x	x

$K_a = 7.2 \times 10^{-4} = \dfrac{x(x)}{1.0 - x} \approx \dfrac{x^2}{1.0}$, $x = [F^-] = 2.7 \times 10^{-2}$ *M*; assumption good.

Next, calculate the Ca^{2+} concentration necessary for $Q = K_{sp,\ CaF_2}$.

$Q = [Ca^{2+}]_0[F^-]_0^2$, $4.0 \times 10^{-11} = [Ca^{2+}]_0(2.7 \times 10^{-2})^2$, $[Ca^{2+}]_0 = 5.5 \times 10^{-8}$ mol/L

$$\text{Mass } Ca(NO_3)_2 = 1.0\ L \times \frac{5.5 \times 10^{-8}\ mol\ Ca^{2+}}{L} \times \frac{1\ mol\ Ca(NO_3)_2}{mol\ Ca^{2+}} \times \frac{164.10\ g\ Ca(NO_3)_2}{mol}$$

$$= 9.0 \times 10^{-6}\ g\ Ca(NO_3)_2$$

For precipitation of CaF_2(s) to occur, we need $Q > K_{sp}$. When 9.0×10^{-6} g $Ca(NO_3)_2$ has been added to 1.0 L of solution, $Q = K_{sp}$. So precipitation of CaF_2(s) will begin to occur when just more than 9.0×10^{-6} g $Ca(NO_3)_2$ has been added.

141. a.

	$Pb(OH)_2(s)$	⇌	Pb^{2+}	+	$2\ OH^-$
Initial	s = solubility (mol/L)		0		1.0×10^{-7} *M* (from water)
Equil.			s		$1.0 \times 10^{-7} + 2s$

$K_{sp} = 1.2 \times 10^{-15} = [Pb^{2+}][OH^-]^2 = s(1.0 \times 10^{-7} + 2s)^2 \approx s(2s^2) = 4s^3$

$s = [Pb^{2+}] = 6.7 \times 10^{-6}$ *M*; assumption is good by the 5% rule.

b.

	$Pb(OH)_2(s)$	⇌	Pb^{2+}	+	$2\ OH^-$	
Initial			0		0.10 *M*	pH = 13.00, $[OH^-] = 0.10$ *M*
	s mol/L $Pb(OH)_2(s)$ dissolves to reach equilibrium					
Equil.			s		0.10	(Buffered solution)

$1.2 \times 10^{-15} = (s)(0.10)^2$, $s = [Pb^{2+}] = 1.2 \times 10^{-13}$ *M*

c. We need to calculate the Pb^{2+} concentration in equilibrium with $EDTA^{4-}$. Since K is large for the formation of $PbEDTA^{2-}$, let the reaction go to completion, and then solve an equilibrium problem to get the Pb^{2+} concentration.

	Pb^{2+}	+ $EDTA^{4-}$	$\rightleftharpoons$	$PbEDTA^{2-}$	$K = 1.1 \times 10^{18}$
Before	0.010 *M*	0.050 *M*		0	
	0.010 mol/L Pb^{2+} reacts completely (large K)				
Change	−0.010	−0.010	→	+0.010	Reacts completely
After	0	0.040		0.010	New initial
	x mol/L $PbEDTA^{2-}$ dissociates to reach equilibrium				
Equil.	x	$0.040 + x$		$0.010 - x$	

$$1.1 \times 10^{18} = \frac{(0.010 - x)}{(x)(0.040 + x)} \approx \frac{0.010}{x(0.040)},\ x = [Pb^{2+}] = 2.3 \times 10^{-19}\ M;\ \text{assumptions good.}$$

Now calculate the solubility quotient for $Pb(OH)_2$ to see if precipitation occurs. The concentration of OH^- is 0.10 *M* since we have a solution buffered at pH = 13.00.

$$Q = [Pb^{2+}]_0[OH^-]_0^2 = (2.3 \times 10^{-19})(0.10)^2 = 2.3 \times 10^{-21} < K_{sp}\ (1.2 \times 10^{-15})$$

$Pb(OH)_2(s)$ will not form since Q is less than K_{sp}.

143. $HC_2H_3O_2 \rightleftharpoons H^+ + C_2H_3O_2^-$; let C_0 = initial concentration of $HC_2H_3O_2$

From normal weak acid setup: $K_a = 1.8 \times 10^{-5} = \dfrac{[H^+][C_2H_3O_2^-]}{[HC_2H_3O_2]} = \dfrac{[H^+]^2}{C_0 - [H^+]}$

$$[H^+] = 10^{-2.68} = 2.1 \times 10^{-3}\ M;\ 1.8 \times 10^{-5} = \frac{(2.1 \times 10^{-3})^2}{C_0 - (2.1 \times 10^{-3})},\ C_0 = 0.25\ M$$

25.0 mL × 0.25 mmol/mL = 6.3 mmol $HC_2H_3O_2$

Need 6.3 mmol KOH = V_{KOH} × 0.0975 mmol/mL, V_{KOH} = 65 mL

145. 0.400 mol/L × V_{NH_3} = mol NH_3 = mol NH_4^+ after reaction with HCl at the equivalence point.

At the equivalence point: $[NH_4^+]_0 = \dfrac{\text{mol } NH_4^+}{\text{total volume}} = \dfrac{0.400 \times V_{NH_3}}{1.50 \times V_{NH_3}} = 0.267\ M$

	NH_4^+	$\rightleftharpoons$	H^+	+	NH_3
Initial	0.267 *M*		0		0
Equil.	$0.267 - x$		x		x

$$K_a = \frac{K_w}{K_b} = \frac{1.0 \times 10^{-14}}{1.8 \times 10^{-5}},\quad 5.6 \times 10^{-10} = \frac{x^2}{0.267 - x} \approx \frac{x^2}{0.267}$$

$x = [H^+] = 1.2 \times 10^{-5}$ *M*; pH = 4.92; assumptions good.

147. $HA + OH^- \rightarrow A^- + H_2O$, where HA = acetylsalicylic acid

$$\text{mmol HA present} = 27.36 \text{ mL OH}^- \times \frac{0.5106 \text{ mmol OH}^-}{\text{mL OH}^-} \times \frac{1 \text{ mmol HA}}{\text{mmol OH}^-} = 13.97 \text{ mmol HA}$$

$$\text{Molar mass of HA} = \frac{2.51 \text{ g HA}}{13.97 \times 10^{-3} \text{ mol HA}} = 180. \text{ g/mol}$$

To determine the K_a value, use the pH data. After complete neutralization of acetylsalicylic acid by OH^-, we have 13.97 mmol of A^- produced from the neutralization reaction. A^- will react completely with the added H^+ and re-form acetylsalicylic acid HA.

$$\text{mmol H}^+ \text{ added} = 15.44 \text{ mL} \times \frac{0.4524 \text{ mmol H}^+}{\text{mL}} = 6.985 \text{ mmol H}^+$$

	A^-	+	H^+	$\rightarrow$	HA	
Before	13.97 mmol		6.985 mmol		0	
Change	−6.985		−6.985	$\rightarrow$	+6.985	Reacts completely
After	6.985 mmol		0		6.985 mmol	

We have back titrated this solution to the halfway point to equivalence, where pH = pK_a (assuming HA is a weak acid). This is true because after H^+ reacts completely, equal milliliters of HA and A^- are present, which only occurs at the halfway point to equivalence. Assuming acetylsalicylic acid is a weak acid, then pH = pK_a = 3.48. $K_a = 10^{-3.48} = 3.3 \times 10^{-4}$.

149. K_{a_3} is so small (4.8×10^{-13}) that a break is not seen at the third stoichiometric point.

Challenge Problems

151. $$\text{mmol HC}_3\text{H}_5\text{O}_2 \text{ present initially} = 45.0 \text{ mL} \times \frac{0.750 \text{ mmol}}{\text{mL}} = 33.8 \text{ mmol HC}_3\text{H}_5\text{O}_2$$

$$\text{mmol C}_3\text{H}_5\text{O}_2^- \text{ present initially} = 55.0 \text{ mL} \times \frac{0.700 \text{ mmol}}{\text{mL}} = 38.5 \text{ mmol C}_3\text{H}_5\text{O}_2^-$$

The initial pH of the buffer is:

$$\text{pH} = \text{p}K_a + \log\frac{[\text{C}_3\text{H}_5\text{O}_2^-]}{[\text{HC}_3\text{H}_5\text{O}_2]} = -\log(1.3 \times 10^{-5}) + \log\frac{\frac{38.5 \text{ mmol}}{100.0 \text{ mL}}}{\frac{33.8 \text{ mmol}}{100.0 \text{ mL}}} = 4.89 + \log\frac{38.5}{33.8} = 4.95$$

Note: Because the buffer components are in the same volume of solution, we can use the mole (or millimole) ratio in the Henderson-Hasselbalch equation to solve for pH instead of using the concentration ratio of $[C_3H_5O_2^-]/[HC_3H_5O_2]$. The total volume always cancels for buffer solutions.

When NaOH is added, the pH will increase, and the added OH^- will convert $HC_3H_5O_2$ into $C_3H_5O_2^-$. The pH after addition of OH^- increases by 2.5%, so the resulting pH is:

$$4.95 + 0.025(4.95) = 5.07$$

At this pH, a buffer solution still exists, and the millimole ratio between $C_3H_5O_2^-$ and $HC_3H_5O_2$ is:

$$pH = pK_a + \log\frac{\text{mmol } C_3H_5O_2^-}{\text{mmol } HC_3H_5O_2},\ 5.07 = 4.89 + \log\frac{\text{mmol } C_3H_5O_2^-}{\text{mmol } HC_3H_5O_2}$$

$$\frac{\text{mmol } C_3H_5O_2^-}{\text{mmol } HC_3H_5O_2} = 10^{0.18} = 1.5$$

Let x = mmol OH^- added to increase pH to 5.07. Because OH^- will essentially react to completion with $HC_3H_5O_2$, the setup to the problem using millimoles is:

	$HC_3H_5O_2$	+	OH^-	$\rightarrow$	$C_3H_5O_2^-$	
Before	33.8 mmol		x mmol		38.5 mmol	
Change	$-x$		$-x$	$\rightarrow$	$+x$	Reacts completely
After	$33.8 - x$		0		$38.5 + x$	

$$\frac{\text{mmol } C_3H_5O_2^-}{\text{mmol } HC_3H_5O_2} = 1.5 = \frac{38.5 + x}{33.8 - x},\ 1.5(33.8 - x) = 38.5 + x,\ x = 4.9 \text{ mmol } OH^- \text{ added}$$

The volume of NaOH necessary to raise the pH by 2.5% is:

$$4.9 \text{ mmol NaOH} \times \frac{1 \text{ mL}}{0.10 \text{ mmol NaOH}} = 49 \text{ mL}$$

49 mL of 0.10 M NaOH must be added to increase the pH by 2.5%.

153. a. Best acid will react with the best base present, so the dominate equilibrium is:

$$NH_4^+ + X^- \rightleftharpoons NH_3 + HX \qquad K_{eq} = \frac{[NH_3][HX]}{[NH_4^+][X^-]} = \frac{K_{a,\ NH_4^+}}{K_{a,\ HX}}$$

Because initially $[NH_4^+]_0 = [X^-]_0$ and $[NH_3]_0 = [HX]_0 = 0$, at equilibrium $[NH_4^+] = [X^-]$ and $[NH_3] = [HX]$. Therefore:

$$K_{eq} = \frac{K_{a,\,NH_4^+}}{K_{a,\,HX}} = \frac{[HX]^2}{[X^-]^2}$$

The K_a expression for HX is: $K_{a,\,HX} = \frac{[H^+][X^-]}{[HX]}, \frac{[HX]}{[X^-]} = \frac{[H^+]}{K_{a,\,HX}}$

Substituting into the K_{eq} expression: $K_{eq} = \frac{K_{a,\,NH_4^+}}{K_{a,\,HX}} = \frac{[HX]^2}{[X^-]^2} = \left(\frac{[H^+]}{K_{a,\,HX}}\right)^2$

Rearranging: $[H^+]^2 = K_{a,\,NH_4^+} \times K_{a,\,HX}$, or taking the –log of both sides:

$$pH = \frac{pK_{a,\,NH_4^+} + pK_{a,\,HX}}{2}$$

b. Ammonium formate = $NH_4(HCO_2)$

$K_{a,\,NH_4^+} = \frac{1.0 \times 10^{-14}}{1.8 \times 10^{-5}} = 5.6 \times 10^{-10}$, $pK_a = 9.25$; $K_{a,\,HCO_2H} = 1.8 \times 10^{-4}$, $pK_a = 3.74$

$$pH = \frac{pK_{a,\,NH_4^+} + pK_{a,\,HCO_2H}}{2} = \frac{9.25 + 3.74}{2} = 6.50$$

Ammonium acetate = $NH_4(C_2H_3O_2)$; $K_{a,\,HC_2H_3O_2} = 1.8 \times 10^{-5}$; $pK_a = 4.74$

$$pH = \frac{9.25 + 4.74}{2} = 7.00$$

Ammonium bicarbonate = $NH_4(HCO_3)$; $K_{a,\,H_2CO_3} = 4.3 \times 10^{-7}$; $pK_a = 6.37$

$$pH = \frac{9.25 + 6.37}{2} = 7.81$$

c. $NH_4^+(aq) + OH^-(aq) \rightarrow NH_3(aq) + H_2O(l)$; $C_2H_3O_2^-(aq) + H^+(aq) \rightarrow HC_2H_3O_2(aq)$

155. a.

$$\begin{array}{lll} CuBr(s) \rightleftharpoons Cu^+ + Br^- & & K_{sp} = 1.0 \times 10^{-5} \\ Cu^+ + 3\,CN^- \rightleftharpoons Cu(CN)_3^{2-} & & K_f = 1.0 \times 10^{11} \\ \hline CuBr(s) + 3\,CN \rightleftharpoons Cu(CN)_3^{2-} + Br^- & & K = 1.0 \times 10^6 \end{array}$$

Because K is large, assume that enough CuBr(s) dissolves to completely use up the 1.0 *M* CN^-; then solve the back equilibrium problem to determine the equilibrium concentrations.

$$CuBr(s) + 3\ CN^- \rightleftharpoons Cu(CN)_3^{2-} + Br^-$$

	CuBr(s)	$3\ CN^-$		$Cu(CN)_3^{2-}$	Br^-
Before	x	1.0 *M*		0	0
	x mol/L of CuBr(s) dissolves to react completely with 1.0 *M* CN^-				
Change	$-x$	$-3x$	$\rightarrow$	$+x$	$+x$
After	0	$1.0 - 3x$		x	x

For reaction to go to completion, $1.0 - 3x = 0$ and $x = 0.33$ mol/L. Now solve the back equilibrium problem.

$$CuBr(s) + 3\ CN^- \rightleftharpoons Cu(CN)_3^{2-} + Br^-$$

	$3\ CN^-$		$Cu(CN)_3^{2-}$	Br^-
Initial	0		0.33 *M*	0.33 *M*
	Let y mol/L of $Cu(CN)_3^{2-}$ react to reach equilibrium.			
Change	$+3y$	$\leftarrow$	$-y$	$-y$
Equil.	3y		$0.33 - y$	$0.33 - y$

$$K = 1.0 \times 10^6 = \frac{(0.33 - y)^2}{(3y)^3} \approx \frac{(0.33)^2}{27y^3},\ y = 1.6 \times 10^{-3}\ M;\ \text{assumptions good.}$$

Of the initial 1.0 *M* CN^-, only $3(1.6 \times 10^{-3}) = 4.8 \times 10^{-3}$ *M* is present at equilibrium. Indeed, enough CuBr(s) did dissolve to essentially remove the initial 1.0 *M* CN^-. This amount, 0.33 mol/L, is the solubility of CuBr(s) in 1.0 *M* NaCN.

b. $[Br^-] = 0.33 - y = 0.33 - 1.6 \times 10^{-3} = 0.33\ M$

c. $[CN^-] = 3y = 3(1.6 \times 10^{-3}) = 4.8 \times 10^{-3}\ M$

157. a. $$SrF_2(s) \rightleftharpoons Sr^{2+}(aq) + 2\ F^-(aq)$$

	$Sr^{2+}(aq)$	$2\ F^-(aq)$
Initial	0	0
	s mol/L SrF_2 dissolves to reach equilibrium	
Equil.	s	$2s$

$[Sr^{2+}][F^-]^2 = K_{sp} = 7.9 \times 10^{-10} = 4s^3$, $s = 5.8 \times 10^{-4}$ mol/L in pure water

b. Greater, because some of the F^- would react with water:

$$F^- + H_2O \rightleftharpoons HF + OH^- \quad K_b = \frac{K_w}{K_{a,\,HF}} = 1.4 \times 10^{-11}$$

This lowers the concentration of F^-, forcing more SrF_2 to dissolve.

c. $SrF_2(s) \rightleftharpoons Sr^{2+} + 2\ F^-$ $\quad K_{sp} = 7.9 \times 10^{-10} = [Sr^{2+}][F^-]^2$

Let s = solubility = $[Sr^{2+}]$; then $2s$ = total F^- concentration.

Since F^- is a weak base, some of the F^- is converted into HF. Therefore:

total F^- concentration = $2s = [F^-] + [HF]$

$$HF \rightleftharpoons H^+ + F^- \quad K_a = 7.2 \times 10^{-4} = \frac{[H^+][F^-]}{[HF]} = \frac{1.0 \times 10^{-2}[F^-]}{[HF]} \text{ (since pH = 2.00 buffer)}$$

$$7.2 \times 10^{-2} = \frac{[F^-]}{[HF]}, \ [HF] = 14[F^-]; \text{ Solving:}$$

$$[Sr^{2+}] = s; \ 2s = [F^-] + [HF] = [F^-] + 14[F^-], \ 2s = 15[F^-], \ [F^-] = 2s/15$$

$$K_{sp} = 7.9 \times 10^{-10} = [Sr^{2+}][F^-]^2 = (s)\left(\frac{2s}{15}\right)^2, \ s = 3.5 \times 10^{-3} \text{ mol/L in pH = 2.00 solution}$$

159. We need to determine $[S^{2-}]_0$ that will cause precipitation of CuS(s) but not MnS(s). For CuS(s):

$$CuS(s) \rightleftharpoons Cu^{2+}(aq) + S^{2-}(aq) \quad K_{sp} = [Cu^{2+}][S^{2-}] = 8.5 \times 10^{-45}$$

$$[Cu^{2+}]_0 = 1.0 \times 10^{-3}\ M, \quad \frac{K_{sp}}{[Cu^{2+}]_0} = \frac{8.5 \times 10^{-45}}{1.0 \times 10^{-3}} = 8.5 \times 10^{-42}\ M = [S^{2-}]$$

This $[S^{2-}]$ represents the concentration that we must exceed to cause precipitation of CuS because if $[S^{2-}]_0 > 8.5 \times 10^{-42}\ M$, $Q > K_{sp}$.

For MnS(s):

$$MnS(s) \rightleftharpoons Mn^{2+}(aq) + S^{2-}(aq) \quad K_{sp} = [Mn^{2+}][S^{2-}] = 2.3 \times 10^{-13}$$

$$[Mn^{2+}]_0 = 1.0 \times 10^{-3}\ M, \quad \frac{K_{sp}}{[Mn^{2+}]} = \frac{2.3 \times 10^{-13}}{1.0 \times 10^{-3}} = 2.3 \times 10^{-10}\ M = [S^{2-}]$$

This value of $[S^{2-}]$ represents the largest concentration of sulfide that can be present without causing precipitation of MnS. That is, for this value of $[S^{2-}]$, $Q = K_{sp}$, and no precipitatation of MnS occurs. However, for any $[S^{2-}]_0 > 2.3 \times 10^{-10}\ M$, MnS(s) will form.

We must have $[S^{2-}]_0 > 8.5 \times 10^{-42}\ M$ to precipitate CuS, but $[S^{2-}]_0 < 2.3 \times 10^{-10}\ M$ to prevent precipitation of MnS.

The question asks for a pH that will precipitate CuS(s) but not MnS(s). We need to first choose an initial concentration of S^{2-} that will do this. Let's choose $[S^{2-}]_0 = 1.0 \times 10^{-10}\ M$ because this will clearly cause CuS(s) to precipitate but is still less than the $[S^{2-}]_0$ required for MnS(s) to precipitate. The problem now is to determine the pH necessary for a 0.1 M H_2S solution to have $[S^{2-}] = 1.0 \times 10^{-10}\ M$. Let's combine the K_{a_1} and K_{a_2} equations for H_2S to determine the required $[H^+]$.

$H_2S(aq) \rightleftharpoons H^+(aq) + HS^-(aq)$ $\quad K_{a_1} = 1.0 \times 10^{-7}$

$HS^-(aq) \rightleftharpoons H^+(aq) + S^{2-}(aq)$ $\quad K_{a_2} = 1 \times 10^{-19}$

$H_2S(aq) \rightleftharpoons 2H^+(aq) + S^{2-}(aq)$ $\quad K = K_{a_1} \times K_{a_2} = 1.0 \times 10^{-26}$

$$1 \times 10^{-26} = \frac{[H^+]^2[S^{2-}]}{[H_2S]} = \frac{[H^+]^2(1 \times 10^{-10})}{0.10}, \ [H^+] = 3 \times 10^{-9}\ M$$

pH = $-\log(3 \times 10^{-9}) = 8.5$. So, if pH = 8.5, $[S^{2-}] = 1 \times 10^{-10}$ *M*, which will cause precipitation of CuS(s) but not MnS(s).

Note: Any pH less than 8.7 would be a correct answer to this problem.

161. $AgCN(s) \rightleftharpoons Ag^+(aq) + CN^-(aq)$ $\quad K_{sp} = 2.2 \times 10^{-12}$

$H^+(aq) + CN^-(aq) \rightleftharpoons HCN(aq)$ $\quad K = 1/K_{a,\,HCN} = 1.6 \times 10^9$

$AgCN(s) + H^+(aq) \rightleftharpoons Ag^+(aq) + HCN(aq)$ $\quad K = 2.2 \times 10^{-12}(1.6 \times 10^9) = 3.5 \times 10^{-3}$

	$AgCN(s) + H^+(aq)$	$\rightleftharpoons Ag^+(aq)$	$+ HCN(aq)$
Initial	1.0 *M*	0	0
	s mol/L AgCN(s) dissolves to reach equilibrium		
Equil.	$1.0 - s$	*s*	*s*

$$3.5 \times 10^{-3} = \frac{[Ag^+][HCN]}{[H^+]} = \frac{s(s)}{1.0 - s} \approx \frac{s^2}{1.0}, \ s = 5.9 \times 10^{-2}$$

Assumption fails the 5% rule (*s* is 5.9% of 1.0 *M*). Using the method of successive approximations:

$$3.5 \times 10^{-3} = \frac{s^2}{1.0 - 0.059}, \ s = 5.7 \times 10^{-2}$$

$$3.5 \times 10^{-3} = \frac{s^2}{1.0 - 0.057}, \ s = 5.7 \times 10^{-2} \text{ (consistent answer)}$$

The molar solubility of AgCN(s) in 1.0 *M* H^+ is 5.7×10^{-2} mol/L.

163. For HOCl, $K_a = 3.5 \times 10^{-8}$ and $pK_a = -\log(3.5 \times 10^{-8}) = 7.46$. This will be a buffer solution because the pH is close to the pK_a value.

$$pH = pK_a + \log\frac{[OCl^-]}{[HOCl]}, \ 8.00 = 7.46 + \log\frac{[OCl^-]}{[HOCl]}, \ \frac{[OCl^-]}{[HOCl]} = 10^{0.54} = 3.5$$

1.00 L × 0.0500 M = 0.0500 mol HOCl initially. Added OH^- converts HOCl into OCl^-. The total moles of OCl^- and HOCl must equal 0.0500 mol. Solving where n = moles:

$$n_{OCl^-} + n_{HOCl} = 0.0500 \text{ and } n_{OCl^-} = (3.5)n_{HOCl}$$

$$(4.5)n_{HOCl} = 0.0500,\ n_{HOCl} = 0.011 \text{ mol};\ n_{OCl^-} = 0.039 \text{ mol}$$

Need to add 0.039 mol NaOH to produce 0.039 mol OCl^-.

0.039 mol = V × 0.0100 M, V = 3.9 L NaOH; *note:* Normal buffer assumptions hold.

165. a. 200.0 mL × 0.250 mmol Na_3PO_4/mL = 50.0 mmol Na_3PO_4

135.0 mL × 1.000 mmol HCl/mL = 135.0 mmol HCl

100.0 mL × 0.100 mmol NaCN/mL = 10.0 mmol NaCN

Let H^+ from the HCl react to completion with the bases in solution. In general, react the strongest base first and so on. Here, 110.0 mmol of HCl reacts to convert all CN^- to HCN and all PO_4^{3-} to $H_2PO_4^-$. At this point 10.0 mmol HCN, 50.0 mmol $H_2PO_4^-$, and 25.0 mmol HCl are in solution. The remaining HCl reacts completely with $H_2PO_4^-$, converting 25.0 mmol to H_3PO_4. The final solution contains 25.0 mmol H_3PO_4, (50.0 – 25.0 =) 25.0 mmol $H_2PO_4^-$, and 10.0 mmol HCN. HCN ($K_a = 6.2 \times 10^{-10}$) is a much weaker acid than either H_3PO_4 ($K_{a_1} = 7.5 \times 10^{-3}$) or $H_2PO_4^-$ ($K_{a_2} = 6.2 \times 10^{-8}$), so ignore it. We have a buffer solution. Principal equilibrium reaction is:

	H_3PO_4	$\rightleftharpoons$	H^+	+	$H_2PO_4^-$	$K_{a_1} = 7.5 \times 10^{-3}$
Initial	25.0 mmol/435.0 mL		0		25.0/435.0	
Equil.	$0.0575 - x$		x		$0.0575 + x$	

$$K_{a_1} = 7.5 \times 10^{-3} = \frac{x(0.0575 + x)}{0.0575 - x};\ \text{normal assumptions don't hold here.}$$

Using the quadratic formula and carrying extra sig. figs.:

$$x^2 + (0.0650)x - 4.31 \times 10^{-4} = 0,\ x = 0.0061\ M = [H^+];\ pH = 2.21$$

b. $[HCN] = \dfrac{10.0 \text{ mmol}}{435.0 \text{ mL}} = 2.30 \times 10^{-2}\ M$; HCN dissociation will be minimal.

167. Major species PO_4^{3-}, H^+, HSO_4^-, H_2O, and Na^+; let the best base (PO_4^{3-}) react with the best acid (H^+). Assume the reaction goes to completion because H^+ is reacting. Note that the concentrations are halved when equal volumes of the two reagents are mixed.

	PO_4^{3-} +	H^+ →	HPO_4^{2-}
Before	0.25 *M*	0.050 *M*	0
After	0.20 *M*	0	0.050 *M*

Major species: PO_4^{3-}, HPO_4^{2-}, HSO_4^-, H_2O, and Na^+; react the best base (PO_4^{3-}) with the best acid (HSO_4^-). Because K for this reaction is very large, assume the reaction goes to completion.

$$PO_4^{3-} + HSO_4^- \rightarrow HPO_4^{2-} + SO_4^{2-} \qquad K = \frac{K_{a,\ HSO_4^-}}{K_{a,\ HPO_4^{2-}}} = 2.5 \times 10^{10}$$

	PO_4^{3-} +	HSO_4^- →	HPO_4^{2-} +	SO_4^{2-}
Before	0.20 *M*	0.050 *M*	0.050 *M*	0
After	0.15 *M*	0	0.100 *M*	0.050 *M*

Major species: PO_4^{3-}, HPO_4^{2-}, SO_4^{2-} (a very weak base with $K_b = 8.3 \times 10^{-13}$), H_2O, and Na^+; because the best base present (PO_4^{3-}) and best acid present (HPO_4^{2-}) are conjugate acid-base pairs, a buffer solution exists. Because K_b for PO_4^{3-} is a relatively large value ($K_b = K_w/K_{a,\ HPO_4^{2-}} = 0.021$), the usual assumptions that the amount of base that reacts to each equilibrium is negligible compared with the initial concentration of base will not hold. Solving using the K_b reaction for PO_4^{3-}:

$$PO_4^{3-} + H_2O \rightleftharpoons HPO_4^{2-} + OH^- \qquad K_b = 0.021$$

	PO_4^{3-}		HPO_4^{2-}	OH^-
Initial	0.15 *M*		0.100 *M*	0
Change	$-x$	→	$+x$	$+x$
Equil.	$0.15 - x$		$0.100 + x$	x

$K_b = 0.021 = \dfrac{(0.100 + x)(x)}{0.15 - x}$; using quadratic equation:

$x = [OH^-] = 0.022\ M$; pOH = 1.66; pH = 12.34

169. H_3A: $pK_{a_1} = 3.00$, $pK_{a_2} = 7.30$, $pK_{a_3} = 11.70$

The pH at the second stoichiometric point is:

$$pH = \frac{pK_{a_2} + pK_{a_3}}{2} = \frac{7.30 + 11.70}{2} = 9.50$$

Thus to reach a pH of 9.50, we must go to the second stoichiometric point. 100.0 mL × 0.0500 *M* = 5.00 mmol H_3A initially. To reach the second stoichiometric point, we need 10.0 mmol OH^- = 1.00 mmol/mL × V_{NaOH}. Solving for V_{NaOH}:

V_{NaOH} = 10.0 mL (to reach pH = 9.50)